Addison Wesley
Mathematics
Makes Sense

Program Overview

Making sense of your needs...

Addison Wesley
Mathematics
Makes Sense

Student understanding
in a manageable and
easy-to-use program

Addison Wesley Mathematics Makes Sense

Program Overview

Kindergarten to Grade 3 Authors

Pat Dickinson
Michelle Jackson
Maggie Martin Connell
Heather Spencer
Susan Gordon
Linden Gray
Nirmala Nutakki
Ken Harper
Lynn Bryan
Peggy Morrow
Ralph Connelly
Don Jones
Michael Davis
Trevor Brown
Brenda Lightburn
Cathy Anderson
Angie Harding
Jennifer Travis
Sharon Jeroski
Carole Saundry
Maureen Dockendorf
Steve Thomas
Jeananne Thomas
Michelle Skene
Sandra Ball
Donna Beaumont

Grade 4 to 8 Authors

Peggy Morrow
Bryn Keyes
Jason Johnston
Ken Harper
Margaret Sinclair
Angela D'Alessandro
Manuel Salvati
Ralph Connelly
Trevor Brown
Michael Davis
Don Jones
Cathy Heideman
Antonietta Lenjosek
Linden Gray
Sharon Jeroski
Maggie Martin Connell
Jeananne Thomas
Steve Thomas
Mary Doucette
Linda Edwards
Sue Gordon

PEARSON
Addison Wesley

Elementary Mathematics Publishing Team

Enid Haley
Lesley Haynes
Mei Lin Cheung
Lynne Gulliver
Tricia Carmichael
Susan Lishman
Ingrid D'Silva
Lynn Pereira
Keltie Thomas
Ellen Davidson
Rosalyn Steiner
Kirsten Vanstone
Susan Ginsberg
Alison Rieger
Kathleen ffolliott
Marg Bukta
Judy Wilson
Nicole Argyropoulos

Elementary Mathematics Production Coordinators

Stephanie Cox
Denise Wake

Product Manager

Anne-Marie Scullion

Mathematics Publishers

Claire Burnett
Susan Green

Program Overview Design

Ezio Lisi

Program Overview Publication 0-321-11825-1

This book contains recycled product and is acid free. Printed and bound in Canada

12 18

PEARSON
Addison Wesley

Table of Contents

Welcome to

Addison Wesley Mathematics Makes Sense

Addison Wesley Mathematics Makes Sense Kindergarten

Core:
- Teacher Guide – binder with 8 modules
- Big Math Book

- *Addison Wesley Little Books*
- Audio
- Website www.pearsoned.ca/mathmakessense
- e tools

Addison Wesley Mathematics Makes Sense Grades 1 and 2

Core:
- Teacher Guide with CD – binder with 15 modules
- Student Book i.e. consumable or BLM
- Big Math Book

- *Addison Wesley Little Books*
- *Together Resource:* Support for Combined Grades
- Audio
- Website www.pearsoned.ca/mathmakessense
- e tools

Addison Wesley Mathematics Makes Sense Grades 3 to 8

Core

- Teacher Guide with CD – binder with 14 modules
- Student Book – hard cover text

- Practice and Homework Book
- *Together Resource:* Support for Combined Grades
- *Addison Wesley Little Books*
- Website www.pearsoned.ca/mathmakessense
- e-tools

French Editions

Addison Wesley Mathematics recognizes the importance of developing a parallel French Edition of *Addison Wesley Mathematics Makes Sense* for French-speaking students.

- Les Editions de la Chenelière is translating all grade levels of *Addison Wesley Mathematics Makes Sense* K-8, therefore ensuring consistency in their translation, Chenelière Mathématiques Un choix logique. Les Editions de la Chenelière is Canada's leading publisher of resources for the French-speaking community outside of Quebec. We look forward to servicing the needs of your French and English students.

Chenelière Mathématiques

Program Principles

- All students need opportunities to learn mathematics in ways that are meaningful to them. A responsible mathematics program recognizes many learning styles and offers guidance to teachers as they plan for individual student differences.

- Teacher understanding of mathematics is a critical factor in their students' success. Teacher understanding can and must be supported in program methodology and pedagogy.

- Students best develop conceptual mathematical understanding when they have opportunities to "do" math, to engage in hands-on experiences in which they explore concepts in a rich mathematical context.

- Students demonstrate conceptual understanding by communicating and modelling their reasoning, and connecting a new concept or strategy to other contexts they have seen before.

- Problem solving is an integral part of learning mathematics. Students best learn new mathematical concepts when they pose and solve problems.

- Mathematics understanding is deepened and enhanced when students have opportunities to make connections between mathematical concepts and other mathematics strands, other disciplines, and the real world.

Part 2
- What patterns can you find in the table?
- What do you notice about the numbers of pieces that have icing on three faces?
- One cake has 16 pieces with icing on two faces. How many pieces are there in the whole cake?
- Suppose you made a 10 by 10 cake. How many of each kind of piece would there be?

Display Your Work

Make a poster display to show all the patterns you found.

Take It Further

Model rectangular cakes with 24 Snap cubes.
- How many different cakes can you model using all 24 cubes?
- How many cakes have pieces with icing on four faces?
- Which cake has the greatest number of pieces with icing on one face? Two faces? Three faces?
- Write about what you found out.

117

- Procedural fluency with number is an essential skill for life. Both mental and written computational strategies must be accurate, efficient, flexible, and adaptable.

- Parents have a significant role to play in student learning, in supporting and reinforcing what is learned in the classroom each day, and promoting a positive attitude toward mathematics in the home.

- The purposeful use of technology in the mathematics classroom can enrich learning experiences for students, allowing them to explore and develop concepts, and extend critical thinking and problem-solving skills.

- A mathematics program should support curriculum implementation and assessment with 100% curriculum fit and practical teacher support – pacing guidelines; combined grades strategies; models for independent and group learning; performance-based assessment suggestions.

- Teachers need a balance of diagnostic, formative, and summative assessment opportunities, with practical assessment tools to track student achievement and meet reporting requirements.

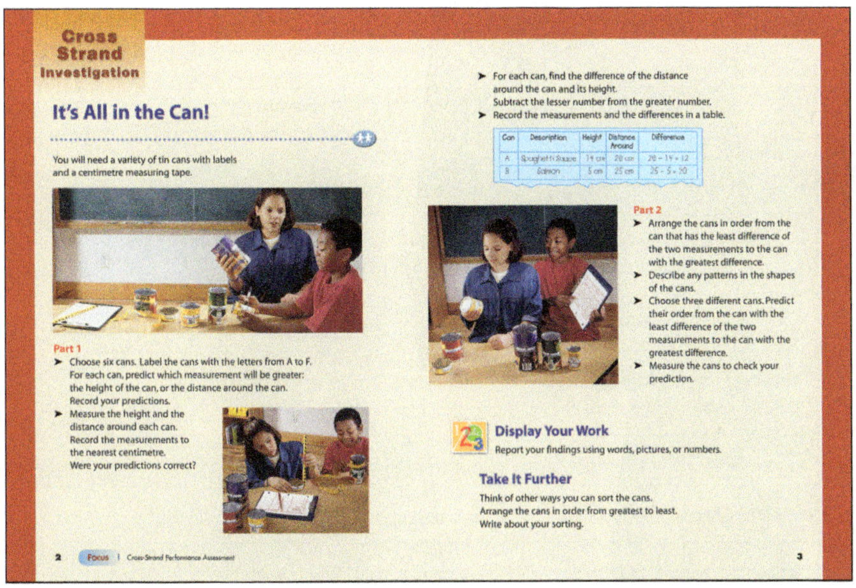

Cross Strand Investigation

It's All in the Can!

You will need a variety of tin cans with labels and a centimetre measuring tape.

Part 1

- Choose six cans. Label the cans with the letters from A to F. For each can, predict which measurement will be greater: the height of the can, or the distance around the can. Record your predictions.
- Measure the height and the distance around each can. Record the measurements to the nearest centimetre. Were your predictions correct?
- For each can, find the difference of the distance around the can and its height. Subtract the lesser number from the greater number.
- Record the measurements and the differences in a table.

Can	Description	Height	Distance Around	Difference
A	Spaghetti Sauce	14 cm	26 cm	26 − 14 = 12
B	Salmon	5 cm	25 cm	25 − 5 = 20

Part 2

- Arrange the cans in order from the can that has the least difference of the two measurements to the can with the greatest difference.
- Describe any patterns in the shapes of the cans.
- Choose three different cans. Predict their order from the can with the least difference of the two measurements to the can with the greatest difference.
- Measure the cans to check your prediction.

Display Your Work

Report your findings using words, pictures, or numbers.

Take It Further

Think of other ways you can sort the cans.
Arrange the cans in order from greatest to least.
Write about your sorting.

2 Focus | Cross-Strand Performance Assessment

3

From Research to Classroom Practice

Addison Wesley Mathematics Makes Sense is based on the most current research about how students learn. The Addison Wesley development team examined published academic research and professional development resources, while we learned about ongoing research into the impact of current issues on classroom practice.

This research was shared with educators across Canada, as the development team assessed its implications for the creation of new mathematics resources for the classroom.

The Addison Wesley development team also met with experienced and new teachers, with principals, parents, and consultants, in a series of symposia, focus groups, and one-on-one interviews. Our purpose was to define the resources that would best suit the needs of student learning and teacher instruction.

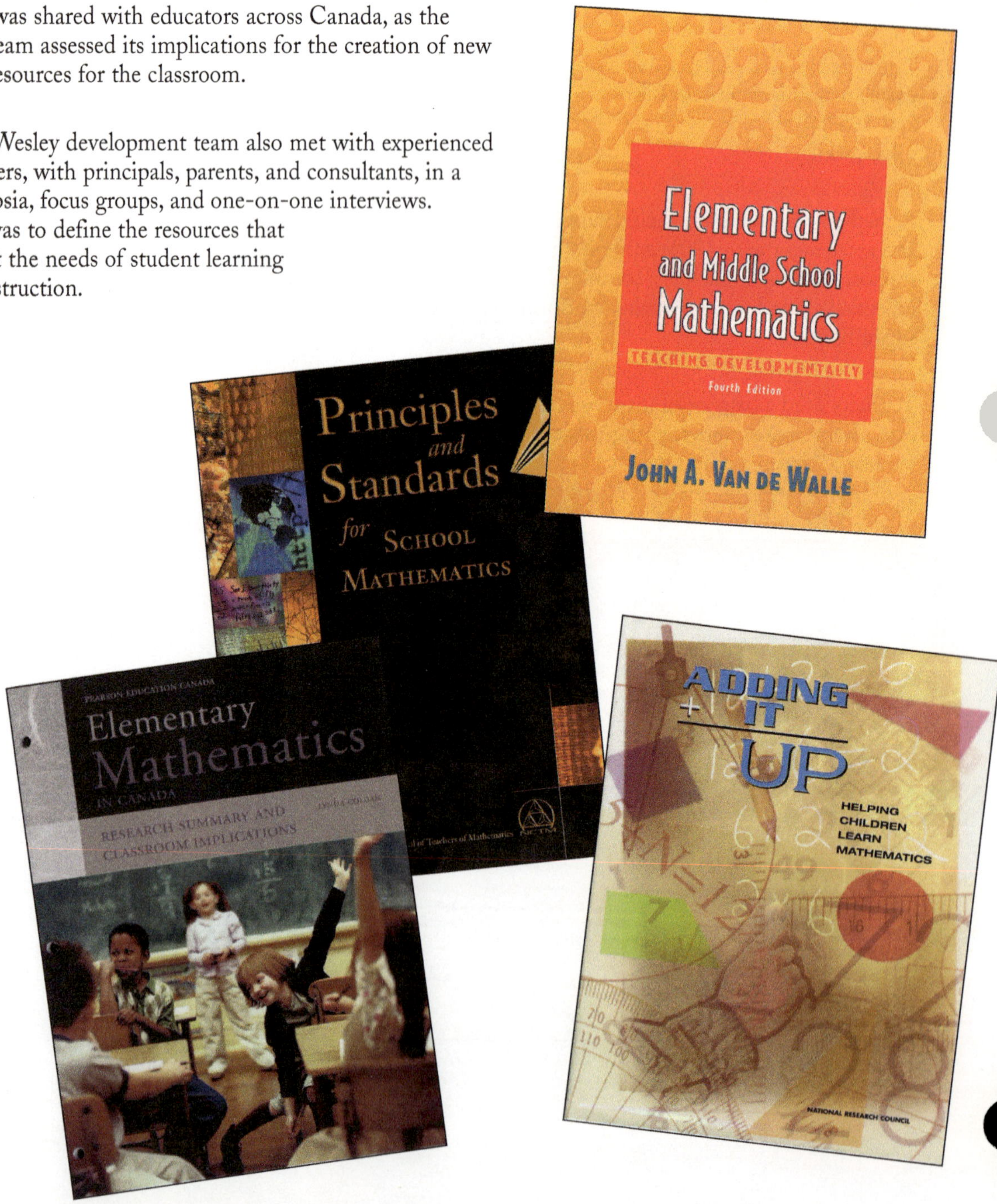

Current research has profound implications for new classroom resources.

– Lynda Colgan, Program Adviser

Program development included field tests at each grade level. In the first year of field testing, 200 classrooms across Canada participated, involving 10,000 students and their teachers to validate program content and organization.

The Addison Wesley development team incorporated field-test teacher input as we refined program design at all levels.

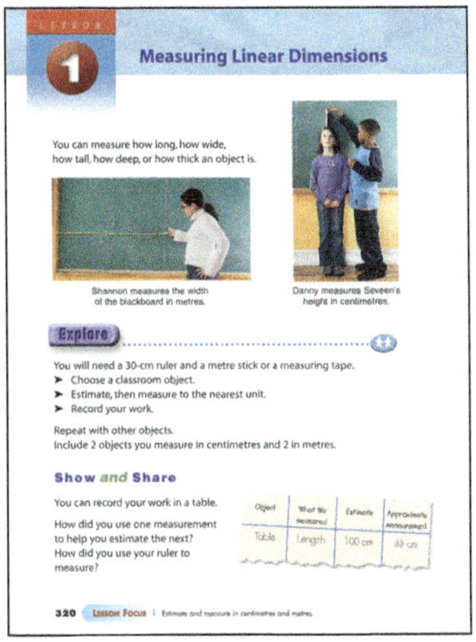
LESSON 1 Measuring Linear Dimensions

You can measure how long, how wide, how tall, how deep, or how thick an object is.

Shannon measures the width of the blackboard in metres.

Danny measures Seveen's height in centimetres.

Explore

You will need a 30-cm ruler and a metre stick or a measuring tape.
- Choose a classroom object.
- Estimate, then measure to the nearest unit.
- Record your work.

Repeat with other objects.
Include 2 objects you measure in centimetres and 2 in metres.

Show and Share

You can record your work in a table.

How did you use one measurement to help you estimate the next?
How did you use your ruler to measure?

Object	What We Measured	Estimate	Approximate Measurement
Table	Length	100 cm	[illegible]

320 Lesson Focus | Estimate and measure in centimetres and metres.

Unit Problem Design a Backyard

Design a backyard for the Rizvi family.

360

Addison Wesley Mathematics Makes Sense is:

- Built from an understanding of current educational research
- Shaped against the backdrop of extensive market research into resource needs
- Field tested in hundreds of schools across Canada

Balanced Instruction

For real understanding, students need a combination of open-ended problem-solving opportunities, meaningful dialogue, and purposeful practice that reinforces, and extends, new learning.

Balanced instruction recognizes four key components that build mathematical literacy, as illustrated here.

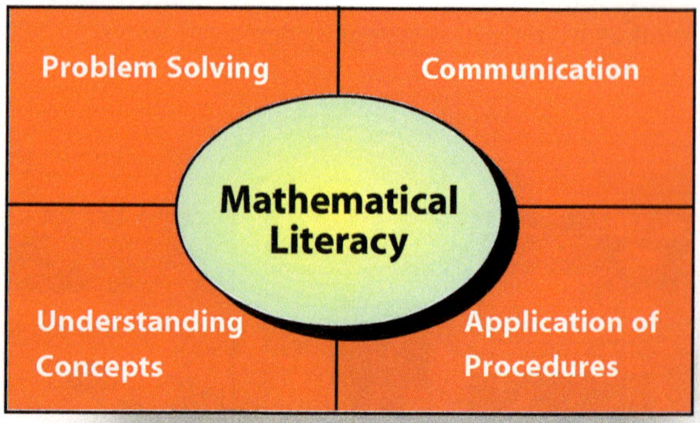

Addison Wesley Mathematics Makes Sense supports each key component in the following ways.

Problem Solving

- Introduces new concepts by presenting a problem to solve.
- Includes whole group, partner, and independent problem-solving activities.

Understanding Concepts

- A variety of activities allows students to bring their own experiences to new concepts.
- Question prompts guide the student dialogue that follows each new learning experience.
- Consolidates key concepts before moving to independent work.

Application of Procedures

- Gives purposeful practice for students to apply, clarify, and extend the learning.
- Provides regular opportunities for calculator or computer applications, or the introduction of new problem-solving strategies.

Communication

- Guides students to represent their thinking in pictures, numbers, or words.
- Provides a balance of oral and written communication opportunities.

It's time for a program that simplifies teacher planning so teachers have more time with their students.
– Peggy Morrow, Program Author

Balanced instruction is delivered in a consistent three-part lesson structure that supports the way students learn, and the way teachers teach.

How Students Learn:

Our Student Book Lesson

How Teachers Teach:

Our Teacher Guide Lesson

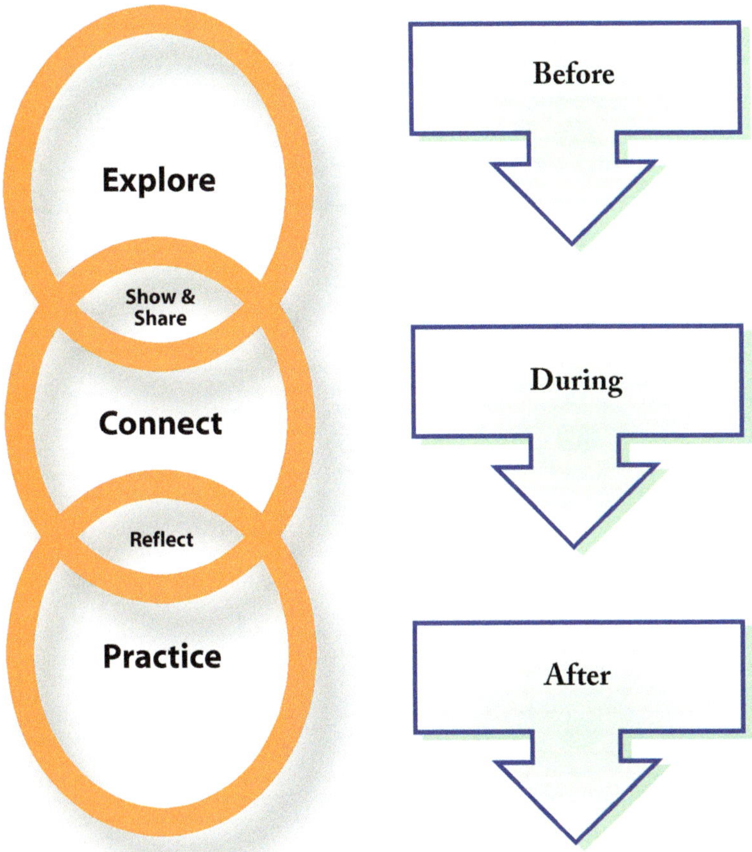

Manageable and Easy-to-Use

The problem-solving approach in *Addison Wesley Mathematics Makes Sense* is balanced with purposeful practice of skills and reinforcement of concepts. *Addison Wesley Mathematics Makes Sense* gives you quick access to ideas for instruction, while your students get clean, clear content appropriately paced.

- An "all-in-one-place" Teacher Guide
- Predictable, consistent format
- Open, readable design

Teaching and Learning for Understanding

Addison Wesley Mathematics Makes Sense has been built on the belief that mathematics is more than a list of isolated facts, that mathematics as a whole can make sense for students, teachers, and parents. Fundamental to this belief is our understanding of the importance of mathematical connections: Math makes sense for students when they see how mathematical ideas are connected to the real world, to other mathematical ideas, and to what they are learning in other subject areas.

Children come to us with experiences and understandings they have already developed into personal networks of understanding. As they work with new ideas, their active engagement leads them to fit new learning within their established understanding. The more ideas students connect, the more solid their understanding.

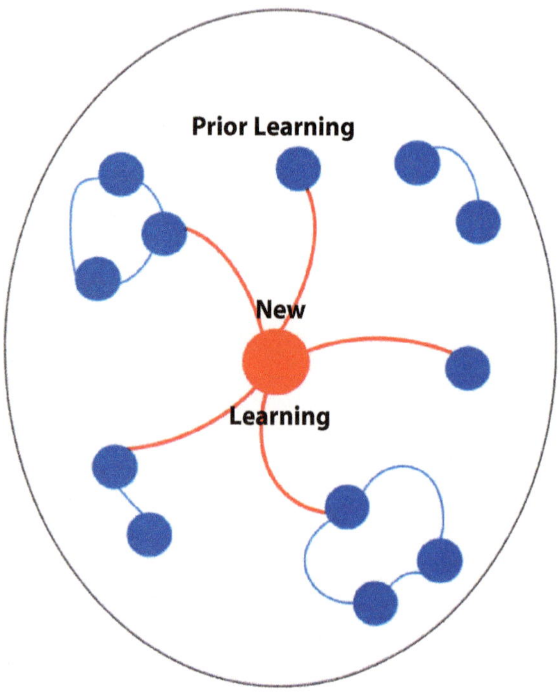

Teaching for understanding reaps many benefits for students:

- When students understand mathematical procedures, they can recall them easily and apply them in a variety of settings.
- When students understand the main concepts and connections of mathematical topics, they rely on reasoning more, and on memory less.
- Conceptual understanding provides the basis for acquiring new knowledge and solving unfamiliar problems.
- Conceptual understanding helps students spot and correct errors in their problem solutions.

The tools that we use to build understanding are our existing ideas, the knowledge that we already possess.
– John A. Van de Walle, Elementary Mathematics Consultant

In *Addison Wesley Mathematics Makes Sense*, the lesson framework delivers instruction in the way in which students learn most effectively.

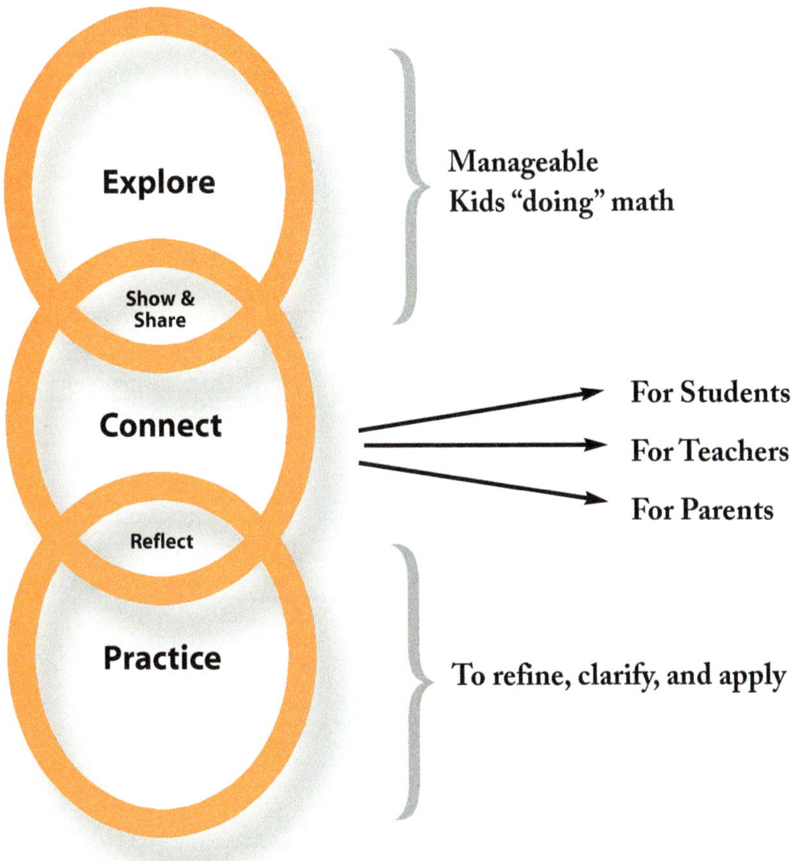

Supporting the lesson framework of *Addison Wesley Mathematics Makes Sense* is an over-arching understanding of how students' mathematical understanding, skills, and strategies develop from the early years (pre-school) through elementary school.

Developmental Continuum — A Useful Tool

- Based on current research on key developmental stages
- Enables teachers to view each student's achievements and challenges within a broader perspective
- Provides a tool for teachers to use with parents and supports teachers when discussing student progress

Purposeful Practice

Educators recognize the important role practice plays within a balanced program. Purposeful practice allows students to clarify, refine, consolidate, and apply new learning through a variety of experiences. In *Addison Wesley Mathematics Makes Sense*, purposeful practice is offered in every lesson to suit a range of learner needs.

At K to 2

Teacher Guide **Practice** suggestions for each core lesson include

- **Reinforcement** for all students
- **Extra Support** for students who may face ESL challenges, or need more experiences with early concepts, problem solving, or applying procedures
- *Extension* for students who are ready to take concepts further

Lessons also regularly include **Numbers Every Day,** and **Activity Banks.** These additional ideas for activities provide hands-on practice.

At grades 1 and 2, the Student Book provides a mechanism for students to record a selection of their mathematics practice.

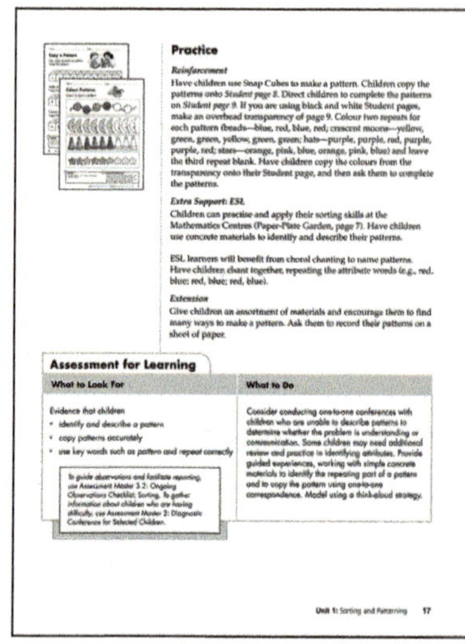

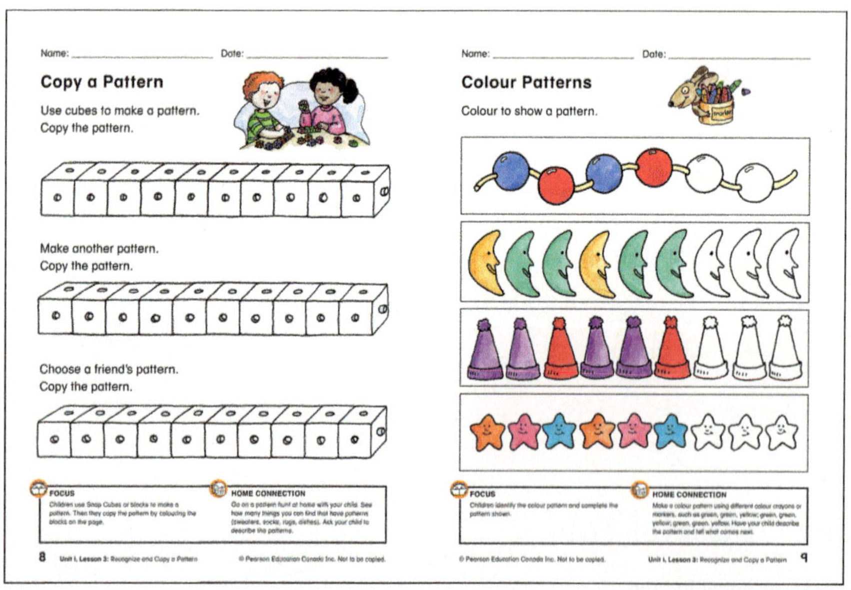

Students naturally solve mathematical problems daily.
Purposeful practice authenticates our classroom instruction.
– Jeananne Thomas, Program Author

At Grades 3 and up

Each lesson in the Student Book provides one to two pages of **Practice**.

This exercise set includes patterning and visual estimation, as well as reinforcement and problem-solving opportunities.

One question in each Practice is identified as an **Assessment Focus:** it provides a good barometer of students' level of conceptual understanding.

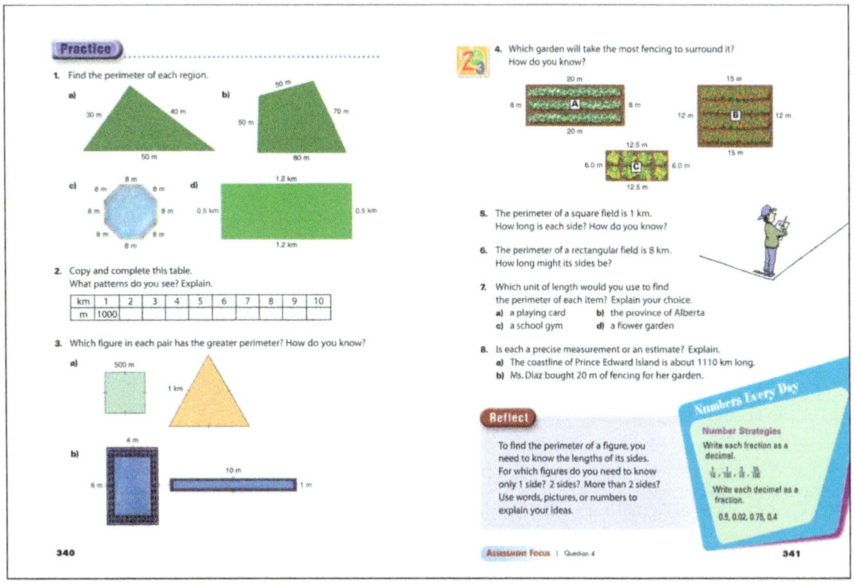
Practice

1. Find the perimeter of each region.

2. Copy and complete this table. What patterns do you see? Explain.

km	1	2	3	4	5	6	7	8	9	10
m	1000									

3. Which figure in each pair has the greater perimeter? How do you know?

4. Which garden will take the most fencing to surround it? How do you know?

5. The perimeter of a square field is 1 km. How long is each side? How do you know?

6. The perimeter of a rectangular field is 8 km. How long might its sides be?

7. Which unit of length would you use to find the perimeter of each item? Explain your choice.
a) a playing card b) the province of Alberta
c) a school gym d) a flower garden

8. Is each a precise measurement or an estimate? Explain.
a) The coastline of Prince Edward Island is about 1110 km long.
b) Ms. Diaz bought 20 m of fencing for her garden.

Reflect

To find the perimeter of a figure, you need to know the lengths of its sides. For which figures do you need to know only 1 side? 2 sides? More than 2 sides? Use words, pictures, or numbers to explain your ideas.

Numbers Every Day

Number Strategies

Write each fraction as a decimal.

Write each decimal as a fraction.

0.5, 0.02, 0.75, 0.4

340 341

In each lesson, **Numbers Every Day** reinforces students'

- Number Sense
- Calculator Skills
- Mental Math

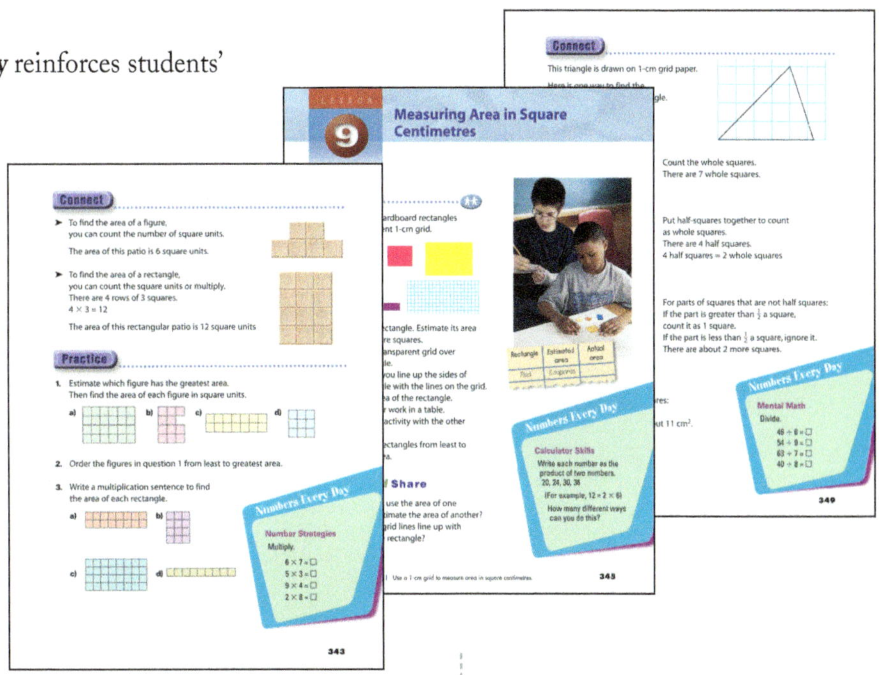
Lesson 9 Measuring Area in Square Centimetres

Connect

To find the area of a figure, you can count the number of square units. The area of this patio is 6 square units.

To find the area of a rectangle, you can count the square units or multiply. There are 4 rows of 3 squares. 4 × 3 = 12

The area of this rectangular patio is 12 square units.

Practice

1. Estimate which figure has the greatest area. Then find the area of each figure in square units.

2. Order the figures in question 1 from least to greatest area.

3. Write a multiplication sentence to find the area of each rectangle.

Numbers Every Day

Number Strategies

Multiply.

6 × 7 = □
5 × 3 = □
9 × 4 = □
2 × 8 = □

Calculator Skills

Mental Math

Divide.

343 345 349

The **Teacher Guide** provides

- Answers and sample responses to **Practice** questions
- Answers and strategy suggestions for **Numbers Every Day**
- **Extra Practice** masters to support specific student needs

Also available at grade 3 and beyond: A **Practice and Homework Book** with two pages of additional support for each lesson in the Student Book

Assessment for Learning

Assessment that informs instruction, with direct links to the curriculum and teacher reporting, is *purposeful, practical,* and *powerful* — a major contributor to how well students learn. In *Addison Wesley Mathematics Makes Sense,* assessment opportunities are woven right into the main flow of instruction, across every unit.

Unit Structure

- Unit Launch
- Core Lessons
- Strategies Toolkit
- Show What You Know
- Unit Problem (Grade 3 and up)

Term Structure

- Cross-Strand Investigation

Diagnostic (Unit Launch, Core Lessons)

Formative (Core Lessons, Strategies Toolkit, Show What You Know)

Summative (Show What You Know, Unit Problem, Cross-Strand Investigation)

Comprehensive Assessment Support

Your Teacher Guide provides detailed assessment support in each unit, with **Planning for Assessment** charts at the start of each unit, **Assessment for Learning** notes in each lesson, and a selection of **Assessment** masters specific to the unit content.

The **Assessment Module** in your Teacher Guide provides additional background support as well as generic assessment tools for use throughout the school year.

> Assessment is not an event, but a continuous process embedded in instruction.
>
> – Sharon Jeroski, Program Author

Diagnostic Assessment

- ☑ To identify students who are at risk in terms of acquiring concepts, procedures, and strategies required in the unit
- ☑ To develop insights into particular needs so that instruction can be adjusted to ensure students have the best possibility to succeed

At Grades 1 and 2

- The **Diagnostic Checklist** lets you record your observations during the **Unit Launch.**
- Mid-unit, use the **Diagnostic Conference** outline with students who appear to be at risk. This form includes scaffolding and observation cues.

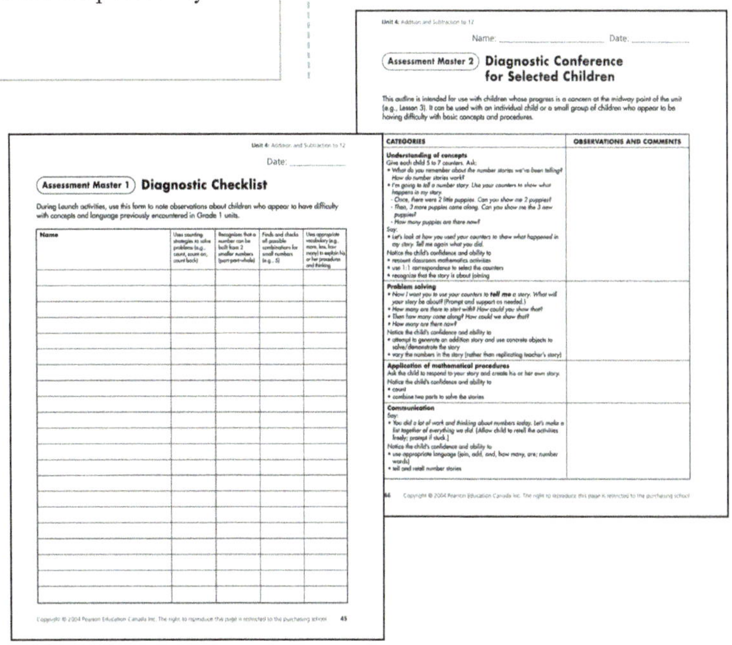

Assessment Master 1 Diagnostic Checklist

During Launch activities, use this form to note observations about children who appear to have difficulty with concepts and language previously encountered in Grade 1 units.

Assessment Master 2 Diagnostic Conference for Selected Children

CATEGORIES	OBSERVATIONS AND COMMENTS
Understanding of concepts	
Problem solving	
Application of mathematical procedures	
Communication	

At Grades 3 to 8

- Each **Unit Launch** in the Student Book is designed to probe children's prior knowledge and skills. The Teacher Guide provides additional diagnostic questions and support.
- The first **Cross-Strand Investigation** in the text lets you start the year with a meaningful context in which students re-visit key concepts from the previous year.
- Use the **Diagnostic Assessment** form; it cues you regarding what to watch for and how to help.

Formative Assessment

- ☑ To gather ongoing information in a variety of ways
- ☑ To provide feedback to students about how they are doing, and how they might improve
- ☑ To adjust instruction
- ☑ To provide additional scaffolding to students who need it
- ☑ To engage students in their own learning and in self-assessment

- At all grades, during all parts of the lesson, the Teacher Guide offers specific questions to probe student understanding.
- Because each lesson engages students directly in **actively exploring** the key concept, teachers have opportunities to observe what students are able to do.

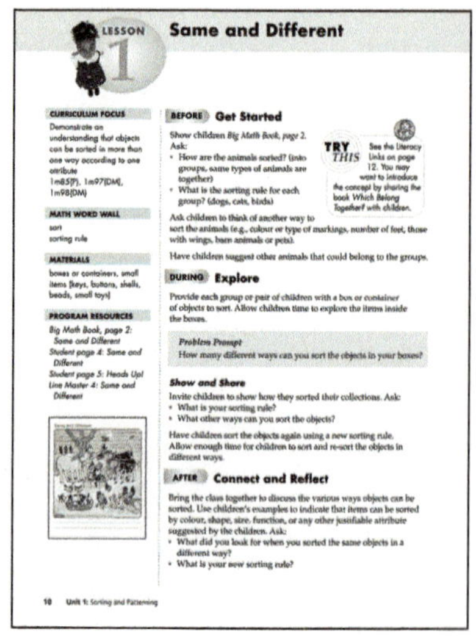

LESSON 1 **Same and Different**

CURRICULUM FOCUS
Demonstrate an understanding that objects can be sorted in more than one way according to one attribute
1m85(P), 1m97(DM), 1m98(DM)

MATH WORD WALL
sort
sorting rule

MATERIALS
boxes or containers, small items (keys, buttons, shells, beads, small toys)

PROGRAM RESOURCES
Big Math Book, page 2: Same and Different
Student page 4: Same and Different
Student page 5: Heads Up!
Line Master 4: Same and Different

BEFORE **Get Started**

Show children *Big Math Book, page 2.*
Ask:
- How are the animals sorted? (into groups, same types of animals are together)
- What is the sorting rule for each group? (dogs, cats, birds)

TRY THIS See the Literacy Links on page 12. You may want to introduce the concept by sharing the book *Which Belong Together?* with children.

Ask children to think of another way to sort the animals (e.g., colour or type of markings, number of feet, those with wings, barn animals or pets).

Have children suggest other animals that could belong to the groups.

DURING **Explore**

Provide each group or pair of children with a box or container of objects to sort. Allow children time to explore the items inside the boxes.

Problem Prompt
How many different ways can you sort the objects in your boxes?

Show and Share
Invite children to show how they sorted their collections. Ask:
- What is your sorting rule?
- What other ways can you sort the objects?

Have children sort the objects again using a new sorting rule. Allow enough time for children to sort and re-sort the objects in different ways.

AFTER **Connect and Reflect**

Bring the class together to discuss the various ways objects can be sorted. Use children's examples to indicate that items can be sorted by colour, shape, size, function, or any other justifiable attribute suggested by the children. Ask:
- What did you look for when you sorted the same objects in a different way?
- What is your new sorting rule?

10 Unit 1: Sorting and Patterning

- At all grades, **Show and Share** provides a key opportunity for eliciting students' understanding through communication.

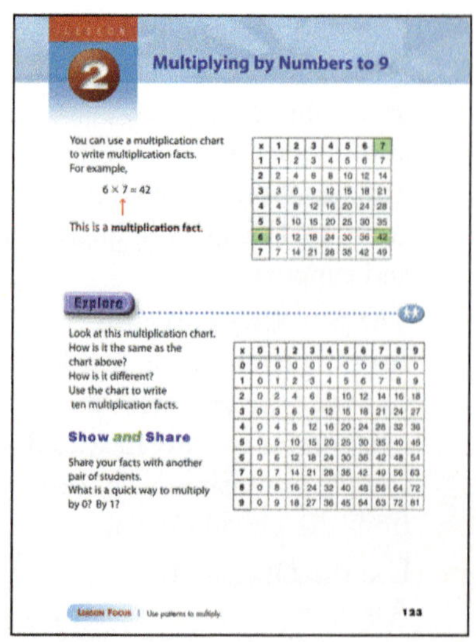

LESSON 2 **Multiplying by Numbers to 9**

You can use a multiplication chart to write multiplication facts.
For example,

$6 \times 7 = 42$

This is a **multiplication fact.**

×	1	2	3	4	5	6	7
1	1	2	3	4	5	6	7
2	2	4	6	8	10	12	14
3	3	6	9	12	15	18	21
4	4	8	12	16	20	24	28
5	5	10	15	20	25	30	35
6	6	12	18	24	30	36	42
7	7	14	21	28	35	42	49

Explore

Look at this multiplication chart.
How is it the same as the chart above?
How is it different?
Use the chart to write ten multiplication facts.

×	0	1	2	3	4	5	6	7	8	9
0	0	0	0	0	0	0	0	0	0	0
1	0	1	2	3	4	5	6	7	8	9
2	0	2	4	6	8	10	12	14	16	18
3	0	3	6	9	12	15	18	21	24	27
4	0	4	8	12	16	20	24	28	32	36
5	0	5	10	15	20	25	30	35	40	45
6	0	6	12	18	24	30	36	42	48	54
7	0	7	14	21	28	35	42	49	56	63
8	0	8	16	24	32	40	48	56	64	72
9	0	9	18	27	36	45	54	63	72	81

Show and Share

Share your facts with another pair of students.
What is a quick way to multiply by 0? By 1?

LESSON FOCUS | Use patterns to multiply

133

> Assessment has taken on new importance in its impact on instructional decisions.
>
> – Ralph Connelly, Program Author

- In the Teacher Guide, **Assessment for Learning** directs your attention to specific behaviours you may see in students' work, and provides practical instructions about what to do to help students who may be struggling.
- **Practice** questions provide more opportunities for you to observe, probe, and provide feedback about student development.

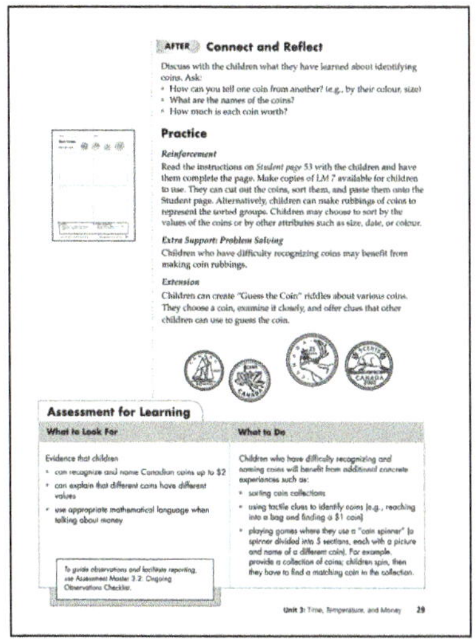

- At grades 3 to 8, Practice sets always include one exercise highlighted as an **Assessment Focus** question: this open-ended problem allows for a range of performance levels, and provides a quick touchstone for you as you circulate to observe students at work.

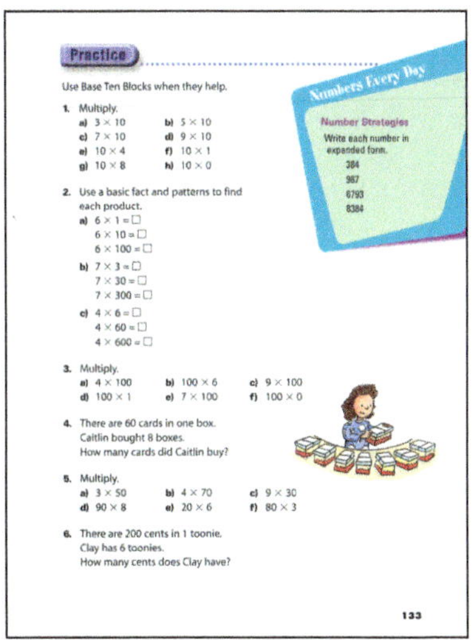

- At grades 3 to 8, the Teacher Guide support for the Practice includes notes on **common misconceptions** and **opportunities for reteaching.**

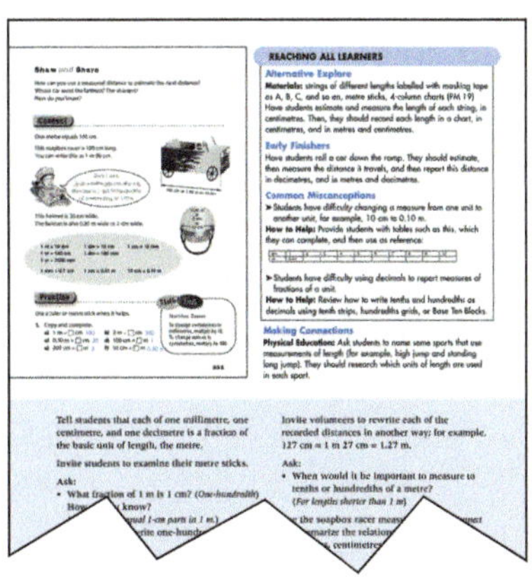

Summative Assessment

- ☑ To make a judgment about a student's achievement of the learning goals for the unit
- ☑ To facilitate reporting

Addison Wesley Mathematics Makes Sense provides a variety of options to meet your summative assessment needs.

At Grades 1 and 2

Show What You Know features performance tasks that enable students to work with concepts from the unit with new materials, or with a new context.

My Journal, in the Student Book, invites students to use pictures, words, or numbers to show their learning.

Cross-Strand Investigations appear once each term. These rich problems have a strong story element. They present an engaging context to students, and allow you to assess the extent to which students are able to synthesize and apply their learning in an integrated way.

The Teacher Guide provides a rubric and supporting notes for each Cross-Strand Investigation, in the **Additional Assessment Support** module that accompanies the Teacher Guide.

At Grades 3 and up

Show What You Know includes a combination of short answer and open-ended questions, all cross-referenced to relevant lessons of the unit.

A **Unit Problem** involves students in the context used to introduce the unit. A **Check List** in the Student Book tells students how their work will be assessed.

Reflect on the Unit presents a journal opportunity that asks students to consolidate their understanding of the big idea for the unit.

Cross-Strand Investigations appear once each term in the Student Book. These rich problems present an engaging context to students, and allow you to assess the extent to which students are able to synthesize and apply their learning in an integrated way.

The Teacher Guide provides a rubric and supporting notes for each Cross-Strand Investigation, in the **Additional Assessment Support** module that accompanies the Teacher Guide.

A three-part **Unit Test** in the Teacher Guide includes a short-answer section, conceptual items, and a problem to be solved.

Teachers are facing increased pressures around accountability. They need some practical support to meet new reporting requirements.

– Jason Johnston, Program Author

Reporting Opportunities

Managing your assessment strategies is a first step in your effective communication regarding student performance, whether informally through parent interviews, or through your preparation of student reports. *Addison Wesley Mathematics Makes Sense* supports your reporting requirements in a number of ways.

- By offering a **Scope and Sequence** that allows you to cover several strands in each term, with each strand appearing at least once in each grade
- With a **Learning Skills Checklist** that lets you summarize observations for possible use in report card comments
- With an **Ongoing Observations Checklist** for each unit that lets you track student performance lesson by lesson, with each lesson tied to your specific curriculum expectations/outcomes
- With specific **rubrics** that match your provincial reporting protocols
- With a **Unit Summary** tracking sheet that lets you record a student's most consistent achievement level in each block of lessons from the unit, with space for anecdotal comments

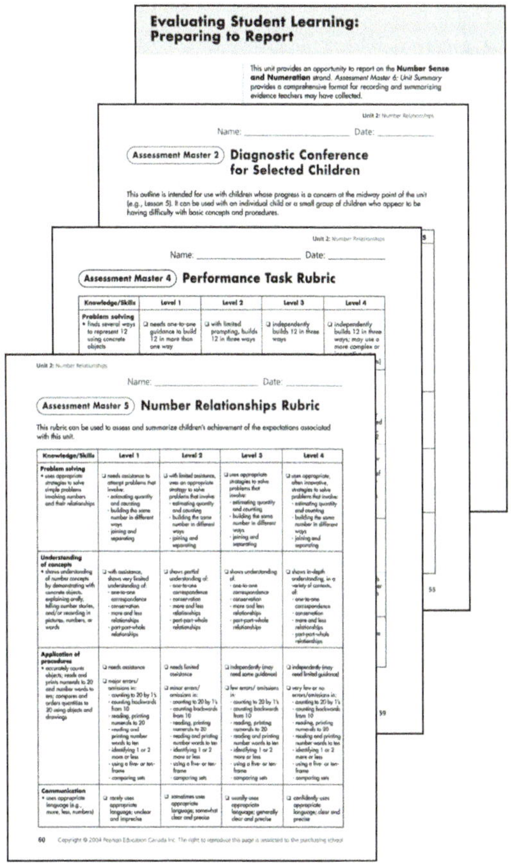

Evaluating Student Learning: Preparing to Report

Assessment Master 2 Diagnostic Conference for Selected Children

Assessment Master 4 Performance Task Rubric

Assessment Master 5 Number Relationships Rubric

At the close of the unit, look for reporting guidelines and sample report card comments in **Evaluating Student Learning: Preparing to Report.**

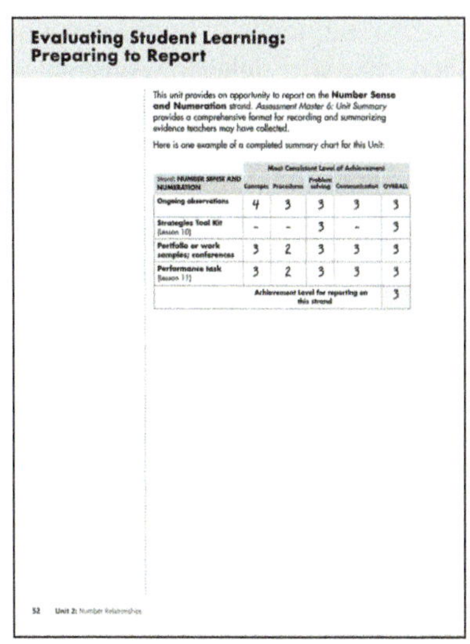

Evaluating Student Learning: Preparing to Report

Your Curriculum Requirements

Addison Wesley Mathematics Makes Sense organizes your curriculum into clusters of expectations/outcomes across and within grades to create a logical, conceptual, and developmental progression of curriculum presentation.

The authors and development team have analyzed your curriculum document carefully, against the backdrop of sound conceptual development. The result is a carefully structured program that makes sense across the grades and, within each grade, designed to enhance student understanding and to recognize students' developmental stages.

Our scope and sequence is designed to meet the demands of your school year calendar. At each grade level, *Addison Wesley Mathematics Makes Sense* has 11 units to keep formal reporting needs to a minimum, while ensuring complete curriculum coverage.

At each grade level, unit by unit, the program filters your curriculum requirements into a selection of "curriculum clusters." Each curriculum cluster represents a "big idea," a building block to creating a deep understanding of mathematics concepts.

- The **Curriculum Overview** in each Teacher Guide unit reveals the "big ideas" of the unit at a glance.

At Grades 1 and 2

For each curriculum cluster at grades 1 and 2, we've organized a logical sequence of core **Lessons**, together with relevant **Activity Banks** to provide additional teaching options.

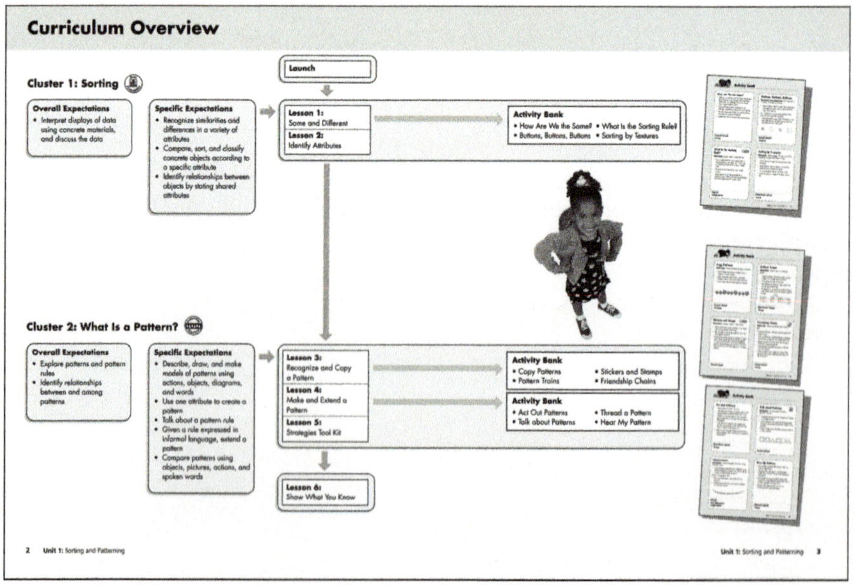
Curriculum Overview

Cluster 1: Sorting

Overall Expectations
- Interpret displays of data using concrete materials, and discuss the data

Specific Expectations
- Recognize similarities and differences in a variety of attributes
- Compare, sort, and classify concrete objects according to a specific attribute
- Identify relationships between objects by stating shared attributes

Launch

Lesson 1: Same and Different

Lesson 2: Identify Attributes

Activity Bank
- How Are We the Same?
- What Is the Sorting Rule?
- Buttons, Buttons, Buttons
- Sorting by Textures

Cluster 2: What Is a Pattern?

Overall Expectations
- Explore patterns and pattern rules
- Identify relationships between and among patterns

Specific Expectations
- Describe, draw, and make models of patterns using actions, objects, diagrams, and words
- Use one attribute to create a pattern
- Talk about a pattern rule
- Given a rule expressed in informal language, extend a pattern
- Compare patterns using objects, pictures, actions, and spoken words

Lesson 3: Recognize and Copy a Pattern

Lesson 4: Make and Extend a Pattern

Lesson 5: Strategies Tool Kit

Lesson 6: Show What You Know

Activity Bank
- Copy Patterns
- Stickers and Stamps
- Pattern Trains
- Friendship Chains

Activity Bank
- Act Out Patterns
- Thread a Pattern
- Talk about Patterns
- Hear My Pattern

2 Unit 1: Sorting and Patterning

Unit 1: Sorting and Patterning 3

A curriculum document sets out overall content goals. It is our responsibility to make that content unfold in the classroom on a daily basis.
– Bryn Keyes, Program Author

At Grades 3 and up

The Curriculum Overview in grades 3 and up shows how the lessons develop across the unit.

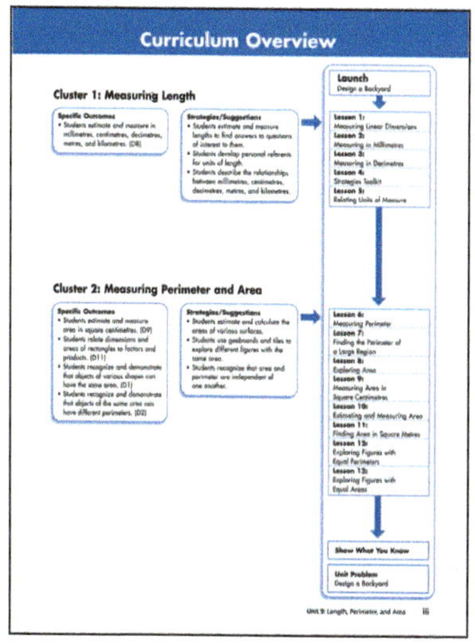

- The **Curriculum Focus** is summarized for each lesson and lists specific outcomes/expectations that relate to the lesson.

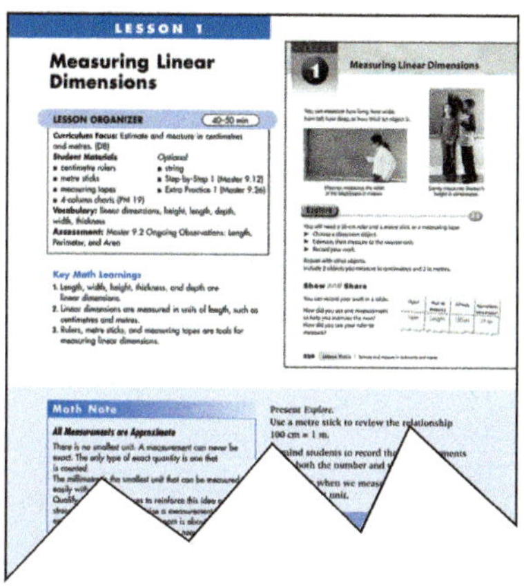

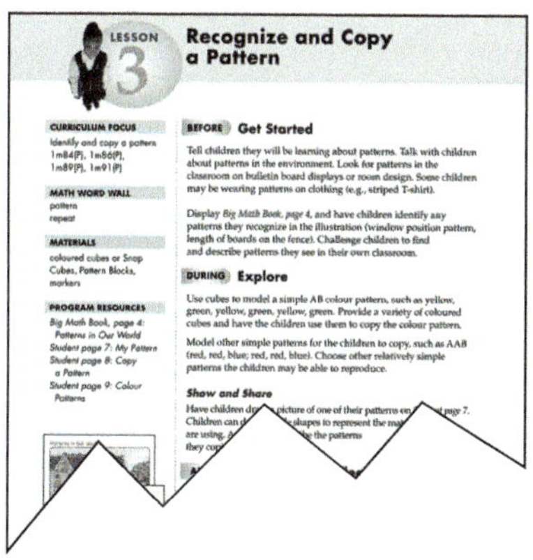

Your regional **Teacher Guide** highlights specific curriculum requirements and

- Year-long planning suggestions
- A **Curriculum Overview** in each unit that clusters and correlates your curriculum to specific lessons
- Specific lesson notes and suggestions
- The CD-ROM that accompanies your Teacher Guide

Making Sense of...

Solutions for Combined Grades

Teachers of combined grades have a special challenge in their task of providing full curriculum coverage for different grade levels, in the same classroom and during the same class period, while addressing the learning needs of all their students. *Addison Wesley Mathematics Makes Sense* offers planning tools for day-to-day support of combined grades classrooms.

Available as a supplement to your Teacher Guide, our **Together Resources** provide practical suggestions for planning and teaching combined grades.

- Background notes outline 3 general lesson approaches, depending on the nature of the content at hand and students' prior knowledge
- Specific unit suggestions identify a day-to-day unit plan with recommended lesson approaches, notes for specific activities, and homework assignments from the unit

In our earliest planning, combined grades have been considered in the creation of the **K to 8 Scope and Sequence.** Wherever the mathematical content allowed, and the curriculum requirements indicated, our development team strove to ensure that unit content aligned across the grades.

Benchmarks for Developing Measurement

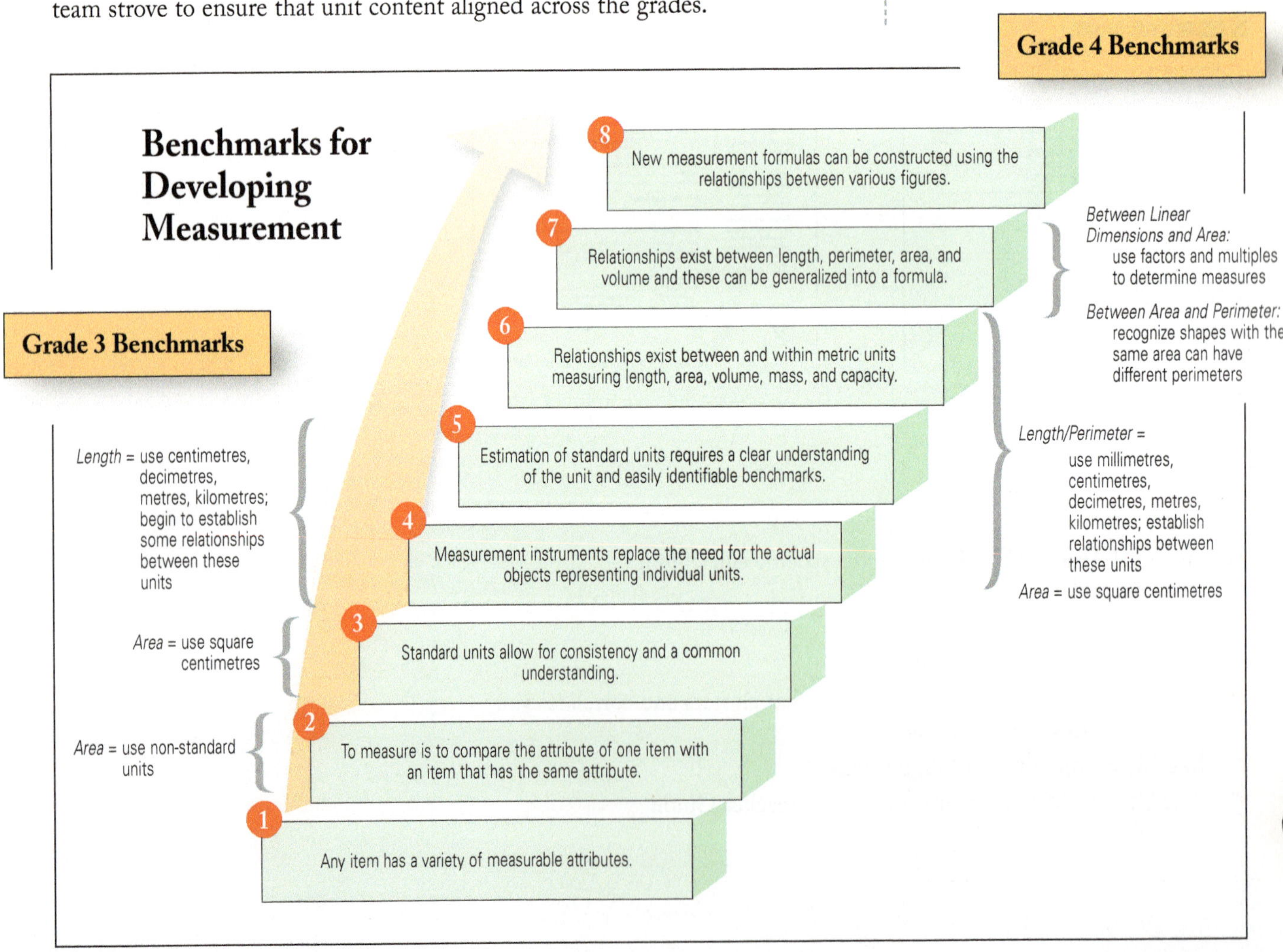

> Understanding developmental stages provides a framework for planning effective mathematics lessons to meet the needs of all students.
> – Craig Featherstone, Program Consultant

K to 2 Scope and Sequence: Supporting Combined Grades

Although headings may change, they accurately reflect content plans.

Kindergarten	Unit	Grade 1	Grade 2
Number Sense and Numeration	1	**Sorting and Patterning**	**Sorting and Patterning**
Measurement	2	**Number Development:** Number Relationships	**Number Development:** Counting and Patterns
Geometry	3	**Measurement:** Time, Temperature, and Money	**Measurement:** Time, Temperature, and Money
		Cross-Strand Investigation	Cross-Strand Investigation
Patterning and Algebra	4	**Number Operations:** Addition and Subtraction to 12	**Number Operations:** Exploring Addition and Subtraction
Data Management	5	**Data Management and Probability**	**Data Management and Probability**
	6	**3-Dimensional Geometry**	**3-Dimensional Geometry**
	7	**Number Operations:** Addition and Subtraction	**Number Operations:** Addition and Subtraction
		Cross-Strand Investigation	Cross-Strand Investigation
	8	**Measurement:** Linear Measurement and Area	**Measurement:** Linear Measurement and Area
	9	**2-Dimensional Geometry**	**2-Dimensional Geometry**
	10	**Number Operations:** Number and Applications	**Number Operations:** Number and Number Patterns
	11	**Measurement:** Mass and Capacity	**Measurement:** Mass and Capacity
		Cross-Strand Investigation	Cross-Strand Investigation

Grades 3 to 6 Scope and Sequence: Supporting Combined Grades

Although headings may change, they accurately reflect content plans.

Unit	Grade 3	Grade 4	Grade 5	Grade 6
1	**Patterns in Number:** Patterns and Place Value	**Patterns in Number**	**Patterns in Number**	**Patterns in Number:** Patterns and Algebra
2	**Number Operations:** Patterns in Addition and Subtraction	**Number Operations:** Whole Numbers and Operations	**Number Operations:** Whole Numbers and Operations	**Number Operations:** Whole Numbers and Operations
3	**Geometry**	**Geometry**	**Geometry**	**Geometry**
	Cross-Strand Investigation	Cross-Strand Investigation	Cross-Strand Investigation	Cross-Strand Investigation
4	**Number Operations:** Multiplication and Division	**Number Operations:** Multiplication and Division	**Number Development:** Decimals	**Number Development:** Fractions and Decimals
5	**Data Management**	**Data Management**	**Data Management**	**Data Management**
6	**Measurement:** Time, Money, and Mass	**Measurement:** Time, Money, and Mass	**Measurement:** Time, Money, and Mass	**Measurement:** Time, Money, and Mass
7	**Geometry:** Transformational Geometry	**Geometry:** Transformational Geometry	**Geometry:** 3-D Geometry and Measurement	**Geometry:** 3-D Geometry and Measurement
	Cross-Strand Investigation	Cross-Strand Investigation	Cross-Strand Investigation	Cross-Strand Investigation
8	**Fractions**	**Fractions and Decimals**	**Fractions and Decimals**	**Fractions:** Ratio, Rate, and Percent
9	**Measurement:** Length, Perimeter, and Area	**Measurement:** Length, Perimeter, and Area	**Measurement:** Length, Perimeter, and Area	**Measurement:** Length, Perimeter, and Area
10	**Patterns and Relationships:** Patterns in Geometry	**Patterns and Relationships:** Patterns in Number and Geometry	**Patterns and Relationships:** Patterns in Number and Geometry	**Patterns and Relationships:** Patterning and Algebra
11	**Probability**	**Probability**	**Probability**	**Probability**
	Cross-Strand Investigation	Cross-Strand Investigation	Cross-Strand Investigation	Cross-Strand Investigation

Grades 7 to 8 Scope and Sequence: Supporting Combined Grades

Although headings may change, they accurately reflect content plans.

Unit	Grade 7	Grade 8
1	**Whole Numbers and Patterns**	**Number and Patterns**
2	**Number Development:** Fractions and Decimals	**Number Development:** Fractions and Decimals
3	**Geometry**	**Geometry**
	Cross-Strand Investigation	Cross-Strand Investigation
4	**Number Development:** Working with Percent	**Number Development:** Working with Percent
5	**Data Management:** Collect, Analyse, and Display	**Data Management:** Collect, Analyse, Display, Infer from Data
6	**Measurement:** Perimeter and Area	**Measurement:** Circle and Triangle Measurement
7	**Geometry and Measurement**	**Geometry and Measurement**
	Cross-Strand Investigation	Cross-Strand Investigation
8	**Ratio and Proportion**	**Ratio and Proportion**
9	**Integers**	**Integers**
10	**Patterning and Algebra:** Linear Equations	**Patterning and Algebra:** Linear Equations
11	**Data Analysis and Probability**	**Data Analysis and Probability**
	Cross-Strand Investigation	Cross-Strand Investigation

Reaching All Learners

Addison Wesley Mathematics Makes Sense meets diverse needs in both the Student Book and Teacher Guide. Through the Teacher Guide, the program also provides strategies for creating an inclusive learning environment while supporting individual student needs.

From the ground up . . . the Lesson Model

A consistent lesson model simplifies the instructional design while offering a balanced approach to learning new concepts.

- **Explore** activities use a variety of groupings and types of materials; their exploratory nature allows for varying background knowledge
  - **Show and Share** highlights opportunities for students to support each other in developing new concepts
- **Connect** consolidates key concepts for all learners
- **Practice** questions cover a range of difficulty levels and learning styles

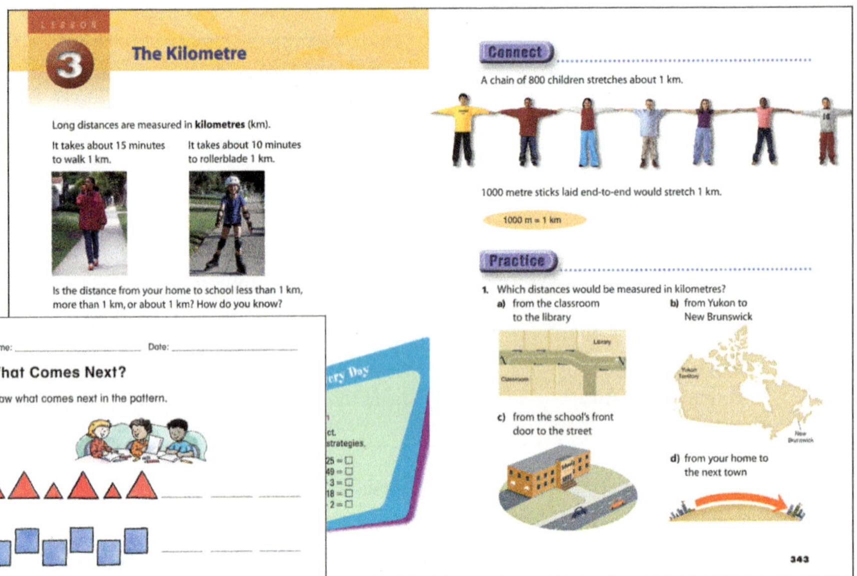

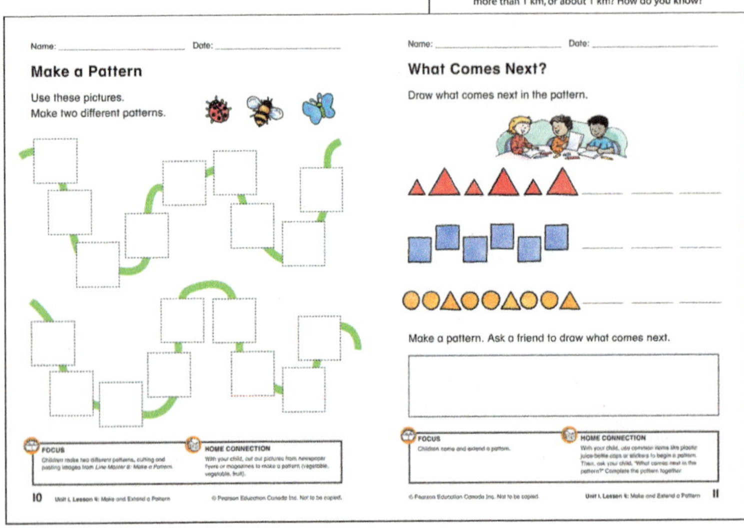

Understanding the elementary-level student:

- An open, inviting design with language at an appropriate reading level
- Content pacing that fits the developmental stage of the learner
- Contexts that are meaningful across cultures — from First Nations people to our multicultural mosaic
- Opportunities to communicate responses in a variety of ways — through words, numbers, pictures, or models

All students need opportunities to apply mathematics skills and concepts in ways that are meaningful to them.
– Sue Gordon, Author

Reaching all learners . . . through support in the Teacher Guide

In the Teacher Guide, additional activities address multiple intelligences, while teaching notes offer suggestions for supporting specific student needs.

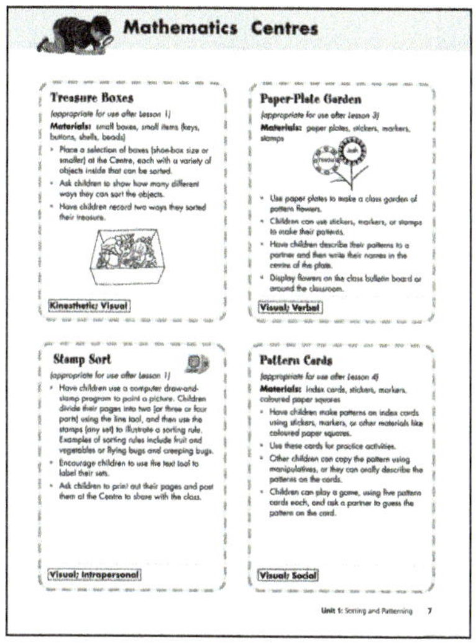

Mathematics Centres

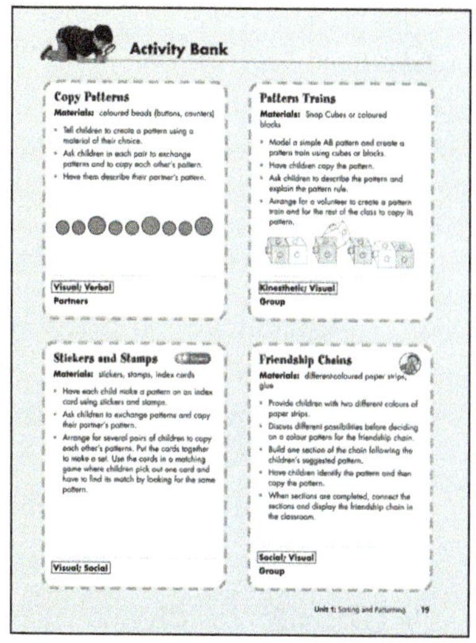

Activity Bank

At Grades 1 and 2

- **Mathematics Centres** provide ideas for extra support and reinforcement throughout the unit
- **Practice** suggestions for core lessons include ideas for **Extra Support** for ESL learners or students who require additional reinforcement
- **Activity Banks** for core lessons identify multiple intelligences and grouping options
- **Assessment for Learning** provides suggestions for identifying and addressing specific student needs

At Grades 3 and up

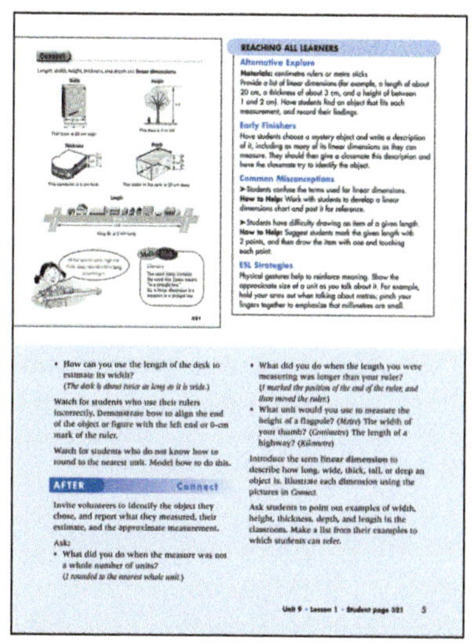

- **Additional Activities** at the start of each unit provide ideas for extra support
- Notes in each lesson provide suggestions for **ESL Strategies; Alternative Explore; Common Misconceptions,** and **How to Help**
- **Assessment for Learning** provides suggestions for identifying and addressing specific student needs
- **Step by Step** offers a scaffolded problem in worksheet form, featuring the Assessment Focus question from the Practice set, provided for every lesson

Building a Math Community

This section in the Grade 4 Planning and Program Masters module in your Teacher Guide gives you:

- Guidelines for creating a supportive environment for learning mathematics
- Suggestions for age-appropriate activities, games, and routines that help to create positive attitudes toward learning mathematics

Making Sense of...

Math Connections

Addison Wesley Mathematics Makes Sense recognizes that mathematical understanding is deepened and enhanced when students make connections between what they are learning and their own experience.

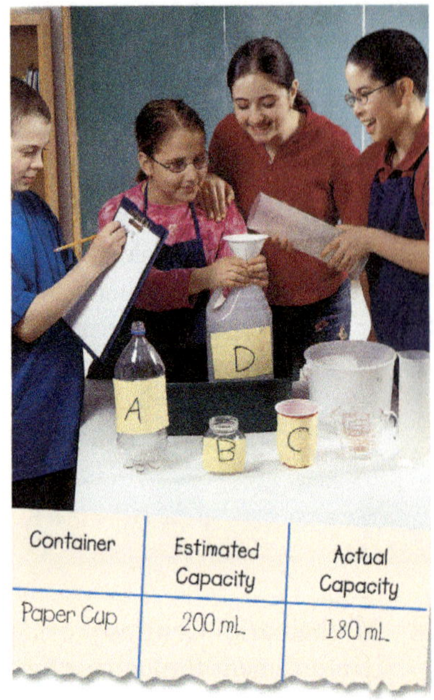

Real-World Contexts

- **Unit Launches** provide contexts to prompt mathematical conversation
- **Problem prompts** and activities in core lessons are relevant to the student's experience
- **Unit Problems** feature applied settings

Numbers Every Day

- Connects "number" to everyday class routines in Kindergarten to Grade 2, threading number concepts through all core learning in Grades 3-8

Cross-Curricular Connections

- At Kindergarten to grade 2, Teacher Guide notes in each lesson provide suggestions for relating mathematics to other subject areas – art, science, social studies, physical education, music
- At grades 3 and up, **Math Link** features in the student book highlight cross-curricular, mathematical, or real-world connections; the Teacher Guide details additional ideas

Across Strands

- Integration of strands occurs within units at the lesson level, and through the **Activity Banks** and **Mathematics Centres.**
- **Cross-Strand Investigations** appear each term, to provide opportunities for rich problem solving that draws on multiple strand concepts.

Students better understand mathematical concepts when they make real-life connections and talk about personal experiences.
– Angela D'Alessandro, Program Author

The Literacy and Numeracy Connection

At K to 2

- **Addison Wesley Mathematics Little Books** and **Lap Books** provide an alternative for launching or extending lessons.
- The **Big Math Book** appeals to primary-level children, many of whom may not yet be comfortable reading print. It includes chants, poems and songs that connect the kinesthetic to the linguistic.
- A take-home book with each **Investigation** in the Student Book provides a shared reading opportunity with mathematical elements.
- The **Literacy Links** feature in the Teacher Guide suggests titles that can be integrated with each lesson or used as a cross-over point with the teaching of language arts.
- Teacher Guide suggestions include use of **cooperative journals**, **pocket charts,** and a **Math Word Wall.**

At Grades 3 to 8

- **Key Words** are listed in the Student Book at the start of each unit
- Students' vocabulary is supported with an illustrated **Glossary** in the Student Book
- **Literature Opportunities** are listed in the Teacher Guide with each Unit Launch; share these literature suggestions before starting the unit to help motivate learning

Home Connections

Parents have a significant role to play in student learning, in supporting and reinforcing what is learned in the classroom each day, and promoting a positive attitude toward mathematics in the home.

Addison Wesley Mathematics Makes Sense provides several tools for communicating with parents, with a changing emphasis as the learner matures from grade 2 to grade 3, and beyond.

At Grades 1 and 2 ...in the Student Book

- Each unit includes a **Dear Family** letter regarding the upcoming unit.
- Each page presents a **Focus** statement to communicate the key learning, and a **Home Connection** suggestion for further reinforcement.
- Between selected units, **Math at Home** – a tear-out, take-home booklet – provides a magazine-style family connection with mathematical information, Canadian trivia, and game suggestions.

Name: ______________ Date: ______________

Dear Family,

In this unit, your child will be learning about time, temperature, and money.

The Learning Goals for this unit are to

- Understand temperature as it relates to seasons and activities.
- Describe and order events, that happen in a day.
- Identify key events, such as birthdays.
- Compare the duration of events, such as recess and lunchtime.
- Name the seasons and days of the week.
- Tell time to the hour.
- Make groups of coins up to 10 cents.

You can help your child reach these goals by doing the activities suggested at the bottom of each page.

44 Unit 3, Launch: Time, Temperature, and Money © Pearson Education Canada Inc. Not to be copied.

At K to 2 ...in the Teacher Guide

- Look for **At Home** line masters that provide a summary of the Big Ideas in the unit, with accompanying activities to reinforce key concepts at home.
- In each unit, content-specific **Assessment Tools** support the teacher when speaking with parents about children's progress.

Students, teachers, and parents are all partners in the learning process.

– Maggie Martin Connell, Program Author

At Grades 3 and up ...in the Student Book

- **Learning Goals** and **Key Words**, presented at the start of each unit, identify the content to be covered for parents as well as students.
- The **Lesson Focus** statement, on the first page of each lesson, identifies the key learning goal for the lesson.
- Parents can use the **Connect** section of each lesson to check the key concepts students have covered in class.
- Regular **At Home** features suggest activities for students to do with family members at home.

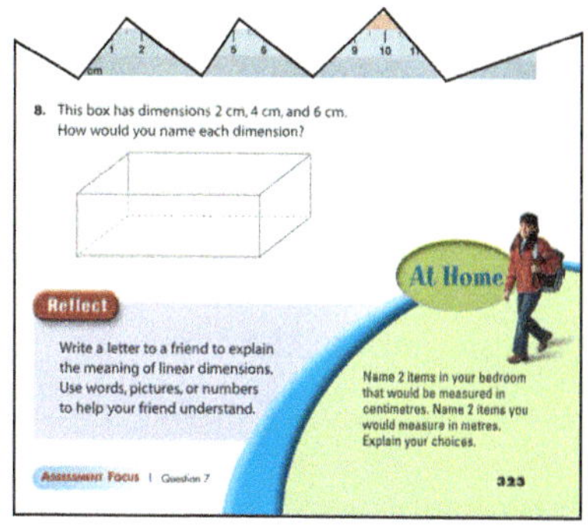
8. This box has dimensions 2 cm, 4 cm, and 6 cm.
How would you name each dimension?

Reflect

Write a letter to a friend to explain the meaning of linear dimensions. Use words, pictures, or numbers to help your friend understand.

At Home

Name 2 items in your bedroom that would be measured in centimetres. Name 2 items you would measure in metres. Explain your choices.

Assessment Focus | Question 7

323

Practice and Homework Book for Grades 3 to 8

- For each lesson, a Quick Review of the key concepts
- For each lesson, graded practice questions that students can complete at home
- Games and activities used for practice when appropriate

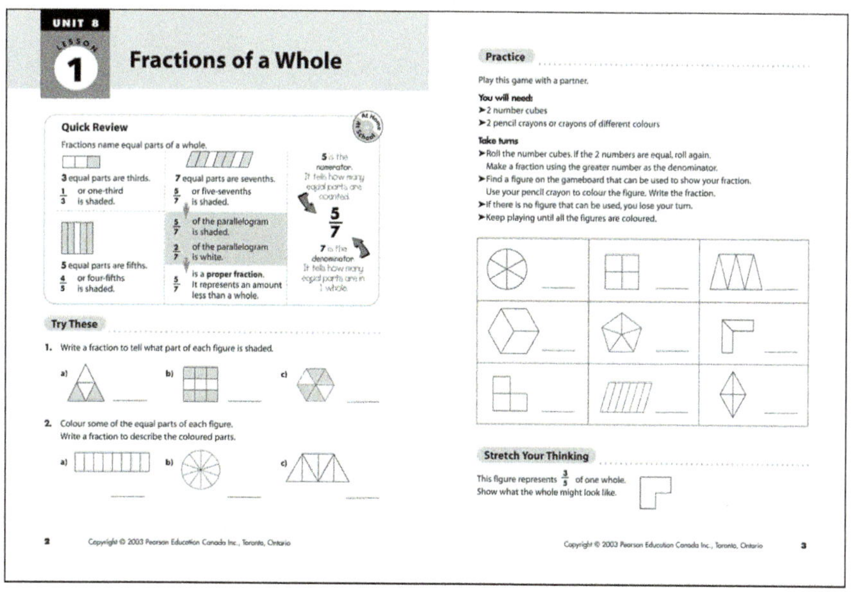
UNIT 8 LESSON 1

Fractions of a Whole

Quick Review

Fractions name equal parts of a whole.

3 equal parts are thirds. $\frac{1}{3}$ or one-third is shaded.

5 equal parts are fifths. $\frac{4}{5}$ or four-fifths is shaded.

7 equal parts are sevenths. $\frac{5}{7}$ or five-sevenths is shaded.

$\frac{5}{7}$ of the parallelogram is shaded.

$\frac{2}{7}$ of the parallelogram is white.

$\frac{5}{7}$ is a **proper fraction**. It represents an amount less than a whole.

5 is the **numerator**. It tells how many equal parts are counted.

7 is the **denominator**. It tells how many equal parts are in 1 whole.

Try These

1. Write a fraction to tell what part of each figure is shaded.

a) b) c)

2. Colour some of the equal parts of each figure.
Write a fraction to describe the coloured parts.

a) b) c)

2 Copyright © 2003 Pearson Education Canada Inc., Toronto, Ontario

Practice

Play this game with a partner.

You will need:

- 2 number cubes
- 2 pencil crayons or crayons of different colours

Take turns

- Roll the number cubes. If the 2 numbers are equal, roll again. Make a fraction using the greater number as the denominator.
- Find a figure on the gameboard that can be used to show your fraction. Use your pencil crayon to colour the figure. Write the fraction.
- If there is no figure that can be used, you lose your turn.
- Keep playing until all the figures are coloured.

Stretch Your Thinking

This figure represents $\frac{3}{5}$ of one whole. Show what the whole might look like.

Copyright © 2003 Pearson Education Canada Inc., Toronto, Ontario 3

Across the Grades

The Pearson Education mathematics Website provides parent information and support.

Technology

Addison Wesley Mathematics Makes Sense integrates technology in the following ways.

- **Technology Lessons** in the student book highlight opportunities for learning new mathematical concepts through the use of the calculator or the computer.

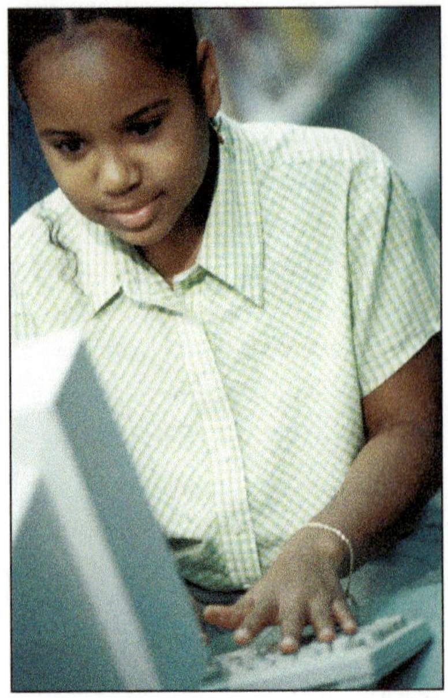

Grade 1

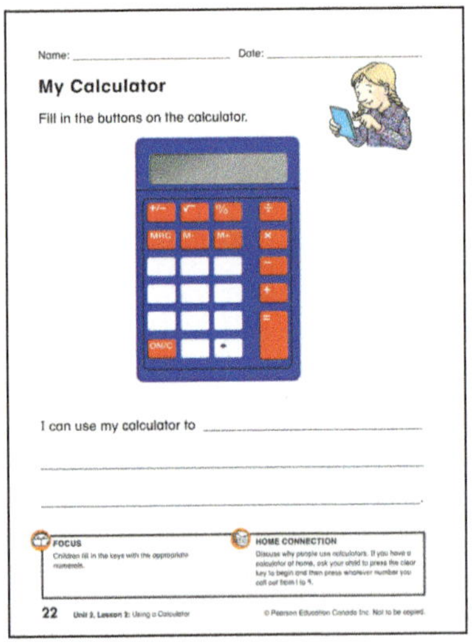

Name: ______________ Date: ______________

My Calculator

Fill in the buttons on the calculator.

I can use my calculator to ______________

____

______________.

FOCUS
Children fill in the keys with the appropriate numerals.

HOME CONNECTION
Discuss why people use calculators. If you have a calculator at home, ask your child to press the clear key to begin and then press whatever number you call out from 1 to 9.

22 Unit 3, Lesson 3: Using a Calculator © Pearson Education Canada Inc. Not to be copied.

Grade 4

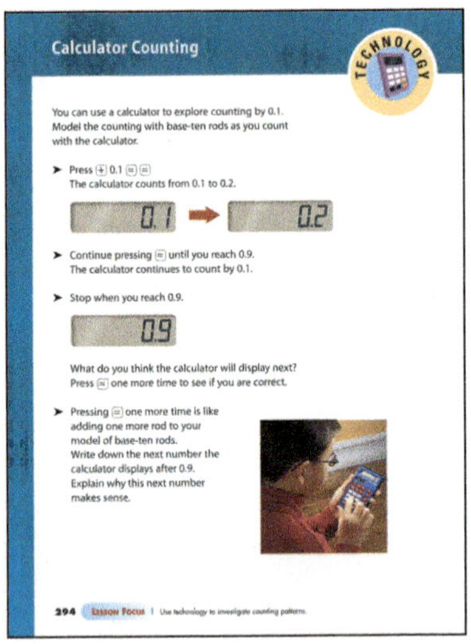

Calculator Counting

You can use a calculator to explore counting by 0.1. Model the counting with base-ten rods as you count with the calculator.

➤ Press + 0.1 = =
The calculator counts from 0.1 to 0.2.

➤ Continue pressing = until you reach 0.9.
The calculator continues to count by 0.1.

➤ Stop when you reach 0.9.

What do you think the calculator will display next?
Press = one more time to see if you are correct.

➤ Pressing = one more time is like adding one more rod to your model of base-ten rods.
Write down the next number the calculator displays after 0.9.
Explain why this next number makes sense.

294 Lesson Focus | Use technology to investigate counting patterns.

- When appropriate, individual activities within the student book suggest the use of a calculator or computer application to enrich and extend the mathematics.
- Suggestions for Numbers Every Day regularly include suggestions related to Calculator Skills.

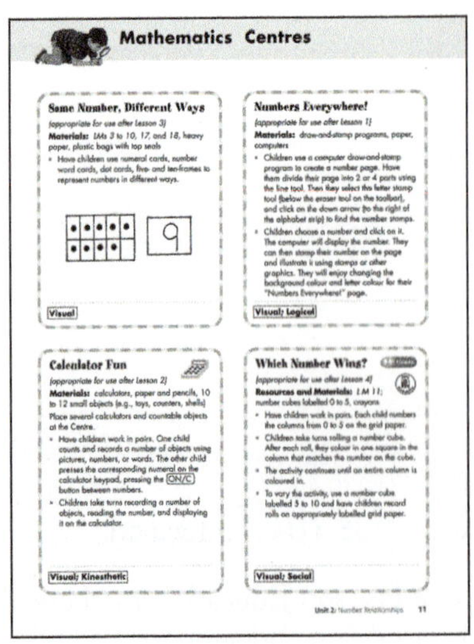

Mathematics Centres

Same Number, Different Ways
(appropriate for use after Lesson 3)
Materials: LMs 3 to 10, 17, and 18, heavy paper, plastic bags with top seals
- Have children use numeral cards, number word cards, dot cards, five- and ten-frames to represent numbers in different ways.

Visual

Numbers Everywhere!
(appropriate for use after Lesson 1)
Materials: draw-and-stamp programs, paper, computers
- Children use a computer draw-and-stamp program to create a number page. Have them divide their page into 2 or 4 parts using the line tool. Then they select the letter stamp tool (below the eraser tool on the toolbar), and click on the down arrow (to the right of the alphabet strip) to find the number stamps.
- Children choose a number and click on it. The computer will display the number. They can then stamp their number on the page and illustrate it using stamps or other graphics. They will enjoy changing the background colour and letter colour for their "Numbers Everywhere!" page.

Visual; Logical

Calculator Fun
(appropriate for use after Lesson 2)
Materials: calculators, paper and pencils, 10 to 12 small objects (e.g., toys, counters, shells)
Place several calculators and countable objects at the Centre.
- Have children work in pairs. One child counts and records a number of objects using pictures, numbers, or words. The other child presses the corresponding numeral on the calculator keypad, pressing the ON/C button between numbers.
- Children take turns recording a number of objects, reading the number, and displaying it on the calculator.

Visual; Kinesthetic

Which Number Wins?
(appropriate for use after Lesson 4)
Resources and Materials: LM 11; number cubes labelled 0 to 5, crayons
- Have children work in pairs. Each child numbers the columns from 0 to 5 on the grid paper.
- Children take turns rolling a number cube. After each roll, they colour in one square in the column that matches the number on the cube.
- The activity continues until an entire column is coloured in.
- To vary the activity, use a number cube labelled 5 to 10 and have children record rolls on appropriately labelled grid paper.

Visual; Social

Unit 2: Number Relationships 11

> The purposeful use of technology in the mathematics classroom can enrich student learning. It allows students to explore and develop concepts, to extend critical thinking and problem-solving skills. – Addison Wesley Mathematics Research Report

Addison Wesley Mathematics e-Tools (K-8) software helps students develop important math concepts using an electronic form of mathematics manipulatives.

- Use to guide class discussion
- Have students use e-Tools as an alternative to concrete materials
- Especially relevant for students who face motor challenges

- Place-Value Blocks
- Counters
- Money
- Time
- Fractions
- Probability
- Spreadsheet-data-grapher
- Geometry Shapes
- Geometry Drawing

Addison Wesley Mathematics Makes Sense **Website** provides a wealth of interactive online resources for teachers, students, and parents. Teachers can access their *Math Makes Sense* Teacher Guide making it easy to customize planning and assessment tools. On-line professional development opportunities, additional activities, samples of student work, sample report card comments, and parent letters in different languages are just a few of the resources teachers will find on this site. Support for students includes additional practice, activities, and web links correlated to their student book. Parents can download our Math@Home magazine filled with background information, Canadian math trivia, and fun games and activities the whole family can do together.

http://www.pearsoned.ca/mathmakessense/

Professional Development

Addison Wesley Mathematics Makes Sense integrates professional development for teachers throughout the program resources, and provides in-service and other tools to ensure success of program implementation.

Professional Development built right into the program. . .

Each unit in the Teacher Guide provides planning detail that includes

- A **Mathematics Background** section, with information for the teacher about the key mathematics concepts to be developed
- **Across the Grades** summary, to show how the topic develops over a three-year window, from the previous grade, to this grade, to the next grade
- Information about how the unit makes connections between various mathematics strands, in **Across the Strands**
- Expert quotes that point to further reading for interested teachers

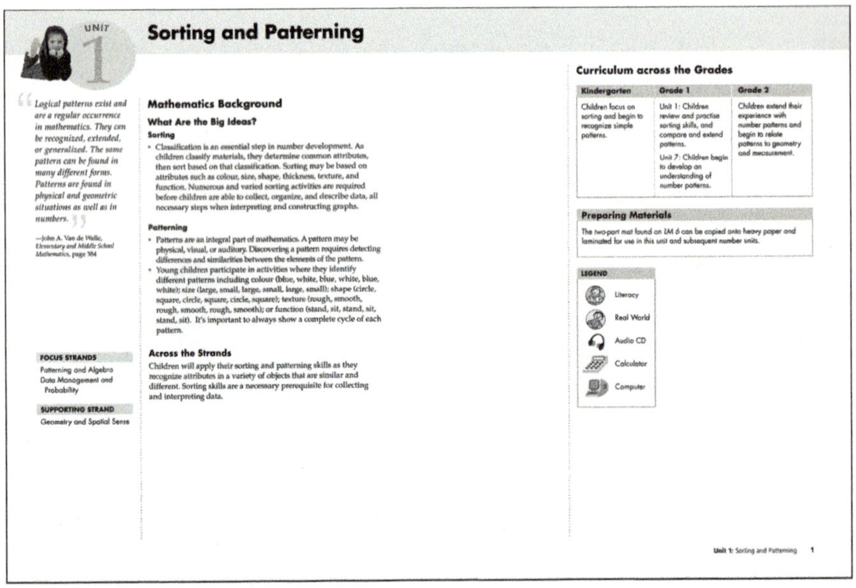

UNIT 1

Sorting and Patterning

"Logical patterns exist and are a regular occurrence in mathematics. They can be recognized, extended, or generalized. The same pattern can be found in many different forms. Patterns are found in physical and geometric situations as well as in numbers."

—John A. Van de Walle, *Elementary and Middle School Mathematics*, page 384

FOCUS STRANDS

Patterning and Algebra
Data Management and Probability

SUPPORTING STRAND

Geometry and Spatial Sense

Mathematics Background

What Are the Big Ideas?

Sorting

- Classification is an essential step in number development. As children classify materials, they determine common attributes, then sort based on that classification. Sorting may be based on attributes such as colour, size, shape, thickness, texture, and function. Numerous and varied sorting activities are required before children are able to collect, organize, and describe data, all necessary steps when interpreting and constructing graphs.

Patterning

- Patterns are an integral part of mathematics. A pattern may be physical, visual, or auditory. Discovering a pattern requires detecting differences and similarities between the elements of the pattern.
- Young children participate in activities where they identify different patterns including colour (blue, white, blue, white, blue, white); size (large, small, large, small, large, small); shape (circle, square, circle, square, circle, square); texture (rough, smooth, rough, smooth, rough, smooth); or function (stand, sit, stand, sit, stand, sit). It's important to always show a complete cycle of each pattern.

Across the Strands

Children will apply their sorting and patterning skills as they recognize attributes in a variety of objects that are similar and different. Sorting skills are a necessary prerequisite for collecting and interpreting data.

Curriculum across the Grades

Kindergarten	Grade 1	Grade 2
Children focus on sorting and begin to recognize simple patterns.	Unit 1: Children review and practise sorting skills, and compare and extend patterns. Unit 7: Children begin to develop an understanding of number patterns.	Children extend their experience with number patterns and begin to relate patterns to geometry and measurement.

Preparing Materials

The two-part mat found on *LM 6* can be copied onto heavy paper and laminated for use in this unit and subsequent number units.

LEGEND

Literacy
Real World
Audio CD
Calculator
Computer

Unit 1: Sorting and Patterning 1

Each lesson further supports professional development in a lesson model that offers

- Connect section to establish the key mathematical understanding of the lesson
- Focus statement to identify the key concepts of the lesson to teachers as well as parents and children
- A variety of instructional strategies detailed in the supporting Teacher Guide notes

Teachers' confidence and understanding of mathematics is an essential criterion for their students' success.
– Trevor Brown, Program Author

Professional Development in direct support of the program

Pearson Education offers flexibility and choice with a range of professional development options.

Customized In-Service and Partnerships

- Workshops, institutes, and on-line in-service led by leading local, national and international math educators such as:

John A. Van de Walle
Elementary Mathematics Advisor

Craig Featherstone
Pearson Education Consultant

Trevor Brown
Toronto, Ontario

Mignonne Wood
Vancouver, British Columbia

Maggie Martin Connell
Atlantic Canada

Jodi Mackie
Edmonton, Alberta

Administrator's Handbook

- Authored by Mignonne Wood, Steve Cairns
- Designed to assist principals in implementing a new mathematics program
- Shows how to foster a positive attitude toward teaching mathematics by building understanding within the school community, with teachers and parents

Van de Walle Facilitator's Guide

- Based on *Elementary and Middle School Mathematics: Teaching Developmentally* by John A. Van de Walle, a teaching methodology resource for the elementary teacher of mathematics
- Provides an organization for a Van de Walle Book Study group model

Pearson Professional Learning

- Quality, sustained, comprehensive teacher professional development at affordable prices

PEARSON Professional Learning

Using Your Teacher Guide...

Addison Wesley Mathematics Makes Sense recognizes that teachers need a program with quick access to ideas for instruction and teacher support features.

Your Teacher Guide has separate modules for each unit of instruction, with additional modules to support your year-long planning:

- **Program Overview** provides detailed information about the overall structure and features of the program.
- **Building a Math Community** (grades 1 and 2) provides a description of a positive environment, and practical suggestions for organizing your classroom and materials, as well as grade-specific ideas for routines and activities.
- The **Additional Assessment Support** module includes a selection of assessment tools that can be used throughout the program for your assessment and reporting needs.
- **Planning and Program Masters** (grades 3 to 8) provide year at a glance planning, materials list, literature connections, and generic program blackline masters. This module includes the feature "Building a Math Community."

The enclosed CD provides additional support and ensures ease of use, with

- A grade-level correlation showing our complete curriculum fit
- Editable versions of unit planning charts, rubrics, and other assessment tools
- Files for selected line masters

Planning a Unit

Each unit module in your Teacher Guide starts with several pages to support your planning for the unit. You'll see **Mathematics Background, Curriculum across the Grades,** and a **Curriculum Overview.**

Planning Charts provide overviews of lessons, materials requirements, assessment opportunities, and suggested times.

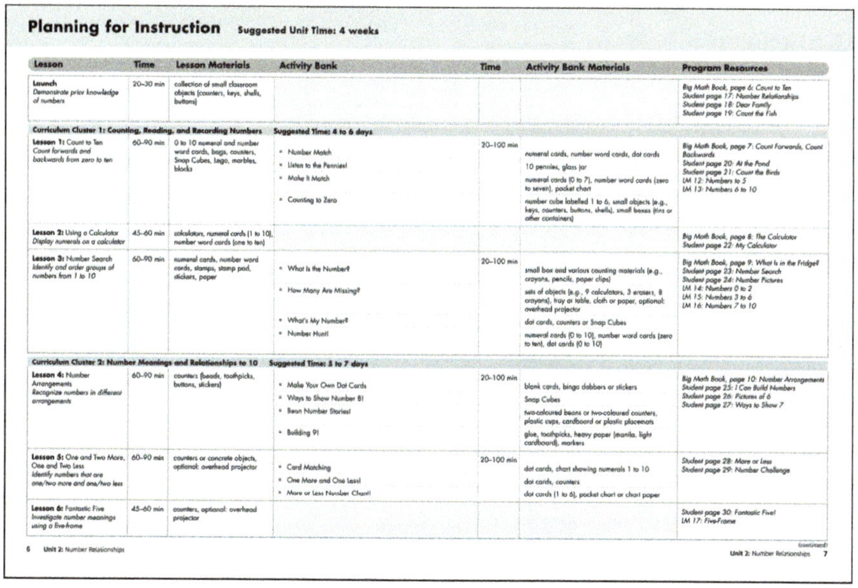
Planning for Instruction Suggested Unit Time: 4 weeks

In grades 1 and 2, one of your planning pages describes **Mathematics Centres** that you can set up in advance for use at various points through the unit. Lesson notes reference centres for support in individualizing instruction.

Grade 1

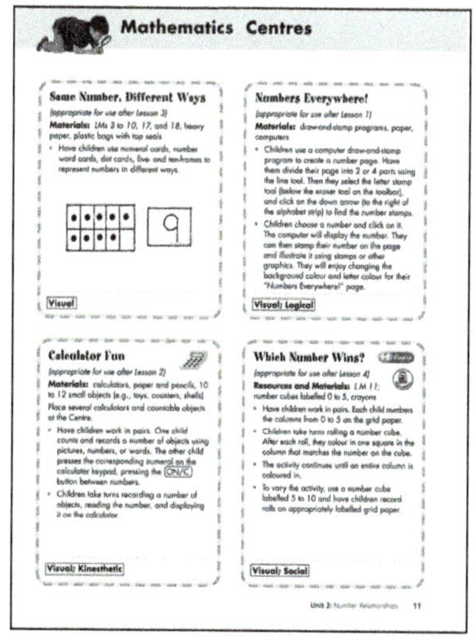
Mathematics Centres

In grades 3 and up, one of your planning pages describes **Additional Activities** that you can organize for use at various points through the unit. Each **Additional Activity** comes with an accompanying activity **Master,** provided at the end of the module.

Grade 4

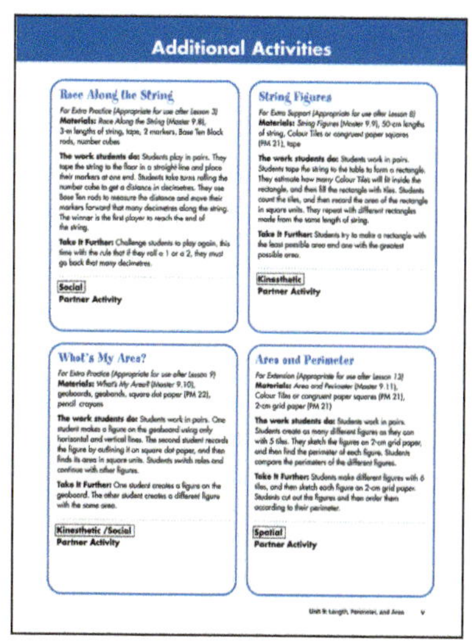
Additional Activities

At Grades 1 and 2

When you're ready to start the unit, the Teacher Guide lessons provide professional choices within a consistent structure.

The suggested **Unit Launch** describes a 20-minute introduction to activate prior knowledge and engage the learner.

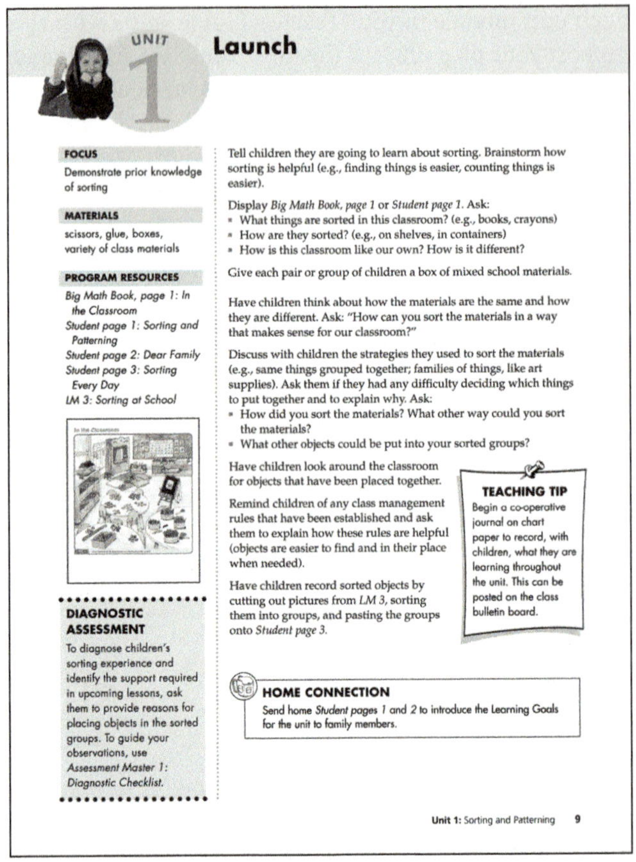

UNIT 1 **Launch**

FOCUS
Demonstrate prior knowledge of sorting

MATERIALS
scissors, glue, boxes, variety of class materials

PROGRAM RESOURCES
Big Math Book, page 1: In the Classroom
Student page 1: Sorting and Patterning
Student page 2: Dear Family
Student page 3: Sorting Every Day
LM 3: Sorting at School

DIAGNOSTIC ASSESSMENT
To diagnose children's sorting experience and identify the support required in upcoming lessons, ask them to provide reasons for placing objects in the sorted groups. To guide your observations, use *Assessment Master 1: Diagnostic Checklist.*

Tell children they are going to learn about sorting. Brainstorm how sorting is helpful (e.g., finding things is easier, counting things is easier).

Display *Big Math Book, page 1* or *Student page 1.* Ask:
- What things are sorted in this classroom? (e.g., books, crayons)
- How are they sorted? (e.g., on shelves, in containers)
- How is this classroom like our own? How is it different?

Give each pair or group of children a box of mixed school materials.

Have children think about how the materials are the same and how they are different. Ask: "How can you sort the materials in a way that makes sense for our classroom?"

Discuss with children the strategies they used to sort the materials (e.g., same things grouped together; families of things, like art supplies). Ask them if they had any difficulty deciding which things to put together and to explain why. Ask:
- How did you sort the materials? What other way could you sort the materials?
- What other objects could be put into your sorted groups?

Have children look around the classroom for objects that have been placed together.

Remind children of any class management rules that have been established and ask them to explain how these rules are helpful (objects are easier to find and in their place when needed).

Have children record sorted objects by cutting out pictures from *LM 3,* sorting them into groups, and pasting the groups onto *Student page 3.*

TEACHING TIP
Begin a co-operative journal on chart paper to record, with children, what they are learning throughout the unit. This can be posted on the class bulletin board.

HOME CONNECTION
Send home *Student pages 1* and *2* to introduce the Learning Goals for the unit to family members.

Unit 1: Sorting and Patterning 9

Notes on **Diagnostic Assessment** help you interpret students' responses, and provide support where needed. Use the supporting master available in the module.

Home Connection highlights opportunities for communication with the home that also appear in the Student Book.

Throughout the teaching notes for the unit, **Teaching Tip** highlights instructional strategies.

As a teacher, I'm looking for lessons I know I can deliver. As an author, I look for ways to embed professional development in the Teacher Guide, in student activities that are developmentally appropriate.
– Michelle Jackson, Program Author

Lessons

Each lesson provides a consistent framework for teaching new concepts and procedural skills: **Explore, Connect and Reflect,** and **Practice.**

LESSON 1

Same and Different

CURRICULUM FOCUS

Demonstrate an understanding that objects can be sorted in more than one way according to one attribute
1m85(P), 1m97(DM), 1m98(DM)

MATH WORD WALL

sort
sorting rule

MATERIALS

boxes or containers, small items (keys, buttons, shells, beads, small toys)

PROGRAM RESOURCES

Big Math Book, page 2: Same and Different
Student page 4: Same and Different
Student page 5: Heads Up!
Line Master 4: Same and Different

BEFORE Get Started

Show children *Big Math Book, page 2.*
Ask:
- How are the animals sorted? (into groups, same types of animals are together)
- What is the sorting rule for each group? (dogs, cats, birds)

TRY THIS See the Literacy Links on page 12. You may want to introduce the concept by sharing the book *Which Belong Together?* with children.

Ask children to think of another way to sort the animals (e.g., colour or type of markings, number of feet, those with wings, barn animals or pets).

Have children suggest other animals that could belong to the groups.

DURING Explore

Provide each group or pair of children with a box or container of objects to sort. Allow children time to explore the items inside the boxes.

Problem Prompt
How many different ways can you sort the objects in your boxes?

Show and Share

Invite children to show how they sorted their collections. Ask:
- What is your sorting rule?
- What other ways can you sort the objects?

Have children sort the objects again using a new sorting rule. Allow enough time for children to sort and re-sort the objects in different ways.

AFTER Connect and Reflect

Bring the class together to discuss the various ways objects can be sorted. Use children's examples to indicate that items can be sorted by colour, shape, size, function, or any other justifiable attribute suggested by the children. Ask:
- What did you look for when you sorted the same objects in a different way?
- What is your new sorting rule?

TEACHING TIP
Begin a math word wall of mathematical words. The children can refer to these words when they are writing. As *sort* and *sorting rule* are modelled, place them on the math word wall.

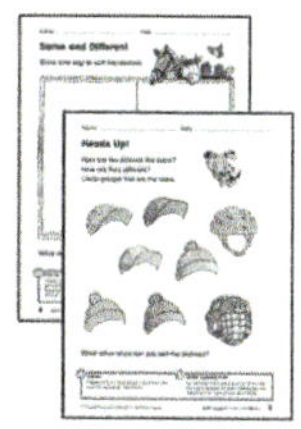

Practice

Reinforcement
Have children cut out pictures from *LM 4*, sort them into groups, and paste the groups onto *Student page 4.*

Read the directions on *Student page 5* with the children. After they have completed the page, discuss the different ways the pictures could have been sorted (summer/winter; brims/no brims; chin strap/no chin strap).

Extra Support: ESL
Children can practise and apply their sorting skills at the Mathematics Centres (Treasure Boxes and Stamp Sort, page 7). Have children describe the objects in detail to enable them to sort by more apparent attributes such as colour and size.

ESL learners will benefit from working with and describing one attribute at a time. Consider providing word cards to help reinforce some of the vocabulary they are learning.

Extension
Have early finishers work in pairs or on their own to create a secret sorting rule game using one attribute. Invite children to explain and share their games with the class or another pair of children.

Assessment for Learning

What to Look For	What to Do
Evidence that children • sort accurately using one attribute • find more than one way to sort • use mathematical language appropriately	Conduct brief conferences to determine why some children are having difficulty. Support them by • posing questions that help children to see that an object can be described by a variety of attributes and sorted accordingly; • asking children to describe objects in detail to help them think of additional attributes for sorting; • modelling mathematical language: "You have sorted these buttons by putting the same colours together. I think your sorting rule is dark colours/light colours.

To guide observations and facilitate reporting, use Assessment Master 3.1: Ongoing Observations Checklist: Sorting.

Here, and in all lessons, check the margin if you need information on curriculum match, or specific materials needed.

- **Curriculum Focus**
- **Materials**
- **Program Resources**

Assessment for Learning appears in every lesson with the main teaching notes, to help shape your formative assessment.

Then, turn the page for additional features that let you deepen the content, or spend additional focused time when needed.

Literacy Links

Providing an alternative way to begin some lessons, using literature and literacy as an entry point for learning

Numbers Every Day

Creating an awareness of number in classroom routine and day-to-day activities

Cross-Curricular Connections

Connecting math to other subject areas

Activity Banks provide up to four additional activity ideas related to the core content of the lesson. Select Activity Banks based on your class needs, and those of individual students. Each activity is keyed to learning style, and grouping requirements.

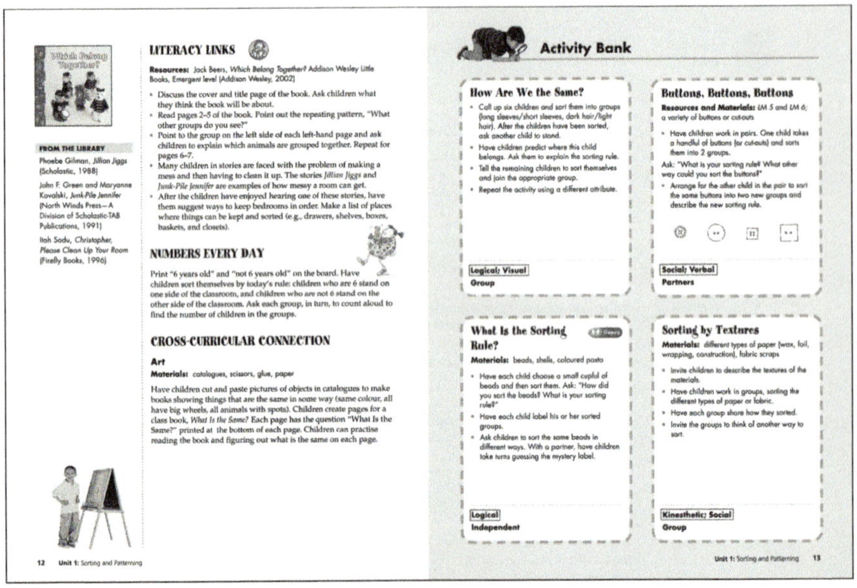

LITERACY LINKS

Resources: Jack Beers, *Which Belong Together?* Addison Wesley Little Books, Emergent level (Addison Wesley, 2002)

- Discuss the cover and title page of the book. Ask children what they think the book will be about.
- Read pages 2–5 of the book. Point out the repeating pattern, "What other groups do you see?"
- Point to the group on the left side of each left-hand page and ask children to explain which animals are grouped together. Repeat for pages 6–7.
- Many children in stories are faced with the problem of making a mess and then having to clean it up. The stories *Jillian Jiggs* and *Junk-Pile Jennifer* are examples of how messy a room can get.
- After the children have enjoyed hearing one of these stories, have them suggest ways to keep bedrooms in order. Make a list of places where things can be kept and sorted (e.g., drawers, shelves, boxes, baskets, and closets).

FROM THE LIBRARY

Phoebe Gilman, *Jillian Jiggs* (Scholastic, 1988)

John F. Green and Maryanne Kovalski, *Junk-Pile Jennifer* (North Winds Press—A Division of Scholastic-TAB Publications, 1991)

Itah Sadu, *Christopher, Please Clean Up Your Room* (Firefly Books, 1996)

NUMBERS EVERY DAY

Print "6 years old" and "not 6 years old" on the board. Have children sort themselves by today's rule: children who are 6 stand on one side of the classroom, and children who are not 6 stand on the other side of the classroom. Ask each group, in turn, to count aloud to find the number of children in the groups.

CROSS-CURRICULAR CONNECTION

Art

Materials: catalogues, scissors, glue, paper

Have children cut and paste pictures of objects in catalogues to make books showing things that are the same in some way (same colour, all have big wheels, all animals with spots). Children create pages for a class book, *What Is the Same?* Each page has the question "What Is the Same?" printed at the bottom of each page. Children can practise reading the book and figuring out what is the same on each page.

12 Unit 1: Sorting and Patterning

Activity Bank

How Are We the Same?

- Call up six children and sort them into groups (long sleeves/short sleeves, dark hair/light hair). After the children have been sorted, ask another child to stand.
- Have children predict where this child belongs. Ask them to explain the sorting rule.
- Tell the remaining children to sort themselves and join the appropriate group.
- Repeat the activity using a different attribute.

Logical; Visual
Group

Buttons, Buttons, Buttons

Resources and Materials: *LM 5* and *LM 6*; a variety of buttons or cut-outs

- Have children work in pairs. One child takes a handful of buttons (or cut-outs) and sorts them into 2 groups.

Ask: "What is your sorting rule? What other way could you sort the buttons?"

- Arrange for the other child in the pair to sort the same buttons into two new groups and describe the new sorting rule.

Social; Verbal
Partners

What Is the Sorting Rule?

Materials: beads, shells, coloured pasta

- Have each child choose a small cupful of beads and then sort them. Ask: "How did you sort the beads? What is your sorting rule?"
- Have each child label his or her sorted groups.
- Ask children to sort the same beads in different ways. With a partner, have children take turns guessing the mystery label.

Logical
Independent

Sorting by Textures

Materials: different types of paper (wax, foil, wrapping, construction), fabric scraps

- Invite children to describe the textures of the materials.
- Have children work in groups, sorting the different types of paper or fabric.
- Have each group share how they sorted.
- Invite the groups to think of another way to sort.

Kinesthetic; Social
Group

Unit 1: Sorting and Patterning 13

Each unit also provides ideas for teaching problem solving, and assessing student performance on the whole unit.

Strategies Tool Kit

Focusing on the strategies and processes children need to master to become effective problem solvers

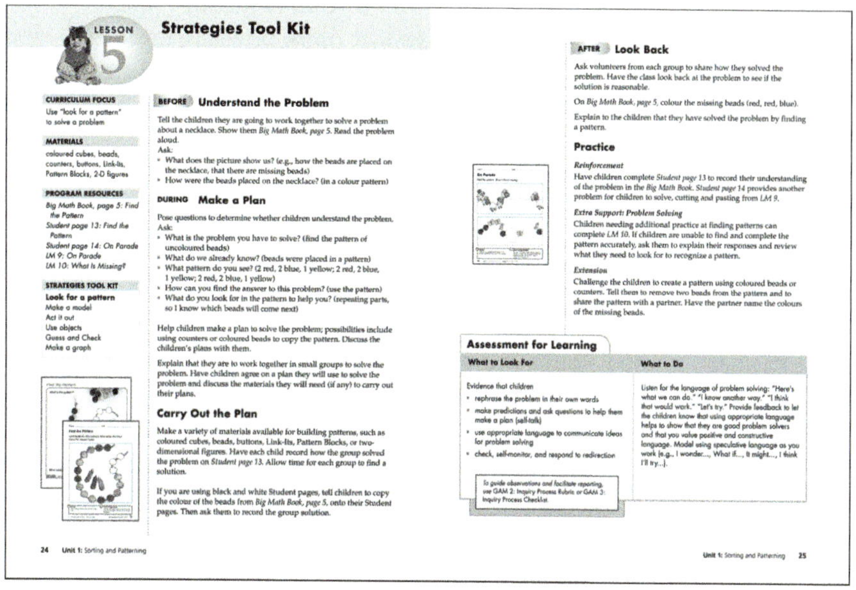

Show What You Know

Your Teacher Guide pages detail a performance task that will allow for demonstration of the learning through the unit.

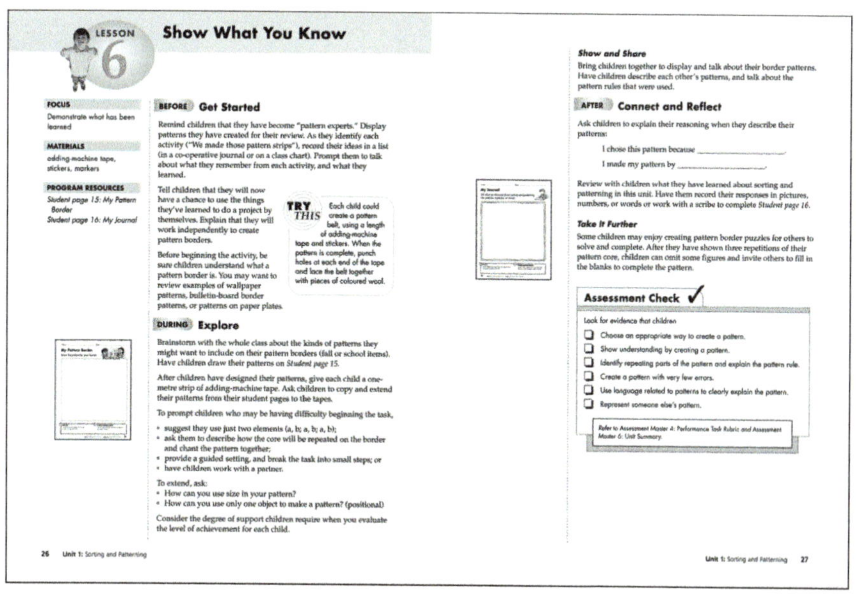

Use the **Assessment Check** checklist to guide your assessment of students' performance. For a more detailed assessment, use the corresponding Assessment Master, which provides a specific rubric.

At Grades 3 and up

Addison Wesley Mathematics Makes Sense moves to a more mature student book format at grade 3. The hard-cover **Student Book** provides a resource for use in the classroom, and at home. For day-to-day planning, the **Teacher Guide** gives reduced pages of the Student Book with accompanying teaching notes.

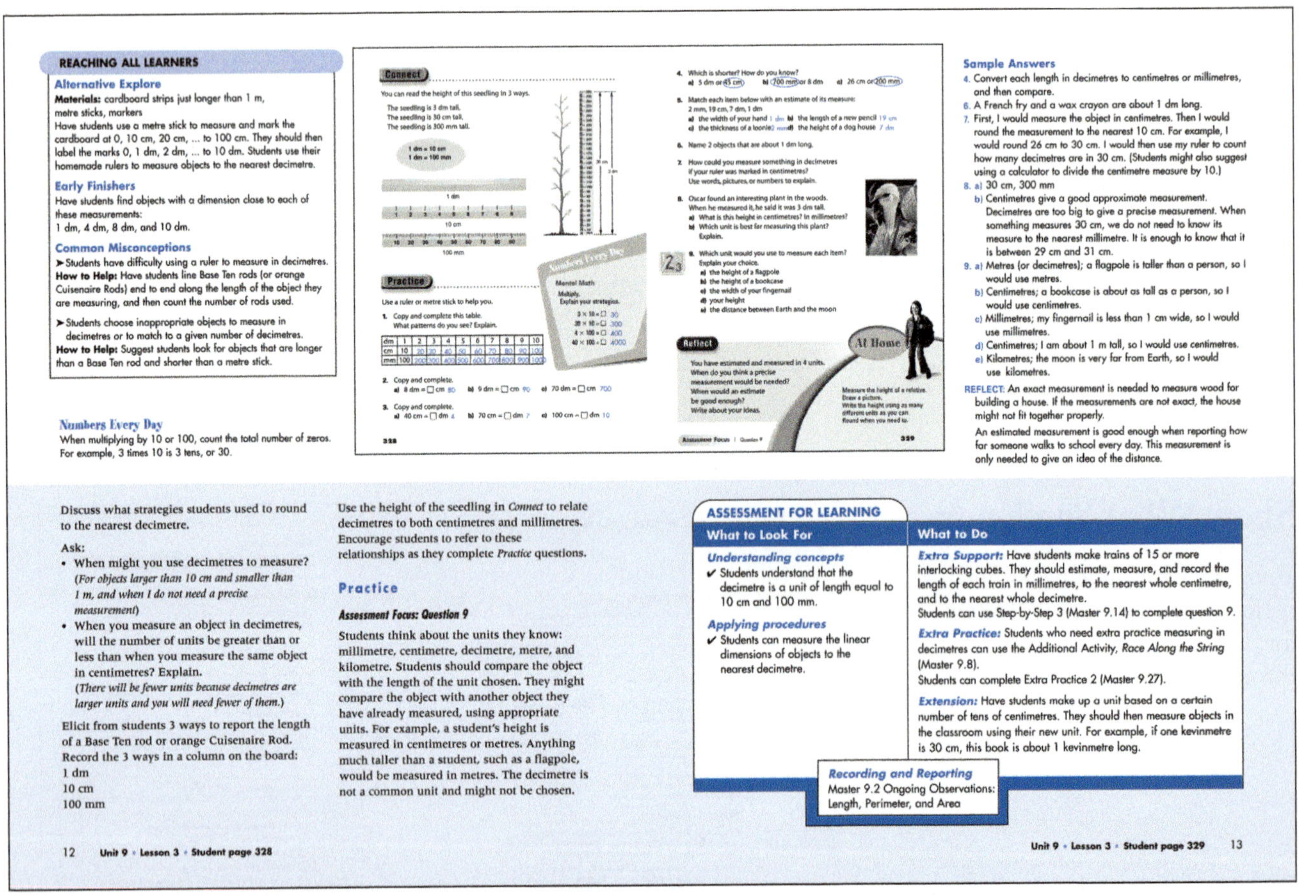

REACHING ALL LEARNERS

Alternative Explore

Materials: cardboard strips just longer than 1 m, metre sticks, markers

Have students use a metre stick to measure and mark the cardboard at 0, 10 cm, 20 cm, ... to 100 cm. They should then label the marks 0, 1 dm, 2 dm, ... to 10 dm. Students use their homemade rulers to measure objects to the nearest decimetre.

Early Finishers

Have students find objects with a dimension close to each of these measurements:
1 dm, 4 dm, 8 dm, and 10 dm.

Common Misconceptions

➤ Students have difficulty using a ruler to measure in decimetres.
How to Help: Have students line Base Ten rods (or orange Cuisenaire Rods) end to end along the length of the object they are measuring, and then count the number of rods used.

➤ Students choose inappropriate objects to measure in decimetres or to match to a given number of decimetres.
How to Help: Suggest students look for objects that are longer than a Base Ten rod and shorter than a metre stick.

Numbers Every Day

When multiplying by 10 or 100, count the total number of zeros. For example, 3 times 10 is 3 tens, or 30.

Sample Answers

4. Convert each length in decimetres to centimetres or millimetres, and then compare.
6. A French fry and a wax crayon are about 1 dm long.
7. First, I would measure the object in centimetres. Then I would round the measurement to the nearest 10 cm. For example, I would round 26 cm to 30 cm. I would then use my ruler to count how many decimetres are in 30 cm. (Students might also suggest using a calculator to divide the centimetre measure by 10.)
8. a) 30 cm, 300 mm
   b) Centimetres give a good approximate measurement. Decimetres are too big to give a precise measurement. When something measures 30 cm, we do not need to know its measure to the nearest millimetre. It is enough to know that it is between 29 cm and 31 cm.
9. a) Metres (or decimetres); a flagpole is taller than a person, so I would use metres.
   b) Centimetres; a bookcase is about as tall as a person, so I would use centimetres.
   c) Millimetres; my fingernail is less than 1 cm wide, so I would use millimetres.
   d) Centimetres; I am about 1 m tall, so I would use centimetres.
   e) Kilometres; the moon is very far from Earth, so I would use kilometres.

REFLECT: An exact measurement is needed to measure wood for building a house. If the measurements are not exact, the house might not fit together properly.

An estimated measurement is good enough when reporting how far someone walks to school every day. This measurement is only needed to give an idea of the distance.

Discuss what strategies students used to round to the nearest decimetre.

Ask:

- When might you use decimetres to measure? *(For objects larger than 10 cm and smaller than 1 m, and when I do not need a precise measurement)*
- When you measure an object in decimetres, will the number of units be greater than or less than when you measure the same object in centimetres? Explain. *(There will be fewer units because decimetres are larger units and you will need fewer of them.)*

Elicit from students 3 ways to report the length of a Base Ten rod or orange Cuisenaire Rod. Record the 3 ways in a column on the board:
1 dm
10 cm
100 mm

Use the height of the seedling in *Connect* to relate decimetres to both centimetres and millimetres. Encourage students to refer to these relationships as they complete *Practice* questions.

Practice

Assessment Focus: Question 9

Students think about the units they know: millimetre, centimetre, decimetre, metre, and kilometre. Students should compare the object with the length of the unit chosen. They might compare the object with another object they have already measured, using appropriate units. For example, a student's height is measured in centimetres or metres. Anything much taller than a student, such as a flagpole, would be measured in metres. The decimetre is not a common unit and might not be chosen.

ASSESSMENT FOR LEARNING

What to Look For	What to Do
Understanding concepts ✔ Students understand that the decimetre is a unit of length equal to 10 cm and 100 mm.	***Extra Support:*** Have students make trains of 15 or more interlocking cubes. They should estimate, measure, and record the length of each train in millimetres, to the nearest whole centimetre, and to the nearest whole decimetre. Students can use Step-by-Step 3 (Master 9.14) to complete question 9.
Applying procedures ✔ Students can measure the linear dimensions of objects to the nearest decimetre.	***Extra Practice:*** Students who need extra practice measuring in decimetres can use the Additional Activity, *Race Along the String* (Master 9.8). Students can complete Extra Practice 2 (Master 9.27).
	Extension: Have students make up a unit based on a certain number of tens of centimetres. They should then measure objects in the classroom using their new unit. For example, if one kevinmetre is 30 cm, this book is about 1 kevinmetre long.

Recording and Reporting
Master 9.2 Ongoing Observations: Length, Perimeter, and Area

12 Unit 9 • Lesson 3 • Student page 328

Unit 9 • Lesson 3 • Student page 329 13

In the Teacher Guide, each **Unit Launch** provides suggestions to support your **Diagnostic Assessment** of students.

Look for **Literature Connections** that relate to the topics at hand.

> In a Teacher Guide I look for daily support for content presentation, classroom management, assessment, and ideas for supporting all learners.
> – Mary Doucette, Program Author

In core lessons, beside the reduced student pages you will find

- **Lesson Organizer** with curriculum information, materials, and vocabulary
- **Key Learnings** for the lesson
- **Reaching All Learners** with suggestions for an **Alternative Explore,** suggested **ESL Strategies,** and **Common Misconceptions/How to Help**
- **Sample Answers** to questions that require a written or diagrammatic response

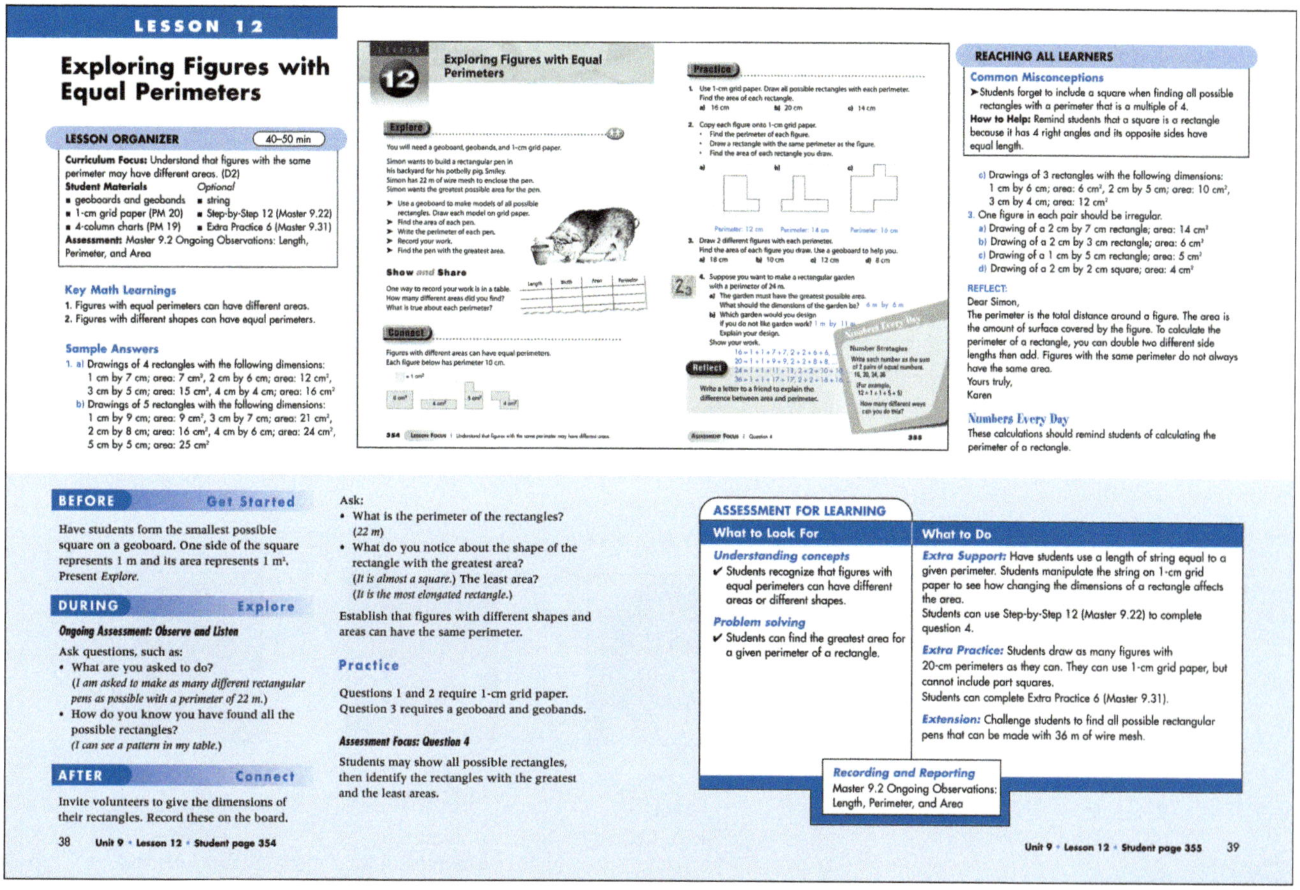

LESSON 12

Exploring Figures with Equal Perimeters

LESSON ORGANIZER 40–50 min

Curriculum Focus: Understand that figures with the same perimeter may have different areas. (D2)

Student Materials
- geoboards and geobands
- 1-cm grid paper (PM 20)
- 4-column charts (PM 19)

Optional
- string
- Step-by-Step 12 (Master 9.22)
- Extra Practice 6 (Master 9.31)

Assessment: Master 9.2 Ongoing Observations: Length, Perimeter, and Area

Key Math Learnings
1. Figures with equal perimeters can have different areas.
2. Figures with different shapes can have equal perimeters.

Sample Answers

1. a) Drawings of 4 rectangles with the following dimensions: 1 cm by 7 cm; area: 7 cm², 2 cm by 6 cm; area: 12 cm², 3 cm by 5 cm; area: 15 cm², 4 cm by 4 cm; area: 16 cm²
   b) Drawings of 5 rectangles with the following dimensions: 1 cm by 9 cm; area: 9 cm², 3 cm by 7 cm; area: 21 cm², 2 cm by 8 cm; area: 16 cm², 4 cm by 6 cm; area: 24 cm², 5 cm by 5 cm; area: 25 cm²

REACHING ALL LEARNERS

Common Misconceptions

➤ Students forget to include a square when finding all possible rectangles with a perimeter that is a multiple of 4.

How to Help: Remind students that a square is a rectangle because it has 4 right angles and its opposite sides have equal length.

c) Drawings of 3 rectangles with the following dimensions: 1 cm by 6 cm; area: 6 cm², 2 cm by 5 cm; area: 10 cm², 3 cm by 4 cm; area: 12 cm²

3. One figure in each pair should be irregular.
   a) Drawing of a 2 cm by 7 cm rectangle; area: 14 cm²
   b) Drawing of a 2 cm by 3 cm rectangle; area: 6 cm²
   c) Drawing of a 1 cm by 5 cm rectangle; area: 5 cm²
   d) Drawing of a 2 cm by 2 cm square; area: 4 cm²

REFLECT:
Dear Simon,
The perimeter is the total distance around a figure. The area is the amount of surface covered by the figure. To calculate the perimeter of a rectangle, you can double two different side lengths then add. Figures with the same perimeter do not always have the same area.
Yours truly,
Karen

Numbers Every Day
These calculations should remind students of calculating the perimeter of a rectangle.

BEFORE Get Started

Have students form the smallest possible square on a geoboard. One side of the square represents 1 m and its area represents 1 m². Present *Explore.*

DURING Explore

Ongoing Assessment: Observe and Listen

Ask questions, such as:
- What are you asked to do? (*I am asked to make as many different rectangular pens as possible with a perimeter of 22 m.*)
- How do you know you have found all the possible rectangles? (*I can see a pattern in my table.*)

AFTER Connect

Invite volunteers to give the dimensions of their rectangles. Record these on the board.

Ask:
- What is the perimeter of the rectangles? (*22 m*)
- What do you notice about the shape of the rectangle with the greatest area? (*It is almost a square.*) The least area? (*It is the most elongated rectangle.*)

Establish that figures with different shapes and areas can have the same perimeter.

Practice

Questions 1 and 2 require 1-cm grid paper. Question 3 requires a geoboard and geobands.

Assessment Focus: Question 4

Students may show all possible rectangles, then identify the rectangles with the greatest and the least areas.

ASSESSMENT FOR LEARNING

What to Look For	What to Do
Understanding concepts ✔ Students recognize that figures with equal perimeters can have different areas or different shapes.	***Extra Support:*** Have students use a length of string equal to a given perimeter. Students manipulate the string on 1-cm grid paper to see how changing the dimensions of a rectangle affects the area. Students can use Step-by-Step 12 (Master 9.22) to complete question 4.
Problem solving ✔ Students can find the greatest area for a given perimeter of a rectangle.	***Extra Practice:*** Students draw as many figures with 20-cm perimeters as they can. They can use 1-cm grid paper, but cannot include part squares. Students can complete Extra Practice 6 (Master 9.31). ***Extension:*** Challenge students to find all possible rectangular pens that can be made with 36 m of wire mesh.

Recording and Reporting
Master 9.2 Ongoing Observations: Length, Perimeter, and Area

38 Unit 9 • Lesson 12 • Student page 354

Unit 9 • Lesson 12 • Student page 355 39

Your lesson plan appears across the bottom half of your lesson pages, with teaching suggestions to support the lesson structure established in the Student Book: **Explore, Connect,** and **Practice.**

Assessment for Learning appears in every lesson with the main teaching notes, to help shape your formative assessment.

Meet our *Addison Wesley Mathematics Makes Sense* In-Service and Professional Development Faculty

Trevor Brown
Toronto, Ontario

Steve Cairns
Burnaby, British Columbia

Lynda Colgan
Kingston, Ontario

Maggie Martin Connell
Atlantic Canada

Marg Craig
Southwestern Ontario

Craig Featherstone
Pearson Education Consultant

Angie Harding
Regina, Saskatchewan

Sharon Jeroski
Assessment Consultant

Jodi Mackie
Edmonton, Alberta

Bill Nimigon
Toronto, Ontario

Carole Saundry
Richmond, British Columbia

Michelle Skene
Ottawa, Ontario

Lynn Strangway
Toronto, Ontario

John A. Van de Walle
Elementary Mathematics Advisor

Mignonne Wood
Vancouver, British Columbia

ADDISON WESLEY

Ontario

Math Makes Sense 7

Ontario

Teacher Guide

Grade 7 Planning and Program Masters

ISBN 0-321-13862-7

9 780321 138620

Teacher Guide Modules

ISBN 0-321-13863-5

9 780321 138637

Complete Teacher Guide package

PEARSON Addison Wesley

Building a Math Community

Contents

Creating a Math Community in the Classroom

> *"Success in mathematics learning requires being positively disposed toward the subject."*
> (Kilpatrick and Swafford 2002, 16)

Each new school year provides fresh opportunities to create a community of learners in the classroom. The goal is to facilitate the development of an inclusive classroom where all students feel safe, valued, and supported in their learning.

As members of a classroom community, teacher and students:

- Demonstrate mutual respect.
- Take risks.
- Seek, evaluate, and apply information to solve problems.
- Make decisions.
- Learn successfully together.

> *"Community building is an ongoing process. Students who feel they are part of a cohesive group take more responsibility for what happens in the classroom and may perform better because of encouragement from their peers."*
> (Barnes 2002, 84)

Helping children acquire "mathematical power" means helping them develop the capacity to apply mathematical knowledge to new or familiar tasks. (Baroody and Coslick 1998, 1 and 2) Mathematics in the classroom must promote a positive disposition to learn and use mathematics.

> *"For students to be comfortable with the processes of mathematical inquiry, they need to explore, reason, solve problems, and communicate about mathematics—and they need regular feedback. When students have these learning opportunities, they begin to develop a deeper understanding of mathematics, enabling them to see connections between mathematical ideas, between mathematics and other subject areas, and between mathematics and everyday life situations."*
> (Baroody and Coslick 1998)

As facilitators of learning, teachers are responsible for creating a classroom environment that allows each student to experience success. The reward is in knowing that students will view math as fun, exciting, engaging, and something they are capable of doing.

Setting the Stage for Community Building

Central to the life of any community is a group meeting time—when the whole class meets to learn what it means to belong to a community. The group meeting should facilitate effective communication—each person has the opportunity to speak, to share successes and challenges, and to listen to and value the ideas of others. Group meetings also reinforce communication skills, such as listening with respect, and speaking clearly and in turn.

Regular meeting times demonstrate to students they have a voice in the classroom. You might consider creating a T-chart with students that describes what an effective meeting should "look like and sound like." Refer to this chart during meeting times through the day as you observe behaviour you identified together as important.

Using the Meeting Time

- Discuss difficulties that occur in the classroom or on the playground. As a community, discuss tools and strategies that may help resolve difficulties or conflicts.
- Share ideas, strategies, or completed work.
- Celebrate successes or provide encouragement.
- Share information about upcoming events in the class or school.
- Trade information about what happened outside the classroom after school hours.

OUR MEETING TIME

LOOKS LIKE	SOUNDS LIKE
• Everyone sits in an arrangement that is conducive to discussion (e.g., desks arranged in a horseshoe formation). • Students are attentive. • The atmosphere is one of respect. • Students come prepared with notebooks. • Student raises a hand to be heard.	• Everyone takes turns to talk. • The student/teacher talks clearly. • Offer positive feedback: "That is an interesting idea. Can you tell us more about it?" • Suggest questions: "Can you share how you solved the problem?"

A math meeting can be held any time. Your needs will direct the activity and discussion. Some possibilities are to:

- Introduce a new math concept.
- Brainstorm students' prior knowledge about a math topic.
- Share a new manipulative or technology and explore possible uses.
- Revisit a math concept to reinforce a specific skill.
- Introduce new math activities.
- Discuss any difficulties arising from the previous math period.
- Share and celebrate student work.

Classroom Seating

Arrange students' desks in groups. Students will then have a sense of belonging. In each group, include students with varied strengths and abilities. This encourages peer modelling and role definition within the group. These groups should not be static; however, they should stay together for at least four weeks so that students can become familiar with one another and feel comfortable in their group.

Regularly reinforce the classroom principles students have agreed to. These principles will be integral to the development of group cohesiveness and classroom norms.

To encourage students to sit beside different classmates have them:

- Sit in alphabetical order by first or last name.
- Sit in order of their birth dates.
- Randomly select name cards from a box, or number sticks from a box.
- Write a proposal of whom they would like to have sit in their groups, providing justification as to why that grouping would work well together.

> *"An effective mathematics learning environment is an environment that encourages the establishment of a community of mathematics learners."*
>
> (Ontario Ministry of Education 2003, 12)

Developing Common Principles

To create a successful classroom community, develop common principles. These principles should reflect the beliefs students and you have about an exemplary learning environment. All students should be encouraged to contribute; and all contributions should be respected.

Characteristics of a Community

- security
- open communication
- mutual liking
- shared goals or objectives
- connectedness
- trust

(Sapon-Shevin 1999, 16 and 17)

Establishing Community Principles

You and your students sit in a circle or horseshoe formation in the classroom.

- Make sure that everyone is together and can see one another. Explain that you are sitting in a circle so that everyone will have a chance to speak and to hear what the others are saying.
- Explain that the meeting you are having now is to decide what will help you learn together and get along in the classroom.
- Tell students that you are excited about beginning a new school year together. You want to make sure that it is a successful year for everyone. To make the class an enjoyable and positive environment to be in, there will be some expectations for all students. These will be your common principles.

Give an example of a class principle, such as, "It is important to help one another."

- Ask for a student volunteer to begin by suggesting a principle. Record the principles on chart paper.
- Go around the room giving each person a turn to contribute. Some students may feel reluctant to share; ensure that students have the opportunity to "pass" when it is their turn to speak. Return to these students later to invite them to participate.

Discuss the principles that were suggested.

- Note principles that were mentioned multiple times, and encourage additional suggestions.
- As the discussion progresses, note all principles mentioned on chart paper or on the blackboard. With the help of the students, summarize the ideas in three to six statements.

Divide students into groups, so that each group can discuss one principle.

- Print each principle on a strip of paper.
- Instruct each group to choose one principle and find a quiet spot in the room to discuss the importance of that principle. (You may need to reread each group's principle as it is selected.)
- Ask each group to decide if it feels that principle should or should not become part of the class rules. The group must provide justification for its decision.

Note

Circulate among the groups to ensure students understand the task and the principle. They may need some discussion prompts:

- Why do you think it is important to include that principle?
- What may happen if we don't include that principle?

This process allows students to take ownership of the class principles. Students are more likely to remember and apply these ideas when they are part of the decision-making process. Throughout the year, revisit these principles with students and discuss their effectiveness. Students may suggest which principles are working well, and which principles could be changed. Encourage students to give reasons.

Bring the groups back.

- Ask each group to put its principle on the chart or write it on the blackboard. Time should be provided for others to comment.
- As a class, decide if any of the groups' decisions should be changed (only after all ideas about the principles have been heard).
- Create the final list of principles based on student decisions. Record the list on chart paper and post it in the classroom.

An Inclusive Math Community

Support Different Learning Styles

Try to get to know your students so you can plan effectively. Students should leave a math class feeling their needs have been addressed and they are successful.

Students have a range of learning styles. To effectively teach all students, it is essential to provide a multitude of classroom experiences. *Addison Wesley Mathematics Makes Sense* uses a variety of approaches to reach all learners.

Different Learning Styles

LEARNING STYLE	STRENGTHS AND PREFERENCES	*MATH MAKES SENSE*
Linguistic	Reading, writing, telling stories, remembering, talking, interacting, hearing, seeing words	Provides learning opportunities to talk, discuss, explain, write, read, and see words
Logical/Mathematical	Experimenting, working with numbers, asking questions, exploring patterns and relationships, math reasoning, applying logic, problem solving, classifying	Provides learning opportunities to experiment, ask questions, explore patterns and relationships, reason mathematically, solve problems, classify items
Visual/Spatial	Drawing, building, designing, creating, visualizing, imagining, working with pictures/colours, doing mazes and puzzles, reading maps and charts	Provides learning opportunities to draw, build, design, create, visualize, imagine, work with pictures/colours, do puzzles, read maps and charts
Musical	Singing, humming, noticing pitches, responding to music, playing instruments, picking up sounds/rhythms/melodies	Provides learning opportunities to work with patterns and make music connections
Kinesthetic	Moving and doing, touching and talking, feeling objects, using body language, physical activities, sports/dance, acting, making crafts, interacting with space	Provides learning opportunities to move and do, touch and talk, feel objects, use body language, work with manipulatives, make models, interact with space
Social (Interpersonal)	Talking to people, joining groups, understanding/leading others, organizing, communicating, mediating, sharing, relating, cooperating, interviewing	Provides learning opportunities to talk to people, work in groups, understand/lead others, organize, communicate, mediate, share, relate, cooperate, interview
Individual (Intrapersonal)	Working alone, pursuing own interests, understanding self, focusing inward, following instincts, pursuing goals, being original, having own space, individual projects	Provides learning opportunities to work individually, build thinking skills, think critically, follow instincts, solve problems, find original solutions, pursue individual projects
Naturalistic	Interest in nature and the environment	Provides learning opportunities by working with objects from nature

Adapted from *Instructor*, Scholastic Inc., 1990.

Preparing Students for Success

"Valuing mathematics implies being productively disposed towards the subject. It involves seeing mathematics as sensible, useful and worthwhile, and seeing oneself as able to learn and use it. Teachers must create a climate whereby all students can make sense of the mathematics they are learning and gain confidence in their mathematics ability."

(*Leading Math Success*, 2004)

When students experience success at math and perceive themselves as doers of math, they can encourage their peers to participate actively in math as well.

Creating Positive Attitudes

Children are more likely to develop a positive attitude toward mathematics when the teacher models the same attitudes.

Activating Prior Knowledge

Students come to the classroom with different experiences and knowledge of math. By determining where students are starting out, you are in a better position to provide appropriate math experiences and to assess ongoing learning.

How to Activate Prior Knowledge

- Pose a question to initiate discussion. For example, "How do you think you would go about adding fractions that do not have like denominators?" "What do you already know about adding fractions that might help you?"
- Brainstorm a class chart when introducing a new concept. For example, provide students with centicubes and pose the question, "How could these manipulatives help you find the volume of a rectangular prism?" Brainstorm and record students' responses on chart paper.
- Use a manipulative to investigate a new type of problem. For example, use two-colour tiles to investigate integers.

Reaching All Learners

Since there is no single way to reach all students, we are challenged to provide a wide variety of instructional strategies and learning experiences. Through observation, you can determine the strengths of each student. This information, combined with what is known about a student's prior knowledge, can help you address learning needs.

The following classroom practices are recommended as appropriate for students' cognitive development:

- New learning must be connected to existing knowledge.
- Examples should be concrete.
- Experiences must be hands-on.
- Lessons need to be active.
- Students must be engaged.
- It is essential to use manipulatives and technology.
- There must be time for active exploration.

Tools for Learning

Working with manipulatives and technology can facilitate math exploration and understanding among a range of learners, especially ESL students. You may also wish to provide each student with a math tool kit (or request that students provide their own) of basic equipment such as a ruler, calculator, two-colour counters, protractor, and so on.

Supporting ESL Students

To comprehend meaning and instruction, ESL students often require other resources in addition to words, such as manipulatives, drawings, and models. You can use these strategies to help ESL learners understand math concepts and language.

- Use facial expressions, gestures, and pantomime to help convey meaning. Repeat key language and concepts, rephrasing concepts in simple words.
- Use manipulatives, drawings, and real-world objects to demonstrate concepts, clarify instructions, and develop language.
- Use charts, graphs, and graphic organizers to introduce and explore concepts. Present additional examples and demonstrations.
- Provide a variety of ways for students to respond and/or show their findings.
- Provide brief previews and reviews of materials to reinforce language and concepts.
- Set a classroom tone that encourages and rewards students who interact, take risks, and use language to express their ideas.

Making Learning Meaningful

When learning is meaningful, students see the connections between themselves and the learning experience. Students do best with activities they find interesting and can actively engage in, including problem scenarios.

To engage learners in meaningful math:

- Use interesting materials.
- Provide students with a choice of tools, manipulatives, and technology.
- Connect new activities to what students already know.
- Pose problems that relate to students, and involve their types of interests.

> *"Children's confidence, competence, and interest in mathematics flourish when new experiences are meaningful and connected with their prior knowledge and experience."*
>
> (NAEYC and NCTM 2002, 6)

Promoting Classroom Communication

It is important to encourage all students to participate in class discussions. As the year progresses, students tend to take more risks at these meetings, especially if they perceive that all ideas are accepted.

To create effective and inclusive collaborative groupings:

- Involve students in discussing and determining appropriate interpersonal and small group skills (class principles).
- Group heterogeneously to promote modelling and diverse thinking. (Include boys and girls.)
- Begin with pairs or with groups of three.
- Keep work groups to 4 students or fewer to encourage positive social behaviours.
- Group students in a way that will encourage positive social behaviours.
- Use strategies such as think-pair-share.
- Use cooperative learning strategies often, but for short periods of time.
- Change group members regularly to promote a variety of interactions. (Leading Math Success, 2004)

Fostering Collaborative Learning

Cooperative/collaborative learning involves students working together towards a common goal. There are five elements involved in successful cooperative/collaborative learning: positive interdependence, face-to-face interaction, individual and group accountability, interpersonal and small group skills. (Johnson and Johnson, 1994, as cited in Bennett and Rolheiser 2001)

It is always important to impress upon students that they are in the classroom together to help each other learn.

It is beneficial for students to experience a variety of groupings. When students work in pairs or small groups, they are provided with more opportunities for interaction and discussion than when they work in larger groups. Providing opportunities to experience math concepts in pairs or small groups enables students to:

- Observe one another.
- Build on one another's ideas by hearing and trying out different strategies.
- Discuss their findings and pose questions.
- Give explanations and demonstrations, using math vocabulary.
- Search for connections and commonalities.

As students work collaboratively, you can glean valuable information by observing their interactions, discussions, explanations, and active involvement. Question students to encourage deeper understanding and reflection. In this way, students identify their own misconceptions and adjust their activity/thinking to reflect their new knowledge.

> *"The kinds of experiences teachers provide clearly play a major role in determining the extent and quality of students' learning... Classroom discourse and social interaction can be used to promote the recognition of connections among ideas and the reorganization of knowledge."*
>
> (Lampert 1986, as cited in NCTM 2000, 21)

Questions to Prompt Discussion and Reflection

- What thought process (steps) did you follow?
- What are you doing right now?
- Why do you think that will work?
- What strategy did you use to solve that problem? How did you solve the problem?
- Is there another way you could solve that problem? Why did you try it that way?
- What are you stuck on?
- How did you figure that out?
- How did you make that happen?
- What are you going to do next?
- What would happen if...?
- What gave you that idea?

The NCTM standards state that mathematics programs should enable all students to:

- Organize and consolidate their math thinking through communication.
- Communicate their math thinking coherently and clearly to peers/teachers.
- Analyse and evaluate the math thinking and strategies of others.
- Use the language of math to express math ideas precisely.

"Although organizing instructions for heterogeneous groups definitely involves a different kind of planning and preparation, many teachers report increased enthusiasm in their students, as well as greater learning and deeper involvement when curricula and instruction are organized around diverse learners working together."

(Sapon-Shevin 1999, 68)

Sharing and Reflecting

Encourage classroom communication to give all students an opportunity to share their thinking and understanding. This also gives you an opportunity to gain an insight into what students are thinking and learning. By providing students with a sharing and reflecting time at the end of a math activity, you offer the opportunity for metacognition. *Reflect and Share* in each section in the Student Book encourages such sharing.

Students are encouraged to:

- Check their own thinking.
- Highlight their own ideas, and see that their solutions are valued.
- Validate their problem-solving strategies and share those ideas.
- Consolidate their learning by explaining it to their peers.
- Ask further questions and learn from their peers as they share their insights.

The Math Journal Entry

Students provide a written or visual reflection of their math experience for the day. You may provide a journal sentence starter to guide their thoughts. Encourage students to write about their thinking using the math vocabulary, pictures, diagrams, symbols, or charts. You may wish to have students respond to *Reflect* at the end of each section in the Student Book. Students may share their entries with a peer or their work group.

Math Routines

Students benefit from a classroom structure that is predictable, follows certain routines, and allows concepts to be revisited regularly. Incorporating math throughout the day gives students the chance to experience more success with math, since they gain more practice with concepts and develop an awareness that math is connected to everyday experiences.

Graph the Class's Favourite Sports Team

Record and graph the scores and win/loss record of a favourite sports team. Have students analyse the data regularly and discuss the probable outcomes of upcoming games based on the opposing teams' win/loss record.

Numbers Every Day

Have students do *Mental Math, Number Strategies,* or *Calculator Skills*, a five- to ten-minute activity in each lesson of the Student Book. Use these activities any time during the day to help students build number sense and skills.

Track a Stock

As a class, choose to buy a fictional stock option in a company. Track the progress of the stock in the newspaper and on the internet. Discuss the stock's profitability (percent increase, decrease, and so on) and make decisions on when it would be best to sell the stock or buy more options in the company.

Games

Incorporate games into your routine once a week to reinforce concepts and give students the opportunity to realize that math can be fun, and to develop strategies. The Student Book contains math games, such as *Product Cover-Up* and *Who Has the Greatest Number?*. You may also wish to have students play with jigsaw puzzles to develop spatial sense.

Math in the Picture

Have the students work together to select an appropriate photograph or picture that identifies each of the math concepts shown. In groups, students can glue the selected pictures on to chart paper and record their ideas about the math found in the picture and the significance of this mathematics.

Some ideas for Math in the Picture are:

- Sports
- Fashion
- Music
- Seasons
- Time of day
- Shapes
- Measuring tools/devices
- Temperature
- Patterns
- Money

Creating the Learning Environment

> *"Students do not want to be embarrassed in front of their peers, and will not take risks unless they feel valued and supported. The classroom therefore must be a safe place. Routines should be established in the classroom that value such behaviours as attentive listening, appreciation, respect, and participation that leaves no occasion for put-downs."*
>
> (Gibbs 2001; Pugalee 2001b in *Leading Math Success* 2004)

A Problem-Solving Approach

Problem solving is a key instructional strategy that enables students to take risks, secure in the knowledge that their thoughts, queries, and ideas are valued. In time, students become well versed in the language of cooperation and collaboration.

After students share their solutions and justifications, you can elaborate on their methods and encourage students to comment or ask questions of their peers. Using student findings and solution methods as a means to guide instruction also allows students to see the value in their work, and encourages peers to share their strategies. While some strategies may be more efficient than others, you can note that several strategies may work and often a combination of strategies is required to solve a problem. Students must use strategies that are meaningful to them and make sense to them.

Classroom Management Tips for Intermediate Mathematics Learners

- Increase emotional safety by including strategies such as framing questions appropriately, using well-planned student groupings and inviting rather than demanding responses.
- Provide positive feedback whenever possible.
- Frequently use positive humour.
- Recognize that intermediate learners will behave inappropriately at times and develop a range of strategies for responding such as, speaking privately to students about inappropriate behaviour using a neutral (not angry) tone of voice. (*Leading Math Success* 2004)

Problem-Solving Strategies

The *Reading and Writing in Math: Choosing a Strategy* sections provide opportunities for students to use these problem-solving strategies:

- Make a table.
- Use a model.
- Draw a diagram.
- Solve a simpler problem.
- Work backward.
- Guess and check.
- Make an organized list.
- Use a pattern.
- Draw a graph.
- Use logical reasoning.

Here are some suggestions to empower students to become problem solvers.

Before

Before students begin:

- Prepare meaningful problem scenarios for students. These should be sufficiently challenging, but easy to solve.
- Ensure the problem is understood by all.
- Begin with a simpler version of the task. Brainstorm possible strategies to use.
- Estimate what the answer might be.
- Explain the expectations for the process and the product.

During

As students work through the problem:

- Let students approach the problem in a way that makes sense to them.
- Listen to conversations to observe student thinking.
- Provide hints or suggestions if students are on the wrong path.
- Encourage students to test their ideas.
- Ask questions to stimulate ideas.
- Assess student understanding of her/his solution.

After

After students have solved their problem:

- Gather for a group meeting to reflect and share.
- Provide ample time for all to discuss the solution.
- Highlight the variety of answers and methods.
- Encourage students to justify their solutions.
- Encourage students to comment positively or ask questions regarding their peers' solutions.

Note

For more detail on using a problem-solving approach to teach mathematics, see John A. Van de Walle, *Elementary and Middle School Mathematics: Teaching Developmentally.* Boston: Allyn and Bacon, 2004, from which these ideas are drawn.

"Problem solving should be a primary goal of all mathematics instruction and an integral part of all mathematical activity."

(NCTM 1989, 23)

Creating the Physical Environment

Building a community of learners can begin with the physical arrangement of the classroom. Students should know where all necessary materials are so they can access them easily. They should also know they are responsible for collecting and returning any materials they have used, and that they are expected to cooperate with other members of the classroom. The classroom set-up should:

- Promote independence for students.
- Provide choices within a structured setting.
- Be organized to encourage sharing.

To set up the physical space:

- Create floor space where you and students can gather for lessons, discussions, and sharing.
- Arrange student desks or tables in groups (about four students per group) to facilitate working together.
- Create a variety of work areas so students have a selection (group areas, individual areas, floor spaces, table spaces, and so on).
- Set up a special area for you to conference with students individually.

Maximizing Classroom Space

Here are some suggestions for maximizing space.

- Establish a bulletin board as a Math Corner where students can display their work. Place a shelf underneath the bulletin board for work that cannot be posted. Include an area where students can write "I wonder about" questions.
- Post Bristol board or a white board to use as a message centre.
- Store math portfolios and games in stackable plastic crates or tubs. Or, turn desks upside down and tape Bristol board around the legs to create a filing cabinet for portfolios and games.
- Create an instant math centre by placing game(s) at a table or meeting space for students to play and work at math challenges or games.

Storage of Materials

Provide a variety of manipulative materials in labelled bins in an accessible area of the classroom. This ensures students know where to find and return what they need. Label the bins clearly.

Organize the mathematics tools. For example, you might want to have math toolkits for each group. These toolkits could contain rulers, measuring tapes, calculators, various counters stored in small plastic bags, string, elastic bands, math vocabulary and definitions, mathematics journal writing starters, and so on. Be sure there are enough items in the kits for the group to work together.

You could also create a materials centre containing pencils, scissors, tape, glue, erasers, crayons, markers, different sizes and types of paper (lined, unlined, graph paper, dot paper, centimetre grid paper), and so on.

You will need a variety of mathematics tools and manipulatives to address different math concepts throughout the year. Students should have access to these materials. Open access allows students to explore manipulatives in greater depth; for example, to further their understanding of a concept, to revisit an activity that was previously provided, or to experiment with their own math problem.

To recognize the importance of personal space while promoting the sharing of materials:

- Provide a personal place in the classroom for each student—for example, the inside of a desk, a cubby, or a mailbox.
- Use labelled bins or shelves to hold math books, workbooks, and journals.

Math Tubs

Math Tubs are a great way to extend and reinforce student learning daily. A Math Tub can be put together following any manipulative activity, game, or problem-solving scenario. Math Tubs should change as the year progresses, to reflect current math topics. You may also want to use these to revisit a particular concept over the course of the year.

Why Use Math Tubs?

- To provide an opportunity to revisit a math concept
- To increase student success by drawing on previously built knowledge
- To provide opportunities to attempt new strategies
- To provide extensions for students who have completed their daily activities
- To reuse materials you have already put together
- To provide further problem-solving activities

Recommended Math Materials

- Algebra Tiles (2-colour) — class set, clear plastic organizer trays, overhead or magnetic set
- Base-ten materials (clearview with interlocking pieces)
- Calculators with fraction key and problem-solving capabilities
- Circular fraction set and frames (decimal, degree, percent, time, fraction and compass points), translucent pieces and overhead set
- Coloured tiles and overhead set
- Coloured relational rods and overhead set (Cuisenaire Rods)
- Connecting cubes (1-cm, 2-cm)
- Connecting plastic figures to build 2-D figures and nets for 3-D solids (Polyhedrons)
- Full circle protractors
- Geoboards (minimum 15 cm by 15 cm) clear, 11 by 11, 5 by 5, circular
- Geobands
- Measuring cups
- Measuring tapes (minimum 150-cm, wind-up tape in protective case, calibrated in centimetres and millimetres)
- Metre sticks (unbreakable plastic, calibrated in centimetres and millimetres)
- Number cubes: 6-faces in two colours; 10-, 12- and 30-faces
- Operation cubes (cubes labelled with operation signs)
- Pattern Blocks and an overhead set
- Pentominoes
- Plastic transparent tools
- Playing cards
- Relational geometric 3-D solids and large demonstration set
- 30-cm rulers
- Safety compasses
- Spinners (number, colour)
- Tangrams
- Trundle wheels
- Two-colour counters and overhead set

(*Leading Math Success* 2004)

Each Math Tub should be in its own bin for easy organization and storage. Each tub should be labelled on the outside with the name of the activity and the number of students that can use that tub at one time. The tub should include:

- instructions for the activity
- any required manipulatives or technology
- a list of common materials required that are not in the tub; for example, glue, scissors
- expectations for the completed activity (whether it is a game or a created piece of work)

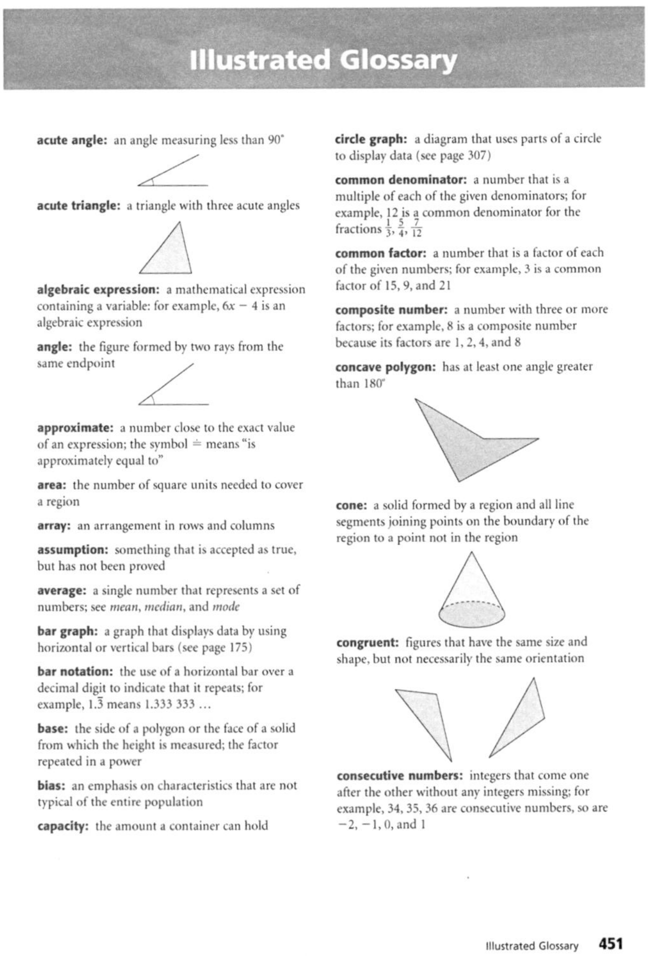

Illustrated Glossary

acute angle: an angle measuring less than 90°

acute triangle: a triangle with three acute angles

algebraic expression: a mathematical expression containing a variable: for example, $6x - 4$ is an algebraic expression

angle: the figure formed by two rays from the same endpoint

approximate: a number close to the exact value of an expression; the symbol $\doteq$ means "is approximately equal to"

area: the number of square units needed to cover a region

array: an arrangement in rows and columns

assumption: something that is accepted as true, but has not been proved

average: a single number that represents a set of numbers; see *mean*, *median*, and *mode*

bar graph: a graph that displays data by using horizontal or vertical bars (see page 175)

bar notation: the use of a horizontal bar over a decimal digit to indicate that it repeats; for example, $1.\overline{3}$ means 1.333 333 …

base: the side of a polygon or the face of a solid from which the height is measured; the factor repeated in a power

bias: an emphasis on characteristics that are not typical of the entire population

capacity: the amount a container can hold

circle graph: a diagram that uses parts of a circle to display data (see page 307)

common denominator: a number that is a multiple of each of the given denominators; for example, 12 is a common denominator for the fractions $\frac{1}{3}, \frac{5}{4}, \frac{7}{12}$

common factor: a number that is a factor of each of the given numbers; for example, 3 is a common factor of 15, 9, and 21

composite number: a number with three or more factors; for example, 8 is a composite number because its factors are 1, 2, 4, and 8

concave polygon: has at least one angle greater than 180°

cone: a solid formed by a region and all line segments joining points on the boundary of the region to a point not in the region

congruent: figures that have the same size and shape, but not necessarily the same orientation

consecutive numbers: integers that come one after the other without any integers missing; for example, 34, 35, 36 are consecutive numbers, so are −2, −1, 0, and 1

Illustrated Glossary 451

Math Terminology

Students should be exposed to mathematics terminology and definitions regularly. This will build their confidence in using mathematics terms and increase their knowledge of the meaning of such terms. You could create a mathematics terminology bulletin board that may include the mathematics term and its corresponding definition. Continue to add to this board throughout the school year. As new terminology is introduced during a lesson, identify the word, its meaning, and add it to the bulletin board. A picture or symbol may accompany the word, if appropriate. This board provides a visual connection for students and helps them identify the word and its meaning.

Another resource for students is the *Glossary* at the end of their text. Students could also create their own personal mathematics dictionaries where they record the terminology and definitions from the bulletin board. This will serve as their own personal reference and could be particularly helpful when students are working independently in class, or when working on homework, or studying for tests.

Key words are listed on the opening page of each unit of the Student Book. These words can be added to language lessons and spelling lists when a particular math concept is being developed.

At times through the year, you can choose a math word and ask students to "Explain what you know about _____" as a math journal entry. This checks prior knowledge or assesses knowledge (as students are using an open-ended forum to share what they know about a math term in pictures, numbers, or words).

Community-Building Activities

The following ideas provide opportunities for students to work together to develop relationships built on co-operation and mutual respect. These activities also provide opportunities to model classroom principles while using math concepts.

Co-Operative Math Posters

Have students work co-operatively to create a math poster when you introduce new concepts/topics. Students can work in groups to develop a poster that shows what they know about the new concepts/topic. The group may wish to select pictures from magazines, draw pictures, print words, label diagrams, or use a combination of the above to create the poster.

Create a Math Bulletin Board

Devote a bulletin board to math. As students work through a concept, all students can contribute work to be displayed. Or, students can work together to create a bulletin board demonstrating a concept they have learned. For example, after a study of symmetry and congruency, students could make a mural depicting various similar, congruent, and symmetrical figures in a futuristic city.

Math Meetings

Use math meetings to gather first-hand information about student attitudes and feelings about math. This is the time to pose a question about a particular math activity, problem, or collaborative group work time. All student responses should be valued and considered for future planning. Students may also have suggestions that could be explored for future learning experiences.

Problem of the Week

At the beginning of the week, pose a math problem to the class and have small groups work on it. Toward the end of the week, invite groups to share their solutions and encourage the class to discuss and compare the different problem-solving strategies presented. You may also wish to have students create similar problems and trade with classmates to solve.

Math through the Day

Students have individual learning styles and strengths in different areas. When math is meaningfully integrated into other subject areas, it can provide significant learning connections for students. Students who demonstrate strengths in other areas of the curriculum can use these strengths to show what they know about mathematics. *Math Link* features in the Student Book highlight connections between the math students are learning and other subject areas as well as the real world.

The math curriculum is extensive; thus, some concepts may be taught early in the year and not revisited in a formal way for some time. By providing students with many opportunities to revisit concepts, you can enhance learning and encourage students to strengthen their understanding. Incorporating math into daily routines provides students with ongoing support and ways to connect math learning to real-life experiences.

LANGUAGE

- Use a math journal to record problem-solving strategies and students' thinking/reflecting on their processes and solutions.
- Read literature related to math concepts.
- Create word or letter patterns.
- Use poems or rhymes during shared reading that include math concepts.
- Create riddles involving math concepts.
- Use math vocabulary in spelling lists and lessons.

NUMBER SENSE AND NUMERATION

- Practise estimation whenever possible: "How much will you save if a $48 pair of jeans is on sale for 30% off?"
- Practise mental math strategies that include ratio, fractions, decimal, percents, integers and exponents: "What is the ratio of students in the class wearing running shoes to those who are not?"

MEASUREMENT

- Regularly have students calculate elapsed time from one activity or one class to the next. Express that time as a fraction, ratio, or percent of the school day, the regular day, the week, and so on.
- Estimate the perimeter and area of irregularly shaped rooms or spaces in and around the school.

PATTERNING AND ALGEBRA

- Begin having students translate simple patterns in the environment into symbolic (variable) representations.

DATA MANAGEMENT AND PROBABILITY

- Discuss relevant data in the media, such as sports statistics, the stock market, or record sales for a student's favourite artist.

GEOMETRY AND SPATIAL SENSE

- Discuss designs in the environment using motion geometry terminology (for example, images that are congruent, will tile a plane, can be translated, rotated or reflected).

Extending the Math Community

Parents and other adults at home need to understand the purpose of a math community in the classroom. Some family members feel uncomfortable with the "new way of doing math" and are unfamiliar with the principles that underlie it.

Here are some ways to open the lines of communication, while providing important information about your math program and each student's progress.

- Keep families informed of current math topics through a biweekly newsletter. Include what, why, and how you are teaching to ensure others understand your instructional strategies.
- Use newsletters to share classroom happenings, procedures, expectations, and celebrations. In each newsletter, publish one problem students have worked through and a few student solutions demonstrating different strategies. Ensure students' names are not published.
- Include in each newsletter an idea or two that families could try at home, to extend the classroom math experiences. Include calculator activities that parents and students can work on together.
- Use a student *Practice and Homework* book as a follow-up to a class experience so that students can re-create a similar experience at home with their families. This should involve interaction and activity, and not be a worksheet students would complete on their own.
- Send home celebratory notes comprising one or two sentences, sharing a student's mathematical success.
- Take photographs of students involved in a variety of math activities and create a photo album with captions. Send this home with students on a rotating basis, providing space for parents to comment, or with a comment sheet that would provide a focus for writing.
- Encourage families to play number games when travelling.
- If students have agendas or day planners, use them to share celebratory notes, as well as other "items."
- Send home mathematics web sites that include problems suitable for grade 7 students.

It is important for families to develop a comfort level with the "what, how, and why" of their children's math learning. Encourage families to become involved in a way that makes sense for them. Family attitudes will have a significant impact on student attitudes regarding math, and you are instrumental in helping others see this "new math" positively.

When you provide support and offer simple ideas about making math real for students at home, you will have succeeded in extending the classroom math community to the homes of students.

REFERENCES

Barnes, Peter. (2002). A Community of Support. *Teaching PreK-8,* August/September, 33, 1, page 84.

Baroody, Arthur J., and Ronald Coslick. (1998). *Fostering Children's Mathematical Power: An Investigative Approach to K-8 Mathematics Instruction.* Mahwah, NJ: Lawrence Erlbaum Associates, pages 1, 2.

Gibbs, J. (2001). *Tribes: A New Way of Learning and Being Together.* Windsor, CA: Center Source Systems.

Kilpatrick, J., and Swafford, J. (Eds.). (2002). *Helping Children Learn Mathematics.* Washington, DC: National Academy Press.

Leading Math Success. (2004). *Mathematical Literacy Grades 7 – 12: The Report of the Expert Panel on Student Success in Ontario.* Toronto: Ontario Ministry of Education

National Council of Teachers of Mathematics. (2000). *Principles and Standards for School Mathematics.* Reston, VA: Author.

National Association for the Education of Young Children (NAEYC) and National Council of Teachers of Mathematics (NCTM). (2002). *Early Childhood Mathematics: Promoting Good Beginnings.* A joint position statement. Adopted April 2002, pages 5, 6.

National Council of Teachers of Mathematics (NCTM). *Curriculum and Evaluation Standards for School Mathematics.* Reston, VA: NCTM, 1989, page 23.

Ontario Ministry of Education. (2003). *Early Math Strategy, The Report of the Expert Panel on Early Math in Ontario; 2003,* Toronto: Queen's Printer for Ontario, page 12.

Pugalee, D.K. (2001b). *Using Communication to Develop Students' Mathematical Literacy.* Mathematics Teaching in the Middle School, 6(5), 296-299.

Sapon-Shevin, Mara. (1999). *Because We Can Change The World; A Practical Guide to Building Cooperative, Inclusive Classroom Communities.* Boston: Allyn and Bacon, pages 16, 17, 68.

Van de Walle, John A. (2004). *Elementary and Middle School Mathematics: Teaching Developmentally.* Boston: Allyn and Bacon.

Addison Wesley Math Makes Sense 7 accommodates these planning needs:

- Each strand is addressed with a major emphasis at least twice through the school year, to provide a rich variety of math experiences for students and to accommodate provincial reporting requirements.
- All units can be completed in about 30 weeks – depending on the needs of the class – to accommodate the normal interruptions that occur during a regular 36-week school year.
- To support the teaching of combined grades, the grade 7 program aligns as much as possible with the grade 6 and grade 8 programs. Unit by unit, students can work on the same strand across grades, with the exception of Unit 9. In this case, the grade 7 program introduces students to integers, a topic that is an important foundation for the future study of algebra.

Some teachers prefer to plan their own sequence of topics through the school year. *Addison Wesley Math Makes Sense* 7 accommodates this, as well, within the larger framework of the mathematics to be developed across the grade 7 program. Some units need to remain in the sequence in which they're placed: for example, it is not wise to change the order of the number units. Other units are independent, and can be shifted if desired: for example, the units on geometry and probability can be shifted, although the teacher needs to bear in mind that the Probability unit does assume prior knowledge of fractions.

If you're teaching *Addison Wesley Math Makes Sense* 7 for the first time, you may prefer to follow the order in the text. This will ensure that the grade-level prerequisites for each unit have been covered previously within the school year. Once you have taught the units in sequence, and become familiar with the content detail in each unit, you will be able to determine whether you prefer a different order.

Here is a suggested timing chart for *Addison Wesley Math Makes Sense* 7:

MONTH		SEPTEMBER	OCTOBER			NOVEMBER	DECEMBER		JANUARY
Text Unit		1 Patterns in Whole Numbers	2 Ratio and Rate	3 Geometry and Measurement		4 Fractions and Decimals	5 Data Management	Vacation	6 Measuring Perimeter and Area
Suggested Timing (weeks)		About 3	About 2–3	3–4		About 4	About 3		About 2

This timing chart shows one possible alternative unit sequence:

MONTH		SEPTEMBER		OCTOBER	NOVEMBER	DECEMBER			JANUARY
Text Unit		3 Geometry and Measurement	5 Patterns in Whole Numbers	2 Ratio and Rate	5 Data Management	4 Fractions and Decimals	Vacation		6 Measuring Perimeter and Area
Suggested Timing (weeks)		3–4	About 3	About 2–3	About 3	About 4			About 2

Cross Strand Investigations

The Cross Strand Investigations are designed for flexible use:

- at the end of each term, as they occur in the text
- to assign during periods of the school year that are prone to interruption of regular class schedules, such as the weeks leading up to holidays
- in a cluster as a closing project – with choice for students – at the end of the school year.

Each Investigation provides an opportunity for students to use the math they have learned in the preceding units, or in earlier years, to solve a problem in context or to investigate an intriguing question or pattern. They can be used to gather assessment information to enable you to fulfill reporting requirements.

Teaching notes, sample responses, and accompanying check lists for the Cross Strand Investigations are in the Additional Assessment Support module.

FEBRUARY		MARCH		APRIL		MAY		JUNE	MONTH
7 Geometry		8 Working with Percents	Vacation	9 Integers	10 Patterning and Algebra	11 Probability			**Text Unit**
About 3		About 3		About 3–4	About 3	About 2			**Suggested Timing (weeks)**

FEBRUARY		MARCH		APRIL		MAY		JUNE	MONTH
8 Working with Percents	7 Geometry		Vacation	9 Integers	11 Probability	10 Patterning and Algebra			**Text Unit**
About 3	About 3			About 3–4	About 2	About 3			**Suggested Timing (weeks)**

Materials List for *Math Makes Sense 7*

Recommended quantities of materials other than program resources provided on Black Line Masters.

For classroom use	For each group of 3 or 4 students	For each pair of students	For each student
• overhead Base Ten Blocks • overhead Pattern Blocks • overhead Cuisenaire Rods • models of geometric solids • newspapers, magazines, grocery flyers **Software** • *The Geometer's Sketchpad* • *Fathom* • *AppleWorks*	• stop watch • empty boxes and cans of different sizes • atlas or almanac	• deck of cards • Base Ten Blocks • measuring tape or metre stick • Interlocking cubes • Colour Tiles or congruent squares • number cubes • glue • Pattern Blocks • sticky tape • empty cereal boxes • labels from canned food • Tangram • spinner • opened metal paper clip • string • paper cups • paper bags • calendar page • cardboard • Cuisenaire Rods	• calculator • scissors • 30-cm ruler • tracing paper • protractor • pushpins • index cards • compass • counters of different colours • 11 by 11 geoboard • geobands

Literature Connections — Grade 7 Math

Clark, Dave. *Tic-Tac-Toe Math: Grades 5–8.* Dale Seymour Publications, 1997. ISBN: 086651547X.

Cook, Shirley. *Math in the Real World of Architecture: Dimensions, Quantities, Shapes, and Patterns.* Incentive Publications Inc., 1999. ISBN: 0865303428.

Forte, Imogene, Marjorie Frank and Terri Breeden. *Geometry and Measurement: Grades 6–8: Inventive Exercises to Sharpen Skills and Raise Achievement (Basic, Not Boring 6 to 8).* Incentive Publications, 1997. ISBN: 0865303673.

Forte, Imogene and Marjorie Frank. *Graphing, Statistics, & Probability: Grades 6–8+: Inventive Exercises to Sharpen Skills and Raise Achievement (Basic, Not Boring 6 to 8).* Incentive Publications, 2000. ISBN: 0865034467.

Forte, Imogene and Marjorie Frank. *Pre-Algebra: Grades 6–8: Inventive Exercises to Sharpen Skills and Raise Achievement (Basic, Not Boring 6 to 8).* Incentive Publications, 2000. ISBN: 0865304475.

Frank, Marjorie. *The Kid's Stuff Book of Math for the Middle Grades.* Incentive Publications, 1988. ISBN: 0865300127.

Fraser, Don and Joan Gideon. *Yesterday's Sports, Today's Math.* Dale Seymour Publications, 1997. ISBN: 1572322004.

Garland, Trudi Hammel. *Fibonacci Fun: Fascinating Activities with Intriguing Numbers.* Dale Seymour Pulications, 1997. ISBN: 1572322659.

Isdell, Wendy. *A Gebra Named Al.* Free Spirit Publishing, 1993. ISBN: 091579358X.

McIntosh, A., Robert E. Reys, and Barbara J. Reys. *Numbersense.* Dale Seymour Publications, 1997. ISBN: 1572322640.

Opie, Brenda, Douglas McAvinn and Lory Jackson. *Fractions, Ratio, Probability, and Standard Measurement: Reproducible Skill Builders and Higher Order Thinking Activities Based on NCTM Standards.* Incentive Publications, 1995. ISBN: 0865303029.

Opie, Brenda. *Masterminds Pre-Algebra: Reproducible Skill Builders and Higher Order Thinking Activities Based on NCTM Standards (Kid's Stuff).* Incentive Publications, 1996. ISBN: 086530338X.

Opie, Brenda and Douglas McAvinn. *Masterminds Skills Boosters for the Reluctant Math Student.* Incentive Publications Inc., 2000. ISBN: 0865304483.

Patriarca, Linda, Marilyn Scheffel, and Sheila Hedeman. *Decimals: A Place Value Approach.* Dale Seymour Publications, 1998. ISBN: 0866519580.

Salvadori, Mario and Joseph P. Wright. *Math Games for Middle School: Challenges and Skill-Builders for Students at Every Level.* Chicago Review Press, 1998. ISBN: 1556522886.

Smoothey, Marion. *Time, Distance and Speed.* New York: Marshall Cavendish Inc., 1993. ISBN: 1854354671.

Program Masters

Contents **Page**

Name ____________________ Date ______________

Program Master 1

Inquiry Process Check List

	Understands Problem		Makes a Plan		Carries out Plan		Looks Back		
Name	Restates problem in own words.	Identifies information given.	Asks questions; makes predictions.	Chooses a strategy.	Applies procedures accurately.	Knows when plan is/is not working.	Explains solution.	Evaluates reasona-bleness of solution.	Describes processes.

Name ____________________ Date ______________

Program Master 2

Self-Assessment

Students can use this format to guide reflection and self-assessment at the end of an activity, lesson, or unit. They can record their ideas on the form or in a journal.

1. What was the main mathematical concept, procedure or strategy you learned?

2. Give an example to show how it works. You can use words, diagrams, symbols, or sketches.

3. Why is it important? When might it be useful to you or others?

4. Check the options below that describe how well you understand it.

- ☐ I could teach it to someone else.
- ☐ I know when and how to use it on my own.
- ☐ I can use it with a bit of help or reminding.
- ☐ I still need a lot of help and practice.

Name ____________________ Date ________________

Program Master 3

Self-Assessment: Problem Solving

Step 1. **Understand.**
State the problem in your own words. Make sure you tell exactly what you are supposed to find or solve.

What information are you given?

How well do you understand this problem?
not at all ☐ partly ☐ a lot ☐

Step 2. **Plan.**
How will you solve the problem? What strategy will you use?

How confident are you that your plan will work?
not at all ☐ partly ☐ a lot ☐

Step 3. **Solve.**
Solve the problem (in your notebook or on paper).
Explain your solution.

Step 4. **Look Back.**
Is your solution reasonable?
not at all ☐ maybe ☐
How certain are you that your solution is correct?
not at all ☐ somewhat ☐ a lot ☐

Describe another way to solve this problem. Compare it to the method you used.

Name ____________________ Date ________________

Program Master 4

Learning Skills Check List

Record ongoing observations of students' learning skills. Use check marks or dates to indicate when behaviours are observed, or use the following key:

Level 1 – very limited; Level 2 – somewhat or limited; Level 3 – satisfactory; Level 4 – thorough

Name	Works independently	Shows initiative	Completes tasks (work habits)	Asks questions (uses information)	Co-operates with others	Resolves conflicts appropriately	Participates in class and group activities	Assesses own work (sets goals)

Name ____________________ Date ______________

Program Master 5

Mathematical Dispositions and Learning Skills

Teachers can record observations about students' dispositions and learning skills once or twice during each unit by noting a rating (for example, 1 to 4) along with brief comments.

Learning Skill	Observation 1		Observation 2	
	Rating*	Date/Evidence	Rating*	Date/Evidence
Independent work • shows self-responsibility • completes work on time and with care				
Initiative • takes risks in performing mathematical tasks • exhibits curiosity • shows enjoyment of mathematical experiences • approaches new tasks confidently				
Work habits • puts forward consistent effort • perseveres in mathematical tasks and projects • shows flexibility				
Class participation • contributes to mathematical discussions • contributes to co-operative problem solving • shares responsibility				
Problem solving • mathematically represents and organizes information • devises plans • carries out plans • self-checks to verify solutions • makes connections among different problems and solutions				
Goal setting • assesses own work; evaluates success • identifies goals • identifies specific steps or actions needed to improve • uses criteria				

Level 1 – very limited; Level 2 – somewhat or limited; Level 3 – satisfactory; Level 4 – thorough

Name ____________________ Date _______________

Program Master 6

Observation Record 1

This form can be used to observe three students who are working together or who are in close proximity.

Unit_____ Lesson _____ Activity _______________

	Observation Notes
Name ____________ ***Focus: PS, UC, AP, CM** **Observed strengths:** **Observed needs:**	
Name ____________ ***Focus: PS, UC, AP, CM** **Observed strengths:** **Observed needs:**	
Name ____________ ***Focus: PS, UC, AP, CM** **Observed strengths:** **Observed needs:**	

*Circle one or more to indicate the focus of your observations and notes:

PS – Problem solving
UC – Understanding of concepts
AP – Application of procedures
CM – Communication

Name ____________________ Date ______________

Program Master 7

Observation Record 2

Use this form to record ongoing observations over a period of time. You can record more than one date/observation in each category.

Observation period from __________ to __________

Observation Notes
Problem solving
Understanding of concepts
Application of procedures
Communication
Summary ***Strengths:*** ***Needs:*** ***Next steps:***

Name ____________________ Date ______________

Program Master 8

Conference Prompts

Teachers can select and develop questions and prompts to use during both formal and informal conferences and interviews with students.
Answers will often provide evidence of more than one category.
Note: The questions are not intended to provide an overall sequence/conference outline. They are examples.

Problem solving	Understanding of concepts
• Explain the problem to me. • What have you tried? • How did you decide where to start/what to do? • Were there any places where you got stuck? How did you get going again? • Why did you choose …? • How did you solve …? • Show/tell me about your thinking. • Show me another way … • What other ways could someone solve this problem? • Have you found all possible solutions/answers? How do you know? • What advice would you give someone else who had to solve a problem like this? • Can you make up another problem like this for me to solve? • Here's what I saw you do …	• Tell me what you know/learned about … • Tell me about your thinking … • How do you know …? • Why does …? • Tell me how you could … • Show me … • What do you predict/think will happen if …? Why? • Does that make sense to you? Tell me why/why not. • How could you explain this to someone who has not learned it yet? • Explain what you need to do … • About how much/how many …? Tell me about your thinking—how did you decide on your estimate? • What is the same/different …? What questions do you have about …?
Application of procedures	**Communication**
• How many …? • Show me how to … • What answer/solution do you have? • Does that make sense to you? • How could you check? • How did you get that answer/solution? • Have you answered all the parts? • Why is this important? How could you use … outside of school? • How is … connected to …? • Have you done work like this before? Tell me about it.	Can be observed as students respond, through speech, writing, and drawing, to questions such as those listed above. Also: • Is there another way to say/show that? • What do you call that? Does it have another name? • How could you tell/show someone else what you learned/found out? • Tell me what you did.

Name ____________________ Date _______________

Program Master 9

Work Sample Records

Teachers can use this form to record key information about a portfolio or collection of work samples they select to keep as evidence of learning.

Unit ______

	Strand circle one or more	**Category** circle one or more*	**What this sample shows about student learning**
Date:________ **Work Sample:**	• Number Sense and Numeration • Measurement • Geometry and Spatial Sense • Patterning and Algebra • Data Management and Probability	PS UC AP CM	
Date:_____ **Work Sample:**	• Number Sense and Numeration • Measurement • Geometry and Spatial Sense • Patterning and Algebra • Data Management and Probability	PS UC AP CM	
Date:_____ **Work Sample:**	• Number Sense and Numeration • Measurement • Geometry and Spatial Sense • Patterning and Algebra • Data Management and Probability	PS UC AP CM	

* **PS** – Problem solving
AP – Application of procedures
UC – Understanding of concepts
CM – Communication

Name ____________________ Date _______________

Program Master 10

Summary Class Records: Strands

Achievement Levels
1 – very limited; simple strategies; major errors; unclear
2 – somewhat or limited; somewhat appropriate strategies; several minor errors; some clarity
3 – satisfactory; appropriate strategies; few minor errors; clear
4 – thorough; rarely makes errors; innovative strategies; clear and precise

Unit ______

	Strand ____________________				**Strand** ____________________			
	Most consistent achievement level				**Most consistent achievement level**			
Name	Observations	Work samples	Performance Assessment	**Overall**	Observations	Work samples	Performance Assessment	**Overall**

Name ____________________ Date _______________

Program Master 11

Summary Class Records: Achievement Categories

Teachers can use this form to keep a class record of the levels achieved on various tasks and activities. Levels can be assigned based on observations, conferences, work samples, and/or performance assessment.

Achievement Levels
1 – very limited; simple strategies; major errors; unclear
2 – somewhat or limited; somewhat appropriate strategies; several minor errors; some clarity
3 – satisfactory; appropriate strategies; few minor errors; clear
4 – thorough; rarely makes errors; innovative strategies; clear and precise

Unit ____ Focus Strand ________________________________

	Level Achieved												
	Problem solving			Understanding of concepts			Application of procedures			Communication			Overall
Name													

Name ____________________ Date ________________

Program Master 12

Summary Record: Individual

Teachers can use this form to maintain an ongoing record of student achievement. For each strand, use records of ongoing observations and conferences, work samples, and performance assessments to determine the level achieved for each category. Record category levels in the boxes, and comments in the space provided.

Achievement Levels

1 – very limited; simple strategies; major errors; unclear
2 – somewhat or limited; somewhat appropriate strategies; several minor errors; some clarity
3 – satisfactory; appropriate strategies; few minor errors; clear
4 – thorough; rarely makes errors; innovative strategies; clear and precise

	Most Consistent Level Achieved				
Category	**Problem solving**	**Understanding of concepts**	**Application of procedures**	**Communication**	**Overall**
NUMBER SENSE AND NUMERATION	level ☐	level ☐	level ☐	level ☐	level ☐
MEASUREMENT	level ☐	level ☐	level ☐	level ☐	level ☐
GEOMETRY AND SPATIAL SENSE	level ☐	level ☐	level ☐	level ☐	level ☐
PATTERNING AND ALGEBRA	level ☐	level ☐	level ☐	level ☐	level ☐
DATA MANAGEMENT AND PROBABILITY	level ☐	level ☐	level ☐	level ☐	level ☐
OVERALL	level ☐	level ☐	level ☐	level ☐	level ☐

Name ____________________ Date ______________

Program Master 13

Hundred Chart

1	2	3	4	5	6	7	8	9	10
11	12	13	14	15	16	17	18	19	20
21	22	23	24	25	26	27	28	29	30
31	32	33	34	35	36	37	38	39	40
41	42	43	44	45	46	47	48	49	50
51	52	53	54	55	56	57	58	59	60
61	62	63	64	65	66	67	68	69	70
71	72	73	74	75	76	77	78	79	80
81	82	83	84	85	86	87	88	89	90
91	92	93	94	95	96	97	98	99	100

Name ____________________ Date ________________

Program Master 14

0.5-cm Grid Paper

Name ____________________ Date ______________

Program Master 15

12 × 12 Multiplication Chart

×	1	2	3	4	5	6	7	8	9	10	11	12
1	1	2	3	4	5	6	7	8	9	10	11	12
2	2	4	6	8	10	12	14	16	18	20	22	24
3	3	6	9	12	15	18	21	24	27	30	33	36
4	4	8	12	16	20	24	28	32	36	40	44	48
5	5	10	15	20	25	30	35	40	45	50	55	60
6	6	12	18	24	30	36	42	48	54	60	66	72
7	7	14	21	28	35	42	49	56	63	70	77	84
8	8	16	24	32	40	48	56	64	72	80	88	96
9	9	18	27	36	45	54	63	72	81	90	99	108
10	10	20	30	40	50	60	70	80	90	100	110	120
11	11	22	33	44	55	66	77	88	99	110	121	132
12	12	24	36	48	60	72	84	96	108	120	132	144

Name ____________________ Date ________________

Program Master 16

Blank 10 by 10 Chart

Name ____________________ Date ______________

Program Master 17

2-Column Chart

Name ____________________ Date ________________

Program Master 18

3-Column Chart

Name ____________________ Date _______________

Program Master 19

4-Column Chart

Name ____________________ Date ________________

Program Master 20

1-cm Grid Paper

Name ____________________ Date _______________

Program Master 21

2-cm Grid Paper

Name ____________________ Date ________________

Program Master 22

Square Dot Paper

Name ____________________ Date _______________

Program Master 23

Isometric Dot Paper

Name ____________________ Date ________________

Program Master 24

Isometric Grid Paper

Name ____________________ Date ______________

Program Master 25

Pattern Blocks

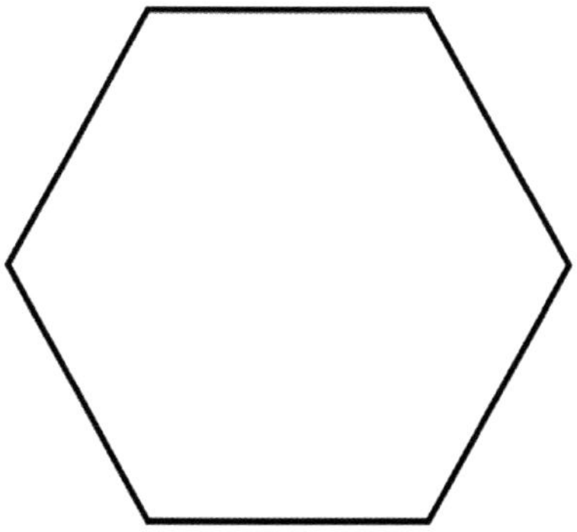

Yellow Hexagon

Orange Square

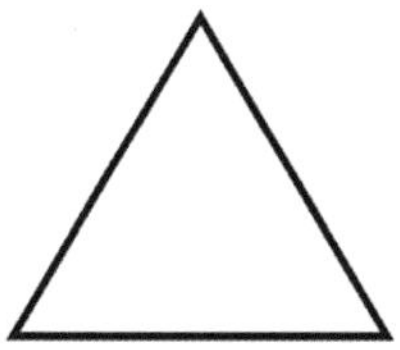

Green Triangle

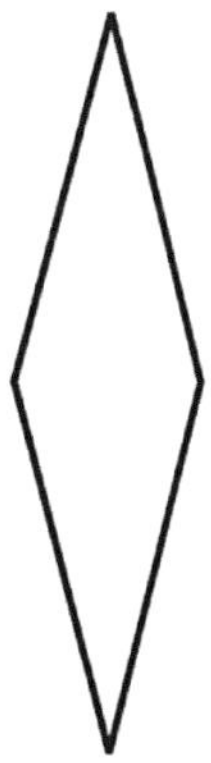

Tan Rhombus

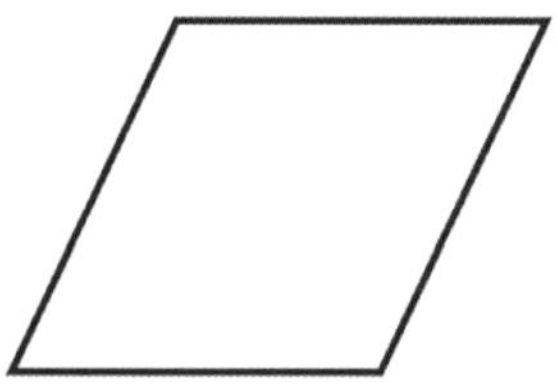

Blue Rhombus

Red Trapezoid

Name ____________________ Date ________________

Program Master 26

Tangram

Name ____________________ Date ________________

Program Master 27

Play Money

Name ____________________ Date ______________

Program Master 28

Venn Diagram

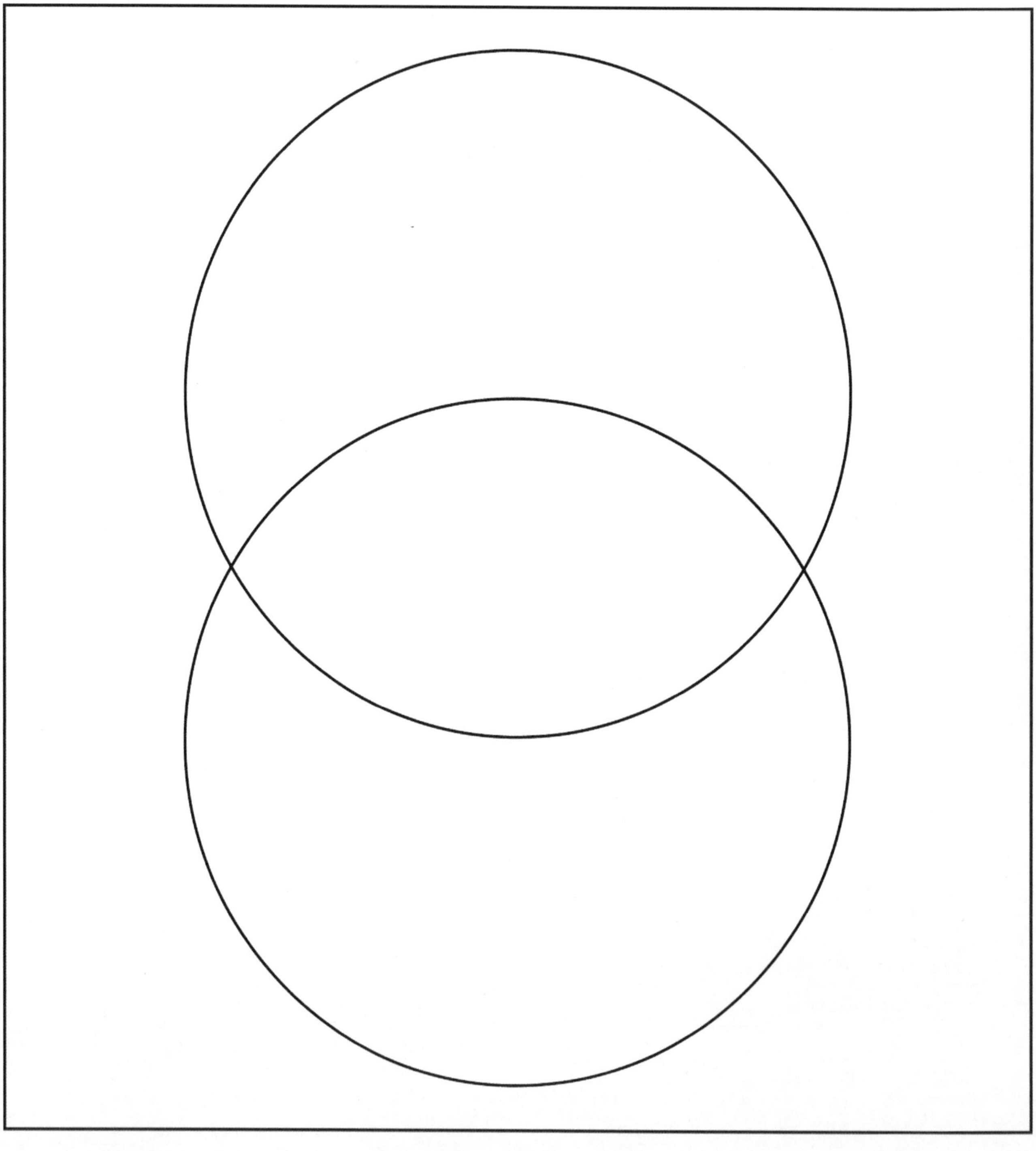

Name ____________________ Date _______________

Program Master 29

5-Column Chart

Name ____________________ Date ________________

Program Master 30

Circle Diagrams

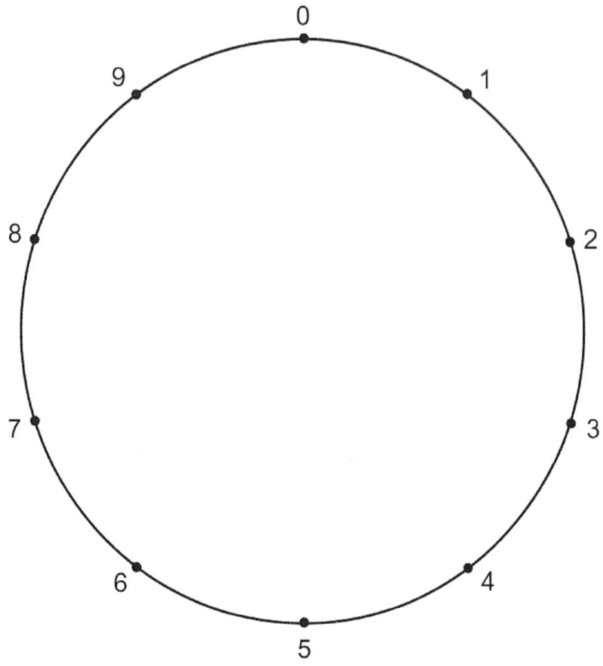

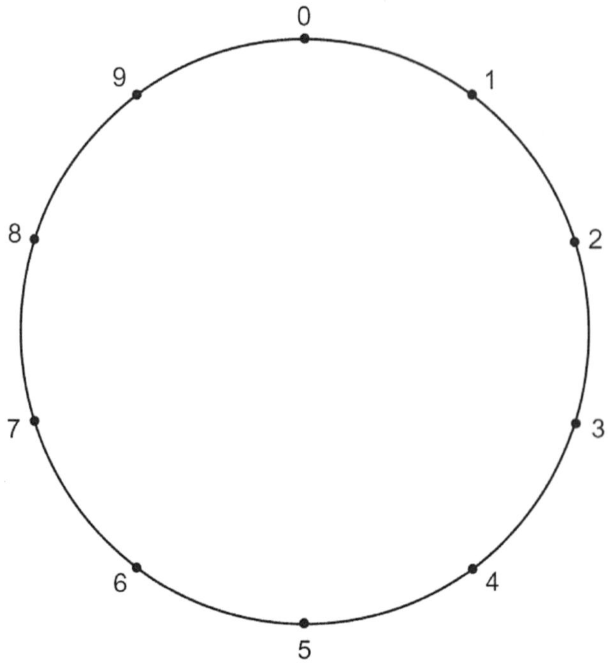

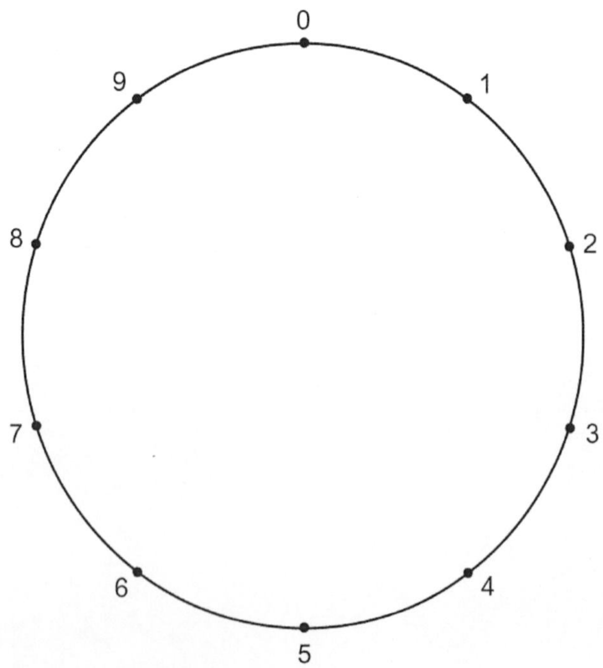

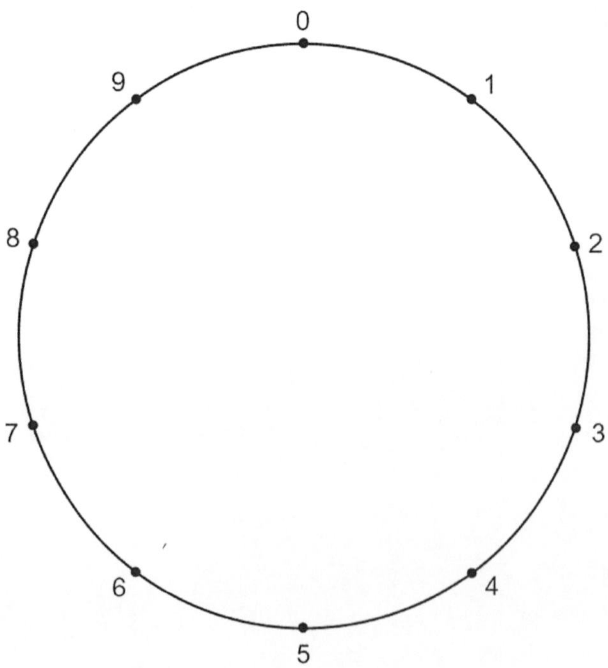

Addison Wesley
Mathematics
Makes Sense

Program Authors

Jason Johnston
Bryn Keyes
Mary Doucette
Antonietta Lenjosek
Steve Thomas
Margaret Sinclair
Trevor Brown
Cathy Heideman
Don Jones
Michael Davis
Jennifer Paziuk
Ken Harper
Sharon Jeroski
Ray Appel
Laura Weatherhead
Betty Milne
Jim Mennie
Lynn Strangway

This book contains recycled product and is acid free.

Printed and bound in Canada

10 17

PEARSON
Education Canada

ADDISON WESLEY

Ontario

Math Makes Sense 7

Ontario

Teacher Guide

Additional Assessment Support

PEARSON
Addison Wesley

ASSESSMENT BACKGROUND

1 An Introduction to Assessment

> *"A problem ... must begin where the students are ... Good* [assessment] *tasks should permit every student in the class ... to demonstrate some knowledge, skill, or understanding."*
>
> (Van de Walle 2004, 62)

Assessment and evaluation in *Addison Wesley Mathematics Makes Sense* are **purposeful** and **possible**—to ensure students are supported in reaching the highest possible levels of achievement, and teachers are supported with tools and strategies that enhance assessment and reporting. Assessment and evaluation reflect the exploratory, hands-on, problem-solving approach that is the foundation of *Addison Wesley Mathematics Makes Sense.*

Improving Student Learning

> *Assessment should support the learning of important mathematics and furnish useful information to both teachers and children.*
>
> (NCTM: *Assessment Principles*)

The primary purpose of assessment and evaluation is to improve student learning. *Diagnostic assessment* helps teachers and students identify learning needs and plan for excellence. *Formative assessment* provides descriptive feedback for teachers and students to monitor their efforts, make adjustments that lead to enhanced learning, and work toward successful achievement. *Summative assessment* allows students to demonstrate and document their achievements, and share them with families, to ensure future effective learning. Student reflection and self-assessment help students become self-directed learners—able to set, work toward, and monitor their own goals.

Assessment strategies and materials in *Addison Wesley Mathematics Makes Sense* reflect the NCTM assessment standards.

Problem Solving

The active, exploratory, problem-solving approach to learning mathematics central to *Addison Wesley Mathematics Makes Sense* is reflected in assessment strategies and techniques. Students demonstrate their knowledge and skills by *doing* mathematics. Many assessment activities focus on performance assessment, where students are asked to demonstrate their knowledge and skills through problems and investigations that connect mathematics to open-ended problems and real-world contexts and issues.

NCTM ASSESSMENT STANDARDS	*ADDISON WESLEY MATHEMATICS MAKES SENSE*
Standard 1: Assessment should reflect the mathematics that all students need to know and be able to do.	Assessment is aligned with the provincial curriculum expectations and content standards that specify what students are to learn at each grade.
Standard 2: Assessment should enhance mathematics learning.	Assessment *for* Learning, a feature in every lesson in the Teacher Guide, focuses on teacher implementation of effective practices to support student learning and performance.
Standard 3: Assessment should promote equity.	At the beginning of every unit, open-ended *diagnostic assessment* helps teachers build on students' prior learning to support student success. *Formative assessment* is particularly helpful in supporting low-achieving students.
Standard 4: Assessment should be an open process.	From grade 1, expectations and criteria are made clear to students and their families. As students gain experience, they are increasingly involved in discussing and setting criteria for their work.
Standard 5: Assessment should promote valid inferences about mathematics learning.	Assessment is based on students *doing* mathematics. To ensure the full spectrum of mathematics achievement is addressed, attention is focused on all aspects of mathematics: understanding concepts and making connections; applying procedures, using problem-solving strategies; and communicating.
Standard 6: Assessment should be a coherent process.	All assessment techniques, tools, and activities are related to the content strands and curriculum expectations, and to student performance.

2 Effective Assessment Practices

> *"Researchers and policy-makers are finally recognizing what teachers have long known: assessment has a powerful effect on student learning."*
>
> (Jeroski 2002)

Goal-Setting, Shared Criteria, Effective Tasks

Learning is enhanced when goals are understood and shared by teachers and students. Recognizing goals and criteria for success is crucial to formative assessment.

Effective performance tasks include complex thinking, where students make choices and decisions. Effective tasks also focus on what students are supposed to **learn** or demonstrate, (not just what they are supposed to **do**).

Self-Assessment

Providing structured, focused opportunities for self-assessment helps students learn, and increases their sense of responsibility. Students engaged in self-assessment become more interested in learning goals, criteria, feedback, and self-improvement.

Provide Meaningful Feedback

Descriptive feedback improves student achievement—feedback that focuses on:

- what students have or have not achieved (rather than comparisons to others)
- timely explanations and corrections (what is incorrect and what is correct and why)
- specific ways in which work can be improved

Adjust Instruction

Teachers who use ongoing assessment results to adjust their teaching help students achieve better results. Thus, teachers are open to adapting their instructional plans to reflect student needs. Teachers should select and develop assessments with a clear sense of purpose—knowing what specific information they and the students need to work toward specific results or expectations.

Motivate Students

Student motivation is one of the keys to learning and improvement. Where assessment results are conveyed in a way that supports learning (rather than questioning ability and effort), teachers have found significant learning gains.

Assessment for learning (formative assessment) and *assessment of learning (summative assessment)* ought first and foremost to support learning. Research by Wynne Harlen and Ruth Deakin Crick found that the effects of summative assessment could support students' learning *when:*

- Assessments were consistent with teacher expectations and student capabilities.
- Students had opportunities to develop self-assessment skills and learning goals.
- The school took a constructive and supportive stance about testing.
- Learning goals were made explicit to low-achieving students, who were shown how to direct effort in learning.
- Assessment results were used to convey a sense of learning progress to students.

3 Diagnostic, Formative, and Summative Assessment

Diagnostic Assessment

Teachers use diagnostic information to make choices about the nature and extent of the learning experiences they provide. Teachers have to consider the varying mathematical knowledge and skills of the whole class as well as individual students.

Purpose

- Help teachers identify students who have difficulty acquiring the necessary concepts, procedures, and strategies.
- Develop insights into particular needs to adjust instruction to ensure at-risk students have the best possibility to succeed.

Diagnostic Opportunities in Addison Wesley Math Makes Sense 7

- The Student Book begins with a group *Cross Strand Investigation* designed to give teachers and students an opportunity to revisit some key concepts and procedures from prior knowledge, and document any gaps or misconceptions. Each unit in the Student Book begins with a *Unit Launch*, designed to activate and build upon students' prior knowledge.
- The notes for the *Unit Launch* in the Teacher Guide include diagnostic questions, and a Diagnostic Assessment feature that cues teachers about what to watch for and what to do. The lesson teaching notes include prompts and questions to help teachers activate prior knowledge to determine whether a student has the skills and understanding required to work on the lesson content.

Generic Tools

The generic tools are available in the *Grade 7 Planning and Program Masters* module.

Helping Teachers Plan

The Planning for Assessment chart at the beginning of each unit in the Teacher Guide includes a section on diagnostic assessment.

Planning for Assessment

Purpose	Tools and Process	Recording and Reporting
Diagnostic	*Unit Launch* Question; conference; scaffold problems throughout the unit	PM 8: Conference Prompts
Formative	*Explore* – Ongoing Assessment: Observe and Listen	Master: 1.2 Ongoing Observations: Patterns in Whole Numbers PM 1: Inquiry Process Check List PM 6: Observation Record 1 PM 7: Observation Record 2 PM 8: Conference Prompts PM 2: Self-Assessment PM 3: Self-Assessment: Problem Solving PM 9: Work Sample Records
Summative	*Unit Review* *Unit Problem* – Performance Assessment Unit Test Review assessment records; add unit results to ongoing records	Master 1.1 Unit Rubric: Patterns in Whole Numbers Master 1.3 Performance Assessment Rubric: Fibonacci Numbers Master 1.4 Unit Summary: Patterns in Whole Numbers PM 10: Summary Class Records: Strands PM 11: Summary Class Records: Achievement Categories PM 12: Summary Record: Individual
Learning Skills/Mathematical Disposition	Observe and record throughout the unit	PM 4: Learning Skills Check List PM 5: Mathematical Dispositions and Learning Skills

Program Masters (PM) are in the *Grade 7 Planning and Program Masters* module.
Extra Practice Masters are on the CD-ROM and are printed in reduced format on page 58 of this module.

Formative Assessment (Assessment for Learning)

> *"Assessment for learning is the process of seeking and interpreting evidence for use by learners and their teachers to decide where the learners are in their learning, where they need to go and how best to get there."*
>
> (Assessment Reform Group 2002)

Assessment *for* learning, at the heart of *Addison Wesley Mathematics Makes Sense*, is designed to help students learn. A comprehensive research summary concluded that *formative assessment* (assessment for learning) improves student achievement substantially, particularly for low achievers (Black and Wiliam 1998). The research indicated that implementing effective formative assessment could be one of the most powerful intervention techniques ever identified, and estimated it could improve average student achievement between 1 to 2 levels.

Purpose

- Provide feedback to students so they know how they are doing, and how they might improve their learning.
- Gather information to adjust instruction for the group, and to provide additional scaffolding to students who need it.
- Engage students in their own learning, goal-setting, and self-assessment.
- Help teachers ensure students are provided with purposeful practice.

Formative Opportunities in Addison Wesley Math Makes Sense 7

Teachers can use the Planning for Assessment chart at the beginning of each unit to create a manageable and purposeful formative assessment plan.

- The Teacher Guide provides specific questions to probe student understanding at various stages of a lesson. Each lesson *(Explore/Show and Share)* engages students in *actively exploring* the key concept. This gives teachers opportunities to observe what students are able to do. *The Explore/Ongoing Assessment: Observe and Listen* sections of the Teacher Guide provide specific cues and questions.
- *Practice* in the Student Book provides opportunities for teachers to observe, probe, and provide feedback about student development. The *Assessment Focus* question in each lesson allows teachers to check various levels of achievement. Numerical and written answers in the Teacher Guide help teachers provide feedback. *Reflect* in the Student Book directs students to focus on what they have learned, and how well they understand the math. Teachers may choose to use these to prompt discussion, demonstration, or journal entries.
- In the Teacher Guide, *Assessment for Learning: What to Look For; What to Do* cues teachers' attention on specific behaviours in students' oral, concrete, or written work. It provides direct, practical instructions about what to do to provide extra support, extra practice, or extensions. *Reaching All Learners* helps teachers identify common misunderstandings and how to alleviate them.

Specific Tools in Each Unit

Name ______________ Date ___________

Master 1.2 **Ongoing Observations: Patterns in Whole Numbers**

The behaviours described under each heading are examples; they are not intended to be an exhaustive list of all that might be observed. More detailed descriptions are provided in each lesson under *Assessment for Learning*.

STUDENT ACHIEVEMENT: Patterns in Whole Numbers				
Student	**Problem solving**	**Understanding of concepts**	**Application of mathematical procedures**	**Communication**
	• Chooses and carries out appropriate strategies to solve multi-step problems and check results (estimates)	• Demonstrates and explains prime and composite numbers, multiples, factors, squares, square roots, exponents • Justifies methods	• Identifies prime and composite numbers; finds factors, multiples • Represents squares, square roots, exponents	• Explains reasoning clearly using appropriate terms and symbols (e.g., prime, factor, square, exponent, power)

Level 1 – very limited; Level 2 – somewhat or limited; Level 3 – satisfactory; Level 4 – thorough

- The *Ongoing Observations* master provides a recording form for teachers to record evidence of student key behaviours in relation to the unit content and the four categories of achievement. Teachers should accumulate observations under each category over the course of the unit.
- The *Unit Rubric* master can be used for both formative and summative assessment. It is based on specific expectations for the entire unit. As a formative assessment master, it can be used to monitor student development during the unit (for example, use a highlighter to indicate which behaviours are observed at different times). It can also be used to assess open-ended tasks or problems, such as the *Assessment Focus* questions in the Student Book, although only parts of the rubric will apply to a specific task.

Generic Tools

The generic tools, *Program Masters,* in the *Grade 7 Planning and Program Masters* module support formative assessment, but are optional. They are not part of the core assessment, but allow teachers to tailor the assessment programs that best suit them.

- *Program Master 1: Inquiry Process Check List* provides criteria and recording forms for teachers to document student development during *Reading and Writing in Math* lessons, where students develop specific problem-solving strategies.
- *Program Master 2: Self-Assessment,* and *Program Master 3: Self-Assessment: Problem Solving* can be used to prompt reflection and self-assessment.
- *Program Masters 6 and 7: Observation Records 1* and *2* are recording formats for making observational notes. They are not specific to a particular unit or activity.

Name ______________ Date ___________

Program Master 8 **Conference Prompts**

Teachers can select and develop questions and prompts to use during both formal and informal conferences and interviews with students.
Answers will often provide evidence of more than one category.
Note: The questions are not intended to provide an overall sequence/conference outline. They are examples.

Problem solving	**Understanding of concepts**
• Explain the problem to me. • What have you tried? • How did you decide where to start/what to do? • Were there any places where you got stuck? How did you get going again? • Why did you choose ...? • How did you solve ...? • Show/tell me about your thinking. • Show me another way ... • What other ways could someone solve this problem? • Have you found all possible solutions/answers? How do you know? • What advice would you give someone else who had to solve a problem like this? • Can you make up another problem like this for me to solve? • Here's what I saw you do ...	• Tell me what you know/learned about ... • Tell me about your thinking ... • How do you know ...? • Why does ...? • Tell me how you could ... • Show me ... • What do you predict/think will happen if ...? Why? • Does that make sense to you? Tell me why/why not. • How could you explain this to someone who has not learned it yet? • Explain what you need to do ... • About how much/how many ...? Tell me about your thinking—how did you decide on your estimate? • What is the same/different ...? What questions do you have about ...?
Application of procedures	**Communication**
• How many ...? • Show me how to ... • What answer/solution do you have? • Does that make sense to you? • How could you check? • How did you get that answer/solution? • Have you answered all the parts? • Why is this important? How could you use ... outside of school? • How is ... connected to ...? • Have you done work like this before? Tell me about it.	Can be observed as students respond, through speech, writing, and drawing, to questions such as those listed above. Also: • Is there another way to say/show that? • What do you call that? Does it have another name? • How could you tell/show someone else what you learned/found out? • Tell me what you did.

- *Program Master 8: Conference Prompts* provides questions teachers can use to probe student understanding, and to help determine the strategies students are using.
- *Program Master 9: Work Sample Records* provides a format for documenting work samples as part of portfolios.

Summative Assessment (Assessment of Learning)

> *"The goal of assessment is to provide a valid set of inferences related to particular expectations for children and schools."*
>
> (Linn and Baker 2002, 3)

Summative assessment involves both assessment (gathering and documenting evidence) and evaluation (judging student development and achievement). Effective summative assessment balances teacher observations and conferences, and student work samples or portfolios, with more structured performance tasks. Effective summative assessment includes assessments that are cumulative and integrated—it allows students to apply what they have learned over a period of time, and to integrate their mathematical understanding across strands.

In *Addison Wesley Mathematics Makes Sense:*

- Students are encouraged to demonstrate and recognize what they have achieved.
- Teachers document evidence and make decisions about student achievement.
- Family members/adults at home understand and have confidence in the reports they receive.

The achievement chart in each *Unit Summary* master in the Teacher Guide provides the framework for most assessments, so teachers can readily combine evidence from various tasks and observations. At the same time, all assessments are linked to the strands and "big ideas" of the math curriculum, supported by references to specific expectations.

Purpose

- Evaluate and judge student achievement of the expectations in the unit.
- Document student achievement to facilitate reporting to families.

Summative Assessment Opportunities in Addison Wesley Math Makes Sense 7

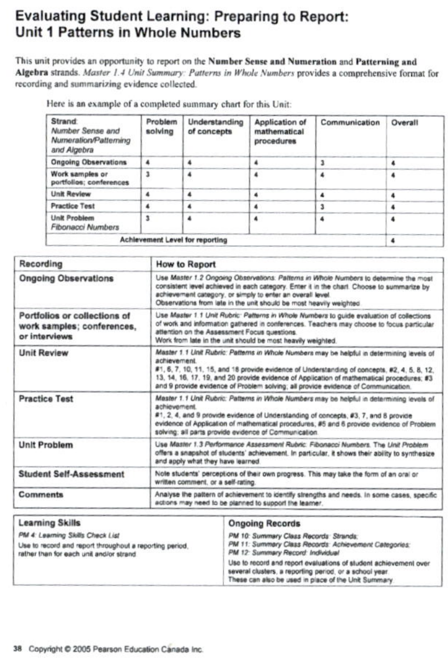

Evaluating Student Learning: Preparing to Report:
Unit 1 Patterns in Whole Numbers

This unit provides an opportunity to report on the **Number Sense and Numeration** and **Patterning and Algebra** strands. *Master 1.4 Unit Summary: Patterns in Whole Numbers* provides a comprehensive format for recording and summarizing evidence collected.

Here is an example of a completed summary chart for this Unit:

Strand: *Number Sense and Numeration/Patterning and Algebra*	Problem solving	Understanding of concepts	Application of mathematical procedures	Communication	Overall
Ongoing Observations	4	4	4	3	4
Work samples or portfolios; conferences	3	4	4	4	4
Unit Review	4	4	4	4	4
Practice Test	4	4	4	3	4
Unit Problem *Fibonacci Numbers*	3	4	4	4	4
Achievement Level for reporting					4

Recording	How to Report
Ongoing Observations	Use *Master 1.2 Ongoing Observations: Patterns in Whole Numbers* to determine the most consistent level achieved in each category. Enter it in the chart. Choose to summarize by achievement category, or simply to enter an overall level. Observations from late in the unit should be most heavily weighted.
Portfolios or collections of work samples; conferences, or interviews	Use *Master 1.1 Unit Rubric: Patterns in Whole Numbers* to guide evaluation of collections of work and information gathered in conferences. Teachers may choose to focus particular attention on the Assessment Focus questions. Work from late in the unit should be most heavily weighted.
Unit Review	*Master 1.1 Unit Rubric: Patterns in Whole Numbers* may be helpful in determining levels of achievement. #1, 6, 7, 10, 11, 15, and 18 provide evidence of Understanding of concepts; #2, 4, 5, 8, 12, 13, 14, 16, 17, 19, and 20 provide evidence of Application of mathematical procedures; #3 and 9 provide evidence of Problem solving; all provide evidence of Communication.
Practice Test	*Master 1.1 Unit Rubric: Patterns in Whole Numbers* may be helpful in determining levels of achievement. #1, 2, 4, and 9 provide evidence of Understanding of concepts; #3, 7, and 8 provide evidence of Application of mathematical procedures; #5 and 6 provide evidence of Problem solving; all parts provide evidence of Communication.
Unit Problem	Use *Master 1.3 Performance Assessment Rubric: Fibonacci Numbers*. The *Unit Problem* offers a snapshot of students' achievement. In particular, it shows their ability to synthesize and apply what they have learned.
Student Self-Assessment	Note students' perceptions of their own progress. This may take the form of an oral or written comment, or a self-rating.
Comments	Analyse the pattern of achievement to identify strengths and needs. In some cases, specific actions may need to be planned to support the learner.

Learning Skills	Ongoing Records
PM 4: Learning Skills Check List Use to record and report throughout a reporting period, rather than for each unit and/or strand.	*PM 10: Summary Class Records: Strands;* *PM 11: Summary Class Records: Achievement Categories;* *PM 12: Summary Record: Individual* Use to record and report evaluations of student achievement over several clusters, a reporting period, or a school year. These can also be used in place of the Unit Summary.

38 Copyright © 2005 Pearson Education Canada Inc.

The Planning for Assessment chart at the beginning of each unit helps teachers plan for summative assessment.

- In the Student Book, the *Unit Review* offers a set of short answer and open-ended questions, keyed to lessons in the unit. The *Practice Test* offers a page of questions that students can use to assess their conceptual understanding and procedural skills in preparation for a unit test. The *Unit Problem* in the Student Book presents a performance task that requires students to apply their learning to an engaging problem or problems. This task allows students to demonstrate various levels of achievement.
- In the Teacher Guide, the *Unit Test* is provided in line master form. The *Unit Test* assesses procedural skills, conceptual understanding, and problem solving skills.
- In each unit of the Teacher Guide, *Evaluating Student Learning: Preparing to Report* offers samples and suggestions on how teachers can summarize the evidence they collect, and make a summative judgment on student achievement. These are organized by strand.

- Each unit in the Student Book concludes with *Reflect,* which focuses student reflection on a key idea in the unit. Use *Reflect* to prompt demonstration, discussion, or journal entries.
- In the Student Book, there are four *Cross Strand Investigations,* one for the start of the school year, and one to close each term. These *Investigations* allow teachers to assess the extent to which students are able to synthesize and apply their learning in an integrated way.

Specific Tools in Each Unit

Name ______________ Date ______________

Master 1.1 **Unit Rubric: Patterns in Whole Numbers**

	Level 1	Level 2	Level 3	Level 4
Problem solving • chooses and carries out a range of strategies (paper and pencil, mental math, calculators, estimation) to solve multi-step problems	with assistance, chooses and carries out a limited range of appropriate strategies, including estimation, rarely resulting in an accurate solution	with limited assistance, chooses and carries out appropriate strategies, including estimation, that frequently result in an accurate solution	chooses and carries out appropriate strategies, including estimation, that usually result in an accurate solution	chooses and carries out appropriate strategies, including estimation; may offer an innovative approach; results in accurate solution
Understanding of concepts • shows understanding by demonstrating and explaining: – how numbers are used to describe our world – justification of methods and strategies – prime and composite numbers; multiples and factors (including GCF and LCM) – squares, square roots – exponents (as repeated multiplication) – number patterns	shows little understanding; may be unable to demonstrate or explain: – numerical information about our world – choice of methods and strategies – prime and composite numbers; multiples and factors (including GCF and LCM) – squares, square roots – exponents and number patterns	shows some understanding; partially able to demonstrate or explain: – numerical information about our world – choice of methods and strategies – prime and composite numbers; multiples and factors (including GCF and LCM) – squares, square roots – exponents and number patterns	shows understanding; able to clearly and appropriately demonstrate or explain: – numerical information about our world – choice of methods and strategies – prime and composite numbers; multiples and factors (including GCF and LCM) – squares, square roots – exponents and number patterns	shows thorough understanding; able to accurately and effectively demonstrate or explain: – numerical information about our world – choice of methods and strategies – prime and composite numbers, multiples and factors (including GCF and LCM) – squares, square roots – exponents and number patterns
Application of mathematical procedures • accurately: – finds factors and multiples (including GCF and LCM) – identifies prime and composite numbers – represents squares and square roots – uses and interprets exponents – identifies and extends number patterns	limited accuracy; major errors or omissions in: – finding factors and multiples (including GCF and LCM) – identifying prime and composite numbers – representing squares and square roots – using and interpreting exponents – identifying and extending number patterns	somewhat accurate; several minor errors or omissions in: – finding factors and multiples (including GCF and LCM) – identifying prime and composite numbers – representing squares and square roots – using and interpreting exponents – identifying and extending number patterns	generally accurate; few minor errors or omissions in: – finding factors and multiples (including GCF and LCM) – identifying prime and composite numbers – representing squares and square roots – using and interpreting exponents – identifying and extending number patterns	accurate and precise; no errors in: – finding factors and multiples (including GCF and LCM) – identifying prime and composite numbers – representing squares and square roots – using and interpreting exponents – identifying and extending number patterns
Communication • explains reasoning and procedures clearly using appropriate terminology and symbols (prime, GCF, LCM, exponent, power) • presents work clearly, including labels and symbols	unable to explain reasoning and procedures clearly; rarely uses appropriate terms and symbols	explains reasoning and procedures with some clarity and use of appropriate terms and symbols	explains reasoning and procedures clearly and precisely, using appropriate terms and symbols	explains reasoning and procedures clearly, precisely, and confidently, using a range of the most appropriate terms and symbols

- The *Unit Rubric* master highlights strategies, concepts, procedures, and communication students are expected to develop over the course of the unit. It can be used to judge the level of achievement demonstrated in portfolios, conference notes, or other tasks. It describes four levels of performance, taking into account the specific expectations for the entire unit. It can also be used to assess performance tasks.
- The *Performance Assessment Rubric* master supports the assessment of the unit problem.
- In the *Unit Summary* master, teachers summarize results of various assessments, and write an overall evaluation of student achievement. In addition to recording and summarizing levels of achievement, teachers are encouraged to comment on the patterns they observe—strengths, needs, and next steps—and to seek student self-assessment.

Generic Tools

The *Grade 7 Planning and Program Masters* module includes several Program Masters teachers may use as part of their summative assessment. These include self-assessment forms and optional summary forms.

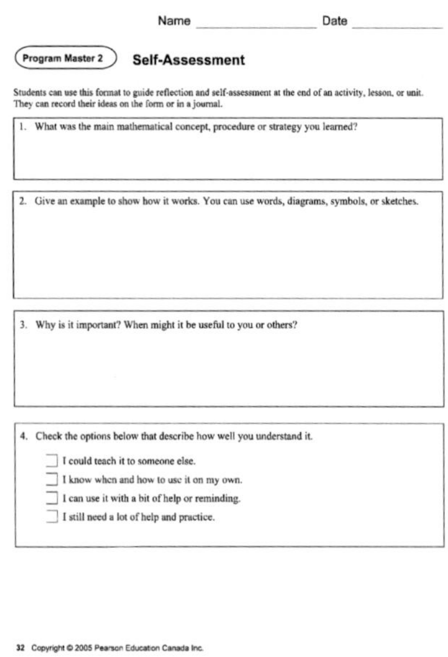

Name ______________ Date ______________

Program Master 2 **Self-Assessment**

Students can use this format to guide reflection and self-assessment at the end of an activity, lesson, or unit. They can record their ideas on the form or in a journal.

1. What was the main mathematical concept, procedure or strategy you learned?

2. Give an example to show how it works. You can use words, diagrams, symbols, or sketches.

3. Why is it important? When might it be useful to you or others?

4. Check the options below that describe how well you understand it.
   - ☐ I could teach it to someone else.
   - ☐ I know when and how to use it on my own.
   - ☐ I can use it with a bit of help or reminding.
   - ☐ I still need a lot of help and practice.

- *Program Master 2: Self-Assessment* prompts students to think about what they have learned and the progress they have made.
- *Program Master 10: Summary Class Records: Strands, Program Master 11: Summary Class Records: Achievement Categories,* and *Program Master 12: Summary Record: Individual,* offer options for record keeping. Teachers might choose one of these forms as an alternative to the *Unit Summary* master, or to create summary records over an extended time.

4 Assessing Student Progress

A. Observe and Listen

> *"Effective assessment involves ongoing, consistent, and focused observations. For a complete picture, we observe students at different times of the day, in different settings, doing different kinds of work."*
>
> (Stenmark and Bush 2001, 38)

Effective Observation

Skilful observation is one key to effective teaching. Teachers routinely adjust their lessons, offer support and feedback to students, modify tasks, ask probing questions, and make plans for future activities based on what they notice.

For many teachers, the most challenging part of observing is documenting what they see and hear. Experienced teachers have developed a variety of ways to observe and record.

Here are some suggestions for effective observation.

- Review provincial and professional documents that offer insights into the typical behaviour and development of students, including those younger and older than the ones you teach.
- Ensure students are actively engaged in exploring and problem solving. When students participate actively, they reveal their thinking and the strategies they use.
- Focus observations on a small number of behaviours or expectations that are central to the content of the lesson. Teachers who observe effectively plan their lessons at the same time as they observe. These lessons will focus on the strengths and weaknesses of students and help students develop the concepts and strategies they need.
- The top priority in observing is student understanding of concepts and use of strategies. Observation can be supplemented with assessment of student work samples and portfolios.
- For each section, choose 2 to 3 students to focus your observation. In this way, teachers ensure they have observed all students over each two- to three-week period.
  Use thoughtful prompts, such as:
  Tell me about your thinking.
  Show me what you have tried.
  How did you decide/know ...?
- Use a recording system compatible with the teaching style and other forms of record keeping.
  - Some teachers prefer to make anecdotal notes.
  - Often, teachers use a check list to identify specific behaviours associated with the lesson by entering a checkmark, date, or code to indicate what they observed.
  - Rubrics can also be used to guide observation and document behaviours.
- Be flexible. Not all observations can be planned and focused. Often, students reveal their mathematical thinking and development during other subjects or outside of class. Some teachers write one sentence at the end of morning, and one sentence immediately after school, to capture these important events and insights. Over time, this can become a rich source of information.
- Frequently skim or reread past observations, especially just before focusing observations on a particular student or group of students. This helps to provide context and continuity.

Observation Features and Tools in Addison Wesley Math Makes Sense 7

Assessment for Learning and Ongoing Observations Check List

- Each lesson includes the feature, *Assessment for Learning,* which cues teachers about key student behaviours. Over the course of a unit, these behaviours should focus on most of the key expectations, and reflect all aspects of achievement—understanding concepts, applying procedures, using problem-solving strategies, and communicating.
- In each unit, the *Ongoing Observations* master provides a manageable form for recording the observations, such as those identified in *Assessment for Learning*. Each aspect of achievement is briefly described, in terms of what to look for within the particular unit. Teachers can make brief notes, enter dates, or use a coding system of their choice.

The tools are tailored to your provincial requirements. Summarize these observations in the *Unit Summary* master to ensure that reporting incorporates a range of evidence.

Other Observation Tools

- *Program Master 6: Observation Record 1* provides a format for teachers to make anecdotal notes about three students who are working together. Teachers can note which strand students are working on, which category of achievement they are observing (for example, concepts, procedures, problem solving, communication), and indicate specific strengths and needs they notice.
- *Program Master 7: Observation Record 2* is designed to help teachers accumulate anecdotal notes about an individual student over time—over an entire school term or reporting period. Four categories of achievements are identified: understanding concepts, applying procedures, problem-solving strategies, and communication. Teachers can use the final section of the form to summarize strengths, needs, and next steps.
- In each unit, the *Unit Rubric* master can be used to guide and record observations. It provides a comprehensive description of four levels of student achievement, and reflects the particular expectations associated with the unit. Some teachers copy a class set of rubrics, such as the *Unit Rubric* master, pre-code one copy with each student's name, then use a highlighter pen to record not only observations, but also evidence from conferences and work samples over the course of a unit. In some cases, teachers use a different colour highlighter pen for different occasions or sources of evidence.

B. Oral Questioning and Conferencing

Oral questioning plays a critical role in assessment:

- It prompts class and group discussion, where teachers are able to both stimulate student thinking and gain insights into their level of understanding.
- It is important in individual interviews or conferences, both formal and informal, where teachers prompt and support students as they explain and justify their thinking, the procedures they are using, and their results and conclusions.

Effective Questioning and Conferencing

- Keep a short list of key questions available for a conversation or short conference. Identify key questions for more formal interviews or conferences ahead of time.
- Respect the student. Focus carefully on what the student is saying.
- Accept the language students use without criticism or correction. Rephrase key ideas, and model appropriate terminology, so students become accustomed to hearing the language of mathematics.
- Ensure students understand that it is their *thinking* that is most interesting to you. Encourage through close attention, positive body language, and non-judgmental comments. However, clarify student language and misconceptions. Use student friendly language to establish comfort level so the student does not feel threatened. Consider prompts such as: *Tell me about ...* or *I wonder how we could ...* or *What if? ...*
- Give students time to think. They need to reflect, self-correct, or confirm what they have said.
- Invite students to pose questions. These questions often reveal more of student understanding than do the responses. Consider the linguistic abilities of the ESL student who may be able to demonstrate mathematical thinking in other ways than talking about it.
- All students, regardless of their language competence, should have access to manipulatives during both informal questioning, and conferences or interviews.

Using the Questioning and Conferencing Features and Tools

Conference and Interview Prompts

Program Master 8: Conference Prompts offers a variety of prompts and questions teachers may choose to use in conferences, interviews, or informal conversations with students. The questions and prompts are organized under four categories: Problem Solving; Understanding of Concepts; Application of Mathematical Procedures; and Communication. They are intended to be samples only, and do not constitute a conference outline. Teachers can add to these from their own repertoire.

Ongoing Assessment: Observe and Listen

Each lesson includes prompts and questions designed to stimulate student thinking, provide scaffolding as needed, and offer insights into students' level of understanding. Under the heading, *Explore/Ongoing Assessment: Observe and Listen,* a short list of questions helps teachers determine how well students are developing lesson concepts. *Connect* often includes one or two key questions that help students formalize lesson concepts and allow teachers to gain insight into their understanding.

C. Performance Assessment

Addison Wesley Mathematics Makes Sense reflects the belief that students must *do* math to *learn* math, and focuses on exploration and problem solving. Performance assessment is a key component at all stages—students have opportunities to apply their learning and demonstrate their achievement through open-ended tasks and investigations.

Effective Performance Assessment

Effective performance assessment depends on effective tasks that help students, teachers, and parents focus on what is important in student learning, and gain insights into student development and achievement. Throughout the resource, a wide variety of open-ended problems, tasks, and investigations, along with rubrics and other scoring guides, have been designed to ensure that they meet the following criteria.

Using the Performance Assessment Features and Tools in Addison Wesley Math Makes Sense 7

Unit Rubric and Performance Assessment Rubric

- Each unit concludes with a performance assessment task linked to the *Unit Launch*.
- Teachers can choose to have students work independently, with a partner, or in a small group. Observing students working together often provides insights into their thinking—as students discuss and debate procedures, their thinking becomes "visible." On the other hand, it is also important to note individual student contributions. Teachers should clearly note on recording forms whether students worked independently, with the support of a peer, or with adult help. Where students work collaboratively, it is often best to have them record their solutions and justification independently.

EFFECTIVE PERFORMANCE ASSESSMENT CHECK LIST

Helps students, teachers, and families focus on learning goals and expectations

- ☑ Learning goals are specified.
- ☑ Expectations and criteria are clear, usually in the form of a rubric.
- ☑ Key mathematical concepts and skills for the grade level are emphasized.
- ☑ Tasks are meaningful to and valued by students and families.
- ☑ Rubrics and scoring guides are designed to provide meaningful feedback to help students see clearly what they are doing well and where they need to improve.

Engages students in applying what they have learned

- ☑ Students are engaged in realistic applications of their understanding and skill.
- ☑ Students are expected to think in complex ways, and to explain or justify their processes and results.

Allows for various levels of performance

- ☑ Tasks allow for a broad range of performance, and lead naturally to extensions—other problems, possibilities, and questions. They are complex and go beyond what could be assessed in a typical paper and pencil test.
- ☑ Students are required to make decisions about the strategies and procedures they use.
- ☑ Make the process open (multiple paths to a solution may be explored); thus the end product is open (multiple correct answers).

- In each unit, the *Performance Assessment Rubric* master can be used to assess students' level of achievement on the *Unit Problem*. The rubric incorporates all parts of the task, and considers concepts, procedures, strategies, and communication.
- The *Unit Summary* master includes space to record these results.

Investigations

- The Student Book has four *Cross Strand Investigations*, designed to take 2 to 4 days for students to complete. The teaching notes are in this *Assessment Module* (pp. 24–39). Each *Investigation* is accompanied by a sample response and check list.
- *Making a Booklet* appears at the beginning of the Student Book and is designed for diagnostic assessment at the beginning of the year. An *Investigation* follows each of Units 3, 7, and 11. These three *Investigations* are placed approximately at the end of each term. Each *Investigation* draws on concepts, skills, and strategies students have already developed.
- The Teacher Guide support for each *Investigation* includes a check list that describes the strand and the expectations addressed by the task. The check lists are cross strand.
- **Option:** Teachers who wish to focus on a specific strand can use the *Unit Rubric* master from previous units. This rubric focuses on generic observations that apply across tasks. For example, the *Unit Rubric* from Unit 1: Patterns in Whole Numbers could be used to assess the patterning aspects of *Cross Strand Investigation: Making a Booklet.*

Reading and Writing in Math

- Each unit includes a *Reading and Writing in Math* feature, where students explore different aspects of problem solving, or solve problems independently.
- The optional assessment tools *Program Master 1: Inquiry Process Check List* helps teachers assess students' strategies for:
  - ➤ Understanding the problem
  - ➤ Making a plan
  - ➤ Carrying out the plan
  - ➤ Looking back
- The same problem-solving strategies may appear in several *Reading and Writing in Math* features—they are not restricted to a particular unit. Using *Program Assessment Master 1: Inquiry Process Check List* across several units can help teachers look for patterns and document ways students' strategies are developing.

Other Opportunities for Performance Assessment

- One question in each *Practice* set is designated *Assessment Focus*. This question may be open-ended, and allows for various levels of achievement.
- Each *Unit Test* includes an open-ended problem. While this does not provide the scope of the *Unit Problem* or an *Investigation*, it does allow teachers to assess students' abilities to solve a problem. This item is particularly useful in assessing the problem-solving strategies students have developed.
- In each unit, the *Unit Rubric* master can be used to assess performance tasks based on unit content. This rubric provides an overall "standard" for the unit, outlining the concepts, procedures, strategies, and communication students are expected to develop. In some cases, teachers may wish to focus on only part of this rubric for a particular task.

D. Work Samples and Portfolios

Collections of student work over time provide both teachers and students with concrete evidence of progress. Portfolios and other collections are often best assessed in conjunction with an interview or conference. It is often difficult to make sense of a written sample without hearing the student's rationale. For ESL students and those who have not developed facility with written English, work samples may not offer an accurate representation of their learning.

Effective Portfolios and Work Samples

- Each item in a collection of work should illustrate something important about a student's development or progress; attitude; understanding of concepts; use of strategies; and application of procedures.
- Engage students in selecting work to collect. Schedule time for students to review, add, delete, and replace material from their portfolios regularly.
- Incorporate students' self-assessment because it is necessary to know the student's thought process. Self-assessment can address questions such as:
  - What does this work show about the math you learned?
  - What does it show about your learning skills or work habits—the way you approach and complete your work?
  - Which of these pieces was most challenging for you? How did you meet the challenge?
  - What are you most proud of in this collection?
  - What is one goal for improvement?
- Use the portfolios or collections as the basis for conferences with students and their parents.
- In assessing portfolios, look for patterns and trends, and try to make an overall or holistic assessment of the student's progress. The *Unit Rubric* master can help teachers make decisions. Some teachers work with students to develop criteria and a rubric for assessing portfolios.

Portfolio and Work Sample Features and Tools in Addison Wesley Math Makes Sense 7

Assessment Focus Questions

In each lesson, one *Practice* question is designated as *Assessment Focus*. These questions may be open ended, and allow students to show various levels of achievement. Responses to these questions can be an integral part of a collection of work samples over a unit.

Portfolio and Work Sample Records

- *Program Master 9: Work Sample Records* is a contents page for a collection of work. It provides space for recording information for up to three samples; teachers can add additional pages as needed. This form can help teachers keep track of the samples they collect, and summarize student achievement. For each unit, teachers record their insights and conclusions about student achievement in the *Unit Summary* master. Collectively, these insights will help teachers decide on a student's overall achievement.

Unit Rubric

- The *Unit Rubric* master guides teachers' decision making when they consider a portfolio or collection of work that reflects student learning over a unit. The *Unit Rubric* describes four levels of achievement, based on the unit expectations, and provides the basis for judging achievement on a collection of work, prior to completing the *Unit Summary*. Some teachers use one copy of the rubric for both observations and work samples.

E. Reflection and Self-Assessment

Opportunities to reflect, self-assess, and set goals improve student learning. Effective self-assessment is constructive and empowering. Students increase their sense of control and responsibility, and are able to focus on how they can improve. Through carefully structured reflection and self-assessment activities, students develop metacognition—they become increasingly aware of what is important in their learning and understand their own progress.

Writing is an important learning tool in mathematics. Students record their thinking, using a combination of pictures, words, or numbers.

Effective Reflection and Self-Assessment

- To become effective at reflection and self-assessment, students need frequent oral modelling and guided practice. Modelling helps students develop the language of self-assessment; they benefit from hearing and seeing examples from their peers, as well as from adults. A collaborative class journal is an excellent way of initiating self-assessment and reflection. In the Student Book, *Show and Share, Connect,* and *Reflect* highlight the importance of bringing students together to collaborate on their learning.
- Provide a variety of formats and media for self-assessment—oral, written, visual, kinesthetic—to ensure a comfort level for all students. It should not depend on a student's linguistic skills. *All* students should have opportunities to consider and assess their learning.
- When students are expected to provide written reflections, offer simple frames to help them get started, for example:
  - ➤ I want to get better at ...
  - ➤ I found out that ...
  - ➤ Look at these two pieces of work. What do you notice? What can you do now that you couldn't do before?
- Provide a concrete "anchor" for students as they self-assess and reflect. This may be a specific representation or piece of work, a portfolio, classroom charts, or a collaborative list of activities they have done. Students will find reflection and self-assessment easier and more natural if it is tied to the specific activities they have done. Provide opportunities for students to share their self-assessments with their families.
- If students are keeping math journals, ensure these are used only as places to share mathematical thinking and ideas. Students should be clear about their purpose and audience—what they are expected to share, to whom they are writing, and what result they can expect.

Reflection and Self-Assessment Features and Tools in Addison Wesley Math Makes Sense 7

Journals

There are questions and prompts for reflection at the end of each lesson, as well as at the end of every unit. Students can respond to these in their notebooks, or in special journals. Encourage students to record their ideas in any way they can. Emphasize that you are only interested in their *mathematical thinking*.

Self-assessment forms

- *Program Master 3: Self-Assessment: Problem Solving* provides a four-step outline for problem solving that includes: Understand, Plan, Solve, and Look Back. At each step, students are asked to assess their work. This form can be used with any problem-solving activity.
- *Program Master 2: Self-Assessment* guides reflection and self-assessment at the end of a lesson or activity. It prompts students to identify and

explain what they have learned, to tell why it is important, and to assess their understanding. It can be used after any activity.

Other reflection and self-assessment tools

Many conference prompts included in *Program Master 8: Conference Prompts* described in *Section 4B: Oral Questioning and Conferencing* (page 11) can be used to prompt reflection and self-assessment.

F. Learning Skills and Dispositions

Comprehensive assessment includes a focus on the learning skills and dispositions that enable student achievement and success. Students need to develop skills that support learning (for example, working independently, showing initiative, completing work, and participating in classroom activities). While these are important to mathematical achievement, they should be assessed and reported separately. It is also important for students to develop a positive attitude toward mathematics.

Effective Assessment of Learning Skills and Dispositions

- Document students' learning skills and dispositions separately from their mathematical development, and report on them separately, as outlined in provincial or local guidelines. Emphasize to students and their families the importance of assessing their skills and dispositions.
- Encourage students to assess their learning skills and set personal goals. Focus on one skill at a time, and focus on a short list of behaviours that a student can reflect on.
- Connect the learning skills students are focusing on in mathematics with those they are developing in other parts of their curriculum. Where possible, use the same recording or self-assessment formats and strategies, while ensuring that you include specific examples from mathematics. Students need to see the connections among various parts of their curriculum and their learning.

Using the Learning Skills and Dispositions Features and Tools in Addison Wesley Math Makes Sense 7

- Teachers can use *Program Master 5: Mathematical Dispositions and Learning Skills* to accumulate observations and notes about an individual student over time. As teachers notice specific behaviours, they can record the data and enter notes and/or a symbol (for example, Level 1 = very limited; Level 2 = somewhat or limited; Level 3 = satisfactory; Level 4 = thorough). Where teachers select specific students to observe each day (see *Section 4A: Observe and Listen,* page 9), they can record observations about learning skills as well as about mathematical development.
- *Program Master 4: Learning Skills Check List* focuses on information similar to that in *Program Master 5: Mathematical Dispositions and Learning Skills,* but in a more condensed form—a class check list. Teachers can use the check list to record assessments of an entire class, using a coding system such as the one described above.

G. Classroom Testing

Teachers recognize that tests have limited utility, and try to balance their assessments—collecting a range of evidence to ensure decisions about achievement are valid.

Effective Classroom Testing

- The development or selection of a test begins with a careful plan or set of specifications to ensure the test is a valid reflection of both the content (the topics and expectations) and the achievement categories (procedures, concepts, strategies) of interest.
- Make sure each question poses a clear task. For this reason, when designing multiple-choice items, a question is usually better than an incomplete statement. After reading the stem, the students should know *exactly* what is required.
- Word questions clearly; use simple straightforward language and short sentences. This is important for ESL students, or others who have difficulty reading.
- Create your own bank of items, organized by topic or expectation.
- Allow students sufficient time to complete the test. A test of mathematics should be a test of *power* (the extent to which the student has acquired the skills, concepts, and strategies required), not a test of the *speed* with which the student answers.
- Before you begin assessing, create a set of sample answers and decide how you will score each item. Apply your criteria and guidelines consistently.

Using the Unit Tests

The Teacher Guide includes a *Unit Test* for each unit. The tests reflect both the content of the unit and the aspects of achievement reflected in the achievement chart. They also present students with a variety of item types.

Sample answers are provided in the Teacher Guide. Teachers can use these to assess each item, then record a raw score, or use the *Unit Rubric* to determine the level of achievement for each section. Teachers can also consider the overall level of mathematical communication students demonstrated in responding to questions throughout the test. Results can be recorded on the *Unit Summary* master. Teachers then determine a student's level of achievement.

Assessing All Learners

Assessment needs to be fair and valid for *all* learners. Teachers also need to be sensitive to the impact assessment can have on students who are struggling.

- Ensure that assessment opportunities include a range of ways that students can represent their learning. Emphasize that you are most interested in students' thinking, rather than in their particular answer or solution.
- Provide opportunities for ESL students and others with limited language skills to demonstrate their learning pictorially and with concrete materials.
- Conduct frequent one-on-one conferences to clarify and extend student learning.
- Look for patterns in students' work that may help to identify those who are having trouble with an aspect that is unrelated to mathematics, such as fine motor control, attention, or language.
- Ensure students are not asked to perform assessment tasks they are incapable of attempting. Select tasks that all students can attempt; then provide adaptations and scaffolding to support them.

5 Summarizing and Reporting Progress

Addison Wesley Mathematics Makes Sense supports a balanced approach to summarizing and reporting. Teachers are encouraged to include observations and portfolios or work samples, as well as formal assessments, in making decisions about a student's progress. In considering evidence from various sources, it is important that teachers:

- establish a tentative plan for reporting at the beginning of each unit or term that includes identifying key evidence that will be collected
- make decisions based on a variety of evidence, collected at various times and in various ways
- ensure the evidence comprehensively addresses the learning expectations
- establish the most consistent level of achievement, rather than the mathematical average
- weight assessments from the end of a cluster, unit, or group of units most heavily
- look for patterns in the results—areas of consistent strength or concern; increasing/ decreasing performance levels over time; characteristic differences from one type of assessment to another
- use a consistent rubric or definition of standards to guide decision making (for example, the *Unit Rubric*)
- invite students to offer their own assessments; conference with them to reconcile any discrepancies between their perceptions and the teacher's record
- base comments on the patterns of achievement noted through observation, conferences, work samples, and performance tasks; be as specific as possible about next steps

Record Keeping, Reporting Features, and Tools

Reporting by Strand

Assessment records and rubrics, as well as the *Unit Summary* master, are organized, first, by strand; then, within strand, by the categories of achievement (concepts, procedures, problem solving, and communication). Teachers are given the flexibility to record and report on each category for a particular strand, or to report on overall level of achievement for the strand.

Features

- As part of *Planning for Assessment,* each unit begins with an outline of diagnostic and formative assessment opportunities and the available tools. This chart identifies both the core assessment tools that are included with the unit, and the optional *Program Masters* in the *Grade 7 Planning and Program Masters* module. The core set of assessment tools and features is consistent throughout.
- At the end of each unit, *Evaluating Student Learning: Preparing to Report* describes how teachers can summarize the evidence they have gathered to determine the most appropriate achievement level for each student. This description includes samples and is tied directly to the *Unit Summary* master. It offers suggestions about how teachers can summarize, record, and combine evidence from observations; problem-solving activities; conferences, portfolios or collections of student work; and performance tasks to complete the *Unit Summary* master.

Unit Rubric

Each unit includes a *Unit Rubric* that focuses on the content of the unit and can be used to assess a variety of student tasks. It can guide a teacher's decisions about the level each student has achieved and demonstrated. The *Unit Rubric* provides descriptions of four levels of achievement for each of the following categories: Problem Solving, Understanding Concepts, Application of Procedures, and Communication.

Unit Summary: The Chart

Name ______________ Date ____________

Master 1.4 **Unit Summary: Patterns in Whole Numbers**

Review assessment records to determine the most consistent achievement levels for the assessments conducted. Some cells may be blank. *Overall* achievement levels may be recorded in each row, rather than identifying levels for each achievement category.

	Most Consistent Level of Achievement*				
Strand: *Number Sense and Numeration/Patterning and Algebra*	**Problem solving**	**Understanding of concepts**	**Application of mathematical procedures**	**Communication**	***Overall***
Ongoing Observations					
Work samples or portfolios; conferences					
Unit Review					
Practice Test					
Unit Problem: Fibonacci Numbers					
Achievement Level for reporting					

* Use Ontario Achievement Levels 1, 2, 3, 4

Self-Assessment:

Comments: (Strengths, Needs, Next Steps)

42 Copyright © 2005 Pearson Education Canada Inc.

A *Unit Summary* master provides a chart to be completed for each student, summarizing the various types of summative evidence gathered. There is space to make notes about students' self-assessment, their strengths and needs, and the next steps needed to ensure their success. Teachers can choose to record information for each category of the achievement chart, or use the overall column.

Teachers use their assessment records to enter the following information:

Ongoing observations—Teachers should use the *Ongoing Observations* master to determine the most consistent level of achievement observed.

Problem solving (*Reading and Writing in Math*)—Teachers who collected evidence of students' inquiry and problem-solving strategies using *Program Master 1: Inquiry Process Check List* during the *Reading and Writing in Math* section can enter the student's level of achievement.

Conferences and interviews; portfolios or collections of work samples—Teachers can use the *Unit Rubric* master to assess a student's level of achievement.

The Unit Review—Teachers can use the *Unit Rubric* master to determine a student's achievement level. *Evaluating Student Learning: Preparing to Report* includes suggestions about which item reflects which category of achievement.

Unit performance task—The *Unit Problem* can be assessed using the *Performance Assessment Rubric* master. This master provides a snapshot of a student's achievement related to the expectations addressed in the unit.

Unit Test—Teachers can enter results of the *Unit Test* (see *Section 4G: Using the Unit Tests,* page 17). Teachers can enter the results as achievement levels, based on the *Unit Rubric,* or as raw scores.

Unit Summary

- Teachers can use the *Unit Summary* master to record brief comments about a student's strengths and needs, and next steps for supporting student progress. The *Unit Rubric* master can help to guide these comments, to ensure they deal with key learnings or big ideas in the strand or unit, as well as specific expectations. For example:

  Strengths: Travis understands that measurement involves a comparison of an item with a unit that has the same attribute. He shows understanding of and ability to use standard units to estimate and measure time, temperature, money, capacity, and mass. This sound grasp of measurement concepts and skills will provide a good foundation when we begin measuring length, perimeter, and area.

  Needs: Travis often makes minor errors, and needs help and reminding to complete all parts of the work required.

  Next steps: Travis may benefit from having a task broken into smaller parts, so that he can focus better on each procedure.

- A student's self-assessment can also be included in the *Unit Summary* master. It is preferable to quote a student's exact oral or written words. These may come from conferences, in-class discussions, journals, or other written reflections.

Report Card Comments

Teachers can synthesize their comments over 3 to 4 units when they are preparing to report. Comments should focus on the student's achievement of the curriculum, and describe areas of strength and growth made throughout the term. The comments should also communicate areas needing further growth and suggest ways to promote this growth.

Learning Skills and Dispositions

- Evidence of learning skills should be ongoing throughout a reporting period, rather than broken down by units or strands. At reporting time, teachers can transfer decisions about the level of students' learning skills directly from *Program Master 5: Mathematical Dispositions and Learning Skills* or *Program Master 4: Learning Skills Check List,* to the report. (See *Section 4F: Learning Skills and Disposition* for further information.)

6 District and Provincial Assessment Programs

In most regions, students at some grades participate in district and/or provincial assessments that are reported at the individual, school, and district level. Often, these are primarily designed to ensure accountability—that students are learning the required expectations or outcomes and achieving high standards.

In some cases—particularly at school and district levels—this may involve aggregating results from a standard performance assessment or test administered in all or a sample of classrooms at a particular grade. In other cases, the assessment is imposed by an external authority (for example, provincial assessments or examinations); the results are released to individual classrooms and students.

Impact of External Testing

While these tests generally have little impact on classroom assessment and reporting for elementary students, research suggests that they can have a powerful effect and (sometimes) negative effect on students' motivation and self-esteem. However, where the following instructional practices are in place, students can respond positively:

- Tests and other assessments are consistent with teacher expectations and student capability.
- Students have opportunities to develop self-assessment skills and learning goals.
- The school takes a constructive and supportive stance about testing.
- Low-achieving students are supported when teachers make learning goals explicit and show students how to direct effort in learning.
- Assessment results are used to convey a sense of learning progress to students.

Enhancing Student Performance on Provincial Assessments

- In the Student Book, assessment and evaluation materials are organized around these four categories of achievement.
  - sound conceptual understanding
  - procedural fluency
  - effective and flexible problem-solving strategies
  - clear and precise mathematical communication
- Each section and unit include assessment items and tasks similar to the types of questions presented on provincial tests. For example:
  - short answer procedural questions
  - items that require students to explain their thinking in words, pictures, or numbers
  - problems to solve
  - timed tests (optional)
  - open-ended performance tasks that integrate the four Achievement Categories
- In each lesson, at least one question in *Practice* provides opportunities for students to display all four levels of performance, which also offers scope for students to demonstrate a Level 4 performance.
- Four *Cross Strand Investigations,* presented at intervals during the year, ensure students approach mathematics as an integrated study. These mirror some question types in the provincial tests.

References

Assessment Reform Group. 1999. *Assessment for Learning: Beyond the Black Box.* Cambridge, UK: University of Cambridge School of Education.

———. 2002. *News/Events: Current activities.* http://www.assessment-reform-group.org.uk

Black, Paul, and Dylan Wiliam. 1998. *Inside the Black Box: Raising Standards through Classroom Assessment.* London, UK: King's College London, School of Education.

———. 1998. Assessment and Classroom Learning. *Assessment in Education* 5 (1): 7–74.

BC Ministry of Education. 2000; 2002. BC Performance Standards: Numeracy. Victoria, BC: Ministry of Education. Available at www.gov.bc.ca/bced

Harlen, Wynne, and Ruth Deakin Crick. 2002. *Review: What is the evidence of the impact of summative assessment and tests on students' motivation for learning?* Presentation, Invitational Conference, Assessment Reform Group, March 5, 2002.

Marzano, Robert J., Debra J. Pickering, and Jane E. Pollock. 2001. *Classroom instruction that works: Research-based strategies for increasing student achievement.* Alexandria, VA: ASCD.

National Education Association in collaboration with Rick Stiggins and the Assessment Training Institute. 2003. *Balanced Assessment.* Washington, DC: National Education Association.

Stenmark, Jean Kerr, and William S. Bush. eds. 2001. *Mathematics Assessment: A Practical Handbook.* Reston, VA: NCTM.

Stiggins, Rick. 2001. *Making Classroom Assessment Instructionally Relevant.* Paper presented at the annual meeting of the American Educational Research Association, Seattle, 2001.

Van de Walle, John A. 2004. *Elementary and Middle School Mathematics: Teaching Developmentally.* 5th ed. Boston: Allyn and Bacon.

Cross Strand Investigation Notes

Making a Booklet

SECTION ORGANIZER (80–100 min)

Curriculum Focus: Cross Strand Performance Assessment: Measurement, Number Sense and Numeration, Patterning and Algebra

Teacher Materials
- a variety of hard and soft cover books

Student Materials
- a sheet of paper $8\frac{1}{2}$ by 11 inches
- sheets of newsprint measuring 25 inches by 38 inches (about 64 cm by 97 cm),
- calculator

Vocabulary: signature, consecutive

Assessment: Cross Strand Observations Check List: Making a Booklet, PM 9 Work Sample Records

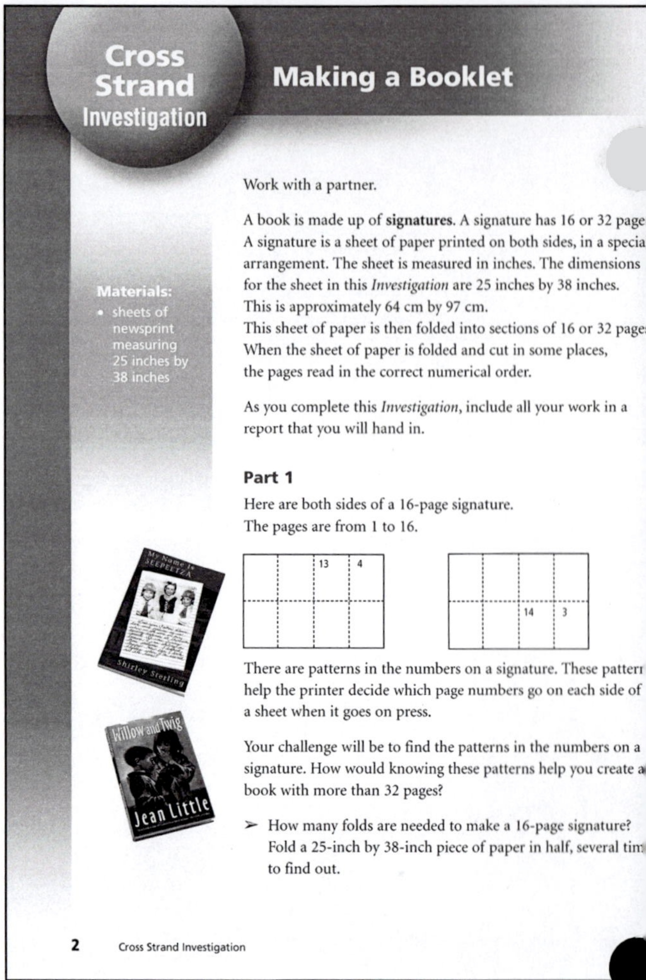

Cross Strand Investigation

Making a Booklet

Work with a partner.

A book is made up of **signatures**. A signature has 16 or 32 page A signature is a sheet of paper printed on both sides, in a specia arrangement. The sheet is measured in inches. The dimensions for the sheet in this *Investigation* are 25 inches by 38 inches. This is approximately 64 cm by 97 cm.
This sheet of paper is then folded into sections of 16 or 32 page When the sheet of paper is folded and cut in some places, the pages read in the correct numerical order.

Materials:
- sheets of newsprint measuring 25 inches by 38 inches

As you complete this *Investigation*, include all your work in a report that you will hand in.

Part 1

Here are both sides of a 16-page signature.
The pages are from 1 to 16.

		13	4

		14	3

There are patterns in the numbers on a signature. These patter help the printer decide which page numbers go on each side of a sheet when it goes on press.

Your challenge will be to find the patterns in the numbers on a signature. How would knowing these patterns help you create a book with more than 32 pages?

➢ How many folds are needed to make a 16-page signature? Fold a 25-inch by 38-inch piece of paper in half, several tim to find out.

2 Cross Strand Investigation

Key Math Learnings

1. Apply and discuss patterning strategies in problem-solving situations.
2. Recognize patterns and use them to make predictions.
3. Present solutions to problems and explain the thinking behind the solution.
4. Explain the process used and any conclusions reached in problem solving and investigations.

TEACHING TIP

At the beginning of the school year, it is worth taking the time to outline expectations and procedures for working with partners and writing reports.

BEFORE — Get Started

Give each pair of students a hard cover and a soft cover book. Have students examine the spines of each book. Ask students:

- What differences do you see in the binding of the pages in a hard cover book and a soft cover book? (*The leaves of a hardcover book are bound in groups. A piece of material is visible between the leaves and the cover. The softcover book leaves may be glued separately or in groups, or stapled together.*)

Have a volunteer read the introductory paragraph of the *Investigation*. Remind students that each side of a leaf of paper is one page. You may wish to tell students that the size of a sheet of paper is traditionally given using Imperial units. For example, a letter-size sheet of paper is $8\frac{1}{2}$ by 11 inches.

Show students a numbered, 4-page book made from a folded sheet of paper. Have students make an 8-page book by folding a sheet of paper from top to bottom, then from left to right. If they number the pages, then open up the sheet, they will see this:

5	4
8	1

3	6
2	7

Present the *Investigation* Part 1.

Demonstrate the folding sequence that will result in the sample shown in the Student Book.

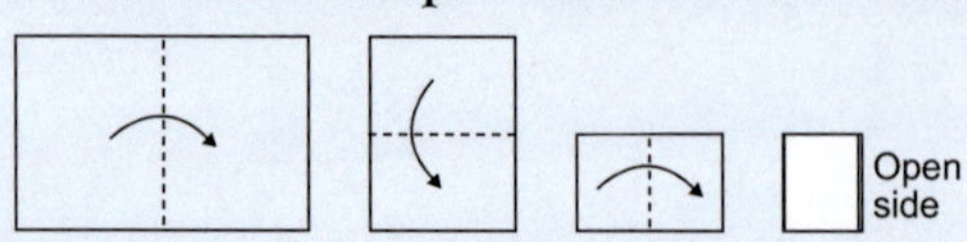

Write the page numbers consecutively on the pages.
Open the sheet of paper.
Where are all the even numbers?
Where are all the odd numbers?
What else do you notice about the page numbers?
What patterns do you see in the page numbers?

- The 2nd signature has pages 17 to 32.
  Draw a sketch. Show both sides of this signature with page numbers in place.
- Look for patterns in the numbers.
  How do these patterns compare with those in the 1st signature?

Part 2

Here are both sides of a 32-page signature.

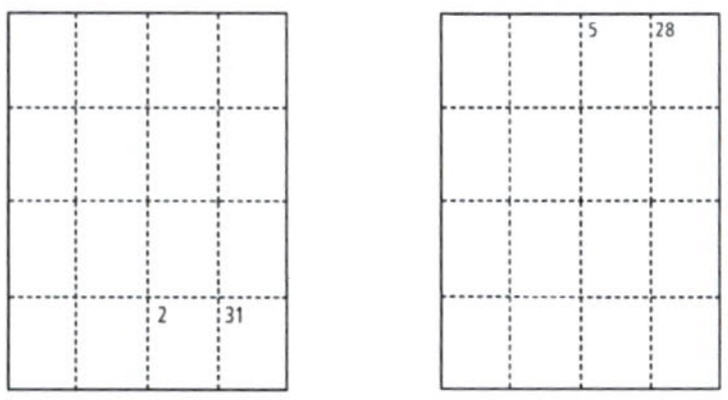

- Repeat the steps in *Part 1* for this 32-page signature.
  Describe all the patterns you discover.
- Find some books in the school or class library.
  Calculate how many signatures each book might have.

Take It Further

Suppose you have to create a 64-page signature.
How can you use the number patterns in *Parts 1* and *2* to help you create a 64-page signature?

Making a Booklet 3

REACHING ALL LEARNERS

Early Finishers

Encourage students to try *Take It Further.* Experiment with alternative sequences in paper folding. How many different page numbering arrangements can be made for a 16-page signature? How are the patterns similar among the different arrangements? How might you create a 12-page signature?

Common Misconceptions

- Students have difficulty numbering the pages on the 32- and 64-page signatures.

How to Help: Help students to number the exposed pages. Hold a finger on the last numbered page while gently unfolding only enough to expose the next page, and then number the page. Remind students of the sequence of folds to keep the pagination consecutive. Alternatively, give them the numbered pages from the *Sample Response.*

- Students have trouble seeing different patterns.

How to Help: Make sure students understand and can describe the patterns in the 4-, then 8-page signature. The number of relationships are fewer but more apparent. Students can then look for similar patterns in the larger signatures.

ESL Strategies

Read the instructions orally, while demonstrating procedures, and prompt with questions to ensure understanding. Partner ESL students with good readers to help follow the directions in the text.

DURING Investigation

Remind students that folding in a different order can yield different yet related patterns.

Encourage students to note the patterns and relationships they see in the page numbers.

Ongoing Assessment: Observe and Listen

Ask questions, such as:

- How have you tried addition to look for patterns? (*I added the numbers vertically. Their sum was 9 or 25.*)
- Do you see any visual patterns? (*All the numbers in each top row are upside down.*)
- How do the patterns compare between signatures? (*The patterns are similar.*)
- Why do you think each pattern exists? (*To ensure that the pages end up in the correct numerical order after printing and folding.*)

Ensure that students have seen the patterns in Part 1 before starting Part 2.

Demonstrate folding that will result in the sample page for Part 2. Help with labelling.

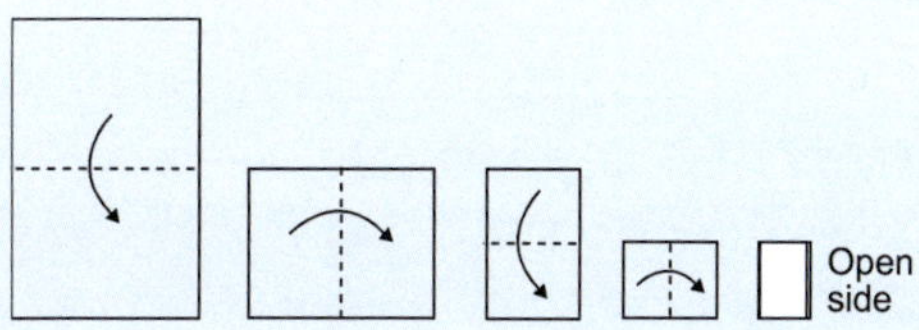

Take It Further: Students may find it time consuming to number the pages in a 64-page signature. To focus on number patterns, you may wish to provide them with the data in the *Sample Response* for the 64-page signature.

AFTER

Have volunteers share their findings. Encourage students to compare their patterns and relationships, trying to explain why they appear. Have them look for similarities and differences between 16- and 32-page signatures, then predict what might happen in *Take It Further.*

Sample Response

Part 1

In a book with more than 32 pages, the patterns and the relationship among the numbers on the signature are similar.

➤ A sheet of paper has two pages. Three folds make a 16-page signature. Each fold doubles the number of pages.

➤ Even and odd numbers are diagonal or they alternate. Odd pages have even pages on their flip side, and vice versa. Vertical sums are either 9 or 25; the sums of corner numbers and horizontally adjacent numbers are 17; the numbers in the upper, lower, right, or left halves have a sum of 34; each side of the signature totals 68; the sum of even numbers on the upper half is equal to the sum of even numbers on the lower half; the same is true for odd numbers. There are diagonal patterns of differences of 7, 8, 9, 11, and so on. Diagonally opposite corners differ by 4.

➤ Results are similar to those above.

17	32	29	20
24	25	28	21

23	26	27	22
18	31	30	19

Part 2

Diagonally opposite corners differ by 4. The sum of the numbers in diagonals differ by multiples of 4. Even and odd numbers alternate. Adjacent numbers in the middle columns have a sum equal to the sums of the numbers on the opposite side of the signature; each row totals 66; upper, lower, right, and left halves each total 132; each side of the signature adds to 264.

27	6	3	30
22	11	14	19
23	10	15	18
26	7	2	31

29	4	5	28
20	13	12	21
17	16	9	24
32	1	8	25

Take It Further

This is one possibility for a 64-page signature.

21	44	37	28	25	40	41	24
21	53	60	5	3	57	56	9
13	52	61	4	1	64	49	16
20	45	36	29	32	33	48	17

23	42	39	26	27	38	43	22
10	55	58	7	6	59	54	11
15	50	63	2	3	29	51	14
18	47	34	31	30	35	46	19

ASSESSMENT FOR LEARNING

What to Look For

Understanding concepts

✔ Students understand and explain the numerical and visual patterns in the signatures.

Applying procedures

✔ Students can determine numerical patterns and relationships, calculating accurately.

Problem solving

✔ Students choose appropriate strategies for determining patterns and relationships. They apply what they have learned to new examples.

Communicating

✔ Students use mathematical terminology to analyse, discuss and defend number patterns.

Recording and Reporting

PM 9 Work Sample Records

Cross Strand Observations Check List: Making a Booklet

Name	Patterning			Number
	Recognizes patterns and uses them to make predictions PS/AP	Applies and discusses patterning strategies in problem-solving situations PS/AP/CM	Presents solutions to patterning problems and explains the thinking behind the solution PS/UC/CM	Explains the process used and any conclusions reached in problem solving and investigations PS/CM

PS – Problem Solving
UC – Understanding of Concepts
AP – Application of Mathematical Procedures
CM – Communication

Ratios in Scale Drawings

SECTION ORGANIZER (80–100 min)

Curriculum Focus: Cross Strand Performance Assessment: Number and Number Sense, Measurement, Geometry and Spatial Sense

Student Materials
- 1-cm grid paper (PM 20)
- 2-cm grid paper (PM 21)
- 0.5-cm grid paper (PM 14)
- isometric grid paper (PM 24)
- ruler

Vocabulary: scale drawing, similar, ratio, polygon, perimeter

Assessment: Cross Strand Observations Check List: Ratios in Scale Drawings, PM 9 Work Sample Records

Cross Strand Investigation

Ratios in Scale Drawings

Work with a partner.

A **scale drawing** is larger or smaller than the original drawing or object, but has the same shape. The scale of the drawing is the rati of a length on the scale drawing to the same length on the original drawing or object.

Materials:
- 1-cm grid paper
  2-cm grid paper
  0.5-cm grid paper
- a ruler

Polygons that have the same shape but different sizes are **similar**.

As you complete this *Investigation*, include all your work in a repo that you will hand in.

Part 1

How are the ratios of corresponding sides in similar polygons related?

➢ Use grid paper.
Draw a polygon with vertices where the grid lines meet.
Trade drawings with your partner.

112 Cross Strand Investigation

Key Math Learnings

1. Identify through investigation the conditions for two figures to be similar.
2. Evaluate data and make conclusions from analysis of the data.
3. Compare the perimeters of similar figures.
4. Compare the areas of similar figures.

TEACHING TIP

In Part 2, a student may draw a polygon whose area is difficult to determine. Encourage students to draw a "simpler" polygon and have them estimate the area before finding it.

BEFORE Get Started

Discuss the differences and similarities among 2-cm, 1-cm, and 0.5-cm grid paper. Use an overhead projector to show transparencies of these grids. Make sure students recall the mathematical meaning of "similar." Ask questions, such as:

- What is the relationship among the squares on the grid paper?
  (The squares are the same shape, but not the same size. They are similar, but not congruent.)
- What is the ratio of the side lengths of the squares drawn on 1-cm and 2-cm grid paper? (*1:2*) The ratio of the perimeters? (*4:8 = 1:2*) The ratio of the areas? (*1:4*)

Present the *Investigation*. Provide each pair of students with 1 sheet of each of the three grid papers.

DURING Investigation

Ongoing Assessment: Observe and Listen

Ask questions, such as:

- How do you know that the polygons you have drawn are similar?
  (The vertices of the polygons are where the grid lines meet on both grid papers, the shape is the same, but the sizes are different.)

- Draw a similar polygon that is larger or smaller than the polygon drawn by your partner. You can use the same sheet of grid paper or a sheet with different grid dimensions. Your drawing is a scale drawing of the polygon.
- Measure and record the lengths of the sides of the two polygons.
- Compare the lengths of corresponding sides of the two polygons. What are the ratios? Are the ratios the same for each pair? Explain.
- Predict the ratio of the perimeters of the polygons. Check your prediction.
- Compare your findings with those of your partner. Explain any differences.

Part 2

How are the ratios of corresponding sides related to the ratios of the areas of the polygons?

- Draw a polygon with vertices where grid lines meet. Draw a similar polygon that is larger. What is the ratio of the corresponding sides?
- Predict the ratio of the area of the original polygon to the area of the second polygon. Explain your reasoning for making this prediction.
- Find the area of each polygon. What is the ratio of the two areas?
- How does your prediction compare to your findings? Explain any differences.
- How is the ratio of the corresponding sides of the polygons related to the ratio of the areas of the polygons?

Take It Further

- Suppose you have to enlarge a polygon so that its area is doubled. Should you double the length of each side? Explain. Use an example in your explanation.
- Suppose you have to enlarge a polygon so that its area is four times its original area. How would you do that?
- What patterns do you see? How could you use these patterns to enlarge a polygon even more?

Ratios in Scale Drawings 113

REACHING ALL LEARNERS

Early Finishers

Encourage students to repeat their investigations using several different polygons, some regular, some irregular, some convex, some concave. If a computer is available, students can explore similar figure drawings using *The Geometer's Sketchpad*. The *Measure* tools, including the calculator, can provide fast calculations for irregular polygons.

Common Misconceptions

- Students have difficulty finding the perimeter and area of a complex polygon.

How to Help: Have students use a rectangle, a rhombus, an isosceles triangle, or a regular polygon. Note that an equilateral triangle cannot easily be drawn on square grid paper. Provide isometric grid paper.

- Students expect the ratio of the areas to be equal to the ratio of the perimeters.

How to Help: Suggest using a simple polygon, such as a square, drawing it on the 0.5-cm grid paper and on both the 1-cm and 2-cm grid papers. A table of values listing the side length of the square, its perimeter, and area should help students see that the ratios are different. Encourage students to predict the final entries before completing the table.

- How did you predict the perimeter of the scale drawing?
  (*I looked at both drawings and the scale drawing appeared to be double the original. Also, to find a perimeter, I add lengths.*)
- How did you predict the area of the scale drawing?
  (*I thought that because the perimeter of the scale drawing was double the original drawing, that area of the scale drawing was doubled too. This was incorrect. It was four times the area.*)
- What relationships can you see between the ratio of corresponding side lengths of the polygons and the ratio of their areas?
  (*The ratio of corresponding sides was 1:2, the ratio of areas was 1:4. I notice that* $4 = 2 \times 2 = 2^2$. *I would need to investigate further to determine if the ratio always doubles, or squares.*)

AFTER

Have volunteers share their reports. Ask students to explain any problems they may have encountered, and how they solved them. Invite pairs to share results from *Take It Further*. Encourage discussion about the patterns they see between the ratios of side lengths and ratio of areas. Ask them to estimate the ratio of side lengths required to produce a ratio of 1:2 in areas. A guess and check strategy, and the use of a calculator, should bring students to a ratio of side lengths that is between 1:1.4 and 1:1.5.

Sample Response

Part 1

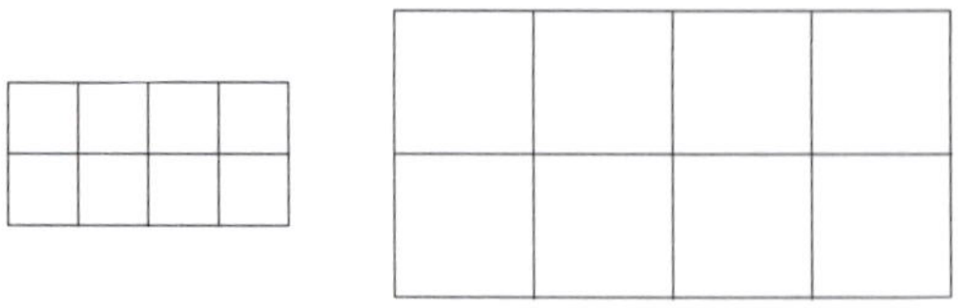

- ➤ The rectangle on the right is similar to the rectangle on the left. The small rectangle has length 4 cm and width 2 cm. The larger rectangle has length 8 cm and width 4 cm.
- ➤ The ratio of lengths is 4:8, or 1:2. The ratio of widths is 2:4, or 1:2. All the ratios of corresponding sides are 1:2. This is because the rectangles are similar.
- ➤ I predict that the ratios of the perimeters will also be 1:2. The perimeter of the small rectangle is 12 cm. The larger rectangle has a perimeter of 24 cm. The ratio of the perimeters is 12:24, or 1:2. This ratio is the same as that for the corresponding sides.
- ➤ My partner's results were the same as mine.

Part 2

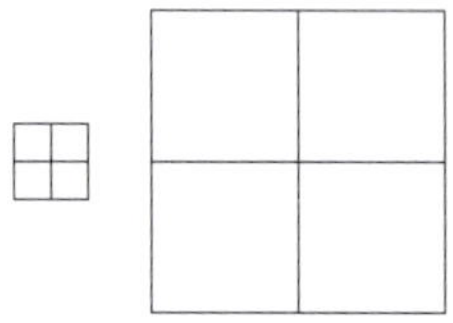

- ➤ The side lengths of the squares are 1 cm and 4 cm. The ratio of the sides is 1:4.
- ➤ I think the ratio of the areas will be 1:16, because it looks as though 16 of the small squares would fit inside the large square.
- ➤ The area of the small square is 1 cm × 1 cm = 1 cm^2. The area of the large square is 4 cm × 4 cm = 16 cm^2.
- ➤ The ratio of the areas is 1:16, as predicted.
- ➤ The ratio of the corresponding side lengths is 1:4, and $16 = 4^2$. So, the ratio of the area of the small square to the large square is the ratio of the squares of the side lengths; that is, 1^2 to 4^2.

Take It Further

- ➤ Doubling the length of each side would more than double the area of a similar polygon. Doubling the length of each side increases the area by 4 times. For example, a rectangle with length 3 cm and width 4 cm has an area of 12 cm^2. If the sides were doubled to 6 cm and 8 cm respectively, the area would be 48 cm^2, or 4 times the area of the first rectangle. By guess and check, I found that if I multiplied each side length by 1.5, then the area approximately doubled.
- ➤ To enlarge a polygon so that its area is four times as large as the original, double the length of each side.
- ➤ To enlarge a polygon so that its area is nine times as large, triple the length of each side. To enlarge a polygon's area sixteen times, each side has to be multiplied by 4.

ASSESSMENT FOR LEARNING

What to Look For

Understanding concepts

✔ Students understand ratio in terms of the comparison of two objects and are able to write a ratio in simplest terms.

Applying procedures

✔ Students are able to draw a similar polygon that is either larger or smaller than an original polygon and can find their perimeter and areas.

Problem solving

✔ Students select appropriate strategies for predicting the ratios of the perimeters and the ratios of the areas of similar polygons.

Communicating

✔ Students use appropriate mathematical terminology to explain their reasoning for any difference between their findings and predictions made.

Recording and Reporting

PM 9 Work Sample Records

Cross Strand Observations Check List: Ratios in Scale Drawings

Name	Geometry	Measurement		Number	
	Draws similar polygons that are either smaller or larger than an original polygon PS/AP	Determines the perimeter of polygons PS/AP	Determines the area of polygons PS/AP	Determines the ratio of corresponding items using appropriate symbols UC/PS/CM	Solves and explains in writing multi-step problems involving simple ratios and fractions PS/CM/AP

PS – Problem Solving
UC – Understanding of Concepts
AP – Application of Mathematical Procedures
CM – Communication

Pick's Theorem

SECTION ORGANIZER 80–100 min

Curriculum Focus: Cross Strand Performance Assessment: Number Sense and Numeration, Patterning and Algebra, Measurement, Geometry and Spatial Sense

Teacher Materials

- overhead projector
- transparent geoboard, suitable for use on an overhead projector
- geobands
- transparency of square dot paper (PM 22)

Student Materials

- geoboard (11 pin by 11 pin)
- geobands
- square dot paper (PM 22)
- 0.5-cm grid paper (PM 14)

Vocabulary: theorem, polygon, conjecture, convex, perimeter, area, scatter plot, trends, algebraic expression

Assessment: Cross Strand Observations Check List: Pick's Theorem, PM 9 Work Sample Records

Key Math Learnings

1. Identify, describe, compare, and classify geometric figures.
2. Use patterns to make a prediction and form generalizations.
3. Complete a table of values and explain a pattern.
4. Translate simple statements into algebraic expressions.
5. Calculate the areas of regular and irregular figures.

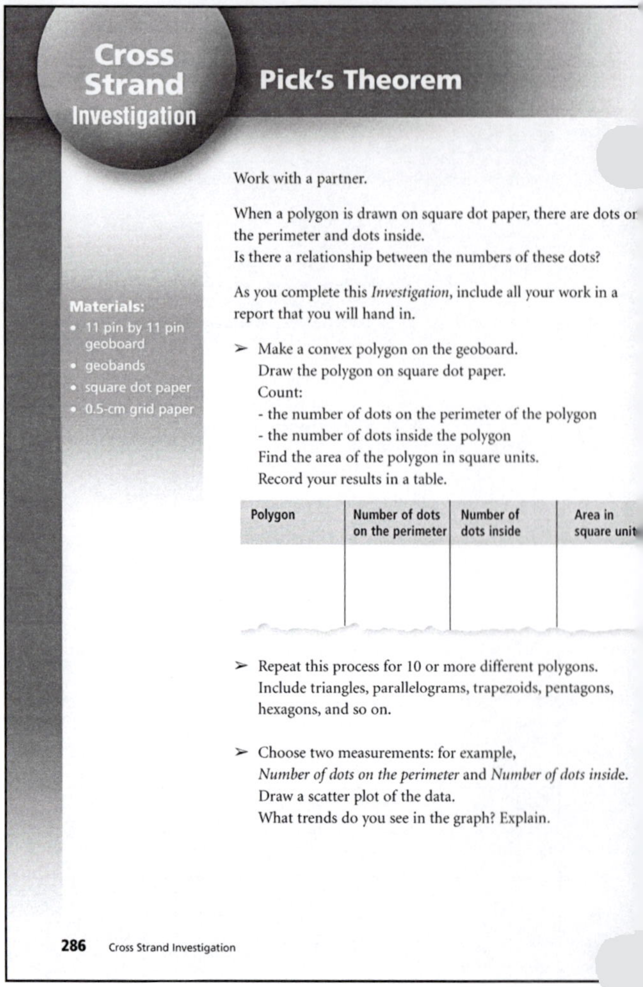

Cross Strand Investigation

Pick's Theorem

Work with a partner.

When a polygon is drawn on square dot paper, there are dots on the perimeter and dots inside.
Is there a relationship between the numbers of these dots?

As you complete this *Investigation*, include all your work in a report that you will hand in.

Materials:
- 11 pin by 11 pin geoboard
- geobands
- square dot paper
- 0.5-cm grid paper

➢ Make a convex polygon on the geoboard.
Draw the polygon on square dot paper.
Count:
- the number of dots on the perimeter of the polygon
- the number of dots inside the polygon
Find the area of the polygon in square units.
Record your results in a table.

Polygon	Number of dots on the perimeter	Number of dots inside	Area in square units

➢ Repeat this process for 10 or more different polygons.
Include triangles, parallelograms, trapezoids, pentagons, hexagons, and so on.

➢ Choose two measurements: for example, *Number of dots on the perimeter* and *Number of dots inside*.
Draw a scatter plot of the data.
What trends do you see in the graph? Explain.

286 Cross Strand Investigation

TEACHING TIP

Some students may not have had much experience using geoboards and geobands. Give all students an opportunity to explore a geoboard with several geobands. Challenge them to create polygons such as an equilateral triangle, a square, and so on.

BEFORE Get Started

Explain that students will explore a theorem, usually known as Pick's theorem, developed by Georg Pick, an Austrian mathematician who died in a concentration camp during the Second World War. If students do not know the meaning of "theorem" have them look it up in a dictionary. Tell students that they will make a conjecture, or informed guess, based on their results, but this will not show that the result is always true for every possible polygon. That is, they will not prove the theorem.

Present the *Investigation*. Have each student work with a partner. Each partner should take turns to create a polygon and record the result. Remind students that a report is required and that these reports will be shared at the conclusion of the investigation.

DURING Investigation

Ongoing Assessment: Observe and Listen

Ask questions, such as:

- How do you know that this polygon is convex? (*All the interior angles of the polygon are less than 180°.*)
- How did you find the area of this polygon? (*I subdivided the polygon into squares, rectangles, and triangles. Then I found the area of each of these, then added the areas.*)

➢ What patterns do you see in the table?
How can you use the patterns to write an expression for the area of a polygon in terms of the number of dots inside the polygon and the number of dots on the perimeter?

➢ Use variables.
Let the number of dots on the perimeter be p.
Let the number of dots inside be i.
Write a formula for the area, A, of a polygon in terms of p and i.
This relationship is called **Pick's Theorem**.

Take It Further

➢ What happens to the area when the number of dots on the perimeter increases while the number of dots inside the polygon stays the same?

➢ What happens to the area when the number of dots inside the polygon increases while the number of dots on the perimeter stays the same?

Pick's Theorem 287

REACHING ALL LEARNERS

Common Misconceptions

➤ Students may be confused about what a convex polygon is and create concave polygons instead.

How to Help: Explain that the internal angles of a convex polygon are less than 180°. A concave polygon has internal angles greater than 180°. Show students that a concave polygon has a vertex that has "caved in."

➤ Students may have difficulty developing the written expression for the area of the polygon based on the internal dots and the dots on the perimeter.

How to Help: Have students focus on one row of data in the table, and determine a possible expression to explain how to use the data relating to the dots to get the area. Then use the same method on another set of data. If it works, try it on a third set, if not try and develop another expression through trial and error.

ESL Strategies

Use the photographs in the Student Book to help students understand the meaning of what they are to do.

- What do you notice about the numbers listed in the table?
  (*The number of dots inside is less than the number of dots on the perimeter.*)
- What strategy did you use to determine the relationship among the area of each polygon, and the numbers of dots inside and on the perimeter of the polygon?
  (*I used a guess and check strategy. I tried to find a connection between the three columns of data.*)

AFTER

Have volunteers share their reports. Ask students to explain any problems they may have encountered as they created the table and the strategies they used to solve the problem. Show students a polygon on a geoboard and ask students how they could use the theorem to find its area. Ask if this method is easier than the methods they studied in Unit 6. Invite pairs to share the results from *Take It Further*. Encourage discussion about how they know the area increases each time.

Sample Response

Polygon	Number of dots on the perimeter	Number of dots inside	Area in square units
Rectangle	10	2	6
Triangle	8	1	4
Rectangle	12	3	8
Square	12	4	9
Hexagon	10	1	5
Hexagon	8	3	6
Triangle	3	0	0.5
Triangle	4	0	1
Trapezoid	12	3	8
Parallelogram	8	3	6
Pentagon	14	12	18

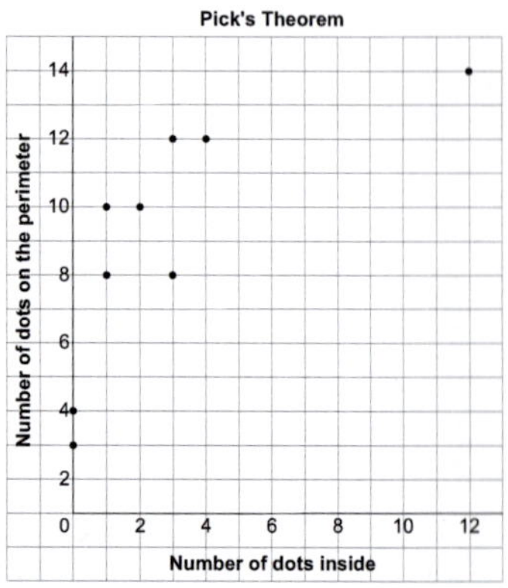

- The graph shows that the number of dots inside has a small range while the number of dots on the perimeter has a much wider range.
- In the table, the data show that the number of dots inside is always less than the number of dots on the perimeter. The range of numbers for the dots inside is, with the exception of one item, between 0 and 4. If you halve the number of dots on the perimeter, then add the number of dots inside the polygon, and then subtract one, you get the area.
- The area of the polygon = Number of Dots on the Perimeter ÷ 2 + Number of Dots Inside − 1

  The formula is: $A = \frac{p}{2} + i - 1$, where p is the number of dots on the perimeter and i is the number of dots inside.

Take It Further

- As the number of dots on the perimeter increases, the area increases while the number of dots inside remains constant.
- As the number of dots inside increases, the area increases while the number of dots on the perimeter remains constant.

ASSESSMENT FOR LEARNING

What to Look For

Understanding concepts

✔ Students systematically collect, organize and analyse data, and identify numerical patterns in the data.
✔ Students understand and describe the attributes of a convex polygon.

Applying procedures

✔ Students can create a table of data, graph the data, and make generalizations.

Problem solving

✔ Students choose appropriate strategies for determining an expression for the area of a polygon from a set of data.

Communicating

✔ Students use mathematical terminology to analyse and discuss identified number patterns and relationships.

Recording and Reporting

PM 9 Work Sample Records

Cross Strand Observations Check List: Pick's Theorem

Name	Patterning and Algebra			Data Management	Number
	Uses patterns to make a prediction and form generalizations PS/AP	Applies and discusses patterning strategies in problem-solving situations PS/AP/CM	Creates an algebraic expression from a statement in words CM/AP	Systematically collects, organizes, analyses, and graphs data PS/US/CM	Explains the process used and any conclusions reached in problem solving and investigations PS/CM

PS – Problem Solving
UC – Understanding of Concepts
AP – Application of Mathematical Procedures
CM – Communication

A Population Simulation

SECTION ORGANIZER 80–100 min

Curriculum Focus: Cross Strand Performance Assessment: Number Sense and Numeration, Patterning and Algebra, Data Management and Probability

Student Materials

- paper cup
- about 40 2-sided counters (pennies, lima beans painted one side, 2-colour tiles)
- 0.5-cm grid paper (PM 14)
- ruler

Vocabulary: population, simulation

Assessment: Cross Strand Observations Check List: A Population Simulation, PM 9 Work Sample Records

Key Math Learnings

1. Systematically collect, organize, and analyse data.
2. Solve problems involving fractions and decimals using the appropriate strategies and calculation methods.
3. Identify, extend, create, and discuss patterns using whole numbers and variables.
4. Present solutions to patterning problems and explain the thinking behind the solution process.

Cross Strand Investigation — **A Population Simulation**

Work with a partner.

An animal population changes from year to year depending on the rates of birth and death, and on the movement of the animals.

A **simulation** is a model of a real situation. You will use a simulation to investigate how an animal population might decline.

As you complete this *Investigation*, include your completed table, graph, and written answers to the questions. You will hand these in.

Materials:

- a paper cup
- 30 to 40 two-sided counters
- 0.5-cm grid paper

➢ The counters are the animals in your population.
Count the number of animals.
Record that number for Year 0 in the *Population* table.

➢ Put the counters in the cup.
Choose which colour will be "face up."
Pour the counters from the cup.
Counters that land face up represent animals that died or moved away during the first year. Set them aside.
Count the number of animals left.

432 Cross Strand Investigation

BEFORE Get Started

Discuss with students what is meant by the population of the school and the community. Ensure students understand that a population of animals refers to the number of a particular type of animal in a specified area. Ask students to describe any simulations they may have experienced, such as computer games, or survivor-type games. Explain that a simulation is a mathematical model that may leave out detail, so will not replicate the real-life situation exactly. Simulations help us to find patterns and so, trends. Tell students that they will use counters as models of animals in a certain population.

Present the *Investigation*. Demonstrate the procedure for the first year, asking students to try the calculations. Make sure that students understand that once a counter has been discarded it is not returned to the cup.

DURING Investigation

Ongoing Assessment: Observe and Listen

Ask questions, such as:

- How did you get the fraction and percent that represents the change in population? (*The decrease in population is the numerator, and the previous year's population the denominator of the fraction. To obtain the percent, I used a calculator to divide the numerator of the fraction by the denominator, then I multiplied by 100%.*)
- What do you expect the next values will be? Why? (*50% less because we are using 2-sided counters. So, there is a 50% chance of the counter landing face up.*)
- What do you expect the graph to show? (*I expect to see a graph that shows a downward trend.*)
- What other graph could you draw? (*I could also graph the Change as a Percent. This would show how the percent changes over time.*)

Record that number as the population for Year 1.
Calculate and record the decrease in population.
Write the decrease as a fraction of the previous year's population.
Write the fraction as a percent.

➢ Place the counters representing live animals back in the cup.
Repeat the experiment for Year 2.
Record the data for Year 2 in the table.
➢ Continue the simulation. Record your data for up to 8 years, or until you run out of animals.
➢ Graph the population data.
Plot *Year* horizontally and *Number of Animals* vertically.
Explain your choice of graph.
What trends do you see in the graph?

Population									
Year	0	1	2	3	4	5	6	7	8
Number of animals									
Decrease in population									
Change as a fraction									
Change as a percent									

➢ Describe the patterns you see in the table. Approximately what fraction and percent of the population remain from year to year?
➢ Use the patterns to predict the population for Year 9.
➢ How long does it take the population of animals to decrease to one-half its original size?
➢ What would happen to a population if there were no births to add to the population each year?

Take It Further

➢ Suppose you repeated this experiment, beginning with more animals. Would you see the same pattern? Explain.
Combine your data with data of other students to find out.
➢ Which environmental factors may cause an animal population to change?

REACHING ALL LEARNERS

Early Finishers

Challenge students to repeat the investigation to simulate population growth. Have them start with 2 counters in the cup and add 1 to the population each time a counter lands face up.

Common Misconceptions

➤ Students record the *Change as a Fraction* using *Number of Animals* as the numerator.
How to Help: Explain that this fraction illustrates different information. Ask students to try both and compare results.

➤ Students cannot explain their choice of graph.
How to Help: Showing students graphs that would be inappropriate helps to clarify why other graphs are more appropriate. If a computer is available, use a spreadsheet to create different types of graphs. Ask students to sort them into appropriate and inappropriate, and explain their rationale.

- What type of graph will you use?
(*A line graph, but I could also draw a bar graph.*)

As students work on *Take It Further*, ask questions such as:

- How do you think your data will compare with those of other students? Why? (*My data may be very different from other students' data. A population of 40 animals is very small.*)
- What do you think will happen when you combine data with other students? (*I expect that when we combine our data the change as a percent will be close to 50% each year.*)

AFTER

Have volunteers share their findings. Ask students questions such as:

- Can you explain why the decline is about 50%?
(*Fair, 2-sided counters have a 50% chance of landing face up.*)
- How could you change the simulation to change the rate of decline?
(*Use number cubes, or other combinations of counters such as 2 counters face up means one loss of animal, or create a counter for births or migration.*)

Invite pairs to share the results from *Take It Further*. Encourage discussion about how results compare from each group and the larger sample size.

Sample Response

Population Decline

Year	0	1	2	3	4	5	6	7	8
Number of Animals	40	19	10	6	3	2	1	0	–
Decrease in Population	–	21	11	4	3	1	1	1	–
Change as a Fraction	–	$\frac{21}{40}$	$\frac{11}{19}$	$\frac{4}{10}$	$\frac{3}{6}$	$\frac{1}{3}$	$\frac{1}{2}$	$\frac{0}{1}$	–
Change as a Percent	–	52.5	57.9	40	50	33.3	50	0	–

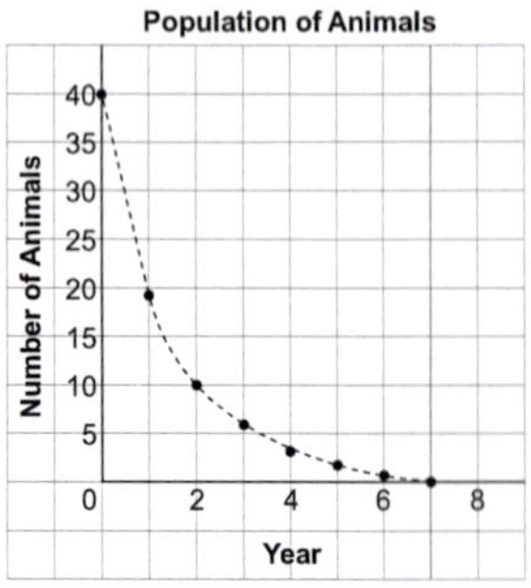

- The line graph shows that the number of animals in the population decreases each year. The decrease is not by the same number of animals each year. The population decreases by about $\frac{1}{2}$, or 50% each year. I could illustrate this by graphing the change as a percent against the year.
- Year 9 will be 0, since the population in year 7 is 0.
- It takes about 1 year for the population to decrease to one-half its original size.
- A population would die out very quickly if there were no births to add to the population.

Take It Further

- With more animals to begin with, the population should decline at the same rate of 50% each year but will likely take longer to reach 0.

Population Decline

Year	0	1	2	3	4	5	6	7	8
Number of Animals	200	100	50	25	12	6	3	1	0
Decrease in Population	–	100	50	25	13	6	3	2	1
Change as a Fraction	–	$\frac{1}{2}$	$\frac{1}{2}$	$\frac{1}{2}$	$\frac{12}{25}$	$\frac{1}{2}$	$\frac{1}{2}$	$\frac{1}{3}$	0
Change as a Percent	–	50	50	50	48	50	50	33.3	0

- Forest fire, disease, weather, famine, drought, flooding, hunting, humans populating an area, and other factors can contribute to animal population change.

ASSESSMENT FOR LEARNING

What to Look For

Understanding concepts

✔ Students systematically collect, organize, and analyse data, identifying numerical patterns in the data.

Applying procedures

✔ Students complete calculations to chart and graph data appropriately.

Problem solving

✔ Students choose appropriate strategies for predicting values and interpreting data tables and graphs.

Communicating

✔ Students use mathematical terminology to analyse, discuss, and defend conclusions from the analysis of data.

Recording and Reporting

PM 9 Work Sample Records

Cross Strand Observations Check List: A Population Simulation

Name	Data Management and Probability		Patterning and Algebra		Number
	Systematically collects, organizes, and displays data using appropriate labels and symbols UC/AP	Interprets displays of data, making conclusions from the analysis of the data UC/CM	Identifies, extends, creates, and discusses patterns using whole numbers and variables UC/CM	Presents solutions to patterning problems and explains the thinking behind the solution process CM/PS	Solves problems involving fractions and decimals using the appropriate strategies and calculation methods AP

PS – Problem Solving
UC – Understanding of Concepts
AP – Application of Mathematical Procedures
CM – Communication

Addison Wesley Mathematics Makes Sense

Program Authors

Jason Johnston
Bryn Keyes
Mary Doucette
Antonietta Lenjosek
Steve Thomas
Margaret Sinclair
Trevor Brown
Cathy Heideman
Don Jones
Michael Davis
Jennifer Paziuk
Ken Harper
Sharon Jeroski
Ray Appel
Laura Weatherhead
Betty Milne
Jim Mennie
Lynn Strangway

Printed and bound in Canada

10 17

PEARSON Education Canada

ADDISON WESLEY

Ontario

Math Makes Sense 7

Ontario

Teacher Guide

Unit 1: Patterns in Whole Numbers

PEARSON
Addison Wesley

UNIT 1

Patterns in Whole Numbers

". . . pattern is not just in numbers and equations but in everything around us. The world is full of pattern and order: in nature, in art, in buildings, in music. Pattern and order are found in commerce, science, medicine, manufacturing, and sociology. Mathematics discovers this order, makes sense of it, and uses it in a multitude of fascinating ways, improving our lives and expanding our knowledge."

John A. Van de Walle

FOCUS STRANDS
Number Sense and Numeration
Patterning and Algebra

SUPPORTING STRAND
Geometry and Spatial Sense

TIPS
Allow opportunities for students to explore, investigate, and communicate mathematically as well as opportunities to practise skills.

Mathematics Background

What Are the Big Ideas?

- When we calculate to solve a problem, the calculation method depends on the context of the problem and the question asked.
- Numbers describe our world and we can use numbers to describe other numbers. We can describe a number by its factors, by the number of its factors, and by the sum of its factors.
- Squaring and taking a square root are inverse operations.
- Exponents represent repeated multiplication.
- Patterns are a regular occurrence in mathematics, and they can be identified, extended, and described.

How Will the Concepts Develop?

Students learn to choose and justify the most effective method for calculations. They use mental math, paper and pencil, estimation, and a calculator to solve problems. These strategies help students determine how appropriate a solution is.

Students find factors and multiples of numbers, and find the greatest common factor and lowest common multiple of two numbers. Students use their knowledge of factors to identify prime and composite numbers.

Students use exponents to represent repeated multiplication, and they are introduced to square roots, square numbers, and cube numbers.

Students explore number patterns and demonstrate their understanding by writing pattern rules. They identify, complete, and extend number patterns.

Why Are These Concepts Important?

Patterns exist in our world, and are found abundantly in mathematics. Finding a pattern is a good problem-solving strategy. A student who is proficient at recognizing and developing patterns should more easily develop algebraic reasoning.

There are many strategies for solving problems. It is important to use the most appropriate and efficient strategy when solving a problem. The ability to choose the appropriate strategy will become increasingly more important as students go further in their study of mathematics.

The ability to find the lowest common multiple of two or more numbers is a valuable tool when finding common denominators for adding and subtracting fractions.

Curriculum Overview

Overall Expectations

- Compare, order, and represent ... multiples, factors, and square roots. (7m1)
- Understand and explain that exponents represent repeated multiplication. (7m4)
- Use estimation to justify or assess the reasonableness of calculations. (7m5)
- Explain, in writing, the process of problem solving using appropriate mathematical language. (7m7)
- Use a calculator to solve number questions that are beyond the proficiency expectations for operations using pencil and paper. (7m8)
- Identify, extend, create, and discuss patterns using whole numbers ... (7m67)
- Apply and discuss patterning strategies in problem-solving situations. (7m69)

Specific Expectations

- Generate multiples and factors of given numbers. (7m11)
- Represent perfect squares and their square roots in a variety of ways. (7m13)
- Understand that repeated multiplication can be represented as exponents. (7m15)
- Justify the choice of method for calculations: estimation, mental computation, concrete materials, pencil and paper, algorithms, or calculators. (7m16)
- Explain the process used and any conclusions reached in problem solving and investigations. (7m24)
- Reflect on learning experiences and describe their understanding using appropriate mathematical language. (7m25)
- Extend a pattern, ..., and write words to explain the pattern. (7m71)
- Recognize patterns and use them to make predictions. (7m72)

Launch

Section 1.1: Numbers All Around Us

Section 1.2: Factors and Multiples

Section 1.3: Squares and Square Roots

Mid-Unit Review

Section 1.4: Exponents

Section 1.5: Number Patterns

Unit Review

Practice Test

Unit Problem
Fibonacci Numbers

Curriculum across the Grades

Grade 6	Grade 7	Grade 8
Students identify and describe the characteristics of multiples and factors, and composite and prime numbers, to 100. They use skip counting to assist in solving questions about factors. Students justify the choice of method for calculations: estimation, mental computation, concrete materials, algorithms, or calculators. Students recognize relationships and use them to summarize and generalize patterns. They identify, extend, and create patterns. Students analyse number patterns and state the rule for any relationships. They discuss and defend the choice of a pattern rule. Students use a calculator and computer applications to explore patterns.	Students generate multiples and factors of given numbers. They represent perfect squares and their square roots in a variety of ways. Students understand that repeated multiplication can be expressed as exponents. Students justify the choice of method for calculations: estimation, mental computation, concrete materials, pencil and paper, algorithms, or calculators. Students explain, in writing, the process of problem solving, and describe their understanding using appropriate mathematical language. Students extend a pattern and write words to explain the pattern. They recognize patterns and use them to make predictions. Students apply and discuss patterning strategies in problem-solving situations.	Students represent whole numbers in expanded form using powers and scientific notation. They represent composite numbers as products of prime factors. Students express repeated multiplication as powers. They estimate the square roots of whole numbers without a calculator, and find the approximate values of square roots using a calculator. Students use trial and error to estimate the square root of a non-perfect square. Students justify the choice of method for calculations, and explain, in writing, the process of problem solving using appropriate mathematical language. Students write an algebraic expression for the *n*th term of a numeric sequence. They describe and justify a rule in a pattern, and find patterns and describe them using words and algebraic expressions. Students apply and discuss patterning strategies in problem-solving situations.

Additional Activities

Rounds of Rounding

For Extra Practice (Appropriate for use after Skills You'll Need)
Materials: *Rounds of Rounding* (Master 1.5a), *Rounds of Rounding* Place-Value Cards (Master 1.5b)

Playing this game reinforces the skills of rounding whole numbers.

The work students do: Students play in pairs. Students round 7-digit numbers to different numbers of decimal places. A student gets a point for each correct rounding. The first student to get 5 points wins.

Take It Further: Students use playing cards. Each student turns over 7 cards, then makes the greatest 7-digit number possible. Students play the game as above.

Mathematical/Social/Logical
Partner Activity

Product Mania

For Extra Support (Appropriate for use after Section 1.2)
Materials: *Product Mania* (Master 1.6), a hundred chart (PM 13), 2 tokens, 2 sets of counters (one colour per player), 2 number cubes labelled 1 to 6

Playing this game provides practice with multiplication facts.

The work students do: Students play in pairs. Students use tokens on a hundred chart and number cubes to find and cover numbers on the chart. The first student to cover 10 squares with counters wins.

Take It Further: Students play the game with octahedral dice, labelled 1 to 8, and a 10 by 10 square numbered from 101 to 200.

Logical/Mathematical/Social
Partner Activity

Squares and Cubes

For Extra Practice (Appropriate for use after Section 1.4)
Materials: *Squares and Cubes* (Master 1.7); a deck of playing cards with the face cards removed, a calculator (optional)

Playing this game reinforces the skills of finding the squares and cubes of whole numbers.

The work students do: Students play in pairs. Students use the numbers on playing cards to find the squares and cubes of numbers. A player receives 1 point if both parts of his answer are correct. Play continues until all cards have been used. The player with the higher score wins.

Take It Further: Students evaluate the number drawn to the exponent 4.

Mathematical/Social
Partner Activity

Pattern Power

For Extra Practice (Appropriate for use after Section 1.5)
Materials: *Pattern Power* (Master 1.8), index cards

The work students do: Students play in pairs. Each student makes 5 number patterns on index cards. Students trade patterns. Students write the pattern rule beside each pattern. Students get 2 points for each correct pattern rule. The student with the higher score after 2 rounds wins.

Take It Further: Students write their patterns on index cards (one per card), then write the corresponding pattern rules on separate index cards. Students shuffle, then trade cards (10 in total). Students sort each other's cards, matching each pattern with its pattern rule. Students get 2 points for each correct match.

Kinesthetic/Visual/Spatial
Partner Activity

Planning for Unit 1

Planning for Instruction

Suggested Unit time: About 3 weeks

Section	Time	Materials	Program Support
Launch, page 2	15–20 min		
Skills You'll Need, page 4	65–80 min	Base Ten Blocks, counters, calculators (optional)	
1.1: Numbers All Around Us, page 8 Justify the choice of strategy when solving problems.	80–100 min	calculators	Master 1.9: Step-by-Step 1 Master 1.17: Extra Practice 1
1.2: Factors and Multiples, page 12 Generate factors and multiples of given numbers.	80–100 min	hundred charts, Venn diagrams, calendar pages (optional)	PM 13: Hundred Chart PM 28: Venn Diagram Master 1.10: Step-by-Step 2 Master 1.18: Extra Practice 2
Game: The Factor Game, page 16		*The Factor Game* game boards, coloured markers, number cubes	Master 1.14: *The Factor Game* Game Board
1.3: Squares and Square Roots, page 17 Find the squares and square roots of whole numbers.	80–100 min	1-cm grid paper and transparency 12 x 12 multiplication charts (optional)	PM 15: 12 x 12 Multiplication Chart PM 20: 1-cm Grid Paper Master 1.11: Step-by-Step 3 Master 1.19: Extra Practice 3
Mid-Unit Review, page 20		calculators, Venn diagrams, hundred charts, 1-cm grid paper	PM 13: Hundred Chart PM 28: Venn Diagram PM 20: 1-cm Grid Paper
1.4: Exponents, page 21 Use exponents to represent repeated multiplication.	80–100 min	interlocking cubes, calculators, 4-column charts	Master 1.12: Step-by-Step 4 Master 1.20: Extra Practice 4
1.5: Number Patterns, page 26 Describe, extend, and explain patterns.	80–100 min	calculators, transparency of Pascal's Triangle (optional), interlocking cubes (optional)	Master 1.13: Step-by-Step 5 Master 1.21: Extra Practice 5
Reading and Writing in Math: Using Different Strategies, page 30			
Unit Review, page 32		Venn diagrams, 1-cm grid paper, calculators, 5-column charts (optional), 0.5-cm grid paper (optional), hundred charts (optional)	PM 20: 1-cm Grid Paper PM 28: Venn Diagram Extra Practice: Student Book page 438
Practice Test, page 35		Venn diagrams, 1-cm grid paper	PM 28: Venn Diagram PM 20: 1-cm Grid Paper
Unit Problem: Fibonacci Numbers, page 36	80–100 min	1-cm grid paper, poster board, 3-column charts, calculators, pencil crayons, glue	PM 20: 1-cm Grid Paper PM 18: 3-Column Charts

etext online tutorial — This web-based tutorial uses voice, animation, and an optional quiz to present each core lesson, so that students can review content with a new approach.

Planning for Assessment

Purpose	Tools and Process	Recording and Reporting
Diagnostic	*Unit Launch* Question; conference; scaffold problems throughout the unit	PM 8: Conference Prompts
Formative	*Explore* – Ongoing Assessment: Observe and Listen	Master 1.2 Ongoing Observations: Patterns in Whole Numbers PM 1: Inquiry Process Check List PM 6: Observation Record 1 PM 7: Observation Record 2 PM 8: Conference Prompts PM 2: Self-Assessment PM 3: Self-Assessment: Problem Solving PM 9: Work Sample Records
Summative	*Unit Review* *Unit Problem* – Performance Assessment Unit Test Review assessment records; add unit results to ongoing records	Master 1.1 Unit Rubric: Patterns in Whole Numbers Master 1.3 Performance Assessment Rubric: Fibonacci Numbers Master 1.4 Unit Summary: Patterns in Whole Numbers PM 10: Summary Class Records: Strands PM 11: Summary Class Records: Achievement Categories PM 12: Summary Record: Individual
Learning Skills/Mathematical Disposition	Observe and record throughout the unit	PM 4: Learning Skills Check List PM 5: Mathematical Dispositions and Learning Skills

Program Masters (PM) are in the *Grade 7 Planning and Program Masters* module.
Extra Practice Masters are on the CD-ROM and are printed in reduced format on page 58 of this module.

SECTION ORGANIZER

15–20 min

Curriculum Focus: Activate prior learning about patterns in whole numbers.

Teacher Materials

Optional

- examples of different types of patterns (for example, pictures of quilts, tiling patterns, growing patterns)

ASSUMED PRIOR KNOWLEDGE

- ☑ Students can recognize mathematical relationships in patterns.
- ☑ Students can identify, extend, and create patterns in a variety of contexts.
- ☑ Students can recognize and discuss patterning rules.

Teaching notes for Cross Strand Investigation *Making a Booklet* are in the *Additional Assessment Support* module.

UNIT 1

Patterns in Whole Numbers

There are many patterns you can see in nature. You can use numbers to describe many of these patterns.

At the end of this unit, you will investigate a famous set of numbers, the Fibonacci Numbers. You will explore these numbers, and find how they can be used to describe the breeding of animals, such as rabbits.

Think about the different patterns you learned in earlier grades. Give an example of each type of pattern.

What You'll Learn

- Use mental math, paper and pencil, calculators, and estimation to solve problems.
- Justify your choice of method for calculations.
- Find factors and multiples of numbers.
- Find the greatest common factor and lowest common multiple of two numbers.
- Identify prime and composite numbers.
- Use exponents to represent repeated multiplication.
- Identify and extend number patterns.
- Choose and justify strategies for solving problems.

Why It's Important

- You need to know an appropriate and efficient method for calculations.
- You need to be able to find common denominators for fraction calculations.

ACTIVATE PRIOR LEARNING

Engage students in a discussion about patterning.

Ask:

- Where can you see patterns around you? (*On a quilt, in wallpaper, in floor tiling, on a checkerboard, in beadwork*)
- What is a type of pattern that you learned in an earlier grade? (*A repeating pattern*) Give an example. (*Star, moon, sun, star, moon, sun, …*)
- What is another type of pattern that you learned in an earlier grade? (*A growing pattern*) Give an example. (*3, 6, 9, 12, …*)
- What is another type of pattern that you learned in an earlier grade? (*A changing-step growing pattern*) Give an example. (*1, 4, 9, 16, …*)

Tell students that, in this unit, they will learn more about patterns in whole numbers. They will describe, extend, and explain patterns, and use patterns to make predictions and to solve problems. At the end of the unit, students will investigate a famous set of numbers, the Fibonacci numbers. They will explore these numbers, and find how they can be used to describe many occurrences in nature. Tell students that the pictures on pages 4 and 5 relate to the *Unit Problem* on Fibonacci numbers.

Key Words

- factor
- prime number
- composite number
- greatest common factor (GCF)
- multiple
- lowest common multiple (LCM)
- square number
- square root
- exponent form
- base
- exponent
- power
- cube number
- perfect square
- perfect cube

FROM THE LIBRARY

Fibonacci Fun: Fascinating Activities with Intriguing Numbers by Trudi Hammel Garland. Dale Seymour Publications, 1997
ISBN: 1572322659
From "Raising Rabbits" to "Prickly Pinecones," 24 easy-to-use, reproducible activities and projects introduce students to Fibonacci numbers and the golden ratio. Topics include geometry, statistics, networks, coordinate graphing, calculators, sequences, number bases, problem solving, and patterns.

Numbersense by A. McIntosh, Robert E. Reys, and Barbara J. Reys. Dale Seymour Publications, 1997
ISBN: 1572322640
Students need good number sense to understand numbers they encounter in life and to effectively use new problem-solving tools. These ten-minute activities help students develop a sense of what numbers represent and how to use them by: exploring relationships and patterns, encouraging mental computation, improving estimation skills, and exploring the idea of reasonableness. Includes activity masters, teacher notes, and ideas for extending the activity.

REACHING ALL LEARNERS

e-tools Some students may benefit from using the virtual manipulatives on the e-Tools CD-ROM. The e-Tool appropriate for this unit is *Place-Value Blocks*.

DIAGNOSTIC ASSESSMENT

What to Look For	What to Do
✔ Students can recognize mathematical relationships in patterns. ✔ Students can identify, extend, and create patterns in a variety of contexts. ✔ Students can recognize and discuss patterning rules.	***Extra Support:*** Students who have difficulty identifying a number pattern should try subtracting consecutive numbers to see if the differences are the same. *Work on this skill during Section 1.5.* Students who have difficulty identifying and extending a number pattern may benefit from transferring the pattern onto a hundred chart, and looking for patterns in the positions of the numbers on the chart. *Work on this skill during Section 1.5.*

SECTION ORGANIZER

65–80 min

Skills in Review
- Rounding
- Multiplying by 10, 100, 1000
- Mental math
- Divisibility rules

Student Materials
- Base Ten Blocks
- counters

Optional
- calculators

Alternative Example 1

Round 183 759:

a) to the nearest ten thousand **b)** to the nearest hundred

Solution

Hundred Thousands	Ten Thousands	Thousands	Hundreds	Tens	Ones
1	8	3	7	5	9

a) The number in the thousands place is 3. Since 3 is less than 5, leave the ten-thousands digit as it is, then replace each number to the right with 0.
183 759 rounded to the nearest ten thousand is 180 000.

b) The number in the tens place is 5. So, add 1 hundred to the number in the hundreds place to get 8 hundreds. Then, replace each number to the right with 0.
183 759 rounded to the nearest hundred is 183 800.

UNIT 1

Skills You'll Need

Rounding

The place-value chart below shows the number 1 234 567.

Millions	Hundred thousands	Ten thousands	Thousands	Hundreds	Tens	Ones
1	2	3	4	5	6	7

To round:
Look at the digit to the right of the place to which you are rounding.
Is this digit 5 or greater?
If it is, add 1 to the place digit.
If it is not, leave the place digit as it is.
Change all the digits to the right of the place digit to 0.

Example 1

a) Round 425 to the nearest ten.

b) Round to the nearest thousand.
i) 2471 **ii)** 13 999

Solution

a)

Hundreds	Tens	Ones
4	2	5

This number is 5.
So, add 1 ten to this number to get 3 tens.
Then, replace 5 with 0.

425 rounded to the nearest ten is 430.

b) i)

Thousands	Hundreds	Tens	Ones
2	4	7	1

This number is less than 5.
So, this number does not change.
Replace each number to the right of 2 with 0.

2471 rounded to the nearest thousand is 2000.

6 UNIT 1: Patterns in Whole Numbers

Rounding

Tell students that rounding is used when estimating.

Ask:

- If you were rounding to the nearest ten thousand, which digit would you look at? (*I would look at the digit in the thousands place.*) To the nearest million? (*I would look at the digit in the hundred-thousands place.*)
- How would the solution for *Example 1* change if you were to round to the nearest hundred? (*Because the number in the tens place is less than 5, I would replace both the 2 and the 5 with zeros. 425 rounded to the nearest hundred is 400.*)

Remind students that if they are rounding to estimate a sum, they may round one number up and the other number down, for a better estimate. For example, to estimate: 345 + 217, round 345 to 340 and 217 to 220 to get 340 + 220 = 560. In this case, we ignore the rule that says round up if the number under consideration is 5 or more. Instead, we "compensate" for rounding one number up by rounding the other number down.

For extra practice, have students play *Rounds of Rounding* (Master 1.5a).

Common Misconceptions

➤ Students think that, in a particular situation, there is only one way to round a number.

How to Help: Tell students that numbers can be rounded in many ways. For example, \$227.99 could be rounded to \$228, \$230, or \$200. Alternatively, the money might be rounded to a friendly number, such as \$225 or \$250, depending on the situation. If you wanted to estimate your monthly spending, you might say, "I spent about \$250." If you wanted to find out whether you had enough money to buy something for \$227.99, you might say, "I round \$227.99 up to \$230, and I have \$230, so I have enough."

ii)

Ten thousands	Thousands	Hundreds	Tens	Ones
1	3	9	9	9

This number is greater than 5.

So, add 1 thousand to this number to get 4 thousands. Replace each number to the right of 4 with 0.

13 999 rounded to the nearest thousand is 14 000.

✓ **Check**

1. Round to the nearest ten.
   a) 36 40 b) 42 40 c) 75 80 d) 361 360

2. Round to the nearest hundred.
   a) 311 300 b) 789 800 c) 625 600 d) 2356 2400

Multiplying by 10, 100, 1000

To multiply a whole number:
– by 10, write 0 after the number.
– by 100, write 00 after the number.
– by 1000, write 000 after the number.

Example 2

Multiply.
a) 32 × 10 b) 478 × 100 c) 51 × 1000
d) 32 × 20 e) 47 × 300

Solution

a) 32 × 10 = 320 b) 478 × 100 = 47 800 c) 51 × 1000 = 51 000

d) 32 × 20 = 32 × 2 × 10
= 64 × 10
= 640

e) 47 × 300 = 47 × 3 × 100
= 141 × 100
= 14 100

Skills You'll Need 7

Alternative Example 2

Multiply.
a) 64 × 30 **b)** 76 × 500

Solution

a) 64 × 30 = 64 × 3 × 10
= 192 × 10
= 1920

b) 76 × 500 = 76 × 5 × 100
= (76 × 5) × 100
= 380 × 100
= 38 000

Multiplying by 10, 100, 1000

If necessary, students could use Base Ten Blocks to model the questions in *Example 2* and explain why each solution makes sense.

Common Misconceptions

➤ Students think that the number of zeros in the answer must always be the same as the total number of zeros in the numbers being multiplied.

How to Help: Write 2 × 500 on the board. Show students this is the same as 2 × 5 × 100, or 10 × 100; and 10 × 100 = 1000. In this case, the answer has 3 zeros, but the numbers being multiplied have only 2 zeros. Tell students they must first multiply the non-zero digits, then write the number of zeros in the numbers being multiplied.

➤ Students have difficulty multiplying two multiples of 10, 100, or 1000.

How to Help: Encourage students to write each number as a product, with one factor being 10, 100, or 1000. For example, for 310 × 40, write 31 × 10 × 4 × 10, then rearrange the factors as 31 × 4 × 10 × 10 = 124 × 100 = 12 400.

Alternative Example 3

Use mental math.

a) 27×60 b) $298 + 365$

Solution

a) 27×60
Since $27 = 30 - 3$, then
$27 \times 60 = 30 \times 60 - 3 \times 60$
$= 1800 - 180$
$= 1620$

b) $298 + 365$
Think:
$298 = 300 - 2$
Then, $300 + 365 - 2$
$= 665 - 2$
Count back to subtract.
$= 663$

Sample Answers

4. When we multiply a number by 10 (by 100, or by 1000), each digit in the place-value chart moves 1 column left (2 columns left or 3 columns left). When the digit is moved, the "space" left behind is filled with one 0 (with two 0s, or with three 0s), as a place holder.

7. a) $28 + 13 + 12 = (28 + 12) + 13$
$= 40 + 13$
$= 53$

b) $2 \times 29 \times 5 = 2 \times 5 \times 29$
$= 10 \times 29$
$= 290$

✓ Check

3. Find.
a) $3 \times 10 = 30$ b) $1000 \times 5 = 5000$ c) $131 \times 10 = 1310$ d) $100 \times 63 = 6300$

4. Use a place-value chart. Explain why we can write zeros after a number when we multiply by 10, 100, or 1000.

5. Multiply.
a) $50 \times 72 = 3600$ b) $18 \times 600 = 10\ 800$ c) $4000 \times 33 = 132\ 000$

Mental Math

Example 3

Use mental math.
a) 53×6 b) $308 + 56 - 6$ c) $197 + 452$

Solution

a) 53×6
Think:
$50 \times 6 + 3 \times 6$
$= 300 + 18$
$= 318$

b) $308 + 56 - 6$
Think:
$56 - 6 = 50$
Then: $308 + 50 = 358$

c) $197 + 452$
Think:
$197 = 200 - 3$
Then: $200 + 452 - 3 = 652 - 3$ Count back to subtract.
$= 649$

✓ Check

6. Use mental math.
a) $4 + 17 = 21$ b) $9 + 8 = 17$ c) $12 + 6 = 18$
d) $20 + 6 = 26$ e) $40 + 30 = 70$ f) $17 - 2 = 15$
g) $22 - 4 = 18$ h) $70 - 20 = 50$ i) $20 - 15 = 5$

7. Use mental math. Explain your strategy.
a) $28 + 13 + 12 = 53$ b) $2 \times 29 \times 5 = 290$ c) $98 + 327 = 425$
d) $4 \times 981 \times 25 = 98\ 100$ e) $99 \times 21 = 2079$ f) $62 \times 8 = 496$

8 UNIT 1: Patterns in Whole Numbers

Mental Math

Encourage students to break down mental math questions into smaller parts that can be solved easily. Remind students of some mental math strategies they used in earlier grades, such as add on; make a "friendly" number; take from one to give to the other; and add to match the ones, then subtract. We can now add the strategy: multiply first to make 10, 100, or 1000. Give examples of the use of each strategy on the board. Tell students there are many mental math strategies and that more than one strategy can be used to solve any particular problem.

Common Misconceptions

➤ Students become confused as they break a multiplication question into parts.

How to Help: Suggest students use grid paper to model the problem and/or use brackets. For example, to find 53×6, students could write $(50 \times 6) + (3 \times 6) = 300 + 18 = 318$.

➤ Students try to use the same mental math strategy to solve all problems.

How to Help: Tell students that a single mental math strategy will not work for all problems. Have a no-paper day where students are encouraged to use mental math. Students need experience with mental math to build both confidence and a solid foundation.

Divisibility Rules

A number is divisible by:

- 2 if the number is even
- 3 if the sum of its digits is divisible by 3
- 4 if the number represented by the last 2 digits is divisible by 4
- 5 if the last digit is 0 or 5
- 6 if the number is divisible by 2 and 3
- 8 if the number represented by the last 3 digits is divisible by 8
- 9 if the sum of the digits is divisible by 9
- 10 if the last digit is 0

Example 4

Which of these numbers is 1792 divisible by?

a) 2 **b)** 3 **c)** 4 **d)** 5 **e)** 6

Solution

a) 1792 is divisible by 2 because 1792 is an even number.

b) $1 + 7 + 9 + 2 = 19$
19 is not divisible by 3, so 1792 is not divisible by 3.

c) The last 2 digits are 92.
$92 \div 4 = 23$
Since the last 2 digits are divisible by 4, 1792 is divisible by 4.

d) 1792 is not divisible by 5 because the last digit is not 0 or 5.

e) Since 1792 is not divisible by 3, 1792 is also not divisible by 6.

✓ Check

8. Which numbers are divisible by 3?
a) 490 No **b)** 492 Yes **c)** 12 345 Yes

9. Write 4 other numbers greater than 400 that are divisible by 3. 510, 612, 702, 423

10. Which numbers are divisible by 6?
a) 870 Yes **b)** 232 No **c)** 681 No

11. Which numbers from 1 to 10 is:
a) 660 divisible by? 1, 2, 3, 4, 5, 6, 10 **b)** 1001 divisible by? 1, 7

Skills You'll Need 9

Alternative Example 4

Use mental math.

a) Write three 3-digit numbers that are divisible by 3.

b) Write a 6-digit number that is divisible by 8.

Solution

a) A number is divisible by 3 if the sum of its digits is divisible by 3. Find 3 numbers for which the sum of the digits of each is divisible by 3.
For example, 243, 108, and 213

b) A number is divisible by 8 if its last 3 digits are divisible by 8. So, one number is 307 888.

c) $98 + 327 = 327 + 100 - 2$
$= 427 - 2$
$= 425$

d) $4 \times 981 \times 25 = 4 \times 25 \times 981$
$= 100 \times 981$
$= 98\ 100$

e) $99 \times 21 = 100 \times 21 - 1 \times 21$
$= 2100 - 21$
$= 2079$

f) $62 \times 8 = 60 \times 8 + 2 \times 8$
$= 480 + 16$
$= 496$

Divisibility Rules

Review divisibility rules with students. Invite 3 or 4 volunteers to stand in front of the class. Give each volunteer a different digit to hold up. Students stand side-by-side to make a 4-digit number. Students decide which numbers this 4-digit number is divisible by, then justify their answers. Have the volunteers trade places to make a different 4-digit number. Students decide which numbers the new 4-digit number is divisible by (for example, if the first number is divisible by 3, then all numbers made with these 4 digits will be divisible by 3, because the divisibility depends on the sum of the digits).

Common Misconceptions

➤ Students think a number can only be divisible by one number.

How to Help: Model divisibility with counters. Give each student 10 counters. Have students arrange the counters into 1 group of 10, 2 groups of 5, and 5 groups of 2. Tell students that 10 is divisible by 1, 2, 5, and 10. Move from modelling concretely to modelling with larger numbers on paper.

➤ Students lose track of the numbers a number is divisible by.

How to Help: Have students make a simple checklist, similar to the list on the top of page 9 in the Student Book. Students check off all the rules that apply to a particular number.

Numbers All Around Us

SECTION ORGANIZER (80–100 min)

Curriculum Focus: Justify the choice of strategy when solving problems. (7m16, 7m24)

Student Materials
- calculators

Optional
- Step-by-Step 1 (Master 1.9)
- Extra Practice 1 (Master 1.17)

Assessment: Master 1.2 Ongoing Observations: Patterns in Whole Numbers

Key Math Learnings

1. Numbers are used to understand and describe our world.
2. There are many strategies that can be used to solve problems: mental math, paper and pencil, estimation, and a calculator.

Mental Math

Encourage students to read across to find the products, and see the pattern that results when 3.6 is multiplied by decreasing powers of 10. In each case, the decimal point in the answer moves 1 place to the left.

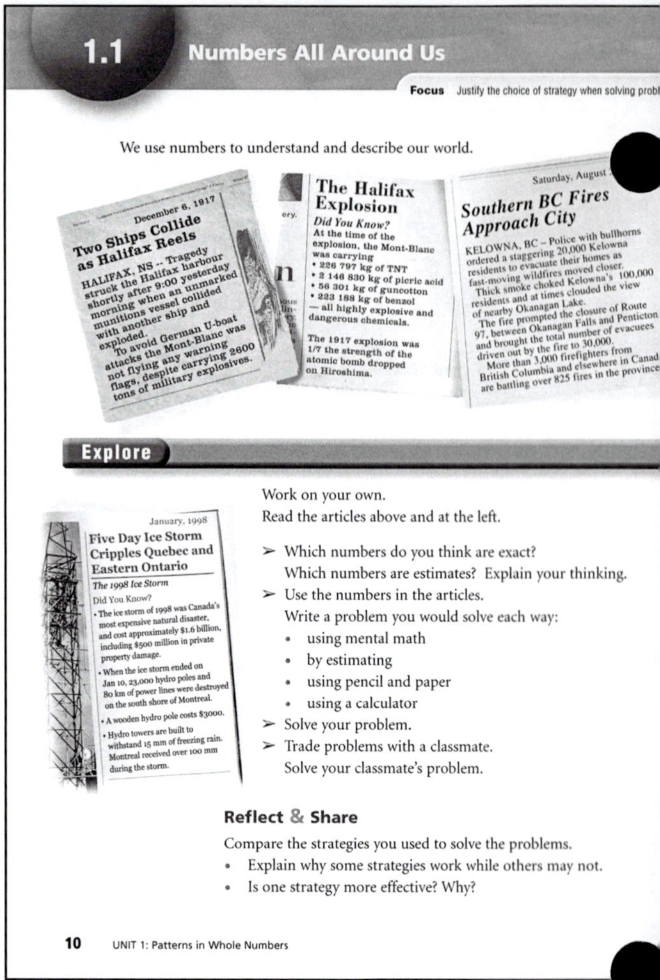

1.1 Numbers All Around Us

Focus Justify the choice of strategy when solving probl

We use numbers to understand and describe our world.

December 6, 1917
Two Ships Collide as Halifax Reels
HALIFAX, NS -- Tragedy struck the Halifax harbour shortly after 9:00 yesterday morning when an unmarked munitions vessel collided with another ship and exploded.
To avoid German U-boat attacks the Mont-Blanc was not flying any warning flags, despite carrying 2600 tons of military explosives.

The Halifax Explosion
Did You Know?
At the time of the explosion, the Mont-Blanc was carrying
- 226 797 kg of TNT
- 2 146 830 kg of picric acid
- 56 301 kg of guncotton
- 223 188 kg of benzol

— all highly explosive and dangerous chemicals.

The 1917 explosion was 1/7 the strength of the atomic bomb dropped on Hiroshima.

Saturday, August
Southern BC Fires Approach City
KELOWNA, BC – Police with bullhorns ordered a staggering 20,000 Kelowna residents to evacuate their homes as fast-moving wildfires moved closer.
Thick smoke choked Kelowna's 100,000 residents and at times clouded the view of nearby Okanagan Lake.
The fire prompted the closure of Route 97, between Okanagan Falls and Penticton and brought the total number of evacuees driven out by the fire to 30,000.
More than 3,000 firefighters from British Columbia and elsewhere in Canad are battling over 825 fires in the province

Explore

January, 1998
Five Day Ice Storm Cripples Quebec and Eastern Ontario
The 1998 Ice Storm
Did You Know?
- The ice storm of 1998 was Canada's most expensive natural disaster, and cost approximately $1.6 billion, including $500 million in private property damage.
- When the ice storm ended on Jan 10, 23,000 hydro poles and 80 km of power lines were destroyed on the south shore of Montreal.
- A wooden hydro pole costs $3000.
- Hydro towers are built to withstand 15 mm of freezing rain. Montreal received over 100 mm during the storm.

Work on your own.
Read the articles above and at the left.

➢ Which numbers do you think are exact?
Which numbers are estimates? Explain your thinking.
➢ Use the numbers in the articles.
Write a problem you would solve each way:
- using mental math
- by estimating
- using pencil and paper
- using a calculator

➢ Solve your problem.
➢ Trade problems with a classmate.
Solve your classmate's problem.

Reflect & Share

Compare the strategies you used to solve the problems.
- Explain why some strategies work while others may not.
- Is one strategy more effective? Why?

10 UNIT 1: Patterns in Whole Numbers

BEFORE — Get Started

Invite students to discuss the use of numbers in our world. Ask:

- Why is it important to be able to read numbers around us?
  (*To compare prices, to read charts and tables, to interpret data in the media*)

Write 3 numbers, rounded to the nearest million, on the board. Write 3 other large numbers, not rounded, on the board. Ask:

- If you had to multiply 2 of the rounded numbers, which strategy would you use?
  (*I would use mental math because it would be an easy calculation.*)
- If you had to multiply 2 of the numbers that are not rounded, which strategy would you use?
  (*I would use a calculator because it would be a difficult calculation.*)
- If you had to solve a problem where an approximate answer is needed, which strategy could you use? (*Estimation*) An exact answer? (*Paper and pencil or a calculator*)

Present *Explore*. Ensure students understand they are to write and solve a problem for each strategy listed, using the data in the articles.

DURING — Explore

Ongoing Assessment: Observe and Listen

Encourage students to use more than one strategy for the same set of numbers.

As students work, ask questions, such as:

- Which numbers do you think are exact? (*226 797 kg, 56 301 kg, 2 146 830 kg, 223 188 kg*) Why? (*These masses were probably listed on the ship's manifest; that is, a list of what the ship is carrying, and the items were probably weighed to ensure the ship wasn't overloaded.*)

Connect

- When the numbers are easy to handle, use mental math.
- When the problem has too many steps, use a paper and pencil.
- When an approximate answer is appropriate and to check reasonableness, estimate.
- When a more accurate answer is needed and the numbers are large, use a calculator.

Example

The population of Canada was 30 750 000 in July 2000. Statistics Canada (Stats Can) data show that there were 6367 telephones per 10 000 people in that year.

a) About how many telephones were there in Canada in 2000?
b) Find the exact number of telephones in Canada in 2000.
c) How did Stats Can know there were 6367 phones per 10 000 people? Explain how this answer affects the answer to part b.

Solution

a) Estimate.
Round 30 750 000 to the nearest ten million: 30 000 000
Round 6367 to the nearest thousand: 6000
10 000 people use about 6000 phones.
10 000 000 people use about 6000 × 1000, or 6 000 000 phones.
30 000 000 people use about 6 000 000 × 3, or 18 000 000 phones.
There were about 18 million phones in Canada in 2000.

b) Find how many groups of 10 000 people there are in 30 750 000.
That is, 30 750 000 ÷ 10 000 = 3075
For each group of 10 000 people, there were 6367 phones.
The number of phones: 3075 × 6367 = 19 578 525
So, there were 19 578 525 phones in Canada in 2000.

Use a calculator.

c) Stats Can conducted a survey of about 40 000 people.
It asked how many phones each person had.
Stats Can then calculated how many phones per 10 000 people.

To find out exactly how many phones there are in Canada, Stats Can would have to survey the entire population. This is impractical. So, the number of phones in part b is an estimate.

REACHING ALL LEARNERS

Alternative Explore

Materials: newspapers and magazines
Have students look through newspapers and magazines to find their own articles about which they write and solve 4 problems.

Early Finishers

Have students round the numbers in the article *The Halifax Explosion*, then write a problem that could be solved each way: using mental math, and by estimating. Students solve their own problems.

Common Misconceptions

➤ Students want to use a calculator to solve every problem.
How to Help: Students need to know the basic addition facts for up to 10 + 10, and the multiplication facts up to 12 × 12. If students always use a calculator, these facts will not be internalized. Provide students (or have them make) a chart for addition facts and a chart for the multiplication facts above. Alternatively, have these charts posted in the classroom.

ESL Strategies

There is much reading and comprehension required in *Explore*. Although it is suggested students work alone, you could pair an ESL student with a student who reads well and have them work together.

However, each mass is probably rounded to the nearest kilogram.)

- Which other numbers are exact?
(1917, because it is a year; 97, because it is the number of a road)
- Which numbers do you think are estimates?
(20 000, 100 000, and 30 000) Why? *(All these numbers refer to numbers of people and, under the circumstances, nobody was counting every person who evacuated her home, or who lived in the area.)*
- Why did you write that problem for pencil and paper?
(I wrote this problem for pencil and paper because there are 3 steps to find the answer.)
- Why did you write that problem for a calculator?
(I wrote this problem for a calculator because the numbers are very large and I wanted an accurate answer.)
- What problem did you write for the mental math strategy?
(About how much will it cost to replace the hydro poles on the south shore of Montreal?)
- How would you solve that problem using mental math?
(To multiply 23 000 by 3000, I first find 23 × 3 = 69; I then write 6 zeros: 23 000 × $3000 = $69 000 000.)
- Are you combining any of the strategies?
(Yes, I solved the problem with paper and pencil, then used a calculator to check my answer.)
- Which strategy do you think is the most difficult to use?
(Pencil and paper; it is much easier to enter the numbers into a calculator.)

AFTER Connect

Invite students to share one of their classmate's problems with the class.
Here are some sample problems and solutions.
- To be solved by estimating: "What was the

Sample Answers

3. a) About 190; I rounded both numbers to the nearest ten.
   b) About 100; I rounded both numbers to the nearest 10.
   c) About 630; I rounded 72 to the nearest ten, then multiplied.
   d) About 6; I rounded both numbers to the nearest ten.
4. a) Eight hundred fifteen million thirty-six thousand dollars
5. I used mental math because the numbers are easy to handle.
6. About 65 000 000 cm, 650 000 m, 650 km; I used mental math because the numbers are easy to handle.
7. I used mental math because the calculations were easy to handle.
9. a) About 1280; my estimate is low because I rounded both numbers down before adding. 580 + 700 = 1280
   b) About 3215; my estimate is low because I subtracted a larger number. 3815 – 600 = 3215
   c) About 4; my estimate is low. 800 ÷ 200 = 4
   I rounded the dividend down, and rounded the divisor up. Each of these actions alone results in a smaller quotient.
   d) About 2; my estimate is low because I used 310 × 2 = 620, which is less than 695.
10. Last week, Sunil worked on Monday, Tuesday, Friday, Saturday, and Sunday. How much money did he earn? (*Answer: $168*)
11. If 111 mm of rain fell in 12 h, about how much rain fell in 1 h? (*Answer: About 9 mm*)
12. a) No, the numbers have been rounded to the nearest hundred or to the nearest thousand. It is unlikely that each province has exactly these numbers, because the numbers change daily.

Practice

1. Solve without a calculator.
   a) 72 + 43 = 115 b) 123 + 85 = 208 c) 672 + 189 = 861
   d) 97 – 24 = 73 e) 195 – 71 = 124 f) 821 – 485 = 336
   g) 65 × 100 = 6500 h) 14 × 75 = 1050 i) 83 × 25 = 2075
   j) 780 ÷ 10 = 78 k) 724 ÷ 4 = 181 l) 245 ÷ 7 = 35
2. Use pencil and paper to find each answer.
   a) 6825 + 127 = 6952 b) 7928 – 815 = 7113 c) 3614 – 278 = 3336
   d) 138 × 21 = 2898 e) 651 ÷ 21 = 31 f) 6045 ÷ 15 = 403
3. Estimate each answer. Explain the strategy you used each time.
   a) 103 + 89 About 190 b) 123 – 19 About 100
   c) 72 × 9 About 630 d) 418 ÷ 71 About 6

Mental Math

Multiply.

3.6 × 1000 3.6 × 100
3.6 × 10 3.6 × 1
3.6 × 0.1 3.6 × 0.01

What patterns do you see in the questions and the answers?

3600, 360, 36, 3.6, 0.36, 0.036

Questions 4 to 7 pose problems about the 1997 Red River Flood in Manitoba. Use mental math, estimation, pencil and paper, or a calculator. Justify your strategy.

4. The 1997 Red River Flood caused over $815 036 000 in damages.
   a) Write this amount in words. Eight hundred fifteen million thirty-six thousand
   b) How close to $1 billion were the damages? $184 964 000
5. Pauline Thiessen and fellow volunteers made an average of 10 000 sandwiches every day for 2 weeks to feed the flood relief workers. How many sandwiches did they make? 140 000 sandwiches
6. Winnipeg used 6.5 million sandbags to hold back the flood. Each sandbag was about 10 cm thick. About how high would a stack of 6.5 million sandbags be in centimetres? Metres? Kilometres?
   About 65 000 000 cm 650 000 m 650 km
7. To help with the flood relief, Joe Morena of St. Viateur Bagels in Montreal trucked 300 dozen of his famous bagels to Manitoba.
   a) How many bagels did he send? 3600
   b) Joe sells bagels for $4.80 a dozen.
   What was the value of his donation? $1440

8. The Monarch butterfly migrates from Toronto to El Rosario, Mexico. This is a distance of 3300 km.
   A monarch butterfly can fly at an average speed of 15 km/h.
   How long does the migration flight take? 220 h

12 UNIT 1: Patterns in Whole Numbers

approximate total mass in tonnes of dangerous chemicals carried by the Mont-Blanc?"
Answer: Round each number to the nearest ten thousand:
230 000 + 2 150 000 + 60 000 + 220 000
Use a calculator: The sum is 2 660 000 kg, which is 2660 t.

- To be solved using paper and pencil: "How many years passed between the Halifax explosion and the fires in BC?" *Answer:* Subtract: 2003 – 1917 = 86 There were 86 years between the two events.
- To be solved using a calculator: "About how many fire-fighters were fighting each fire in BC?" *Answer:* 3000 ÷ 825 = 3.6; round up because the 3000 is a low estimate. About 4 fire-fighters are fighting each fire. This seems too few. Perhaps the data in the newspaper are wrong.

Use *Connect* to help students understand when each strategy should be used.

There is often more than one strategy that might be used to solve any one problem, or a combination of strategies may be used.

Practice

Students might require a calculator for some of questions 4 to 7, and questions 10 to 12.

Assessment Focus: Question 12

Students will have to distinguish between Atlantic and non-Atlantic provinces. For part e, some students may write a problem that does not involve any computations such as, *"Which province has the greatest population?"* Stress that students should write problems that require the use of the strategies discussed in this section.

Students who need extra support to complete Assessment Focus questions may benefit from the Step-by-Step masters (Masters 1.9–1.13).

9. Estimate each answer. Is each estimate high or low? How do you know?
a) 583 + 702 b) 3815 − 576 c) 821 ÷ 193 d) 695 ÷ 310
About 1280; low About 3215; low About 4; low About 2; low

For questions 10 and 11: Make up a problem using the given data. Have a classmate solve your problems.

10. Sunil earns $7 per hour. He works 4 h per day during the week and 6 h per day on the weekends.

11. In October 1954, Hurricane Hazel blew through Toronto, Ontario. Winds reached 124 km/h, 111 mm of rain fell in 12 h, and over 210 mm of rain fell over 2 days.

12. **Assessment Focus** The table shows the populations of some Canadian provinces in 1999.

Province	Population
NF and Labrador	541 000
PEI	138 000
Nova Scotia	939 800
New Brunswick	755 000
Ontario	11 513 800

The mean of a set of numbers is the sum of the numbers divided by how many numbers there are.

a) Do you think these numbers are exact? Explain.
b) Find the total population of the 4 Atlantic provinces. 2 373 800
c) Find the mean population of the Atlantic provinces. 593 450
d) Approximately how many times as many people are in Ontario as are in the Atlantic provinces? About 5 times as many
e) Make up your own problem about these data. Solve it.

Take It Further

13. Find 2 whole numbers that:
a) have a sum of 10 and a product of 24 4 and 6
b) have a difference of 4 and a product of 77 7 and 11
c) have a sum of 77 when added to 3 1 and 73

Which of parts a to c have more than one answer? Explain.

Reflect

Write an example of a problem you would solve:
• by estimation • by using a calculator
Justify your choice.

1.1 Numbers All Around Us 13

e) What is the total population of Ontario and the 4 Atlantic provinces? (*Answer: 13 887 600*)

13. Part c has more than one answer. The numbers could be any pair of whole numbers that add to 74, such as 1 and 73, 2 and 72, 3 and 71, … 35 and 39, 36 and 38, 37 and 37.

REFLECT: By estimation: For lunch, Dana has a hot dog with 395 calories, a granola bar with 270 calories, and a yogurt with 138 calories. About how many calories are in Dana's lunch?
Using a calculator: A grocery store sold 374 bags of milk on Monday, 278 bags on Tuesday, 401 bags on Wednesday, 189 bags on Thursday, 422 bags on Friday, 321 bags on Saturday, and 162 bags on Sunday. How many bags of milk did the store sell that week?

Assignment Guidelines

If your students do not have time to complete all the *Practice* questions on pages 12 and 13, these questions provide minimum curriculum coverage: 1, 3, 5, 9, 11, 12, *Reflect*
To assess the 4 Achievement Chart categories listed in the curriculum document, have students complete these *Practice* questions:
Understanding Concepts: 3
Communication: 9
Problem Solving: 11
Application: 12

ASSESSMENT FOR LEARNING

What to Look For

Understanding concepts
✔ Students understand there are many strategies that can be used to solve problems.
✔ Students understand some strategies are more effective than others.

Applying procedures
✔ Students can choose the best strategy to solve a problem, then solve the problem.

Communication
✔ Students can justify the choice of strategy when solving problems.

What to Do

Extra Support: Students who have difficulty choosing the most effective strategy may benefit from asking themselves these questions: "Are the numbers easy to handle?", "Do I need an approximate answer?", "Do I need an accurate answer and are the numbers large?", "Are there many steps involved?"
Students can use Step-by-Step 1 (Master 1.9) to complete question 12.

Extra Practice: Have students complete each part of *Practice* question 1 using estimation and using a calculator. They then compare the 3 answers for each question. Two of the answers should be the same in each case.
Students can complete Extra Practice 1 (Master 1.17).

Extension: Have students write problems similar to those in question 13, then trade problems with a classmate and solve the classmate's problems.

Recording and Reporting
Master 1.2 Ongoing Observations: Patterns in Whole Numbers

Factors and Multiples

SECTION ORGANIZER (80–100 min)

Curriculum Focus: Generate factors and multiples of given numbers. (7m11, 7m25)

Student Materials
- Venn diagrams (PM 28)
- hundred charts (PM 13)

Optional
- calendar pages
- Step-by-Step 2 (Master 1.10)
- Extra Practice 2 (Master 1.18)

Vocabulary: factor, prime number, composite number, greatest common factor (GCF), multiple, lowest common multiple (LCM)

Assessment: Master 1.2 Ongoing Observations: Patterns in Whole Numbers

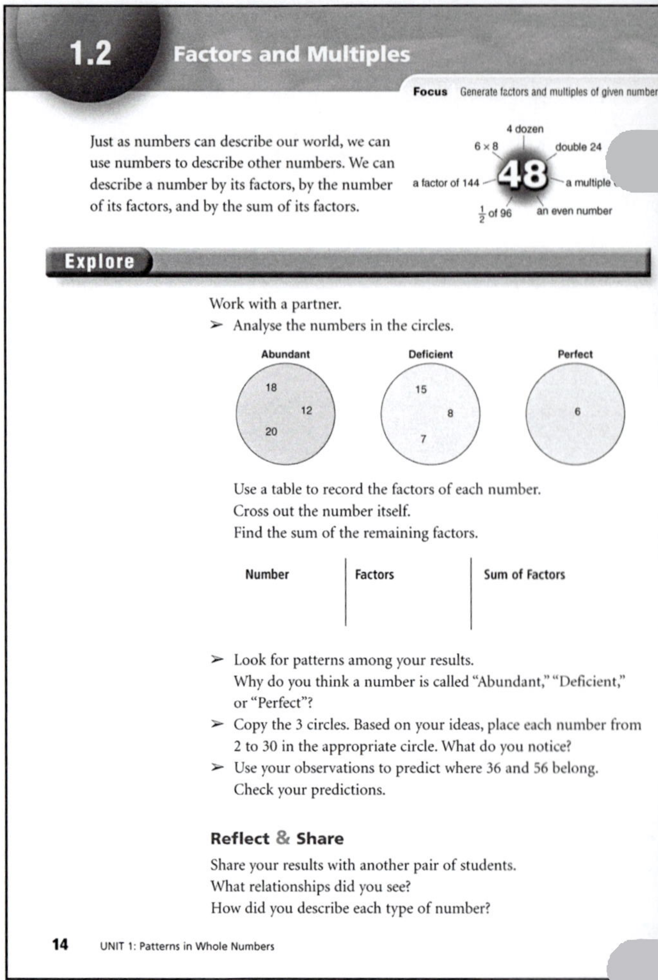

1.2 Factors and Multiples

Focus Generate factors and multiples of given number

Just as numbers can describe our world, we can use numbers to describe other numbers. We can describe a number by its factors, by the number of its factors, and by the sum of its factors.

Explore

Work with a partner.

➢ Analyse the numbers in the circles.

Use a table to record the factors of each number.
Cross out the number itself.
Find the sum of the remaining factors.

Number	Factors	Sum of Factors

➢ Look for patterns among your results.
Why do you think a number is called "Abundant," "Deficient," or "Perfect"?

➢ Copy the 3 circles. Based on your ideas, place each number from 2 to 30 in the appropriate circle. What do you notice?

➢ Use your observations to predict where 36 and 56 belong.
Check your predictions.

Reflect & Share

Share your results with another pair of students.
What relationships did you see?
How did you describe each type of number?

14 UNIT 1: Patterns in Whole Numbers

Key Math Learnings

1. A factor is a number that divides exactly into another number.
2. The multiples of a number are found by multiplying the number by 1, by 2, by 3, by 4, and so on, or by skip counting.
3. Factors that are the same for 2 or more numbers are called common factors. Multiples that are the same for 2 or more numbers are called common multiples.

BEFORE Get Started

Invite students to look at the web for the number 48 on page 14 of the Student Book. Ask:

- What does the web show us?
  (It shows us that we can use many other numbers to describe the number 48.)
- How else could you describe 48?
  (It is a multiple of 8; it is a factor of 192; it is $\frac{1}{3}$ of 144; 12 × 4 = 48; and 16 + 16 + 16 = 48.)

Present *Explore*. Ensure students understand they are to analyse all the numbers in the circles, and record their findings in a table.

DURING Explore

Ongoing Assessment: Observe and Listen

As students work, ask questions, such as:

- What do you notice as you place each number from 2 to 30 in the appropriate circle?
  (All numbers with only 2 factors, 1 and itself, are deficient numbers. Most numbers are deficient numbers.)
- What strategy are you using to predict where 36 and 56 belong?
  (I am looking at the number of factors that each number has. Since both of them have many factors, I predict they both belong in the "Abundant" circle.)
- Where do 36 and 56 belong?
  (The factors of 36, excluding 36, are: 1, 2, 3, 4, 6, 9, 12, and 18. The sum of the factors is 55, which is greater than 36. 36 is an "Abundant" number. The factors of 56, excluding 56, are: 1, 2, 4, 7, 8, 14, and 28. The sum of the factors is 64, which is greater than 56. 56 is an "Abundant" number.)

Students who are having difficulty may need to take another look at the table they created. In each case, ensure students cross out the number itself. If students cannot see patterns in their tables, have students check to see that they have found all possible factors for each number.

Connect

➢ Recall that a factor is a number that divides exactly into another number.
For example, 1, 2, 3, and 6 are the factors of 6.
Each number divides into 6 with no remainder.

A **prime number** has only 2 factors, itself and 1.
2, 3, and 5 are prime numbers.
All prime numbers are deficient.

A **composite number** has more than 2 factors.
8 is a composite number because its factors are 1, 2, 4, and 8.
Composite numbers can be deficient, abundant, or perfect.

1 has only one factor, so 1 is neither prime nor composite.

When we find the factors that are the same for 2 numbers, we find **common factors**.

Example 1

Show the factors of 12 and 30 in a Venn diagram.
What is the **greatest common factor** (**GCF**) of 12 and 30?

Solution

Find pairs of numbers that divide into 12 exactly.

Use the divisibility rules.

12 ÷ 1 = 12	1 and 12 are factors.
12 ÷ 2 = 6	2 and 6 are factors.
12 ÷ 3 = 4	3 and 4 are factors.

Stop at 3 because the next number, 4, is already a factor.
The factors of 12 are 1, 2, 3, 4, 6, and 12.

Find the factors of 30.

30 ÷ 1 = 30	1 and 30 are factors.
30 ÷ 2 = 15	2 and 15 are factors.
30 ÷ 3 = 10	3 and 10 are factors.
30 ÷ 5 = 6	5 and 6 are factors.

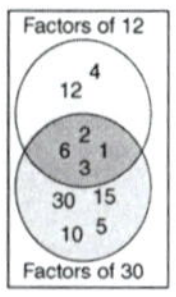

Mark the factors on the Venn diagram.
Place the common factors in the overlapping region.
The GCF of 12 and 30 is 6.

REACHING ALL LEARNERS

Alternative Explore

Materials: 0.5-cm grid paper (PM 14)
Have students find all the factors for each number from 1 to 30. They then draw a bar graph, with each number along the horizontal axis, and the number of factors along the vertical axis. Note that in *Explore* in Section 1.3, students look for patterns in these data, specifically relating to square numbers.

Early Finishers

Have students extend *Explore* by placing each number from 31 to 60 in the appropriate circle, then report their findings.

Common Misconceptions

➤ Students confuse factors and multiples.
How to Help: Create a *factor web*, similar to the web on page 14 of the Student Book, by writing the factors of the chosen number around the outside. Create a *multiple web* for the same number by writing multiples around the outside.

➤ Students have difficulty finding common multiples.
How to Help: Have students make flashcards with pairs of numbers, such as 3 and 4, or 6 and 9. They should write the LCM on the back of each card. Students should include pairs that are prime, such as 11 and 5.

ESL Strategies

Make full use of the hundred chart and take the opportunity to use a calendar page for *Practice*, Question 9. Diagrams, pictures, and charts are very important when teaching the concept of multiples to students for whom English is a second language.

AFTER Connect

What you might see:

Number	Factors	Sum of Factors
18	1, 2, 3, 6, 9, ~~18~~	21
12	1, 2, 3, 4, 6, ~~12~~	16
20	1, 2, 4, 5, 10, ~~20~~	22
15	1, 3, 5, ~~15~~	9
8	1, 2, 4, ~~8~~	7
7	1, ~~7~~	1
6	1, 2, 3, ~~6~~	6

Invite students to share their findings with the class.

Ask questions, such as:

- Where did you place each of the numbers from 2 to 30?
  ("Abundant:" 12, 18, 20, 24, 30; "Deficient:" 2, 3, 4, 5, 7, 8, 9, 10, 11, 13, 14, 15, 16, 17, 19, 21, 22, 23, 25, 26, 27, 29; "Perfect:" 6, 28)
- What relationships did you see?
  (Excluding the number itself, the sum of the factors of an abundant number exceeds the number, a deficient number exceeds the sum of its factors, and the sum of the factors of a perfect number is the number itself.)

Have students write a definition of each type of number in their math notebooks or journals.

Introduce *Connect* to review the terms *factor, prime number, composite number, common factors, multiple* and *common multiple,* and introduce the terms *greatest common factor* and *least common multiple.* Tell students that it is important to be able to find greatest common factors when reducing fractions to lowest terms. It is also important to be able to find the lowest common multiple when finding common denominators for fraction calculations. Review the examples with the class.

Number Strategies

Students could round each number to the nearest dollar. Since \$8.18 is 18¢ more than \$8, and \$7.88 is 12¢ less than \$8, the estimate will be close to the answer.

Sample Answers

4. a) Composite; the number has more than 2 factors.
   b) Prime; the number has only 2 factors, itself and 1.
   c) Composite; the number has more than 2 factors.
   d) Prime; the number has only 2 factors, itself and 1.
   e) Prime; the number has only 2 factors, itself and 1.
   f) Prime; the number has only 2 factors, itself and 1.
5. I used the divisibility rules, then wrote the factors on a Venn diagram. I placed the common factors in the overlapping region, then found the greatest common factor.
7. a) Yes; for example, I will use the numbers 3 and 4:

Number	Multiples
3	3, 6, 9, **12**, 15, 18, 21, **24**, 27, 30, 33, **36**, …
4	4, 8, **12**, 16, 20, **24**, 28, 32, **36**, 40, …

The numbers 3 and 4 have common multiples 12, 24, 36, …

b) Yes; for example, I will use the numbers 30 and 24:

Number	Multiples
30	**1**, **2**, **3**, 5, **6**, 10, 15, 30
24	**1**, **2**, **3**, 4, **6**, 8, 12, 24

The numbers 30 and 24 have 1, 2, 3, and 6 as common factors.

8. a) There could be 1 or 3 bars in a package.

Number of Bars	Factors (Number in a package)
15	**1**, **3**, 5, 15
12	**1**, 2, **3**, 4, 6, 12

(Answers continue, below right.)

➢ The **multiples** of a number are found by multiplying the num
by 1, by 2, by 3, by 4, and so on, or by skip counting.
When we find multiples that are the same for 2 numbers, we fi
common multiples.
We can use a 100 chart to find multiples and common

Example 2

a) Use a 100 chart to find the common multiples of 12 and 21.
b) Find the **lowest common multiple** (**LCM**) of 12 and 21.

Solution

a)

1	2	3	4	5	6	7	8	9	10
11	12	13	14	15	16	17	18	19	20
21	22	23	24	25	26	27	28	29	30
31	32	33	34	35	36	37	38	39	40
41	42	43	44	45	46	47	48	49	50
51	52	53	54	55	56	57	58	59	60
61	62	63	64	65	66	67	68	69	70
71	72	73	74	75	76	77	78	79	80
81	82	83	84	85	86	87	88	89	90
91	92	93	94	95	96	97	98	99	100

The multiples of 12 are blue.
The multiples of 21 are shaded green.
The common multiple is blue and shaded green.

b) Multiples of 12 are 12, 24, 36, 48, 60, 72, **84**, 96, …
Multiples of 21 are 21, 42, 63, **84**, …
The LCM is 84.

Practice

1. List 4 multiples of each number.
   a) 5 b) 7 c) 8
   For example, 10, 15, 20, 25; For example, 14, 21, 28, 35; For example, 16, 24, 32, 40
2. Find the factors of each number. Explain how you did it.
   a) 18 b) 20 c) 28 d) 36 e) 37 f) 45
   1, 2, 3, 6, 9, 18; 1, 2, 4, 5, 10, 20; 1, 2, 4, 7, 14, 28; 1, 2, 3, 4, 6, 9, 12, 18, 36; 1, 37; 1, 3, 5, 9, 1
3. Find the factors of each number.
   a) 50 b) 51 c) 67 d) 75 e) 84 f) 120
   1, 2, 5, 10, 25, 50; 1, 3, 17, 51; 1, 67; 1, 3, 5, 15, 25, 75; 1, 2, 3, 4, 6, 7, 12, 14, 21, 28, 42, 84
   1, 2, 3, 4, 5, 6, 8, 10, 12, 15, 20, 24, 30, 40, 60, 120

16 UNIT 1: Patterns in Whole Numbers

Practice

Encourage students to use hundred charts and Venn diagrams to help them find greatest common factors and lowest common multiples. Question 6 requires hundred charts. When students complete question 10, have them write a definition of a "near-perfect" number in their notebooks or journals.

Assessment Focus: Question 9

Students could use a hundred chart or a calendar page. Students could place symbols on the multiples of the days, using a different symbol for each worker. They find days that have all 3 symbols. If students do solve the problem this way, have them explain how its solution relates to the work of this unit.

(Sample Answers, continued)

b) There could be 1, 2, 3, or 6 bars in a package.

Number of Bars	Factors (Number in a package)
18	**1**, **2**, **3**, **6**, 9, 18
24	**1**, **2**, **3**, 4, **6**, 8, 12, 24

9. In 12 days; I used a hundred chart. I circled all the multiples of 2. I put a line through all the multiples of 3. I put a dot on all the multiples of 4. The numbers that had all three symbols were: 12, 24, 36, 48, … The numbers start at 12 and increase by 12 each time. Kevin, Alison, and Fred will work together again in 12 days. Twelve is the lowest common multiple of 2, 3, and 4.
10. The numbers 4 and 16 could each be called "near-perfect" because the sum of the factors, excluding the number itself, is one less than the number. The number 8 is another example of a near-perfect number. I looked at my table from *Explore* and found a number whose sum of factors was one less than the number.

Number Strategies

...s cost $12.99, ...d $7.88 ...uded).
Approximately how much change should there be from $40.00?

About $11

4. Is each number prime or composite? How do you know?

a) 18 b) 13 c) 9 d) 19 e) 61 f) 2

Composite Prime Composite Prime Prime Prime

5. Find the GCF of each pair of numbers.
Which strategy did you use?

a) 10, 5 b) 12, 8 c) 15, 25 d) 9, 12 e) 18, 15

5 4 5 3 3

6. Use a 100 chart. Find the LCM of each pair of numbers.

a) 3, 4 b) 2, 5 c) 12, 18 d) 10, 25 e) 27, 18

12 10 36 50 54

7. Can a pair of numbers have:
a) more than one common multiple?
b) more than one common factor?
Use a diagram to explain your thinking.

8. Julia and Sandhu bought packages of granola bars.
1 or 3 bars a) Julia had 15 bars in total. Sandhu had 12 bars in total. How many bars could there be in one package?
1, 2, 3, or 6 bars b) What if Julia had 24 bars and Sandu had 18 bars? How many bars could there be in one package?
Draw a diagram to explain your thinking.

9. **Assessment Focus** Kevin, Alison, and Fred work part-time. Kevin works every second day. Alison works every third day. Fred works every fourth day. Today they all worked together. When will they work together again? Explain how you know.

10. The numbers 4 and 16 could be called "near-perfect".
Why do you think this name is appropriate?
Find another example of a near-perfect number.
What strategy did you use?

Reflect

What is the difference between a factor and a multiple?
Is a factor ever a multiple? Is a multiple ever a factor?
Use diagrams, pictures, or a 100 chart to explain.

1.2 Factors and Multiples 17

REFLECT: A factor is a number that divides exactly into another number. A multiple is a product of a given number and a counting number.
I will use the number 12 as an example.
Factors of 12: 1, 2, 3, 4, 6, 12
Multiples of 12: 12, 24, 36, 48, …
12 is both a factor and a multiple of 12:
12 ÷ 1 = 12 and 12 × 1 = 12.
Therefore, a number is both a factor and a multiple of itself.

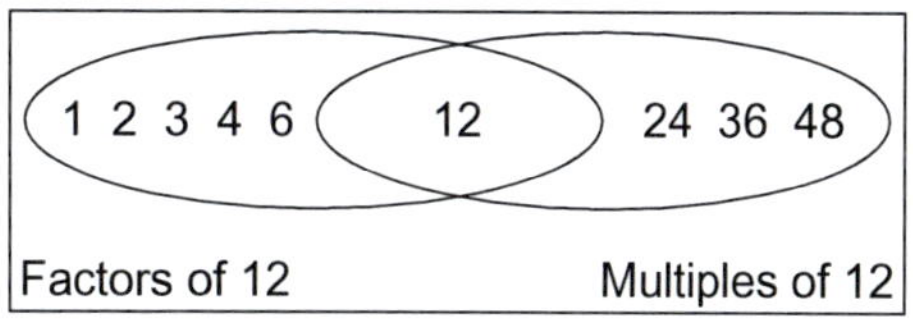

Assignment Guidelines

If your students do not have time to complete all the *Practice* questions on pages 16 and 17, these questions provide minimum curriculum coverage: 1, 2, 4, 5, 6, 8, 9, *Reflect*
To assess the 4 Achievement Chart categories listed in the curriculum document, have students complete these *Practice* questions:
Communication: 2
Application: 6
Understanding Concepts: 7
Problem Solving: 8

ASSESSMENT FOR LEARNING

What to Look For	What to Do
Understanding concepts ✔ Students understand how to generate factors and multiples of given numbers. ***Applying procedures*** ✔ Students can identify a number as prime or composite. ✔ Students can find the greatest common factor and the least common multiple for a given set of numbers. ***Communicating*** ✔ Students use appropriate mathematical terminology to describe the meanings of the terms "Abundant," Deficient," and "Perfect" numbers.	***Extra Support:*** Students can play the Additional Activity *Product Mania* (Master 1.6). Students can use Step-by-Step 2 (Master 1.10) to complete question 9. ***Extra Practice:*** Have students find the LCM for each pair of numbers in *Practice,* question 5, and the GCF for each pair of numbers in *Practice,* question 6, parts c, d, and e. Students can complete Extra Practice 2 (Master 1.18). ***Extension:*** Have students choose 3 numbers, then find their LCM and GCF.

Recording and Reporting
Master 1.2 Ongoing Observations: Patterns in Whole Numbers

The Factor Game

SECTION ORGANIZER

Student Materials
- number cubes
- *The Factor Game* game board (Master 1.14)
- different coloured markers

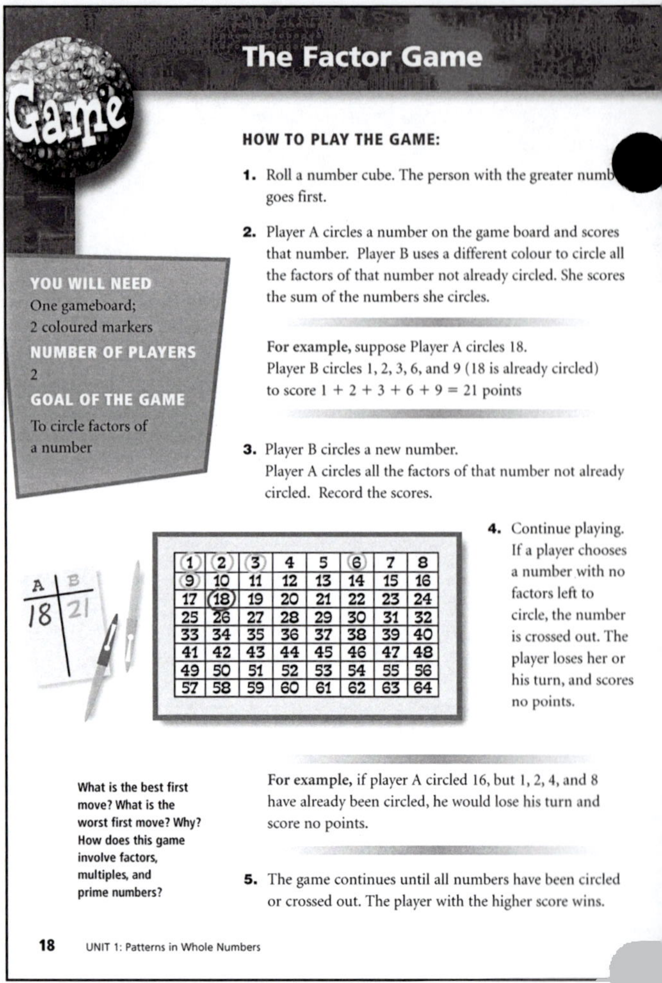

The Factor Game

YOU WILL NEED
One gameboard;
2 coloured markers

NUMBER OF PLAYERS
2

GOAL OF THE GAME
To circle factors of a number

HOW TO PLAY THE GAME:

1. Roll a number cube. The person with the greater number goes first.
2. Player A circles a number on the game board and scores that number. Player B uses a different colour to circle all the factors of that number not already circled. She scores the sum of the numbers she circles.

For example, suppose Player A circles 18.
Player B circles 1, 2, 3, 6, and 9 (18 is already circled) to score 1 + 2 + 3 + 6 + 9 = 21 points

3. Player B circles a new number.
Player A circles all the factors of that number not already circled. Record the scores.
4. Continue playing. If a player chooses a number with no factors left to circle, the number is crossed out. The player loses her or his turn, and scores no points.

1	2	3	4	5	6	7	8
9	10	11	12	13	14	15	16
17	18	19	20	21	22	23	24
25	26	27	28	29	30	31	32
33	34	35	36	37	38	39	40
41	42	43	44	45	46	47	48
49	50	51	52	53	54	55	56
57	58	59	60	61	62	63	64

A	B
18	21

For example, if player A circled 16, but 1, 2, 4, and 8 have already been circled, he would lose his turn and score no points.

5. The game continues until all numbers have been circled or crossed out. The player with the higher score wins.

What is the best first move? What is the worst first move? Why? How does this game involve factors, multiples, and prime numbers?

18 UNIT 1: Patterns in Whole Numbers

Take It Further

Students can play the game again, this time using a hundred chart as the game board.

Invite a volunteer to read the game rules.

Ensure students understand that a number can only be circled once.

As students play, ask questions such as:

- What is the best first move?
  (*To circle a prime number*)
  Why? (*My opponent will score 1 point because he or she will only be able to circle the number 1.*)
- What is the worst first move? (*To circle a large number that has many factors, such as 64.*)
  Why? (*My opponent will be able to circle many numbers and score a lot of points.*)
- How does this game involve factors, multiples, and prime numbers?
  (*The best first move is to circle a prime number because it only has 2 factors, 1 and itself. When a player circles a number, the other player circles all the factors of that number. Before I circle a number, I check to see that it is a multiple of a number already circled. On the game board on page 18, I would circle 36, because it is a multiple of 18, and most of the factors of 36 have already been circled – my opponent gets only 16 points. I always try to choose a deficient number because the sum of the factors is less than the number, so I get more points than my opponent.*)
- Will you ever be forced to lose your turn?
  (*Yes, there will come a time when only prime numbers are left, and the number 1 has already been circled.*)

After students have played the game a few times, have students who achieved high scores explain their strategies.

Squares and Square Roots

1.3 Squares and Square Roots

Focus Find the squares and square roots of whole numbers.

Explore

Work with a partner
This chart shows the number of factors of each whole number.

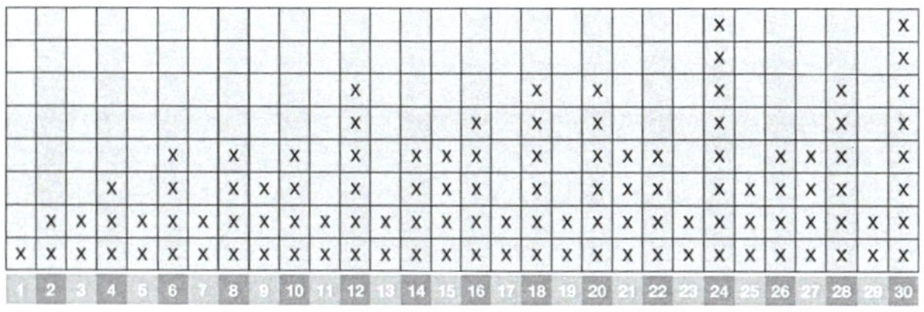

Look for patterns and relationships in this chart.
Find the factors of the numbers with two factors.
What do you notice?
Describe the numbers with four or more factors.
Describe the numbers that have an odd number of factors.

Reflect & Share

One way to describe a number with an odd number of factors is to call it a **square number**.
Why do you think this name is used?
Draw pictures to support your explanation.

Connect

The factors of a composite number occur in pairs.
For example, $48 \div 2 = 24$ 2 and 24 are factors of 48.
When the quotient is equal to the divisor, the dividend is a square number.
For example, $49 \div 7 = 7$, so 49 is a square number.
dividend divisor quotient

SECTION ORGANIZER 80–100 min

Curriculum Focus: Find the squares and square roots of whole numbers. (7m13)

Teacher Materials
- overhead transparency of 1-cm grid paper (PM 20)

Student Materials
- 1-cm grid paper (PM 20)

Optional
- 12 × 12 multiplication chart (PM 15)
- Step-by-Step 3 (Master 1.11)
- Extra Practice 3 (Master 1.19)

Vocabulary: square number, square root

Assessment: Master 1.2 Ongoing Observations: Patterns in Whole Numbers

Key Math Learnings

1. A square number can be written as the product of two equal factors.
2. A square root is a number which, when multiplied by itself, results in a given number.
3. Squaring and taking a square root are inverse operations.

BEFORE Get Started

Present *Explore*. Remind students of the work they did in the previous lesson, listing the factors of numbers from 2 to 30. Explain that the factors (including the number itself) are graphed in *Explore*.

DURING Explore

Ongoing Assessment: Observe and Listen

As students work, ask questions, such as:
- What do you notice about the factors of the numbers with two factors?
  (*The factors are always 1 and the number itself. The numbers are prime numbers.*)
- How can you describe the numbers with four or more factors? (*They are composite numbers.*)
- How can you describe the numbers that have an odd number of factors?
  (*They have a multiplication fact in which both factors are the same; for example, 4 × 4 = 16.*)
- Which numbers in the chart have an odd number of factors? (*1, 4, 9, 16, and 25*)

AFTER Connect

Have students share their findings with the class.

Ask:
- Why do you think a number with an odd number of factors is called a square number?
  (*A square with side length 1, 2, 3, 4, or 5 units has an area of 1, 4, 9, 16, or 25 square units. For example, a square with side length 3 cm has an area of 9 cm²: 3 × 3 = 9. Therefore, 3 is a factor of 9 but we only list it once.*)

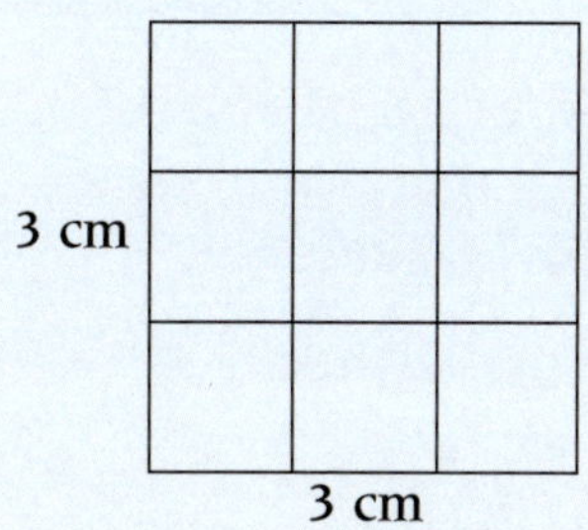

Area = 3 cm × 3 cm
= 9 cm²

REACHING ALL LEARNERS

Early Finishers

Have students extend the line plot in *Explore* for numbers from 31 to 60.

Common Misconceptions

➤ Students confuse squaring a number with doubling a number.

How to Help: Show students that the square of a number is the product of a number multiplied by itself; for example, 25 is the square of 5: $5 \times 5 = 25$. When we double a number, we multiply it by 2; for example, double 5 is 10: $5 \times 2 = 10$. Point out that 2 is the only number for which squaring and doubling produce the same answer.

Number Strategies

Students should find the pattern rule for the amount spent each month. Students should extend the pattern until the amount remaining is less than $5.

Sample Answers

8. 1: $\sqrt{1} = 1$; 4: $\sqrt{4} = 2$; 9: $\sqrt{9} = 3$; 16: $\sqrt{16} = 4$; 25: $\sqrt{25} = 5$; 36: $\sqrt{36} = 6$; 49: $\sqrt{49} = 7$; 64: $\sqrt{64} = 8$, 81: $\sqrt{81} = 9$; 100: $\sqrt{100} = 10$; 121: $\sqrt{121} = 11$; 144: $\sqrt{144} = 12$; 169: $\sqrt{169} = 13$; 196: $\sqrt{196} = 14$; 225: $\sqrt{225} = 15$; 256: $\sqrt{256} = 16$; 289: $\sqrt{289} = 17$; 324: $\sqrt{324} = 18$; 361: $\sqrt{361} = 19$; 400: $\sqrt{400} = 20$
   I squared each whole number from 1 to 20 to find the numbers with the corresponding square roots.

We can get 49 by multiplying the whole number, 7, by itself.
$49 = 7 \times 7$
We write: $7 \times 7 = 7^2$
We say: 7 squared

- One way to model a square number is to draw a square.
  This square has area 9 square units.
  The side length is $\sqrt{9}$, or 3 units.
  We say: A **square root** of 9 is 3.

9 square units

Other inverse operations are addition and subtraction, multiplication and division

- When we multiply a number by itself, we square the number. Squaring a number and taking its square root are inverse operations. That is, they undo each other.
  $7 \times 7 = 49$
  so, $7^2 = 49$
  $\sqrt{49} = \sqrt{7^2}$
  $= 7$

Example 1

Find the square of each number.
a) 5 b) 15 c) 32

Solution

a) $5^2 = 5 \times 5 = 25$
b) $15^2 = 15 \times 15 = 225$
c) $32^2 = 32 \times 32 = 1024$
Use a calculator.

Example 2

Draw a diagram to find a square root of each number.
a) 16 b) 36

Solution

a) On grid paper, draw a square with area 16 square units.
The side length of the square is 4 units.
So, $\sqrt{16} = 4$

16 square units

b) On grid paper, draw a square with area 36 square units.
The side length of the square is 6 units.
So, $\sqrt{36} = 6$

36 square units

20 UNIT 1: Patterns in Whole Numbers

We write $3 \times 3 = 3^2$, and we say 3 squared. Tell students that 9 is a *square number*.

A square with area 36 square units has side length $\sqrt{36}$, or 6 units. We say: A *square root* of 36 is 6.

When you review *Example 1*, part c, have students use their calculators to check. If students have a calculator with a key that squares a number (usually x^2), have them use that key.

Mathematical Note

We say that *a* square root of 9 is 3, because 9 has two square roots, 3 and –3. In grade 8, students will multiply integers and learn that $(-3) \times (-3) = +9$. At that time, students can comprehend the negative square root.

Review the examples in *Connect*.

Practice

Question 4 requires grid paper.

Assessment Focus: Question 8

Students could work backward and square each whole number from 1 to 20 to find the whole numbers with the corresponding square roots. Some students may not include 1 and 20 as the question states numbers *between* 1 and 20.

Practice

1. Find.
   a) $8^2 = 64$ b) $16^2 = 256$ c) $1^2 = 1$ d) $29^2 = 841$

2. Find the square of each number.
   a) 4 16 b) 17 289 c) 13 169 d) 52 2704

3. a) Find the square of each number.
   i) 1 1 ii) 10 100 iii) 100 10 000 iv) 1000 1 000 000
   b) Use the results of part a. Predict the square of each number.
   i) 10 000 100 000 000 ii) 1 000 000 1 000 000 000 000

4. Use grid paper. Find a square root of each number.
   a) 16 4 b) 4 2 c) 900 30 d) 144 12

5. Calculate the side length of a square with each area.
   a) 100 m² 10 m b) 64 cm² 8 cm c) 81 m² 9 m

6. Order from least to greatest.
   a) $\sqrt{36}$, 36, 4, $\sqrt{9}$ — $\sqrt{9}$, 4, $\sqrt{36}$, 36
   b) $\sqrt{400}$, $\sqrt{100}$, 19, 15 — $\sqrt{100}$, 15, 19, $\sqrt{400}$

7. Which whole numbers have squares between 50 and 200?
   8; 9; 10; 11; 12; 13; 14

8. **Assessment Focus** Which whole numbers have square roots between 1 and 20? How do you know?

9. A large square room has an area of 144 m².
   a) Find the length of a side of the room. 12 m
   b) How much baseboard is needed to go around the room? 48 m
   c) Each piece of baseboard is 2.5 m long. How many pieces of baseboard are needed? 20 pieces

10. A garden has an area of 400 m². The garden is divided into 16 congruent square plots. What is the side length of each plot? 5 m — $400 \div 16 = 25$; $\sqrt{25} = 5$

Number Strategies

Chris had saved $145.98 by June. He spent $2.25 in July, $4.50 in August, and $9.00 in September. If Chris' spending pattern continues, when will he have less than $5.00?

December

Reflect

How can you find the perimeter of a square when you know its area? Use an example to explain.

1.3 Squares and Square Roots 21

9. c) 20 pieces: 48 ÷ 2.5 = 19.2 To have enough baseboard, 20 full pieces should be ordered. But since I haven't allowed for a doorway that will be about 1 m wide and not need baseboard, 19 pieces are probably enough.

REFLECT: For example, the area of a square is 81 cm². The side length is $\sqrt{81}$, or 9 cm. The perimeter is the distance around the square, which is the sum of the lengths of its sides, or 4 times its side length.

9 cm + 9 cm + 9 cm + 9 cm = 4 × 9 cm
= 36 cm

The perimeter of a square with area 81 cm² is 36 cm.

Assignment Guidelines

If your students do not have time to complete all the *Practice* questions on page 21, these questions provide minimum curriculum coverage: 1, 3, 4, 6, 8, 9, *Reflect*

To assess the 4 Achievement Chart categories listed in the curriculum document, have students complete these *Practice* questions:

Understanding Concepts: 3
Application: 4
Communication: 8
Problem Solving: 9

ASSESSMENT FOR LEARNING

What to Look For

Understanding concepts

✔ Students understand the difference between squares and square roots.

✔ Students understand that squaring a number and taking its square root are inverse operations.

Applying procedures

✔ Students can use grid paper to find a square root of a given number, and to find the side length of a square with a given area.

Problem solving

✔ Students can use square roots to solve problems relating to area and perimeter.

What to Do

Extra Support: Students having difficulty may benefit from using a 12 × 12 multiplication chart (PM 15) to find the square of each number from 1 to 12, and to find square roots of numbers to 144. The main diagonal from top left to bottom right contains square numbers, and a square root of a number is read from the chart by moving up to the top row from that number in the main diagonal. Students can use Step-by-Step 3 (Master 1.11) to complete question 8.

Extra Practice: Have students cut out squares of various sizes from a sheet of grid paper (for example, 3 by 3, 8 by 8), then glue them into a notebook. For each square, have students label its area and side length, then write two statements; for example, 3 × 3 = 9; $\sqrt{9} = 3$.
Students can complete Extra Practice 3 (Master 1.19).

Recording and Reporting

Master 1.2 Ongoing Observations: Patterns in Whole Numbers

SECTION ORGANIZER

Student Materials

- calculators
- Venn diagrams (PM 28)
- 1-cm grid paper (PM 20)
- hundred charts (PM 13)

Assessment:

Masters 1.1 Unit Rubric: Patterns in Whole Numbers, 1.4 Unit Summary: Patterns in Whole Numbers

Mid-Unit Review

LESSON

1.1 **1.** The table shows the most common surnames for adults in the United Kingdom.

Surname	Number
Smith	538 369
Jones	402 489
Williams	279 150

a) Approximately how many adults have one of these three names? [About 1 220 000 adults] To which place value did you estimate? Explain your choice.

b) Exactly how many more Smiths are there than Jones? Explain. [135 880]

c) Write your own problem about these data. Solve your problem. Justify your strategy.

2. In one week, Joe worked 23 h cutting grass. He was paid \$9/h. From this money, Joe bought 5 tickets for a football game, at \$15 per ticket, and 2 DVDs for \$21 each, including tax. How much money did Joe have left?

1.2 **3.** Find all the factors of each number.

a) 35 [1, 5, 7, 35] b) 24 [1, 2, 3, 4, 6, 8, 12, 24]

4. Find 2 factors of each number.

a) 6 b) 10
c) 14 d) 15
e) 9 f) 21

5. Organize the first 8 multiples of 6 and 8 in a Venn diagram.

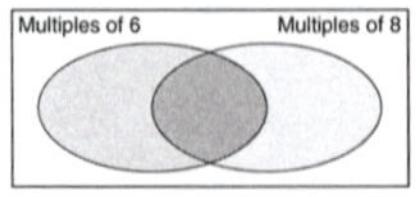

6. For the numbers 15 and 6, find:

a) the GCF [3] b) the LCM [30]

7. a) Why is 7 a prime number?
b) Why is 8 not a prime number?

1.3 **8.** Can three consecutive whole numbers all be primes? Justify your answer. [No]

9. A square patio has an area of 81 m². How long is each side? [9 m]

10. Find.

a) $\sqrt{49}$ [= 7] b) 8^2 [= 64]
c) $\sqrt{100}$ [= 10] d) the square of 9 [= 81]

11. Find two squares with a sum of 100. [$6^2 + 8^2 = 100$]

12. Write 100 as a square number and as a square root of a number. [$100 = 10^2 = \sqrt{10\ 000}$]

13. Explain why: $\sqrt{1} = 1$

22 UNIT 1: Patterns in Whole Numbers

Sample Solutions

1. a) About 1 220 000 adults; I rounded each number to the nearest ten thousand because the numbers are easy to work with. My answer is a reasonable estimate because 2 numbers were rounded up and 1 number was rounded down.
   b) 135 880; I used paper and pencil, then checked my answer with a calculator.
   c) Exactly how many adults have one of these three names? (*Answer:* 1 220 008)
   I used a calculator because I needed an exact answer and the numbers are large.
2. In one week, Joe earned 23 × \$9 = \$207.
   Joe spent 5 × \$15 = \$75 on football tickets and 2 × \$21 = \$42 on DVDs. To find the money Joe had left, I subtracted the amount spent from the amount earned: \$207 – \$75 – \$42 = \$90.
4. a) Any two of: 1, 2, 3, 6 b) Any two of: 1, 2, 5, 10
   c) Any two of: 1, 2, 7, 14 d) Any two of: 1, 3, 5, 15
   e) Any two of: 1, 3, 9 f) Any two of: 1, 3, 7, 21
5.

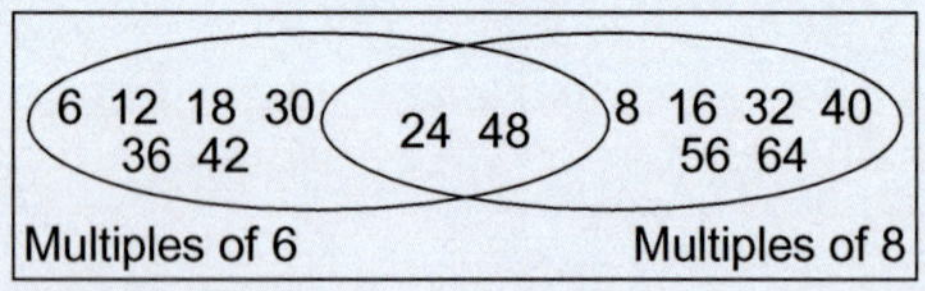

7. a) It has only 2 factors, itself and 1.
   b) It has more than 2 factors: 1, 2, 4, 8.
8. No, because at least one of the three numbers will be an even number greater than 2, and each even number greater than 2 has 2 as a factor, so has at least 3 factors. If I chose the numbers 1, 2, 3, then 2 and 3 are prime numbers, but 1 is neither prime nor composite.
11. $6^2 + 8^2 = 36 + 64$
    $= 100$
12. $100 = 10^2$
    $\sqrt{10\ 000} = 100$
13. Since 1 × 1 = 1, $1^2 = 1$. Therefore, $\sqrt{1} = \sqrt{1^2} = 1$

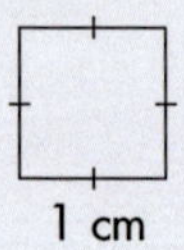

A = 1 cm²

A square with area 1 cm² has side length 1 cm.

1.4 Exponents

Focus Use exponents to represent repeated multiplication.

Explore

Work with a small group.
You will need 65 interlocking cubes.
The edge length of each cube is 1 unit.
The volume of each cube is 1 cubic unit.

- How many different ways can you make a larger cube?
- What is the volume of each larger cube you make? What is its edge length?
- Use factors to write the volume of each cube.
- Record your results in a table.

Number of Cubes	Volume (cubic units)	Edge Length (units)	Volume As a Product
1	1	1	$1 \times 1 \times 1$

Reflect & Share

Observe how the volume grows. Describe the growth using pictures or numbers. What other patterns do you see in the table?
Use these patterns to help you write the volumes of the next 3 cubes in the pattern.

Connect

When numbers are repeated in multiplication, we can write them in **exponent form**.

For example, we can write $2 \times 2 \times 2 \times 2$ as 2^4.
2 is the **base**.
4 is the **exponent**.
2^4 is the **power**.

base 2^4 exponent power

We say: 2 to the power of 4, or
2 to the 4th
2^4 is a power of 2.

1.4 Exponents 23

Exponents

SECTION ORGANIZER (80–100 min)

Curriculum Focus: Use exponents to represent repeated multiplication. (7m15)

Teacher Materials
- interlocking cubes

Student Materials
- interlocking cubes (65 per group)
- calculators
- 4-column charts (PM 19)

Optional
- Step-by-Step 4 (Master 1.12)
- Extra Practice 4 (Master 1.20)

Vocabulary: exponent form, base, exponent, power, cube number, perfect square, perfect cube

Assessment: Master 1.2 Ongoing Observations: Patterns in Whole Numbers

Key Math Learnings

1. Exponents represent repeated multiplication.
2. A number written as a power has a base and an exponent.
3. A power with exponent 2 is a square number. A power with exponent 3 is a cube number.
4. A number can be written in standard form, in expanded form, and in exponent form.

BEFORE Get Started

Have students use 3, 4, or 5 interlocking cubes to make rectangular prisms.

Ask:
- How many cubes did you use to make your rectangular prism? (*4*)
- What is the volume of your prism? (*4 cubic units*) How do you know? (*The volume of a rectangular prism is length × width × height; $1 \times 1 \times 4 = 4$*)
- Did anyone make a different rectangular prism with 4 cubes? (*Yes*) What is its volume? (*4 cubic units; $2 \times 2 \times 1 = 4$*)

Present *Explore*. Arrange students into groups of 3 or 4. Assign one student in each group to record the results in a table.

DURING Explore

Ongoing Observations: Observe and Listen

As students work, ask questions, such as:
- How many different ways can you make a larger cube? (*3; I can use 8 cubes, 27 cubes, and 64 cubes.*)
- What is the volume of each larger cube you made? (*8 cubic units, 27 cubic units, and 64 cubic units*) What are the corresponding edge lengths? (*2 units, 3 units, and 4 units*)
- What patterns do you see in the table? (*The number of cubes is equal to the volume each time. The edge length starts at 1 and increases by 1 each time. The volume starts at $1 \times 1 \times 1$ cubic units. The number multiplied by itself 3 times increases by 1 each time.*)
- How could you describe how the volume grows? (*The volume increases by 7 cubes, by 19 cubes, and by 37 cubes.*)

REACHING ALL LEARNERS

Early Finishers

Give students a hundred chart. Have them shade all the numbers that are perfect squares red and all the numbers that are perfect cubes blue. Students find any numbers that are both perfect squares and perfect cubes (64).

Common Misconceptions

➤ Students multiply the base by the exponent when writing a power in standard form.

How to Help: Tell students that the exponent, shown in smaller size and raised, tells how many times the number before it is used as a factor; for example, 4 is the exponent in 6^4: $6^4 = 6 \times 6 \times 6 \times 6$. The factor 6 is written 4 times.

ESL Strategies

Have students draw a square on an index card and beneath the square write the square numbers: 1, 4, 9, 16, 25, 36, 49, 64, 81, 100. Have students draw a cube on an index card and beneath the cube write the cube numbers: 1, 8, 27, 64, 125, 216, 343, 512, 729, 1000.

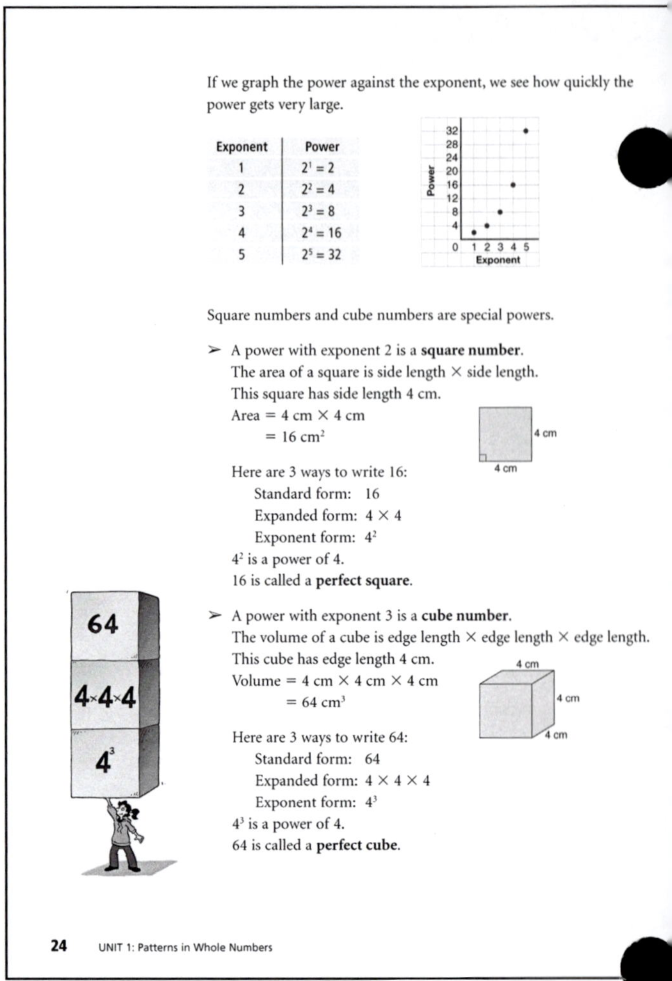

If we graph the power against the exponent, we see how quickly the power gets very large.

Exponent	Power
1	$2^1 = 2$
2	$2^2 = 4$
3	$2^3 = 8$
4	$2^4 = 16$
5	$2^5 = 32$

Square numbers and cube numbers are special powers.

➢ A power with exponent 2 is a **square number**.
The area of a square is side length × side length.
This square has side length 4 cm.
Area = 4 cm × 4 cm
= 16 cm^2

Here are 3 ways to write 16:
Standard form: 16
Expanded form: 4 × 4
Exponent form: 4^2
4^2 is a power of 4.
16 is called a **perfect square**.

➢ A power with exponent 3 is a **cube number**.
The volume of a cube is edge length × edge length × edge length.
This cube has edge length 4 cm.
Volume = 4 cm × 4 cm × 4 cm
= 64 cm^3

Here are 3 ways to write 64:
Standard form: 64
Expanded form: 4 × 4 × 4
Exponent form: 4^3
4^3 is a power of 4.
64 is called a **perfect cube**.

24 UNIT 1: Patterns in Whole Numbers

AFTER Connect

Have volunteers share their tables, cubes or pictures, and findings with the class.

What you might see:

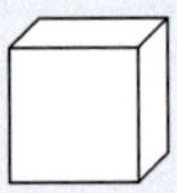

$V = 1$ cubic unit

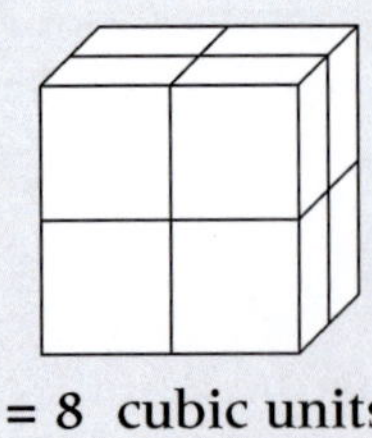

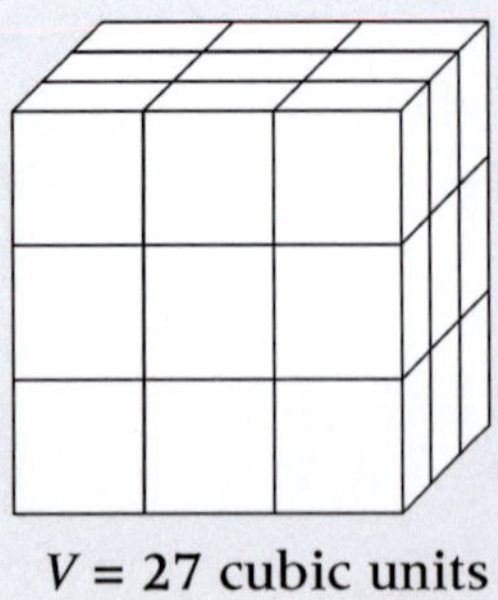

$V = 8$ cubic units $V = 27$ cubic units

Number of Cubes	Volume (cubic units)	Edge Length (units)	Volume As a Product
1	1	1	1 × 1 × 1
8	8	2	2 × 2 × 2
27	27	3	3 × 3 × 3
64	64	4	4 × 4 × 4

Ask:

- Use the patterns to predict what the volumes of the next 3 cubes in the pattern will be? (*The volumes in cubic centimetres will be: 5 × 5 × 5 = 125, 6 × 6 × 6 = 216, and 7 × 7 × 7 = 343.*)

Tell students that we use exponents to represent repeated multiplication. Remind students of the exponent 2 they used in Section 1.3 to write the square of a number.
Have students write each volume in *Explore* in exponent form.

Example 1

Write in exponent form.

a) 6×6 b) $5 \times 5 \times 5$ c) 32

Solution

a) $6 \times 6 = 6^2$ b) $5 \times 5 \times 5 = 5^3$

c) $32 = 2 \times 2 \times 2 \times 2 \times 2 = 2^5$

Example 2

Write in expanded form and standard form.

a) 3^5 b) 7^4

Solution

a) $3^5 = 3 \times 3 \times 3 \times 3 \times 3 = 243$

b) $7^4 = 7 \times 7 \times 7 \times 7 = 2401$

A calculator can be used to simplify a power such as 3^5.
For a scientific calculator, the keystrokes are:

[3] [^] [5] [ENTER] or [3] [y^x] [5] [ENTER] to display 243

For a non-scientific calculator, use repeated multiplication.
The keystrokes are:

[3] [×] [=] [=] [=] [=] to display 243

Practice

1. Write the base of each power.
a) 2^4 2 b) 3^2 3 c) 7^3 7 d) 10^5 10 e) 6^9 6 f) 8^3 8

2. Write the exponent of each power.
a) 2^5 5 b) 3^2 2 c) 7^1 1 d) 9^5 5 e) 8^{10} 10 f) 10^4 4

3. Write in expanded form.
a) 2^4 $2 \times 2 \times 2 \times 2$ b) 10^3 $10 \times 10 \times 10$ c) 6^5 $6 \times 6 \times 6 \times 6 \times 6$ d) 4^2 4×4 e) 2^1 2 f) 5^4 $5 \times 5 \times 5 \times 5$

4. Write in exponent form.
a) $3 \times 3 \times 3 \times 3$ 3^4 b) $2 \times 2 \times 2$ 2^3 c) $5 \times 5 \times 5 \times 5 \times 5 \times 5$ 5^6
d) $10 \times 10 \times 10$ 10^3 e) 79×79 79^2 f) $2 \times 2 \times 2 \times 2 \times 2 \times 2 \times 2 \times 2$ 2^8

1.4 Exponents 25

Sample Answers

9. In each pair, the base and the exponent have been interchanged. I used a calculator to find out which number was greater.
a) 3^2; $9 > 8$ **b)** 2^5; $32 > 25$
c) 3^4; $81 > 64$ **d)** 4^5; $1024 > 625$

10. From least to greatest: 5^2, 3^4, 6^3, 3^5
I wrote each base the number of times indicated by the exponent, then multiplied. I ordered the products, then wrote each number in its power form.

12. a) i) 16^1, 4^2, 2^4 **ii)** 81^1, 3^4, 9^2 **iii)** 64^1, 2^6, 4^3, 8^2

b) 256: 256^1, 2^8, 4^4, 16^2

$$\begin{aligned} 256 &= 2^8 \\ &= 2 \times 2 \times 2 \times 2 \times 2 \times 2 \times 2 \times 2 \\ &= (2 \times 2 \times 2 \times 2) \times (2 \times 2 \times 2 \times 2) \\ &= 16 \times 16 \\ &= 16^2 \end{aligned}$$

$$\begin{aligned} 256 &= 2^8 \\ &= (2 \times 2) \times (2 \times 2) \times (2 \times 2) \times (2 \times 2) \\ &= 4 \times 4 \times 4 \times 4 \\ &= 4^4 \end{aligned}$$

REFLECT: I factor the number. If the number can be written as the product of two equal factors, it is a perfect square. If the number can be written as the product of three equal factors, it is a perfect cube. If neither of these things can be done, the number is neither a perfect square nor a perfect cube.

Use *Connect* to introduce the terms *perfect square, cube number*, and *perfect cube*, and to introduce the different ways to write numbers: standard form, expanded form, and exponent form. Review the examples in *Connect*.

Tell students that any number can be written in exponent form, by using the exponent 1. For example: $6 = 6^1$; $103 = 103^1$.

Practice

Question 11 requires a calculator.

Assessment Focus: Question 12

Students should try different numbers for the base each time, and possibly use their calculators to determine which bases can be used. For other numbers in part b, students could look at the patterns of numbers in part a; for example, 64 is 4×16, so both 16 and 64 can be written as powers of 4, and use the same or a similar pattern.

Calculator Skills

Students find how much the variety store brings in for every 24 cans of pop that it sells, then subtract the cost of a case of pop to find how much money the store makes per case.

Assignment Guidelines

If your students do not have time to complete all the *Practice* questions on pages 25 and 26, these questions provide minimum curriculum coverage: 3, 4, 6, 7, 10, 11, 12, *Reflect*

To assess the 4 Achievement Chart categories listed in the curriculum document, have students complete these *Practice* questions:

Understanding Concepts: 3
Communication: 8
Application: 10
Problem Solving: 12

Calculator Skills

A case of 24 cans of pop costs $7.49 at a local grocery store. A variety store charges customers $1.25 for 1 can. How much more money is the variety store making?

$22.51 per case

5. Write in exponent form, then in standard form.

a) 5×5 $5^2 = 25$ b) $3 \times 3 \times 3 \times 3$ $3^4 = 81$
c) $10 \times 10 \times 10 \times 10 \times 10$ d) $2 \times 2 \times 2$ $2^3 = 8$
e) $9 \times 9 \times 9$ $10^5 = 100\,000$ f) $2 \times 2 \times 2 \times 2 \times 2 \times 2 \times$
$9^3 = 729$ $2^7 = 128$

6. Write in standard form.

a) $2^4 = 16$ b) $10^3 = 1000$ c) $3^5 = 243$ d) $7^3 = 343$ e) $2^8 = 256$ f) $4^1 = 4$

7. Write as a power of 10. How did you do it?

a) $100 = 10^2$ b) $10\,000 = 10^4$ c) $100\,000 = 10^5$
d) $10 = 10^1$ e) $1000 = 10^3$ f) $1\,000\,000 = 10^6$
I counted the number of zeros, then put that number as the expor

8. Write as a power of 2. Explain your method.

a) $4 = 2^2$ b) $16 = 2^4$ c) $64 = 2^6$ d) $256 = 2^8$ e) $32 = 2^5$ f) $2 = 2^1$
I multiplied 2 by itself until I got the given number. In each case, the exponent represents th number of 2s that were multiplied.

9. What patterns do you see in the pairs of numbers? Which is the greater number in each pair? Explain how you know.

a) 2^3 or 3^2 $<$ b) 2^5 or 5^2 $>$ c) 3^4 or 4^3 $>$ d) 5^4 or 4^5 $<$

10. Write these numbers in order from least to greatest: $3^5, 5^2, 3^4, 6^3$. How did you do this? $5^2, 3^4, 6^3, 3^5$

11. Simplify.

a) 3^{12} 531 441 b) 7^3 343 c) 5^6 15 625 d) 4^8 65 536 e) 9^8 43 046 721 f) 2^{23} 8 388 608

12. Assessment Focus

a) Express each number in exponent form in as many different ways as you can.
i) 16 ii) 81 iii) 64
b) Find other numbers that can be written in exponent form, in more than one way. Show your work.

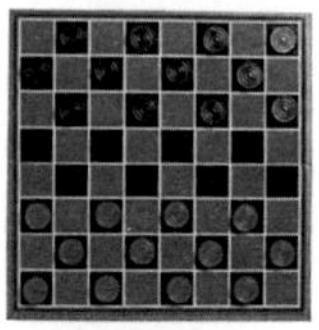

13. Write in exponent form:

a) the number of small squares on a checkerboard 2^6, 4^3, or 8^2
b) the area of a square with side length 5 units 5^2 square units
c) the volume of a cube with edge length 9 units 9^3 cubic units

Reflect

When you see a number, how can you find out if it is a perfect square, or a perfect cube, or neither? Give examples.

26 UNIT 1: Patterns in Whole Numbers

ASSESSMENT FOR LEARNING

What to Look For	What to Do
Understanding concepts ✔ Students understand that exponents can be used to represent repeated multiplication.	***Extra Support:*** Students who have difficulty simplifying numbers in exponent form should write the numbers in expanded form first; for example, $2^3 = 2 \times 2 \times 2$. Students can use Step-by-Step 4 (Master 1.12) to complete question 12.
Applying procedures ✔ Students can write a number in standard form, in expanded form, and in exponent form.	***Extra Practice:*** Have students write the numbers in *Practice* questions 1, 2, and 11 in expanded and standard form. Students can complete Extra Practice 4 (Master 1.20). Students can play the Additional Activity *Squares and Cubes* (Master 1.7).
Communicating ✔ Students can explain how to find out if a number is a perfect square, a perfect cube, or neither.	

Recording and Reporting
Master 1.2 Ongoing Observations: Patterns in Whole Numbers

The World of Work

Hospital Administrator

The administrator of a busy hospital makes hundreds of decisions every day, many of which involve whole number computations and conversions. Should she purchase more 'standard' 24-tray carts for the orderlies to deliver meals to the new 84-bed hospital wing? The administrator calculates she would need four of these carts to take enough meals to the new wing. In the cart supplier's catalogue, there are also 32-tray carts which are more expensive, but priced within budget. Only three of the 32-tray carts would deliver all the meals, and they would cost less than four of the standard carts.

When the orderlies look at the catalogue picture of the 32-tray cart, they tell the administrator that the cart is too low. It is tiring and slower to bend so far down, so they wouldn't use the lowest eight tray bins. So, it's back to the calculator for the administrator. Which cart would *you* choose now? Give reasons for your answer.

Math Link

Your World

Carpet and tile prices are given per square unit. A paint can label tells the area the paint will cover in square units. Wallpaper is sold in rolls with area in square units.

The World of Work: Hospital Administrator 27

Hospital Administrator

Sample Solution

Four 24-tray carts would have $4 \times 24 = 96$ tray spaces, which would be fine as the hospital wing has 84 beds. These carts are easy to use, and they cost less than the 32-tray carts. Three 32-tray carts would have $3 \times 32 = 96$ tray spaces, which would also be fine. However, if the lowest eight tray bins aren't used, only $32 - 8 = 24$ tray spaces would be used on each cart; $24 \times 3 = 72$ tray spaces in total. Three carts would not be enough; they would need four 32-tray carts. Since the same number of each cart would be required, and the 24-tray cart costs less, I would choose the 24-tray cart.

Here are some careers that involve whole number computations.

Software Design Engineer: Part of a software design engineer's job is to simulate what a user might experience when interacting with a program, and to record any unexpected "bugs" or "viruses." With the fear of computer viruses shutting down an entire company or city network, this job is a very important one. He or she would need to be aware of how viruses might grow exponentially within a network.

Marine Researcher: Fish are an important food source. A marine researcher helps fisheries estimate the abundance of specific breeds. They create mathematical formulas based on past fishing activities and numbers of breeds, and use these formulas to predict stock depletion, to protect certain species of fish. A marine researcher needs to be able to see patterns in fish populations over time, and predict fish stocks based on these number patterns.

Carpenter or **Architect:** A carpenter is someone who is skilled in the trade or art of building, finishing, and repairing wooden objects or structures. An architect is a person trained in the science or art of building; someone whose work is designing buildings and supervising their construction. Few occupations use numbers as much as carpenters and architects. They need to measure everything they do. Carpenters have to know how to use fractions easily and determine length, width, height, depth, area, and volume. They must be able to use math to solve problems. Architects need a good knowledge of ratios when doing their initial scale drawings.

Number Patterns

SECTION ORGANIZER

80–100 min

Curriculum Focus: Describe, extend, and explain patterns. (7m71, 7m72, 7m25)

Teacher Materials

Optional

- transparency of Pascal's Triangle

Student Materials

- calculators

Optional

- interlocking cubes
- Step-by-Step 5 (Master 1.13)
- Extra Practice 5 (Master 1.21)

Assessment: Master 1.2 Ongoing Observations: Patterns in Whole Numbers

Key Math Learnings

1. Pascal's Triangle is a number triangle that can be extended by using number patterns.
2. A table can be used to display, identify, and extend a pattern.
3. A pattern rule describes a number pattern and can be used to extend it. The pattern rule for a number pattern may be stated in more than one way.

1.5 Number Patterns

Focus Describe, extend, and explain patterns.

Explore

Work on your own.
Blaise Pascal lived in France in the 17th century.
He was 13 years old when he constructed the triangle below.
This triangle is called Pascal's Triangle.

```
                1                    row 1
              1   1                  row 2
            1   2   1                row 3
          1   3   3   1              row 4
        1   4   6   4   1            row 5
      1   5  10  10   5   1          row 6
```

➢ What patterns do you see in the triangle?
➢ What symmetry do you see in the triangle?

Reflect & Share

Compare your patterns with those of a classmate.
Together, write about three different patterns you see in the triangle.

Connect

Here are some of the patterns in Pascal's Triangle.

➢ Each row begins and ends with 1.
After the second row, each number is the sum of the 2 numbers above it.
To write row 7:
Start with 1.
Add: 1 + 5 = 6
Add: 5 + 10 = 15
Add: 10 + 10 = 20, and so on

```
                                 Sum
            1                     1
          1   1                   2
        1   2   1                 4
      1   3   3   1               8
    1   4   6   4   1            16
  1   5  10  10   5   1          32
1   6  15  20  15   6   1        64
```

➢ The sum of the numbers in each row is shown above, and in the table on the next page.
From the 2nd row on, the sums can be written as powers.

28 UNIT 1: Patterns in Whole Numbers

BEFORE — Get Started

Write the following number patterns on the board:

2, 4, 6, 8, 10, …
5, 15, 35, 65, …
3, 2, 4, 3, 5, 4, 6, …

Ask:

- How would you describe the first pattern? (*Start at 2. Add 2 to get the next number.*)
- How would you describe the second pattern? (*Start at 5. Add 10. Increase the number added by 10 each time.*)
- How would you describe the third pattern? (*Start at 3. Subtract 1 to get the next number. Add 2 to get the next number. Continue to add and subtract in this way.*)
- What are the next 3 terms in each pattern? (*Pattern 1: 12, 14, 16; Pattern 2: 105, 155, 215; Pattern 3: 5, 7, 6*)

Present *Explore.* Tell students they will explore Pascal's Triangle by looking for as many different number patterns as they can.

DURING — Explore

Ongoing Assessment: Observe and Listen

Ask questions, such as:

- What patterns do you see in the triangle? (*If I choose a number on the triangle and subtract the number above it and to the left, the difference is the number above and to the right of the chosen number: 4 – 1 = 3. The number of numbers in a row starts at 1 and increases by 1 each time.*)
- What are some other number patterns in the triangle? (*There are patterns in the diagonals. For the diagonal containing the numbers 1, 2, 3, 4, 5, the pattern rule is: Start at 1. Add 1 each time. For the diagonal containing the numbers 1, 3, 6, 10, the pattern rule is: Start at 1. Add 2. Increase the number added by 1 each time.*)

Row	2	3	4	5	6	7
Sum in standard form	2	4	8	16	32	64
Sum in exponent from	2^1	2^2	2^3	2^4	2^5	2^6

We can use this table to predict the sum of the numbers in any row. All sums are powers of 2.
The exponent is 1 less than the row number.
So, the 10th row has sum: $2^9 = 512$
And the 19th row has sum: $2^{18} = 262\ 144$

➢ The 3rd numbers in each row have this pattern: 1, 3, 6, 10, 15, ...
To get each term in the pattern, we add 1 more than we added before. We can use this to extend the pattern.
The 5th term: 15
The 6th term: 15 + 6 = 21
The 7th term: 21 + 7 = 28, and so on

Example

Describe each pattern in words. Write the next 3 terms.

a) 4, 9, 14, 19, … b) 1, 3, 9, 27, … c) 1, 3, 7, 13, 21, …

Solution

a) 4, 9, 14, 19, …
Start at 4.
Add 5 to get the next number.
The next 3 terms are 24, 29, 34.

b) 1, 3, 9, 27, …
Start at 1.
Multiply by 3 to get the next number.
The next 3 terms are 81, 243, 729.

c) 1, 3, 7, 13, 21, …
Start at 1.
Add 2.
Increase the number added by 2 each time.
The next 3 terms are 31, 43, 57.

1.5 Number Patterns 29

REACHING ALL LEARNERS

Early Finishers

Have students describe each pattern in *Practice* questions 1 and 2 in words.

Common Misconceptions

➤ Students forget to include the start number when describing a pattern.

How to Help: Remind students that the start number is very important. Demonstrate this using the pattern rule: Add 2. Increase the number added by 1 each time. If I start at 1, the pattern is: 1, 3, 6, 10, … If I start at 2, the pattern is: 2, 4, 7, 11, … The patterns are different.

➤ Students do not include enough terms in their number patterns.

How to Help: Show students the number pattern 2, 4, … Tell students the pattern could be extended using the pattern rule: Start at 2. Add 2 to get the next number: 2, 4, 6, 8, 10, … The pattern could also be extended using the pattern rule: Start at 2. Multiply by 2 to get the next number: 2, 4, 8, 16, 32, … The pattern could also be extended using the pattern rule: Start at 2. Add 2. Increase the number added by 1 each time: 2, 4, 7, 11, 16, … Tell students they should include enough numbers (usually 4 or more) in a pattern so the pattern is clear and cannot be misinterpreted.

ESL Strategies

Provide students for whom English is a second language with copies of Pascal's Triangle so they can use coloured lines or symbols to indicate the patterns. Describing the patterns in words may be difficult for them.

- What symmetry do you see in the triangle? *(The triangle has line symmetry about a vertical line drawn through the numbers 1, 2, 6, …)*

Show students a transparency of Pascal's Triangle. Draw a line through the numbers 1, 2, and 6. Fold the triangle along the line. Show students how matching numbers coincide. Ensure students understand that if we ignore the orientation of the numbers, this is an example of line symmetry.

AFTER Connect

Review *Connect.* Explain to students that patterns can often be described in more than one way. Look at the pattern for the sum of the numbers in each row. The pattern could be written as: Start at 2. Multiply by 2 to get the next number. The pattern could also be written as: Start at 2^1. Increase the exponent by 1 each time.

Practice

Have interlocking cubes available for question 7 and calculators for question 8.

Assessment Focus: Question 8

Students should find a repeating pattern with core 2, 4, 8, 6 for the units digits. They can either extend the pattern for a total of 40 terms, or use logical reasoning and relate 40 as a multiple of 4 to the units digit being the 4th digit in the core.

Sample Answers

3. a) Start at 200. Subtract 1. Add 2. Increase the number you add or subtract by 1 each time. 202, 197, 203
   b) Start at 4. Add 3. Increase the number you add by 2 each time. 28, 39, 52
   c) Start at 100. Subtract 1. Increase the number you subtract by 1 each time. 90, 85, 79
   d) Start at 2. Add 4. Increase the number you add by 2 each time. 30, 42, 56
   e) Start at 50. Subtract 2. Increase the number you subtract by 2 each time. 30, 20, 8
   f) Start at 2. Multiply by 3 to get the next number. 162, 486, 1458
4. 2, 4, 12, 48, ... Start at 2. Multiply by 2. Increase the number you multiply by, by 1 each time. 240, 1440, 10 080
5. a),b),c)

Row	Next 6 Terms
1	109 989, 1 099 989, 10 999 989, 109 999 989, 1 099 999 989, 10 999 999 989
2	219 978, 2 199 978, 21 999 978, 219 999 978, 2 199 999 978, 21 999 999 978
3	329 967, 3 299 967, 32 999 967, 329 999 967, 3 299 999 967, 32 999 999 967
Column	
1	4356, 5445, 6534, 7623, 8712, 9801
2	43956, 54945, 65934, 76923, 87912, 98901

My predictions were correct.

(Answers continue below.)

Practice

1. Write the next 3 terms in each pattern.
   a) 7, 9, 11, 13, ... 15, 17, 19
   b) 1, 5, 25, 125, ... 625, 3125, 15 625
   c) 4, 7, 10, 13, ... 16, 19, 22
   d) 1, 10, 100, 1000, ...
   e) 20, 19, 18, 17, ... 16, 15, 14
   f) 79, 77, 75, 73, ... 71, 69, 67

   1. d) 10 000, 100 000, 1 000 000
2. Write the next 3 terms in each pattern.
   a) 3, 4, 6, 9, ... 13, 18, 24
   b) 1, 4, 9, 16, ... 25, 36, 49
   c) 101, 111, 121, 131, ... 141, 151, 161
   d) 1, 12, 123, 1234, ...
   e) 1, 4, 16, 64, ... 256, 1024, 4096
   f) 256, 128, 64, 32, ... 16, 8, 4

   2. d) 12 345, 123 456, 1 234 567
3. Describe each pattern in words.
   Write the next 3 terms.
   a) 200, 199, 201, 198, ... 202, 197, 203
   b) 4, 7, 12, 19, ... 28, 39, 52
   c) 100, 99, 97, 94, ... 90, 85, 79
   d) 2, 6, 12, 20, ... 30, 42, 56
   e) 50, 48, 44, 38, ... 30, 20, 8
   f) 2, 6, 18, 54, ... 162, 486, 1458
4. Create your own number pattern. Trade patterns with a classmate. Describe your classmate's pattern. Write the next 3 terms.
5. a) Copy this pattern. Find each product.

$99 \times 11 = \square$	$99 \times 111 = \square$	...
$99 \times 22 = \square$	$99 \times 222 = \square$	...
$99 \times 33 = \square$	$99 \times 333 = \square$	...
⋮	⋮	

   b) Extend this pattern sideways and down. Predict the next 6 terms in each row and column.
   c) Check your predictions with a calculator.

Number Strategies

One can of pop contains 355 mL. About how many 2-L pop bottles can be filled with one case of 24 cans of pop?
About 4 bottles

6. This pattern shows the first 3 triangular numbers.

   a) Draw the next 3 terms in the pattern.
   b) List the first 6 triangular numbers. 1, 3, 6, 10, 15, 21
   c) Find the next 2 triangular numbers without drawing pictures. Explain how you did this. 28 and 36

30 UNIT 1: Patterns in Whole Numbers

(Sample Answers, continued)

6. a)

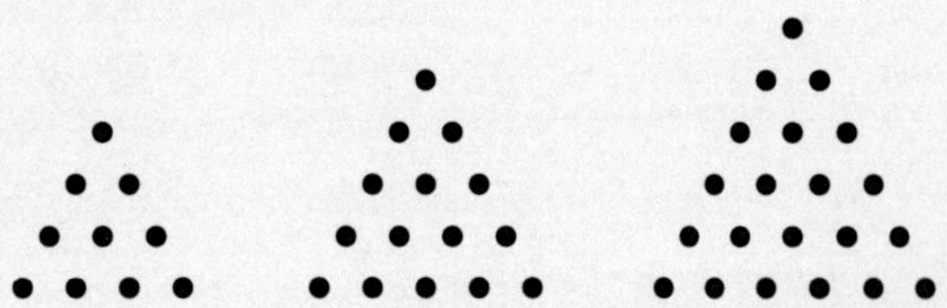

10 15 21

   c) I used the pattern rule: Start at 1. Add 2. Increase the number added by 1 each time.
8. b) The units digits follow the repeating pattern: 2, 4, 8, 6, 2, 4, 8, 6, ...
   c) Every fourth term has 6 as the units digit. 2^{40} is the fortieth term, and 40 is divisible by 4. Therefore, 2^{40} will have 6 as its unit digit.
   d) The first 10 powers of 3: 3, 9, 27, 81, 243, 729, 2187, 6561, 19 683, 59 049. The units digits follow the repeating pattern: 3, 9, 7, 1, 3, 9, 7, 1, ... Every fourth term has 1 as the units digit. 3^{63} is the sixty-third term, and 63 is 1 less than 64, which is divisible by 4. Therefore, 3^{63} will have 7 as its unit digit (the same units digit as the 3rd term).

REFLECT: Three different types of patterns:
1, 4, 7, 10, 13, ... The pattern is: Start at 1. Add 3 to get the next number. To predict the next term, I added 3 to the last given term to get 16.
1, 4, 9, 16, ... The pattern is: Start at 1. Add 3. Increase the number you add by 2 each time. To predict the next term, I saw that 7 was added to get 16, so I added 7 + 2, or 9 to get 25.
20, 19, 18, 17, ... The pattern is: Start at 20. Subtract 1 to get the next number. To predict the next term, I subtracted 1 from the last given term to get 16.

d) Add consecutive triangular numbers;
that is, Term 1 + Term 2; Term 2 + Term 3; and so on.
What pattern do you see? 4, 9, 16, 25, 36, 49, 64, ...
Write the next 3 terms in this pattern. 81, 100, 121

e) Subtract consecutive triangular numbers;
that is, Term 2 − Term 1; Term 3 − Term 2; and so on.
What pattern do you see? 2, 3, 4, 5, 6, 7, 8, ...
Write the next 3 terms in this pattern. 9, 10, 11.

7. This pattern shows the first 3 cube numbers.

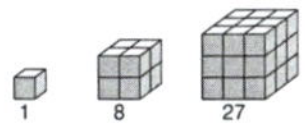

a) Sketch the next 3 cube numbers in the pattern.
Use interlocking cubes if they help. 64, 125, 216

b) Write the next 3 cube numbers without drawing pictures.
Explain how you did this. 343, 512, 729

8. **Assessment Focus**

a) Write the first 10 powers of 2; that is, 2^1 to 2^{10}, in standard form. 2, 4, 8, 16, 32, 64, 128, 256, 512, 1024

b) What pattern do you see in the units digits?

c) How can you use this pattern to find the units digit of 2^{40}?

d) Investigate powers of other numbers.
Look for patterns in the units digits.
Explain how you can use these patterns to find units digits for powers too large to display on the calculator.

Take It Further

9. Some sequences of numbers may represent different patterns.
Extend each pattern in as many different ways as you can.
Write the pattern rule for each pattern.

a) 1, 2, 4, ... 7, 11, 16, ...
b) 1, 4, 9, ... 12, 17, 20 ...
c) 5, 25, ... 55, 95, 145, ...

Reflect

Choose 3 different types of patterns from this section.
Describe each pattern.
Explain how you can use the pattern to predict the next term.

1.5 Number Patterns 31

Number Strategies

Students could multiply 355 × 24 to find the total number of millilitres in one case of pop. They could convert this amount to litres, then divide by 2 to get the number of 2-L bottles that can be filled with one case of pop. Students should recognize that the question asks "About," and therefore an exact answer is not required.

Assignment Guidelines

If your students do not have time to complete all the *Practice* questions on pages 30 and 31, these questions provide minimum curriculum coverage: 1, 3, 4, 6, 8, *Reflect*

To assess the 4 Achievement Chart categories listed in the curriculum document, have students complete these *Practice* questions:

Understanding Concepts: 3
Communication: 4
Application: 5
Problem Solving: 8

ASSESSMENT FOR LEARNING

What to Look For

Understanding concepts

✔ Students understand that Pascal's Triangle can be reproduced using number patterns.

Applying procedures

✔ Students can display, identify, and extend a pattern.
✔ Students can use a pattern rule to make predictions.

Communicating

✔ Students can describe a number pattern in more than one way.

What to Do

Extra Support: Students may benefit from using counters or isometric grid paper to model and draw the patterns of triangular numbers in *Practice*, question 6.
Students can use Step-by-Step 5 (Master 1.13) to complete question 8.

Extra Practice: Students can play the Additional Activity *Pattern Power* (Master 1.8).
Students can complete Extra Practice 5 (Master 1.21).

Extension: Have students write pattern rules for the patterns of triangular and cube numbers in questions 6 and 7.

Recording and Reporting
Master 1.2 Ongoing Observations: Patterns in Whole Numbers

Using Different Strategies

SECTION ORGANIZER

Vocabulary: line segment, reasoning

Strategies to Consider

- Make a table.
- Use a model.
- Draw a diagram.
- Solve a simpler problem.
- Work backward.
- Guess and check.
- Make an organized list.
- Use a pattern.
- Draw a graph.
- Use logical reasoning.

Using Different Strategies

Problem

There are 8 people at a party.
Each person shakes hands with everyone else.
How many handshakes are there?

Think of a strategy

Strategy 1: **Draw a diagram and count.**

Draw 8 dots. Join every dot to every other dot.
Count the line segments.

Number of line segments
$= 8 + 5 + 5 + 4 + 3 + 2 + 1$
$= 28$

There are 28 handshakes.

Strategy 2: **Solve simpler problems, then look for a pattern.**

2 people 1 handshake | 3 people 3 handshakes | 4 people 6 handshakes | 5 people 10 handshakes

Make a table.
Each time you add a person, you add one more handshake than the time before.
So, 6 people: 10 + 5, or 15 handshakes
7 people: 15 + 6, or 21 handshakes
8 people: 21 + 7, or 28 handshakes

Number of People	Number of Handshakes	
2	1	
3	3	+2
4	6	+3
5	10	+4

32 UNIT 1: Patterns in Whole Numbers

Using different strategies helps to double check or confirm reasonableness and accuracy of solutions. It also shows flexibility and understanding of the problem and the mathematics involved. It may reveal more than one answer.

BEFORE

- Remind students of the problem solving strategies to consider. It is useful to have these posted.
- Without student books open, demonstrate the problem with student volunteers.
- Briefly introduce each strategy, one at a time. Allow students to finish the strategy and compare answers.
- Discuss the level of confidence in the answer each time. (*Each new strategy yields the same answer, increasing confidence in the accuracy and reasonableness of the solution*). To make this point more obvious, begin with strategy 3, then 2 and finally 1, moving from higher levels of abstraction to levels closer to the actual event. They may even do the actual handshakes to confirm their solutions.
- Show the student page to compare their strategies with those in the text.
- Read *Look Back* together and discuss.
- Introduce the *Problems.*

DURING

- As the purpose is to experiment with different strategies, allow students to work in pairs or small groups to stimulate different approaches, and discuss the reasonableness of strategies and solutions.
- Circulate and monitor the work, redirecting solutions when necessary by questioning. It is acceptable to have incorrect solutions at this point. When solutions are shared, inaccuracies will become apparent to the students.

Reading and Writing in Math

Strategy 3: **Use reasoning.**

Each of 8 people shakes hands with 7 other people.
That is, 8×7, or 56 handshakes
But we have counted each handshake twice.
We have said that A shaking hands with B is different from B shaking hands with A.
So, we divide by 2: $\frac{56}{2} = 28$
There are 28 handshakes.

Look back

- Look at the numbers of handshakes for 2 to 8 people. Where have you seen this pattern before?
- What if there were 9 people at the party? How many handshakes would there be? How do you know?

Problems

Solve each problem. Try to use more than one strategy.

1. A ball is dropped from a height of 16 m. Each time it hits the ground, the ball bounces to one-half its previous height. The ball is caught when its greatest height for that bounce is 1 m. How far has the ball travelled?
2. A rectangular garden is 100 m long and 44 m wide. A fence encloses the garden. The fence posts are 2 m apart. How many posts are needed?
3. Here is a 5 by 5 square. How many squares of each different size can you find in this large square?

Reflect

Why might you want to solve a problem more than one way?

Reading and Writing in Math: Using Different Strategies 33

Sample Solutions

1. Draw a diagram and add the lengths of the segments.
   $16 + 8 + 8 + 4 + 4 + 2 + 2 + 1 = 45$
   Make a table.

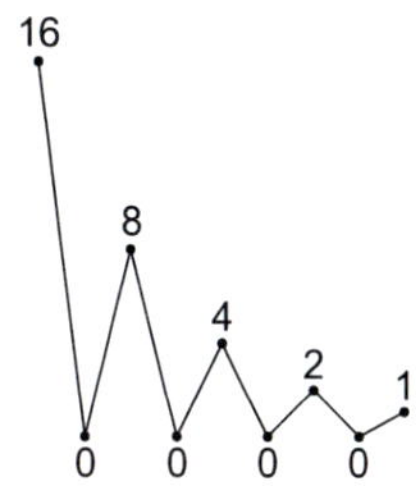

Down	Up
16	8
8	4
4	2
2	1

Bounce	Down	Up	Total
1	16	8	24
2	8	4	12
3	4	2	6
4	2	1	3

Add distances down and up. $30 + 15 = 45$
or total for each bounce $24 + 12 + 6 + 3 = 45$
The ball travelled 45 m.

2. Solve simpler problems, then look for a pattern.

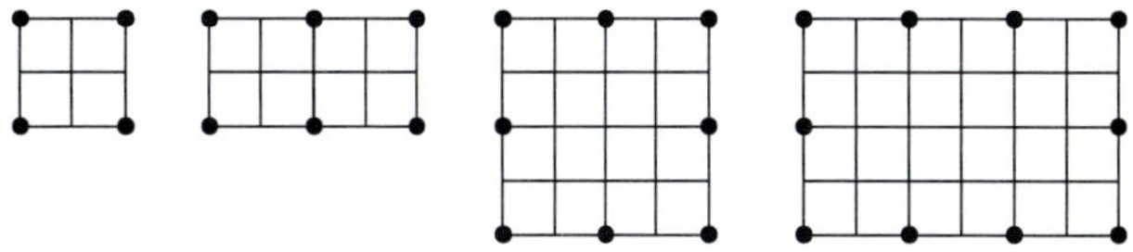

(Solutions continue below)

- Highlight new and different strategies as they arise. At different times, suggest that students circulate to different groups to pick up new ideas, or to confirm the direction they are headed.

AFTER

- Share strategies and answers for each problem.
- When groups or individuals have different answers, this is a perfect opportunity for them to justify their solution, analyse the reasonableness, and finally to reach consensus with a high degree of confidence. Some will have different but correct answers, the difference being from the interpretation of the problem (see problem 1).

(Sample Solutions, continued.)

Dimensions	2×2	4×2	4×4	6×4	8×12
Perimeter	8	12	16	20	40
Posts	4	6	8	10	20

Number of posts = perimeter ÷ 2
Perimeter of 100 m × 44 m garden is $2(100) + 2(44) = 288$
Number of posts = $288 \div 2 = 144$
Alternatively, the number of posts is equal to the sum of the length and width, $100 + 44 = 144$
Use Reasoning.
One side is 100 m with a post every 2 m starting at the corner. That is $100 \div 2$, or 50 posts. The opposite side is the same. $50 + 50 = 100$ posts
There are two sides of 44 m with a post at every 2 m, or $44 \div 2 = 22$ each side. Two sides = 44 posts
100 posts + 44 posts = 144 posts

3. Make an organized list.
   1×1 squares = 25
   2×2 squares = 16
   3×3 squares = 9
   4×4 squares = 4
   5×5 squares = 1
   Total $25 + 16 + 9 + 4 + 1 = 55$

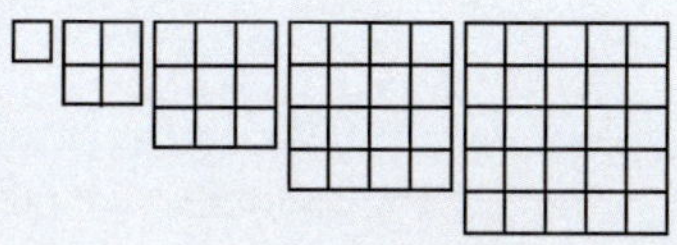

SECTION ORGANIZER

Student Materials
- Venn diagrams (PM 28)
- 1-cm grid paper (PM 20)
- calculators

Optional
- 5-column charts (PM 29)
- 0.5-cm grid paper (PM 14)
- hundred charts (PM 13)

Assessment:
Masters 1.1 Unit Rubric: Patterns in Whole Numbers, 1.4 Unit Summary: Patterns in Whole Numbers

Correlation of Extra Practice questions on page 438:

Section	Questions
1.1	1, 2, 3, 4, 5
1.2	6, 7, 8, 10
1.3	9, 11
1.4	12, 13, 14, 15
1.5	15, 16, 17

Unit Review

Review any lesson with etext online tutorial

What Do I Need to Know?

✓ A *factor* of a number divides into the number exactly; that is, there is no remainder.
For example, $6 \div 2 = 3$, so 2 is a factor of 6.

✓ A *prime number* has only 2 factors, itself and 1.
For example, the only factors of 17 are 17 and 1, so 17 is a prime number.

✓ A *composite number* has more than 2 factors.
For example, 12 has factors 1, 2, 3, 4, 6, and 12, so 12 is a composite number.

✓ A *square number*, or *perfect square*, has an odd number of factors.
It can also written as a power with exponent 2.
For example, the factors of 9 are 1, 3, and 9, so 9 is a perfect square.
We write $9 = 3^2$.

✓ A *square root* of a number is a factor that is squared to get the number.
For example, 9 is a square root of 81 because $9^2 = 81$.
We write $\sqrt{81} = 9$.

✓ When a number is written in *exponent form*, it is written as a *power*.
For example, for the power 5^3:
5 is the *base*.
3 is the *exponent*.
$5 \times 5 \times 5$ is the *expanded form*.
125 is the *standard form*.

✓ A *cube number*, or *perfect cube*, is a power with exponent 3.
For example, $1^3 = 1$, $2^3 = 8$, $3^3 = 27$, $4^3 = 64$,
so 1, 8, 27, and 64 are perfect cubes.

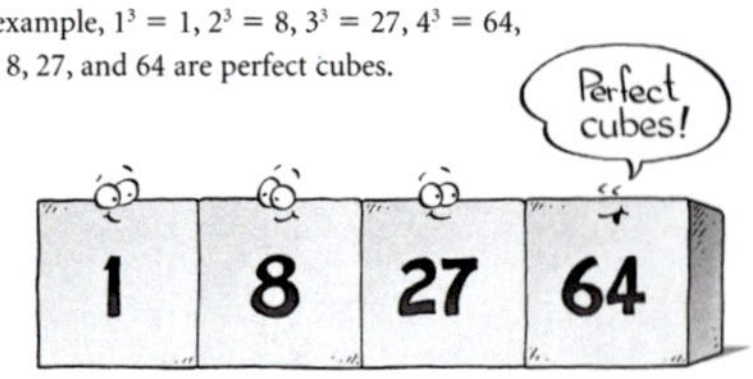

34 UNIT 1: Patterns in Whole Numbers

Sample Solutions

2. b) How many more points did Karl Malone score than Wilt Chamberlain? (*Answer: 1500*)
I used mental math because the numbers are easy to subtract. 32 919 − 31 419 = 1500

3. a) For example: 99 + 100 + 101 = 300,
58 + 59 + 60 + 61 + 62 = 300,
13 + 14 + 15 + 16 + 17 + 18 + 19 + 20 + 21 + 22 + 23 + 24 + 25 + 26 + 27 = 300

b) The number of terms is equal to 300 divided by the middle number; for example,
$300 \div 60 = 5$: 5 terms are added.
The sum of the first and last number is double the middle number; for example,
13 + 27 = 40; $20 \times 2 = 40$.
The sums of pairs of numbers that are equal distances from the middle number are double the middle number; for example, 59 + 61 = 120; $60 \times 2 = 120$.

c) Yes, unless the 3-digit number is a prime number, such as 101.
For example, 138 = 45 + 46 + 47
$138 \div 46 = 3$; 3 terms are added.
45 + 47 = 92; $46 \times 2 = 92$

4. a) 45 min; I assumed that Armin continued to walk at the same rate and that he did not make any stops.

b) $220; I assumed there were 4 weekends in a month and that Tana continued to baby-sit the same amount of time, and for the same rate. If there were 5 weekends in the month, Tana would make $275.

8.

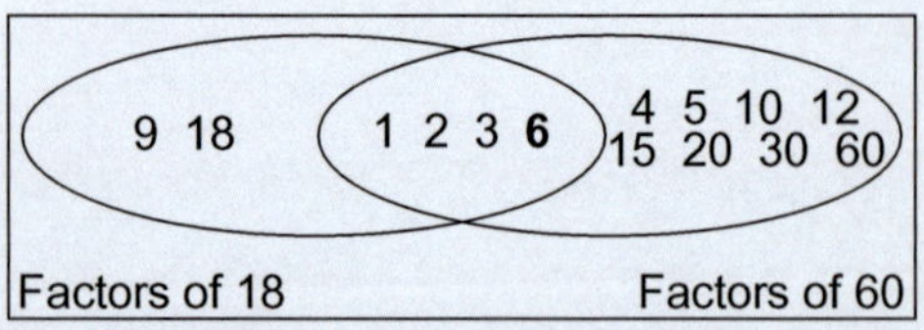

9. One, the number 2; a prime number has only 2 factors, itself and 1.
The factors of 2 are 1 and 2. Any other even number would have more than 2 factors, and would not be a prime number.

13. The side length of a square with area 81 m^2 is $\sqrt{81}$ m = 9 m.
The perimeter is the distance around the square:
9 m + 9 m + 9 m + 9 m = 36 m

What Should I Be Able to Do?

For extra practice, go to page 438.

1. Find each answer. Use pencil and paper.
   a) 3621 + 8921 = 12 542
   b) 5123 − 4123 = 1000
   c) 35 × 12 = 420
   d) 125 × 27 = 3375
   e) 815 + 642 − 85 = 1372
   f) 1638 ÷ 21 = 78

2. This table shows the highest all-time scorers at the end of the 2000–2001 NBA season.

Kareem Abdul-Jabbar	38 387
Karl Malone	32 919
Wilt Chamberlain	31 419
Michael Jordan	29 277

   a) What is the total number of points? 132 002 points
   b) Write a problem about these data. Solve your problem. Justify the strategy you used.

3. a) Write the number 300 as the sum of 2 or more consecutive whole numbers. Find as many ways to do this as you can.
   b) What patterns do you see in the numbers added?
   c) Suppose you started with another 3-digit number. Will you see similar patterns? Investigate to find out.

4. Solve each problem. State any assumption you made.
   a) Armin's house is 3 km from a mall. He walks 1 km in 15 min. How long does it take Armin to walk to the mall? 45 min
   b) Tana makes \$15, \$21, and \$19 for baby-sitting one weekend. How much will Tana make in a month? \$220

5. The table shows the ticket prices and number of tickets sold for a popular movie.

	Ticket Price (\$)	Number of Tickets Sold
Adults	12	125
Seniors	10	34
Youths	8	61

   Calculate the total cost of the ticket sales. \$2328

1.2 6. Find all the factors of each number.
   a) 36 b) 50 c) 75 d) 77
   1, 2, 3, 4, 6, 9, 12, 18, 36
   1, 2, 5, 10, 25, 50
   1, 3, 5, 15, 25, 75
   1, 7, 11, 77

7. Find the first 10 multiples of each number.
   a) 9 b) 7 c) 12 d) 15
   9, 18, 27, 36, 45, 54, 63, 72, 81, 90
   7, 14, 21, 28, 35, 42, 49, 56, 63, 70
   12, 24, 36, 48, 60, 72, 84, 96, 108, 120
   15, 30, 45, 60, 75, 90, 105, 120, 135, 150

8. For the numbers 18 and 60, find:
   a) the GCF 6 b) the LCM 180
   Draw a Venn diagram to illustrate part a.

Unit Review 35

YOUR NOTES

14. The area of the grill is 40 cm × 40 cm = 1600 cm^2.
The area of a hamburger is 8 cm × 8 cm = 64 cm^2.
To find how many hamburgers can be grilled at one time, I divide 1600 ÷ 64 = 25.
Because the side length of a hamburger divides exactly into the side length of the grill (40 ÷ 8 = 5), my answer seems reasonable.

15.

	Exponent Form	Base	Exponent	Expanded Form	Standard Form
a)	3^4	3	4	3 × 3 × 3 × 3	81
b)	2^5	2	5	2 × 2 × 2 × 2 × 2	32
c)	10^7	10	7	10 × 10 × 10 × 10 × 10 × 10 × 10	10 000 000
d)	5^4	5	4	5 × 5 × 5 × 5	625
e)	4^4	4	4	4 × 4 × 4 × 4	256

18. b) i) Start at 3. Add 2. Add 1. Continue to alternate the number added.
ii) Start at 1. Multiply by 2 to get the next number.
iii) Start at 1. Add 3. Increase the number you add by 2 each time.
iv) Start at 3. Add 1. Increase the number you add by 1 each time.

19. c) The pattern is the sums of consecutive square numbers. The sums can be found two ways: by adding consecutive square numbers or by using this pattern rule: Start at 5. Add 8. Increase the number you add by 4 each time.

20. a) $1^2 + 2^2 + 3^2 + 4^2 + 5^2 = 55$
$1^2 + 2^2 + 3^2 + 4^2 + 5^2 + 6^2 = 91$
b) The pattern is the sums of consecutive square numbers; each new sum is found by adding the next square number. A pattern rule is: Start at 1. Add 2^2. Add 3^2. Continue to increase the number squared by 1 each time.

YOUR NOTES

LESSON

9. How many prime numbers are even? One: 2
Justify your answer.

1.3 **10.** Find a square root of each number.
a) 121 11 b) 169 13 c) 225 15

11. Find each square root. Draw a picture if it helps.
a) $\sqrt{25}$ 5 b) $\sqrt{100}$ 10 c) $\sqrt{81}$ 9

12. Calculate the area of a square with each side length.
a) 7 cm $49\ cm^2$ b) 17 cm $289\ cm^2$ c) 93 m $8649\ m^2$

13. The area of a square is $81\ m^2$. What is the perimeter of the square? How do you know? 36 m

14. Raquel cooks 8-cm square hamburgers on a grill. The grill is a rectangle with dimensions 40 cm by 40 cm. How many hamburgers can be grilled at one time? 25 hamburgers
Justify your answer.

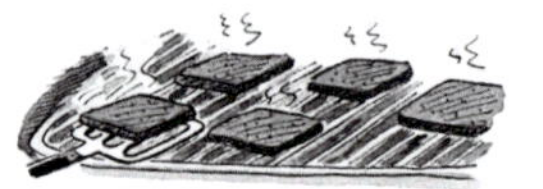

1.4 **15.** Copy and complete this table.

	Exponent Form	Base	Exponent	Expanded Form	Standard Form
a)	3^4				
b)	2^5				
c)	10^7				
d)		5	4		
e)				4×4×4×4	

1.5 **16.** A perfume formula requires 4 g of an essential oil per bottle.
a) How many grams are needed for 2500 bottles? 10 000 g
b) Write this number in exponent form. 10^4 g

17. Write these numbers in order from greatest to least.
$3^4, 4^4, 5^3, 2^6$ $4^4, 5^3, 3^4, 2^6$

18. a) Write the next 3 terms in each pattern.
i) 3, 5, 6, 8, 9, … 11, 12, 14
ii) 1, 2, 4, 8, … 16, 32, 64
iii) 1, 4, 9, 16, … 25, 36, 49
iv) 3, 4, 6, 9, … 13, 18, 24
b) Describe each pattern in part a.

19. a) Copy and complete this pattern.
$1^2 + 2^2 = \square$ 5
$2^2 + 3^2 = \square$ 13
$3^2 + 4^2 = \square$ 25
$4^2 + 5^2 = \square$ 41
b) Write the next two rows in the pattern. $5^2 + 6^2 = 61$
c) Describe the pattern. $6^2 + 7^2 = 85$

20. $1^2 = 1$
$1^2 + 2^2 = 5$
$1^2 + 2^2 + 3^2 = 14$
$1^2 + 2^2 + 3^2 + 4^2 = 30$
a) Write the next two lines in the pattern.
b) What pattern do you see?

36 UNIT 1: Patterns in Whole Numbers

ASSESSMENT FOR LEARNING

What to Look For

Understanding concepts

✔ **Questions 6 and 7:** Student can generate factors and multiples of given numbers.
✔ **Questions 10, 11, and 12:** Student can find the squares and square roots of whole numbers.
✔ **Question 17:** Student understands that exponents are used to represent repeated multiplication.

Applying procedures

✔ **Question 8:** Student understands how to find the greatest common factor and the lowest common multiple for a pair of numbers.
✔ **Question 4:** Student can use factors to solve a problem.

Communicating

✔ **Question 2:** Student can justify the choice of strategy when solving a problem.

Problem solving

✔ **Question 13:** Student can use patterns to solve a problem.

Recording and Reporting

Master 1.1 Unit Rubric: Patterns in Whole Numbers
Master 1.4 Unit Summary: Patterns in Whole Numbers

Practice Test

1. Estimate. Describe your strategy.
   a) 624 + 1353 About 1970 b) 897 ÷ 23 About 45 c) 752 × 36 About 30 000
2. Use mental math to evaluate 2 × 395 × 5. Explain your strategy. 3950
3. Use a Venn diagram to show the factors of 48 and 18. Circle the GCF.

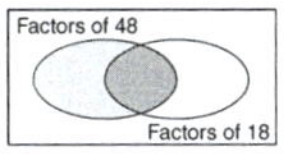

4. Use patterns to find the first 6 common multiples of 15 and 6.
5. Use the clues below to find the mystery number. Explain your strategy and reasoning. 78
   Clue 1: I am a 2-digit number.
   Clue 2: I am less than 9^2.
   Clue 3: I have 26 and 6 as factors.
6. Sharma plays basketball every third day of the month. She baby-sits her little brother every seventh day of the month. How many times in a month will Sharma have a conflict between basketball and baby-sitting? Explain your thinking. Once a month, on the 21st day
7. Write these numbers in order from least to greatest.
   a) $5^2, 2^5, \sqrt{25}, 10^2, 3^3$ $\sqrt{25}, 5^2, 3^3, 2^5, 10^2$
   b) $10 \times 10 \times 10, 2^3, \sqrt{400}, 3^2, 17$ $2^3, 3^2, 17, \sqrt{400}, 10 \times 10 \times 10$
8. The perimeter of a square is 32 cm. What is the area of the square? Explain your thinking. Include a diagram. 64 cm^2
9. Write the next 3 terms in each pattern. Describe each pattern.
   a) 1, 3, 6, 10, … 15, 21, 28 b) 23, 25, 27, … 29, 31, 33 c) 100, 81, 64, 49, … 36, 25, 16
10. Write the number 35 as:
   a) the sum of 3 squares $1^2 + 3^2 + 5^2 = 35$
   b) the difference between 2 squares $6^2 - 1^2 = 35$
   c) the sum of a prime number and a square $19 + 4^2 = 35$

Practice Test 37

SECTION ORGANIZER

Student Materials
- Venn diagrams (PM 28)
- 1-cm grid paper (PM 20)

Assessment:
Master 1.1 Unit Rubric: Patterns in Whole Numbers

Assignment Guidelines

To assess the 4 Achievement Chart categories listed in the curriculum document, use these test questions:
Communication: 1
Understanding Concepts: 3
Application: 5
Problem Solving: 6

Sample Solutions

1. a) I rounded each number to the nearest ten.
   b) I rounded each number to the nearest ten.
   c) I rounded each number to the nearest ten.
2. I first multiplied 2 × 5 to get 10, then multiplied 395 by 10.
3.

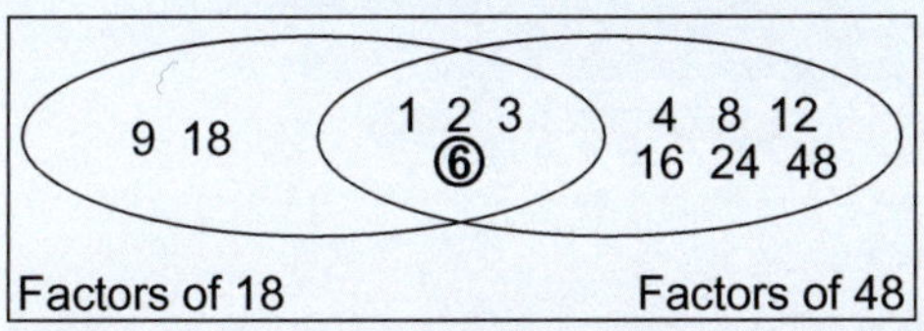

4. Multiples of 6: 6, 12, 18, 24, **30**, 36, 42, 48, 54, **60**, …
   Multiples of 15: 15, **30**, 45, **60**, 75, …
   The common multiples of 15 and 6 are the multiples of 30.
   The first 6 common multiples are: 30, 60, 90, 120, 150, 180
5. I found the 2-digit multiples of 6: 12, 18, 24, 30, 36, 42, 48, 54, 60, 66, 72, **78**, 84, 90, 96
   I found the 2-digit multiples of 26: 26, 52, **78**
   The number is less than 9^2, or 81.
   The number must be 78.
6. Days Sharma plays basketball: 3, 6, 9, 12, 15, 18, **21**, 24, 27, 30
   Days Sharma baby-sits: 7, 14, **21**, 28
   Sharma will have a conflict between basketball and baby-sitting once a month, on the 21st day.
8. The perimeter is the distance around the outside of the square. A square has 4 sides of equal length, so the side length of the square is 32 cm ÷ 4 = 8 cm.
   The area of a square is the square of its side length = 8 cm × 8 cm = 64 cm^2.

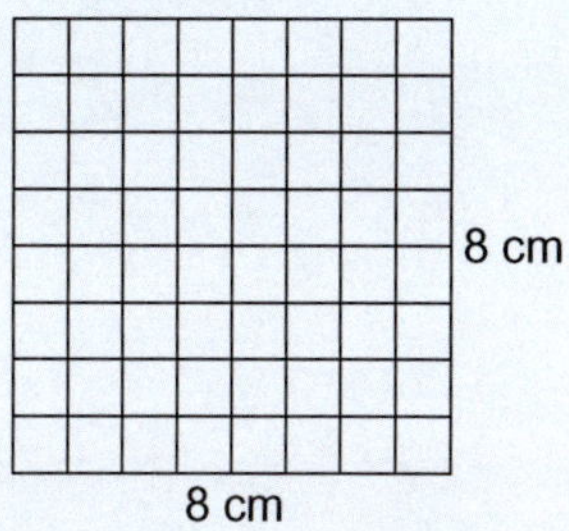

9. a) Start at 1. Add 2. Increase the number you add by 1 each time.
   b) Start at 23. Add 2 to get the next number.
   c) Start at 100. Subtract 19. Decrease the number you subtract by 2 each time. Alternatively, start at 100. Write the square numbers less than 100 in order.

Fibonacci Numbers

SECTION ORGANIZER 80–100 min

Student Grouping: 2–4
Student Materials
- 1-cm grid paper (PM 20)
- poster board
- 3-column charts (PM 18)
- calculators
- pencil crayons
- glue

Assessment:
Masters 1.3 Performance Assessment Rubric: Fibonacci Numbers, 1.4 Unit Summary: Patterns in Whole Numbers

Sample Solutions

1. a)

Beginning of Month	Number of Pairs	Number of Rabbits
6	8	16
7	13	26

b) A term is equal to the sum of the two preceding terms, for example, Term 5 = Term 3 + Term 4 = 2 + 3 = 5
Term 5 is 5.
To find Term 8, I add Term 6 and Term 7.
Term 8 = 8 + 13
= 21

(*Solutions continue, below right.*)

Unit Problem Fibonacci Numbers

One of greatest mathematicians of the Middle Ages was an Italian, Leonardo Fibonacci.

Fibonacci is remembered for this problem:

A pair of rabbits is placed in a large pen.
When the rabbits are two months old, they produce another pair of rabbits.
Every month after that, they produce another pair of rabbits.
Each new pair of rabbits does the same.
None of the rabbits dies.
How many rabbits are there at the beginning of each month?

This table shows the rabbits at the beginning of the first 5 months.

Beginning of Month	Number of Pairs	Number of Rabbits
1	1	
2	1	
3	2	
4	3	
5	5	

1. a) Continue the pattern for two more months.
Use different colours to show the new rabbits.
b) Write the number of pairs of rabbits at the beginning of each month, for the first 7 months.
These are the Fibonacci numbers.
What pattern do you see?
Explain how to find the next number in the pattern.

2. The Fibonacci sequence appears in the family tree of the drone, or male bee.
The drone has a mother, but no father.
Female bees are worker bees or queens.
They have a mother and a father.
The family tree of a male bee back to its grandparents is shown on the next page.

38 UNIT 1: Patterns in Whole Numbers

Remind students that they should use the *Check List* to assess their work before handing it in. You may also wish to provide students with copies of Master 1.3 Performance Assessment Rubric: Fibonacci Numbers so they will know how their work will be assessed.

Before students begin, ask volunteers to explain a growing pattern, a pattern on a grid, squares, and factors. Ensure students know they are to record each pattern they make, find patterns within the Fibonacci sequence, and create a poster to show the results of their exploration of the Fibonacci numbers. Encourage students to use their imagination and research skills when creating their posters.

For more information about Fibonacci numbers, try www.mcs.surrey.ac.uk/Personal/R.Knott/Fibonacci/fibnat.html.

(*Sample Solutions, continued*)

2. b) The Fibonacci numbers are the numbers of bees in each generation going back:
1, 1, 2, 3, 5, 8, 13, 21

3. The first 15 Fibonacci numbers:
1, 1, 2, 3, 5, 8, 13, 21, 34, 55, 89, 144, 233, 377, 610
a) Every third number is an even number.
b) 3 is a factor of every fourth number.
c) 5 is a factor of every fifth number.

4. Sum of the squares of the second and third terms:
$1^2 + 2^2 = 5$
Sum of the squares of the third and forth terms:
$2^2 + 3^2 = 13$
Sum of the squares of the forth and fifth terms:
$3^2 + 5^2 = 34$
I notice that the sums of the squares are also Fibonacci numbers. They are the Fibonacci numbers, starting with the fifth term, 5, and skipping a term each time.
The next two lines of this pattern are:
Sum of the squares of the fifth and sixth terms: $5^2 + 8^2 = 89$
Sum of the squares of the sixth and seventh terms:
$8^2 + 13^2 = 233$

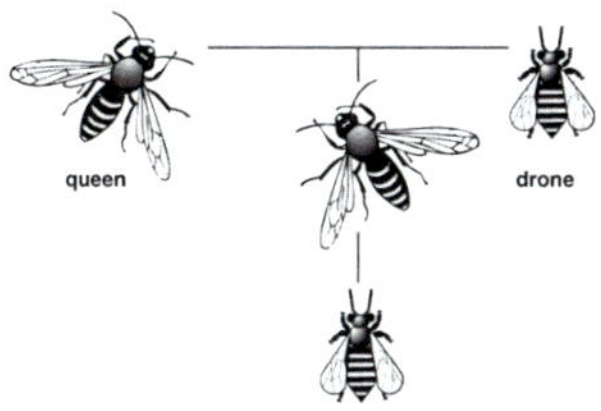

a) Copy the diagram. Trace the male bee's ancestors back 5 more generations.
b) Explain how you can use this pattern to find the Fibonacci numbers.

Check List

Your work should show:

✓ how you used patterns to find your answers
✓ all diagrams and charts, clearly presented
✓ a clear explanation of your results
✓ your understanding of Fibonacci numbers

There are many patterns you can find in the Fibonacci sequence.

3. Write the first 15 Fibonacci numbers.
a) What type of number is every third number? even
b) Which number is a factor of every fourth number? 3
c) Which number is a factor of every fifth number? 5

4. Add the squares of the:
2nd and 3rd terms 5
3rd and 4th terms 13
4th and 5th terms 34
What do you notice?
Write the next two lines of this pattern.

5. Research Fibonacci numbers. Make a poster to show your work.

Reflect on the Unit

What have you learned about whole numbers?
What have you learned about number patterns?
Write about some of the things you have learned.

Unit Problem: Fibonacci Numbers 39

5. Students' posters could include information about how the Fibonacci numbers are found in the family trees of rabbits and bees; in petals on flowers; in pine cones; in seed heads; in leaf arrangements; in the Nautilus sea shell; and on cauliflower, broccoli, bananas, and pineapples. Encourage students to explore these patterns in nature, as they create their posters. For more information about Fibonacci numbers, students could read *Fibonacci Fun: Fascinating Activities with Intriguing Numbers* as referred to in the *Unit Launch*.

REFLECT ON THE UNIT: Whole numbers have factors, and a set of numbers may have common factors. A prime number is a whole number that has only 2 factors. A composite number is a whole number with more than 2 factors. Multiples of whole numbers are found by multiplying the number by 1, by 2, by 3, by 4, and so on. Multiples that are the same for two or more whole numbers are called common multiples. When we multiply a whole number by itself, we square the number. Squaring and taking a square root are inverse operations. When we multiply a whole number by itself three times, we cube the number. Exponents are used to represent the repeated multiplication of whole numbers.
Number patterns are all around us. Number patterns can be described and extended, and can be used to make predictions. Number patterns can even be found in nature, for example in the family tree of bees and rabbits. Pascal's Triangle and the Fibonacci sequence contain many number patterns.

ASSESSMENT FOR LEARNING

What to Look For

Understanding concepts

✔ Students understand that many patterns can be found in the Fibonacci sequence.

Applying procedures

✔ Students can find patterns in the Fibonacci sequence.

Communicating

✔ Students use mathematical language effectively to describe patterns, and to explain how patterns can be extended.

What to Do

Extra Support: Make the problem accessible.
Some students may have difficulty recognizing and extending patterns. These students may benefit from having each part of the *Unit Problem* structured, using tables and manipulatives.

Other students may have difficulty describing their patterns and explaining their research in writing. Assess these students verbally. Are they able to communicate their ideas orally, using appropriate mathematical language?

Some students may have difficulty creating a poster. Brainstorm a list of examples of the Fibonacci numbers found in nature. Record the list on the board for all students to refer to as they create their posters.

Recording and Reporting

Master 1.3 Performance Assessment Rubric: Fibonacci Numbers
Master 1.4 Unit Summary: Patterns in Whole Numbers

Evaluating Student Learning: Preparing to Report: Unit 1 Patterns in Whole Numbers

This unit provides an opportunity to report on the **Number Sense and Numeration** and **Patterning and Algebra** strands. *Master 1.4 Unit Summary: Patterns in Whole Numbers* provides a comprehensive format for recording and summarizing evidence collected.

Here is an example of a completed summary chart for this Unit:

Strand: *Number Sense and Numeration/Patterning and Algebra*	**Problem solving**	**Understanding of concepts**	**Application of mathematical procedures**	**Communication**	***Overall***
Ongoing Observations	4	4	4	3	4
Work samples or portfolios; conferences	3	4	4	4	4
Unit Review	4	4	4	4	4
Practice Test	4	4	4	3	4
Unit Problem Fibonacci Numbers	3	4	4	4	4
Achievement Level for reporting					4

Recording	**How to Report**
Ongoing Observations	Use *Master 1.2 Ongoing Observations: Patterns in Whole Numbers* to determine the most consistent level achieved in each category. Enter it in the chart. Choose to summarize by achievement category, or simply to enter an overall level. Observations from late in the unit should be most heavily weighted.
Portfolios or collections of work samples; conferences, or interviews	Use *Master 1.1 Unit Rubric: Patterns in Whole Numbers* to guide evaluation of collections of work and information gathered in conferences. Teachers may choose to focus particular attention on the Assessment Focus questions. Work from late in the unit should be most heavily weighted.
Unit Review	*Master 1.1 Unit Rubric: Patterns in Whole Numbers* may be helpful in determining levels of achievement. #1, 6, 7, 10, 11, 15, and 18 provide evidence of Understanding of concepts; #2, 4, 5, 8, 12, 13, 14, 16, 17, 19, and 20 provide evidence of Application of mathematical procedures; #3 and 9 provide evidence of Problem solving; all provide evidence of Communication.
Practice Test	*Master 1.1 Unit Rubric: Patterns in Whole Numbers* may be helpful in determining levels of achievement. #1, 2, 4, and 9 provide evidence of Understanding of concepts; #3, 7, and 8 provide evidence of Application of mathematical procedures; #5 and 6 provide evidence of Problem solving; all parts provide evidence of Communication.
Unit Problem	Use *Master 1.3 Performance Assessment Rubric: Fibonacci Numbers*. The *Unit Problem* offers a snapshot of students' achievement. In particular, it shows their ability to synthesize and apply what they have learned.
Student Self-Assessment	Note students' perceptions of their own progress. This may take the form of an oral or written comment, or a self-rating.
Comments	Analyse the pattern of achievement to identify strengths and needs. In some cases, specific actions may need to be planned to support the learner.

Learning Skills	**Ongoing Records**
PM 4: Learning Skills Check List Use to record and report throughout a reporting period, rather than for each unit and/or strand.	*PM 10: Summary Class Records: Strands;* *PM 11: Summary Class Records: Achievement Categories;* *PM 12: Summary Record: Individual* Use to record and report evaluations of student achievement over several clusters, a reporting period, or a school year. These can also be used in place of the Unit Summary.

Name ____________________ Date ______________

Master 1.1

Unit Rubric: Patterns in Whole Numbers

	Level 1	Level 2	Level 3	Level 4
Problem solving • chooses and carries out a range of strategies (paper and pencil, mental math, calculators, estimation) to solve multi-step problems	with assistance, chooses and carries out a limited range of appropriate strategies, including estimation, rarely resulting in an accurate solution	with limited assistance, chooses and carries out appropriate strategies, including estimation, that frequently result in an accurate solution	chooses and carries out appropriate strategies, including estimation, that usually result in an accurate solution	chooses and carries out appropriate strategies, including estimation; may offer an innovative approach; results in accurate solution
Understanding of concepts • shows understanding by demonstrating and explaining: – how numbers are used to describe our world – justification of methods and strategies – prime and composite numbers; multiples and factors (including GCF and LCM) – squares, square roots – exponents (as repeated multiplication) – number patterns	shows little understanding; may be unable to demonstrate or explain: – numerical information about our world – choice of methods and strategies – prime and composite numbers; multiples and factors (including GCF and LCM) – squares, square roots – exponents and number patterns	shows some understanding; partially able to demonstrate or explain: – numerical information about our world – choice of methods and strategies – prime and composite numbers; multiples and factors (including GCF and LCM) – squares, square roots – exponents and number patterns	shows understanding; able to clearly and appropriately demonstrate or explain: – numerical information about our world – choice of methods and strategies – prime and composite numbers; multiples and factors (including GCF and LCM) – squares, square roots – exponents and number patterns	shows thorough understanding; able to accurately and effectively demonstrate or explain: – numerical information about our world – choice of methods and strategies – prime and composite numbers; multiples and factors (including GCF and LCM) – squares, square roots – exponents and number patterns
Application of mathematical procedures • accurately: – finds factors and multiples (including GCF and LCM) – identifies prime and composite numbers – represents squares and square roots – uses and interprets exponents – identifies and extends number patterns	limited accuracy; major errors or omissions in: – finding factors and multiples (including GCF and LCM) – identifying prime and composite numbers – representing squares and square roots – using and interpreting exponents – identifying and extending number patterns	somewhat accurate; several minor errors or omissions in: – finding factors and multiples (including GCF and LCM) – identifying prime and composite numbers – representing squares and square roots – using and interpreting exponents – identifying and extending number patterns	generally accurate; few minor errors or omissions in: – finding factors and multiples (including GCF and LCM) – identifying prime and composite numbers – representing squares and square roots – using and interpreting exponents – identifying and extending number patterns	accurate and precise; no errors in: – finding factors and multiples (including GCF and LCM) – identifying prime and composite numbers – representing squares and square roots – using and interpreting exponents – identifying and extending number patterns
Communication • explains reasoning and procedures clearly using appropriate terminology and symbols (prime, GCF, LCM, exponent, power) • presents work clearly, including labels and symbols	unable to explain reasoning and procedures clearly; rarely uses appropriate terms and symbols	explains reasoning and procedures with some clarity and use of appropriate terms and symbols	explains reasoning and procedures clearly and precisely, using appropriate terms and symbols	explains reasoning and procedures clearly, precisely, and confidently, using a range of the most appropriate terms and symbols

Name ____________________ Date ______________

Master 1.2

Ongoing Observations: Patterns in Whole Numbers

The behaviours described under each heading are examples; they are not intended to be an exhaustive list of all that might be observed. More detailed descriptions are provided in each lesson under *Assessment for Learning*.

STUDENT ACHIEVEMENT: Patterns in Whole Numbers				
Student	**Problem solving** ▪ Chooses and carries out appropriate strategies to solve multi-step problems and check results (estimates)	**Understanding of concepts** ▪ Demonstrates and explains prime and composite numbers, multiples, factors, squares, square roots, exponents ▪ Justifies methods	**Application of mathematical procedures** ▪ Identifies prime and composite numbers; finds factors, multiples ▪ Represents squares, square roots, exponents	**Communication** ▪ Explains reasoning clearly using appropriate terms and symbols (e.g., prime, factor, square, exponent, power)

Level 1 – very limited; Level 2 – somewhat or limited; Level 3 – satisfactory; Level 4 – thorough

Name ____________________ Date ______________

Master 1.3

Performance Assessment Rubric: Fibonacci Numbers

	Level 1	Level 2	Level 3	Level 4
Problem solving • chooses appropriate patterning strategies (e.g., diagrams, tables, charts, calculators, simpler problems) to solve problems involving the Fibonacci sequence	uses few simple strategies to solve problems involving the Fibonacci sequence; limited success	uses some appropriate strategies to solve problems involving the Fibonacci sequence; some success	uses appropriate strategies to solve problems involving the Fibonacci sequence; successful	uses innovative and appropriate strategies to solve problems involving the Fibonacci sequence; successful and effective
Understanding of concepts • shows understanding of number patterns by giving appropriate explanations and illustrations of: – how to find the next number in a Fibonacci sequence – how to use the family tree of a drone to find the Fibonacci numbers – a variety of patterns in the Fibonacci numbers – other findings about Fibonacci numbers	shows very limited understanding by giving few appropriate illustrations and examples of patterns in Fibonacci numbers	shows limited understanding by giving some appropriate but incomplete illustrations and examples of patterns in Fibonacci numbers	shows understanding by giving appropriate illustrations of examples of patterns in Fibonacci numbers	shows thorough understanding by giving appropriate and complete illustrations and examples of patterns in Fibonacci numbers
Application of mathematical procedures • identifies and extends a pattern • identifies factors, and prime and composite numbers	limited accuracy; major errors or omissions in: – identifying and extending patterns – identifying factors, and prime and composite numbers	somewhat accurate; several minor errors or omissions in: – identifying and extending patterns – identifying factors, and prime and composite numbers	generally accurate; few minor errors or omissions in: – identifying and extending patterns – identifying factors, and prime and composite numbers	accurate and precise; practically no minor errors or omissions in: – identifying and extending patterns – identifying factors, and prime and composite numbers
Communication • explains reasoning clearly using appropriate mathematical terminology • presents work, including diagrams, clearly	explains reasoning unclearly and imprecisely using few mathematical terms presents work with little clarity	explains reasoning with some clarity using some appropriate mathematical terms presents work with some clarity	explains reasoning clearly and precisely using appropriate mathematical terms presents work clearly	explains reasoning clearly, precisely, and confidently using a range of appropriate mathematical terminology presents work clearly and precisely

Name ____________________ Date ________________

Master 1.4

Unit Summary: Patterns in Whole Numbers

Review assessment records to determine the most consistent achievement levels for the assessments conducted. Some cells may be blank. *Overall* achievement levels may be recorded in each row, rather than identifying levels for each achievement category.

	Most Consistent Level of Achievement*				
Strand: *Number Sense and Numeration/Patterning and Algebra*	**Problem solving**	**Understanding of concepts**	**Application of mathematical procedures**	**Communication**	***Overall***
Ongoing Observations					
Work samples or portfolios; conferences					
Unit Review					
Practice Test					
Unit Problem: Fibonacci Numbers					
Achievement Level for reporting					

* Use Ontario Achievement Levels 1, 2, 3, 4

Self-Assessment:

Comments: (Strengths, Needs, Next Steps)

Name ____________________ Date ______________

Master 1.5a

Additional Activity 1: Rounds of Rounding

Play with a partner.

You will need a set of place-value cards, and pencil and paper.

How to Play:

1. Each player records a 7-digit number on paper. No digit may be written more than two times.
2. Shuffle the place-value cards and place them face down in a pile.
3. One player turns over a place-value card, then rounds his number to that place value.
   One point is awarded for a correct answer.
   If the player is incorrect, his partner tries to round the number.
   If she is correct, she gets 1 point.
4. The other player turns over a place-value card, then rounds her number to that place-value.
5. Repeat *Steps 1* to *4* several times.
   The first player to get 5 points wins.

Take It Further:
Use playing cards (Ace to 9, and King, where Ace = 1, and King = 0).
Each player turns over 7 cards, then makes the greatest 7-digit number possible.
Play the game as above.

Name ____________________ Date ________________

Master 1.5b

Place-Value Cards

Tens	Hundreds
Thousands	Ten Thousands
Hundred Thousands	Millions

Name ____________________ Date _______________

Master 1.6

Additional Activity 2: Product Mania

Play with a partner.

You will need a hundred chart, 2 tokens, 2 sets of counters (one colour per player), and 2 number cubes labelled 1 to 6.

How to Play:

1. Each player rolls a number cube. Place your token on that square of the hundred chart.
2. One player rolls both number cubes, then adds the numbers rolled.
   Both players race to cover the product of the total rolled and each number in the square containing a token. For example, if the tokens are on 3 and 5, and the total of the numbers rolled is 9, cover the numbers 27 (9×3) and 45 (9×5) with counters. Only one counter can be in any one square.
3. Take turns to roll the number cubes. The first player to cover 10 squares with counters wins.

Take It Further:
Play the game with regular octahedrons labelled 1 to 8.
Use a 10 by 10 square to make a chart for 101 to 200.

Name ____________________ Date ________________

Master 1.7

Additional Activity 3: Squares and Cubes

Work with a partner.

You will need a deck of playing cards with the face cards removed, a calculator (optional)

How to Play:

1. Shuffle the cards. Place the cards face down in a pile.
2. Player A turns over the top card.
   She says the square and cube of the number drawn.
   For example, if a 4 is drawn, she says, "16 and 64."
3. Player B checks Player A's answer, using a calculator if necessary.
4. Player A receives 1 point if both parts of her answer are correct.
   Player A receives no points if she gets either part wrong.
5. Player B takes a turn. Play continues until all cards have been used.
   The player with the higher score wins.

Take It Further:
Play the game again. This time, evaluate the number drawn to the exponent 4 as well.

Name ____________________ Date ________________

Master 1.8

Additional Activity 4: Pattern Power

Play with a partner.

You will need index cards.

Make 5 different number patterns on 5 index cards.
List the first 4 numbers for each pattern; for example, 4, 10, 18, 28, …

Trade patterns with your partner.
Identify your partner's patterns.
Write the pattern rule beside each pattern; for example,
Start at 4. Add 6. Increase the number you add by 2 each time.

You get 2 points for each correct pattern rule.
The player with the higher score after 2 rounds wins.

Take It Further:
Write your patterns on index cards (one per card).
Write the pattern rules on separate index cards. Shuffle your cards.
Trade cards (10 in total) with your partner. Sort each other's cards.
Match each pattern with its pattern rule.
Players get 2 points for each correct match.

Name ____________________ Date ________________

Master 1.9

Step-by-Step 1

Section 1.1, Question 12

Step 1 Do you think these numbers have been rounded?
Do you think these numbers are exact? ______ Why?

____

Step 2 Add the populations of NF and Labrador, PEI, Nova Scotia and New Brunswick.
What is the total population? __________________

Step 3 Divide your answer in *Step 2* by 4 (the number of provinces).
What is the mean population? __________________

Step 4 Round your answer from *Step 2* to the nearest hundred thousand.

____

Step 5 Round the population of Ontario to the nearest hundred thousand.

____

Step 6 Divide the number in *Step 5* by the number in *Step 4*. Approximately how many times as many people are in Ontario as are in the Atlantic provinces?

____

Step 7 Write your own problem about these data.

____

____

Solve your problem.

____

____

Name ____________________ Date ______________

Master 1.10

Step-by-Step 2

Section 1.2, Question 9

Use a calendar.

Sun	Mon	Tues	Wed	Thurs	Fri	Sat
		1	2	3	4	5
6	7	8	9	10	11	12
13	14	15	16	17	18	19
20	21	22	23	24	25	26
27	28	29	30			

Kevin red   Alison green   Fred orange

Step 1 Let red represent Kevin. Draw a red circle on all the days that are multiples of 2.
Let green represent Alison. Draw a green circle on all the days that are multiples of 3.
Let orange represent Fred. Draw an orange circle on all the days that are multiples of 4.

Step 2 Which days have all 3 colours of circles?

____

Step 3 When did the people first all work together? ____________________

Step 4 When will they work together again? ____________________
How do you know?

____

____

Name ____________________ Date ______________

Master 1.11 **Step-by-Step 3**

Section 1.3, Question 8

Which numbers have square roots between 1 and 20?

Step 1 Complete the table. Square each square root from 4 to 22.

Square root	1	2	3	4	5	6	7	8	9	10	11
Number	$1^2 = 1$	$2^2 = 4$	$3^2 = 9$								
Square root	12	13	14	15	16	17	18	19	20	21	22
Number											

Step 2 Look at the numbers and square roots in the table.
Which whole numbers have square roots between 1 and 20?

____

How do you know?

____

____

Name ____________________ Date _______________

Master 1.12

Step-by-Step 4

Section 1.4, Question 12

Step 1 Write each number as a product of equal factors.
Then write the product as a power.

16: Try 2 as a factor. ______________________ Power = _____

Try 4 as a factor. ______________________ Power = _____

81: Try 3 as a factor. ______________________ Power = _____

Try 9 as a factor. ______________________ Power = _____

64: Try 2 as a factor. ______________________ Power = _____

Try 4 as a factor. ______________________ Power = _____

Try 8 as a factor. ______________________ Power = _____

Step 2 Remember that any number can be written as a power by using the exponent 1. Write each number in *Step 1* with exponent 1.

____

Step 3 Use the ideas above.
Find other numbers that can be written in exponent form, in more than one way.
Show your work.

Name ____________________ Date ______________

Master 1.13

Step-by-Step 5

Section 1.5, Question 8

Step 1 Complete the table.

Standard Form	2	4								
Exponent Form	2^1	2^2	2^3	2^4	2^5	2^6	2^7	2^8	2^9	2^{10}

Step 2 Write the units digit for each number written in standard form.

2, 4, ___ ___ ___ ___ ___ ___ ___ ___

What pattern do you see?

____

Step 3 Extend the pattern to the 40th term.

2, 4, ___

___ ___ ___ ___ ___ ___ ___ ___ ___ ___ ___ ___ ___ ___ ___ ___ ___ ___

What is the units digit of 2^{40}? _______

Step 4

Standard Form	3	9								
Exponent Form	3^1	3^2	3^3	3^4	3^5	3^6	3^7	3^8	3^9	3^{10}

Repeat *Steps 1* and *2* for the first 10 powers of 3.
Use the pattern in the units digit to find the units digit of 3^{27}.
Show your work.

Name ____________________ Date ________________

Master 1.14

The Factor Game Game Board

1	2	3	4	5	6	7	8
9	10	11	12	13	14	15	16
17	18	19	20	21	22	23	24
25	26	27	28	29	30	31	32
33	34	35	36	37	38	39	40
41	42	43	44	45	46	47	48
49	50	51	52	53	54	55	56
57	58	59	60	61	62	63	64

Name ____________________ Date ________________

Master 1.15a

Unit Test: Unit 1
Patterns in Whole Numbers

1. Solve each problem. Which strategy did you use?
Why did you choose that strategy?

a) Fong has 353 pennies, 227 nickels, 132 dimes, 53 quarters, and 27 toonies.
How much money does she have altogether?

b) Jason estimates that he drinks about 300 mL of orange juice in a day. About how much orange juice does he drink in a month?

c) Josephine bought a ruler for $1, a pencil sharpener for $1, a clipboard for $3, some glue for $2, a geometry set for $5, and a binder for $2.
How much money did she spend altogether, before tax?

2. Find the common factors of 16 and 36. What is their GCF?

3. Find the first 9 multiples of 8 and 6. What is their LCM?

Name ____________________ Date ______________

Master 1.15b **Unit Test continued**

4. Find:

a) $\sqrt{169}$ **b)** 6^3 **c)** the square of 7

5. Write the next 3 terms in each number pattern.

a) 7, 10, 15, 22, …

b) 7, 14, 28, 56, …

6. Siew takes violin lessons every third day of the month.
She plays softball every fifth day of the month.
How many times in a month will Siew have the two activities on the same day?
Which days of the month will they be?
Explain your thinking.

7. Use the clues to find a mystery number. Explain your thinking.
Clue 1: I am a 2-digit number.
Clue 2: I am greater than $\sqrt{144}$, but less than 6^2.
Clue 3: I have 17 as a factor.
Clue 4: I am not a prime number.
What am I?

Name ____________________ Date ________________

Master 1.15c

Unit Test continued

8. Misha, Sasha, and Devon bought hockey cards.
Each package contains the same number of cards.
Misha bought 120 cards. Sasha bought 180 cards. Devon bought 96 cards.
What is the greatest number of cards that could come in one package?

9. Extend the following pattern in as many different ways as you can.
State the pattern rule for each pattern you write.
Why are so many different patterns possible?
3, 6, …

Name ____________________ Date ______________

Master 1.16 Sample Answers

Unit Test – Master 1.15

1. a) $95.33; I used a calculator because there are many steps, the numbers are large, and I need an exact answer.
   b) About 9000 mL or 9 L; I used mental math. I assumed 30 days in a month. I calculated 30×30 mentally.
   c) $14; I used mental math because the numbers are easy to handle.
2. Common factors: 1, 2, and 4
   GCF: 4
3. Multiples of 8: 8, 16, 24, 32, 40, 48, 56, 64, 72
   Multiples of 6: 6, 12, 18, 24, 30, 36, 42, 48, 54
   LCM: 24
4. a) 13 b) 216 c) 49
5. a) 31, 42, 55 b) 112, 224, 448
6. Twice; on the 15th and 30th days
   I assumed there were 30 days in a month.
   The common multiples of 3 and 5 are 15 and 30.
7. 34; the number is greater than 12 but less than 36.
   The numbers between 12 and 36 that have a factor of 17 are: 17 and 34.
   Of these 2 numbers, 17 is a prime number as it has only 2 factors, itself and 1.
8. 12 cards
9. Some possible patterns:
   3, 6, 9, 12, 15, …
   Start at 3. Add 3 to get the next number.
   3, 6, 10, 15, 21, …
   Start at 3. Add 3. Increase the number you add by 1 each time.
   3, 6, 12, 24, 48, …
   Start at 3. Multiply by 2 to get the next number.
   3, 6, 18, 72, 360, …
   Start at 3. Multiply by 2. Increase the number you multiply by, by 1 each time.
   Many patterns are possible because there are not enough given terms to define the pattern.

Extra Practice Masters 1.17–1.22

Go to the CD-ROM to access editable versions of these Extra Practice Masters

Name ______________ Date ____________

Master 1.17 **Extra Practice 1**

Section 1.1: Numbers All Around Us

1. Solve without a calculator.
   a) 86 + 124   b) 174 – 63   c) 22 × 1000   d) 525 ÷ 25

2. Estimate. Explain the strategy you used each time.
   a) 82 + 77   b) 234 – 18   c) 51 × 11   d) 319 ÷ 80

3. Dana runs 15 km per day during the week and 25 km per day on weekends.
   a) How far does Dana run in a week?

   b) How far would Dana run in one month?

   What assumptions did you make?

4. Mrs. Wong bought 6 sweatshirts at $39.95 each, including tax.
   a) About how much money did she spend?

   b) She gave the cashier $250.
   She got $9.30 in change.
   Does this seem right? Explain.

5. The Grade 7 students are divided into 3 classes.
   There are 29 students in Mr. Haley's class,
   32 students in Mr. Chua's class,
   and 28 students in Mrs. Davis' class.
   a) About how many students are in Grade 7?

   b) What is the actual number of students in Grade 7?

   c) Was your estimate high or low? Why?

Name ______________ Date ____________

Master 1.18 **Extra Practice 2**

Section 1.2: Factors and Multiples

1. List 6 multiples of each number.
   a) 6   b) 9   c) 10   d) 4

2. Find the factors of each number.
   a) 17   b) 32   c) 48   d) 54

3. Is each number prime or composite? How do you know?
   a) 23   b) 34   c) 56   d) 61

4. Find the GCF of each pair of numbers.
   a) 16, 8   b) 6, 9   c) 10, 35   d) 4, 12

5. Find the LCM of each pair of numbers.
   a) 7, 9   b) 3, 5   c) 12, 10   d) 14, 8

6. Frances has piano lessons every fourth day.
   She has ballet lessons every fifth day.
   She has soccer every second day.
   On which day will she first have all three activities?
   Explain how you know.

Name ______________ Date ____________

Master 1.19 **Extra Practice 3**

Section 1.3: Squares and Square Roots

1. Find the square of each number.
   a) 12   b) 15   c) 6   d) 11

2. Find a square root of each number.
   a) 196   b) 400   c) 169   d) 1

3. Order from least to greatest.
   a) 4^2, $\sqrt{400}$, 15, $\sqrt{144}$ b) 3^2, $\sqrt{100}$, 8, $\sqrt{169}$

4. Which whole numbers have squares between 10 and 65?

5. Calculate the area of a square with each side length.
   a) 8 m   b) 23 cm   c) 1 cm

6. A drawer is divided into 12 congruent square sections.
   The drawer has a total area of 432 cm^2.
   What is the side length of each section?

Name ______________ Date ____________

Master 1.20 **Extra Practice 4**

Section 1.4: Exponents

1. Write the base, then the exponent of each power.
   a) 5^{12} b) 7^4 c) 2^9 d) 10^1

2. Write in expanded form.
   a) 1^6 b) 6^3 c) 7^5 d) 8^4

3. Write in exponent form, then in standard form.
   a) 41 × 41 × 41   b) 11 × 11 × 11 × 11 × 11

   c) 4 × 4 × 4 × 4 × 4 × 4 × 4   d) 9 × 9 × 9 × 9

4. Write as a power of 4.
   a) 64   b) 16   c) 4   d) 256   e) 1024

5. Write these numbers in order from least to greatest.
   4^3, 5^2, 2^4, 3^5

6. Write each number in exponent form in as many different ways as you can.
   a) 625   b) 256

7. Use a calculator. Simplify.
   a) 11^6 b) 6^7 c) 8^5 d) 12^5

Name ______________ Date ____________

Master 1.21 **Extra Practice 5**

Section 1.5: Number Patterns

1. Write the next 3 terms in each pattern.
   a) 5, 10, 16, 23, …   b) 2, 5, 3, 6, …
   c) 63, 59, 55, 51, …   d) 4, 8, 16, 32, …

2. Write the next 3 terms in each pattern.
   a) 5, 6, 8, 11, …   b) 1, 8, 27, 64, …
   c) 46, 44, 40, 34, …   d) 3, 34, 345, 3456, …

3. Describe each pattern in words.
   a) 4, 7, 10, 13, …   b) 3, 8, 5, 10, …
   c) 66, 65, 63, 60, …   d) 3, 5, 10, 18, …

4. Extend each pattern in as many different ways as you can.
   Describe each pattern.
   a) 2, 4, 8, …   b) 1, 3, 9, …

5. Find each product. What pattern do you see?
   Write the next two rows in the pattern.

   7 × 7 = □

   67 × 67 = □

   667 × 667 = □

Name ______________ Date ____________

Master 1.22 **Sample Answers**

Extra Practice 1 – Master 1.17

Section 1.1

1. a) 210   b) 111
   c) 22 000   d) 21
2. a) About 160; I rounded both numbers to the nearest 10: 80 + 80 = 160
   b) About 214; I rounded 18 to the nearest 10, then subtracted: 234 – 20 = 214
   c) About 550; I rounded 51 to the nearest 10, then multiplied 50 × 11 to get 550
   d) About 4; I rounded 319 to the nearest 10, then divided: 320 ÷ 80 = 4
3. a) 125 km
   b) About 542 km; I assumed Dana continued to run the same distances and that he did not miss a day.
   15 × 5 + 25 × 2 = 125 × 52 ÷ 12
   I multiplied by 52, the number of weeks in a year, to get the distance run in a year. Then I divided by 12, the number of months a year, to get the distance run in 1 month.
4. a) About $240
   b) No, I rounded the cost of a sweatshirt up, so my estimate is high. Mrs. Wong should get more than $10 in change. She received only $9.30.
5. a) About 90 students; 30 + 30 + 30 = 90
   b) 89 students
   c) High; I rounded 2 numbers up by a total of 3, and I rounded one number down by 2. I rounded up by a greater amount so my estimate is high.

Extra Practice 2 – Master 1.18

Section 1.2

1. a) 6, 12, 18, 24, 30, 36
   b) 9, 18, 27, 36, 45, 54
   c) 10, 20, 30, 40, 50, 60
   d) 4, 8, 12, 16, 20, 24
2. a) 1, 17   b) 1, 2, 4, 8, 16, 32
   c) 1, 2, 3, 4, 6, 8, 12, 16, 24, 48
   d) 1, 2, 3, 6, 9, 18, 27, 54
3. a) Prime; the number has only 2 factors, itself and 1.
   b) Composite; the number has more than 2 factors.
   c) Composite; the number has more than 2 factors.
   d) Prime; the number has only 2 factors, itself and 1.
4. a) 8   b) 3   c) 5   d) 4
5. a) 63   b) 15   c) 60   d) 56
6. On day 20; 20 is the LCM of 2, 4, and 5.

Extra Practice 3 – Master 1.19

Section 1.3

1. a) 144   b) 225   c) 36   d) 121
2. a) 14   b) 20   c) 13   d) 1
3. a) $\sqrt{144}$, 15, 4^2, $\sqrt{400}$ b) 8, 3^2, $\sqrt{100}$, $\sqrt{169}$
4. 4, 5, 6, 7, and 8
5. a) 64 m^2 b) 529 cm^2 c) 1 cm^2
6. 6 cm

Extra Practice 4 – Master 1.20

Section 1.4

1. a) 5, 12   b) 7, 4   c) 2, 9   d) 10, 1
2. a) 1 × 1 × 1 × 1 × 1 × 1   b) 6 × 6 × 6
   c) 7 × 7 × 7 × 7 × 7   d) 8 × 8 × 8 × 8
3. a) 41^3, 68 921   b) 11^5, 161 051
   c) 4^7, 16 384   d) 9^4, 6561
4. a) 4^3 b) 4^2 c) 4^1
   d) 4^4 e) 4^5
5. 2^4, 5^2, 4^3, 3^5
6. a) 5^4, 25^2, 625^1 b) 2^8, 4^4, 16^2, 256^1
7. a) 1 771 561   b) 279 936
   c) 32 768   d) 248 832

Extra Practice 5 – Master 1.21

Section 1.5

1. a) 31, 40, 50   b) 4, 7, 5
   c) 47, 43, 39   d) 64, 128, 256
2. a) 15, 20, 26   b) 125, 216, 343
   c) 26, 16, 4
   d) 34 567, 345 678, 3 456 789
3. a) Start at 4. Add 3 to get the next number.
   b) Start at 3. Alternate adding 5 and subtracting 3.
   c) Start at 66. Subtract 1. Increase the number you subtract by 1 each time.
   d) Start at 3. Add 2. Increase the number you add by 3 each time.
4. a) 2, 4, 8, 16, 32, 64, …
   Start at 2. Multiply by 2 to get the next number.
   2, 4, 8, 14, 22, 32, …
   Start at 2. Add 2. Increase the number you add by 2 each time.
   b) 1, 3, 9, 27, 81, 243, …
   Start at 1. Multiply by 3 to get the next number.
   1, 3, 9, 19, 33, 51, …
   Start at 1. Add 2. Increase the number you add by 4 each time.
5. 7 × 7 = 49
   67 × 67 = 4489
   667 × 667 = 444 889
   6667 × 6667 = 44 448 889
   66 667 × 66 667 = 4 444 488 889
   The number of 4s in the product starts at 1 and increases by 1 each time. The 4s always come first in the number.
   The number of 9s in the product is always 1, and it is always the last digit.
   The number of 8s in the product starts at 0 and increases by 1 each time. The 8s come between the 4s and the 9.

Addison Wesley

Mathematics
Makes Sense

Program Authors

Jason Johnston
Bryn Keyes
Mary Doucette
Antonietta Lenjosek
Steve Thomas
Margaret Sinclair
Trevor Brown
Cathy Heideman
Don Jones
Michael Davis
Jennifer Paziuk
Ken Harper
Sharon Jeroski
Ray Appel
Laura Weatherhead
Betty Milne
Jim Mennie
Lynn Strangway

Printed and bound in Canada

10 17

PEARSON
Education Canada

ADDISON WESLEY

Ontario

Math Makes Sense 7

Ontario

Teacher Guide

Unit 2: Ratio and Rate

PEARSON
Addison Wesley

UNIT 2

Ratio and Rate

"Where proportional reasoning is concerned . . . the rush to rules is a serious error. Time must be allowed for development of intuitive ideas."

John A. Van de Walle

FOCUS STRAND
Number Sense and Numeration

SUPPORTING STRAND
Patterning and Algebra

TIPS
Each lesson should appeal to auditory, kinesthetic, and visual learners. Appealing to all these preferences deepens the understanding of all students.

Mathematics Background

What Are the Big Ideas?

- A ratio is a comparison of two numbers, quantities, or measures with the same units.
- Some ratios are comparisons of one part of a whole to another part, while other ratios are comparisons of one part of the whole to the whole.
- Equivalent ratios are equal. Equal ratios result from multiplying or dividing all terms of a ratio by the same number.
- Equivalent ratios can be used to compare ratios.
- A rate is a comparison of two different things or two quantities with different units. A unit rate compares a quantity to 1 unit.
- Ratios and rates can be used to solve problems.

How Will the Concepts Develop?

Students use models and diagrams to investigate ratios. Students use factors and multiples to find equivalent ratios. Students use diagrams and tables to model and solve ratio problems. They apply their understanding of ratios to scale drawings and maps.

Students investigate rates, and use diagrams, tables, and graphs to find unit rates. They use unit rates to solve problems.

Why Are These Concepts Important?

An understanding of a ratio is crucial to the development of a student's ability to be a proportional thinker.

The ability to think proportionally enables students to apply ratios and rates to many everyday activities. For example, ratios and rates are used to compare numbers and quantities, to compare prices when shopping, and to read maps. They are also used in carpentry, cooking, sports, finance, and architecture.

Curriculum Overview

Overall Expectations
- Explain, in writing, the process of problem solving using appropriate mathematical language. (7m7)
- Identify, extend, create, and discuss patterns using whole numbers ... (7m67)
- Apply and discuss patterning strategies in problem-solving situations. (7m69)

Specific Expectations
- Explain numerical information in their own words and respond to numerical information in a variety of media. (7m12)
- Perform three-step problem solving that involves whole numbers ... related to real-life experiences, ... (7m14)
- Explain the process used and any conclusions reached in problem solving and investigations. (7m24)
- Reflect on learning experiences and describe their understanding using appropriate mathematical language. (7m25)
- Extend a pattern, complete a table, and write words to explain the pattern. (7m71)
- Recognize patterns and use them to make predictions. (7m72)
- Present solutions to patterning problems and explain the thinking behind the solution process. (7m75)

Launch

Section 2.1: What Is a Ratio?

Section 2.2: Equivalent Ratios

Section 2.3: Comparing Ratios

Mid-Unit Review

Section 2.4: Applications of Ratios

Section 2.5: What Is a Rate?

Unit Review
Practice Test

Unit Problem
Who's the Smartest?

Curriculum across the Grades

Grade 6	Grade 7	Grade 8
Students relate fractions to decimals, percents, rates, and ratios using concrete materials, drawings, and symbols. Students demonstrate an understanding of ratio. They solve simple rate and ratio problems. Students relate time and distance and speed: kilometres per hour.	Ratio and rate is not a requirement of the Grade 7 curriculum. This unit has been included to provide continuity between Grades 6 and 8.	Students demonstrate an understanding of and apply unit rates in problem-solving situations. Students solve problems that involve converting between fractions, decimals, percents, unit rates, and ratios.

Additional Activities

LCM

For Extra Practice (Appropriate for use after Skills You'll Need)
Materials: *LCM* (Master 2.5), number cards for prime numbers 2, 3, 5, 7, 11, 13, 17, and 19; and composite numbers 4, 6, 8, 9, 10, 12, 14, 15, 16, 18, and 20; 2-column charts (PM 17). The 2 types of numbers should be on different colours of card to denote the two different types of numbers.

This activity reinforces the meaning of the lowest common multiple and enables the student to distinguish between prime numbers and composite numbers.

The work students do: Students work alone. The student draws two cards, one from the "prime number" pile and one from the "composite number" pile. The numbers are recorded in a table similar to the one shown below. The student writes the multiples of each number in the chart until he discovers the lowest common multiple (LCM). After completing several rounds of this activity, the student looks for patterns between the numbers drawn and the LCM. Is there an easy way to find the LCM without using a table?

Prime 5	**Composite 4**
10	8
15	12

Take It Further: The student uses the composite number cards only. She draws 2 cards, then finds the LCM.

Mathematical/Logical
Individual Activity

Buzz

For Extra Support (Appropriate for use after Skills You'll Need)
Materials: *Buzz* (Master 2.6)

This game provides practice with multiple and factor recognition.

The work students do: Students work in a group. A student selects a target number between 1 and 10. Students begin counting, with each player taking turns to say one number as quickly as he or she can. If one of the digits of a number is the target number, or if a number is a multiple of the target number, the student must say, "buzz" instead of the number. For example, if the target number is 7, students would count 1, 2, 3, 4, 5, 6, buzz, 8, 9, 10, 11, 12, 13, buzz, 15, 16, buzz, and so on. This is an elimination game. If a student fails to say "buzz" when required, that student is eliminated. Play continues until only 1 player remains or a set amount of time has elapsed.

Take It Further: Students use a target number greater than 9, and say "buzz" on multiples of the target number, as well as numbers containing any of the digits.

Logical/Mathematical/Social
Group Activity

Planning for Unit 2

Planning for Instruction

Suggested Unit time: About 2–3 weeks

Section	Time	Materials	Program Support
Launch, page 2	15–20 min		
Skills You'll Need, page 4	65–80 min	12 by 12 multiplication charts (optional)	PM 15: 12 × 12 Multiplication Chart
2.1: What Is a Ratio?, page 7 Use models and diagrams to investigate ratios.	80–100 min	counters (red, blue, and yellow) calculators (optional)	Master 2.7: Step-by-Step 1 Master 2.14: Extra Practice 1
2.2: Equivalent Ratios, page 11 Write equivalent ratios.	80–100 min	1-cm grid paper and transparency	PM 20: 1-cm Grid Paper Master 2.8: Step-by-Step 2 Master 2.15: Extra Practice 2
2.3: Comparing Ratios, page 15 Use equivalent ratios to compare ratios.	80–100 min		Master 2.9: Step-by-Step 3 Master 2.16: Extra Practice 3
Mid-Unit Review, page 19			
2.4: Applications of Ratios, page 20 Use ratios to solve problems.	80–100 min	1-cm grid paper and transparency 0.5-cm grid paper calculators metre sticks or measuring tapes (optional)	PM 20: 1-cm Grid Paper PM 14: 0.5-cm Grid Paper Master 2.10: Step-by-Step 4 Master 2.17: Extra Practice 4
2.5: What Is a Rate?, page 24 Investigate rates.	80–100 min	stopwatches or clock calculators newspapers and magazines	Master 2.11: Step-by-Step 5 Master 2.18: Extra Practice 5
Reading and Writing in Math: Organizing a Math Notebook, page 28			
Unit Review, page 31		calculators counters (optional) 1-cm grid paper (optional)	Extra Practice: Student Book page 439
Practice Test, page 33		0.5-cm grid paper calculators	PM 14: 0.5-cm Grid Paper
Unit Problem: Who's the Smartest?, page 34	40–50 min	calculators	

etext online tutorial

This web-based tutorial uses voice, animation, and an optional quiz to present each core lesson, so that students can review content with a new approach.

Planning for Assessment

Purpose	Tools and Process	Recording and Reporting
Diagnostic	*Unit Launch* Question; conference; scaffold problems throughout the unit	 PM 8: Conference Prompts
Formative	*Explore* – Ongoing Assessment: Observe and Listen	Master 2.2 Ongoing Observations: Ratio and Rate PM 1: Inquiry Process Check List PM 6: Observation Record 1 PM 7: Observation Record 2 PM 8: Conference Prompts PM 2: Self-Assessment PM 3: Self-Assessment: Problem Solving PM 9: Work Sample Records
Summative	*Unit Review* *Unit Problem* – Performance Assessment Unit Test Review assessment records; add unit results to ongoing records	Master 2.1 Unit Rubric: Ratio and Rate Master 2.3 Performance Assessment Rubric: Who's the Smartest? Master 2.4 Unit Summary: Ratio and Rate PM 10: Summary Class Records: Strands PM 11: Summary Class Records: Achievement Categories PM 12: Summary Record: Individual
Learning Skills/ Mathematical Disposition	Observe and record throughout the unit	PM 4: Learning Skills Check List PM 5: Mathematical Dispositions and Learning Skills

Program Masters (PM) are in the *Grade 7 Planning and Program Masters* module.
Extra Practice Masters are on the CD-ROM and are printed in reduced format on page 51 of this module.

SECTION ORGANIZER

15–20 min

Curriculum Focus: Activate prior learning about ratio and rate.

ASSUMED PRIOR KNOWLEDGE

- ☑ Students have a basic understanding of ratio and rate.
- ☑ Students can use information to make comparisons.
- ☑ Students can relate time, distance, and speed.

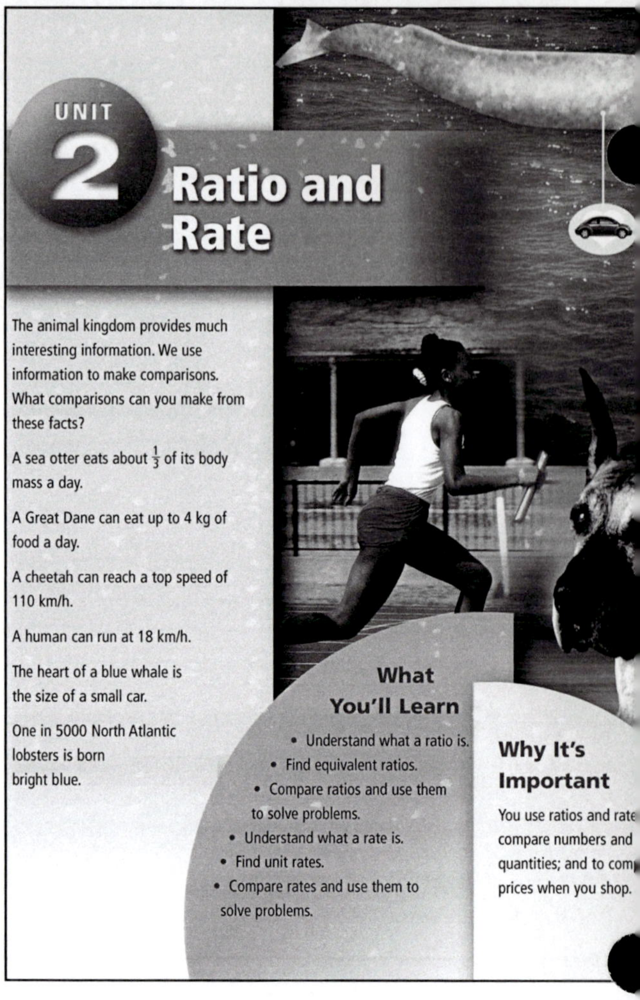

UNIT 2 Ratio and Rate

The animal kingdom provides much interesting information. We use information to make comparisons. What comparisons can you make from these facts?

A sea otter eats about $\frac{1}{3}$ of its body mass a day.

A Great Dane can eat up to 4 kg of food a day.

A cheetah can reach a top speed of 110 km/h.

A human can run at 18 km/h.

The heart of a blue whale is the size of a small car.

One in 5000 North Atlantic lobsters is born bright blue.

What You'll Learn

- Understand what a ratio is.
- Find equivalent ratios.
- Compare ratios and use them to solve problems.
- Understand what a rate is.
- Find unit rates.
- Compare rates and use them to solve problems.

Why It's Important

You use ratios and rate compare numbers and quantities; and to com prices when you shop.

ACTIVATE PRIOR LEARNING

Invite students to look at the pictures on pages 40 and 41 of the Student Book.

Ask questions, such as:

- What does it mean when we say a human can run at 18 km/h?
  (*In one hour, a human can run a distance of 18 km.*)
- Who runs faster, a cheetah or a human?
  (*A cheetah*)
- How do you know? (*A speed of 110 km/h is much faster than a speed of 18 km/h.*)
- About how many times as fast as a human is a cheetah? (*About 6 times*) How do you know? (*I rounded 18 to 20 and I rounded 110 to 120 to get a multiple of 20; 120 = 6 × 20, so the cheetah is about 6 times as fast as a human.*)
- How long would it take a sea otter to eat its body mass? (*About 3 days*)
  How do you know? ($\frac{1}{3} + \frac{1}{3} + \frac{1}{3} = 1$)
- How long do you think it would take you to eat 4 kg of food? (*About 4 or 5 days*)
- What ratio represents the number of North Atlantic lobsters born bright blue?
  (*1 in 5000, or 1 to 5000, or 1:5000*)
- What other ratio or rate can you think of?
  (*My heart beats about 70 times in one minute.*)

Tell students that we use ratios and rates every day. For example, we measure the speed of a car in kilometres per hour; when cooking rice, we add $2\frac{1}{2}$ cups of water for every cup of rice; we use a scale to help us read a map; and we use ratios to compare prices when shopping.

Tell students that they will use models and diagrams to investigate ratios, then find equivalent ratios. They will investigate rates, and then compare both ratios and rates and use them to solve problems. At the end of the unit, students will demonstrate what they have learned by finding which of 3 animals is the smartest.

Key Words

- ratio
- part-to-whole rati
- part-to-part ratio
- terms of a ratio
- equivalent ratios
- simplest form
- rate
- unit rate
- average speed

FROM THE LIBRARY

Time, Distance and Speed by Marion Smoothey. New York: Marshall Cavendish Inc., 1993.
ISBN: 1854354671
Text and activities explain how time, distance, and speed can be measured.

DIAGNOSTIC ASSESSMENT

What to Look For	What to Do
✔ Students demonstrate a basic understanding of rate and ratio. ✔ Students can use information to make comparisons. ✔ Students can relate time, distance, and speed.	***Extra Support:*** Students who have difficulty relating time, distance, and speed may benefit from writing speeds in words, for example, a speed of 25 km/h means that in 1 hour, I travel a distance of 25 km. *Work on this skill during Section 2.5.* Students who have difficulty solving ratio problems may benefit from modelling the problem with counters. For example, to solve the problem, "Benjamin drinks 3 glasses of milk per day. How many glasses will he drink in 4 days?" students could model the problem with 4 groups of 3 counters to get 12 glasses of milk. *Work on this skill during Section 2.5.*

SECTION ORGANIZER

65–80 min

Skills in Review
- Finding the greatest common factor
- Finding the lowest common multiple
- Converting among metric units

Student Materials
Optional
- 12 × 12 multiplication chart (PM 15)

Alternative Example 1

Find the GCF of 27 and 36.

Solution
Draw a factor tree for each number.

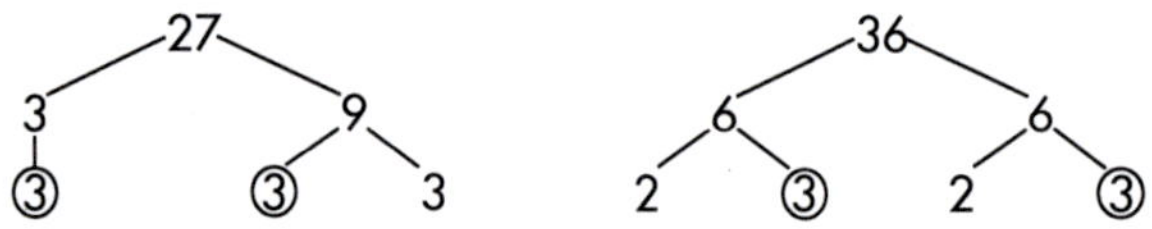

Circle the numbers that appear in the bottom row of both factor trees. 3 and 3 are common to both factor trees.
The GCF of 27 and 36 is 3 × 3 = 9.
When students use this method to find the GCF of 3 numbers (*Check* question 1d), they circle numbers that appear in the bottom row of all 3 factor trees.

UNIT 2 **Skills You'll Need**

Greatest Common Factor

Recall that the greatest common factor (GCF) of a set of numbers is the greatest number that will divide exactly into the given numbers.
For example, 6 is the greatest common factor of 18 and 24.

Example 1
Find the GCF of 24 and 30.

Solution
Draw a factor tree for each number.

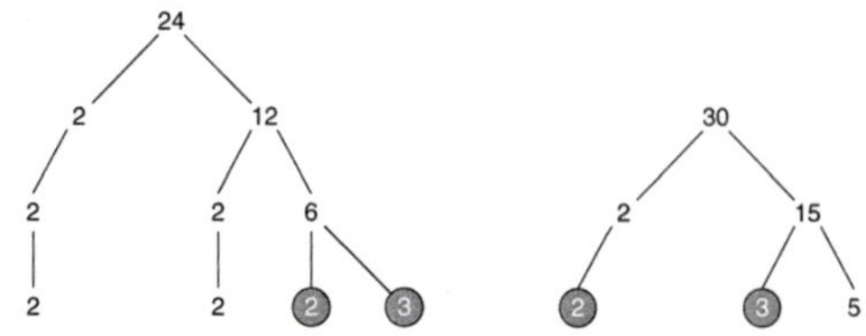

Circle the numbers that appear in the bottom row of both factor trees.
2 and 3 are common to both factor trees.
The GCF of 24 and 30 is 2 × 3 = 6.

✓ Check

1. Find the GCF of the numbers in each set.
   a) 30, 75 — 15
   b) 27, 63 — 9
   c) 42, 56 — 14
   d) 12, 18, 42 — 6

42 UNIT 2: Ratio and Rate

Greatest Common Factor

Have students examine the factor trees for 24 and 30. Ask:

- How do you make a factor tree for 24? (*I write 24 on the top, then write 2 numbers that multiply to give 24 on the next row. I continue in this way for any number that can be factored further. I carry any numbers that cannot be factored further to the bottom row.*)
- What are all the numbers on the bottom row? (*They are prime numbers.*)
- Is there another possible factor tree for 24? (*Yes. The numbers that appear in the bottom row would be the same.*)

Draw this factor tree on the board to show students how the end result is the same.

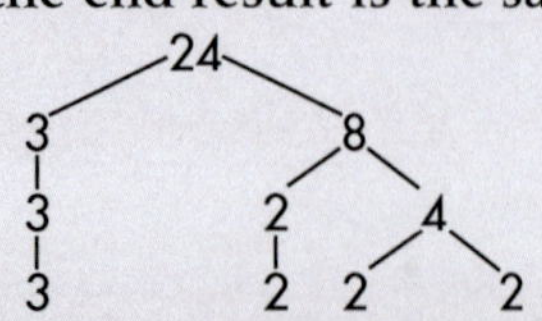

For extra support, have students play *Buzz* (Master 2.6).

Common Misconceptions

➤ Students do not take the factor trees far enough.

How to Help: Tell students that all the numbers in the bottom row must be prime numbers. Remind students that a prime number has only two factors, itself and 1. Suggest students make a list of the prime numbers to 50 on an index card for quick reference.

➤ Students have trouble finding the factors of a number.

How to Help: Tell students that they need to know the basic multiplication facts. Give students a copy of a 12 × 12 multiplication chart (PM 15) that they can refer to for factoring.

Lowest Common Multiple

Recall that the lowest common multiple (LCM) of a set of numbers is the least number that is a multiple of each number in the set. This also means that each number in the set is a factor of the lowest common multiple.

Example 2

Find the LCM of 18 and 32.

Solution

Draw a factor tree for each number.

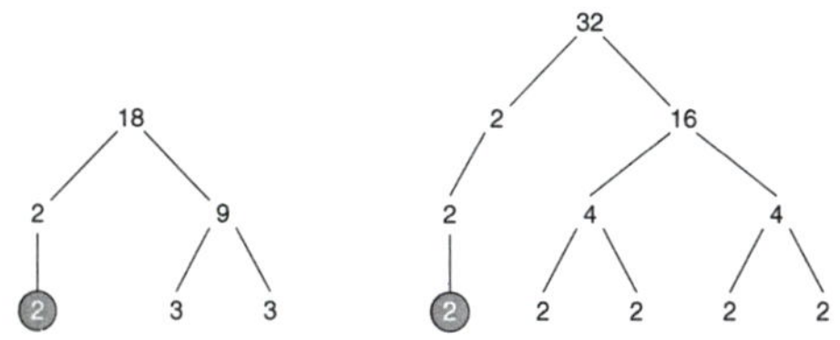

Circle the numbers that appear in the bottom row of both factor trees.
Multiply the numbers not circled and one each of the circled numbers:
$3 \times 3 \times 2 \times 2 \times 2 \times 2 \times 2 = 288$
The LCM of 18 and 32 is 288.

✓ Check

2. Write the first 6 multiples of each number.
   a) 4 b) 7 c) 9 d) 12
   a) 4, 8, 12, 16, 20, 24
   b) 7, 14, 21, 28, 35, 42
   c) 9, 18, 27, 36, 45, 54
   d) 12, 24, 36, 48, 60, 72
3. Find the LCM of the numbers in each pair.
   a) 9, 12 — 36 b) 14, 35 — 70 c) 16, 40 — 80
4. Find the LCM of the numbers in each set.
   a) 36, 45 — 180 b) 3, 4, 6 — 12 c) 12, 15, 20 — 60

Alternative Example 2

Find the LCM of 12 and 10.

Solution

Draw a factor tree for each number.

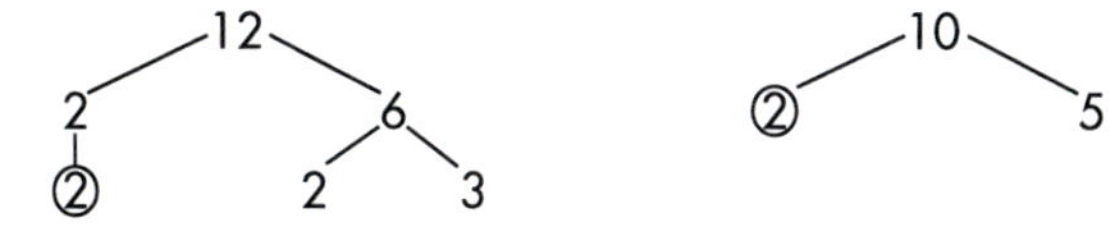

Circle the numbers that appear in the bottom row of both factor trees.
Multiply the numbers not circled and one each of the circled numbers.
$2 \times 3 \times 5 \times 2 = 60$
The LCM of 12 and 10 is 60.
When students use this method to find the LCM of 3 numbers (*Check* question 4b, c), they circle numbers that appear in the bottom row of any 2 of the 3 factor trees.

Lowest Common Multiple

Show students that there are often several factor trees for each number and there is no "correct" tree. Showing all the trees for 18 and 32 will help students see they do not need to know all the factors of a number to begin. Starting with 2 as a factor is always an option when the number is even, although trees that have a 2 in the first row can often be long. Beginning the first row with two factors that are close in value usually results in a smaller factor tree.

Ask:

- How do you use the factor trees to find the lowest common multiple?
  (*I multiply all the numbers that are not circled and one from each pair of circled numbers.*)
- What are the numbers in the bottom row of the trees? (*They are prime numbers.*)

For extra practice, have students play *LCM* (Master 2.5).

Common Misconceptions

➤ Students circle all the numbers that are the same in the bottom row of both factor trees; for example, they circle all the 2s in the bottom rows of *Example 2.*

How to Help: Tell students that the numbers in the bottom rows must be circled in pairs; for example, for each 2 circled in the factor tree for 18, there must be a 2 circled in the factor tree for 32.

➤ Students think that the LCM of two numbers is their product.

How to Help: If the two numbers have no common factors, then the LCM is their product. If the two numbers have common factors, then their LCM is the product divided by the common factor. For example, the LCM of 12 and 10 is 60, which is $12 \times 10 \div 2$. Have students find the LCM by listing multiples until they reach the matching common multiple.

Alternative Example 3

Convert.

a) 2700 m to kilometres
b) 14.5 L to millilitres
c) 32 cm to millimetres
d) 458 mm to centimetres

Solution

a) 2700 m $= \frac{2700}{1000}$ km
$= 2.7$ km

b) 14.5 L $= 14.5 \times 1000$ mL
$= 14\,500$ mL

c) 32 cm $= 32 \times 10$ mm
$= 320$ mm

d) 458 mm $= \frac{458}{10}$ cm
$= 45.8$ cm

Converting among Metric Units

100 cm = 1 m
1000 m = 1 km
1000 g = 1 kg
1000 mL = 1 L

- To convert centimetres to metres, divide by 100.
- To convert:
  metres to kilometres
  grams to kilograms
  millilitres to litres
  } Divide by 1000.

Divide to convert to a larger unit.

- To convert metres to centimetres, multiply by 100.
- To convert:
  kilometres to metres
  kilograms to grams
  litres to millilitres
  } Multiply by 1000.

Multiply to convert to a smaller unit.

Example 3

Convert.

a) 650 cm to metres
b) 82 km to metres
c) 2.4 kg to grams
d) 2840 mL to litres

Solution

a) 650 cm $= \frac{650}{100}$ m
$= 6.5$ m

b) 82 km $= 82 \times 1000$ m
$= 82\,000$ m

c) 2.4 kg $= 2.4 \times 1000$ g
$= 2400$ g

d) 2840 mL $= \frac{2840}{1000}$ L
$= 2.84$ L

✓ **Check**

5. Convert.

12.8 m **a)** 1280 cm to metres
b) 680 m to kilometres 0.68 km
2.454 kg **c)** 2454 g to kilograms
d) 1987 mL to litres 1.987 L
820 cm **e)** 8.2 m to centimetres
f) 1.25 km to metres 1250 m
450 g **g)** 0.45 kg to grams
h) 2.3 L to millilitres 2300 mL

44 UNIT 2: Ratio and Rate

Converting among Metric Units

Hold up a metre stick. Ask:

- How many centimetres are in 1 m? (*100*) In 2 m? (*200*) In 1.5 m? (*150*)

Record 1 m = 100 cm and 100 cm = 1 m on the board.

To convert metres to centimetres, multiply by 100. Ask:

- How would we convert from centimetres to metres? (*We would divide by 100.*)

At this point, do not tell students to "move the decimal point two places to the left or right" as they divide or multiply, as they will focus on the mechanics of moving decimal points, rather than on the meaning of converting between the units.

Common Misconceptions

➤ Students multiply by 1000 when converting from metres to kilometres.

How to Help: Tell students that to convert from a smaller unit to a larger unit, we always divide. Provide students with a visual aid to help them decide whether to multiply or divide, such as:

mm cm m km
(*divide*)

mm cm m km
(*multiply*)

➤ Students are unsure which is the larger of two units.

How to Help: Provide students with benchmarks for commonly used units. For example, tell students one millimetre is about the thickness of a dime, one centimetre is about the width of a fingernail, one metre is about the length of a baseball bat, and one kilometre is about the distance from the school to the gas station.

2.1 What Is a Ratio?

Focus Use models and diagrams to investigate ratios.

There are different ways to compare numbers.
Look at these advertisements.

How are the numbers in each advertisement compared?
Which advertisement is most effective? Explain.

Explore

Work with a partner.

How can you compare the number of blue counters to the number of yellow counters?
How many different ways can you compare the counters?
Write each way you find.

2.1 What Is a Ratio? 45

What Is a Ratio?

SECTION ORGANIZER

80–100 min

Curriculum Focus: Use models and diagrams to investigate ratios. (7m12, 7m24)

Student Materials
- counters (red, blue, and yellow)

Optional
- calculators
- Step-by-Step 1 (Master 2.7)
- Extra Practice 1 (Master 2.14)

Vocabulary: ratio, terms of a ratio, part-to-whole, part-to-part

Assessment: Master 2.2 Ongoing Observations: Ratio and Rate

Key Math Learnings

1. A ratio is a comparison of two numbers, quantities, or measures.
2. A part-to-whole ratio compares one part of a whole to the whole.
3. A part-to-part ratio compares one part of a whole to another part of the whole.

BEFORE Get Started

Explain to students that advertisers often use numbers to convince people to buy their products and that it is important for consumers to be able to interpret the advertising slogans. When presented with two numbers, we can compare them in different ways:

- 2 out of 3 means for every 3 people asked, 2 preferred this type of corn and 1 preferred another type. Have students use their calculators to illustrate that 7036 out of 10 554 can be simplified to 2 out of 3, by dividing each number by 3518.
- "Twice as many people" is another way of saying 2 out of 3. Two people are for this type of corn, one person is not, and 2 is twice 1.
- Numbers can be compared by subtracting.
  $10\ 554 - 7036 = 3518$

However, the last advertisement does not state how many people were surveyed.

If 1 000 000 people were surveyed, a difference of 3518 is not significant.

Ask:

- What differences are there among these advertisements?
  (*The first and third advertisements use small numbers to compare; the second and fourth advertisements use large numbers; only the first two advertisements tell us how many people were surveyed.*)
- Do you think only 3 people were surveyed in the first advertisement? (*No, these numbers have been reduced; it could have been 200 out of 300 people, or 2000 out of 3000 people, and so on.*)
- How does the third advertisement differ from the others? (*It doesn't use a number; it uses the words "twice as many" instead.*)
- How many people do you think were surveyed for each advertisement?
  (*As few as 3 people could have been surveyed for the first and third advertisements; as few as 3519 people could have been surveyed for the fourth*

REACHING ALL LEARNERS

Alternative Explore

Students work in groups to compare the students in the class in as many ways as they can.

Early Finishers

Have students add 3 green counters to the counters in *Explore*, then make and record additional comparisons.

Common Misconceptions

➤ Students confuse part-to-part ratios with part-to-whole ratios.
How to Help: When you give examples, state both types of ratios in numbers and in words. Have students use both types of ratios in their responses.

ESL Strategies

Have students for whom English is a second language draw diagrams or pictures with numerical notations to represent ratios, instead of words.

Sample Answers

2. a) The ratio of green counters to red counters is 9:7.
   b) The ratio of girls to boys is 8:3.
   c) The ratio of fiction to non-fiction books is 2:5.
4. Assume there are 11 boys and 16 girls in the class.
   a) 11:16 b) 16:11 c) 11:27 d) 9:25

Reflect & Share

Share your list with another pair of classmates.
Add any new comparisons to your list.
Talk about the different ways you compared the counters.

Connect

Here is a collection of models.

This is a part-to-whole ratio.

➢ We can use a **ratio** to compare one part of the collection to the whole collection.
There are 9 cars compared to 13 models.
The ratio of cars to models is written as 9 to 13 or 9:13.

This is a part-to-part ratio.

➢ We can use a ratio to compare one part of the collection to another part.
There are 9 cars compared to 4 planes.
The ratio of cars to planes is written as 9 to 4 or 9:4.
9 and **4** are called the **terms** of the ratio.
9 is the first term and 4 is the second term.

Example

At a class party, there are 16 boys, 15 girls, and 4 adults.
What is each ratio?
a) boys to girls b) girls to adults
c) adults to total number of people at the party

Solution

a) There are 16 boys and 15 girls.
So, the ratio of boys to girls is 16:15.
b) There are 15 girls and 4 adults.
So, the ratio of girls to adults is 15:4.
c) The total number of people is 16 + 15 + 4 = 35.
So, the ratio of adults to total number of people is 4:35.

46 UNIT 2: Ratio and Rate

advertisement; 10 554 people were surveyed for the second advertisement.)

- Which advertisement do you think is most effective? Why? (*I think the third advertisement is most effective because it is simple and gets right to the point. I think the second advertisement is most effective because it shows the large number of people that were surveyed.*)

Students who do not understand the significance of the possible range of people surveyed may benefit from a demonstration: Ask 3 students if they prefer chocolate or strawberry ice cream. If 2 students answer chocolate, tell students that we can say that 2 out of 3 students or "twice as many" students prefer chocolate ice cream. Have students comment on the accuracy of this statement.

Present *Explore*. Distribute 12 red, 6 blue, and 9 yellow counters to pairs of students.

DURING Explore

Ongoing Assessment: Observe and Listen

As students work, note students who do not realize that the red counters are not necessary to answer the first question. If some students generate only one or two ways, help them continue the investigation with questions, such as:

- Can you use numbers instead of, or as well as words?
- Can you use mathematical symbols in any of your comparisons?

Ask questions, such as:

- How can you compare the number of blue counters to the number of yellow counters? (*There are 6 blue counters and 9 yellow counters; 6 out of 15 counters are blue; 3 more counters are yellow; of the blue and yellow counters,* $\frac{2}{5}$ *are blue and* $\frac{3}{5}$ *are yellow.*)

Practice

1. Look at the crayons below. Write each ratio.
   a) red crayons to the total number of crayons 3:15
   b) yellow to the total number of crayons 1:15
   c) blue crayons to green crayons 7:4

2. Use words, numbers, or pictures.
   Write a ratio to compare the items in each sentence.
   a) A student had 9 green counters and 7 red counters on his desk. green:red = 9:7
   b) In a dance team, there were 8 girls and 3 boys. girls:boys = 8:3
   c) The teacher had 2 fiction and 5 non-fiction books on her desk. fiction:non-fiction = 2:5

3. The ratio of T-shirts to shorts in Frank's closet is 5:2.
   Write the ratio of T-shirts to the total number of garments. 5:7

4. a) What is the ratio of boys to girls in your class?
   b) What is the ratio of girls to boys?
   c) What is the ratio of boys to the total number of students in your class?
   d) What if two boys leave the room?
   What is the ratio in part c now?

5. a) Draw two different diagrams to show the ratio 3:5.
   b) Draw a diagram to show the ratio 7:1.

6. Maria shares some seashells with Jeff.
   Maria says, "Two for you, three for me, two for you, three for me ..."
   Tonya watches.
   At the end, she says, "So Jeff got $\frac{2}{3}$ of the shells."
   Do you agree with Tonya? Give reasons for your answer. No

5. a) part to part: △ △ △ ☺ ☺ ☺ ☺ ☺

   part to whole: △ △ △ ☺ ☺

   b) part to part: □ □ □ □ □ □ □ ●

6. No. The ratio of shells for Jeff to Maria is 2:3. Therefore, for every 5 shells, Jeff got 2 shells and Maria got 3 shells. Jeff got $\frac{2}{5}$ of the shells and Maria got $\frac{3}{5}$ of the shells.

8. e) Patrick adds 1 cup of chopped green pepper to his salad. What is the ratio of green pepper to the total amount of ingredients? (*Answer: 1:12*)

9. a) For example: The ratio of green triangles to red triangles is 1:3.
   The ratio of green figures to red figures is 2:8.
   The ratio of blue figures to all figures is 1:11.
   The ratio of circles and squares to triangles is 6:5.
   b) If I change one red circle to a green square, the ratio of red figures to green figures is 7:3, and the ratio of circles to triangles is 2:5.

REFLECT: A ratio is a comparison of two numbers, quantities, or measures. I found several examples of ratios in the newspaper. There was an advertisement for a health product that said, "Two out of three doctors recommend ..." This is a part-to-whole ratio. I found a recipe for a float that called for 1 part ice cream to 2 parts root beer. I also found an advertisement for carpet shampoo. It suggested mixing 1 part shampoo to 8 parts water. These are both part-to-part ratios. I can add the 2 terms of each ratio to get the whole amount.

- What other ways can you compare the counters? (*There are twice as many red counters as there are blue counters; 12 out of 27 counters are red; there are 3 more red counters than yellow counters; for every blue counter, there are 2 red counters.*)

Summarize the activity as a class. Have students add to their lists as other students share their comparisons. Note comparison words, such as "to," "more than," "for every," "as many as," and "out of."

AFTER Connect

Use *Connect* to introduce the terms **ratio, part-to-whole ratio, part-to-part ratio,** and **terms of the ratio.** Tell students that in a part-to-whole ratio, the number of items in the whole is always written last. In a part-to-part ratio, the order of the terms does not matter, but we must clearly communicate the meaning; for example, we must say whether the ratio is cars to planes or planes to cars.

Practice

Assessment Focus: Question 8

Students should demonstrate that they understand the difference between individual amounts and the total amount. Their own problem may be modelled after one of the text questions with only one detail changed (for example, in part b, using celery instead of macaroni) or by using different amounts of the given ingredients. A level 4 response may add or subtract given ingredients, or include new ingredients in the recipe.

Students who need extra support to complete Assessment Focus questions may benefit from the Step-by-Step masters (Masters 2.7–2.11).

Number Strategies

Students list all the prime numbers between 1 and 30, then find the sum of the numbers listed.

Assignment Guidelines

If your students do not have time to complete all the *Practice* questions on pages 47 and 48, these questions provide minimum coverage: 1, 3, 5, 6, 7, 8, *Reflect*

To assess the 4 Achievement Chart categories listed in the curriculum document, have students complete these *Practice* questions:

Understanding Concepts: 1
Communication: 2
Application: 5
Problem Solving: 6

Number Strategies

What is the sum of all the prime numbers between 1 and 30?
2 + 3 + 5 + 7 + 11 + 13 + 17 + 19 + 23 + 29 = 129

7. A box contains 8 red, 5 green, 2 brown, 3 purple, 1 blue, and 6 yellow candles.
   a) Write each ratio.
      i) red:purple 8:3 ii) green:blue 5:1
      iii) purple:green 3:5 iv) brown and yellow:total
   b) What if 3 red, 2 green, and 4 yellow candles were burn
      Write the new ratios for part a. i) 5:3 ii) 3:1 iii) 3:3

8. **Assessment Focus** Patrick plans to make salad. The re calls for 3 cups of cooked macaroni, 3 cups of sliced orang 2 cups of chopped apple, 1 cup of chopped celery, and 2 c of mayonnaise.
   a) What is the total amount of ingredients? 11 cups
   b) What is the ratio of oranges to apples? 3:2
      Mayonnaise to macaroni? 2:3
   c) What is the ratio of apples and oranges to the total am of ingredients? 5:11
   d) Patrick makes a mistake. He uses 2 cups of oranges ins What are the new ratios in parts b and c? 2:2, 4:10
   e) Write your own ratio problem about this salad. Solve your problem.

Take It Further

9. a) Create four different ratios using these figures.

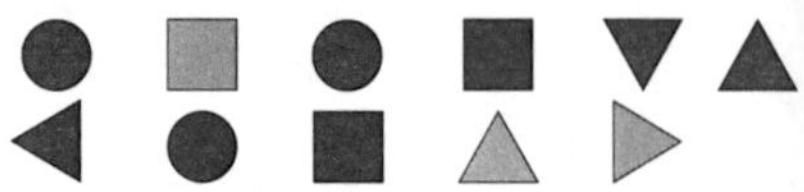

   b) How can you change one figure to create ratios of 2:5 7:3? Explain.

Reflect

Look in newspapers and magazines for examples of ratios.
Cut out the examples. Paste them in your notebook.
Explain how the ratios are used.
What information can you get from them?

48 UNIT 2: Ratio and Rate

ASSESSMENT FOR LEARNING

What to Look For	What to Do
Understanding concepts ✔ Students understand that a ratio is a comparison of two numbers, quantities, or measures. ***Applying procedures*** ✔ Students can write part-to-whole and part-to-part ratios. ✔ Students can use manipulatives or diagrams to model a ratio. ***Communicating*** ✔ Students can read ratios using words like "to" or "for every" to convey meaning.	***Extra Support:*** Students who have difficulty with part-to-part ratios may benefit from modelling the ratio with counters. Students put the counters into 2 groups. The number of counters in each group represents each term of the ratio. Students can use Step-by-Step 1 (Master 2.7) to complete question 8. ***Extra Practice:*** Have students use words, numbers, *and* pictures to model each ratio in *Practice* questions 2 to 4. Students can complete Extra Practice 1 (Master 2.14). ***Extension:*** Have students generate other ratios to describe the students in their class (for example, hair colour, length of hair).

Recording and Reporting
Master 2.2 Ongoing Observations: Ratio and Rate

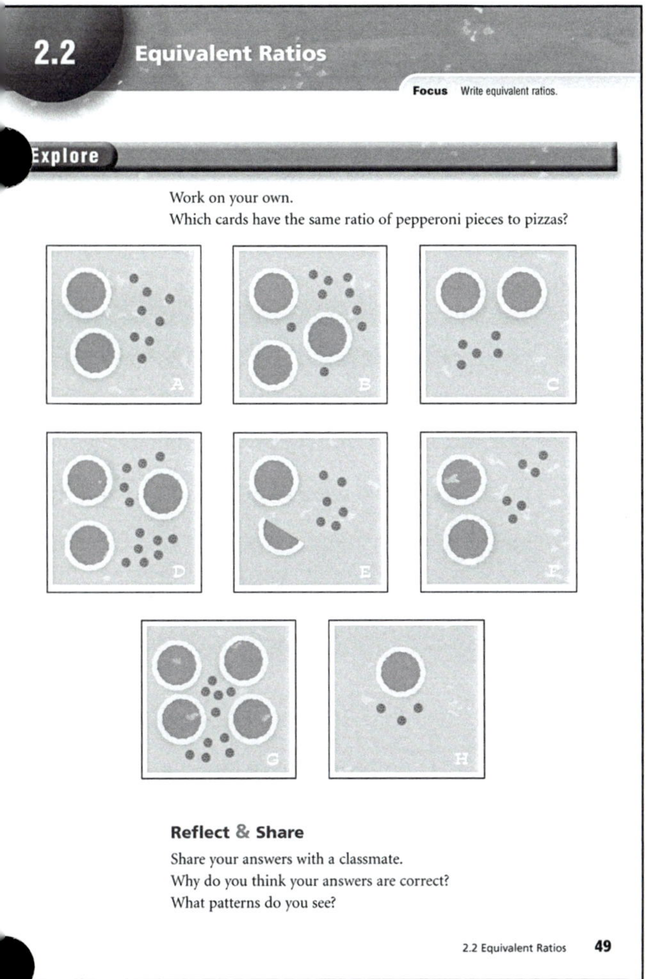
2.2 Equivalent Ratios

Focus Write equivalent ratios.

Explore

Work on your own.
Which cards have the same ratio of pepperoni pieces to pizzas?

Reflect & Share

Share your answers with a classmate.
Why do you think your answers are correct?
What patterns do you see?

2.2 Equivalent Ratios 49

Equivalent Ratios

SECTION ORGANIZER (80–100 min)

Curriculum Focus: Write equivalent ratios.
(7m71, 7m72, 7m25)

Teacher Materials

- transparency of 1-cm grid (PM 20)

Student Materials

Optional

- 1-cm grid paper (PM 20)
- Step-by-Step 2 (Master 2.8)
- Extra Practice 2 (Master 2.15)

Vocabulary: equivalent ratios, simplest form

Assessment: Master 2.2 Ongoing Observations: Ratio and Rate

Key Math Learnings

1. Equivalent ratios are equal.
2. An equivalent ratio can be formed by multiplying or dividing the terms of a ratio by the same number.
3. A ratio is in simplest form when its terms have no common factors.

BEFORE Get Started

Initiate a discussion about beverages that are made from powders. Write a list of these beverages on the board, such as coffee, iced tea, Kool-Aid, and hot chocolate. Ask:

- The can of hot chocolate powder suggests that you mix 3 spoonfuls of powder to 1 cup of hot water. How many spoonfuls would you need to make 2 cups of hot chocolate? (*6*) 3 cups? (*9*) 4 cups? (*12*)
- What pattern do you see in the numbers? (*As the number of cups increases by 1, the number of spoonfuls increases by 3.*)

Present *Explore.* Tell students they will examine the ratios of pepperoni pieces to pizzas on 8 different cards, then try to find equal ratios. Suggest students think of multiples as they compare the ratios.

DURING Explore

Ongoing Assessment: Observe and Listen

As students work, ask questions, such as:

- What is the ratio of pepperoni pieces to pizzas on Card C? (*5:2*)
- What is the ratio of pepperoni pieces to pizzas on Card G? (*10:4*)
- Are these ratios the same? Explain. (*Yes, I can divide the pepperoni and pizzas on Card G into 2 equal groups. Each group has 2 pizzas and 5 pepperoni pieces, which matches Card C.*)
- Which other cards have the same ratios? (*Cards B and H, Cards F and B, and Cards D and E*)
- How many cards have the same ratio as Card H? (*2*) Which ones? (*Cards B and F*) How do you know? (*I divide the pepperoni and pizzas on Card B into 3 equal groups. Each group has 1 pizza and 3 pepperoni pieces, which matches Card H. I divide the pepperoni and pizzas on Card F*

REACHING ALL LEARNERS

Alternative Explore

Materials: 2 number cubes, red and green counters
Students work in pairs. One student rolls 2 number cubes, then adds the numbers rolled. This is the first term of a ratio. This procedure is repeated to get the second term. Students model the ratio with red and green counters. Students make a different set of counters to model the same ratio, then record their findings.

Early Finishers

Have students find a simple recipe. Students rewrite the recipe to make enough for twice as many people, and to make enough for one-half as many people.

Common Misconceptions

➤ Students think they can add or subtract the same number to get an equivalent ratio.

How to Help: Start with the ratio 2:1. Keep adding 1 to each term to get ratios 3:2, 4:3, 5:4, and 6:5. Plot these points on a grid to show that they do not lie on a straight line, so they are not equivalent ratios.

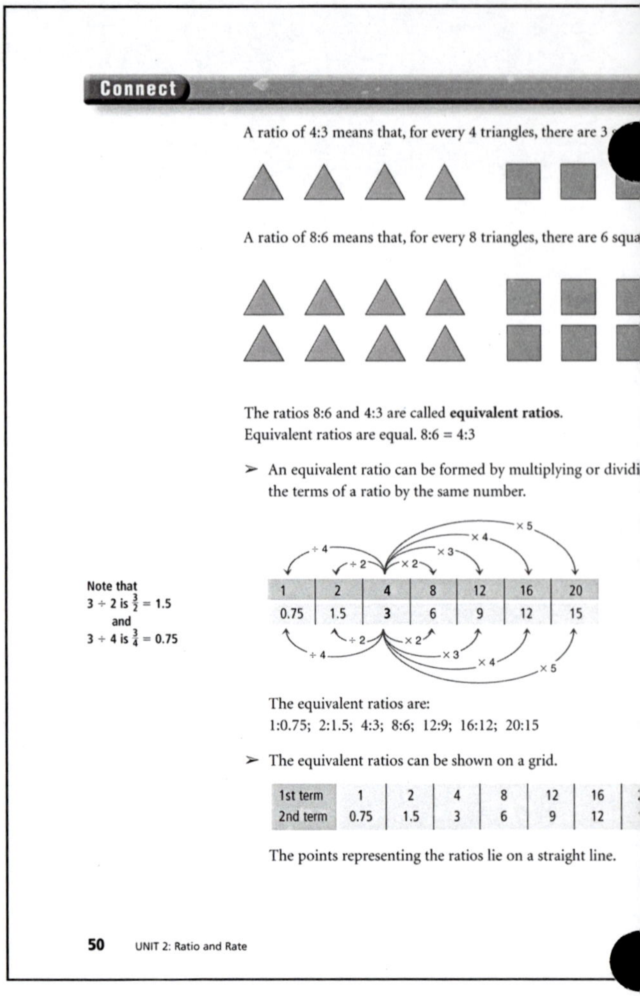

Connect

A ratio of 4:3 means that, for every 4 triangles, there are 3

A ratio of 8:6 means that, for every 8 triangles, there are 6 squa

The ratios 8:6 and 4:3 are called **equivalent ratios.**
Equivalent ratios are equal. 8:6 = 4:3

➤ An equivalent ratio can be formed by multiplying or dividi the terms of a ratio by the same number.

Note that
$3 \div 2$ is $\frac{3}{2} = 1.5$
and
$3 \div 4$ is $\frac{3}{4} = 0.75$

1	2	4	8	12	16	20
0.75	1.5	3	6	9	12	15

The equivalent ratios are:
1:0.75; 2:1.5; 4:3; 8:6; 12:9; 16:12; 20:15

➤ The equivalent ratios can be shown on a grid.

1st term	1	2	4	8	12	16
2nd term	0.75	1.5	3	6	9	12

The points representing the ratios lie on a straight line.

50 UNIT 2: Ratio and Rate

Sample Answers

1. a)

1.5	**3**	6	9	12
2	**4**	8	12	16

b)

7	**14**	28	42	56
2	**4**	8	12	16

2. a) The ratio of girls to boys is 5:4.
   b) The ratio of American cars to Japanese cars is 1:3.

into 2 equal groups. Each group has 1 pizza and 3 pepperoni pieces, which matches Card H.)

- How do you know Cards D and E have the same ratios?
  (If I cut one pizza on Card D in half, then I can make 2 equal groups. Each group has $1\frac{1}{2}$ pizzas and 6 pepperoni pieces, which matches Card E.)
- How could you draw a card to show a ratio that is the same as Card A?
  (I could draw 4 pepperoni slices and 1 pizza.)
  Why? *(I divide the pepperoni and pizza on Card A into 2 equal groups. Each group has 1 pizza and 4 pepperoni pieces, and this is what I draw.)*
- What patterns do you see?
  (When I compare two ratios that are the same, I can get one ratio from the other by dividing or multiplying the terms by the same number.)

AFTER Connect

Review the examples in *Connect.*

Ask questions, such as:

- If there were 12 triangles, how many squares would there be? *(9)* How do you know?
  (The number of triangles was multiplied by 3, so I multiplied the number of squares by 3.)
- If there were 2 triangles, how many squares would there be? *($1\frac{1}{2}$)* How do you know?
  (The number of triangles was divided by 2, so I divided the number of squares by 2.)
- Is the ratio 6:9 in simplest form? Why?
  (No, both terms can be divided by 3.)
- What is 6:9 in simplest form? *(2:3)*

Use a 1-cm grid transparency to graph the number of connectors against the number of short rods from the *Example,* for Kits C, D, E, and the Regular Kit.

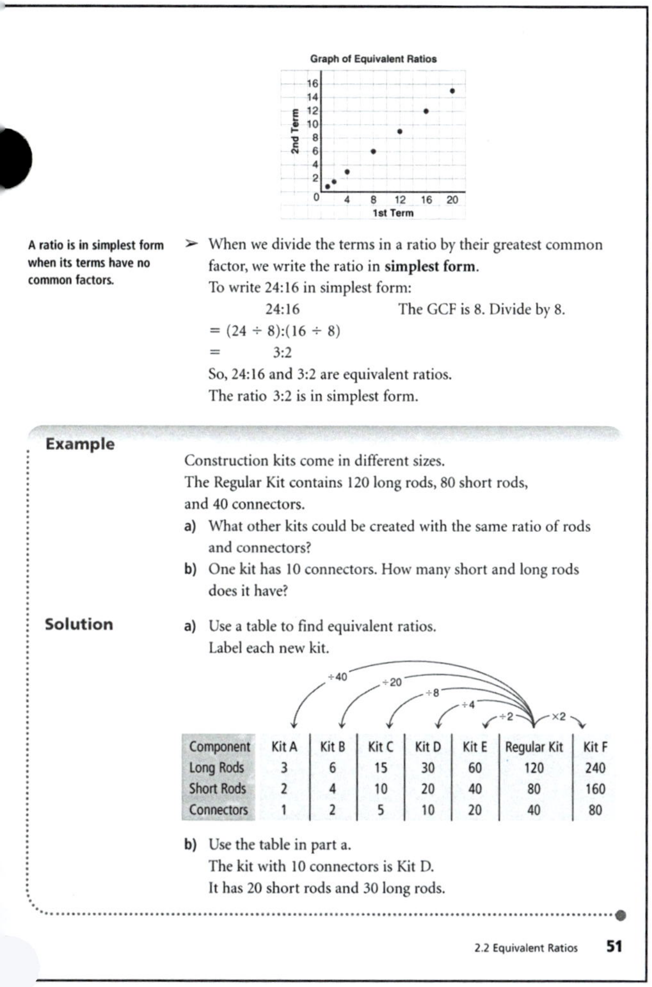

Graph of Equivalent Ratios

A ratio is in simplest form when its terms have no common factors.

➢ When we divide the terms in a ratio by their greatest common factor, we write the ratio in **simplest form**.
To write 24:16 in simplest form:
24:16 The GCF is 8. Divide by 8.
= (24 ÷ 8):(16 ÷ 8)
= 3:2
So, 24:16 and 3:2 are equivalent ratios.
The ratio 3:2 is in simplest form.

Example

Construction kits come in different sizes.
The Regular Kit contains 120 long rods, 80 short rods, and 40 connectors.

a) What other kits could be created with the same ratio of rods and connectors?
b) One kit has 10 connectors. How many short and long rods does it have?

Solution

a) Use a table to find equivalent ratios.
Label each new kit.

Component	Kit A	Kit B	Kit C	Kit D	Kit E	Regular Kit	Kit F
Long Rods	3	6	15	30	60	120	240
Short Rods	2	4	10	20	40	80	160
Connectors	1	2	5	10	20	40	80

b) Use the table in part a.
The kit with 10 connectors is Kit D.
It has 20 short rods and 30 long rods.

2.2 Equivalent Ratios 51

c) The ratio of blue paint to white paint is 3:1.
d) The ratio of Canadian stamps to American stamps is 1:2.

3. 2:3 and 6:9; both terms of the first ratio were multiplied by 3 to get the second ratio.
9:12 and 3:4; both terms of the first ratio were divided by 3 to get the second ratio.
8:5 and 16:10; both terms of the first ratio were multiplied by 2 to get the second ratio.
1:2 and 3:6; both terms of the first ratio were multiplied by 3 to get the second ratio.
4. a) There could be 30 non-fiction books and 10 fiction books.
b) There are many possible answers. The ratio of non-fiction books to fiction books is 3:1. As long as the ratio of non-fiction books to fiction books is equivalent to 3:1, the answer is possible. However, since it is a class library, reasonable answers would be between 30 and 120 non-fiction books and between 10 and 40 fiction books.
5. 30 cm by 15 cm

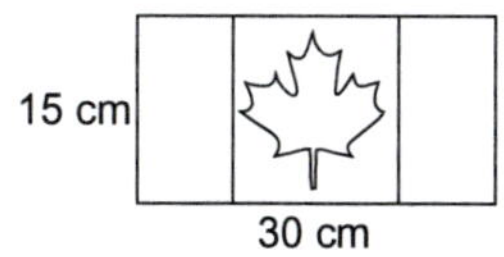

6. There could be 5 red counters, 6 blue counters, and 8 green counters, or there could be 10 red counters, 12 blue counters, and 16 green counters. There are many more ways to do this, as we can continue to multiply each number of counters in the first set by whole numbers greater than 2 to get different sets.

REFLECT: I chose the ratio 2:5. To find an equivalent ratio, I can multiply both terms of the ratio by 2 to get 4:10. To find another equivalent ratio, I can multiply both terms of the original ratio by 3 to get 6:15.

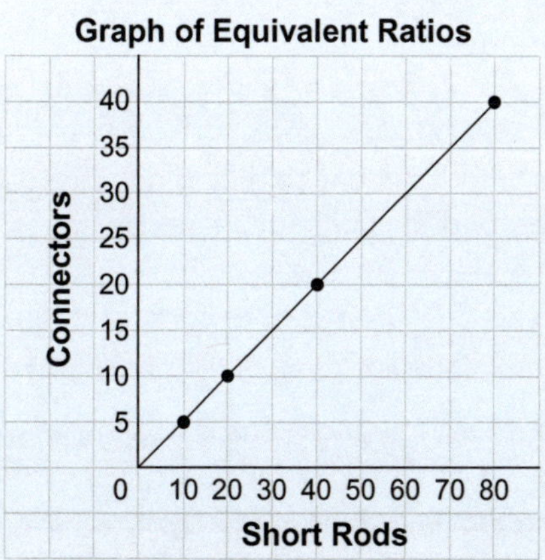

Ensure students understand that since the points representing the ratios lie on a straight line, the ratios are equivalent.

Practice

Encourage students to draw diagrams and tables to help them answer the questions.

Assessment Focus: Question 6

Students need to understand that the ratio of red:blue is 5:6, so they need 5 red counters to 6 blue counters. The ratio of blue:green is 3:4, so students find an equivalent ratio with 6 blue counters; that is, blue:green is 6:8.

Number Strategies

Students could draw factor trees for each number, or could begin by listing the factors of each number. Stronger math students might be able to identify the greatest common factors without listing factors first.

Assignment Guidelines

If your students do not have time to complete all the *Practice* questions on page 52, these questions provide minimum coverage: 1, 2, 3, 4, 6, *Reflect*

To assess the 4 Achievement Chart categories listed in the curriculum document, have students complete these *Practice* questions:

Understanding Concepts: 1
Communication: 3
Application: 5
Problem Solving: 6

Practice

Number Strategies

Find the greatest common factor of the numbers in each set.

- 16, 40, 24 8
- 33, 77, 88 11
- 45, 75, 30 15
- 150, 75, 225 75

1. Write three ratios equivalent to each ratio.
Use tables to show your work.
a) 3:4 = 6:8 = 9:12 = 12:16 **b)** 14:4 = 7:2 = 28:8 = 42:12

2. Rewrite each sentence as a ratio statement in simplest form.
a) In a class, there are 15 girls and 12 boys. 15:12 = 5:4
b) In a parking lot, there were 4 American cars and 12 Japanese cars. 4:12 = 2:6 = 1:3
c) A paint mixture is made up of 6 L of blue paint and 2 L of white paint. 6:2 = 3:1
d) A stamp collection contains 12 Canadian stamps and 24 American stamps. 12:24 = 1:2

3. Name the pairs of equivalent ratios:
2:3, 9:12, 8:5, 1:2, 2:1, 16:10, 3:6, 6:9, 5:8, 3:4
Tell how you know they are equivalent.

4. In a class library, 3 out of 4 books are non-fiction.
The rest are fiction.
a) How many non-fiction books could there be?
How many fiction books?
b) How many different answers can you find for part a?
Which answers are reasonable? Explain.

5. The official Canadian flag has a length to width ratio of 2:1.
Doreen has a sheet of paper that measures 30 cm by 20 cm.
What are the length and width of the largest Canadian flag Doreen can draw? Sketch a picture of the flag. 30 cm by 1

6. **Assessment Focus** Use red, blue, and green counters.
Make a set of counters with these two ratios:
red:blue = 5:6 blue:green = 3:4
How many different ways can you do this?
Record each way you find.

Reflect

Choose a ratio. Use pictures, numbers, or words to show how t
two equivalent ratios.

52 UNIT 2: Ratio and Rate

ASSESSMENT FOR LEARNING

What to Look For	What to Do
Understanding concepts ✔ Students understand that equivalent ratios are equal. ***Applying procedures*** ✔ Students can recognize and write equivalent ratios. ✔ Students can write a ratio in simplest form. ✔ Students can use equivalent ratios to solve word problems. ***Communicating*** ✔ Students can explain the reasonableness of an answer.	***Extra Support:*** Students who have difficulty finding equivalent ratios could use a calculator, and multiply each term by the same number. Students can use Step-by-Step 2 (Master 2.8) to complete question 6. ***Extra Practice:*** Have students draw more cards like those in *Explore* to show different pairs of equivalent ratios. Students can complete Extra Practice 2 (Master 2.15). ***Extension:*** Have students graph the number of long rods against the number of short rods from the *Example* in *Connect* for Kits A to E. Students explain their results.

Recording and Reporting
Master 2.2 Ongoing Observations: Ratio and Rate

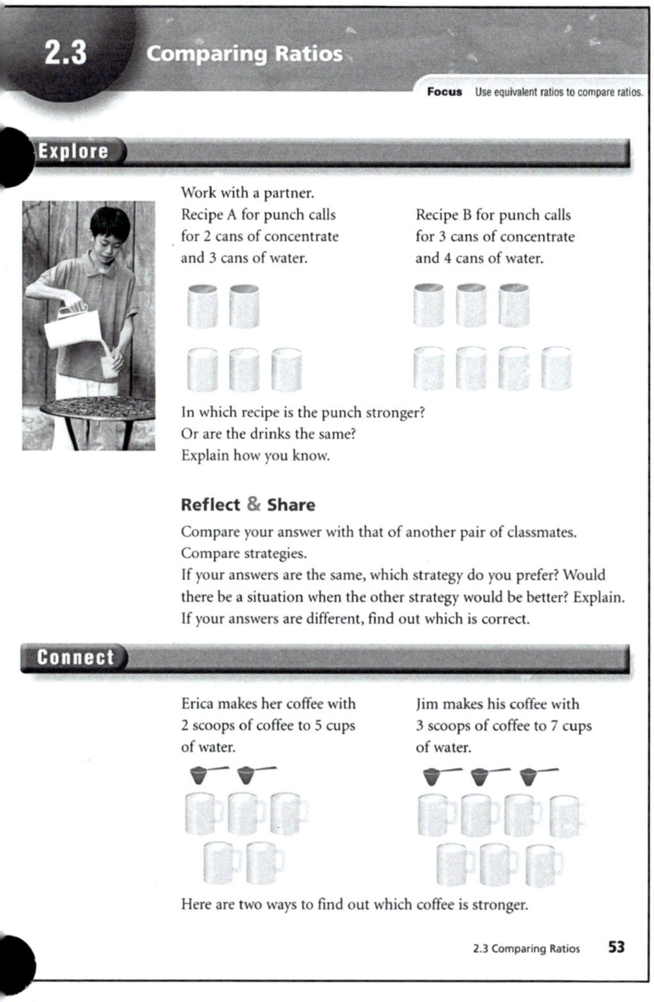
2.3 Comparing Ratios

Focus Use equivalent ratios to compare ratios.

Explore

Work with a partner.

Recipe A for punch calls for 2 cans of concentrate and 3 cans of water.

Recipe B for punch calls for 3 cans of concentrate and 4 cans of water.

In which recipe is the punch stronger?
Or are the drinks the same?
Explain how you know.

Reflect & Share

Compare your answer with that of another pair of classmates.
Compare strategies.
If your answers are the same, which strategy do you prefer? Would there be a situation when the other strategy would be better? Explain.
If your answers are different, find out which is correct.

Connect

Erica makes her coffee with 2 scoops of coffee to 5 cups of water.

Jim makes his coffee with 3 scoops of coffee to 7 cups of water.

Here are two ways to find out which coffee is stronger.

2.3 Comparing Ratios 53

Comparing Ratios

SECTION ORGANIZER 80–100 min

Curriculum Focus: Use equivalent ratios to compare ratios. (7m14, 7m71, 7m75)
Student Materials
Optional
- Step-by-Step 3 (Master 2.9)
- Extra Practice 3 (Master 2.16)

Assessment: Master 2.2 Ongoing Observations: Ratio and Rate

Key Math Learning

Ratios can be compared by writing them with the second terms the same, and with the first terms the same.

BEFORE Get Started

Have students recall the class discussion about drink mixes. Ask:

- What makes the drink taste stronger? (*More mix or less water*)
  Weaker? (*Less mix or more water*)
- What do you do when you use 2 packages of drink mix? (*I add twice as much water.*)
- What if you want to use only half a package of mix? (*I would add half as much water.*)

Present *Explore.* Tell students they will use their knowledge of ratios and equivalent ratios to determine which punch is stronger. Ensure students understand they are to justify their answers.

DURING Explore

Ongoing Assessment: Observe and Listen

Observe the strategies students use to solve the problem. If students focus on the amount of water only (4 cans compared to 3 cans), remind them that the amount of concentrate is also different in each recipe.

Ask questions, such as:

- What is the ratio of concentrate to water in recipe A? (*2:3*) In recipe B? (*3:4*)
- How did you find which punch is stronger? (*I used equivalent ratios: For recipe A, 2:3 = 4:6 = 6:9 = 8:12; for recipe B, 3:4 = 6:8 = 9:12. I kept writing equivalent ratios until the second terms were the same. Then I looked at the first terms. Recipe B uses more concentrate, so its punch is stronger.*)

REACHING ALL LEARNERS

Alternative Explore

Tell students to pretend they are carpet cleaners. There are 2 carpet shampoos available to them. Shampoo A requires 3 parts of shampoo for every 7 parts of water. Shampoo B requires 2 parts of shampoo for every 5 parts of water. Which shampoo would make the stronger mixture? Students should explain how they know.

Early Finishers

Have students redo the *Example* in *Connect* using the strategy "make the first terms the same." Students compare their answers to the answer given in the *Example*.

Common Misconceptions

➤ Students think that a ratio with terms that are numerically larger is the greater ratio.

How to Help: Use an example such as 7:10 and 4:5, to show that 4:5 = 8:10, and hence 4:5 is greater than 7:10. Remind students that it is not the individual terms that tell about ratio; it is the 2 terms together that indicate its value.

Sample Answers

1. Mixture A: C C C C C C C C C W W W

   Mixture B: C W W W

2. a) Write equivalent ratios until the sums of the terms are equal.
   4:3 = 20:15 — sum of terms is 20 + 15 = 35.
   3:2 = 21:14 — sum of terms is 21 + 14 = 35.
   The total number of pictures is 70.

➤ Find how much water is used for 1 scoop of coffee.

1 scoop of coffee to $2\frac{1}{2}$ cups of water. | 1 scoop of coffee to $2\frac{1}{3}$ cups of water.

Since $2\frac{1}{3}$ is less than $2\frac{1}{2}$,
Jim uses less water to 1 scoop of coffee.
So, Jim's coffee is stronger.

➤ Find how much coffee is used for the same amount of water.
Write each mixture as a ratio.
Write each ratio with the same second term,
then compare the first terms.
Use equivalent ratios.

Erica: 2:5; ×2 4:10; ×3 6:15; ×4 8:20; ×5 10:25; ×6 12:30; ×7 14:35

Jim: 3:7; ×2 6:14; ×3 9:21; ×4 12:28; ×5 15:35

Since 2:5 = 14:35,
Erica uses 14 scoops of coffee to 35 cups of water.

Since 3:7 = 15:35,
Jim uses 15 scoops of coffee to 35 cups of water.

Jim uses more coffee. So, Jim's coffee is stronger.
Notice that, as we multiply to get equivalent ratios,
we get multiples of the terms of the ratios.
That is, the first terms in Erica's equivalent ratios are multiples of 2 and the second terms are multiples of 5.

54 UNIT 2: Ratio and Rate

- Did anyone use a different strategy? Explain. (*I found how much concentrate was used for each can of water. For Recipe A, I divided the recipe by 3 to get $\frac{2}{3}$ can of concentrate and 1 can of water. For recipe B, I divided the recipe by 4 to get $\frac{3}{4}$ can of concentrate and 1 can of water. Since $\frac{3}{4} > \frac{2}{3}$, recipe B makes the stronger punch.*)
- Are any other strategies possible? Explain. (*Yes, I could find how much water is used for each can of concentrate. The recipe that uses the lesser amount of water would make the stronger punch. Recipe A uses $\frac{3}{2}$, or $1\frac{1}{2}$ cans of water to 1 can of concentrate. Recipe B uses $\frac{4}{3}$, or $1\frac{1}{3}$ cans of water to 1 can of concentrate. Since $1\frac{1}{3} < 1\frac{1}{2}$, recipe B uses less water, so it makes the stronger punch.*)

AFTER Connect

Review the strategies in *Connect*. Some students may not be familiar with making coffee. Remind students that "stronger" or "weaker" in these questions depends on the amount of water used. Tell students that we assume both Erica and Jim are using the same type of coffee.

Some students may suggest another strategy to find how much water is used for the same amount of coffee. To do this:

Write each mixture as a ratio.
Write each ratio with the same first term,
then compare the second terms.
Use equivalent ratios.

Erica: 2:5; ×2 4:10; ×3 6:15

Jim: 3:7; ×2 6:14

A quicker way to write each ratio with the same second term is to find the lowest common multiple of the second terms.
That is, the lowest common multiple of 5 and 7 is 35.

Example

At the outdoor centre, there were the same numbers of boys and girls. Five out of every 8 boys wanted to kayak. Two out of every 3 girls wanted to kayak. Do more boys than girls want to kayak? Explain.

Solution

Five out of every 8 boys want to kayak.
This is a ratio of 5:8.
Two out of every 3 girls want to kayak.
This is a ratio of 2:3.
To compare the ratios, write them with the second terms the same.
The lowest common multiple of 8 and 3 is 24.
Multiply to make the second term of each ratio 24.

Boys	Girls
5:8	2:3
= (5 × 3):(8 × 3)	= (2 × 8):(3 × 8)
= 15:24	= 16:24
15 out of 24 boys want to kayak	16 out of 24 girls want to kayak

Since 16 is greater than 15, more girls want to kayak.

Practice

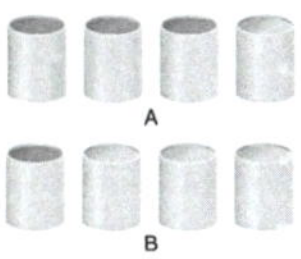

1. The concentrate and water in each picture are mixed.
   Which mixture is stronger: A or B? Mixture A
   Draw a picture to show your answer.

2. Two boxes contain pictures of hockey and basketball players.
   In one box, the ratio of hockey players to basketball players is 4:3.
   In the other box, the ratio is 3:2.
   The boxes contain the same number of pictures.
   a) What could the total number of pictures be? 70
   b) Which box contains more pictures of hockey players?
   Draw a picture to show your answer.

2.3 Comparing Ratios **55**

b) The box with ratio 3:2 has more hockey players. Students' pictures should show the numbers of players in the equivalent ratios above.

3. I found how many shots would be made for the same number of free shots. Since 6:13 = 54:117 and 5:9 = 65:117, Madhu made more shots.

4. a) The mixture of 5 cans of white paint and 7 cans of blue paint. I found how many cans of white paint are needed for the same number of cans of blue paint. Since 3:4 = 21:28 and 5:7 = 20:28, the second mixture uses less white paint, so it will give the darker shade of blue.
   b) The mixture of 3 cans of white paint and 4 cans of blue paint requires more white paint because 21 > 20.

5. b) If I add 1 can of concentrate to B, the ratio becomes 4:2 which is the same as 2:1, ratio A.
   B [C][C][C][C][W][W] 4:2
   A [C][C][W] 2:1 The ratios are equivalent.

6. a) Write equivalent ratios until the 2nd term in each ratio is 30.
   Ms. Arbuckle
   7:5 = 14:10 = 21:15 = 28:20 = 35:25 = 42:30
   Mr. Albright
   4:3 = 8:6 = 12:9 = 16:12 = 20:15 = 24:18 = 28:21 = 32:24 = 36:27 = 40:30
   Ms. Arbuckle's class has 2 more fiction books.
   b) If Mr. Albright added 2 non-fiction books to his class library, the ratio of fiction to non-fiction books would become 40:32, which is the same as 5:4. The ratio in Ms. Arbuckle's class is 7:5. If I make both second terms the same, 5:4 = 25:20 and 7:5 = 28:20. The two ratios are not the same.

Since 2:5 = 6:15, Erica uses 6 scoops of coffee to 15 cups of water.	Since 3:7 = 6:14, Jim uses 6 scoops of coffee to 14 cups of water.

Jim uses less water. So, Jim's coffee is stronger.

Ask questions, such as:

- When would the strategy "make the second terms the same" be preferred?
  (*When you can find the lowest common multiple of the second terms in fewer steps.*)
- When would the strategy "make the first terms the same" be preferred? (*When you can find the lowest common multiple of the first terms in fewer steps, as in the example of Erica and Jim.*)

Tell students that to check for equivalency, students could plot the points (at least three) representing the ratios on a grid. The points lie on a straight line if the ratios are equivalent.

Practice

Encourage students to draw diagrams and tables as necessary to help them answer the questions. For question 4, ensure students understand that the more white paint added, the lighter the shade will be.

Assessment Focus: Question 6

Students should use equivalent ratios to compare the ratios. They should recognize that adding 2 non-fiction books to Mr. Albright's library will not make the ratios the same. Students should use equivalent ratios to explain their answers.

7. Write equivalent ratios for each ratio until the 2nd terms (the numbers of people) are the same. Since 2:3 = 14:21 and 5:7 = 15:21, the people at Amin's party get more pizza.

REFLECT: In the first store, a ratio of 7:5 could be 21 DVDs and 15 videos. In the second store, a ratio of 4:3 could be 20 DVDs to 15 videos. In this case, the first store has more DVDs. However, a ratio of 7:5 could also be 42 DVDs and 30 videos, and a ratio of 4:3 could be 60 DVDs and 45 videos, so the second store has more DVDs.
Since we do not know how the two ratios are related, we cannot say which store has more DVDs.

Number Strategies

Students could use different strategies, such as guess and check; make a diagram; or make a table.

Assignment Guidelines

If your students do not have time to complete all the *Practice* questions on pages 55 and 56, these questions provide minimum coverage: 1, 3, 4, 6, 7, *Reflect*
To assess the 4 Achievement Chart categories listed in the curriculum document, have students complete these *Practice* questions:
Understanding Concepts: 1
Communication: 3
Application: 4
Problem Solving: 6

Number Strategies

There are 10 coins that total $0.60.
What are the coins?
8 nickels and 2 dimes

3. In a basketball game, Alison made 6 of 13 free shots.
Madhu made 5 of 9 free shots. Who played better? Explain. M

4. The principal is deciding which shade of blue to have the classrooms painted. One shade of blue requires 3 cans of paint mixed with 4 cans of blue paint. Another shade of blue requires 5 cans of white paint mixed with 7 cans of blue paint.
a) Which mixture will give the darker shade of blue? Explain.
b) Which mixture will require more white paint? 3:4

5. Look at the two mixtures.
a) What is the ratio of concentrate to water in A and in B?

A 2:1

B 3:2

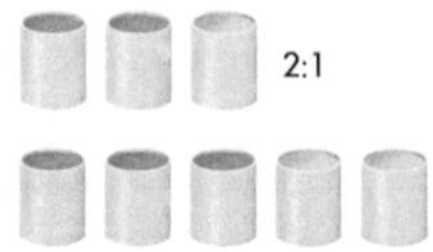

b) Explain how you could add concentrate or water to make both ratios the same.
Draw a picture to show your answer.

6. Assessment Focus The ratio of fiction to non-fiction book in Ms. Arbuckle's class library is 7:5.
The ratio of fiction to non-fiction books in Mr. Albright's class library is 4:3.
Each classroom has 30 non-fiction books.
a) Which room has more fiction books? How many more?
b) Mr. Albright added two non-fiction books to his class librar
Does this make the ratio the same in both classes? Explain.

7. At Ria's party, there were 2 pizzas for every 3 people.
At Amin's party, there were 5 pizzas for every 7 people.
At which party did each person get more pizza? Explain.
Amin's p

Reflect

In one store, the ratio of DVDs to videos is 7:5.
In another store, the ratio of DVDs to videos is 4:3.
Explain why you cannot say which store has more DVDs.

56 UNIT 2: Ratio and Rate

ASSESSMENT FOR LEARNING

What to Look For	What to Do
Understanding concepts ✔ Students understand that equivalent ratios can be used to compare ratios. ***Applying procedures*** ✔ Students can choose an appropriate strategy to solve problems involving the comparison of ratios. ✔ Students can compare ratios by writing them with the second terms the same, and by writing them with the first terms the same. ***Communicating*** ✔ Students can draw diagrams and use words to justify their answers.	***Extra Support:*** Students who have difficulty deciding whether to make the first terms the same or the second terms the same could use one method for all questions, and not analyse the situation to decide which method is more efficient. Students can use Step-by-Step 3 (Master 2.9) to complete question 6. ***Extra Practice:*** Have students write problems similar to the problems in *Explore* and *Connect*, then solve their own problems. Students can complete Extra Practice 3 (Master 2.16). ***Extension:*** Students compare three ratios of scoops of coffee to cups of water to find which coffee is the strongest: 2:3, 1:2, or 3:5 (*Answer: 2:3*).

Recording and Reporting
Master 2.2 Ongoing Observations: Ratio and Rate

Mid-Unit Review

LESSON

2.1 **1.** In the school parking lot, there are 4 Japanese cars, 7 American cars, 3 German cars, and 2 Korean cars. Write each ratio.

a) American cars to Japanese cars 7:4

b) German cars to Korean cars 3:2

c) American cars to total number of cars 7:16

d) German cars to Japanese cars and American cars 3:11

2. A box contains 5 cream chocolates, 2 chocolate-covered almonds, and 3 caramel chocolates.

a) What is each ratio? Sketch a picture for each ratio.

i) almond chocolates to caramel chocolates 2:3

ii) cream chocolates to caramel chocolates 5:3

iii) cream chocolates to all chocolates 5:10 or 1:2

b) Lesley ate one of each kind of chocolate. What is each new ratio for part a?

i) 1:2, ii) 4:2 or 2:1, iii) 4:7

3. In Mary's closet, there are 7 T-shirts, 4 pairs of shorts, and 3 sweaters. Write each ratio.

a) T-shirts to shorts 7:4

b) sweaters to shorts 3:4

c) sweaters to T-shirts and shorts 3:11

2.2 **4.** For each ratio, write three equivalent ratios.

a) 5:3 5:3 = 10:6 = 15:9 = 20:12

b) 6:24 = 1:4 = 3:12 = 12:48

5. a) Write each ratio below in simplest form.

i) green squares to red squares 1:3

ii) yellow squares to purple squares 3:1

iii) red squares to total number of squares 3:8

b) State the colours for each ratio.

i) 1:6 purple:blue

ii) 2:5 yellow:red purple:green

6. In Ms. Bell's class, the ratio of boys to girls is 5:4.

a) There are 15 boys in the class. How many girls are there? 12 girls

b) Two girls leave. What is the new ratio of boys to girls? 15:10 = 3:2

2.3 **7.** A jug of orange juice requires 3 cans of orange concentrate and 5 cans of water.

a) Accidentally, 4 cans of concentrate were mixed with 5 cans of water. Is the mixture stronger or weaker than it should be? Explain. Stronger

b) Suppose 6 cans of water were mixed with 3 cans of concentrate. Is the mixture stronger or weaker than it should be? Explain. Weaker

Mid-Unit Review 57

SECTION ORGANIZER

Assessment: Masters 2.1 Unit Rubric: Ratio and Rate, 2.4 Unit Summary: Ratio and Rate

Sample Solutions

2. a) i) Almond to caramel = 2:3

A A Ca Ca Ca

ii) Cream to caramel = 5:3

Cr Cr Cr Cr Cr Ca Ca Ca

iii) Cream to all chocolates = 5:10 or 1:2

Cr Cr Cr Cr Cr Ca Ca Ca A A

b) i) Almond to caramel = 1:2

ii) Cream to caramel = 4:2 or 2:1

iii) Cream to all chocolates = 4:7

5. There are 15 red squares, 6 yellow squares, 12 blue squares, 5 green squares, and 2 purple squares, for a total of 40 squares.

a) i) Green squares to red squares = 5:15 = 1:3

ii) Yellow squares to purple squares = 6:2 = 3:1

iii) Red squares to total number of squares = 15:40 = 3:8

b) i) Purple squares to blue squares = 2:12 = 1:6

ii) Purple squares to green squares = 2:5

Yellow squares to red squares = 6:15 = 2:5

6. The ratio of boys to girls is 5:4.

a) Find equivalent ratios until the number of boys is 15.

5:4 = 10:8 = 15:12

There are 12 girls.

b) Two girls leave, so 10 girls remain.

Boys to girls = 15:10 = 3:2

7. Juice requires 3 cans of concentrate to 5 cans of water.

a) Since 1 more can of concentrate was mixed with the same amount of water, the mixture is stronger than it should be.

b) Since 1 more can of water was mixed with the same amount of concentrate, the mixture is weaker than it should be.

Applications of Ratios

SECTION ORGANIZER (80–100 min)

Curriculum Focus: Use ratios to solve problems. (7m14, 7m24, 7m75)

Teacher Materials
- transparency of 1-cm grid (PM 20)

Student Materials
- 1-cm grid paper (PM 20)
- 0.5-cm grid paper (PM 14)
- calculators

Optional
- metre stick or measuring tape for *Connect*
- Step-by-Step 4 (Master 2.10)
- Extra Practice 4 (Master 2.17)

Assessment: Master 2.2 Ongoing Observations: Ratio and Rate

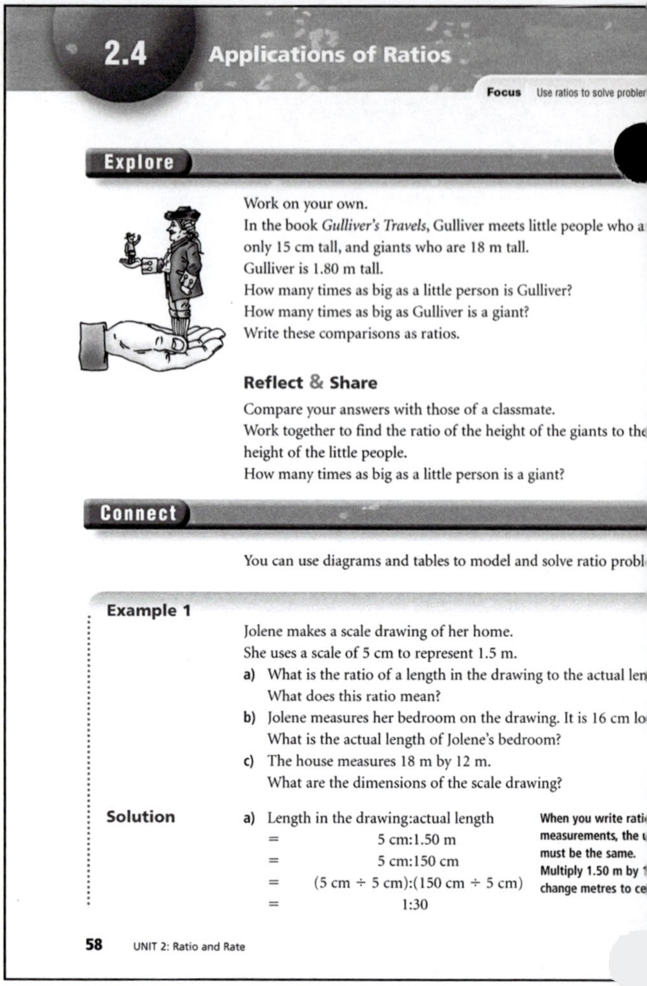
2.4 Applications of Ratios

Focus Use ratios to solve probler

Explore

Work on your own.
In the book *Gulliver's Travels*, Gulliver meets little people who a
only 15 cm tall, and giants who are 18 m tall.
Gulliver is 1.80 m tall.
How many times as big as a little person is Gulliver?
How many times as big as Gulliver is a giant?
Write these comparisons as ratios.

Reflect & Share

Compare your answers with those of a classmate.
Work together to find the ratio of the height of the giants to the
height of the little people.
How many times as big as a little person is a giant?

Connect

You can use diagrams and tables to model and solve ratio probl

Example 1

Jolene makes a scale drawing of her home.
She uses a scale of 5 cm to represent 1.5 m.
a) What is the ratio of a length in the drawing to the actual len
What does this ratio mean?
b) Jolene measures her bedroom on the drawing. It is 16 cm lo
What is the actual length of Jolene's bedroom?
c) The house measures 18 m by 12 m.
What are the dimensions of the scale drawing?

Solution

a) Length in the drawing:actual length
= 5 cm:1.50 m
= 5 cm:150 cm
= (5 cm ÷ 5 cm):(150 cm ÷ 5 cm)
= 1:30

When you write rati
measurements, the u
must be the same.
Multiply 1.50 m by 1
change metres to ce

58 UNIT 2: Ratio and Rate

Key Math Learnings

1. Diagrams and tables can be used to model and solve ratio problems.
2. The units must be the same when you write ratios of measurements.

BEFORE Get Started

Engage students in a discussion about *Gulliver's Travels* by Jonathan Swift. Many students may have seen the movie or the cartoon; some may even have read the book. Explain that Lemuel Gulliver travels to various mythical locations, including Lilliput, where people are tiny, and Brobdignag, a land of giants.

Review how students can compare two lengths.

Ask questions, such as:

- A ruler is 30 cm long. How many rulers will fit along a table 210 cm long? How do you know? (*7 rulers; I divided 210 by 30.*)
- How many times as long as the ruler is the table? (*7 times*)

Present *Explore.* Tell students they will compare Gulliver's height to that of a little person and to that of a giant. Ensure students understand that when they compare two measurements, the units must be the same; for example, both heights could be in metres.

DURING Explore

Ongoing Observations: Observe and Listen

Watch for students who do not use the same units in their ratios.

Ask:

- How tall is Gulliver? (*1.80 m*) A little person? (*15 cm*)
- How many times as big as a little person is Gulliver? (*12 times*) How do you know? (*I converted 1.80 m to centimetres, then divided 180 cm by 15 cm to get 12.*)
- Did anyone use a different strategy? Explain. (*I converted 15 cm to metres, then divided 1.80 by 0.15 to get 12.*)
- Does it matter if both units are metres or centimetres? Explain. (*No, you can make comparisons as long as both units are the same.*)

Each 1 cm in the drawing represents 30 cm in the home.

b) Draw a diagram.

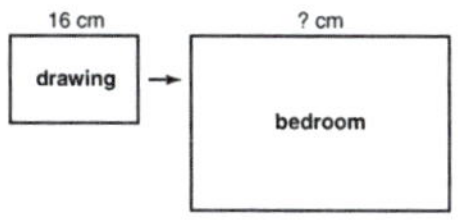

The length in the drawing is 16 cm.
Each 1 cm in the drawing represents 30 cm in the bedroom.
So, the length of the bedroom is 16 × 30 cm = 480 cm
= 4.8 m

c) Draw a diagram.

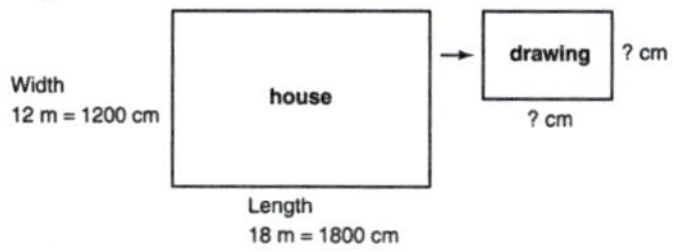

1 cm in the drawing represents 30 cm in the house.
Divide each measurement in the house to find the measurement on the drawing.

Length in the drawing = $\frac{1800 \text{ cm}}{30}$
= 60 cm

Width in the drawing = $\frac{1200 \text{ cm}}{30}$
= 40 cm

The dimensions of the scale drawing are 60 cm by 40 cm.

Example 2

Wallpaper paste can be made by mixing flour and water.
The table shows the volume of water to be mixed with flour to make different quantities of paste.

Water (mL)	16	32	48
Flour (mL)	3	6	9

a) What is the ratio of the volume of water to the volume of flour?
b) How much water is required for 15 mL of flour?

2.4 Applications of Ratios 59

REACHING ALL LEARNERS

Alternative Explore

An eraser is 5 cm long. A ruler is 30 cm long.
The classroom is 6 m wide.
How many times as long as the eraser is the ruler?
How many times as long as the ruler is the width of the classroom?
How many times as long as the eraser is the width of the classroom?
Students write these comparisons as ratios.

Early Finishers

Students measure their own heights in centimetres, then compare their heights to Gulliver's height, to a little person's height, and to a giant's height. They write these comparisons as ratios, in simplest form if possible.

Common Misconceptions

➤ Students convert the units so that all measurements are in the same units, but do not simplify the resulting ratio.

How to Help: Encourage students to write ratios in simplest form. Have them check that the terms of the ratio have no common factors. Use a calculator to check whether 2, 3, 4, ..., and so on, divide exactly into the numbers.

- How many times as big as Gulliver is the giant? (*10 times*) How do you know? (*18 ÷ 1.80 = 10*)
- What is the ratio of the little person's height to Gulliver's height? (*15:180 = 1:12*)
Gulliver's height to the giant's height? (*1.80:18 = 18:180 = 1:10*)

AFTER Connect

Invite volunteers to share their answers with the class. Ask:

- What is the ratio of the height of the giants to the height of the little people? (*1800:15 or 120:1*)
- How many times as big as a little person is the giant? (*120 times*)

Tell students that ratios can be used to make drawings of items that are very large or very small. These are called scale drawings.

Diagrams drawn "to scale" are accurate representations of their relative sizes.

Model how to make a scale drawing using a 1-cm grid transparency on the overhead projector. Tell students that, in this diagram, you will use the scale 1 cm represents 1 m. Have a volunteer measure the length of the classroom to the nearest 0.5 m. Have another volunteer measure the width. Ask:

- How long is the classroom? (*18 m*) How many centimetres is that, using the scale 1 cm represents 1 m? (*18 cm*)
- How wide is the classroom? (*14.5 m*) How many centimetres is that, using the scale 1 cm represents 1 m? (*14.5 cm*)
- How can we write the scale 1 cm represents 1 m as a ratio? (1:100) Why? (*There are 100 cm in 1 m, so a ratio of 1 cm to 1 m is 1 cm to 100 cm, or 1:100.*)

Sample Answers

1. e) I would need 20 cans of orange concentrate, 10 cans of cranberry concentrate, and 30 cans of water. I know the quantities of each ingredient required to make 3 L of punch, so I multiplied each quantity by 5 to get the amounts required to make 15 L.

2. b) Ship: 88 m; Model: 176 cm

   c) Model: 27 cm; Ship: 13.5 m

3. d) 0.5 cm × 20 = 10 cm
   I multiplied the height of the model by 20 (the scale is 1 cm represents 20 cm or 1:20) to get the actual height.

4. The scale is 2 cm represents 3 m. I convert metres to centimetres so that both units are the same:
   3 m = 3 × 100 cm = 300 cm.
   The scale is 2 cm represents 300 cm.
   The ratio is 2:300 or 1:150. William is incorrect.

5. a) The ratio of water to salt is 1:9, so the amount of salt needed for 7 L of water is 7 × 9 g = 63 g.
   b) 10 L; the ratio of water to salt is 1:9, so the amount of water needed for 90 g of salt is 90 L ÷ 9 = 10 L.

Mental Math

Students could recall all the basic multiplication facts for each number.

Solution

a) Volume of water:volume of flour = 16:3

b) Use a pattern to continue the table in part a.
For the water, the pattern rule is: Start at 16, then add 16.
The next three terms are 64, 80, 96.
For the flour, the pattern rule is: Start at 3, then add 3.
The next three terms are 12, 15, 18.
Extend the table to include these numbers.

Water (mL)	16	32	48	64	80	96
Flour (mL)	3	6	9	12	15	18

From the table, 80 mL of water are needed for 15 mL of flour.

Practice

Mental Math

Find all the factors of each number.
7, 15, 27, 36, 48, 51

7: 1, 7
15: 1, 3, 5, 15
27: 1, 3, 9, 27
36: 1, 2, 3, 4, 6, 9, 12, 18, 36
48: 1, 2, 3, 4, 6, 8, 12, 16, 24, 48
51: 1, 3, 17, 51

1. This table shows the quantities of concentrate and water needed to make punch.

Orange concentrate (cans)	2	4	6	8	10
Cranberry concentrate (cans)	1	2	3	4	5
Water (cans)	3	6	9	12	15
Punch (L)	1.5	3	4.5	6	7.5

a) What are the next two numbers in each row of the table?
b) What is the ratio of cranberry concentrate to water? 1:3
c) Suppose you use 10 cans of orange concentrate. How much punch would you get? 7.5 L
d) Suppose you use 12 cans of concentrate in total. How much punch would you get? 6 L
e) How much of each ingredient would you need to make 15 L of punch? Explain your reasoning.

Remember to convert the units so you work with all measurements in the same units.

2. Jenny makes models of Canadian Coast Guard ships. She uses a scale of 3 cm to 1.5 m.
a) What is the ratio of a length on the model to a length on the ship? 3:150 or 1:50
b) The Terry Fox ship is 88 m long. How long is the model? 176
c) The model of the Otter Bay is 27 cm long. What is the actual length of the Otter Bay? 13.5 m
Draw diagrams to show your answers.

60 UNIT 2: Ratio and Rate

Draw a rectangle on the transparency as a scale diagram of the classroom.

Tell students we could use a different scale, such as 1 cm represents 2 m. Ask:

- How long would the rectangle be? (*9 cm*)
- What is this scale as a ratio? (*1:200*) Explain. (*A ratio of 1 cm to 2 m is 1 cm to 200 cm, or 1:200.*)

Tell students this idea is extended to using the scale on a map.

Use the examples in *Connect* to show students how diagrams and tables can be used to model and solve ratio problems.

Practice

Have 1-cm grid paper (PM 20) and 0.5-cm grid paper (PM 14) available for questions 2, 3, and 4.

Assessment Focus: Question 6

Most students will realize that Aston's father will win the race. Students' diagrams should show the position of Aston when his father crosses the finish line. This drawing should enable students to see how much of a head start Aston's father could give his son so they reach the finish line together.

3. A set designer builds a model of the stage and the different pieces of furniture on it. He uses a scale of 5 cm to 1 m.
   a) What is the ratio of a length on the model to a length on the stage? 5:100 or 1:20
   b) The length of a table is 1.4 m. What is the length of the model? 7 cm
   c) The height of the model of a lamp is 3 cm. What is the actual height of the lamp? 60 cm
   d) The height of the model of an ornament is 0.5 cm. What is the actual height of the ornament? 10 cm How did you find out?

   Draw diagrams to show your answers.

Math Link

Social Studies

A scale on a provincial map is 1:1 500 000. This means that 1 cm on the map represents 1 500 000 cm on the ground, which is $\frac{1\,500\,000}{100}$ m, or 15 000 m on the ground. And, 15 000 m is $\frac{15\,000}{1000}$ km, or 15 km. So, a scale of 1:1 500 000 is 1 cm to 15 km.

4. Janice builds a model using a scale of 2 cm to represent 3 m. Her friend William says she is using a ratio of 2:3. Is William correct? Explain. No

5. This table shows the quantities of salt and water needed to make salt solutions.

Water (L)	2	4	6	8
Salt (g)	18	36	54	72

   a) How much salt would be needed for 7 L of water? 63 g
   b) How much water would be needed for 90 g of salt? 10 L

6. **Assessment Focus** Aston challenges his father to a 100-m race. Aston runs 4 m for every 5 m his father runs.
   a) Who wins the race? Draw a diagram to show your answer. Aston's father
   b) How far will Aston have run when his father crosses the finish line? 80 m
   c) Aston asks to race again but wants to be given a head start. How much of a start should Aston's father give him to make it a close race? Explain your answer.

Reflect

Make up your own ratio problem.
Solve your problem. Show your work.

6. a) Aston's father

0 5 10 15 20 25 30 35 40 45 50 55 60 65 70 75 80 85 90 95 100

Aston

0 4 8 12 16 20 24 28 32 36 40 44 48 52 56 60 64 68 72 76 80

c) Aston's father could give his son a head start of 18 m or 19 m. The head start must be less than 20 m or the two runners will tie.

REFLECT: The length of a June bug in a picture in my science textbook is 1.5 cm. The scale is 1:2. What is the length of the actual June bug?
Answer: The scale is 1:2. To find the actual length, I multiply 1.5 cm × 2 to get 3 cm. The actual length of the June bug is 3 cm.

Assignment Guidelines

If your students do not have time to complete all the *Practice* questions on pages 60 and 61, these questions provide minimum coverage: 1, 2, 4, 6, *Reflect*

To assess the 4 Achievement Chart categories listed in the curriculum document, have students complete these *Practice* questions:

Understanding Concepts: 1
Application: 2
Communication: 4
Problem Solving: 6

ASSESSMENT FOR LEARNING

What to Look For

Understanding concepts

✔ Students understand that diagrams and tables can be used to model and solve ratio problems.

✔ Students understand that the units must be the same when you write ratios of measurements.

Applying procedures

✔ Students can apply equivalent ratios to find the dimensions of a scale drawing.

Problem Solving

✔ Students can solve problems that involve ratios.

What to Do

Extra Support: Students who have difficulty interpreting scales may benefit from using a table to write the relationships in different ways. For example, to use the scale 1 cm represents 25 m, students could copy and extend a table, like that below, as far as they need.

1	2	3	4	
25	50	75	100	

Students can use Step-by-Step 4 (Master 2.10) to complete question 6.

Extra Practice: Have students use a ruler or tape measure and grid paper to make a scale drawing of one new item in the classroom, such as a desktop, a bookcase, a chair seat, and so on. Students can complete Extra Practice 4 (Master 2.17).

Extension: Have students redraw the house and bedroom in *Connect* using a different scale.

Recording and Reporting

Master 2.2 Ongoing Observations: Ratio and Rate

What Is a Rate?

SECTION ORGANIZER (80–100 min)

Curriculum Focus: Investigate rates. (7m14, 7m24)

Student Materials
- stopwatches or a clock
- calculators
- newspapers and magazines

Optional
- Step-by-Step 5 (Master 2.11)
- Extra Practice 5 (Master 2.18)

Vocabulary: rate, unit rate, average speed

Assessment: Master 2.2 Ongoing Observations: Ratio and Rate

Key Math Learnings

1. A rate is a comparison of two different things.
2. A unit rate compares a quantity to 1 unit.
3. Diagrams, tables, and graphs can be used to find unit rates.
4. The rate at which a car travels is its average speed.

2.5 What Is a Rate?

Focus Investigate rates.

Explore

Work with a partner.
You will need a stopwatch.
One person is the "blinker." The other person is the timekeeper.
The blinker blinks as many times as possible.
Count the number of times the blinker blinks in 20 s.
Reverse roles.
Count the number of times the blinker blinks in 30 s.

➢ Who was the faster blinker?
How do you know?

➢ Estimate how many times each person would blink in 1 h.
What assumptions do you make?
Are these assumptions reasonable?

Reflect & Share

Compare your results with those of another pair of classmates.
How can you decide who is the fastest blinker?

Connect

When we compare two different things, we have a **rate**.
Here are some rates.

- We need 5 sandwiches for every 2 people.
- Oranges are on sale at $1.49 for 12.
- Gina earns $4.75 per hour for baby-sitting.
- There are 500 sheets on one roll of paper towels.

The last two rates above are **unit rates**.
Each rate compares a quantity to 1 unit.

Jamal skipped rope 80 times in 1 min.
We say that Jamal's rate of skipping is 80 skips per minute.
We write this as 80 skips/min.

To find unit rates, we can use diagrams, tables, and graphs.

62 UNIT 2: Ratio and Rate

BEFORE — Get Started

Engage students in a discussion about things that are timed.

Ask:

- What are some things that people time? (*The amount of time it takes to run a certain distance, the number of heartbeats in 1 minute, the number of words that can be typed in a minute*)
- A person can run 100 m in 15 s.
How far can she run in 30 s? (*About 200 m*)
How do you know? (*100 × 2 = 200*)
- What assumptions do you make? (*That she can run 200 m at the same rate as she runs 100 m*)
- How far can she run in 1 min? (*About 400 m*)
Explain. (*There are 60 s in 1 min; 60 s ÷ 15 s = 4; 4 × 100 m = 400 m. I assume that she can maintain the rate.*)

Present *Explore.* Tell students they will count, then predict, the number of times a person can blink in two different time periods. Distribute a stopwatch to each pair of students. Suggest students practise using the stopwatches before starting the activity. It may be difficult for the timer to watch the stopwatch and count the blinks at the same time. Suggest students work in groups of 3 rather than in pairs, with one student as the blinker, the second student as the timer, and the third student as the counter. Ensure students understand they are to blink as many times as possible.

DURING — Explore

Ongoing Assessment: Observe and Listen

Ask questions, such as:

- How many times did you blink in 20 s? (*50 times*) How many times did your partner blink in 30 s? (*80 times*)
- Who was the faster blinker? (*My partner*) How do you know? (*In 1 min, I would have*

Example 1

The doctor took Marjorie's pulse. He counted 25 beats in 20 s. What was Marjorie's heart rate in beats per minute?

Solution

Draw a diagram.
There are 25 beats in 20 s.
There are 60 s in 1 min.
We multiply 20 s by 3 to get 60 s.
So, multiply the number of beats in 20 s by 3 to get the number of beats per minute.

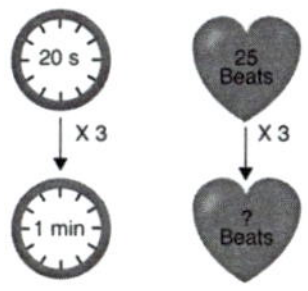

25 beats × 3 = 75 beats

Marjorie's heart rate is 75 beats/min.

Example 2

A printing press prints 120 sheets in 3 min.

a) Express the printing as a rate.
b) How many sheets are printed in 1 h?
c) How long will it take to print 1000 sheets?

Solution

a) Draw a diagram.
The press prints 120 sheets in 3 min.
So, in 1 min, the press prints:
120 sheets ÷ 3 = 40 sheets
The rate of printing is 40 sheets/min.

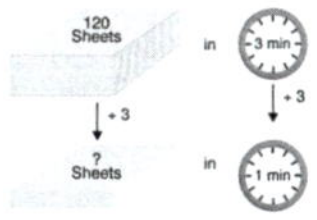

b) In 1 min, the press prints 40 sheets.
One hour is 60 min.
So, in 60 min, the press prints:
60 × 40 sheets = 2400 sheets
The press prints 2400 sheets in 1 h.

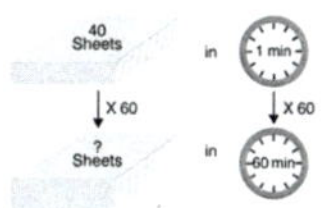

c) *Method 1*
In 1 min, the press prints 40 sheets.
So, in 5 min, the press prints: 5 × 40 = 200 sheets
Make a table. Every 5 min, 200 more sheets are printed.
Extend the table until you get 1000 sheets.

2.5 What Is a Rate? **63**

REACHING ALL LEARNERS

Alternative Explore

Students work in pairs. They will need a stopwatch. One person is the "drawer." The other person is the timekeeper. The drawer draws as many happy faces as possible. Count the number of happy faces the drawer draws in 20 s. Students switch roles. Count the number of happy faces the drawer draws in 30 s. How many happy faces can each person draw in 1 minute? Explain.

Early Finishers

Students can find the unit rate for a different activity, such as the number of knee bends in 1 minute.

Common Misconceptions

➤ Students are unsure whether to multiply or divide to find the unit rate.

How to Help: Have students record the following in their notebooks:

Greater number → Lesser number Divide
Lesser number → Greater number Multiply

For example, to find the unit rate for 120 sheets printed in 3 min, I want the number of sheets in 1 min, so I divide both terms by 3. To find the unit rate for 25 beats in 20 s, I want the number of beats in 1 min, so I multiply both terms by 3, as 20 s × 3 = 60 s.

ESL Strategies

Students for whom English is a second language will enjoy the social nature of the activity in *Explore*. There is minimal language needed for maximum participation.

blinked 150 times. There are 60 s in 1 min; 60 ÷ 20 = 3; 3 × 50 blinks = 150 blinks. In 1 min, my partner would have blinked 160 times. There are 60 s in 1 min; 60 ÷ 30 = 2; 2 × 80 blinks = 160 blinks.)

- About how many times would you blink in 1 h? (*About 9000 times*) Your partner? (*About 9600 times*) How did you estimate? (*I multiplied the number of blinks in 1 min by 60 to get the number of blinks in 1 h.*)
- What assumptions did you make? (*I assumed that each of us would continue to blink at the same rate.*)
- Is this assumption reasonable? (*No, my partner and I blinked as many times as possible in a short period of time. I don't think either of us could continue to blink at this rate for an hour.*)

AFTER Connect

Invite students to share their results.

Ask:

- How can you decide who is the fastest blinker in the class? (*We can use the results for 20 s and 30 s to find how many times each person would blink in 1 min. We could then order the results from least to greatest to find the fastest blinker, the person with the greatest number of blinks in 1 min.*)

Use *Connect* to introduce the terms **rate** and **unit rate**. Tell students that the numbers of blinks in 1 h found in *Explore* are unit rates because they compare the numbers of blinks to one unit, 1 h. Ensure students understand that "/" represents *per*. For example, we write 150 blinks/min. We say 150 blinks per minute.

Tell students they have already used unit rates in earlier sections. For example, students worked with cups of water per scoop of coffee in Section 2.3. Ensure students understand they are building on their prior knowledge of ratios.

Sample Answers

3. 120 beats/min; the heart rate increases with increased activity.

5. a) 25 km
   b) 25 km/h
      In 1 h, the cyclist travels 25 km.
      In 2 h, the cyclist travels 50 km.
      In 3 h, the cyclist travels 75 km.
      The unit rate is 25 km/h. The average speed is the unit rate.

7. 3 h 20 min = 180 min + 20 min = 200 min; so running rate is 200 min ÷ 25 km = 8 min/km.

8. a) i) 7 min/km ii) 8 min/km iii) 8.5 min/km
   b) About 9 min/km
      I think it will take him about 6 h 40 min. The farther Scott runs, the greater the time it takes him to run 1 km.
      9 min/km × 44 km = 396 min; 396 min is almost 6 h 40 min.

REFLECT: Three different examples of rates from newspapers and magazines:

Bananas are advertised at $0.39/kg. The rate tells people that 1 kg of bananas costs 39¢.

The winning golfer averaged 19 putts per round. The rate is used to show readers how well the golfer played during the tournament.

A 1-L can of paint covers a surface area of about 9.29 m^2. The rate helps people estimate how much paint they need to cover their walls.

Time (min)	5	10	15	20	25
Sheets printed	200	400	600	800	1000

Method 2
The press prints 40 sheets in 1 min.
Think: What do we multiply 40 by to get 1000?
Use division: 1000 ÷ 40 = 25
So, 40 × 25 = 1000
We multiply the time by the same number.
1 min × 25 = 25 min
The press takes 25 min to print 1000 sheets.

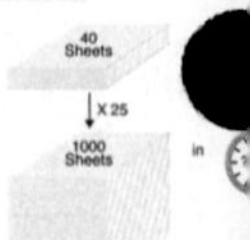

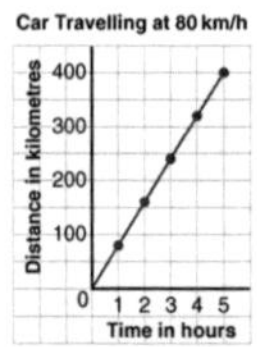

The rate at which a car travels is its **average speed**.
When a car travels at an average speed of 80 km/h, it travels:
80 km in 1 h
160 km in 2 h
240 km in 3 h
320 km in 4 h
400 km in 5 h … and so on
We can show this motion on a graph.
An average speed of 80 km/h is a unit rate.

Practice

1. Express as a unit rate.
   a) Morag typed 60 words in one minute. 60 words/min
   b) Peter swam 25 m in one minute. 25 m/min
   c) Abdu read 20 pages in one hour. 20 pages/h

2. Express as a unit rate.
   a) June cycled 30 km in 2 h. 15 km/h
   b) An elephant travelled 18 km in 30 min. 36 km/h
   c) A plane flew 150 km in 15 min. 600 km/h

3. Before running in a 100-m race, Gaalen's heart rate was 70 beats/min. Which do you think is more likely after the race: 60 beats/min or 120 beats/min? Explain. 120 beats/min

64 UNIT 2: Ratio and Rate

Remind students that ratios compare two measures of the same type of thing. A rate compares measures of two different things or quantities; the measuring unit is different for each value.

Ask:

- What are some different examples of rates? *(70 km per hour, number of centimetres of tape per roll, number of passengers per busload, number of square metres covered per litre of paint)*

Another strategy for *Example 1* is to make a table.
Every 20 s, 25 beats are counted.
1 min = 60 s

To find the number of beats in 60 s, multiply each initial number by 2, then by 3, and so on.

Time (s)	20	40	60
Beats	25	50	75

Marjorie's heart rate is 75 beats per 60 s or 75 beats/min.

Practice

Students require newspapers and magazines for *Reflect*. Note that students need to complete question 7 before they attempt question 8, because question 7 explains running rate in minutes per kilometre.

Assessment Focus: Question 8

Students should compare the three running rates to find that the farther Scott runs, the greater his running rate. To estimate how long it takes Scott to run 44 km, students should base their estimates on the Day 20 running rate or an even greater running rate. Students who use the rates from Day 1 or Day 10 do not fully understand the question. Students should report the time in hours and minutes.

Mental Math

nd a square root
each number.
49, 25, 81, 16, 64,
144, 4, 121
5, 9, 4, 8, 12, 2, 11

4. Ribbon costs $1.44 for 3 m.
  a) What is the cost per metre? $0.48/m
  b) How much would 5 m of ribbon cost? $2.40
  c) How much ribbon could you buy for $12? 25 m

5. The graph shows the distance travelled by a cyclist in 3 h.
  a) How far did the cyclist travel in 1 h? 25 km
  b) What is the average speed of the cyclist? 25 km/h
  How do you know?

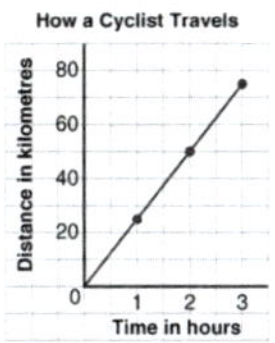

In England, the currency is pennies and pounds. There are 100 pennies in one pound, £1.

6. James and Lucinda came to Canada on holiday from England. The rate of exchange for their money was $2.50 Can to £1.
  a) How many Canadian dollars would James get for £20? $50
  b) What is the value in English pounds of a gift Lucinda bought for $30 Can? £12

7. When a person runs a long-distance race, she thinks of the time she takes to run 1 km (min/km), rather than the distance run in 1 min (km/min).
On a training run, Judy took 3 h 20 min to run 25 km.
What was Judy's rate in minutes per kilometre? 8 min/km

8. **Assessment Focus** Scott trained for the marathon.
On day 1, he took 70 min to run 10 km.
On day 10, he took 2 h 40 min to run 20 km.
On day 20, he took 4 h 15 min to run 30 km.
  a) What was Scott's running rate, in minutes per kilometre, for each day?
  i) Day 1 7 min/km ii) Day 10 8 min/km iii) Day 20 8.5 min/km
  b) What do you think Scott's running rate, in minutes per kilometre, might be for the 44 km of the marathon?
  How long do you think it will take him? Explain.

Reflect

Look through newspapers and magazines to find three different examples of rates. Explain how the rates are used.

2.5 What Is a Rate? **65**

Mental Math

Students know that the square root of a number is the side length of a square for which that number is the area. Students can visualize each square. Students could recall basic multiplication facts in which both factors are the same.

Assignment Guidelines

If your students do not have time to complete all the *Practice* questions on pages 64 and 65, these questions provide minimum coverage: 2, 4, 6, 7, 8, *Reflect*
To assess the 4 Achievement Chart categories listed in the curriculum document, have students complete these *Practice* questions:
Understanding Concepts: 2
Application: 6
Problem Solving: 8
Communication: *Reflect*

ASSESSMENT FOR LEARNING

What to Look For

Understanding concepts

✔ Students understand that a rate is a comparison of two different things.

✔ Students understand that the rate at which a car travels is its average speed.

Applying procedures

✔ Students can use diagrams, tables, and graphs to find unit rates.

Problem Solving

✔ Students can use unit rates to solve problems.

What to Do

Extra Support: Students who have difficulty finding rates would probably find the method of making a table the easiest to use, and should use that method for all questions.
Students can use Step-by-Step 5 (Master 2.11) to complete question 8.

Extra Practice: Students can find the unit rates for the first 2 rates listed in *Connect*, page 62.
Students can complete Extra Practice 5 (Master 2.18).

Extension: Have students find examples of rates in newspapers or advertising flyers, then calculate the unit rates.

Recording and Reporting
Master 2.2 Ongoing Observations: Ratio and Rate

Organizing a Math Notebook

SECTION ORGANIZER

Vocabulary: legible, well-organized, reasonable

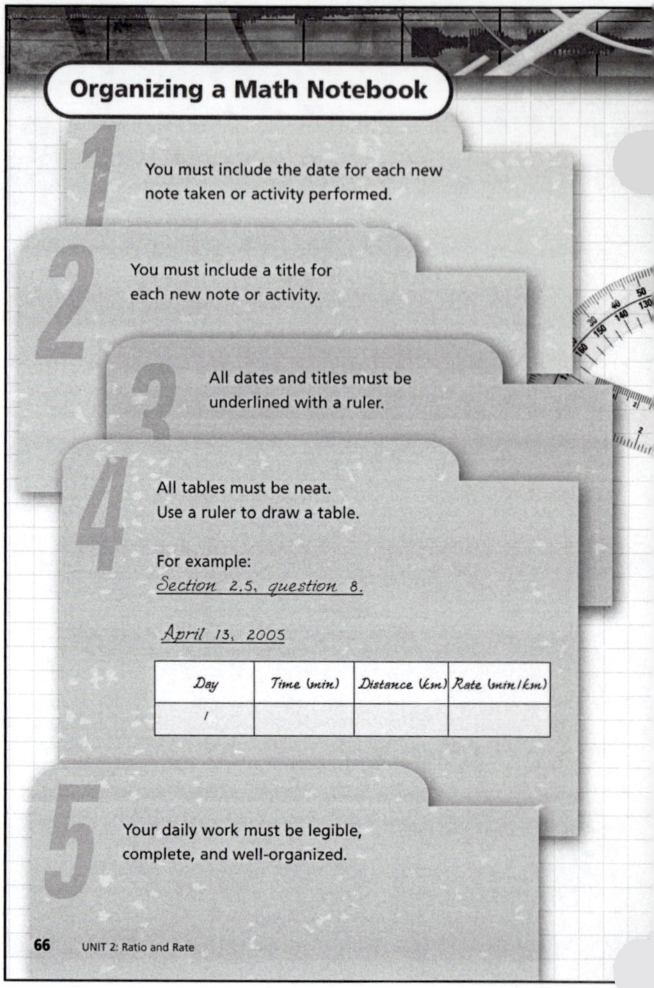

Organizing a Math Notebook

1 You must include the date for each new note taken or activity performed.

2 You must include a title for each new note or activity.

3 All dates and titles must be underlined with a ruler.

4 All tables must be neat. Use a ruler to draw a table.

For example:
Section 2.5, question 8.

April 13, 2005

Day	Time (min)	Distance (km)	Rate (min/km)
1			

5 Your daily work must be legible, complete, and well-organized.

66 UNIT 2: Ratio and Rate

Mathematical learning occurs through the process of problem solving. When keeping a record of problem solving, students should represent their mathematical thinking as well as their solutions. This requires that they have the ability to communicate orally and symbolically; for example, using pictures, numbers, words, and models. Capturing and preserving mathematical thinking through a written *record* is an important element of learning. It helps students remember, reflect, and communicate in a way that others can understand.

BEFORE

Review, with students, these 3 ways to record their learning:

- **Math Notebook** is a *detailed* record of ongoing learning through *specific* problems.
- **Math Journal** is a reflective summary of *general* observations, ideas, conjectures, and conclusions from a *group* of problems or an investigation.
- **Study Sheet** is a *brief synopsis* of key ideas and procedures for *quick reference.*

The Math Notebook is useful as a reference tool. Students can refer to it for solutions to problems, for ideas and strategies, and for corrected solutions. The notebook also informs the teacher what the student understands. To be effective, the book should be organized and legible. Solving a mathematical problem is often a messy process. Rough calculations, notes, and sketches may be on scraps of paper, and models may be made with manipulatives. The notes in the notebook should capture these recordings in an organized manner to make them understandable to teachers, peers, parents, as well as themselves. Discuss the attributes of an acceptable notebook throughout the year, and show students model notebooks. Note-taking skills develop gradually and improve with practice.

Have volunteers read aloud the 7-step process outlined in the Student Book. After each step, ask students why the step is useful.
(*For example, the date and title helps me find the work again; underlining allows features of the text to stand out; making corrections allows me to see where I went wrong and is useful when studying for tests.*)

Model expectations. Work through a previous *Practice* question as a class to show students how the notes should be organized.

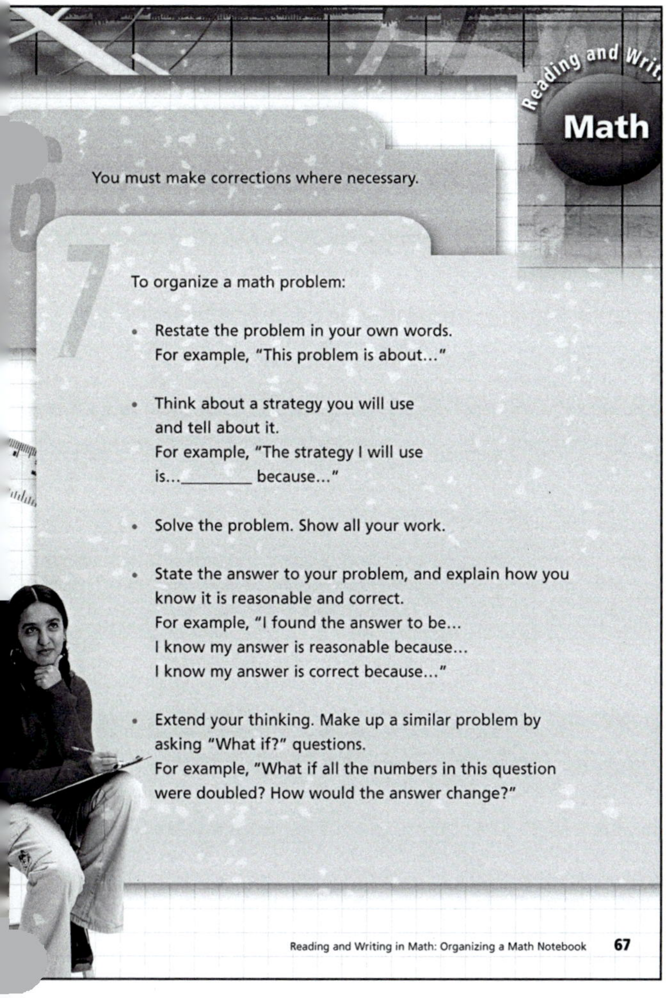

Reading and Writing in Math

You must make corrections where necessary.

7

To organize a math problem:

- Restate the problem in your own words.
  For example, "This problem is about…"
- Think about a strategy you will use
  and tell about it.
  For example, "The strategy I will use
  is…________ because…"
- Solve the problem. Show all your work.
- State the answer to your problem, and explain how you
  know it is reasonable and correct.
  For example, "I found the answer to be…
  I know my answer is reasonable because…
  I know my answer is correct because…"
- Extend your thinking. Make up a similar problem by
  asking "What if?" questions.
  For example, "What if all the numbers in this question
  were doubled? How would the answer change?"

Reading and Writing in Math: Organizing a Math Notebook 67

REACHING ALL LEARNERS

Early Finishers

Students for whom English is a second language may have difficulty communicating their thinking in writing. Encourage these students to use pictures, charts, and numbers, and to explain their thinking orally. Pair these students with students whose first language is English, and use peer editing often. Have ESL students concentrate on one or two problems for the notebook. Always highlight *growth* in an ESL student's work.

DURING

Circulate and comment on the mathematics displayed and the organization of students' notebooks. Show positive examples of work to redirect students and to stimulate ideas for improvement. Encourage individuality, both in the strategies and procedures used and in the way they represent their understanding. Encourage students to defend their thinking when they communicate a solution.

AFTER

Suggest students exchange notebooks with a classmate. Students can use sticky notes to comment on each of the 7 steps, suggesting where improvement is needed.

On the bulletin board, post a list of those attributes that add to the quality of a notebook as they arise in class; for example, the use of subheadings, sidebars or word bubbles to explain procedures, numbered steps, photos to explain procedures using manipulatives, and multiple solutions. This list will help students critique both their own notebooks as well as those of their peers.

Highlight anonymous student work. Anonymity provides a sense of pride for the student who produced the work without potential embarrassment in front of her or his peers. Post exemplary student work with clear labels, identifying the attributes that make it effective; for example, use labels such as legible, well-organized, and reasonable. Encourage students to extend their thinking, as this will demonstrate the depth of their understanding. Model and share exemplary work often, as this will encourage students to take pride in their work and to develop creative mathematical thinking.

Race Engineer

Sample Solution

A car could reach a top speed of 536 km/h but still have a lower average speed and hence take a longer time.
For example, I could drive my car for 70 km and take 1 h to do it. My average speed is 70 km/h. At some point in the journey, I was travelling at 95 km/h for a time. This is my greatest speed.

You could drive your car for 70 km and take less than 1 h to do it because your average speed is 80 km/h. At no time in the journey were you travelling faster than 85 km/h. This is your greatest speed.

So, the person with the greatest speed at some point is not the person with the "fastest time."

The World of Work

Race Engineer

The equivalent of the 100-m sprint in the world of cars is th drag race. One-quarter of one mile is about 400 m. The rac engineers (men and women who help design, build, and tun cars) are an important part of the racing team. Theirs is a world filled with gear ratios, cylinder compression ratios, fuel mixture ratios, acceleration, and speed. It's a constant cycle of theory, real-world application, testing, and evaluating. And, sometimes, these take place during a few hours between race runs! Helping t dragster team driver get to the finish line $\frac{1}{1000}$ th of a second fast than a previous run could mean the difference between winning losing the race.

In October, 2003, a top fuel dragster recorded a new "fastest tim 4.441 s for the $\frac{1}{4}$-mile drag race. But another car and driver continued to hold the record for the fastest recorded speed achie during a race—an incredible 536 km/h! Why do you suppose th second car doesn't hold the record for fastest time?

Here are some careers/hobbies that involve rate and ratio.

Cartographers: Cartographers or mapmakers design maps, and define the specifications of a map, such as projection, scale, size, and colour. They analyse survey data, photographs, satellite data, and other records to create a map. Cartographers use ratios when drawing a map; for example, if the distance between two places is 15 km and the scale on the map is 1 cm represents 10 km, the mapmaker must ensure the distance is accurately represented.

Chefs: In general, chefs measure, mix, and cook ingredients according to recipes. Chefs are also responsible for directing the work of other kitchen workers, estimating food requirements, and ordering food supplies. Chefs must be able to cook for between 1 person and hundreds of people. Chefs use ratios to adjust a recipe for more people or fewer people than the recipe is written.

People who participate in Orienteering: Orienteering is a competitive form of land navigation. The object of orienteering is to locate control points by using a map and compass to navigate through the woods. Orienteering is often called the "thinking sport" because it involves map reading, decision-making, and physical challenges. Any kind of map may be used for orienteering (even a street map), but it is crucial that participants are strong map-readers who can relate the scale of a map to actual distances.

Unit Review

Review any lesson with etext online tutorial

What Do I Need to Know?

✓ A ratio is a comparison of quantities.
For example, 3 dogs to 7 cats is 3:7.

✓ An equivalent ratio can be formed by multiplying or dividing the terms of a ratio by the same number.

For example:

5:8	and	36:30
$= (5 \times 3):(8 \times 3)$		$= (36 \div 6):(30 \div 6)$
$=$ 15:24		$=$ 6:5
5:8 and 15:24 are equivalent ratios.		36:30 and 6:5 are equivalent ratios.

✓ Two ratios can be compared when the second terms are the same.
For example, Scott's scoring record was 16:5.
Brittany's scoring record was 10:3.
To find who had the better record, use equivalent ratios to make the second term of each ratio 15.

Scott	Brittany
16:5	10:3
$= (16 \times 3):(5 \times 3)$	$= (10 \times 5):(3 \times 5)$
$=$ 48:15	$=$ 50:15

Brittany had the better record.

✓ A rate is a comparison of two quantities with different units.
For example:
Heart rate is measured in beats per minute (beats/min).
Average speed is measured in kilometres per hour (km/h).
Fuel consumption of an aircraft is measured in litres per hour (L/h).

Unit Review 69

SECTION ORGANIZER

Student Materials
- calculators

Optional
- counters
- 1-cm grid paper (PM 20)

Assessment: Masters 2.1 Unit Rubric: Ratio and Rate, 2.4 Unit Summary: Ratio and Rate

Correlation of Extra Practice questions on page 439:

Section	Questions
2.1	1
2.2	2, 3, 4, 5, 7, 9
2.3	6, 8
2.4	10

Sample Solutions

2. The ratio of yellow to blue squares is 9:6 or 3:2.
The ratio of green to yellow and blue squares is 4:15.
The ratio of red and yellow to blue and green squares is 11:10.
The ratio of blue to red, green, and yellow squares is 6:15 or 2:5.

3. One way to get a ratio equivalent to 25:10 is to divide both terms by 5. An equivalent ratio is 5:2.
A second way to get a ratio equivalent to 25:10 is to multiply both terms by 2.
An equivalent ratio is 50:20.

4. I made a table of ratios equivalent to 3:2. The length cannot be greater than 25 cm and the width cannot be greater than 20 cm.
So, the largest flag Jake can draw is 24 cm by 16 cm.

Length	Width
3	**2**
6	4
9	6
12	8
15	10
18	12
21	14
24	**16**
27	18
30	20

5. Ms. Beveridge's class has more computers.
I found how many computers there are for the same number of students. Since 2:3 = 10:15, and 3:5 = 9:15, the first class, Ms. Beveridge's class, has more computers because 10 > 9. She has 10 computers for each 15 students; Mr. Walker has 9 computers for each 15 students.

6. a) 1.8×100 cm = 180 cm; 8:180 or 2:45
b) 320 cm or 3.2 m

Plane: 72 m; Model: 3.2 m

c) 13.5 m

Model: 60 cm; Plane: 13.5 m

9. a) The average speed of a lion is 22 m/s.
The average speed of a zebra is 18 m/s.
So, the lion is faster.
b) The ratio of the average speed of the lion to that of the zebra is 22:18, or 11:9.

YOUR NOTES

What Should I Be Able to Do?

For extra practice, go to page

LESSON

2.1 **1.** On a school trip, there are 9 boys, 10 girls, and 4 adults.
Write each ratio.
a) girls to boys 10:9
b) boys and girls to adults 19:4
c) adults to boys and girls 4:19

2.2 **2.** Write four ratios to describe the coloured squares.

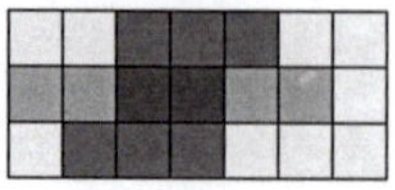

3. Explain two different ways to get ratios equivalent to 25:10.

4. Jake has to draw a flag with a length to width ratio of 3 to 2. What is the largest flag Jake can draw on a 25-cm by 20-cm sheet of paper? 24 cm by 16 cm

2.3 **5.** The ratio of computers to students in Ms. Beveridge's class is 2:3. The ratio of computers to students in Mr. Walker's class is 3:5. Each class has the same number of students.
Which room has more computers? Explain.
Ms. Beveridge's class

2.4 **6.** Ali builds model planes. He uses a scale of 8 cm to represent 1.8 m.
a) What is the ratio of a length on the model to the actual length on the plane?
b) A plane has a length of
What is the length of
the model? 3.2 m or 320
c) A model has a length of 60
What is the actual length of
the plane? 13.5 m
Draw pictures to show your answers.

7. Red and white paint is mixed i
the ratio of 3 to 2.
a) How many cans of red pain
would be needed with 6 car
of white paint? 9 cans
b) How many cans of each colour are needed to make 20 cans of mixture? 12 cans
red paint and 8 cans of white

2.5 **8.** Express as a unit rate.
a) A bus travelled 120 km in 3 40
b) An athlete ran 1500 m in 6 min. 250 m/min
c) A student earned $16 for 2 h work. $8/h

9. A lion can run 550 m in 25 s.
A zebra can run 270 m in 15 s
a) Which animal is faster? Th
b) What is the ratio of their average speeds? 11:9

70 UNIT 2: Ratio and Rate

ASSESSMENT FOR LEARNING

What to Look For

Understanding of concepts

✔ **Questions 1 and 2:** Student can write a ratio.
✔ **Question 6:** Student understands that the units must be the same when you write ratios of measurements.
✔ **Question 8:** Student can express a rate as a unit rate.

Application of mathematical procedures

✔ **Questions 4 and 5:** Student can use equivalent ratios to solve word problems.
✔ **Question 6:** Student can apply equivalent ratios to find the dimensions of a model.

Communicating

✔ **Question 3:** Student can explain how to find equivalent ratios.

Problem solving

✔ **Question 9:** Student can use unit rates to solve a problem.

Recording and Reporting

Master 2.1 Unit Rubric: Ratio and Rate
Master 2.4 Unit Summary: Ratio and Rate

Practice Test

1. a) Write each ratio in simplest form.

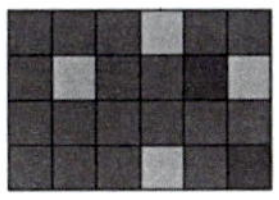

i) red squares to blue squares 9:1
ii) blue squares to green squares 1:2
iii) red squares and blue squares to total numbers of squares 5:6

b) Suppose the grid is increased to a rectangle measuring 9 units by 4 units. The ratios of the colours remain the same. How many red squares will there be in the new rectangle? 27 red squares

2. In the league, the Leos play 8 games. Their win to loss ratio is 5:3. The Tigers play 11 games. Their win to loss ratio is 7:4.
a) Which team has the better record? Explain. The Tigers
b) Suppose the Leos win their next game and the Tigers lose theirs. Which team would have the better record? Explain. The Leos

3. Hessa is building a scale model of a park. She uses a scale of 12 cm to represent 1.5 m.
a) The actual length of the bridge is 20 m. What is the length of the model bridge? 1.6 m or 160 cm
b) In the model, the height of the climbing frame is 10 cm. What is the actual height of the frame? 125 cm or 1.25 m

4. Look at this graph.
a) What is the speed of each car? Car A: 5 m/s Car B: 4.5 m/s
b) How far apart are the cars after 4 s? 2 m

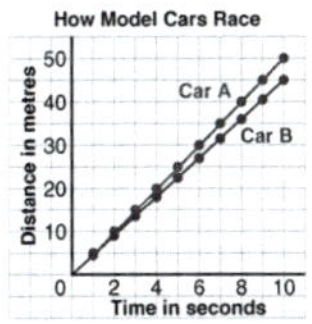

5. Trevor's mark on a math test was 10 out of 15. Anne's mark on another test was 15 out of 20. Trevor said, "Each of us got 5 wrong. So, our marks are equal." Do you agree? Give reasons for your answer. No

Practice Test 71

SECTION ORGANIZER

Student Materials
- 0.5-cm grid paper (PM 14)
- calculators

Assessment: Masters 2.1 Unit Rubric: Ratio and Rate, 2.4 Unit Summary: Ratio and Rate

Assignment Guidelines

To assess the 4 Achievement Chart categories listed in the curriculum document, use these test questions:
Understanding Concepts: 1
Problem Solving: 2
Application: 4
Communication: 5

Sample Solutions

1. b) 27 red squares
I found how many red and blue squares there are for 36 squares.
Since 5:6 = 30:36, there are 30 red and blue squares.
The ratio of red squares to blue squares is 9:1. So, there must be 27 red squares and 3 blue squares as 9:1 and 27:3 are equivalent ratios.

2. a) The Tigers have the better record.
I found how many wins each team would have for the same number of losses.
Since 5:3 = 20:12, and 7:4 = 21:12, the second team, the Tigers, has the better record because 21 > 20.
b) If the Leos win their next game, their win to loss ratio would be 6:3. If the Tigers lose their next game, their win to loss ratio would be 7:5. I found how many wins each team would have for the same number of losses.
Since 6:3 = 30:15, and 7:5 = 21:15, the first team, the Leos, would have the better record because 30 > 21.

3. a) 1.6 m or 160 cm (The ratio of a length of the model to the actual length of the bridge is 2:25.)
b) 125 cm or 1.25 m

5. No, I do not agree.
I found each student's mark for the same number of questions.
Since 10:15 = 40:60, and 15:20 = 45:60, the second mark, Anne's mark, is the better mark because 45 > 40.
They do not have equal marks.

Who's the Smartest?

SECTION ORGANIZER 40–50 min

Student Grouping: 2
Student Materials
- calculators

Assessment: Masters 2.3 Performance Assessment Rubric: Who's the Smartest?, 2.4 Unit Summary: Ratio and Rate

Sample Solution

1.

Animals	Ratio of Body Mass to Brain Mass
Human	40:1
Monkey	70:1
Camel	800:1

The human's body mass is 40 times its brain mass.
The monkey's body mass is 70 times its brain mass.
The camel's body mass is 800 times its brain mass.
According to Mr. Peabody's hypothesis, the human is the smartest. The ratio of a human's body to brain mass is the least. The mass of the brain and the mass of the body are closest in size in the human.

Unit Problem Who's the Smartest?

A hypothesis is something that seems likely to be true. It needs to be tested and proved or disproved.

Mr. Peabody believes you can predict an animal's intelligence by looking at the size of its brain.
He uses ratios to compare body size to brain size.
Investigate this strategy.

Analyse the data below to test Mr. Peabody's **hypothesis**.

The mass of a human brain is about the same mass as your math textbook.

Species	Comparing Mass (g)		Comparing Length (cm)	
	Body	Brain	Body	Brain
Human	56 000	1400	150	15
Monkey	7 000	100	30	5
Camel	520 000	650	200	15

1. Compare masses: find the ratio of body mass to brain mass.
   - How does a human compare to a monkey? 40:1
   - How does a human compare to a camel? 70:1
   - How does a camel compare to a monkey? 800:1

   According to Mr. Peabody's hypothesis, which animal is smartest? Explain your reasoning.

72 UNIT 2: Ratio and Rate

Have students turn to pages 40 and 41 of the Student Book.

Review *What You'll Learn,* the learning goals of the unit, and discuss the meanings of the *Key Words.* Tell students they will use the skills and concepts they learned in this unit to complete the *Unit Problem.*

Present the *Unit Problem.* Invite volunteers to read the introduction and questions aloud. Ensure students understand what they are expected to do.

Have one student read the *Check List* aloud. Remind students that they should use the *Check List* to assess their work before handing it in. You may also wish to provide students with copies of Master 2.3 Performance Assessment Rubric: Who's the Smartest? so they will know how their work will be assessed.

Tell students their work should be presented clearly, both in words and with numbers. Encourage students to use diagrams, pictures, or tables to help them answer the questions. If Mr. Peabody should have any questions about the opinions and conclusions received, he should be able to look at the work accompanying the letters to see how the opinions have been supported and justified.

Before starting the *Unit Problem,* have students predict the smartest animal: the human, the monkey, or the camel. Students can later check their predictions.

2. Compare lengths: find the ratio of body length to brain length.
- How does a human compare to a monkey?
- How does a human compare to a camel?
- How does a camel compare to a monkey?

According to Mr. Peabody's hypothesis, which animal is smartest? Explain your reasoning.

Check List

Your work should show:
- ✓ how you calculated each ratio
- ✓ your reasoning for which animal is the smartest
- ✓ your conclusions about the hypothesis
- ✓ the correct use of mathematical language

3. The dinosaur, diplodocus, lived about 150 million years ago. The brain of a diplodocus was about 9 cm long. The body of a diplodocus was about 27 m long.
   - How long would a human's brain be if it had the same brain length to body length ratio as a diplodocus? 0.5 cm

   A frog's brain is about 2 cm long. A frog's length is about 10 cm long
   - How long would a human's brain be if it had the same brain length to body length ratio as a frog? 30 cm

4. Review your results. Write a short letter to Mr. Peabody telling him whether you agree with his hypothesis, and why. Use mathematical language to support your opinion.

Reflect on the Unit

How is a rate like a ratio?
How is it different?
Use examples in your explanation.

Unit Problem: Who's the Smartest? 73

2.

Animals	Ratio of Body Length to Brain Length
Human	10:1 (30:3)
Monkey	6:1 (18:3)
Camel	40:3

According to Mr. Peabody's hypothesis, the monkey is the smartest. The ratio of a monkey's body to brain length is the least. The length of the brain and the length of the body are closest in size in monkeys.

3. The ratio of brain length to body length of a diplodocus was 9:2700 or 1:300. If a human had the same brain length to body length ratio as a diplodocus, a human's brain would be 0.5 cm long. The human body is 150 cm long. 300 cm ÷ 2 = 150 cm; 1 cm ÷ 2 = 0.5 cm. The ratio of brain length to body length of a frog is 2:10 or 1:5. If a human had the same brain length to body length ratio as a frog, a human's brain would be 30 cm long. The human body is 150 cm long. 5 cm × 30 = 150 cm; 1 cm × 30 = 30 cm

REFLECT ON THE UNIT: A rate is a special ratio. Both a ratio and a rate are comparisons of two things. They are different in that both terms in a ratio use the same units, while the terms in a rate use different units. A ratio is a comparison of two similar things; a rate is a comparison of two different things. For example:
- The ratio of green counters to red counters is 4:5. Both terms in the ratio represent counters.
- $8/h is a rate. It is a comparison of two different things, dollars and hours.

ASSESSMENT FOR LEARNING

What to Look For	What to Do
Understanding concepts ✔ Students understand that equivalent ratios can be used to compare ratios. ✔ Students understand that the units must be the same when you write ratios of measurements. ***Applying procedures*** ✔ Students can apply their understanding of ratios and equivalent ratios to compare data and solve problems. ***Communicating*** ✔ Students can use mathematical language effectively to support their opinions about the hypothesis.	***Extra Support:*** Make the problem accessible. Some students may have difficulty comparing ratios. Encourage students to reduce ratios to simplest form before finding, then comparing, equivalent ratios. Other students may have difficulty finding equivalent ratios. Encourage these students to model the ratios with Pattern Blocks, or to draw arrows from the original term to the equivalent term, then labelling each arrow. Some students may have difficulty writing a short letter. Tell students they must convince Mr. Peabody to accept their opinions. Students should include the ratios used in questions 1, 2, and 3 to help support their opinions.

Recording and Reporting
Master 2.3 Performance Assessment Rubric: Who's the Smartest?
Master 2.4 Unit Summary: Ratio and Rate

Evaluating Student Learning: Preparing to Report: Unit 2 Ratio and Rate

This unit provides an opportunity to report on the **Number Sense and Numeration** strand.
Master 2.4 Unit Summary: Ratio and Rate provides a comprehensive format for recording and summarizing evidence collected.

Here is an example of a completed summary chart for this Unit:

Strand: *Number Sense and Numeration*	**Problem solving**	**Understanding of concepts**	**Application of mathematical procedures**	**Communication**	***Overall***
Ongoing Observations	3	3	3	2	3
Work samples or portfolios; conferences	3	4	3	3	3
Unit Review	2	3	3	3	3
Practice Test	3	2	2	2	2
Unit Problem Who's the Smartest?	3	4	4	4	4
Achievement Level for reporting					3

Recording	**How to Report**
Ongoing Observations	Use *Master 2.2 Ongoing Observations: Ratio and Rate* to determine the most consistent level achieved in each category. Enter it in the chart. Choose to summarize by achievement category, or simply to enter an overall level. Observations from late in the unit should be most heavily weighted.
Portfolios or collections of work samples; conferences, or interviews	Use *Master 2.1 Unit Rubric: Ratio and Rate* to guide evaluation of collections of work and information gathered in conferences. Teachers may choose to focus particular attention on the Assessment Focus questions. Work from late in the unit should be most heavily weighted.
Unit Review	*Master 2.1 Unit Rubric: Ratio and Rate* may be helpful in determining levels of achievement. #1, 2, 6, and 8 provide evidence of Understanding of concepts; #4, 5, and 6 provide evidence of Application of mathematical procedures; #9 provides evidence of Problem solving; #3 provides evidence of Communication.
Practice Test	*Master 2.1 Unit Rubric: Ratio and Rate* may be helpful in determining levels of achievement. #1 provides evidence of Understanding of concepts; #4 provides evidence of Application of mathematical procedures; #2 provides evidence of Problem solving; #5 provides evidence of Communication.
Unit Problem	Use *Master 2.3 Performance Assessment Rubric: Who's the Smartest?* The *Unit Problem* offers a snapshot of students' achievement. In particular, it shows their ability to synthesize and apply what they have learned.
Student Self-Assessment	Note students' perceptions of their own progress. This may take the form of an oral or written comment, or a self-rating.
Comments	Analyse the pattern of achievement to identify strengths and needs. In some cases, specific actions may need to be planned to support the learner.

Learning Skills	**Ongoing Records**
PM 4: Learning Skills Check List Use to record and report throughout a reporting period, rather than for each unit and/or strand.	*PM 10: Summary Class Records: Strands* *PM 11: Summary Class Records: Achievement Categories* *PM 12: Summary Record: Individual* Use to record and report evaluations of student achievement over several clusters, a reporting period, or a school year. These can also be used in place of the Unit Summary.

Name ____________________ Date ______________

Master 2.1

Unit Rubric: Ratio and Rate

	Level 1	Level 2	Level 3	Level 4
Problem solving • chooses and carries out a range of strategies (e.g., tables, rates, and ratios) to create and solve multi-step problems related to real life where comparisons of numbers and quantities are required	with assistance, chooses and carries out a limited range of appropriate strategies to create and solve problems related to real-life comparisons of numbers and quantities; rarely resulting in an accurate solution	with limited assistance, chooses and carries out appropriate strategies to create and solve problems related to real-life comparisons of numbers and quantities that frequently result in accurate solutions	chooses and carries out appropriate strategies to create and solve problems related to real-life comparisons of numbers and quantities that usually result in accurate solutions	chooses and carries out appropriate strategies to create and solve problems related to real-life comparisons of numbers and quantities; may offer an innovative approach; results in accurate solution
Understanding of concepts • shows understanding of ratios and rates by explaining and illustrating what they are and how they relate to real-life problems	shows little understanding; may be unable to explain or illustrate rates and ratios, and their application in real-life situations	shows some understanding; partially able to explain and illustrate rates and ratios, and their application in real-life situations	shows understanding; able to clearly and appropriately explain and illustrate rates and ratios, and their application in real-life situations	shows thorough understanding; able to accurately and effectively explain and illustrate rates and ratios and their application in real-life situations
Application of mathematical procedures • applies understanding of number and number computations to: – find equivalent ratios and unit rates – compare ratios and rates	limited accuracy; major errors or omissions in: – finding equivalent ratios and unit rates – comparing ratios and rates	somewhat accurate; several minor errors or omissions in: – finding equivalent ratios and unit rates – comparing ratios and rates	generally accurate; few minor errors in: – finding equivalent ratios and unit rates – comparing ratios and rates	accurate and precise; no errors in: – finding equivalent ratios and unit rates – comparing ratios and rates
Communication • explains reasoning and procedures clearly, including appropriate terminology (for example, rate, ratio)	unable to explain reasoning and procedures clearly	partially explains reasoning and procedures	explains reasoning and procedures clearly	explains reasoning and procedures clearly, precisely, and confidently
• presents work clearly, including appropriate symbols	presents work with little clarity; rarely uses appropriate symbols	presents work with some clarity; uses some appropriate symbols	presents work clearly and precisely; uses appropriate symbols	presents work clearly and precisely; uses a range of appropriate symbols

Name ____________________ Date ______________

Master 2.2

Ongoing Observations: Ratio and Rate

The behaviours described under each heading are examples; they are not intended to be an exhaustive list of all that might be observed. More detailed descriptions are provided in each lesson under *Assessment for Learning*.

STUDENT ACHIEVEMENT: Ratio and Rate				
Student	**Problem solving** ▪ Chooses and carries out appropriate strategies to solve multi-step problems involving comparisons of numbers, quantities, and prices	**Understanding of concepts** ▪ Explains and illustrates rates and ratios and their application to real-life problems (for example, comparing prices)	**Application of mathematical procedures** ▪ Finds equivalent rates ▪ Finds unit rates ▪ Compares ratios and rates	**Communication** ▪ Explains reasoning clearly ▪ Presents work clearly

Level 1 – very limited; Level 2 – somewhat or limited; Level 3 – satisfactory; Level 4 – thorough

Name ____________________ Date ______________

Master 2.3

Performance Assessment Rubric: Who's the Smartest?

	Level 1	Level 2	Level 3	Level 4
Problem solving				
• chooses appropriate strategies (ratios, tables, patterns) to solve single- and multi-step problems involving comparisons; checks reasonableness of solutions	uses few simple strategies to solve single- and multi-step problems involving comparisons; limited success	uses some appropriate strategies to solve single- and multi-step problems involving comparisons; some success	uses appropriate strategies to solve single- and multi-step problems involving comparisons; successful	uses innovative and appropriate strategies to solve single- and multi-step problems involving comparisons; successful and effective (efficient)
Understanding of concepts				
• shows understanding of number comparisons (ratios) by using relevant mathematical concepts in explaining processes and conclusions related to Mr. Peabody's hypothesis	shows very limited understanding by using few relevant mathematical concepts in explanations and conclusions related to the hypothesis	shows limited understanding by using some relevant concepts in appropriate but incomplete explanations and conclusions related to the hypothesis	shows understanding by using relevant concepts in appropriate and complete explanations and conclusions related to the hypothesis	shows thorough understanding by using all relevant concepts in appropriate, complete, and insightful explanations and conclusions
Application of mathematical procedures				
• calculates and compares ratios accurately	limited accuracy; major errors or omissions in calculating and comparing ratios	somewhat accurate; several minor errors or omissions in calculating and comparing ratios	generally accurate; few minor errors or omissions in calculating and comparing ratios	accurate and precise; no errors in calculating and comparing ratios
Communication				
• explains reasoning clearly, using appropriate mathematical terminology	explains reasoning unclearly and imprecisely, using few mathematical terms	explains reasoning with some clarity, using some appropriate mathematical terms	explains reasoning clearly and precisely, using appropriate mathematical terms	explains reasoning clearly, precisely, and confidently, using a range of appropriate mathematical terminology
• presents work clearly	presents work with little clarity	presents work with some clarity	presents work clearly	presents work clearly and precisely

Name ____________________ Date ______________

Master 2.4

Unit Summary: Ratio and Rate

Review assessment records to determine the most consistent achievement levels for the assessments conducted. Some cells may be blank. *Overall* achievement levels may be recorded in each row, rather than identifying levels for each achievement category.

	Most Consistent Level of Achievement*				
Strand: *Number Sense and Numeration*	**Problem solving**	**Understanding of concepts**	**Application of mathematical procedures**	**Communication**	***Overall***
Ongoing Observations					
Work samples or portfolios; conferences					
Unit Review					
Practice Test					
Unit Problem: Who's the Smartest?					
Achievement Level for reporting					

* Use Ontario Achievement Levels 1, 2, 3, 4

Self-Assessment:

Comments: (Strengths, Needs, Next Steps)

Name ____________________ Date ________________

Master 2.5

Additional Activity 1: LCM

Work on your own.

You will need: numeral cards for the prime numbers 2, 3, 5, 7, 11, 13, 17, 19, and the composite numbers 4, 6, 8, 9, 10, 12, 14, 15, 16, 18, and 20; and a 2-column chart.

How to Play:

1. Place all the cards face down in 2 piles: prime and composite.
2. Use a 2-column chart to make a table.
   Label the columns *Prime* and *Composite*.
   Take 1 card from each pile. Record it in the correct column.
3. List the common multiples of each number until you reach the lowest common multiple (LCM). Record the LCM.
4. Repeat *Steps 2* and *3* for a different pair of prime and composite numbers.
5. Look for patterns in your tables.
   What is an easy way to find the LCM of a prime and composite number?

Take It Further: Use the composite number cards only. Label each column *Composite.* Repeat *Step 3* for several pairs of composite numbers.
How can you find the LCM of two composite numbers without using a table?

Name ____________________ Date ______________

Master 2.6

Additional Activity 2: Buzz

Work in a group.

How to Play:

Players agree at the beginning of the game how much time is allowed for a player to say the number.

1. Player A selects a target number from 2 to 9.

2. The other players take turns to count by 1s. You must say "buzz" when a multiple of the target number is reached or when any number containing the target number as a digit is reached. For example, suppose the target number is 4. The players take turns to count from 1: "1, 2, 3, buzz, 5, 6, 7, buzz, 9, 10, 11, buzz, 13, buzz," and so on.

3. A player is eliminated if:
   - he says "buzz" at the wrong time.
   - she does not say "buzz" when she should.
   - he takes too long to say the number or "buzz."

   The last player in the game is the winner.

4. When you can play this game well, do not allow any pauses in the count.

Take It Further: Use a 2-digit target number and include saying "buzz" when a number contains either of the two digits.

Name ____________________ Date ______________

Master 2.7

Step-by-Step 1

Section 2.1, Question 8

Step 1 Write the amount of each ingredient.
Macaroni: _____ cups
Oranges: _____ cups
Apples: _____ cups
Celery: _____ cups
Mayonnaise: _____ cups
Add to find the total amount of ingredients. ______

Step 2 Look at the numbers in *Step 1.*
Write the ratio of oranges to apples. _____:_____
Write the ratio of mayonnaise to macaroni: _____:_____

Step 3 What is the total amount of apples and oranges? _____ cups
Write the ratio of the total amount of apples and oranges to the total amount of ingredients (from *Step 1*). _____:_____

Step 4 Patrick uses only 2 cups of oranges.
What is the new total amount of ingredients? _____
Repeat *Steps 2* and *3* for the new amount of oranges.

Step 5 Write your own ratio problem about this salad.

____

____

Solve your problem.

Name ____________________ Date ______________

Master 2.8 **Step-by-Step 2**

Section 2.2, Question 6

Use red, blue, and green counters.

Step 1 The ratio of red to blue counters is 5:6.
Draw a diagram to show this ratio.

Step 2 The ratio of blue to green counters is 3:4.
Write an equivalent ratio with 6 blue counters. __________
Draw a diagram to show this ratio.

Step 3 There are 5 red and 6 blue counters.
How many green counters are there? _____

Step 4 Multiply each number of counters by 2.
How many of each colour counter are there? ____________________

Step 5 Multiply the number of counters in *Step 3* by 3.
How many of each colour counter are there? ____________________

Step 6 How many more ways can you find numbers of counters with the ratios in *Steps 1* and *2*?
Explain.

____

____

Name ____________________ Date ______________

Master 2.9

Step-by-Step 3

Section 2.3, Question 6

Step 1 Write equivalent ratios for 7:5 until the second term is 30.

____

There are 30 non-fiction books in Ms. Arbuckle's class library.

How many fiction books are there? ________________

Step 2 Write equivalent ratios for 4:3 until the second term is 30.

____

There are 30 non-fiction books in Mr. Albright's class library.

How many fiction books are there? ________________

Step 3 Use your answers to *Steps 1* and *2*.
Which room has more fiction books? ____________________

How many more books does this room have? _________

Step 4 Mr. Albright adds 2 non-fiction books to his class library.
How many non-fiction books does he have now? ___________

Write the new ratio of fiction to non-fiction books. ______:______

Step 5 Is the ratio in *Step 4* the same as that for Ms. Arbuckle's class in *Step 1*? Explain.

____

____

Name ____________________ Date ______________

Master 2.10 **Step-by-Step 4**

Section 2.4, Question 6

Step 1 What is the ratio of the distance run by Aston to the distance run by Aston's father?
_____:_____

Step 2 Complete this table to find equivalent ratios.

Distance Aston Runs (m)	Distance His Father Runs (m)
4	5
8	
12	
20	
40	
60	
80	

Step 3 How long is the race? _______

Who wins the race? ________________
Use the table you completed in *Step 1*.
When Aston's father crosses the finish line,
how far has Aston run? ______

How much farther has Aston to run? _________

Step 4 Aston's father wants to win the second race.
How much head start should Aston's father give his son to make
the race close? ____________

Explain. ____

Step 5 Aston's father wants his son to win the second race.
How much head start should Aston's father give his son to make
the race close? ______________

Explain. ____

Name ____________________ Date _______________

Master 2.11

Step-by-Step 5

Section 2.5, Question 8

Step 1 Scott took 70 min to run 10 km.

How many minutes does Scott take to run 1 km? ___________

What is his running rate for day 1? _________ min/km

Step 2 Scott took 2 h 40 min to run 20 km.

How many minutes is this? ___________

What is Scott's running rate for day 10? _________ min/km

Step 3 Scott took 4 h 15 min to run 30 km.

How many minutes is this? ___________

What is Scott's running rate for day 20? _________ min/km

Step 4 Look at the running rates for *Steps 1* to *3*.

How do the rates change?

____

Estimate the running rate for a 44-km race. _______________

What time will Scott take to run 44 km? ___________________

Explain how you got your answers.

____

____

Name ____________________ Date ________________

Master 2.12a

Unit Test: Unit 2
Ratio and Rate

1. Look at the figures below.

□ △ △ □ □ △ ○ ○ △

a) Write each ratio.

i) squares to triangles

ii) triangles to circles and squares

iii) circles to the total number of figures

b) Which figure could you add to show a ratio 3:10?

2. The ratio of the length of a rectangle to its width is 3:2.
Give 3 possible dimensions of the rectangle.

3. Express as a unit rate.

a) A car travelled 120 km in 2 h.

b) Sean's heart beat 23 times in 20 s.

c) An employee made $48.00 for 4 h work.

d) A hockey player scored 36 goals in 9 games.

4. The price of 2 dozen cobs of corn is $7.20.
Joanna wants to buy 3 cobs of corn.
How much will she pay?

5. In a recent basketball game, Les made 3 of 5 free throws, Janice made 2 of 3 free throws, and Kam made 6 of 12 free throws. Who played best? Explain.

Name ____________________ Date _______________

Master 2.12b Unit Test continued

6. Emily looks at a picture. A car in this picture is 30 cm long.
The scale of the drawing is 1:14.

a) What is the actual length of the car?

b) An umbrella in the same picture is 5 cm long.
What is the actual length of the umbrella?

c) Emily added a fire hydrant to the picture.
The actual fire hydrant is 77 cm high.
Emily used the same scale. The hydrant in the drawing is 4 cm high.
Did Emily draw the fire hydrant accurately? Explain.

Name ____________________ Date ______________

Master 2.13 Sample Answers

Unit Test – Master 2.12

1. **a) i)** 3:4 **ii)** 4:5 **iii)** 2:9
   b) I could add 1 circle, then circles to total number of figures is 3:10.
2. For example,
   3 cm by 2 cm; 6 m by 4 m; 1.5 m by 1 m
3. **a)** 60 km/h **b)** 69 beats/min
   c) $12/h **d)** 4 goals/game
4. 90¢
5. Janice played the best.
   I found how many free throws each player made for the same number of shots.
   Since 3:5 = 18:30, 2:3 = 20:30, and 6:12 = 1:2 = 15:30, the second player, Janice, played the best. 20 > 18 > 15
6. **a)** 4.2 m **b)** 70 cm or 0.7 m
   c) No, Emily did not draw the fire hydrant accurately. A height of 4 cm in the drawing represents an actual height of 14 × 4 cm = 56 cm. The height of the drawing of the hydrant should have been 5.5 cm; 5.5 cm × 14 = 77 cm.

Extra Practice Masters 2.14–2.19

Go to the CD-ROM to access editable versions of these Extra Practice Masters

Name ______________ Date ____________

Master 2.14 **Extra Practice 1**

Section 2.1: What Is a Ratio?

1. A baseball team has 3 outfielders, 4 infielders, and a battery (the pitcher and the catcher). Write each ratio.
   a) outfielders to infielders
   b) infielders to the battery
   c) the battery to the entire team

2. Write each ratio.
   a) a tricycle's wheels to a bicycle's wheels
   b) a tricycle's wheels to a car's wheels
   c) a tricycle's wheels to a bicycle's and a car's wheels

3. There are 5 cows and 2 chickens in a farmer's field.
   a) What is the ratio of tails to legs?
   b) What is the ratio of wings to tails?

4. a) Draw two different diagrams to show the ratio 2:3.
   b) Draw a diagram to show the ratio 5:3.

5. a) Which rows below show the same ratio?

A	♣♣♣♣	♥♥♥
B	♠♠	♦♦♦
C	■■■■■ ■■■	☼☼☼☼☼☼
D	♥♥♥	♠♠♠♠
E	♦♦♦♦	►►►►►►►
F	►►►	■■■■■■

   b) Use the ratios above.
      i) Use the ratios in row A. If there are 16 clubs, how many hearts are there?
      ii) Use the ratios in row B. If there are 24 diamonds, how many spades are there?
      iii) Use the ratios in row C. If there are 72 squares, how many suns are there?
      iv) Use the ratios in row D. If there are 28 spades, how many hearts are there?
      v) Use the ratios in row E. If there are 48 diamonds, how many arrows are there?
      vi) Use the ratios in row F. If there are 30 squares, how many arrows are there?

Name ______________ Date ____________

Master 2.15 **Extra Practice 2**

Section 2.2: Equivalent Ratios

1. Write an equivalent ratio for each ratio.
   a) 4:5 b) 18:12
   c) 7:2 d) 50:10
   e) 15:3 f) 4:9

2. Three out of every 5 students watch hockey. How many students watch hockey in a class of 30?

3. Name the pairs of equivalent ratios:
   10:18, 3:6, 2:7, 9:18, 2:5, 5:9, 20:50, 8:28
   How do you know they are equivalent?

4. A basketball player scored 8 points in the first quarter of the game. Suppose she continues to score at this rate. How many points will she score in the game?

5. Rewrite each sentence as a ratio statement in simplest form.
   a) On the bus, there are 14 girls and 12 boys.
   b) In the garden, there are 12 rose bushes and 4 lilac bushes.
   c) On the bookshelf, there are 7 mystery books and 21 science-fiction books.

6. How many equivalent ratios are there for 3:4 in which the sum of all the digits is less than 10? Write the ratios you find.

Name ______________ Date ____________

Master 2.16 **Extra Practice 3**

Section 2.3: Comparing Ratios

1. Mr. James' class has a ratio of 2 boys to 3 girls. Ms. Singh's class has a ratio of 1 girl to 2 boys. Both classes have 30 students. How many boys and girls are in each class?

2. At the carnival, the Ring Toss advertises that 3 of every 7 players win a prize. The Pop the Balloon game advertises that 4 of every 9 players win a prize. Which game would you play? Explain.

3. The Blazers hockey team has won 7 of its first 12 games. No game was tied. The Rockets' record is 5 wins and 3 losses. Which team has the better record?

4. Concentrate and water are mixed to make juice. Which is the stronger mixture: A or B? Explain.
   Mixture A: 3 parts concentrate to 5 parts water
   Mixture B: 4 parts concentrate to 7 parts water

5. Here are the ratios of cats to dogs in different kennels in the city. In each case, state which kennel has the greater number of dogs.
   a) Kennel A, 5:6 or Kennel B, 7:9
   b) Kennel C, 8:11 or Kennel D, 15:19
   c) Kennel E, 3:4 or Kennel F, 2:3

6. There is a total of 600 blue, yellow, and red balls in a machine. The ratio of blue balls to the total number of balls is 1:4. The ratio of yellow balls to blue balls is 7:3. The ratio of blue balls to red balls is 3:2. Which colour of balls is most common?

Name ______________ Date ____________

Master 2.17 **Extra Practice 4**

Section 2.4: Applications of Ratios

1. The ratio of the height of an object in a photograph to the actual height is 1:100. The height of a statue in the photograph is 5 cm. How tall is the statue?

2. At a certain time of day, a person's shadow is twice her height.
   a) What ratio describes this relationship?
   b) At this time of day, Gene's shadow measures 320 cm. What is his height?

3. A model car is constructed using a scale of 1 cm to 0.20 m.
   a) What is the ratio of a length on the model to the length on the car?
   b) The length of the model car is 15 cm. How long is the car?

4. A flea is very difficult for the human eye to see. Jose looks at a drawing of a flea in a book. The drawing uses the scale 5:1. The actual length of a flea is 2 mm. How long is the drawing?

5. A scale on a map is 1 cm to 250 km. What does this mean?

6. When Tammy was 4, the ratio of Tammy's age to her father's age was 1:7. What will the ratio of their ages be when Tammy's father is 48?

Name ______________ Date ____________

Master 2.18 **Extra Practice 5**

Section 2.5: What Is a Rate?

1. Express as a unit rate.
   a) The bus travelled 80 km in 2 h.
   b) Marco's heart beat 35 times in 30 s.
   c) Inga walked 12 km in 4 h.

2. Sal earns $24 in 3 h. Josh earns $13 in 2 h. Komal earns $44 in 4 h.
   a) Who makes the most money per hour?
   b) How much will the person who earns the most money per hour earn in 8 h?

3. Fran bought 3 cans of soup for $1.45. At this rate, how much will 6 cans cost?

4. James read 48 pages in 90 min. How many pages could he read in 5 h?

5. a) A car travels at an average speed of 50 km/h. How long will it take to travel 200 km?
   b) A car travels at an average speed of 40 km/h. Will it take more or less time to travel 200 km?

6. a) Tyson can type 49 words per minute. About how long will he take him to type a 1000-word essay?
   b) Taylor typed 1000 words in half an hour. At about what rate was she typing?

Name ______________ Date ____________

Master 2.19 **Sample Answers**

Extra Practice 1 – Master 2.14
Section 2.1

1. a) 3:4 b) 4:2, or 2:1 c) 2:9
2. a) 3:2 b) 3:4 c) 3:6, or 1:2
3. a) 5:24 b) 4:5
4. a) □□ ▽▽▽ or □□▽
   b) ♥♥♥♥♥ ♦♦♦
5. a) A = C = 4:3; B = E = 2:3
   b) i) 12 ii) 16 iii) 54 iv) 21 v) 72 vi) 15

Extra Practice 2 – Master 2.15
Section 2.2

1. a) 16:20 b) 3:2
   c) 14:4 d) 5:1
   e) 30:6 f) 8:18
2. 18 students
3. 10:18 and 5:9; I can divide both terms in the 1st ratio by 2 to get the 2nd ratio.
   3:6 and 9:18; I can multiply both terms in the 1st ratio by 3 to get the 2nd ratio.
   2:7 and 8:28; I can multiply both terms in the 1st ratio by 4 to get the 2nd ratio.
   2:5 and 20:50; I can multiply both terms in the 1st ratio by 10 to get the 2nd ratio.
4. 32 points
5. a) The ratio of girls to boys is 7:6.
   b) The ratio of rose to lilac bushes is 3:1.
   c) The ratio of mystery to science-fiction books is 1:3.
6. There are two ratios: 15:20 and 30:40

Extra Practice 3 – Master 2.16
Section 2.3

1. Mr. James' class has 12 boys and 18 girls. Ms. Singh's class has 10 girls and 20 boys.
2. Pop the Balloon
   I found the number of prizes for the same number of players.
   Since 3:7 = 27:63, and 4:9 = 28:63, the second game, Pop the Balloon, is the game where more players win a prize because 28 > 27.
3. The Rockets; Wins to losses for Blazers is 7:5 or 21:15. Wins to losses for Rockets is 5:3 or 25:15.
4. Mixture A
   I found the number of parts of concentrate for the same number of parts of water.
   Since 3:5 = 21:35, and 4:7 = 20:35, the first mixture, Mixture A, is the stronger mixture because 21 > 20.
5. a) Kennel B
   b) Kennel C
   c) Kennel F
   For example, in part a:
   Kennel A
   dogs:total animals = 6:11 = 96:176
   Kennel B
   dogs:total animals = 9:16 = 99:176
6. yellow; 150 blue, 350 yellow, 100 red balls

Extra Practice 4 – Master 2.17
Section 2.4

1. 500 cm or 5 m
2. a) The ratio of the length of a shadow to a person's height is 2:1.
   b) Gene is 160 cm or 1.6 m tall.
3. a) 1:20 b) 300 cm or 3 m
4. 10 mm or 1 cm
5. Each distance of 1 cm on the map represents an actual distance of 250 km. The ratio of the distance on the map to the actual distance is 1:25 000 000.
6. 24:48 = 1:2

Extra Practice 5 – Master 2.18
Section 2.5

1. a) 40 km/h b) 70 beats/min
   c) 3 km/h
2. a) Komal; he makes $11/h.
   b) In 8 h, Komal will earn $88.
3. $2.90
4. 160 pages
5. a) 4 h b) More time; it takes 5 h.
6. a) About 20 min
   b) About 33 words/min

Addison Wesley
Mathematics Makes Sense

Program Authors

Jason Johnston
Bryn Keyes
Mary Doucette
Antonietta Lenjosek
Steve Thomas
Margaret Sinclair
Trevor Brown
Cathy Heideman
Don Jones
Michael Davis
Jennifer Paziuk
Ken Harper
Sharon Jeroski
Ray Appel
Laura Weatherhead
Betty Milne
Jim Mennie
Lynn Strangway

Printed and bound in Canada

10 17

PEARSON
Education Canada

ADDISON WESLEY

Ontario

Math Makes Sense 7

Ontario
Teacher Guide

Unit 3: Geometry and Measurement

PEARSON
Addison Wesley

UNIT 3

Geometry and Measurement

"Measurement and geometry are presented together . . . in the development of formulas . . . Developing the formulas and seeing how they are connected and interrelated is significantly more important than blindly plugging numbers into formulas . . ."

John A. Van de Walle

FOCUS STRAND
Geometry and Spatial Sense
Measurement

SUPPORTING STRAND
Patterning and Algebra

TIPS
Adolescent learners enjoy learning that is connected to their lives, encourages risk-taking, and seeing things from different points of view.

Mathematics Background

What Are the Big Ideas?

- Different two-dimensional views of a three-dimensional object can be drawn.
- A three-dimensional object can be built from a two-dimensional pattern called a net.
- A three-dimensional object can be drawn to show depth.
- The surface area and volume of a rectangular prism can be calculated using formulas.

How Will the Concepts Develop?

Students will build on their previous experience with three-dimensional objects and investigate other ways to represent them: two-dimensional views, isometric drawings, pictorial diagrams, nets, and models built from nets.

The students' experiences with perimeter and area formulas will be expanded to develop formulas for the surface area and volume of a rectangular prism.

Why Are These Concepts Important?

The presentation and solution of many problems require drawing a diagram or making a model. A student needs to be able to draw an accurate diagram that does not mislead him. A student may need these skills when she is involved in home renovations or design, comparison shopping, or various art projects.

The investigations, concepts, and skills related to measurement formulas will be continued throughout students' school careers and beyond, as they learn about other types of solids and other algebraic expressions.

Curriculum Overview

Cluster 1: Drawing and Building Solids

Overall Expectations

- Identify, draw, and construct three-dimensional geometric figures from nets. (7m47)
- Use mathematical language effectively to describe geometric concepts, reasoning, and investigations. (7m52)

Specific Expectations

- Recognize the front, side, and back views of three-dimensional figures. (7m53)
- Sketch front, top, and side views of three-dimensional figures with or without the use of a computer application. (7m54)
- Sketch three-dimensional objects from models and drawings. (7m55)
- Build three-dimensional figures and objects from nets. (7m56)

Cluster 2: Measuring Rectangular Prisms

Overall Expectations

- Demonstrate a verbal and written understanding of and ability to apply accurate measurement strategies that relate to their environment. (7m28)
- Apply volume formulas to problem-solving situations involving rectangular prisms. (7m31)

Specific Expectations

- Interpret a variable as a symbol that may be replaced by a given set of numbers. (7m73)
- Write statements to interpret simple formulas. (7m74)
- Develop the formula for finding the surface area of a rectangular prism using nets. (7m42)
- Develop the formula for finding the volume of a rectangular prism using concrete materials. (7m43)
- Understand the relationship between the dimensions and the volume of a rectangular prism. (7m44)
- Calculate the surface area and the volume of a rectangular prism in a problem-solving context. (7m45)
- Sketch a rectangular prism given its volume. (7m46)

Launch

Section 3.1: Sketching Views of Solids
Technology: Using a Computer to Draw Views of Solids
Section 3.2: Sketching Solids
Section 3.3: Building Objects from Nets
Mid-Unit Review

Section 3.4: Using Variables in Measurement Formulas
Section 3.5: Surface Area of a Rectangular Prism
Section 3.6: Volume of a Rectangular Prism

Unit Review
Practice Test

Unit Problem
Making Food for a Bake Sale

Curriculum across the Grades

Grade 6	Grade 7	Grade 8
Students identify nets for a variety of polyhedra from drawings. Students design nets of cubes and pyramids, and sketch the net for an object. Students build an object with interlocking cubes, then draw it. Students estimate and calculate the volume of a rectangular prism. Students develop rules and formulas for calculating the volume of a rectangular prism.	Students recognize and sketch the front, side, and back views of objects, with and without the use of a computer. Students sketch objects from models and drawings, and build objects from nets. Students develop the formulas for finding the surface area and volume of a rectangular prism. Students use these formulas to solve problems related to rectangular prisms.	Students recognize objects from their top, side, and front views, then sketch and build them. Students develop the formulas for finding the surface area and volume of a triangular prism, then use the formulas to solve problems. Students understand the relationship between the dimensions and the volume of a triangular prism.

Materials for This Unit

You will need a variety of solids, linking cubes, empty cereal boxes, and grocery flyers. Tape the open face of the cereal box so it is closed for student use.

Additional Activities

Match It

For Extra Practice (Appropriate for use after Section 3.1)
Materials: *Match It* (Master 3.5); *Match It cards* (Master 3.15); scissors

Playing this game reinforces the skills of spatial visualization, and recognizing the different views of a solid.

The work students do: The view cards from Master 3.15 are cut apart and placed face down. The object cards are placed face up. Students take turns to find 5 views of one of the object cards. If no match is made, the student turns the cards back down and her partner has a turn. The winner has the most matches.

Take It Further: Have students create their own view cards and object cards.

Logical/Spatial/Kinesthetic
Partner Activity

Slide Design

For Extra Practice (Appropriate for use after Section 3.2)
Materials: *Slide Design* (Master 3.6); isometric dot paper (PM 23), linking cubes, pencil crayons

Doing this activity reinforces the skills of isometric drawing, translations, and designing a pattern.

The work students do: A student builds a solid from 4 linking cubes. He draws this solid in the upper left corner of a piece of isometric dot paper and repeats the picture several times so the object is drawn several times beside and below itself (slide). The student colours top faces one colour, front faces another colour, and side faces a third colour. The student attempts to fill the page, and make a design.

Take It Further: The student could reflect the isometric drawing in vertical, horizontal, or diagonal lines to produce a design.

Spatial/Logical
Individual Activity

Net a Cube

For Extra Practice (Appropriate for use after Section 3.3)
Materials: *Net a Cube* (Master 3.7); square dot paper (PM 22), scissors, 2 differently coloured markers

Playing this game reinforces the skills of recognizing and drawing a net of a cube, and spatial awareness.

The work students do: On dot paper, students draw a 12 by 12 square. They attempt to fill the space with as many different nets of a cube as possible.

Each person uses a different colour to outline her net. A student scores two points for each different net, and one point for filling in a space with a previously used design. Students use extra dot paper to build the cube if one person challenges another's net design. The student gets no points if his design is not a net. The challenger misses her turn if the design *is* a cube. The winner has the higher score when all possible space has been filled.

Take It Further: Draw different nets of a rectangular prism on a sheet of dot paper.

Spatial/Logical
Partner Activity

SAVO

For Extra Practice (Appropriate for use after Section 3.6)
Materials: *SAVO* (Master 3.8); three number cubes labelled 1 to 6, four matching counters for each person, game board (Master 3.16)

Playing this game reinforces the skills of using formulas to find the surface area and volume of a rectangular prism.

The work students do: Four students can play. Each person takes a turn rolling the three cubes to represent the dimensions of a rectangular prism. The student must calculate the surface area of a prism with these dimensions to move the number of spaces equal to the sum of the numbers on the cubes. If the student correctly calculates the volume as well, she may move 3 more spaces. After the first counter is in play, a player may move another marker into play on each next turn.

Mathematical/Social
Group Activity

Planning for Unit 3

Planning for Instruction

Suggested Unit time: 3–4 weeks

Section	Time	Materials	Program Support
Launch, page 2	15–20 min	different kinds of boxes, cans, and other packages	
Skills You'll Need, page 4	65–80 min	polyhedra, isometric dot paper, linking cubes	PM 23: Isometric Dot Paper
Section 3.1: Sketching Views of Solids, page 6 Recognize and sketch different views of objects.	80–100 min	square dot paper or grid paper, linking cubes, polyhedra, rulers	Master 3.9: Step-by-Step 1 PM 22: Square Dot Paper PM 20: 1-cm Grid Paper Master 3.33: Extra Practice 1
Technology: Using a Computer to Draw Views of Solids, page 10 Use technology to sketch views of objects.	40–50 min	computers with *The Geometer's Sketchpad* software, linking cubes	
Section 3.2: Sketching Solids, page 12 Sketch pictures of objects from models and drawings.	80–100 min	isometric dot paper, linking cubes, square dot paper or grid paper	Master 3.10: Step-by-Step 2 Master 3.34: Extra Practice 2 PM 23: Isometric Dot Paper PM 22: Square Dot Paper PM 20: 1-cm Grid Paper
Section 3.3: Building Objects from Nets, page 17 Build objects from nets.	80–100 min	scissors, tape, polyhedra nets (as listed in *Program Support*)	Masters 3.17–3.20: Nets for *Explore* and *Connect* Masters 3.21–3.27: Nets for *Practice* Questions 1, 2, 3, 4, 5, 7 Master 3.11: Step-by-Step 3 Master 3.35: Extra Practice 3
Mid-Unit Review, page 21		isometric dot paper, square dot paper or grid paper, net of a pentagonal prism	PM 22: Square Dot Paper PM 23: Isometric Dot Paper PM 20: 1-cm Grid Paper Master 3.28: Net for Mid-Unit Review, Question 5
Section 3.4: Using Variables in Measurement Formulas, page 22 Use measurement formulas to introduce the concept of a variable.	80–100 min		Master 3.12: Step-by-Step 4 Master 3.36: Extra Practice 4
Section 3.5: Surface Area of a Rectangular Prism, page 25 Use a formula to calculate the surface area of a rectangular prism.	80–100 min	empty cereal boxes, scissors, rulers, grid paper, linking cubes	Master 3.13: Step-by-Step 5 Master 3.37: Extra Practice 5 PM 20: 1-cm Grid Paper
Section 3.6: Volume of a Rectangular Prism, page 29 Use a formula to calculate the volume of a rectangular prism.	80–100 min	empty cereal boxes, rulers, linking cubes	Master 3.14: Step-by-Step 6 Master 3.38: Extra Practice 6
Reading and Writing in Math: Decoding Word Problems, page 32			
Unit Review, page 34		isometric dot paper, square dot paper or grid paper	Master 3.29: Net for Unit Review, Question 3 PM 23: Isometric Dot Paper PM 20: 1-cm Grid Paper PM 22: Square Dot Paper Extra Practice: Student Book page 440

Section	Time	Materials	Program Support
Practice Test, page 37		isometric dot paper, square dot paper or grid paper	PM 23: Isometric Dot Paper PM 20: 1-cm Grid Paper PM 22: Square Dot Paper Master 3.30: Net for Practice Test, Question 2
Unit Problem: Making Food for a Bake Sale, page 38	80–100 min	grocery flyers, isometric dot paper, 1-cm grid paper, sketch paper	PM 23: Isometric Dot Paper PM 20: 1-cm Grid Paper PM 14: 0.5-cm Grid Paper

etext online tutorial

This web-based tutorial uses voice, animation, and an optional quiz to present each core lesson, so that students can review content with a new approach.

Planning for Assessment

Purpose	Tools and Process	Recording and Reporting
Diagnostic	*Unit Launch* Question; conference; scaffold problems throughout the unit	PM 8: Conference Prompts
Formative	*Explore* – Ongoing Assessment: Observe and Listen	Master 3.2 Ongoing Observations: Geometry and Measurement PM 1: Inquiry Process Check List PM 6: Observation Record 1 PM 7: Observation Record 2 PM 8: Conference Prompts PM 2: Self-Assessment PM 3: Self-Assessment: Problem Solving PM 9: Work Sample Records
Summative	*Unit Review* *Unit Problem* – Performance Assessment Unit Test Review assessment records; add unit results to ongoing records	Master 3.1 Unit Rubric: Geometry and Measurement Master 3.3 Performance Assessment Rubric: Making Food for a Bake Sale Master 3.4 Unit Summary: Geometry and Measurement PM 10: Summary Class Records: Strands PM 11: Summary Class Records: Achievement Categories PM 12: Summary Record: Individual
Learning Skills/Mathematical Disposition	Observe and record throughout the unit	PM 4: Learning Skills Check List PM 5: Mathematical Dispositions and Learning Skills

Program Masters (PM) are in the *Grade 7 Planning and Program Masters* module.
Extra Practice Masters are on the CD-ROM and are printed in reduced format on page 75 of this module.

SECTION ORGANIZER 15–20 min

Curriculum Focus: Activate prior learning about three-dimensional geometry and the volume of a rectangular prism.
Vocabulary: polyhedron, polyhedra, prism, pyramid, net
Teacher Materials
Optional
- different sizes of boxes; for example, cereal, gift, crackers
- different sizes of cans
- other shaped packages; for example, perfume boxes

ASSUMED PRIOR KNOWLEDGE

☑ Students can identify nets for various polyhedra.

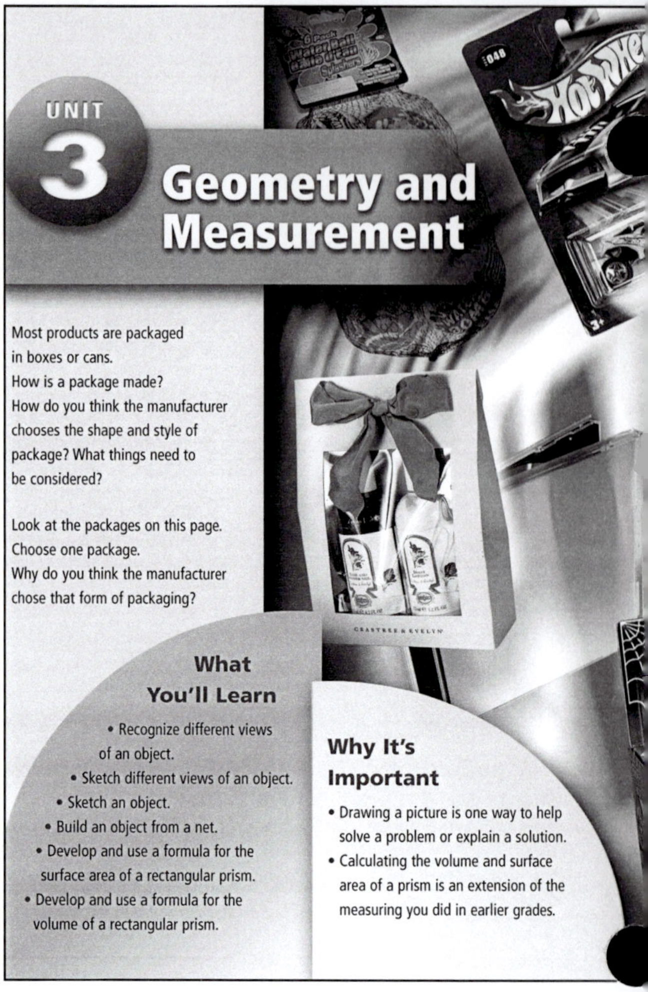

UNIT 3

Geometry and Measurement

Most products are packaged in boxes or cans.
How is a package made?
How do you think the manufacturer chooses the shape and style of package? What things need to be considered?

Look at the packages on this page.
Choose one package.
Why do you think the manufacturer chose that form of packaging?

What You'll Learn
- Recognize different views of an object.
- Sketch different views of an object.
- Sketch an object.
- Build an object from a net.
- Develop and use a formula for the surface area of a rectangular prism.
- Develop and use a formula for the volume of a rectangular prism.

Why It's Important
- Drawing a picture is one way to help solve a problem or explain a solution.
- Calculating the volume and surface area of a prism is an extension of the measuring you did in earlier grades.

ACTIVATE PRIOR LEARNING

Engage students in a discussion about the packages in the picture. Have them consider others that they have in their lunch boxes, and others that they see in the classroom or on store shelves. Have a variety of packages available for students to refer to.

Discuss the first 3 questions on page 74. Record students' answers under the following categories: Materials, Design, Shape and Style, Considerations. Let students decide on the appropriate category.

(Materials: cardboard, metal, plastic, layers of different materials)

(Design: patterns folded together, pieces welded together, heating and moulding)

(Shape and Style: eye-appeal, shelf space, stacking of product)

(Considerations: type of product in package, amount to be packaged, production costs, environmentally friendly, keeping product sterile and airtight)

For the fourth question, students could refer to the answers above. *(Shoebox: cardboard material would be folded and pasted from a net or pattern to create a rectangular prism and a lid that is large enough to hold the boots. The box stacks easily. Cost of material would be amount of cardboard used.)*

Tell students that, in this unit, they will learn more about representing three-dimensional objects and finding the surface area and volume of boxes—rectangular prisms. Students will demonstrate what they have learned by creating their own package for a bake sale item.

Key Words

- polyhedron (polyhedra)
- prism
- pyramid
- regular polyhedron
- cube
- tetrahedron
- isometric
- pictorial diagram
- icosahedron
- octahedron
- dodecahedron
- frustum
- variable
- surface area

FROM THE LIBRARY

Math in the Real World of Architecture: Dimensions, Quantities, Shapes, and Patterns by Shirley Cook. Incentive Publications Inc., 1999
ISBN: 0865303428
Students discover how the art and science of architecture is built upon basic dimensions, quantities, shapes, and patterns. Students learn how these mathematical theorems and concepts can be used to create plans for homes and buildings.

REACHING ALL LEARNERS

Some students may benefit from using the virtual manipulatives on the e-Tools CD-ROM.
The e-Tools appropriate for this unit include *Geometry Shapes* and *Geometry Drawing*.

DIAGNOSTIC ASSESSMENT

What to Look For	What to Do
✔ Students understand that a net is a two-dimensional pattern that folds to make a three-dimensional object. ✔ Students can identify nets for various polyhedra.	***Extra Support:*** Students who have difficulty with three-dimensional spatial sense will need actual objects to use throughout the unit, such as boxes that can be taken apart to form nets for finding surface area, linking cubes, and polyhedra models.

SECTION ORGANIZER

65–80 min

Skills in Review
- Recognizing and identifying three-dimensional objects.
- Using isometric dot paper to draw three-dimensional objects

Teacher Materials
- polyhedra
- isometric chart paper or isometric dot paper transparency

Student Materials
- isometric dot paper (PM 23)

Optional
- polyhedra
- linking cubes

Vocabulary: polyhedron, prism, pyramid, regular polyhedron, cube, tetrahedron, isometric

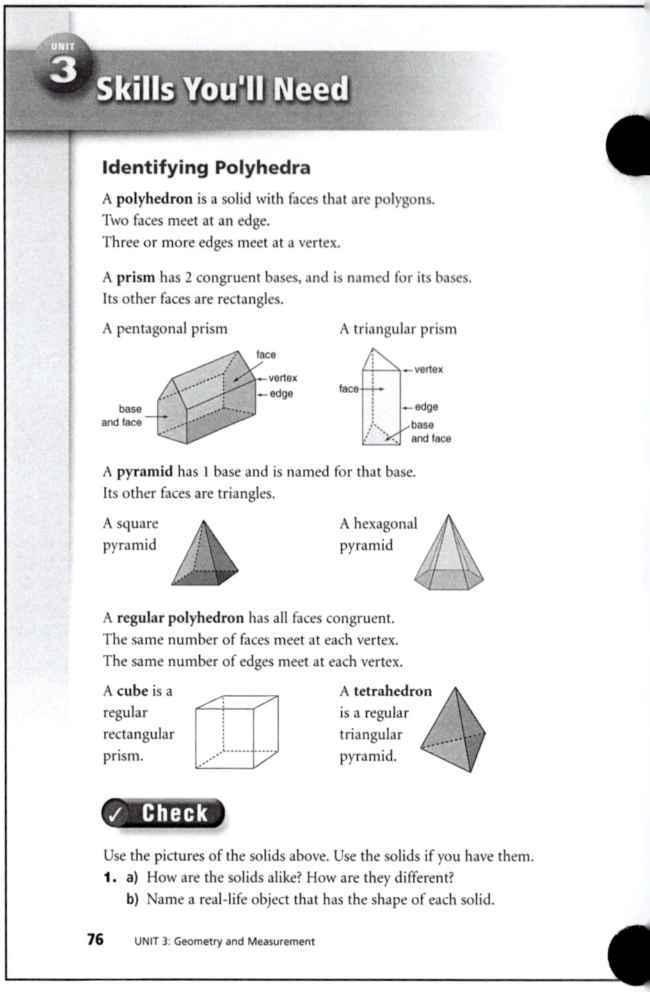

UNIT 3 Skills You'll Need

Identifying Polyhedra

A **polyhedron** is a solid with faces that are polygons.
Two faces meet at an edge.
Three or more edges meet at a vertex.

A **prism** has 2 congruent bases, and is named for its bases.
Its other faces are rectangles.

A pentagonal prism — face, vertex, edge, base and face

A triangular prism — vertex, face, edge, base and face

A **pyramid** has 1 base and is named for that base.
Its other faces are triangles.

A square pyramid

A hexagonal pyramid

A **regular polyhedron** has all faces congruent.
The same number of faces meet at each vertex.
The same number of edges meet at each vertex.

A **cube** is a regular rectangular prism.

A **tetrahedron** is a regular triangular pyramid.

✓ Check

Use the pictures of the solids above. Use the solids if you have them.

1. a) How are the solids alike? How are they different?
   b) Name a real-life object that has the shape of each solid.

76 UNIT 3: Geometry and Measurement

Identifying Polyhedra

Briefly review the names of the polyhedra presented. The base of a prism is the face for which it is named. The two bases are joined by rectangular faces. The base of a pyramid is the face for which it is named. Each triangular face is connected to the base. The triangular faces meet at a point.

Give students time to do the *Check*, then have them take turns to record an answer on the board under the headings: SAME/DIFFERENT or REAL-LIFE OBJECT.

(Same: all the faces are polygons; Different: numbers of faces, edges, and vertices, shapes, cross-sections)

(Prisms: house, crystal, chocolate bar, packages; Pyramids: tent, gazebo roof, Pharaoh's tomb, lighthouse base; Regular polyhedron: number cubes for games, sugar cubes, packages)

Ask students if they see any relationship between the numbers of faces, edges, and vertices of the solids. Some may know *Euler's formula: vertices + faces − edges = 2*. Do not give this formula to students; have them investigate this relationship during the unit.

Common Misconceptions

➤ Students confuse a prism with a pyramid.
How to Help: For any given prism or pyramid, have students decide whether it has two congruent parallel faces. If it does, it is a prism. If it does not, it is a pyramid.

➤ Students think that the base of a prism or pyramid is the face upon which it sits.
How to Help: Have students first identify whether the solid is a prism or pyramid. If it is a prism, then have students identify the two congruent parallel faces that are the bases. If the solid is a pyramid, have students identify the polygon to which each triangular face is attached. This polygon is the base of the pyramid.

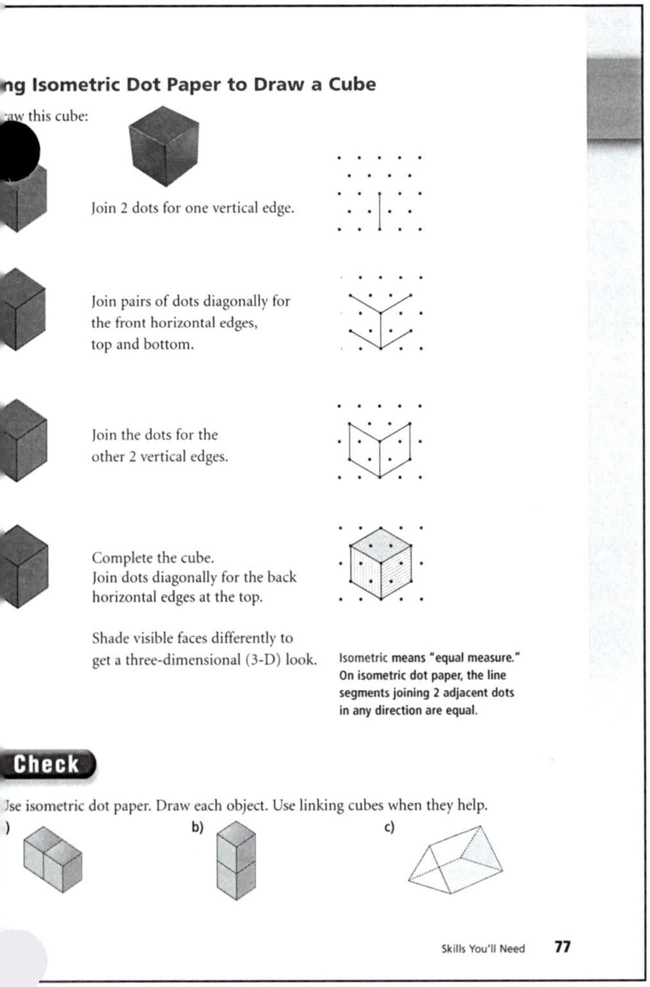

ng Isometric Dot Paper to Draw a Cube

aw this cube:

Join 2 dots for one vertical edge.

Join pairs of dots diagonally for the front horizontal edges, top and bottom.

Join the dots for the other 2 vertical edges.

Complete the cube.
Join dots diagonally for the back horizontal edges at the top.

Shade visible faces differently to get a three-dimensional (3-D) look.

Isometric means "equal measure." On isometric dot paper, the line segments joining 2 adjacent dots in any direction are equal.

Check

Jse isometric dot paper. Draw each object. Use linking cubes when they help.

) b) c)

Skills You'll Need 77

Sample Answers

1. a) For example: All of them have a base, faces, edges, and vertices. They have different shapes.
   b) For example: Pentagonal prism—barn; triangular prism—Toblerone chocolate bar; square pyramid—pyramid in Egypt; hexagonal pyramid—top of church tower; cube—sugar cube; tetrahedron—juice pack

2. a)  b)  c) 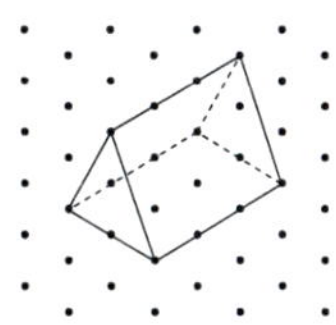

Using Isometric Dot Paper to Draw a Cube

Students may draw a cube in an order that is different from the steps presented. Whichever order is used, three faces should be visible. Model the steps on the board, overhead projector, or chart paper. If students are unsure of the steps, do *Check* question 2a together. Let students take turns to draw a line segment until the drawing is complete. As students finish *Check*, have them draw the diagrams on the board or overhead transparency for questions 2b and c. Be sure to observe as students are drawing to determine those who have trouble with three-dimensional drawing.

For information about 3-D and a simple test for students about 3-D vision, try *http://www.vision3d.com/stereo.html.*

Common Misconceptions

➤ Students do not know how to start their drawing.

How to Help: Have students place the object so one vertical edge is facing them. This edge should be the line segment they draw first. Students could highlight this edge with coloured tape so they can refer back to it as they draw. All other line segments are drawn relative to this segment.

Alternatively, have a student work with another student, who can model the steps for her. As each face of a cube is completed, have the student match the drawing to the face of the object.

Sketching Views of Solids

SECTION ORGANIZER (80–100 min)

Curriculum Focus: Recognize and sketch different views of objects. (7m53, 7m54)

Teacher Materials
- polyhedra solids
- linking cubes
- square dot transparency or grid chart paper

Student Materials
- linking cubes
- square dot paper (PM 22) or 1-cm grid paper (PM 20)
- ruler

Optional
- compass
- Step-by-Step 1 (Master 3.9)
- Extra Practice 1 (Master 3.33)

Assessment: Master 3.2 Ongoing Observations: Geometry and Measurement

Key Math Learnings

1. A three-dimensional object may have different two-dimensional views.
2. A three-dimensional object can be described by its two-dimensional views.

3.1 Sketching Views of Solids

Focus Recognize and sketch different views of objects.

Which objects do you see in this picture?

Choose an object. What does it look like from the top? From the side? From the back?

Explore

Work on your own.
Choose a classroom object.

Sketch the object from every view possible. Label each view.
Use dot paper or grid paper if it helps.
Describe each sketch.

Reflect & Share

Trade sketches with a classmate.
Try to identify the object your classmate drew.

Connect

We can use square dot paper to draw each view of the object at the left.
We ignore the holes in each face.

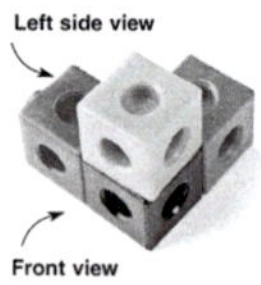

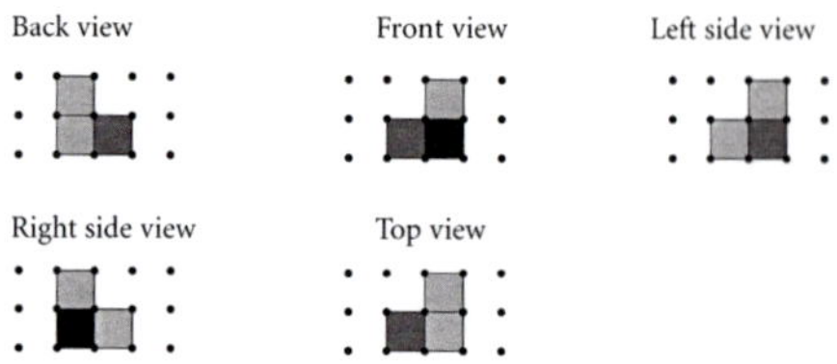

78 UNIT 3: Geometry and Measurement

BEFORE — Get Started

Choose one object from the picture on page 78, or in your classroom. Have a student draw a top, side, or back view of it on grid chart paper or a square dot transparency on the overhead projector. Label the view. Be sure the view does not show any depth, only height and width. Have other students draw other views so students can refer to this sample during the *Explore*.

DURING — Explore

Ongoing Assessment: Observe and Listen

As students are drawing their views, make sure they use rulers for objects that have straight edges (a compass may be needed if circular objects are drawn). Watch for students who use shading or depth on their diagrams. Encourage them to sketch only the shape of each view, not the details of it.

Ask:
- Which figures are you drawing?
  (*Rectangles, squares, triangles, circles*)
- Are some views the same?
  (*Yes, some solids have same front and back or left and right side views.*)
- Could some of the views represent another object?
  (*Yes, a rectangle may be a desk top, a computer screen, a textbook, a recycle bin, and so on.*)

After students have exchanged sketches and identified each other's objects, have students share problems they had drawing.

Example

A triangular prism fits on top of a rectangular prism. The bases of the triangular prism are right isosceles triangles. The rectangular prism has two square faces. Sketch the front, back, side, and top views.

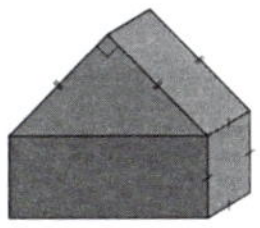

A right isosceles triangle has a 90° angle and two equal sides.

Solution

The front view and back view are the same. Sketch a right isosceles triangle on top of a rectangle.

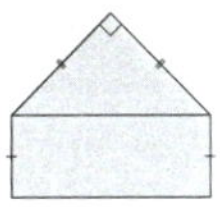

Front view

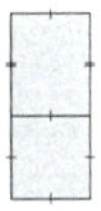

Side view

The two side views are the same. The side face of the triangular prism is a rectangle. Sketch a rectangle on top of a square.

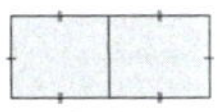

Top view

The top view is two congruent rectangles.

Practice

Use linking cubes when they help.

1. Many signs are views of objects. Identify the view (front, back, side, or top) and the object on each sign.

a) Child care — front view

Adult and child

b) Airport transportation — top or bottom view

Airplane

c) Fully accessible — side

Person in a wheelchair

REACHING ALL LEARNERS

Early Finishers

Have students draw composite objects that they build by combining different polyhedra.

Common Misconceptions

➤ Students identify congruent objects as being different because they have different orientations.

How to Help: Give students enough linking cubes so that when they make all possible arrangements with, for example, 4 linking cubes in question 7, they can compare each new object with those they have previously made.

ESL Strategies

ESL students benefit from having pictures associated with key words. Have them sketch different simple views of themselves. Have them label each view with the words "front," "back," "top," "right side," and "left side."

AFTER Connect

Use linking cubes to make the object in *Connect*. For the *Example*, show a triangular prism on top of a rectangular prism to help those students who have poor spatial visualization. For students with spatial difficulties, draw the views, step-by-step, with them or make a simpler model to review with them. Discuss where 2-D views are used (*animation sketches, architecture sketches, topographical maps).*

Practice

Many students will benefit from using linking cubes to make the objects given, and to help match the views to the model.

Although question 4 is a sketch, rather than an accurate diagram, students could use grid paper, with a scale of 1 cm to represent 2 cm or 4 cm on the birdhouse. The roof of the birdhouse is steep, so its top view will be 2 adjacent rectangles, with width much less than the length.

Students may need other polyhedra for question 8.

Assessment Focus: Question 7

There are many possible arrangements for four linking cubes—all in a row or a column, one cube placed in three different places on top, in front, behind or on the bottom, and pairs of cubes on top or behind each other. Most students will not draw all 5 possible arrangements. Students could repeat this question after they have learned how to use *The Geometer's Sketchpad* in the next lesson.

Students who need extra support to complete the Assessment Focus questions may benefit from the Step-by-Step masters (Masters 3.9 to 3.14).

Sample Answers

2.

	Top	Front	Back	Left Side	Right Side
A	P	N	N	N	N
B	N	N	N	Q	L
C	Q	Q	L	Q	L
D	J	Q	L	Q	L
E	K	Q	L	M	M

3.

Object	Front	Back	Side	Top
a	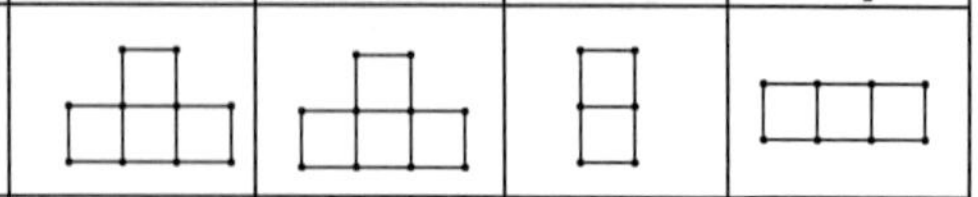			
b	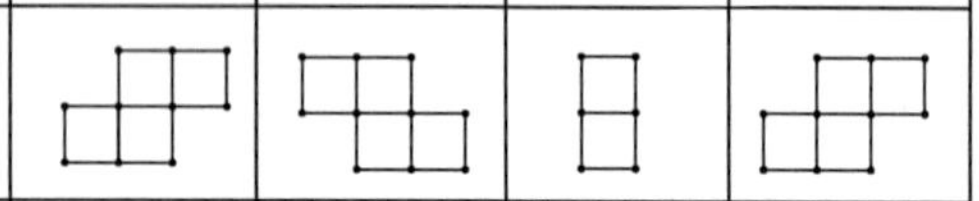			
c	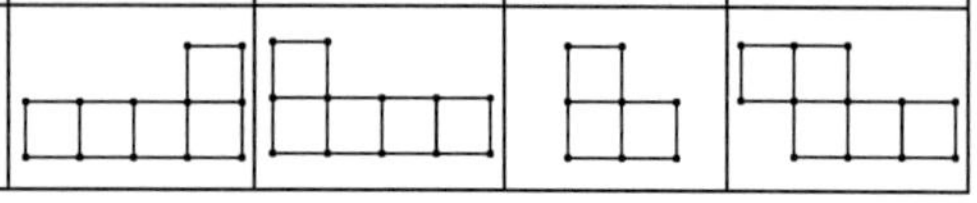			

4. top front side back

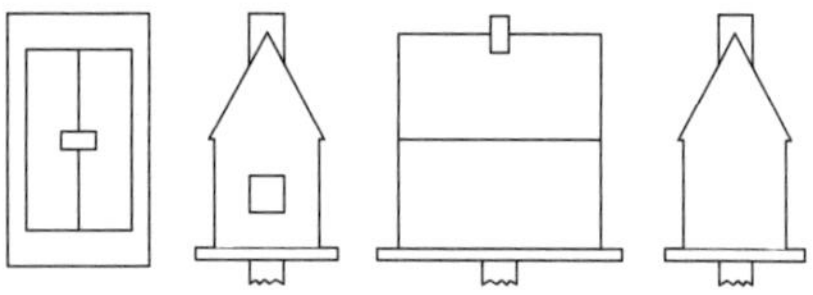

5. a) side b) side c) side d) front

(*Answers continue below.*)

2. Use linking cubes. Make each object A to E. Figures J to Q are views of objects A to E. Match each view (J to Q) to each object (A to E), in as many ways as you can.

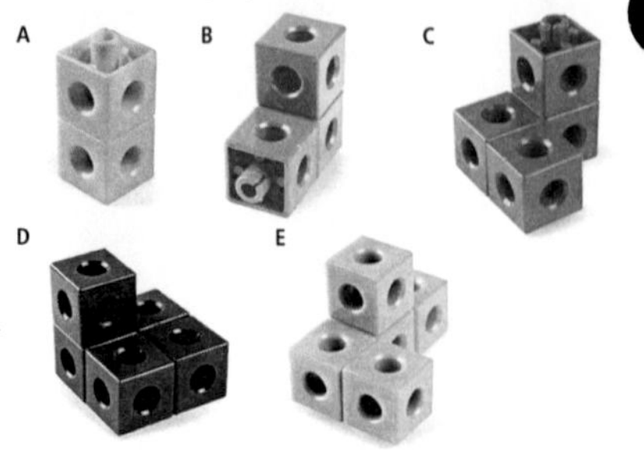

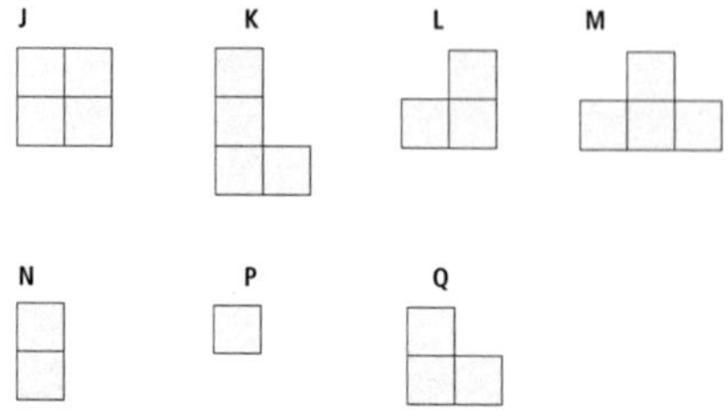

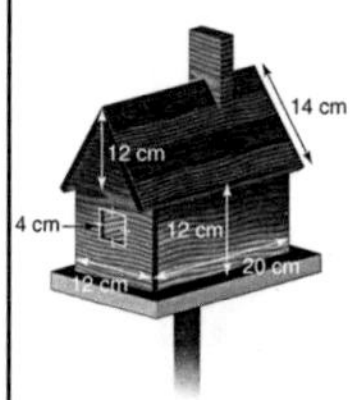

3. Use linking cubes. Make each object. Use square dot paper. Draw the front, back, side, and top views of each object.
a) b) c)

4. Sketch the top, front, side, and back views of the birdhouse at the left. Label each view.

80 UNIT 3: Geometry and Measurement

(*Sample Answers, continued.*)

6. a) front back top side

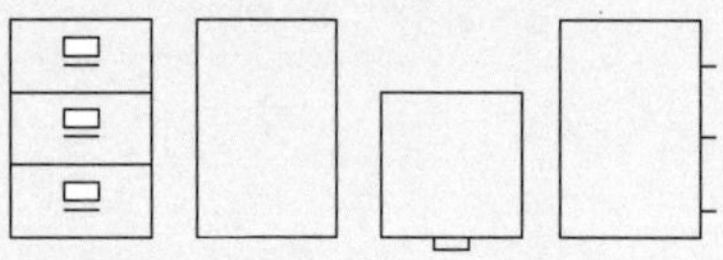

b) front back top side

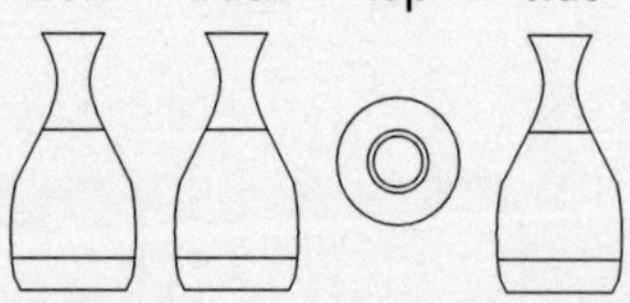

c) front back top side

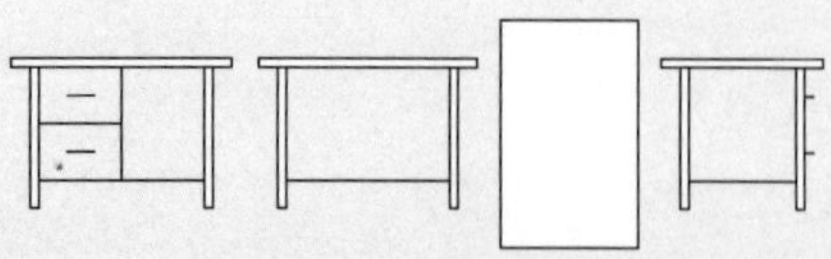

7. There are 5 possible arrangements.

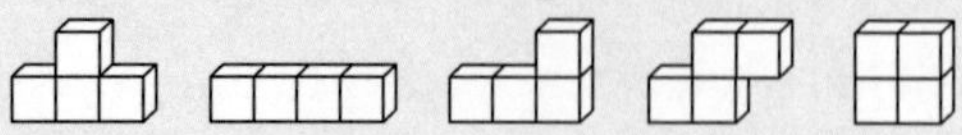

A B C D E

Here are the views for each arrangement.

front back top side

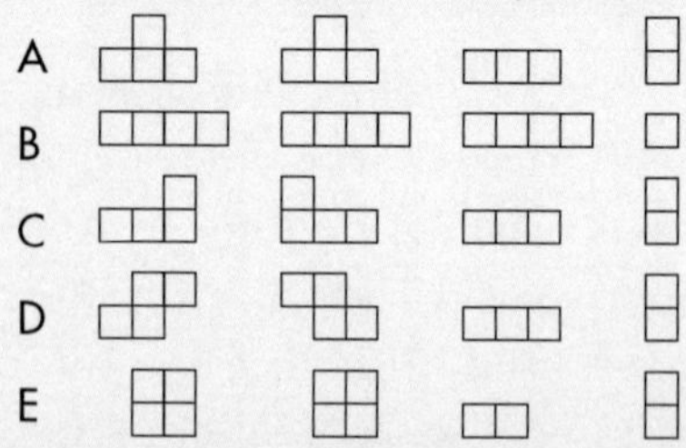

8. a) No. A prism has rectangular faces, so for all the views to be the same, the bases and side faces must be squares.
b) Square-based prism, square-based pyramid
c) The linking cubes in questions 2a and 2b
d) A chair

9. a) back b) top c) side

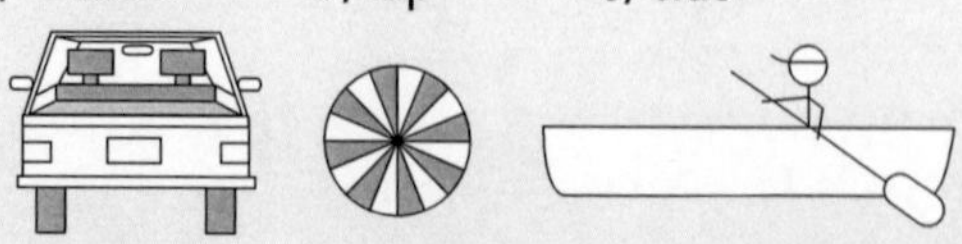

REFLECT: I chose the table. The top view is a rectangle. The front view shows the legs and the edge of the top. I think that is enough to identify it.

top view side view

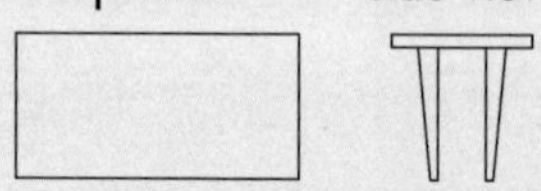

5. Design a road safety or information sign for each situation. Tell which view you used. Explain how each sign shows the information.
a) playground ahead b) tennis court
c) skateboarding allowed d) no flash cameras allowed

6. Find each object in the classroom.
Sketch the front, back, top, and side views of each object.
a) filing cabinet b) vase c) teacher's desk

Mental Math

How many:
- days in a year? 365
- months in a year? 12
- days in a week? 7
- hours in a day? 24
- minutes in an hour? 60
- seconds in a minute? 60

7. **Assessment Focus** Use 4 linking cubes. Make as many different objects as possible. Draw the front, back, top, and side views for each object. Label each view. Use your sketches to explain how you know all the objects you made are different.

8. All 5 views of a cube are the same.
Use the solids in the classroom.
a) Are there any other prisms with all views the same? Explain. No.
b) Which solid has 4 views the same? Square-based prism
c) Which solid has only 3 views the same?
d) Which solid has no views the same? A chair
If you cannot name a solid for parts b to d, use linking cubes to make a solid.

9. Here is one view of an object.
Sketch a possible different view of the object.
a)  b)  c) 

Reflect

Choose an object. How many views do you need to sketch, so someone else can identify it? Explain. Sketch the views you describe.

Mental Math

Students can look at calendars to find the days in a year and a week, and the months in a year. They can look at clocks to determine the other relationships.

Assignment Guidelines

If your students do not have time to complete all the *Practice* questions on pages 79-81, the following questions provide minimum curriculum coverage: 3, 4, 5, 7, 8, *Reflect*
To assess the 4 Achievement Chart categories listed in the curriculum document, have students complete these questions:
Understanding Concepts: 3
Application: 4
Communication: 5
Problem Solving: 8

ASSESSMENT FOR LEARNING

What to Look For	What to Do
Understanding concepts ✔ Students understand that a two-dimensional view shows height and width, not depth. ***Applying procedures*** ✔ Students can draw different views of simple objects. ***Communicating*** ✔ Students can draw and label two-dimensional views on grid or square dot paper.	***Extra Support:*** Pair a student who has good spatial sense with a student who needs help drawing. Students can use Step-by-Step 1 (Master 3.9) to complete question 7. ***Extra Practice:*** Students can play *Match It* (Master 3.5). Students can complete Extra Practice 1 (Master 3.33). ***Extension:*** Students can create more game cards for *Match It*.

Recording and Reporting
Master 3.2 Ongoing Observations: Geometry and Measurement

Using a Computer to Draw Views of Solids

SECTION ORGANIZER

40–50 min

Curriculum Focus: Use technology to sketch views of objects. (7m54)

Teacher Materials

Optional

- posters with screenshots of *The Geometer's Sketchpad* tools and menus

Student Materials

- computer with *The Geometer's Sketchpad* software

Optional

- linking cubes

Vocabulary: *The Geometer's Sketchpad* Menu and Toolbox words

Assessment: Master 3.2 Ongoing Observations: Geometry and Measurement

Key Math Learning

Computer software can be used to make accurate drawings of the views of an object.

Using a Computer to Draw Views of Solids

Focus Use technology to sketch views of objects.

Software, such as *The Geometer's Sketchpad*, can be used to draw different views of solids.

Follow these steps.

1. Open *The Geometer's Sketchpad*.

To make a "dot paper" screen:

2. From the **Edit** menu, choose **Preferences**.
   Select the Units tab. Check the Distance units are cm.
   Click **OK**.
3. From the **Graph** menu, choose **Define Coordinate System**.
   Click on a point where the grid lines intersect.
   The grid is now highlighted in pink.
4. From the **Display** menu, choose **Line Width**, then **Dotted**.
   There are dots at the grid intersections.
   Click anywhere on the screen other than the dots.
   The dots are no longer highlighted. Hold down the shift key.
   Click on each numbered axis and the two red dots.
   Release the shift key.
   The axes and the dots are now highlighted.
5. From the **Display** menu, choose **Hide Objects**.
   The axes and dots disappear.
   The screen now appears like a piece of dot paper.
   From the **Graph** menu, choose **Snap Points**.

Make this object with linking cubes.
Follow the steps below to create views of this object.

Front view

6. From the **Toolbox** menu, choose **A** (Text Tool).
   Move the cursor to the screen and a finger appears.
   Click and drag to make a box at the top left.
   Inside the box, type: Front View

82 UNIT 3: Geometry and Measurement

Use a poster or sketch on the board to indicate where the Toolbox Menu and menus are. Review how to log on to the computer and access this software. Students need to read each instruction carefully and in order.

As students work individually or in pairs on the computers, be prepared to troubleshoot computer problems. Problems occur if a student misses a step in the instructions.

Have the student use a ruler to move down from one instruction to the next. If a student has not used **Snap Points,** the endpoints of line segments will slide off the dots. Encourage students to explore other menu and Toolbox commands.

The computer drawn views of linking cubes are neat, accurate, and colourful.

7. From the **Toolbox** menu, choose (Straightedge Tool).

Move to a dot on the screen below the title.
Click and drag to draw a line segment.
Release the mouse button.
Continue to draw line segments to draw the front view.
Click to select each line segment.
From the **Display** menu, choose **Line Width**, then **Dashed**.
This draws the line segments as broken lines.

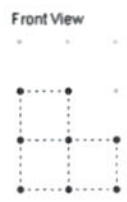

8. From the **Toolbox** menu, click on (Selection Arrow Tool).

Click to select the four corners of the top square, in clockwise order.
From the **Construct** menu, choose **Quadrilateral Interior**.
From the **Display** menu, choose **Color**, then choose blue.

9. Repeat *Step 8* to make the bottom squares red and green.

10. Repeat *Step 6* to *9* to draw and label the left side view and the back view.

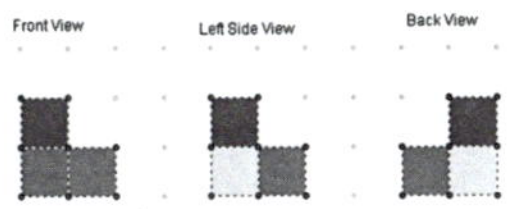

11. Draw the top view and right side view.

✓ Check

1. Open a new sketch. Draw different views of objects from *Section 3.1, Practice* question 3. Compare the hand-drawn views with the computer-drawn views.

Technology: Using a Computer to Draw Views of Solids 83

REACHING ALL LEARNERS

Early Finishers

Have students investigate what else they can do with *The Geometer's Sketchpad.*

Common Misconceptions

➤ Students have difficulty following the step-by-step instructions.
How to Help: Have two students work together. One student reads the steps while the other student does them. Students should switch roles to be sure both can complete the activity.

ESL Strategies

There is much to read and decode, as well as learning the technology. Pair an ESL student with a student who reads well and is comfortable with computers. Make sure this student does not do all the work and exclude the ESL student.

ASSESSMENT FOR LEARNING

What to Look For

Understanding concepts

✔ Students understand the Toolbox and menu commands of the software.

Applying procedures

✔ Students can use the software to produce views of solids built with linking cubes.

What to Do

Extra Support: Pair a student who has good computer skills with a student who needs help.

Extra Practice: Students can build the linking cube arrangements for question 7, page 81, then draw their views. Students then print the views and attach an isometric drawing of the solid to the views.

Extension: Students can remove **Snap Points**, and draw the birdhouse in question 4, page 80.

Recording and Reporting

Master 3.2 Ongoing Observations: Geometry and Measurement

SECTION 3.2

Sketching Solids

SECTION ORGANIZER 80–100 min

Curriculum Focus: Sketch pictures of objects from models and drawings. (7m55)

Teacher Materials
- isometric dot transparency or chart paper

Student Materials
- isometric dot paper (PM 23)
- grid paper or square dot paper (PM 20 or PM 22)
- linking cubes

Optional
- Step-by-Step 2 (Master 3.10)
- Extra Practice 2 (Master 3.34)

Vocabulary: pictorial diagram

Assessment: Master 3.2 Ongoing Observations: Geometry and Measurement

Key Math Learnings

1. Isometric dot paper can be used to show three dimensions of an object.
2. A pictorial drawing uses translations of a view to give the impression of three dimensions.

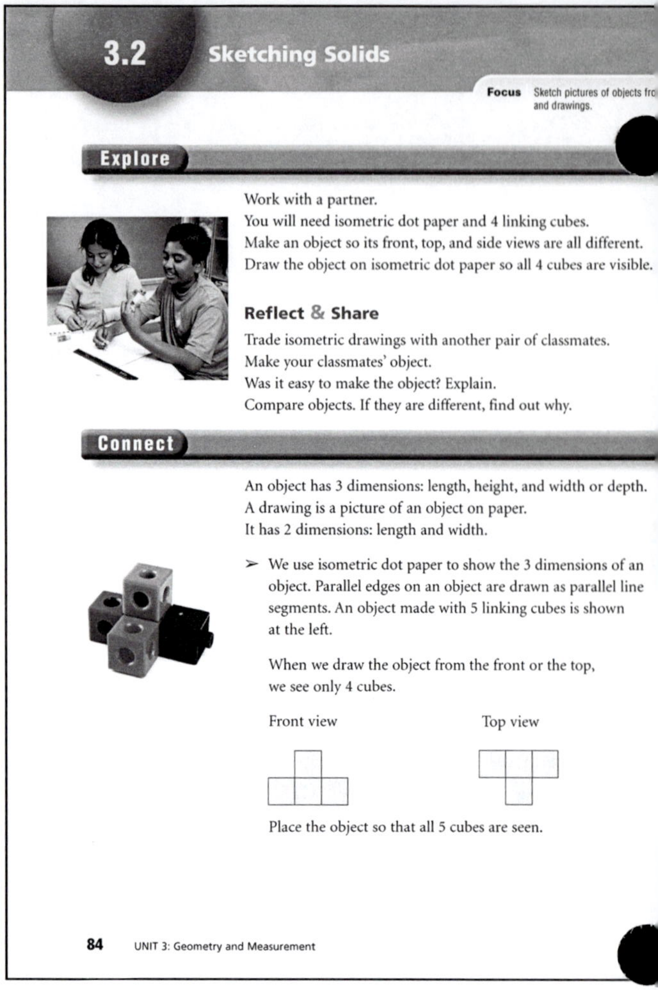

3.2 Sketching Solids

Focus Sketch pictures of objects fro and drawings.

Explore

Work with a partner.
You will need isometric dot paper and 4 linking cubes.
Make an object so its front, top, and side views are all different.
Draw the object on isometric dot paper so all 4 cubes are visible.

Reflect & Share

Trade isometric drawings with another pair of classmates.
Make your classmates' object.
Was it easy to make the object? Explain.
Compare objects. If they are different, find out why.

Connect

An object has 3 dimensions: length, height, and width or depth.
A drawing is a picture of an object on paper.
It has 2 dimensions: length and width.

➢ We use isometric dot paper to show the 3 dimensions of an object. Parallel edges on an object are drawn as parallel line segments. An object made with 5 linking cubes is shown at the left.

When we draw the object from the front or the top, we see only 4 cubes.

Front view Top view

Place the object so that all 5 cubes are seen.

84 UNIT 3: Geometry and Measurement

BEFORE Get Started

Remind students about the arrangements of 4 linking cubes they made in Section 3.1, question 4, page 81. For the *Explore*, students choose an arrangement that has different views.

If necessary, review *Skills You'll Need*, page 77, and/or have one partner in each pair have her book open at that page, so students can review how to draw on isometric dot paper.

Math Note

The restriction in *Explore* for the top, front, and side views to be different was to prevent students making a rectangular prism that is 1 by 1 by 4, or 2 by 2 by 1. There are 3 other possible arrangements with 4 cubes.

DURING Explore

Ongoing Assessment: Observe and Listen

Allow students who have difficulty with three-dimensional drawing to choose a simpler arrangement of the four cubes, rather than one with several different views. Encourage students who need practice in three-dimensional drawing to do the drawing, while their partners coach.

As students work on the *Explore*, watch for the steps students use to make their drawings. Record those students with good strategies and have them share these with the class during *Connect*.

Draw the edges in this order:
- vertical edges (red)
- horizontal edges that appear to go down to the right (blue)
- horizontal edges that appear to go up to the right (green)

Shade faces to produce a 3-D effect.

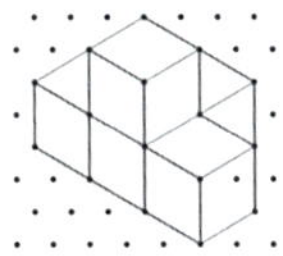

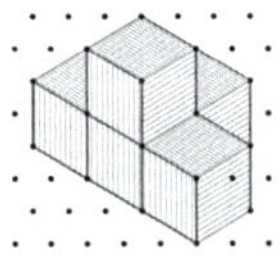

Number Strategies

Simplify.
Use order of operations.
- 17 − 7 × 2 + 3 6
- 15 − 6 ÷ 2 12
- 14 ÷ 2 × 3 21
- 8 × 2 + 21 − 6 31
- 15 + 3 × 5 30

➢ We can use translations to draw a **pictorial diagram**.
A pictorial diagram shows the shape of an object in 2 dimensions.
It gives the impression of 3 dimensions.
To sketch the rectangular prism above right:

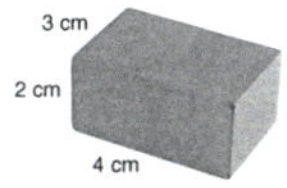

Draw a rectangle 4 cm by 2 cm.

Draw another rectangle that is the image of the first rectangle after a translation up and to the right.

Join corresponding vertices for a sketch of a rectangular prism.
Label the dimensions.

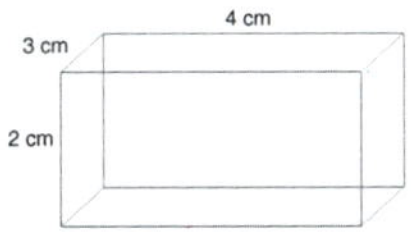

Note that the depth of the prism is 3 cm but, on the drawing, this distance is less than 3 cm. In a pictorial drawing, the depth of an object is drawn to a smaller scale than the length and width. This gives the appearance of 3 dimensions.

3.2 Sketching Solids 85

REACHING ALL LEARNERS

Early Finishers

Have students sketch a different arrangement of the 4 cubes; or make, then sketch an arrangement with 5 cubes.

Common Misconceptions

➤Students have difficulty transferring what they see in 3 dimensions to a drawing in 2 dimensions.

How to Help: Make sure students follow the steps in the student text or have them work with stronger students who can coach them step by step.

Making Connections

In art, students may be learning to make drawings appear 3-dimensional by having one or two vanishing points. Students could practice this skill in their drawings.

Number Strategies

Remind students of the order of operations: brackets, multiplication and division from left to right, addition and subtraction from left to right.

Ask:
- How did you know where to start your drawing?
  (I held my object so I could see the top and side views. I drew the 6 vertical line segments I could see, first.)
- What did you do next?
  (I drew the diagonal lines for the front horizontal edges at the bottom and top; I did this by joining the vertical segments.)
- How did you finish your diagram?
  (I drew the line segments for the side and back horizontal edges.)
- Did the object you made using your classmates' drawing match their object?
  (Yes, the drawing made it easy to see how the 4 cubes were joined.)

AFTER Connect

Students with good three-dimensional drawing strategies should demonstrate these on chart paper or the overhead projector. Point out that, on isometric dot paper, all the edges of a cube have the same length, and opposite edges are parallel. In art, students may be learning about perspective drawings with lines that converge to a vanishing point. These are different kinds of drawings.

If necessary, review how to draw the object in *Connect* made with 5 linking cubes. Then show students a pictorial diagram. Students may find it easier to draw this type of diagram on square dot paper or grid paper.

Sample Answers

1. a) 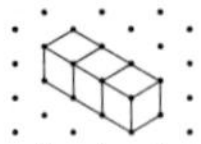 b) 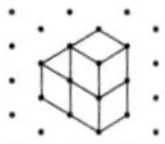

2. a) 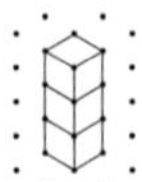 b) 

3. a)  b) 

4. 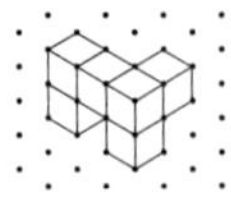

5. a) 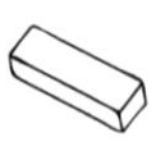 b)  c) 

6. b) 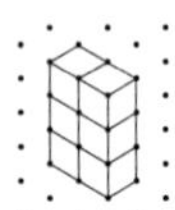

   d) Yes, making the shelving unit 2 cubes high and 3 cubes long will reduce side faces by one or making the shelving unit 3 cubes high and 2 cubes long will reduce the top/bottom faces by one.

7. a) 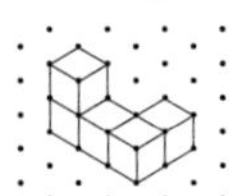 b) 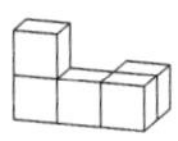

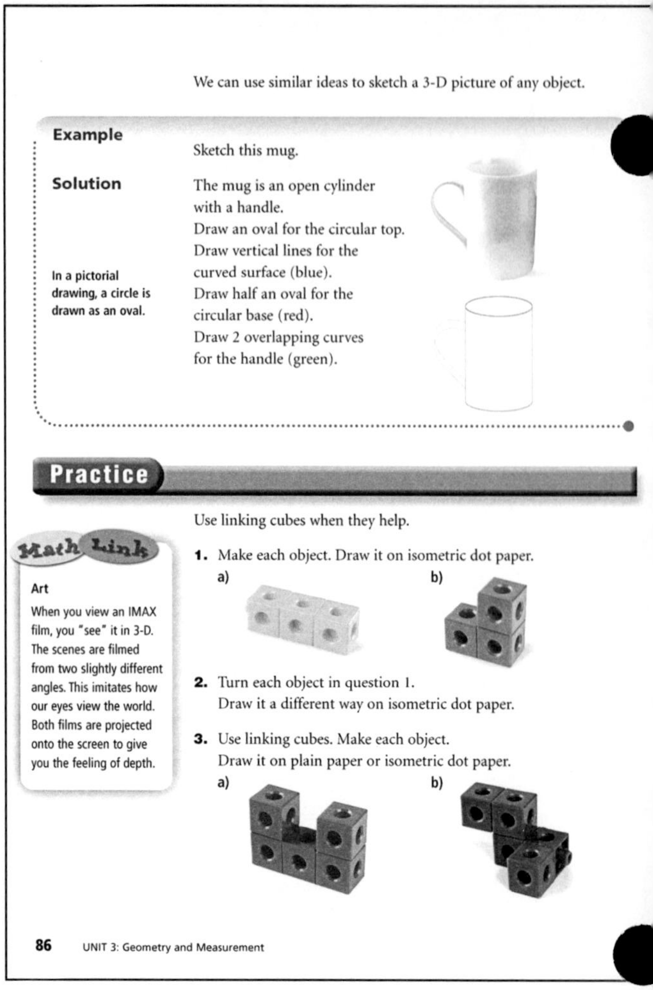

We can use similar ideas to sketch a 3-D picture of any object.

Example

Sketch this mug.

Solution

The mug is an open cylinder with a handle.
Draw an oval for the circular top.
Draw vertical lines for the curved surface (blue).
Draw half an oval for the circular base (red).
Draw 2 overlapping curves for the handle (green).

In a pictorial drawing, a circle is drawn as an oval.

Practice

Use linking cubes when they help.

Math Link

Art

When you view an IMAX film, you "see" it in 3-D. The scenes are filmed from two slightly different angles. This imitates how our eyes view the world. Both films are projected onto the screen to give you the feeling of depth.

1. Make each object. Draw it on isometric dot paper.
a) b)

2. Turn each object in question 1.
Draw it a different way on isometric dot paper.

3. Use linking cubes. Make each object.
Draw it on plain paper or isometric dot paper.
a) b)

86 UNIT 3: Geometry and Measurement

Then review the *Example*, which illustrates how to draw an object with a circular cross section.

Practice

Ensure students build the models before they draw the objects. Question 6 may need different coloured squares to represent the different types of faces rather than linking cubes. A top face of one cube is the bottom face of the cube above it.

Assessment Focus: Question 7

A student will build any arrangement of the 5 linking cubes. A student who is struggling will probably build a 1 by 1 by 5 rectangular prism. A student who is comfortable with the concept will probably build an object that has at least one cube stacked on top of another.

4. Here are different views of an object made with linking cubes.

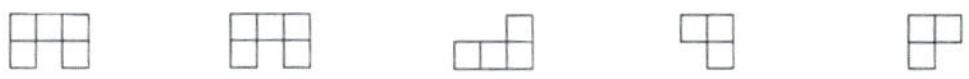

Make the object.
Draw it on isometric dot paper or plain paper.

5. Sketch a 3-D picture of each object on plain paper.

a)  b)  c) 

6. Square pieces of shelving snap together to make cube-shaped stacking shelves. All the faces are square and measure 30 cm by 30 cm. A side face costs $1.50.
A top or bottom face costs $1.30. The back face costs $1.10.
Kate built shelves using 9 side faces, 6 back faces, and 9 top/bottom faces.

a) Use linking cubes to build a possible design.
b) Draw a picture of your design on isometric dot paper.
c) How much did the shelving cost? $31.80
d) Is it possible to have the same number of cubes but use fewer pieces? Explain. Yes
e) If your answer to part d is yes, what is the new cost of shelving? Explain. $30.30 or $30.50

7. Assessment Focus Use 5 linking cubes. Make a solid.

a) Sketch the solid on isometric dot paper.
b) Sketch a 3-D picture of the solid on plain paper.
c) How is sketching a solid on isometric paper different from sketching it on plain paper? How are the methods alike? Use your sketches to explain.

Reflect

How do you draw an object to show its 3 dimensions?
Use words and pictures to explain.

3.2 Sketching Solids **87**

c) Different: The dots are a fixed distance apart on isometric paper but distances must be measured or scales used on plain paper. Draw vertical edges and then horizontal edges up to the right or down to the right to complete isometric drawing. Draw a 2-dimensional view on plain paper, then repeat this view translated up and to the right a distance appropriate for the depth, and draw "depth" lines in the same direction. Alike: Best to work from front to back; keeping all parts in correct relative positions, use ruler.

REFLECT: I used isometric paper: I used 5 linking cubes. I arranged 4 cubes in a square and put the 5th cube on the top. I held my object so I could see all 5 cubes. I drew vertical lines to show the vertical edges I could see. I then drew diagonal lines to show the horizontal edges that appear to go down to the right. I then drew diagonal lines to show the horizontal edges that appear to go up to the right. Finally, I used 3 different colours for the faces; one colour for the horizontal faces; a second colour for the faces that face to the right; and a third colour for the faces that face to the left.

Assignment Guidelines

If your students do not have time to complete all the *Practice* questions on pages 86 and 87, the following questions provide minimum curriculum coverage: 1b, 3b, 4, 5c, 7, *Reflect*
To assess the 4 Achievement Chart categories listed in the curriculum document, have students complete these questions:
Understanding Concepts: 3b
Application: 5c
Problem Solving: 4
Communication: *Reflect*

ASSESSMENT FOR LEARNING

What to Look For	What to Do
Understanding concepts ✔ Students understand some different methods for drawing solids.	***Extra Support:*** As students produce drawings for the *Practice* questions, post these around the room under the headings *Isometric* and *Pictorial* so other students may refer to them if they experience difficulty. Students can use Step-by-Step 2 (Master 3.10) to complete question 7.
Applying procedures ✔ Students can use the methods to draw solids.	***Extra Practice:*** Have students sketch other objects in the classroom. Students can complete the Additional Activity *Slide Design* (Master 3.6). Students can complete Extra Practice 2 (Master 3.34).
Communicating ✔ Students can describe steps for drawing a solid.	***Extension:*** Have students use prisms, pyramids, cones, cylinders, and so on, to make an object, which they then sketch different ways.

Recording and Reporting
Master 3.2 Ongoing Observations: Geometry and Measurement

Forensic Graphics Specialist

Forensic Graphics Specialist

The World of Work

A forensic investigator collects information from a crime scene to find out who was involved and exactly what happened. The forens investigator also presents evidence in court as required by law.

The forensic graphics specialist visits the crime scene to take photographs and measurements. She may research to compose technical drawings to help with the investigation. When she prepares these drawings, the graphics specialist pays attention to shading and relative line thickness. It is important that she does not present optical illusions such as an object appearing to be "inside out."

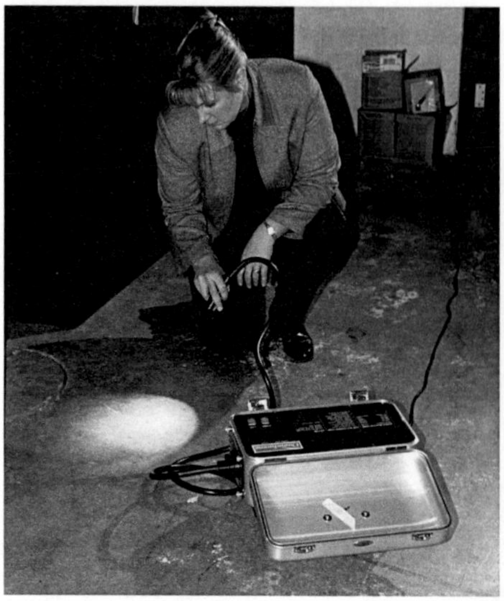

The forensic graphics specialist needs to make "field sketches" to refer to when making drawings in the office. The type of drawings made need to convey the important features of problem locations but eliminate distracting details.

Have students suggest other careers or times in daily life that require the use of accurate 2-dimensional and 3-dimensional drawings.

Archeologist: The location of an artifact in a dig must be recorded carefully so it may be matched with other finds. This would require top views for north/south/east/west locations and side views to show in which layer of the excavation the artifact was found.

Art Authenticator: Valuable works of art are catalogued by owners with specific details recorded to verify the originality of the work and to protect against fraud. Different views of the art work are made to record methods of mounting.

Interior Design: Sketches of rooms from different views show the ideas a designer has for a space.

Other possibilities: 3-D Modelling and Animation, Web Design, Illustrator, Map Making

3.3 Building Objects from Nets

Focus Build objects from nets.

In earlier grades, you designed nets for prisms and pyramids.
Now, you will fold nets to make prisms, pyramids, and other polyhedra.

Explore

Work with a partner.
You will need scissors and tape.
Your teacher will give you large copies of the nets below.

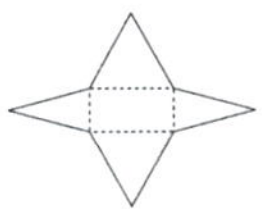

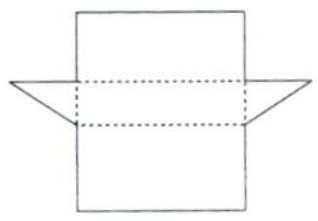

➢ Identify the polyhedron for each net above.
➢ Use a copy of each net.
Cut it out. Fold, then tape it to make a polyhedron.
➢ Identify congruent faces on each polyhedron.

Reflect & Share

Look at each polyhedron from the top, front, back, and sides.
Which views are the same? Explain.

Connect

There are 5 regular polyhedra.
You reviewed 2 of them, the cube and the tetrahedron,
in *Skills You'll Need*, page 76.

One regular polyhedron is an **icosahedron**.
Here is a net for one-half of an icosahedron.

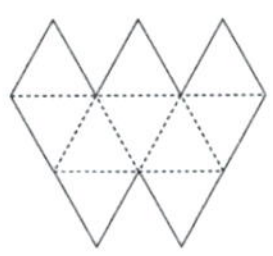

3.3 Building Objects from Nets 89

Building Objects from Nets

SECTION ORGANIZER (80–100 min)

Curriculum Focus: Build objects from nets. (7m56)

Teacher Materials
- net of an icosahedron (2 copies of Master 3.19)
- net of a frustum of a square pyramid (Master 3.20)
- polyhedra

Optional
- nets of a cube and a tetrahedron

Student Materials
- nets for *Explore* and *Practice* questions 1-5, 7, 9 (Masters 3.17, 3.18, 3.21 to 3.27)
- scissors and tape

Optional
- shoeboxes to store finished polyhedra
- Step-by-Step 3 (Master 3.11)
- Extra Practice 3 (Master 3.35)

Vocabulary: icosahedron, octahedron, dodecahedron

Assessment: Master 3.2 Ongoing Observations: Geometry and Measurement

Key Math Learnings

1. Three-dimensional objects can be built from polygons.
2. A net is a pattern that folds to form a three-dimensional solid.
3. Polyhedra can be classified by certain characteristics; for example, regular, prism, pyramid.

BEFORE Get Started

Students can use a shoebox to store the solids they build. Remind students of the work they did in grade 6. Model the construction techniques by building a cube and/or tetrahedron from its net. Ensure students understand the task in *Explore*.

DURING Explore

Ongoing Assessment: Observe and Listen

Watch as students cut and fold. Accuracy is needed if edges are to meet and complete solids can be built.

As students work on the ***Explore***, ask:

- Which solid will your net make? How do you know?
  (*Most of the faces are triangles, so it will be a pyramid. There is only one rectangle for the base so it is a rectangular pyramid.*)
- Which solid will the other net make? How do you know?
  (*Most of the faces are rectangles so it will be a prism. There are 2 congruent triangular faces for bases, so it is a triangular prism.*)
- Could you make the same solid with a different net?
  (*Yes. For the rectangular pyramid, all the triangles are arranged around the base but the net could have all the triangles joined and the base attached to only one of them.*)
- How many faces, edges, and vertices does each solid have?
  (*Rectangular pyramid: 5, 8, 5; triangular prism: 5, 9, 6*)
- Which attributes are easier to determine using the net?
  (*Number of faces and which are congruent*)
- Which attributes are easier to find using the solid?
  (*The type of solid, the number of edges and vertices*)

REACHING ALL LEARNERS

Early Finishers

Have students cut and fold nets for the icosahedron and the frustum of a square pyramid that are used in *Connect.* Students can determine the characteristics of these solids.

ESL Strategies

The visual part of this unit should be meaningful to ESL students, but the vocabulary may be confusing. Many of the words have two meanings in English such as *faces, nets, edges* or have close pronunciations, such as *prism* and *prison*. Have students keep a word list of these double meanings.

Sample Answers

1. a) triangular prism
   b) a prism with 5 faces, 2 are congruent right triangles and 3 are rectangles. There are 6 vertices and 9 edges.
2. a) This is a polyhedron because the faces are polygons.
   b) The 6-sided polygons are parallel. These polygons are perpendicular to all the other faces. Alternate rectangles are parallel. Adjacent rectangles are perpendicular.
3. a) It has 8 faces and "octa" means 8.
   b) The octagon appears to be a double pyramid. It has 8 faces, 6 vertices, and 12 edges.
   It is regular because all the faces are equilateral triangles; the same number of edges (4) meet at each vertex; and the same number of faces (4) meet at each vertex.
4. a) It is a trapezoid pyramid because the base is a trapezoid and all the other faces are triangles. It has 5 faces, 8 edges, and 5 vertices.

This net can be cut out and folded.
The net has 10 congruent triangles.

Two of these pieces are taped together to make an icosahedron.

An icosahedron has 20 congruent faces.
Each face is an equilateral triangle.
In the *Practice* questions, you will make the other 2 regular polyhedra.

A regular **octahedron**

A regular **dodecahedron**

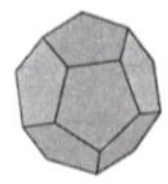

In previous grades, you designed and sketched nets of prisms and pyramids.
In the *Example* that follows, and in *Practice* questions, you will investigate nets for other objects.

Example

Fold this net to make an object.
Describe the object.

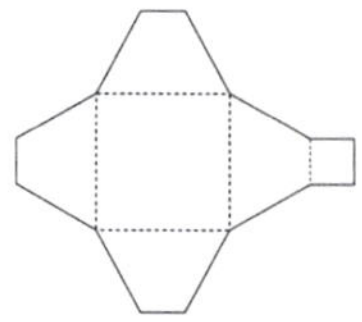

Solution

The net is folded along the broken line segments. Each edge touches another edge. The edges are taped.

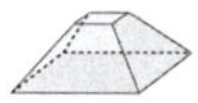

90 UNIT 3: Geometry and Measurement

- What changes as the solid is placed on different faces?
  (*The views of the solid change.*)

AFTER Connect

Review students' responses to the questions in *Reflect & Share.*

For the rectangular pyramid: front and back views are the same because opposite faces are congruent triangles. The two side views are the same, for a similar reason. The top view is a rectangle with a line segment from each vertex to the centre.

For the triangular prism: If the prism is resting on a triangular base, then its front and side views are rectangles; the back view is a rectangle divided into 2 smaller rectangles with a vertical line segment, and the top view is a triangle.

If the prism is resting on a rectangular face, then its front and back views are triangles, the side views are rectangles, and the top view is a rectangle divided into 2 congruent rectangles with a horizontal line segment.

Review the net for an icosahedron in *Connect,* and the net for the frustum of a square pyramid in the *Example.* Have students count the numbers of faces, edges, and vertices.

You could set up a Polyhedra Summary Sheet on chart paper. Make a table with 8 columns, and these headings: Sketch of Net; 3-D Picture; Name; Regular (yes/no); Shape of Base; Number and Type of Faces; Number of Edges; Number of Vertices. Fill in the table for the rectangular pyramid and triangular prism from *Explore,* and for the regular icosahedron and frustum of a square pyramid in *Connect.*
As students fold the nets to make objects in *Practice,* fill in the table for these solids.

The object looks like the bottom of a pyramid; that is, a pyramid with the top part removed. The object is called a **frustum** of a pyramid.

The object has 2 non-congruent square faces, and 4 congruent trapezoid faces. The 2 square faces are parallel.

Practice

Your teacher will give you a large copy of each net.

1. Fold this net to make a polyhedron.
   a) Identify the polyhedron. Triangular prism
   b) Describe the polyhedron.

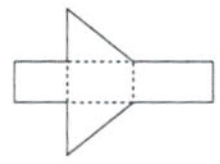

2. Fold this net.
   a) Is the object a polyhedron? Yes
   If so, what are the attributes that make it a polyhedron?
   b) Identify parallel faces and perpendicular faces.

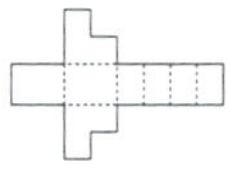

Calculator Skills

Find three prime numbers that have a sum of 43 and a product of 1085.
+ 7 + 31 = 43
× 7 × 31 = 1085

3. Fold two of these nets to make two square pyramids with no base.
Tape the two pyramids together at their missing bases.
You have made a regular octahedron.
   a) Why does it have this name?
   b) Describe the octahedron.
   How do you know it is regular?

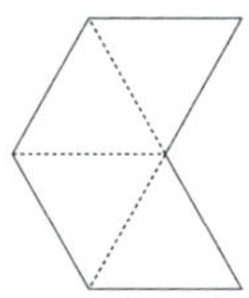

4. Fold each net. Describe each object.
How are the objects the same? How are they different?

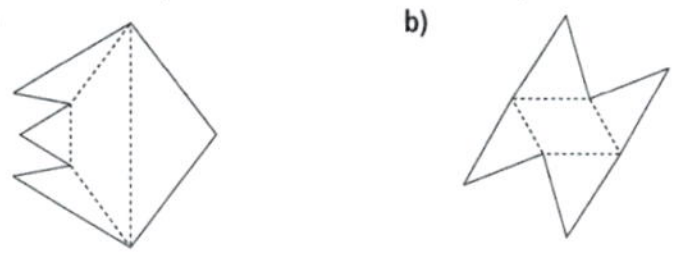

a) Trapezoid pyramid   b) Parallelogram pyramid

3.3 Building Objects from Nets **91**

b) It is parallelogram pyramid because the base is a parallelogram and all the other faces are triangles. It has 5 faces, 8 edges, and 5 vertices.
The two objects have the same numbers of faces, edges, and vertices but different shaped bases.

5. The dodecahedron has 12 congruent faces that are regular pentagons, 30 edges, and 20 vertices. It is a regular dodecahedron because the same numbers of edges and faces (3) meet at each vertex.

6. There are 12 regular pentagons and 20 regular hexagons. Five hexagons surround one pentagon. Each hexagon has a pentagon on every other edge.

7. a) This is a prism with 7 faces, 2 of which are congruent regular parallel pentagons and 5 are congruent rectangles. There are 15 edges and 10 vertices.
   b) The side faces are rectangles so it is a prism. It is a pentagonal prism because the congruent parallel bases are pentagons.

8. The sides of the polygons that meet at edges must be the same length. As faces meet, other faces must not overlap.

9. The object is a pentagonal prism. The two congruent bases are concave pentagons.

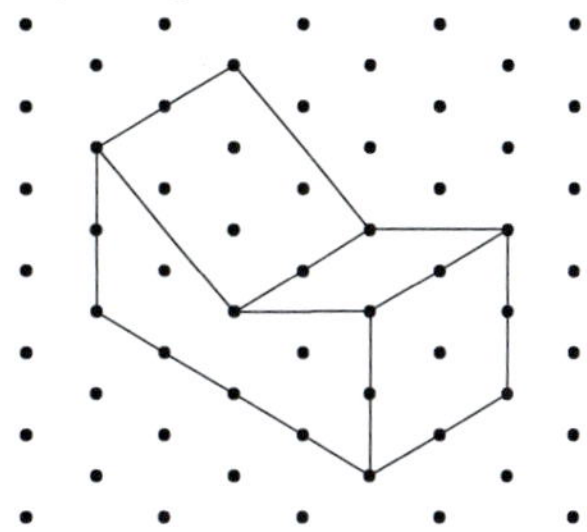

Practice

Students may need to continue to work in pairs to share resources and to assist in taping. Distribute copies of Masters 3.21 to 3.27. By the end of the *Practice*, students may have found Euler's Formula:

numbers of faces + vertices − edges = 2. This is true for all polyhedra.

Assessment Focus: Question 7

Students should be able to build and describe this solid from previous practice. Descriptions may include different views; number and shapes of faces and whether they are congruent; number of edges; and number of vertices.

REFLECT: I chose a box of salt. It is 17 cm high, 10 cm wide, and 5 cm deep. I think this shape was chosen because it is easy to hold and pour the salt from the opening on a side face, close to the top.
I could not think of a better shape for the packaging.
(Note that students' work should include a sketch of the package and a net of the package.)

Calculator Skills

Students need to consider numbers that are factors of 1085. The first obvious factor is 5, so the product of the other two numbers is 217. Since this number is odd, 2 is not a factor, and the sum of the digits is not divisible by 3, so that is not a factor. Test the next prime number: 7, so 217 ÷ 7 = 31, which is also prime.
5 + 7 + 31= 43

Assignment Guidelines

If your students do not have time to complete all the *Practice* questions on pages 91 and 92, the following questions provide minimum curriculum coverage:
1, 3, 6, 7, 8, *Reflect*
To assess the 4 Achievement Chart categories listed in the curriculum document, have students complete these questions:
Understanding Concepts: 3
Application: 6
Communication: 8
Problem Solving: 9

5. Fold two of these nets. Put the open parts together. Tape the pieces to make a regular dodecahedron. Describe the dodecahedron.

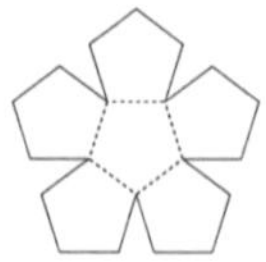

6. A soccer ball is not a sphere. It is a polyhedron. Look at a soccer ball. Explain which polygons are joined to make the ball. How are the polygons joined?

7. **Assessment Focus** Fold the net shown.

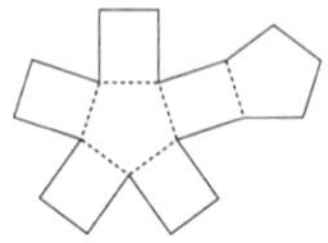

a) Describe the object formed.
b) Name the object. Justify your answer. Pentagonal prism

8. All the nets you have used fold to make objects. Which features must be true for this to happen?

Take It Further

9. Use isometric dot paper or plain paper. Draw the object that has this net. Explain your thinking.

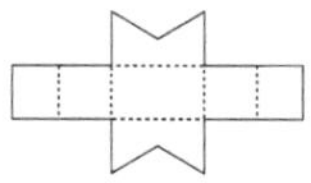

Reflect

Choose a product that has a package in the shape of a polyhedron.
Sketch the package. Include appropriate dimensions.
Cut along the edges to make the net.
Why do you think the manufacturer used this shape for the package?
Can you find a better shape for the packaging? Explain.

92 UNIT 3: Geometry and Measurement

ASSESSMENT FOR LEARNING

What to Look For	What to Do
Understanding concepts ✔ Students understand that nets fold to make polyhedra, and regular polyhedra have congruent faces. ***Applying procedures*** ✔ Students can build a polyhedra from a net. ***Communicating*** ✔ Students can describe the attributes of the polyhedra they build.	***Extra Support:*** Some students have difficulty cutting and folding accurately. Pair each student with someone able to assist her or him. Students can use Step-by-Step 3 (Master 3.11) to complete question 7. ***Extra Practice:*** Students can complete the Additional Activity *Net a Cube* (Master 3.7). Students can complete Extra Practice 3 (Master 3.35). ***Extension:*** Students can cut apart the figures on a net, then try to tape the figures together a different way, to form a different net.

Recording and Reporting
Master 3.2 Ongoing Observations: Geometry and Measurement

Mid-Unit Review

LESSON

3.1 **1.** Sketch the front, back, top, and side views of each object. Label each view.

a) Television

b) Baseball mitt

c) Chair

3.2 **2.** Make each object. Sketch a 3-D view of the object on isometric dot paper.

a)

b)

3. Sketch a 3-D view of each object on plain paper.

a)

b)

4. Suppose you had to construct an object from linking cubes. Which would you prefer to use: a drawing of the object on isometric dot paper, or 5 different views on plain paper? Justify your choice. Use diagrams to support your choice.

3.3 **5.** Use a large copy of this net. Fold the net to make an object. Name the object. List its attributes.

Pentagonal prism

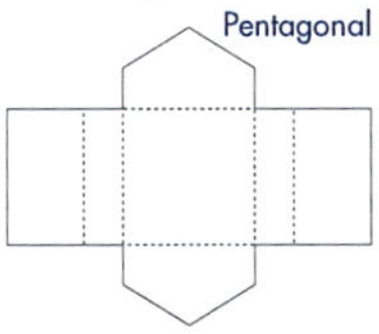

6. Which polyhedra could have each view shown below? Find as many polyhedra as you can for each view.

a)

b)

Mid-Unit Review 93

SECTION ORGANIZER

Student Materials
- net for question 5 (Master 3.28)
- square grid or dot paper (PM 20 or PM 22)
- isometric dot paper (PM 23)

Assessment: Master 3.2 Ongoing Observations: Geometry and Measurement

Sample Solutions

1. a) front back top side

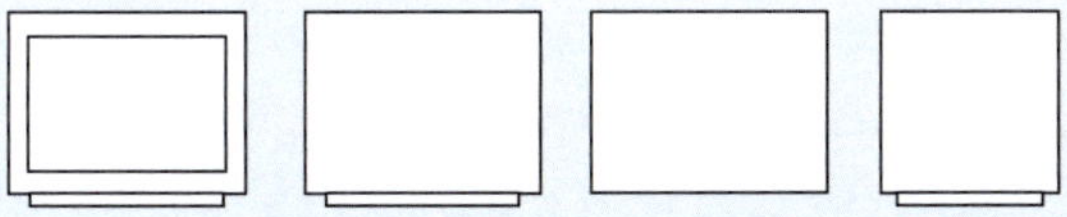

b) front back top side

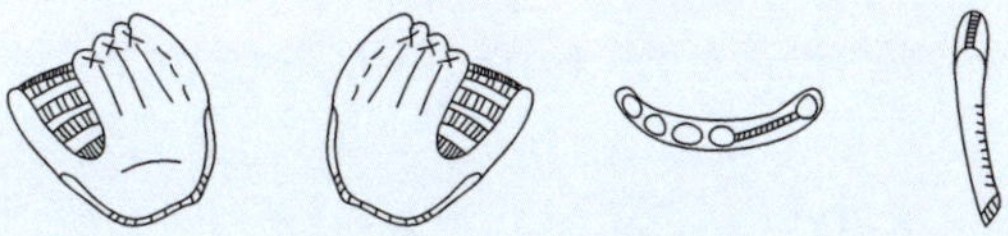

c) front back top side

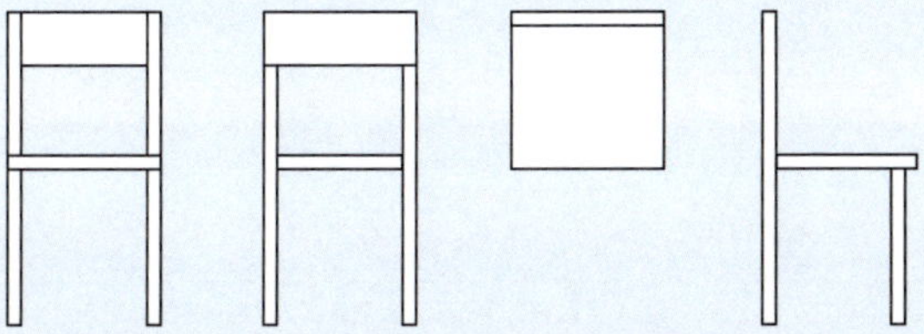

2. a)

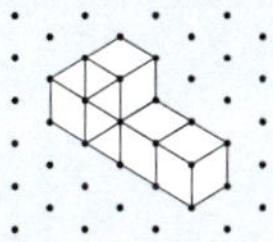

b)

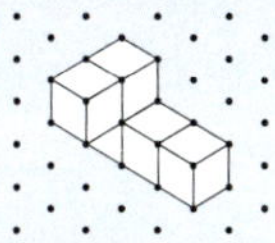

3. a)

b)

4. I would prefer to use a drawing on isometric dot paper: it shows three dimensions at once but does not show hidden parts.
If I had to use 5 different views, I would need to think about how the pictures fit together to construct the object.

5. This is a pentagonal prism. It has 2 congruent pentagonal faces as the bases and 5 rectangular faces, not all congruent, for a total of 7 faces. There are 15 edges and 10 vertices.

6. a) Square view: a square prism, a cube, a pentagonal prism with a square face, and so on

b) Isosceles triangle: a triangular pyramid or prism, a rectangular pyramid

Using Variables in Measurement Formulas

SECTION ORGANIZER 80–100 min

Curriculum Focus: Use measurement formulas to introduce the concept of a variable. (7m73, 7m76)
Student Materials
Optional
- Step-by-Step 4 (Master 3.12)
- Extra Practice 4 (Master 3.36)

Vocabulary: area, perimeter, base, height, variable, substitute
Assessment: Master 3.2 Ongoing Observations: Geometry and Measurement

Key Math Learnings

1. The perimeter and area of a rectangle and a square can be expressed using formulas.
2. Measurement formulas use variables to represent the dimensions of a figure.

Number Strategies

GCF is the greatest common factor. For these numbers, it is 5.
LCM is the least common multiple. It is the least number that all 3 numbers divide into exactly.

LCM = 2 × 3 × 5 × 5 = 150

3.4 Using Variables in Measurement Formulas

Focus Use measurement formulas to introduce the concept of a variable.

Explore

Work with a partner.

➢ Find the area of each rectangle below, in square units.

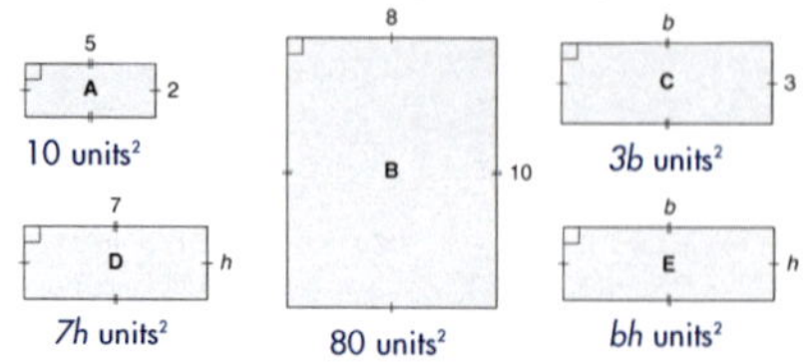

➢ Find the perimeter of each rectangle above, in units.
A: $P = 14$ units; B: $P = 36$ units; C: $P = 2(b + 3)$ units; D: $P = 2(7 + h)$ units; E: $P = 2(b + h)$ units

Reflect & Share

Compare your results with those of another pair of classmates.
How did you find the area when you did not know:
- the base?
- the height?
- the base and height?

How did you find the perimeter in each case?

Connect

When we do not know the dimensions of a figure, we use letters to represent them.
For a rectangle, we use *b* to represent the length of the base, and *h* to represent the height.

One way to find the area of a rectangle is to use a formula.
The formula for the area of a rectangle is:
A = base × height
Then $A = b \times h$
We write $A = b \times h$ as $A = bh$.

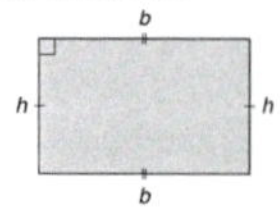

94 UNIT 3: Geometry and Measurement

BEFORE Get Started

Remind students of the word formulas for the perimeter and area of squares and rectangles that they learned in grade 6. Ask:
- What does area mean?
(*The number of congruent square units that fit in a figure*)
- What does perimeter mean? (*The distance around a figure measured in units*)

Ensure students recall that the area of a rectangle is base times height. Students need to understand that the base of a rectangle is the side perpendicular to the height and, when we say "base times height," we mean the length of the base multiplied by the length of the height.
Ensure students understand the task in *Explore.* Perimeter measurements are in units, and area measurements in square units.

DURING Explore

Ongoing Assessment: Observe and Listen

As students work on *Explore,* ask:
- How did you find the area of rectangle A?
(*I multiplied 5 units by 2 units to get 10 square units.*)
- How did you find the perimeter of rectangle B?
(*I added the side lengths: 8 units + 10 units + 8 units + 10 units to get 36 units.*)
- Which way did you use to find the perimeter of rectangle B?
(*I added the two unequal sides, then multiplied by 2: 8 units + 10 units = 18 units; multiply: 2 × 18 units = 36 units.*)
- How did you find the area of rectangle C?
(*I multiplied 3 × b to get 3 × b square units.*)

The formula for the perimeter of a rectangle is:
$P = 2 \times$ (base + height)
Then $P = 2 \times (b + h)$
We write $P = 2 \times (b + h)$ as $P = 2(b + h)$.

The letters we use to represent the base and height are called **variables**. Variables in a formula can represent different numbers. When we know the values of the variables, we **substitute** for the variables. That is, we replace each variable with a number.

A square is a rectangle with all sides equal.
The formula for the area of a square is:
A = side length × side length
Use the variable s for the side length.
Then, $A = s \times s$
or $A = s^2$

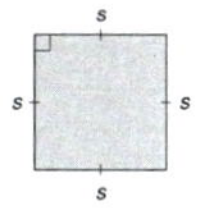

We use exponents to represent repeated multiplication.

The formula for the perimeter of a square is:
$P = 4 \times$ side length
or $P = 4 \times s$
We write $P = 4 \times s$ as $P = 4s$.

Example

A rectangle has base 15 cm and height 3 cm. Use formulas to find its area and perimeter.

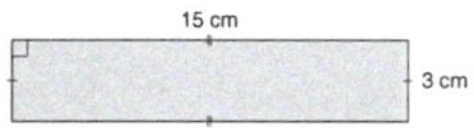

Solution

Area, $A = bh$
$b = 15$ and $h = 3$
Substitute for b and h in the formula.
$A = 15 \times 3$
$A = 45$
The area is 45 cm².

Perimeter, $P = 2(b + h)$
Substitute for b and h.
$P = 2(15 + 3)$
$P = 2(18)$
$P = 36$
The perimeter is 36 cm.

Use order of operations. Do the operation in brackets first. Then multiply.

3.4 Using Variables in Measurement Formulas 95

REACHING ALL LEARNERS

Early Finishers

Have students draw a rectangle that has a rectangle or square removed from the inside. How do they find the area of the remaining figure? How is a formula useful? (*Use the formula for the area of a rectangle twice. Subtract the area of the rectangle removed from the area of the original rectangle.)*

Common Misconceptions

➤ Students have difficulty understanding that variables represent numbers.

How to Help: Have students use words to describe the steps for finding the perimeter and area of a rectangle and a square. Have them try to simplify the steps to fewer and fewer words. Compare a variable with a short form for a dimension that must be identified each time. The operations used are the same, the measurements change.

ESL Strategies

Students may not understand that words such as *base* and *height* have two meanings: the line segment itself, in each case, and its measure. The word *length* has three meanings: the line segment, its measure, and also the measure of any other line segment; that is, *length* is a generic term for the measure of any line segment. Have students draw and label diagrams to show these meanings.

- How did you find the perimeter of rectangle E?
  (*I added the 2 sides: b + h, then I multiplied by 2: (b + h) × 2.*)

AFTER Connect

Some students may suggest using length and width to describe the dimensions of a rectangle. Ask what the formulas would be if l and w were used. We use base and height because the formulas developed will generalize to more figures. Students need to understand that any letter can be used for a dimension, provided there is an explanation of what the letter represents. It helps promote understanding when the letter used is related to the dimension represented.

Practice

Assessment Focus: Question 6

Students should explain that multiplying each of two numbers by 2, then adding gives the same result as adding the two numbers first, then multiplying by 2.

Assignment Guidelines

If your students do not have time to complete all the *Practice* questions on page 96, the following questions provide minimum curriculum coverage:
1b, 2b, 3, 4a, 5a, 6, *Reflect*
To assess the 4 Achievement Chart categories listed in the curriculum document, have students complete these questions:
Understanding Concepts: 1b, 2b
Application: 4a, 5a
Problem Solving: 6
Communication: *Reflect*

Sample Answers

3. b) The values of b and h change for each rectangle.
   c) $b = h$; they are the same.
6. Perimeter is double the base plus double the height.
   Both formulas are different ways to say the same thing.
   For $P = 2b + 2h$; we double the base and height, then add them.
   For $P = 2(b + h)$; we add the base and height, then double this sum.
   In each case, we get the sum of the lengths of the sides of the rectangle.
7. a) Perimeter formula of a rectangle is $P = 2(b + h)$
   In words: Perimeter is double the sum of the base and height.
   For a square, base = height = side length
   The sentence becomes: Perimeter is double the sum of side and side.
   A side plus a side is two sides, so returning to variables
   $P = 2(2s) = 4s$
   b) Area formula of a rectangle is $A = bh$
   In words: Area is the product of the base and height
   For a square, base = height = side length
   The sentence becomes: Area is the product of side and side.
   Returning to variables: $A = s \times s = s^2$

REFLECT: A variable is a letter that represents a number that can change. The variable is replaced by a number. We use variables in measurement formulas so the formulas can be written in a shorter form.

Practice

1. Use the formula: $P = 4s$
   Find the perimeter of the square with each side length.
   a) 5 cm — 20 cm b) 9 cm — 36 cm c) 2 cm — 8 cm d) 8 cm — 32 cm
2. Use the formula for the area of a rectangle: $A = bh$
   Find the area of each rectangle.
   a) base: 6 cm; height: 3 cm — $A = 18\ cm^2$
   b) base: 11 cm; height: 2 cm — $A = 22\ cm^2$
3. a) For each rectangle, what is the value of b and the value of h?
   i) $b = 3$, $h = 2$ ii) $b = 5$, $h = 4$ iii) $b = 2$, $h = 2$

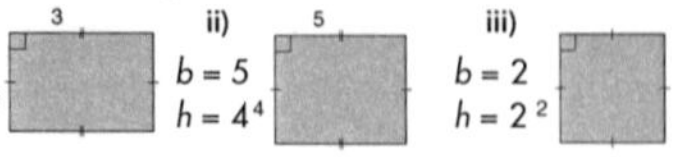

   b) Use your answers to part a to explain why we call b and h variables.
   c) What is true about b and h in part a, iii?
4. Find the area and perimeter of each rectangle.
   a) base: 12 cm; height: 4 cm — $A = 48\ cm^2$; $P = 32$ cm
   b) base: 10.5 cm; height: 3.0 cm — $A = 31.5\ cm^2$; $P = 27$ cm
5. Find the perimeter and area of each square.
   a) side length: 2.8 cm — $P = 11.2$ cm, $A = 7.84\ cm^2$
   b) side length: 3.1 cm — $P = 12.4$ cm; $A = 9.61\ cm^2$
6. **Assessment Focus**
   Here is another formula for the perimeter of a rectangle:
   $P = 2b + 2h$
   Write this formula in words.
   Explain why there are two formulas for the perimeter of a rectangle.

Number Strategies

Find the LCM and GCF of 10, 15, and 25.
LCM = $2 \times 3 \times 5 \times 5 = 150$
GCF = 5

Take It Further

7. a) How could you use the formula for the perimeter of a rectangle to get the formula for the perimeter of a square? $P = 4s$
   b) How could you use the formula for the area of a rectangle to get the formula for the area of a square? $A = s^2$

Reflect

What is a variable?
Why do we use variables to write measurement formulas?

96 UNIT 3: Geometry and Measurement

ASSESSMENT FOR LEARNING

What to Look For

Understanding concepts

✔ Students understand that a variable in a formula represents a number.

Applying procedures

✔ Students can choose and use the correct measurement formulas for squares and rectangles.

Problem Solving

✔ Students can describe the relationship between formulas for squares and rectangles.

Communicating

✔ Students can explain a formula in words.

What to Do

Extra Support: Students who find difficult the abstract concept of a letter representing any number may benefit from seeing the repetitive steps of perimeter and area calculations using word formulas that are gradually reduced to the first letter of each word. Students can use Step-by-Step 4 (Master 3.12) to complete question 6.

Extra Practice: Students can complete Extra Practice 4 (Master 3.36).

Extension: Students can write an algebraic formula for the relationship between the numbers of vertices, edges, and faces for the polyhedra in Section 3.3. They should test the formula on several polyhedra.

Recording and Reporting

Master 3.2 Ongoing Observations: Geometry and Measurement

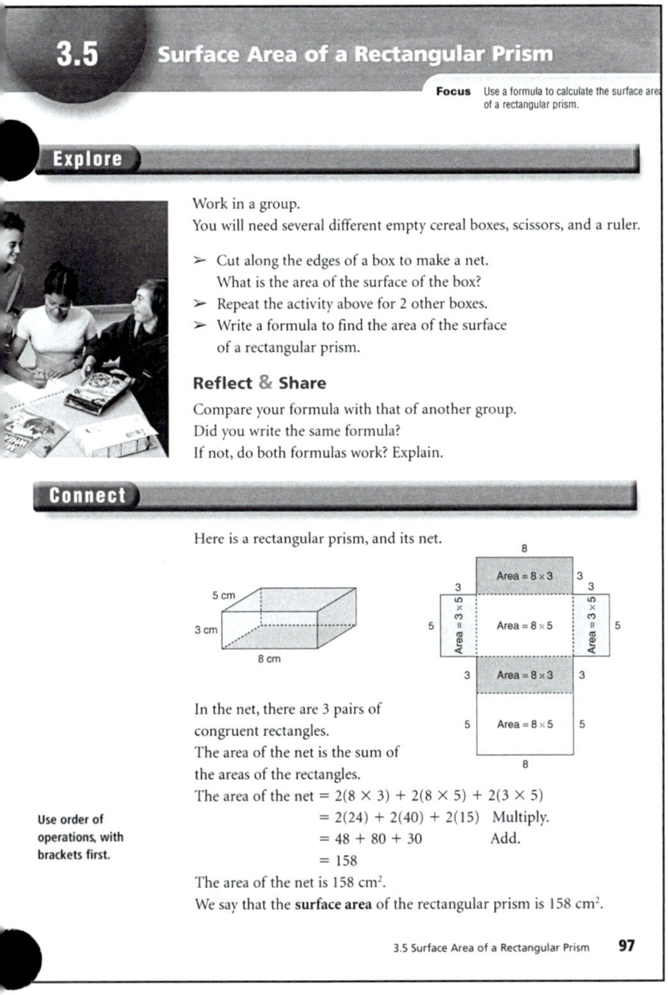
3.5 Surface Area of a Rectangular Prism

Focus Use a formula to calculate the surface area of a rectangular prism.

Explore

Work in a group.
You will need several different empty cereal boxes, scissors, and a ruler.

- ➢ Cut along the edges of a box to make a net. What is the area of the surface of the box?
- ➢ Repeat the activity above for 2 other boxes.
- ➢ Write a formula to find the area of the surface of a rectangular prism.

Reflect & Share

Compare your formula with that of another group.
Did you write the same formula?
If not, do both formulas work? Explain.

Connect

Here is a rectangular prism, and its net.

In the net, there are 3 pairs of congruent rectangles.
The area of the net is the sum of the areas of the rectangles.

Use order of operations, with brackets first.

The area of the net $= 2(8 \times 3) + 2(8 \times 5) + 2(3 \times 5)$
$= 2(24) + 2(40) + 2(15)$ Multiply.
$= 48 + 80 + 30$ Add.
$= 158$

The area of the net is 158 cm^2.
We say that the **surface area** of the rectangular prism is 158 cm^2.

3.5 Surface Area of a Rectangular Prism 97

Surface Area of a Rectangular Prism

SECTION ORGANIZER (80–100 min)

Curriculum Focus: Use a formula to calculate the surface area of a rectangular prism. (7m42, 7m73, 7m76)

Teacher Materials
- a cereal box cut to form a net

Student Materials
- at least 3 empty cereal boxes for each group
- scissors
- rulers
- linking cubes (question 4)

Optional
- 1-cm grid paper (PM 20)
- Step-by-Step 5 (Master 3.13)
- Extra Practice 5 (Master 3.37)

Vocabulary: surface area

Assessment: Master 3.2 Ongoing Observations: Geometry and Measurement

Key Math Learning

A formula for the surface area of a rectangular prism can be developed from its net.

BEFORE Get Started

To explain surface area, use a cereal box already cut along some edges to form a net. Tell students not to include overlapping flaps for surface area calculations. Remind students that a formula is a short form to represent the steps used for a calculation. All students should participate in *Explore*, so assign roles—cutter, measurer, recorder, tracker—to ensure this happens. Make sure students understand the task in *Explore*.

DURING Explore

Ongoing Assessment: Observe and Listen

As students work on *Explore*, watch and listen for students:
- finding congruent faces and areas
- recognizing that the three dimensions of a prism require three variables in the formula
- understanding that different organizations of steps are possible, similar to the perimeter formula for a rectangle

Ask:
- How many congruent faces are there? *(Three pairs)*
- What dimensions of the prism are represented on each face? *(Length and width, length and height, width and height)*
- How can the calculations be organized? *(Find the areas of 6 rectangles using A = bh; then add the areas. Or find the area of each different rectangle, double it, then add these numbers. Or find the area of each different rectangle, add the areas, then double this sum.)*
- How did you write the surface area as a formula? *(I labelled the rectangles A, B, C, D, E, F, then wrote the formula as: Surface area = the areas of rectangles A + B + C + D + E + F.)*

REACHING ALL LEARNERS

Alternative Explore

Materials: plain paper, 1-cm grid paper

Have students use their skills from Section 3.2 to draw a variety of rectangular prisms on plain paper (3 cm by 5 cm by 6 cm, 1 cm by 5 cm by 5 cm, 4 cm by 4 cm by 4 cm). Have them draw the corresponding nets on 1-cm grid paper, then calculate the surface area, as in *Explore*. They can cut out the nets to be sure they form rectangular prisms. Have students compare the diagrams and calculations with others, then summarize their calculations and develop a formula.

Early Finishers

Have students investigate the surface areas of rectangular prisms that have one face missing, such as a shoebox without a lid. How does this affect the formula they created?

Common Misconceptions

➤Students have difficulty using the algebraic formula.

How to Help: Have students find the surface area from first principles; that is, do not use an algebraic formula. Students can calculate the area of each face from a net, then add the areas. Note that the curriculum does not specify an algebraic formula, and a formula that is the sum of the areas of 6 rectangles is acceptable.

We can use the net of a rectangular prism to write a formula for its surface area.
We use a variable to label each dimension.
The prism has length l, width w, and height h.

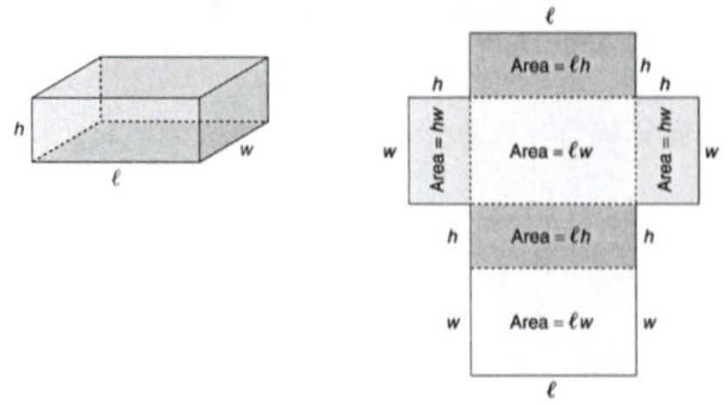

In the net, there are 3 pairs of congruent rectangles.
The surface area of the prism is the sum of the areas of the rectangles.
The surface area of the prism = $2lh + 2lw + 2hw$
We write: $SA = 2lh + 2lw + 2hw$

Remember that lw means $l \times w$.

We can use this formula to find the surface area of a rectangular prism, without drawing a net first.

Example

Find the surface area of this rectangular prism.

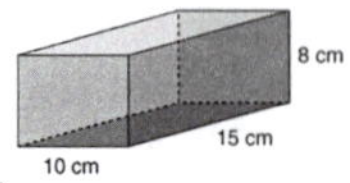

Solution

Use the formula:
$SA = 2lh + 2lw + 2hw$
Substitute: $l = 15$, $h = 8$, and $w = 10$

$SA = 2(15 \times 8) + 2(15 \times 10) + 2(8 \times 10)$
$= 2(120) + 2(150) + 2(80)$
$= 240 + 300 + 160$
$= 700$

The surface area of the rectangular prism is 700 cm^2.

- How is your formula different?
  (I used variables for length (l), width (w), and height (h), then wrote the formula as the sum of the areas. Surface area = lw + lw + lh + lh + wh + wh)

AFTER Connect

Be sure students understand that there must be three variables for any measurement formula for a prism. We use *l*, *w*, and *h* since *b* for base refers to the rectangular base of the prism. The calculations in the student text double each area, and then add. Show students the alternative method of adding the areas and then doubling, if you think it worthwhile. It does involve brackets within brackets, which students who have not mastered the order of operations may have difficulty with.

In the net, each rectangle appears twice.

The area of the net
$= 2[(8 \times 3) + (8 \times 5) + (3 \times 5)]$
$= 2[24 + 40 + 15]$
$= 2[79]$
$= 158$

This leads to the alternative formula
$SA = 2(lh + lw + hw)$

Practice

Students need to develop organized solutions and use variables correctly. Students can draw the nets on 1-cm grid paper for question 1 and other questions, if they need diagrams to work from. Have linking cubes available for question 4. In question 6, students need to determine which dimensions are the length, width, and height of the room. Students review equivalent ratios in question 10.

Practice

Visualize the net. How does that help to find the surface area?

1. Find the surface area of each rectangular prism.

a) b) c)

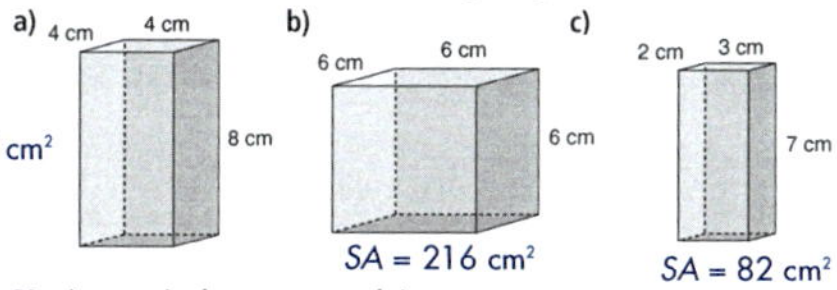

$SA = 160\ cm^2$ $SA = 216\ cm^2$ $SA = 82\ cm^2$

2. Use isometric dot paper or plain paper. Sketch a rectangular prism with these dimensions: 6 cm by 3 cm by 2 cm. Find the surface area of the prism. $SA = 72\ cm^2$

3. Find the surface area of each rectangular prism.

a) b) c)

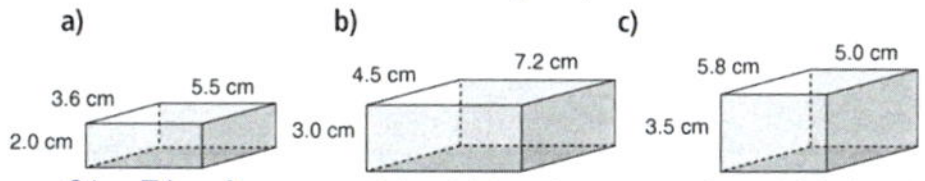

$SA = 76\ cm^2$ $SA = 135\ cm^2$ $SA = 133.6\ cm^2$

Mental Math

Estimate each product. What strategies did you use?

Order the products from least to greatest.

- 24.8×3.2 75
- 35.2×2.8 105
- 13.2×5.7 78
- 5.5×15.5 90

4. Use linking cubes.
   a) Find the surface area of a cube with edge length 1 unit. $SA = 6\ units^2$
   b) What if the edge length is doubled? What happens to the surface area? $24\ units^2$ Make a new cube to find out.
   c) What if the edge length is tripled? What happens to the surface area? $54\ units^2$ Make a new cube to find out.
   d) Predict the surface area of a cube with edge length 4 units. Explain your prediction. Make a new cube to check. $96\ units^2$

5. a) Find a rectangular prism in the classroom. Measure its length, width, and height. Find its surface area.
   b) Suppose each dimension of the prism is halved. What happens to the surface area? Explain.
   The surface area is $\frac{1}{4}$ of the original surface area.

3.5 Surface Area of a Rectangular Prism 99

Mental Math

Students may round to the nearest unit: $25 \times 3 = 75$; $35 \times 3 = 105$; $13 \times 6 = 78$; $6 \times 15 = 90$. The order for these estimates is first, third, fourth, and second. The order for the calculations is third, first, fourth, and second. The first and third estimates are close; 75 and 78.

Sample Answers

2.

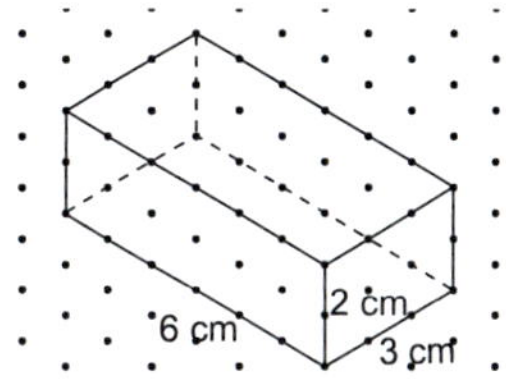

4. b) Each edge length is 2 units. The surface area is 4 times as great: 24 $units^2$
   c) Each edge length is 3 units. The surface area is 9 times as great: 54 $units^2$
   d) The surface area will be 16 times as great. Doubling produced 2^2 or 4 times the surface area. Tripling produced 3^2 or 9 times the surface area. If the pattern continues, quadrupling each edge length will produce 4^2 or 16 times the surface area: 96 $units^2$.
5. a) Students may measure the classroom itself, a filing cabinet, cupboard, or box. If the prism is 2 m by 3 m by 5 m, the surface area is 62 m^2.
   b) Halving each dimension: 1 m by 1.5 m by 2.5 m. The new surface area is 15.5 m^2. The surface area is $\frac{1}{4}$ of the original surface area.

(Answers continue below.)

Assessment Focus: Question 7

Students need to show that doubling one dimension will not double the surface area and halving one dimension will not halve the surface area.

(Sample Answers continued.)

6. a) The amount of paint depends on which values are used for each dimension.
   If the ceiling and floor are 4 m by 7 m, then the wall area is 66 m^2.
   Tanya needs to buy $66 \times 2 \div 40 = 3.3$; round to 4 cans of paint.
   If the ceiling and floor are 3 m by 7 m, then the wall area is 80 m^2.
   Tanya needs to buy $80 \times 2 \div 40 = 4$ cans of paint.
   b) The assumptions are the values used for each dimension, as shown above. Using a 3 m by 4 m ceiling/floor dimensions would mean the room is 7 m high, which is not a reasonable assumption. Also, we do not consider the areas of the door or possible windows. These will not be painted.

7.

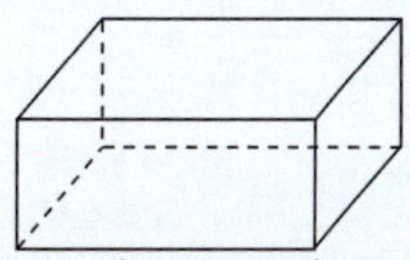

The surface area increases when the length is doubled and decreases when the length is halved. For a prism with dimensions 2 cm by 4 cm by 6 cm, the surface area is 88 cm^2. When the length is doubled, the surface area is 160 cm^2 and when the length is halved, the surface area is 52 cm^2. Students can show nets of these situations and indicate that 4 of the 6 faces have their areas doubled, so the surface area increases but does not double. Similarly, when the length is halved, 4 of the 6 faces have their areas halved, so the surface area decreases but not by half.

11. Base dimensions are 2 m by 2 m since the base is a square with area 4 m^2.
    Surface area − 2 base areas = Area of 4 faces = 40 m^2
    Area of 4 side faces ÷ 4 = Area of 1 side face = 10 m^2
    Area of 1 side face ÷ width = height = 5 cm
    The prism is 2 m by 2 m by 5 m.
12. Each dimension must be a common factor of two face areas.
    A common factor of 24 and 18 is 6:
    $6 \times 4 = 24$ and $6 \times 3 = 18$
    4 is a common factor of 24 and 12.
    3 is a common factor of 18 and 12.
    $3 \times 4 = 12$
    The dimensions are 6 m by 4 m by 3 m.

REFLECT: To find the surface area of a rectangular prism, label each dimension as length (*l*), width (*w*), or height (*h*). Replace each letter of the formula ($SA = 2lh + 2lw + 2hw$) with the measurement. Remember that $2lh$ means $2 \times l \times h$.

Example: To find the surface area of a rectangular prism with length 5 cm, width 2 cm, and height 6 cm:

Use $SA = 2lh + 2lw + 2hw$

Substitute: $l = 5$, $h = 6$, $w = 2$

$SA = 2(5 \times 6) + 2(5 \times 2) + 2(6 \times 2)$
$= 2(30) + 2(10) + 2(12)$
$= 60 + 20 + 24$
$= 104$

The surface area is 104 cm^2.

6. Tanya paints the walls of her family room.
The room measures 3 m by 4 m by 7 m.
The walls need 2 coats of paint. A 4-L can of paint covers 40 m^2.
a) How much paint should Tanya buy? 4 cans
b) What assumptions do you make? Explain.

7. Assessment Focus Sketch a rectangular prism. Label its dimensions. What do you think happens to the surface area of a prism when its length is doubled? Its length is halved? Investigate to find out. Show your thinking.

8. Each object has the shape of a rectangular prism, but one face or parts of faces are missing. Find each surface area.

a)

$SA = 832$ cm^2

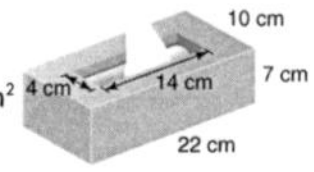

b)

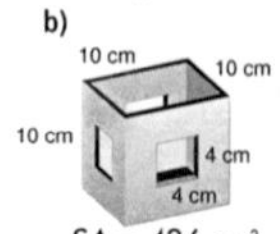

$SA = 436$ cm^2

c)

$SA = 1580$ cm^2

9. The surface area of a cube is 54 cm^2.
a) What is the area of one face of the cube? 9 cm^2
b) What is the length of one edge of the cube? 3 cm

Take It Further

10. A 400-g cereal box measures 20 cm by 7 cm by 31 cm.
A 750-g cereal box measures 24 cm by 9 cm by 33 cm.
a) Find the surface area of each box. 1954 cm^2, 2610 cm^2
b) What is an approximate ratio of surface areas? 10:13
What is an approximate ratio of masses? 1:2
c) Compare the ratios in part b.
Do you expect the ratios to be equal? Explain.

11. A rectangular prism has a square base with area 4 m^2.
The surface area of the prism is 48 m^2.
What are the dimensions of the prism? 2 m by 2 m by 5 m

12. A rectangular prism has faces with these areas: 12 cm^2, 24 cm^2, and 18 cm^2. What are the dimensions of the prism? Explain.
6 m by 4 m by 3 m

Reflect

Explain how to find the surface area of a rectangular prism using a formula. Include an example in your explanation.

100 UNIT 3: Geometry and Measurement

Assignment Guidelines

If your students do not have time to complete all the *Practice* questions on pages 99 and 100, the following questions provide minimum curriculum coverage: 1, 5, 6, 7, 8ac, *Reflect*

To assess the 4 Achievement Chart categories listed in the curriculum document, have students complete these questions:

Understanding Concepts: 1
Communication: 5b
Problem Solving: 7
Application: 8

ASSESSMENT FOR LEARNING

What to Look For	What to Do
Understanding concepts ✔ Students understand how a formula for surface area is developed. ***Applying procedures*** ✔ Students can use the formula for the surface area of a rectangular prism. ***Problem Solving*** ✔ Students solve surface area problems involving changes in dimensions or working backward from given information. ***Communicating*** ✔ Students can present organized solutions to surface area problems.	***Extra Support:*** Have students draw a net on grid paper for each prism before they use the formula. Relate each area calculation to its place in the formula. Students can use the Step-by-Step 5 (Master 3.13) to complete question 7. ***Extra Practice:*** Students can find rectangular prisms in the classroom, measure their dimensions, and calculate their surface areas. Students can complete Extra Practice 5 (Master 3.37). ***Extension:*** Students can create their own problems similar to questions 9, 11, and 12 and trade with other students. Have them describe strategies they used to solve these problems.

Recording and Reporting
Master 3.2 Ongoing Observations: Geometry and Measurement

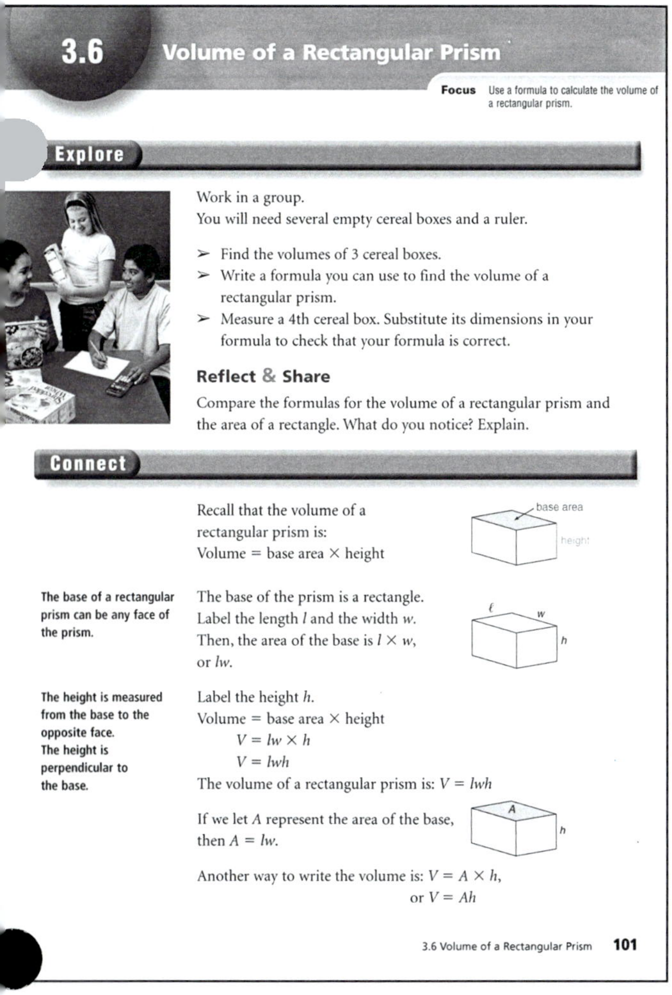

3.6 Volume of a Rectangular Prism

Focus Use a formula to calculate the volume of a rectangular prism.

Explore

Work in a group.
You will need several empty cereal boxes and a ruler.

- ➢ Find the volumes of 3 cereal boxes.
- ➢ Write a formula you can use to find the volume of a rectangular prism.
- ➢ Measure a 4th cereal box. Substitute its dimensions in your formula to check that your formula is correct.

Reflect & Share

Compare the formulas for the volume of a rectangular prism and the area of a rectangle. What do you notice? Explain.

Connect

Recall that the volume of a rectangular prism is:
Volume = base area × height

base area
height

The base of a rectangular prism can be any face of the prism.

The base of the prism is a rectangle.
Label the length l and the width w.
Then, the area of the base is $l \times w$, or lw.

ℓ w h

The height is measured from the base to the opposite face. The height is perpendicular to the base.

Label the height h.
Volume = base area × height
$V = lw \times h$
$V = lwh$
The volume of a rectangular prism is: $V = lwh$

If we let A represent the area of the base, then $A = lw$.

A h

Another way to write the volume is: $V = A \times h$, or $V = Ah$

3.6 Volume of a Rectangular Prism 101

Volume of a Rectangular Prism

SECTION ORGANIZER (80–100 min)

Curriculum Focus: Use a formula to calculate the volume of a rectangular prism. (7m31, 7m43, 7m44, 7m45, 7m46)

Teacher Materials

Optional

- boxes smaller than cereal boxes
- 1-cm cubes

Student Materials

- empty cereal boxes
- rulers
- linking cubes for *Practice* question 7

Optional

- Step-by-Step 6 (Master 3.14)
- Extra Practice 6 (Master 3.38)

Vocabulary: volume

Assessment: Master 3.2 Ongoing Observations: Geometry and Measurement

Key Math Learning

A formula for the volume of a rectangular prism is the area of its base multiplied by its height.

BEFORE Get Started

In grade 6, students developed a word formula for the volume of a rectangular prism. Review the meaning of the volume of a rectangular prism as the amount of space it fills, measured in cubic units. Fill a small box with 1-cm cubes to illustrate. Ensure students understand the problem in *Explore,* and have each group identify a different role for each person.

DURING Explore

Ongoing Assessment: Observe and Listen

As students work together on *Explore,* watch for students who begin by measuring the dimensions of a box. They need to be sure each member of the group understands the reason for this.

Ask:

- How is the number of 1-cm cubes on the bottom layer related to the dimensions of the base?
  (*The number of blocks is the product of the length and width.*)
- How many layers of 1-cm cubes will there be?
  (*The number of layers is equal to the height in centimetres.*)
- How can the number of layers and the number of cubes in each layer be used to find the volume in cubic centimetres?
  (*The volume is the product of the number of layers and the number of cubes in each layer.*)
- Will the volume of the box be different if it sits on a different face?
  (*No, the volume does not change. The box takes up the same amount of space.*)
- What are the variables for the boxes?
  (*Length, width, and height*)

REACHING ALL LEARNERS

Early Finishers

Have students choose one cereal box and find different dimensions for a box that has the same volume. Students calculate the surface areas of both boxes to find out which uses less material.

Common Misconceptions

➤ Students have difficulty understanding the conservation of volume; that is, the volume does not change when the prism sits on a different face.

How to Help: Have students fill a box with 1-cm cubes, then place the box on each different face. The number of 1-cm cubes does not change, so the volume does not change.

➤ Students confuse volume and surface area, and do not know which formula to use.

How to Help: Have students think about the meaning of the word *surface*. Remind students that area is measured using 2 dimensions, and volume is measured using 3 dimensions.

Sample Answers

3. 1 by 1 by 36, 1 by 2 by 18, 1 by 3 by 12, 1 by 4 by 9, 1 by 6 by 6, 2 by 2 by 9, 2 by 3 by 6, 3 by 3 by 4;
I found all prisms with one dimension of 1 unit, then repeated this for one dimension of 2 units, and so on. I made sure I did not repeat combinations of dimensions.

4. c) Nine cuts along the 20-cm edge, to make 10 strips, each 2 cm wide. Two cuts along the 21-cm edge, to make 3 strips, each 7 cm wide.

6. Double one dimension. The surface area does not double because not all the faces are affected by the increase in one dimension.

Example

A deck of 54 cards fits in a box with dimensions 6.5 cm by 9.0 cm by 1.6 cm. What is the volume of the box? Give the answer to the nearest cubic centimetre.

Solution

Recall that, when the dimensions are measured in centimetres (cm), the volume is measured in cubic centimetres (cm^3).

Draw a diagram.

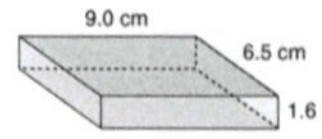

The box is a rectangular prism.
Label each dimension.
Use the formula: $V = lwh$
Substitute: $l = 9.0$, $w = 6.5$, and $h = 1.6$
$V = 9.0 \times 6.5 \times 1.6$ Use a calculator.
$= 93.6$
The volume is 93.6 cm^3, or about 94 cm^3.

Practice

Use a calculator when it helps.

1. For each rectangular prism: find the area of its base, then find its volume.

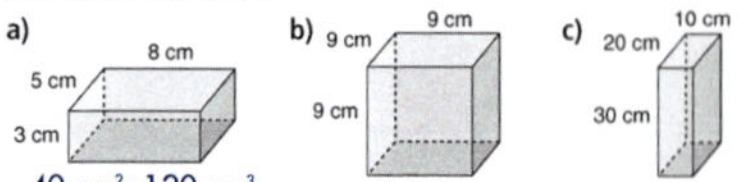

a) 40 cm^2; 120 cm^3 b) 81 cm^2; 729 cm^3 c) 200 cm^2; 6000 cm^3

2. Find the volume of each rectangular prism.

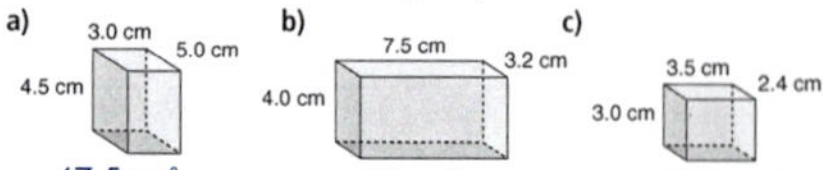

a) 67.5 cm^3 b) 96 cm^3 c) 25.2 cm^3

3. Use linking cubes.
Make all possible rectangular prisms with volume 36 $units^3$.
Sketch each prism you make.
Label each prism with its dimensions in units.
How do you know you have found all possible prisms?

102 UNIT 3: Geometry and Measurement

AFTER Connect

Have students share the formulas the groups developed or remembered. The symbols for the variables may be different but all the formulas should use the product of three dimensions or the product of the base area and the height. Compare finding the volume and finding the surface area of a rectangular prism. Both require knowing the dimensions and can be expressed as a formula. Remind students that changing the letter in a formula is acceptable provided they identify what the letter represents. The text uses $l \times w$ rather than $b \times h$ for the area of a rectangle to match the variables used for the surface area. Review the explanation and *Example* in *Connect*.

Assessment Focus: Question 7

Students show that a volume that is a prime number results from only one set of dimensions, and a volume with two prime factors results from 2 possible sets of dimensions, then they extend this pattern.

Assignment Guidelines

If your students do not have time to complete all the *Practice* questions on pages 102 and 103, the following questions provide minimum curriculum coverage: 1, 3, 4, 5, 7, *Reflect*

To assess the 4 Achievement Chart categories listed in the curriculum document, have students complete these questions:
Understanding Concepts: 1c
Application: 3
Problem Solving: 4
Communication: 5

4. Philip made fudge that filled a 20-cm by 21-cm by 3-cm pan.
   a) What is the volume of the fudge? 1260 cm^3
   b) Philip shares the fudge with his classmates. There are 30 people in the class. How much fudge will each person get? 42 cm^3
   c) How should Philip cut the fudge so each person gets the same size piece? Sketch the cuts he should make.
   d) What are the dimensions of each piece of fudge? 2 cm by 7cm by 3 cm
5. Sketch a rectangular prism. Label its dimensions.
   What do you think happens to the volume of the prism when:
   a) its length is doubled? The volume is doubled.
   b) its length and width are doubled? The volume is multiplied by 4.
   c) its length, width, and height are doubled? The volume is multiplied by 8.
   Investigate to find out. Show your work.
   Will the results be true for all rectangular prisms?
   How do you know?

Mental Math

Estimate each quotient.
What strategies did you use?

Order the quotients from least to greatest.

- 3572 ÷ 71 ≐ 50
- 4675 ÷ 58 ≐ 80
- 5007 ÷ 43 ≐ 100
- 6729 ÷ 95 ≐ 67

Least to greatest: 50, 67, 80, 100

6. How can you double the volume of a rectangular prism? Does its surface area double, too? Explain.
7. **Assessment Focus** Use linking cubes.
   a) How many rectangular prisms can you make with 2 cubes? 3 cubes? 4 cubes? 5 cubes? 6 cubes? and so on, up to 20 cubes?
   b) How many cubes do you need to make exactly 1 prism? Exactly 2 prisms? Exactly 3 prisms? Exactly 4 prisms?
   c) What patterns do you see in your answers to part b?
8. a) Sketch 3 different rectangular prisms with volume 24 cm^3.
   b) Which prism has the greatest surface area? The least surface area?
   c) Try to find a prism with a greater surface area. Describe the shape of this prism.
   d) Try to find a prism with a lesser surface area. Describe the shape of this prism.

Reflect

Suppose you know the volume of a rectangular prism. How can you find its dimensions? Use words and pictures to explain.

3.6 Volume of a Rectangular Prism 103

7. a)

Number of Cubes	2	3	4	5	6	7	8	9	10	11	12	13	14	15	16	17	18	19	20
Number of Prisms	1	1	2	1	2	1	3	2	2	1	4	1	2	2	4	1	4	1	4

b) 1 prism: 2, 3, 5, 7, 11, 13, 17, 19; 2 prisms: 4, 6, 9, 10, 14, 15; 3 prisms: 8; 4 prisms: 12, 16, 18, 20
c) When the volume is a prime number, only 1 prism can be made. When the volume is the product of 1 and 2 prime factors, 2 prisms can be made. When the volume is the product of 3 prime factors, 3 prisms can be made. When the volume has 6 factors, or can be written as the product of 2 factors three different ways, 4 prisms can be made.

8. Assume all dimensions are in whole numbers of centimetres.
   a), b) Sample prisms: 1 cm by 1 cm by 24 cm, (greatest) surface area 98 cm^2; 1 cm by 2 cm by 12 cm, surface area 76 cm^2; 2 cm by 3 cm by 4 cm (least) surface area 52 cm^2
   c) It has maximum length and minimum width and height – the prism is long, thin, and narrow.
   d) It has a shape that is closest to a cube; that is, its length, width, and height are close in value.

REFLECT: Find 3 numbers that multiply to make the volume. Then, these numbers are the length, width, and height. For example, for a prism with volume 17 cm^3, its dimensions are 1 cm by 1 cm by 17 cm.

Mental Math

Round to friendly numbers to make the division easier.

ASSESSMENT FOR LEARNING

What to Look For	What to Do
Understanding concepts ✔ Students understand that the volume of a rectangular prism is the product of its dimensions.	***Extra Support:*** Have students use 1-cm cubes to calculate volume or to check their answers. Students can use Step-by-Step 6 (Master 3.14) to complete question 7.
Applying procedures ✔ Students can use a formula to solve problems involving the volume of a rectangular prism.	***Extra Practice:*** Students can play *SAVO* (Master 3.8). Students can complete Extra Practice 6 (Master 3.38).
Problem solving ✔ Students can investigate how changing dimensions affects the volume of a rectangular prism.	***Extension:*** Students can create and solve their own problems, similar to question 8.

Recording and Reporting

Master 3.2 Ongoing Observations: Geometry and Measurement

Decoding Word Problems

SECTION ORGANIZER

Vocabulary: decoding

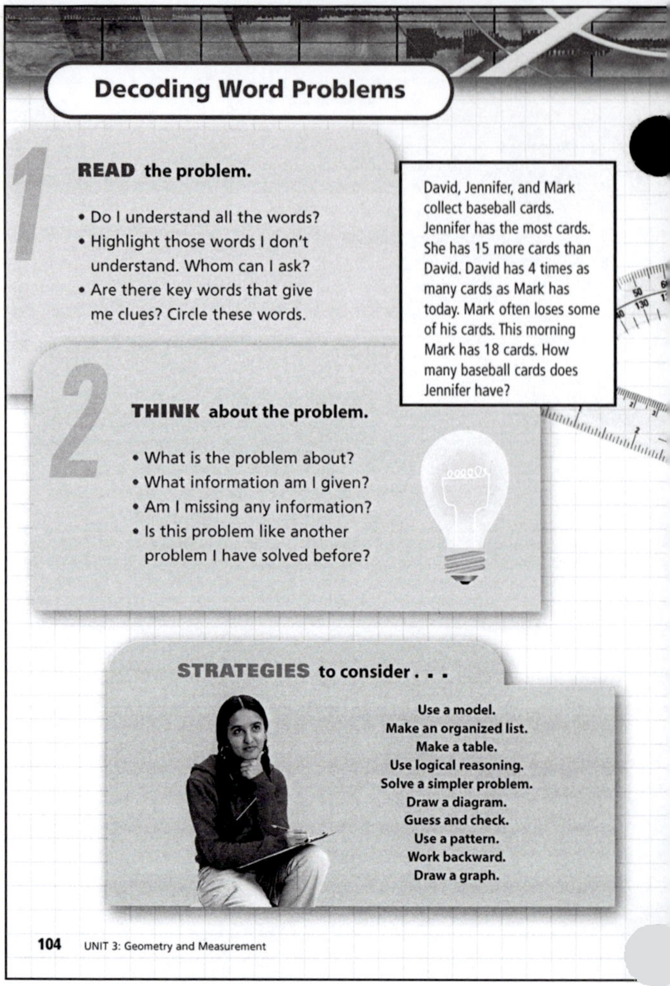

Decoding Word Problems

1 READ the problem.

- Do I understand all the words?
- Highlight those words I don't understand. Whom can I ask?
- Are there key words that give me clues? Circle these words.

David, Jennifer, and Mark collect baseball cards. Jennifer has the most cards. She has 15 more cards than David. David has 4 times as many cards as Mark has today. Mark often loses some of his cards. This morning Mark has 18 cards. How many baseball cards does Jennifer have?

2 THINK about the problem.

- What is the problem about?
- What information am I given?
- Am I missing any information?
- Is this problem like another problem I have solved before?

STRATEGIES to consider . . .

Use a model.
Make an organized list.
Make a table.
Use logical reasoning.
Solve a simpler problem.
Draw a diagram.
Guess and check.
Use a pattern.
Work backward.
Draw a graph.

104 UNIT 3: Geometry and Measurement

BEFORE

Step 1: Write the problem on an overhead transparency. Read the problem aloud together. Guide students through the questions. Follow the directions by highlighting and circling words as you go. Students may use sticky notes to highlight and flag instead of circling words in their math books.

Step 2: Ask the questions orally. Students should eliminate any unnecessary or extraneous information; for example, *Mark often loses some of his cards*. It is a good idea to **estimate** an answer, or to make a reasonable guess before continuing.

Step 3: Consider different ways the problem can be represented and solved. Brainstorm strategies and how they might be used. At this point, encourage students to focus on strategy rather than on numbers; for example, *"I would take the number of cards Mark has and multiply to find the number of cards David has."*

DURING

Step 4: Allow students to work in small groups or with partners, using the strategy of their choice. They should keep their estimates in mind as they determine if the plan is working. Encourage students to change strategies if necessary.

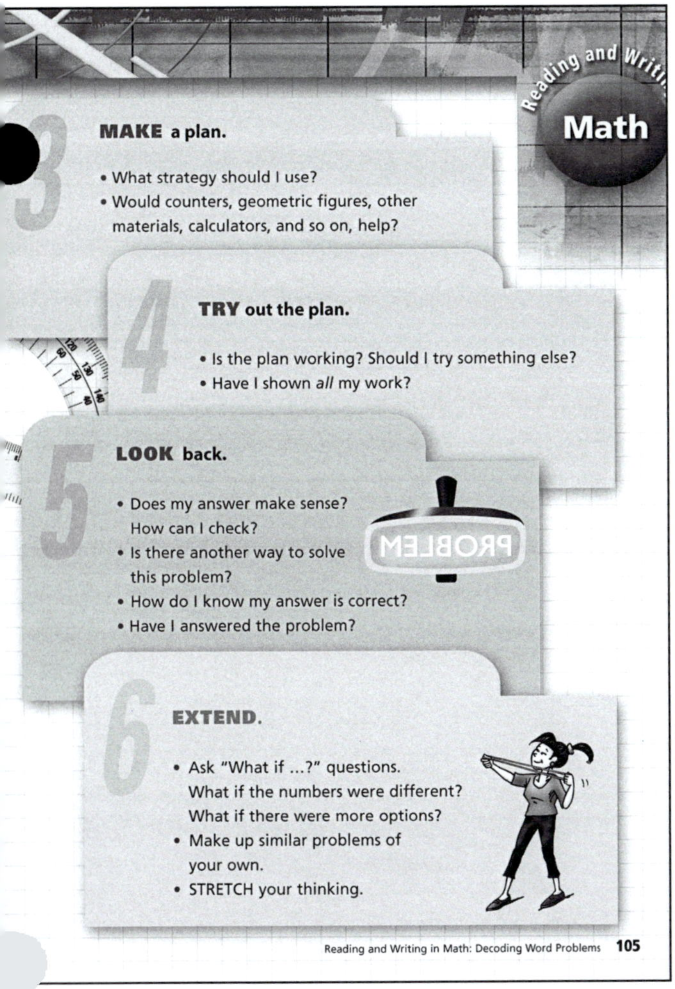

Reading and Writing in Math

3 **MAKE** a plan.

- What strategy should I use?
- Would counters, geometric figures, other materials, calculators, and so on, help?

4 **TRY** out the plan.

- Is the plan working? Should I try something else?
- Have I shown *all* my work?

5 **LOOK** back.

- Does my answer make sense? How can I check?
- Is there another way to solve this problem?
- How do I know my answer is correct?
- Have I answered the problem?

6 **EXTEND.**

- Ask "What if ...?" questions. What if the numbers were different? What if there were more options?
- Make up similar problems of your own.
- STRETCH your thinking.

Reading and Writing in Math: Decoding Word Problems 105

REACHING ALL LEARNERS

ESL Strategies

- ➤ Steps 1 and 2 are especially useful for ESL students.
- ➤ Read the instructions orally, while demonstrating or sketching the given information. Prompt students with questions to ensure understanding.
- ➤ Partner ESL students with good readers to help follow the directions in the text, and to help with questions that require written responses.
- ➤ Read answers orally to a partner to ensure the words make sense.

Sample Answer

Key information:
Mark has 18 cards.
David has 4 times as many cards as Mark: $18 \times 4 = 72$
Jennifer has 15 more cards than David: $72 + 15 = 87$
Jennifer has 87 baseball cards.

Step 5: Compare answers and strategies, including both which strategy was used, and how it was recorded. Emphasize sensible answers that answer the actual problem. Many students follow correct procedures and calculate correctly only to answer the wrong problem.

Step 6: Students use different numbers and options to write similar word problems.

Exchange word problems with other groups. Writing word problems helps students to understand the structure of a problem.

AFTER

- Repeat this exercise with problems from the Unit Review.
- Post the steps for decoding word problems in the classroom and refer to them often. Don't forget *estimation*.
- You may wish to use student-developed criteria for rating a good word problem; for example, all required information, some redundant information, challenging, clear question, realistic.
- There are many logic puzzles that help to develop the reading skills used in Steps 1 and 2. These puzzles are readily available on the Internet or in books and magazines.

SECTION ORGANIZER

Student Materials
- square dot paper (PM 22)
- isometric dot paper (PM 23)
- net of an octahedron for question 3 (Master 3.29)

Optional
- linking cubes

Assessment: Master 3.2 Ongoing Observations: Geometry and Measurement

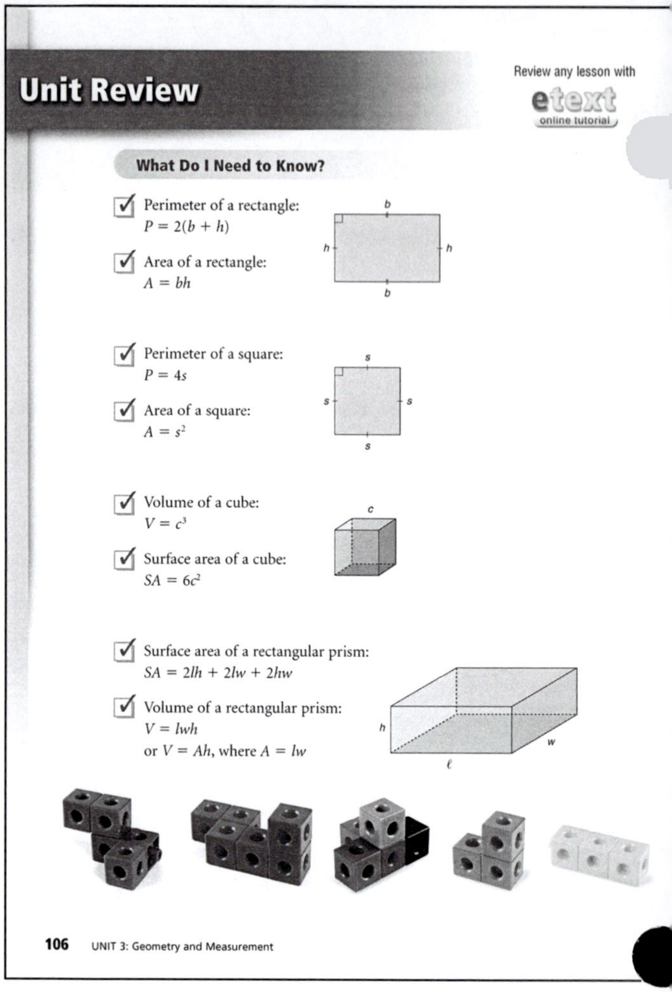

Unit Review

Review any lesson with etext online tutorial

What Do I Need to Know?

- Perimeter of a rectangle: $P = 2(b + h)$
- Area of a rectangle: $A = bh$
- Perimeter of a square: $P = 4s$
- Area of a square: $A = s^2$
- Volume of a cube: $V = c^3$
- Surface area of a cube: $SA = 6c^2$
- Surface area of a rectangular prism: $SA = 2lh + 2lw + 2hw$
- Volume of a rectangular prism: $V = lwh$ or $V = Ah$, where $A = lw$

106 UNIT 3: Geometry and Measurement

Correlation of Extra Practice questions on page 440:

Section	Questions
3.1	1, 2
3.2	3, 4, 5
3.4	6
3.5	7, 8, 9
3.6	7

Discuss the skills students learned in the first three sections:

- Drawing different 2-D views of solids on grid paper and with technology
- Sketching 3-D diagrams of solids using isometric dot paper and pictorial diagrams
- Building objects from nets and describing them

If students have learned alternative formulas for the perimeter of a rectangle and the surface area of a rectangular prism, include those in the *What Do I Need to Know?* list.
[$P = 2b + 2h$ and $SA = 2(lh + lw + hw)$]

Practice

As students work through the review, use the Ongoing Observations master to record students' performance on those questions with which they had difficulty. Encourage students to try questions without looking at previous examples. When they do have difficulty, have them review the questions from the indicated section and try the question again.

What Should I Be Able to Do?

For extra practice, go to page 440.

LESSON

3.1 **1.** Sketch the front, back, side, and top views of each object. Use square dot paper, plain paper, or *The Geometer's Sketchpad*.

a)

b)

c)

3.2 **2.** a) Identify the view and the objects on each sign.

i) Railway Crossing Ahead

Top view
Road over railway tracks

ii) Fishing Area

Side view
Fish

b) Design a new sign from a different view. Sketch your design.

3.3 **3.** This is a net for an octahedron.

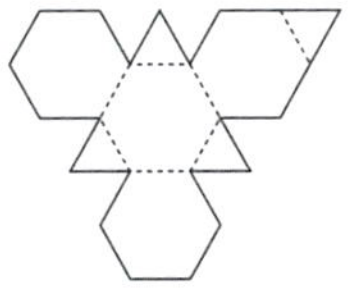

a) Fold a large copy of the net. Describe the object. Why do you think it is called an octahedron?

b) How is the object you built different from a regular octahedron?

3.4 **4.** Find the area of each figure.

49 cm² a) a square with side length 7 cm

36 m² b) a rectangle with base 12 m and height 3 m

5. A cube has edge length *c*.

a) Write a formula for the surface area of the cube. $SA = 6c^2$

b) Use the formula to find the surface area when *c* is 4 cm. 96 cm²

6. A children's play area is 90 m long and 44 m wide. A fence will enclose the area.

268 m a) How much fencing is needed?

b) Fencing comes in 12-m bundles. Each bundle costs $35. How much will the fence cost? Justify your answer. 23 bundles $805

YOUR NOTES

Sample Solutions

1.

	Front	Back	Side	Top
a)	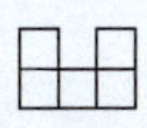	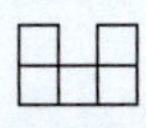	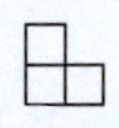	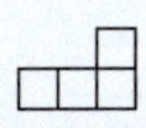
b)	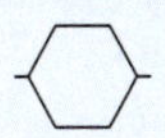	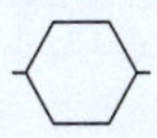	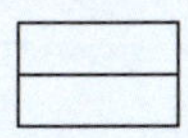	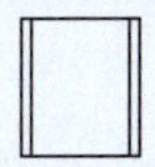
c)	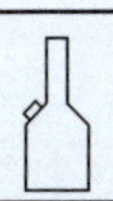	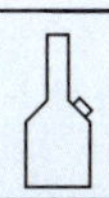		

2. a) i) Top view of a road crossing over railway tracks

ii) Side view of a fish with fishing line and hook

b) Front view of a person walking for a pedestrian crossing sign

3. a) This has 8 faces (4 congruent regular hexagons and 4 congruent equilateral triangles), 18 edges, and 12 vertices. It is an octahedron because it has 8 faces.

b) A regular octahedron has congruent faces; the same number of faces meet at each vertex; the same number of edges meet at each vertex.

6. a) Perimeter = 2 (90 + 44)
= 268
268 m of fencing are required.

b) Number of bundles = 268 ÷ 12 = $22.\overline{3}$
23 bundles are needed
Cost = 23 x $35 = $805
The fence will cost $805.

8. a) 1 can of paint; 11 rolls of wallpaper

b) Assume the height of the room is 3 m. Assume Elizabeth will do two coats of paint. No allowance has been made for windows (which will not be painted) or door (which may not be painted). Not much allowance has been made for extra wallpaper needed in case it has to match across strips.

9. There is only one answer. For the values to be the same, *s* = 6 units to match the 6 in the surface area formula. That will result in 6^3 for both expressions. The cube is 6 units by 6 units by 6 units.

YOUR NOTES

LESSON

3.5
3.6

7. Find the surface area and volume of each rectangular prism.

a) 6 m, 2 m, 3 m — 72 m², 36 m³

b) 8 cm, 3 cm, 3 cm — 114 cm², 72 cm³

c) 50 cm, 50 cm, 50 cm — 15 000 cm², 125 000 cm³

8. Elizabeth pastes wallpaper on 3 walls of her bedroom. She paints the 4th wall. This is one of the smaller walls. The dimensions of the room are 3 m by 5 m by 6 m. A roll of wallpaper covers about 5 m². A 4-L can of paint covers about 40 m².

a) How much wallpaper and paint should Elizabeth buy? 11 rolls of wallpaper 1 can of paint

b) What assumptions do you make?

9. The surface area and volume of a cube have the same numerical value. Find the dimensions of this cube. How many answers can you find? 6 units by 6 units by 6 units

10. Sketch all possible rectangular prisms with a volume of 28 m³. Each edge length is a whole number of metres. Label each prism with its dimensions. Calculate the surface area of each prism.

11. In *Gulliver's Travels* by Jonathan Swift, Gulliver visits a land where each of his dimensions is 12 times as large as that of the inhabitants.

a) Assume you can be modelled as a rectangular prism. Measure your height, width, and thickness.

b) Suppose you were one of the inhabitants. What would Gulliver's dimensions be?

c) Use your dimensions. Calculate your surface area and volume.

d) Calculate Gulliver's surface area and volume. 286.56 m², 259.2 m³

12. The volume, V, and base area, A, of a rectangular prism are given. Find the height of each prism. Sketch the prism. What are possible dimensions for the prism? Explain.

a) $V = 18$ m³, $A = 6$ m²

b) $V = 60$ cm³, $A = 15$ cm²

13. Samya is making candles. She uses a 1-L milk carton as a mould. Its base is a 7-cm square. Samya pours 500 mL of wax into the carton. Recall that 1 mL = 1 cm³. Approximately how tall will the candle be? Justify your answer.
About 10 cm

108 UNIT 3: Geometry and Measurement

10.

Dimensions	Surface Area
1 m by 1 m by 28 m	114 m²
1 m by 2 m by 14 m	88 m²
1 m by 4 m by 7 m	78 m²
2 m by 2 m by 7 m	64 m²

11. a) Use $h = 1.25$ m, $w = 0.4$ m, $t = 0.3$ m
b) $h = 15$ m, $w = 4.8$ m, $t = 3.6$ m
c) 1.99 m²; 0.15 m³
d) 286.56 m²; 259.2 m³

12. a) Possible dimensions: 1 m by 6 m by 3 m or 2 m by 3 m by 3 m. The height is fixed (3 cm) but the area of the base could have any 2 dimensions whose product is 6.
b) Possible dimensions: 1 cm by 4 cm by 15 cm or 3 cm by 5 cm by 4 cm; the height is 4 cm; assume that each dimension is a whole number of centimetres.

13. 1 L = 1000 mL = 1000 cm³
Base area of a candle is 7 cm × 7 cm = 49 cm². Since the volume of the candle is 500 mL or 500 cm³, the height of the candle in centimetres will be 500 ÷ 49, which is about 10 cm.

SECTION ORGANIZER

Student Materials
- square dot paper (PM 22)
- isometric dot paper (PM 23)
- net of a frustum for question 2 (Master 3.30)

Assessment: Master 3.2 Ongoing Observations: Geometry and Measurement

Practice Test

1. Build the letter H with linking cubes.
   Draw the front, back, side, and top views.
2. Fold a copy of this net.
   a) Describe the object.
   What name could you give it?
   Justify your answer.
   b) Sketch the object.

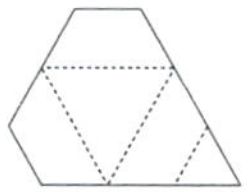

3. Find the surface area and volume of this rectangular prism.

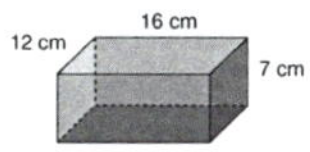

SA = 776 cm², *V* = 1344 cm³

4. Each edge length of a rectangular prism is 7 cm.
   a) Sketch the prism.
   b) Use formulas to find its volume and surface area. *V* = 343 cm³, *SA* = 294 cm²
5. Here are the dimensions of two designs for a sandbox for the primary playground. Each sandbox is a rectangular prism.
   One design is 3 m by 3 m by 30 cm.
   A second design is 3.25 m by 3.25 m by 25 cm.
   a) Sketch each sandbox. Include its dimensions.
   b) Compare the designs. For each design, calculate the area of material needed to build it and the volume of sand it will hold.
   c) Which sandbox should be built? Justify your answer.
6. Think about the nets you have folded and the solids you have made.
   Suppose you are a tent manufacturer.
   Which net would you use to make a tent?
   Explain why it would be a good tent design.

Practice Test 109

Remind students to use appropriate papers for sketches and to be aware of the different units in question 5.

Sample Solutions

1.

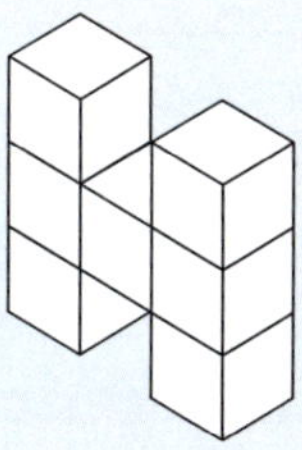

Front **Back** **Side** **Top**

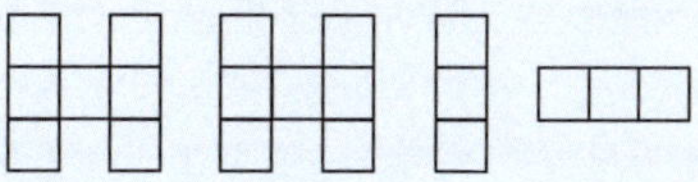

2. a) This has 5 faces (2 similar equilateral triangles and 3 congruent trapezoids), 9 edges, and 6 vertices.
   It looks like a triangular pyramid with its top sliced off.
   It could be called a truncated tetrahedron.
   b)

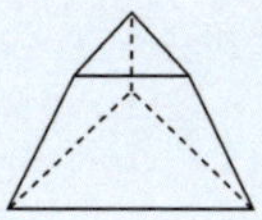

3. $SA = 776$ cm²; $V = 1344$ cm³

4. a)

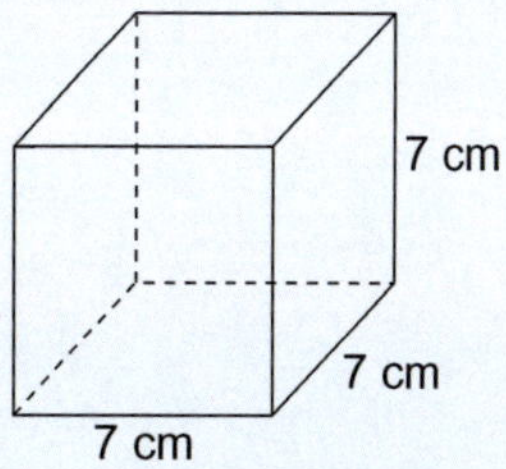

   b) $V = 343$ cm³; $SA = 294$ cm²
5. b) The first design has a greater depth but a smaller base area than the second design.
   1st design: $SA = 12.6$ m², $V = 2.7$ m³;
   2nd design: $SA = 13.8$ m²; $V = 2.6$ m³
   c) The first design uses less material but holds more sand, so it should be the design built.
6. If I were making a one-person tent, an equilateral triangular prism sitting on a rectangular face would have good head space for sitting up. It uses several congruent pattern pieces with few seams. It would have a good runoff for rain.

Making Food for a Bake Sale

SECTION ORGANIZER 80–100 min

Student Grouping: 2 to 3

Teacher Materials

- magazines or other material with advertisements
- Performance Assessment Rubric: Making Food for a Bake Sale (Master 3.3)
- Unit Summary: Geometry and Measurement (Master 3.4)

Student Materials

- grocery flyers
- isometric dot paper (PM 23)
- sketch paper
- grid paper (PM 14, PM 20)

Optional

- Performance Assessment Rubric: Making Food for a Bake Sale (Master 3.3)

Assessment: Masters 3.3 Performance Assessment Rubric: Making Food for a Bake Sale, 3.4 Unit Summary: Geometry and Measurement

Teaching notes for Cross Strand Investigation *Ratios in Scale Drawings* are in the *Additional Support* module.

Unit Problem **Making Food for a Bake Sale**

Suppose you are planning to sell baked goods at the local charity bake sale.
You have to decide the selling price for your baked goods.
You want to make sure that the price covers the cost of the ingredients and the packaging.

Decide on the baked goods you will sell.
For example, here is a recipe for Rice Krispies Treats.

Rice Krispies Treats

50 mL margarine
250 g marshmallows
1.5 L Rice Krispies

Melt the margarine.
Add marshmallows and stir until melted.
Remove from heat.
Add Rice Krispies.
Stir until the Rice Krispies are coated.
Press mixture into greased 32-cm by 23-cm pan.
When mixture is cool, cut into squares.

Use this recipe or find your own recipe for treats.
How many batches of treats will you make?
Calculate how much of each ingredient you need.
Use grocery flyers to find how much the ingredients will cost.

110 UNIT 3: Geometry and Measurement

Explain that students will work in groups to complete all 5 questions. Invite volunteers to read each question aloud. Ensure students understand what they are expected to do. Remind students to show their work.

Have a volunteer read the *Check List*. Remind students that they should use the *Check List* to assess their work before handing it in. You may also wish to provide students with copies of the Performance Assessment Rubric: Making Food for a Bake Sale, Master 3.3, so they will know how their performance will be assessed.

As students complete the *Unit Problem*, circulate to answer questions, to provide help with interpreting the questions, and to record notes on observations. Encourage students to use the skills they developed in this unit.

Sample Solutions

Our group will make 6 batches of treats so that most of our ingredients will be completely used.

We will need: 6×50 mL, or 300 mL margarine
6×250 g, or 1500 g marshmallows
6×1.5 L, or 9 L Rice Krispies

Estimating grocery costs (Size and price have been rounded for easy calculations—size rounded down and price rounded up to be sure to cover costs): 400 g of margarine is about \$1.20, 450 g of marshmallows is about \$1.50, and 700 g of Rice Krispies is \$4.50.

1. Cost for 1 batch of treats:
   50 mL of margarine is about 50 g.
   3 L of Rice Krispies is about 700 g.
   Cost for 1 batch = \$20.70 ÷ 6 = \$3.45
2. The pan of treats is 32 cm by 23 cm and is 3.5 cm deep. If three cuts are made each way in the pan, there will be 16 treats. Each treat is about 8 cm by 6 cm by 3.5 cm. We will sell 2 treats to a package. The box would be 8 cm by 6 cm by 7 cm. This is almost a cube so it will have a smaller surface area. We will design a closed topped box to keep our treats fresh.

1. Calculate the cost of 1 batch of treats.

2. How many treats will you sell in 1 package?
Design a box as the package for your treats.
Decide if the box is open and covered with plastic wrap, or if the box is closed.
Draw a 3-D picture of your box.
Sketch a net for your box.

3. Calculate the surface area and volume of your box.
Suppose the cost of cardboard is 50¢/m^2.
How many boxes can you make from 1 m^2 of cardboard?
How much does each box cost?
What other costs are incurred to make the boxes?
What assumptions do you make?

4. Draw the top, front, back, and side views of your box.

5. How much will you sell 1 box of treats for? Justify your answer. Show how the selling price of the treats covers the cost of all the things you bought.

Check List

Your work should show:

✓ all calculations in detail

✓ all sketches clearly labelled

✓ a clear explanation of your results

✓ how you decided the selling price of 1 box of treats

Reflect on the Unit

Write a paragraph to tell what you have learned about polyhedra in this unit. Try to include something from each lesson in the unit.

Unit Problem: Making Food for a Bake Sale 111

3. $SA = 292$ cm^2
$V = 336$ cm^3
15 nets fit on 1 m^2 of cardboard.
Cost of one box = \$0.50 ÷ 15 = \$0.0033 per box
The cost of tape or glue to secure the boxes needs to be considered along with any design to be printed on the boxes.

5. Cost for 1 package of treats = Cost for 1 batch ÷ (number of treats per batch ÷ number of treats per package) = \$3.45 ÷ (16 ÷ 2) = \$3.45 ÷ 8 = \$0.44. Since we need to cover the cost of packaging and advertising, and we want to make a profit for the charity, we will sell our treats for \$1.00. This will give at least a 50¢ profit and be an easy price for people to pay without having to make change very often. If we sell all 6 batches, our profit will be \$0.50 × 8 × 6 = \$24.

REFLECT ON THE UNIT: Polyhedra are solids whose faces are polygons. Different sketches of polyhedra are possible. Two-dimensional views show only what is visible from the top, front, back or side. These are drawn on square grid paper or by using technology. Three-dimensional sketches show length, width, and height. These include isometric drawings using isometric dot paper, pictorial diagrams using translations of a 2-D view, or vanishing point diagrams (studied in art). There are formulas to find the surface area and volume of a rectangular prism ($SA = 2lh + 2lw + 2hw$, $V = lwh$).

ASSESSMENT FOR LEARNING

What to Look For

Understanding concepts

✔ Students can calculate surface area and volume of a rectangular prism.

Applying procedures

✔ Students can choose dimensions for a package.

Problem solving

✔ Students can calculate the selling price for 1 box of treats.

Communicating

✔ Students create neat, well-labelled sketches.

What to Do

Extra Support: Students may need some scaffolding of the steps. Use questions, such as:

- Do any measurements need to be converted?
- How can you calculate how many batches you can make from those ingredients?
- How much will you buy altogether?
- How large is each treat?
- How does this affect the size of package?
- How much does each treat cost?
- What shape will be best for your treats? Why?
- Will you be able to use all the cardboard to make your boxes?

Recording and Reporting

Master 3.3 Performance Assessment Rubric: Making Food for a Bake Sale
Master 3.4 Unit Summary: Geometry and Measurement

Evaluating Student Learning: Preparing to Report: Unit 3 Geometry and Measurement

This unit provides an opportunity to report on the **Geometry and Spatial Sense** and **Measurement** strands. *Master 3.4 Unit Summary: Geometry and Measurement* provides a comprehensive format for recording and summarizing evidence collected.

Here is an example of a completed summary chart for this Unit:

Strand: *Geometry and Spatial Sense/ Measurement*	**Problem solving**	**Understanding of concepts**	**Application of mathematical procedures**	**Communication**	***Overall***
Ongoing Observations	3	3	2	3	2/3
Work samples or portfolios; conferences	2	3	3	3	3
Unit Review	3	3	3	3	3
Practice Test	2	3	2	3	2/3
Unit Problem Making Food for a Bake Sale	3	3	2	3	3
Achievement Level for reporting					3

Recording	How to Report
Ongoing Observations	Use *Master 3.2 Ongoing Observations: Geometry and Measurement* to determine the most consistent level achieved in each category. Enter it in the chart. Choose to summarize by achievement category, or simply to enter an overall level. Observations from late in the unit should be most heavily weighted.
Portfolios or collections of work samples; conferences, or interviews	Use *Master 3.1 Unit Rubric: Geometry and Measurement* to guide evaluation of collections of work and information gathered in conferences. Teachers may choose to focus particular attention on the Assessment Focus questions. Work from late in the unit should be most heavily weighted.
Unit Review	*Master 3.1 Unit Rubric: Geometry and Measurement* may be helpful in determining levels of achievement. #1, 2, 3, 4, and 7 provide evidence of Understanding of concepts; #5, 6, 10, and 12 provide evidence of Application of mathematical procedures; #8, 9, 11, and 13 provide evidence of Problem solving; #6 provides evidence of Communication.
Practice Test	*Master 3.1 Unit Rubric: Geometry and Measurement* may be helpful in determining levels of achievement. #1 and 2 provide evidence of Understanding of concepts; #3 and 4 provide evidence of Application of mathematical procedures; #5 provides evidence of Problem solving; #6 provides evidence of Communication.
Unit Problem	Use *Master 3.3 Performance Assessment Rubric: Making Food for a Bake Sale*. The *Unit Problem* offers a snapshot of students' achievement. In particular, it shows their ability to synthesize and apply what they have learned.
Student Self-Assessment	Note students' perceptions of their own progress. This may take the form of an oral or written comment, or a self-rating.
Comments	Analyse the pattern of achievement to identify strengths and needs. In some cases, specific actions may need to be planned to support the learner.

Learning Skills	Ongoing Records
PM 4: Learning Skills Check List Use to record and report throughout a reporting period, rather than for each unit and/or strand.	*PM 10: Summary Class Records: Strands* *PM 11: Summary Class Records: Achievement Categories* *PM 12: Summary Record: Individual* Use to record and report evaluations of student achievement over several clusters, a reporting period, or a school year. These can also be used in place of the Unit Summary.

Name ____________________ Date ________________

Master 3.1

Unit Rubric: Geometry and Measurement

	Level 1	Level 2	Level 3	Level 4
Problem solving • chooses and carries out a range of strategies to solve problems involving objects, their volume and surface area (e.g., using a formula, drawing a picture, using concrete objects)	with assistance, chooses and carries out a limited range of appropriate strategies to solve problems and design investigations that involve data and statistical methods	with limited assistance, chooses and carries out appropriate strategies for problems involving objects, their volume and surface area, that frequently result in an accurate solution	chooses and carries out appropriate strategies for problems involving objects, their volume and surface area, that usually result in an accurate solution	chooses and carries out appropriate strategies for problems involving objects, their volume and surface area, may offer an innovative approach; results in accurate solution
Understanding of concepts • shows understanding by demonstrating and explaining: – various representations of an object – relationship between a net and an object – formula for volume of a rectangular prism – formula for surface area of a rectangular prism	shows little understanding; may be unable to demonstrate, explain or justify choice of method for: – various representations of an object – relationship between a net and an object – formula for volume of a rectangular prism – formula for surface area of a rectangular prism	shows some understanding; partially able to demonstrate, explain, and justify choice of method for: – various representations of an object – relationship between a net and an object – formula for volume of a rectangular prism – formula for surface area of a rectangular prism	shows understanding; able to clearly and appropriately demonstrate, explain, and justify choice of method for: – various representations of an object – relationship between a net and an object – formula for volume of a rectangular prism – formula for surface area of a rectangular prism	shows thorough understanding; able to accurately and effectively demonstrate, explain, and justify choice of method for: – various representations of an object – relationship between a net and an object – formula for volume of a rectangular prism – formula for surface area of a rectangular prism
Application of mathematical procedures • accurately: – recognizes and sketches various views of specific objects – constructs objects from nets – calculates surface area and volume of a rectangular prism	limited accuracy; major errors or omissions in: – recognizing and sketching various views of specific objects – constructing objects from nets – calculating surface area and volume of a rectangular prism	somewhat accurate; several minor errors or omissions in: – recognizing and sketching various views of specific objects – constructing objects from nets – calculating surface area and volume of a rectangular prism	generally accurate; few minor errors or omissions in: – recognizing and sketching various views of specific objects – constructing objects from nets – calculating surface area and volume of a rectangular prism	accurate and precise; very few or no errors in: – recognizing and sketching various views of specific objects – constructing objects from nets – calculating surface area and volume of a rectangular prism
Communication • explains concepts, reasoning and procedures clearly, using appropriate mathematical language	unable to explain reasoning and procedures clearly	partially explains reasoning and procedures	explains reasoning and procedures clearly	explains reasoning and procedures clearly, precisely, and confidently
• presents work clearly including appropriate formulas and symbols	presents calculations with little clarity; rarely uses appropriate symbols	presents calculations with some clarity; uses some appropriate symbols	presents calculations clearly and precisely; uses appropriate symbols	presents calculations clearly and precisely; uses a range of appropriate symbols

Name ____________________ Date ________________

Master 3.2

Ongoing Observations: Geometry and Measurement

The behaviours described under each heading are examples; they are not intended to be an exhaustive list of all that might be observed. More detailed descriptions are provided in each lesson under *Assessment for Learning.*

STUDENT ACHIEVEMENT: Geometry and Measurement				
Student	**Problem solving** ▪ Chooses and carries out appropriate strategies to solve problems involving objects, surface area, and volume	**Understanding of concepts** ▪ Explains and demonstrates: – various representations of an object – formulas for surface area and volume of a rectangular prism	**Application of mathematical procedures** ▪ Recognizes and sketches various views of an object ▪ Constructs objects from nets ▪ Calculates surface area and volume of a rectangular prism	**Communication** ▪ Explains concepts, reasoning, and procedures clearly ▪ Presents work clearly

Level 1 – very limited; Level 2 – somewhat or limited; Level 3 – satisfactory; Level 4 – thorough

Name ____________________ Date ________________

Master 3.3

Performance Assessment Rubric: Making Food for a Bake Sale

	Level 1	Level 2	Level 3	Level 4
Problem solving • chooses appropriate strategies to design a package (box) and determine the selling price for 1 box of treats (e.g., using formulas, drawing a picture, using concrete objects)	uses few simple strategies to design a package and decide on selling price of 1 box of treats; limited success	uses some appropriate strategies to design a package and decide on selling price of 1 box of treats; some success	uses appropriate strategies to design a package and decide on selling price of 1 box of treats; successful	uses innovative and appropriate strategies to design a package and decide on selling price of 1 box of treats; successful and effective
Understanding of concepts • shows understanding of geometry and measurement by sketching or explaining: – the box, its net, and top, front, back, and side views – assumptions made in calculating cost per box – justification for selling price of 1 box	shows very limited understanding; may be unable to give appropriate explanations, illustrations or justifications	shows limited understanding by giving some appropriate but incomplete explanations, illustrations or justifications	shows understanding by giving appropriate explanations, illustrations or justifications	shows thorough understanding by giving appropriate and complete explanations, illustrations or justifications, using all relevant concepts
Application of mathematical procedures • calculates costs accurately (1 batch of treats, cardboard for 1 box; profit per box) • calculates surface area and volume accurately	limited accuracy; major errors or omissions in calculating: – costs – surface area – volume	somewhat accurate; several minor errors or omissions in calculating: – costs – surface area – volume	generally accurate; few minor errors or omissions in calculating: – costs – surface area – volume	accurate and precise; with no errors or omissions in calculating: – costs – surface area – volume
Communication • explains reasoning clearly using appropriate mathematical terminology	explains reasoning unclearly and imprecisely using few mathematical terms	explains reasoning with some clarity using some appropriate mathematical terms	explains reasoning clearly and precisely using appropriate mathematical terms	explains reasoning clearly, precisely, and confidently using a range of appropriate mathematical terminology
• presents work, including sketches, formulas, and calculations, clearly	presents work with little clarity	presents work with some clarity	presents work clearly	presents work clearly and precisely

Name ____________________ Date ______________

Master 3.4

Unit Summary: Geometry and Measurement

Review assessment records to determine the most consistent achievement levels for the assessments conducted. Some cells may be blank. *Overall* achievement levels may be recorded in each row, rather than identifying levels for each achievement category.

	Most Consistent Level of Achievement*				
Strand: *Geometry and Spatial Sense/ Measurement*	**Problem solving**	**Understanding of concepts**	**Application of mathematical procedure**	**Communication**	***Overall***
Ongoing Observations					
Work samples or portfolios; conferences					
Unit Review					
Practice Test					
Unit Problem Making Food for a Bake Sale					
Achievement Level for reporting					

*Use Ontario Achievement Levels 1, 2, 3, 4.

Self-Assessment:

Comments: (Strengths, Needs, Next Steps)

Name ____________________ Date ________________

Master 3.5

Additional Activity 1: Match It!

Work with a partner.

You will need a copy of Master 3.15 and scissors.

1. Cut out all the cards on Master 3.15.
2. Keep the object cards face up.
3. Place the view cards face down. Mix them up.
4. Take turns to turn over 5 views. If all the views match one of the objects, take all six cards from the game. If any or all the views do not match, turn all of them face down. The next person has a turn.
5. Continue playing until all the pieces have been claimed.
6. The winner is the person with the most pieces.

Take It Further:
Use linking cubes to make an object and dot paper to draw the views. Combine your object and views with those of 5 other students to make your own *Match It!* game.

Name ____________________ Date ________________

Master 3.6

Additional Activity 2: Slide Design

Work on your own.

You will need isometric dot paper (PM 23), linking cubes, and pencil crayons.

1. Build an object from 4 linking cubes.

2. Make an isometric drawing of this object in the upper left-hand corner of the isometric dot paper.

3. Draw a translation of the isometric drawing, so that the new drawing touches the original drawing.

4. Repeat *Step 3* several times to fill the page. Be sure that each image touches a previous image.

5. Choose 3 different colours of pencil crayons. Use one colour for all top faces drawn.
Use a second colour for all front faces drawn. Use a third colour for all side faces.
Use your drawings to make a design.

Take It Further:
Reflect the isometric drawing in vertical, horizontal, or diagonal lines to produce a design.

Name ____________________ Date ________________

Master 3.7

Additional Activity 3: Net a Cube

Work with a partner.

You will need square dot paper (PM 22), coloured markers, and scissors.

1. On the square dot paper, draw a 12 by 12 square. Each of you has a different colour marker.

2. Take turns to fill the square with as many *different* nets of a cube as possible.

3. Score two points for a net not yet used.
Score one point for a net already used.

4. If your partner draws a design that you think does not form a cube, you may challenge him. Check his design by drawing it on another piece of dot paper, cut it out, then fold it. If it does not form a cube, no points are scored. If it does form a cube, you miss your next turn.

5. Play ends when no one can draw any more nets in the square.

6. The winner is the person with the most points.

Take It Further:
Repeat the activity. This time, draw different nets for a rectangular prism.

Name ____________________ Date ________________

Master 3.8

Additional Activity 4: SAVO

Work in a group.

You will need counters, 3 number cubes labelled 1 to 6, and a game board (Master 3.16).

1. Each player chooses four counters the same colour and places them on the *Start* squares outside the board.

2. Roll a number cube for the highest number to see who starts.

3. Each turn, 3 number cubes are rolled. The three numbers that show are the dimensions of a rectangular prism. The sum of these numbers is the number of squares the player moves. The player must correctly calculate the surface area of the prism before moving one counter. She may use another marker to move 3 more spaces if she correctly calculates the volume of the prism.

4. Counters move counterclockwise around the board. A player may move a counter toward *Home* when it has been around the board once.

5. A player may send another player's counter back to the *Start* if her marker lands on an occupied space. On each turn, a player may move one new marker into play.

6. The game ends when one player has all four markers inside the *Home* square.

If time is limited:
Play with fewer markers.
Don't send a player back to the *Start* – share the space.

Name ____________________ Date ______________

Master 3.9

Step-by-Step 1

Section 3.1, Question 7

You will need square dot paper and 4 linking cubes.

Step 1 Join the linking cubes in a row.

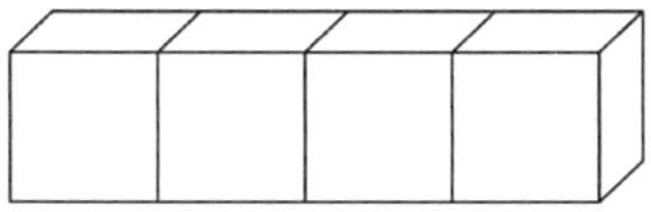

Draw the front, back, top, and side views.

Step 2 Move one end cube and place it on top of another cube.

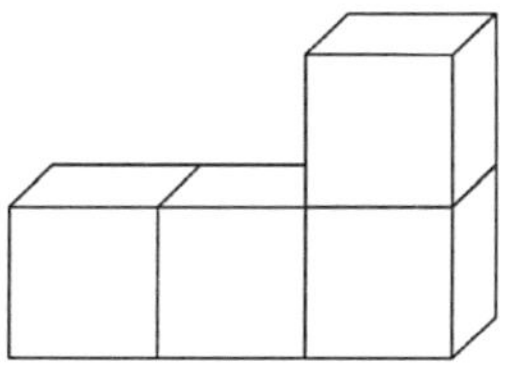

Draw the front, back, top, and side views.

Step 3 Move the same cube. Place it on top of a different cube.

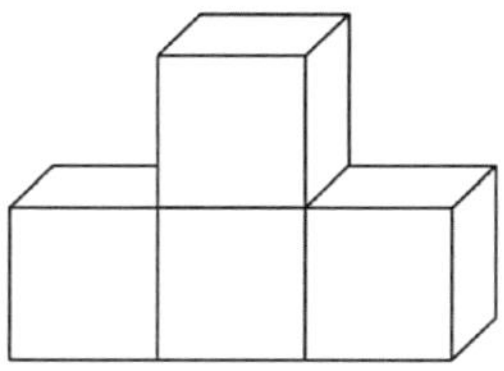

Draw the front, back, top, and side views.

Step 4 Find a different arrangement.
Draw all the views.

Step 5 Find one more different arrangement.
Draw all the views.

Name ____________________ Date _______________

Master 3.10

Step-by-Step 2

Section 3.2, Question 7

You will need isometric dot paper and 5 linking cubes.

Step 1 Build this object.

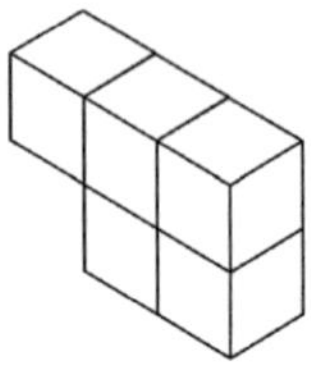

Step 2 Place it as shown. Turn it so one vertical edge is facing you.

Isometric Drawing

Step 3 Draw the vertical edges for this object on the isometric dot paper.

Step 4 Draw the horizontal edges that appear to go down to the right.

Step 5 Draw the horizontal edges that appear to go up to the right.

Pictorial Diagram

Step 6 Draw the front view of the solid above on plain paper.

Step 7 Draw the front view again.
Draw it so that it is up and to the right of the first front view.

Step 8 Join the corresponding vertices.

Step 9 How is sketching on isometric paper like sketching on plain paper?

____

____

Step 10 How is sketching on isometric paper different from sketching on plain paper?

____

____

Name ____________________ Date _______________

Master 3.11

Step-by-Step 3

Section 3.3, Question 7

Step 1 Cut along the solid lines of the net.

Step 2 Write your name on the pentagon with all the rectangles attached to it. This will be the outside surface.

Step 3 Fold along the dotted lines toward the inside.

Step 4 Place the pentagon with your name on it face down.

Step 5 Fold up the rectangles to form faces.

Step 6 Fold the other pentagon onto the top.

Step 7 Tape the sides.

Step 8 Describe the object.

Is it a prism, a pyramid, or neither? ____________________

How many faces? _______________

How many edges? _______________

How many vertices? _____________

How many bases? _______________

Shape of the base(s): _____________

Step 9 Use your answers from *Step 8* to name the object. ______________

Name ______________ Date ______________

Master 3.12

Step-by-Step 4

Section 3.4, Question 6

Step 1 Sketch a rectangle.
Label its base *b*,
and its height *h*.
Choose values for *b* and *h*.

Step 2 Write this formula in words: $P = 2b + 2h$

____

Step 3 How do you use the formula in *Step 2* to find the perimeter of a rectangle?
Explain by using the formula to find the perimeter of the rectangle in *Step 1*.

____

____

Step 4 Write this formula in words: $P = 2(b + h)$

____

____

Step 5 How do you use the formula in *Step 4* to find the perimeter of a rectangle?
Explain by using the formula to find the perimeter of the rectangle in *Step 1*.

____

____

Step 6 Why are there two formulas for the perimeter of a rectangle?

____

____

Name ____________________ Date ________________

Master 3.13

Step-by-Step 5

Section 3.5, Question 7

Step 1 Sketch a rectangular prism with dimensions 2 cm by 4 cm by 6 cm.

Step 2 Find the surface area of the prism in *Step 1*. ________________________________

Step 3 Sketch a rectangular prism with dimensions 2 cm by 4 cm by 12 cm.

Step 4 Find the surface area of the prism in *Step 3*. ________________________________

Step 5 Look at your answers to *Steps 2 and 4*.
What happens to the surface area of a rectangular prism when its length is doubled?

____

Step 6 Sketch a rectangular prism with dimensions 2 cm by 4 cm by 3 cm.

Step 7 Find the surface area of the prism in *Step 6*. ________________________________

Step 8 Look at your answers to *Steps 2 and 7*.
What happens to the surface area of a rectangular prism when its length is halved?

____

Name ____________________ Date ________________

Master 3.14 **Step-by-Step 6**

Section 3.6, Question 7

You will need 20 linking cubes.

Step 1 How many rectangular prisms can you make with each number of cubes?
On a separate sheet of paper, write the dimensions of each prism you make.

2: ______	3: ______	4: ______	5: ______
6: ______	7: ______	8: ______	9: ______
10: ______	11: ______	12: ______	13: ______
14: ______	15: ______	16: ______	17: ______
18: ______	19: ______	20: ______	

Step 2 Look at your answers in *Step 1*.
How many cubes made exactly 1 prism? ____________________

How many cubes made exactly 2 prisms? ____________________

How many cubes made exactly 3 prisms? ____________________

How many cubes made exactly 4 prisms? ____________________

Step 3 What is special about the numbers of cubes that make exactly 1 prism?

____

What is special about the numbers of cubes that make exactly 2 prisms?

____

What is special about the numbers of cubes that make exactly 3 prisms?

____

What is special about the numbers of cubes that make exactly 4 prisms?

____

Name ____________________ Date ________________

Master 3.15

Match It! Cards

Name ____________________ Date ______________

Master 3.16

Game Board for SAVO

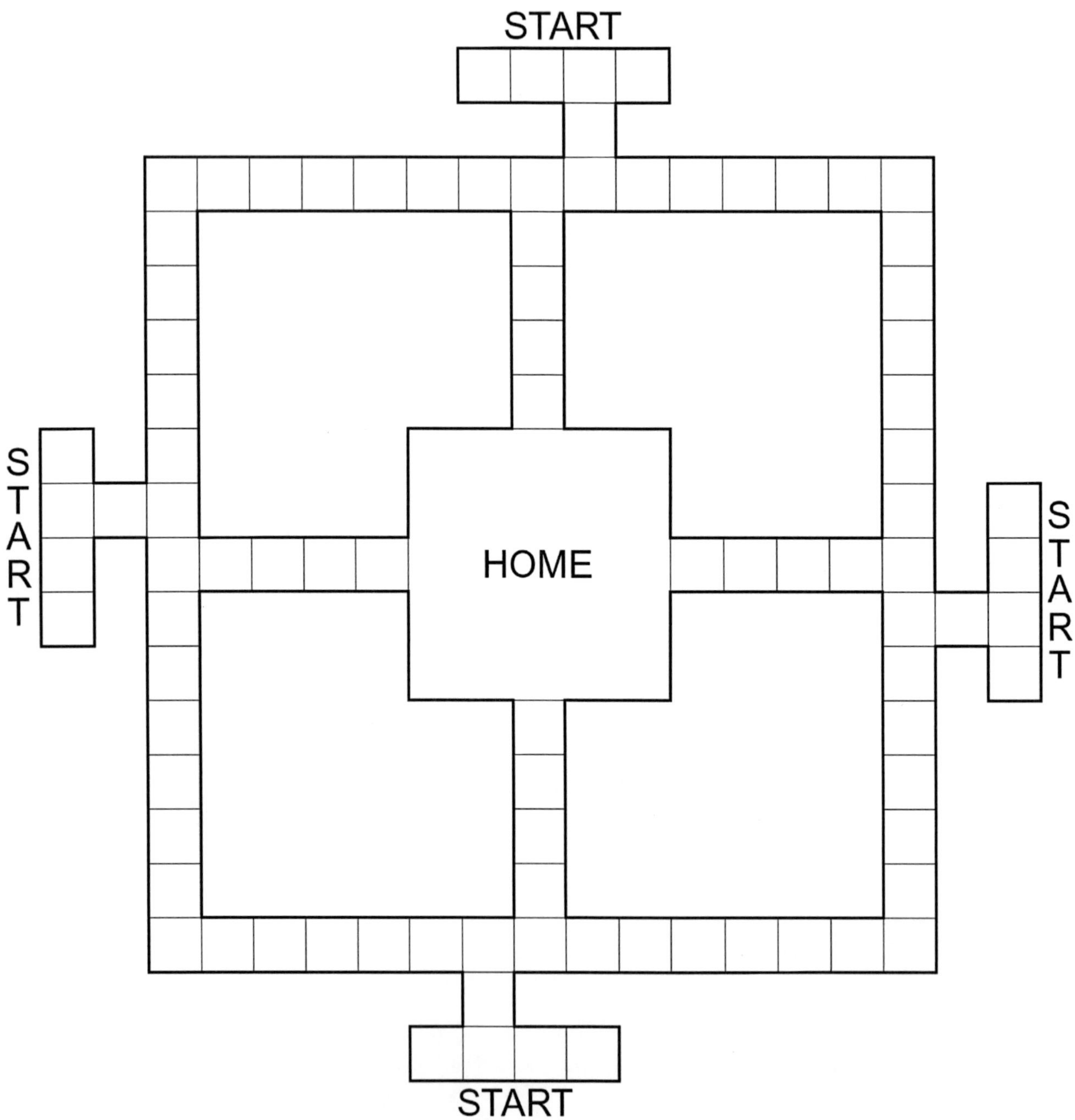

Name ____________________ Date ________________

Master 3.17

Net for Section 3.3 *Explore*

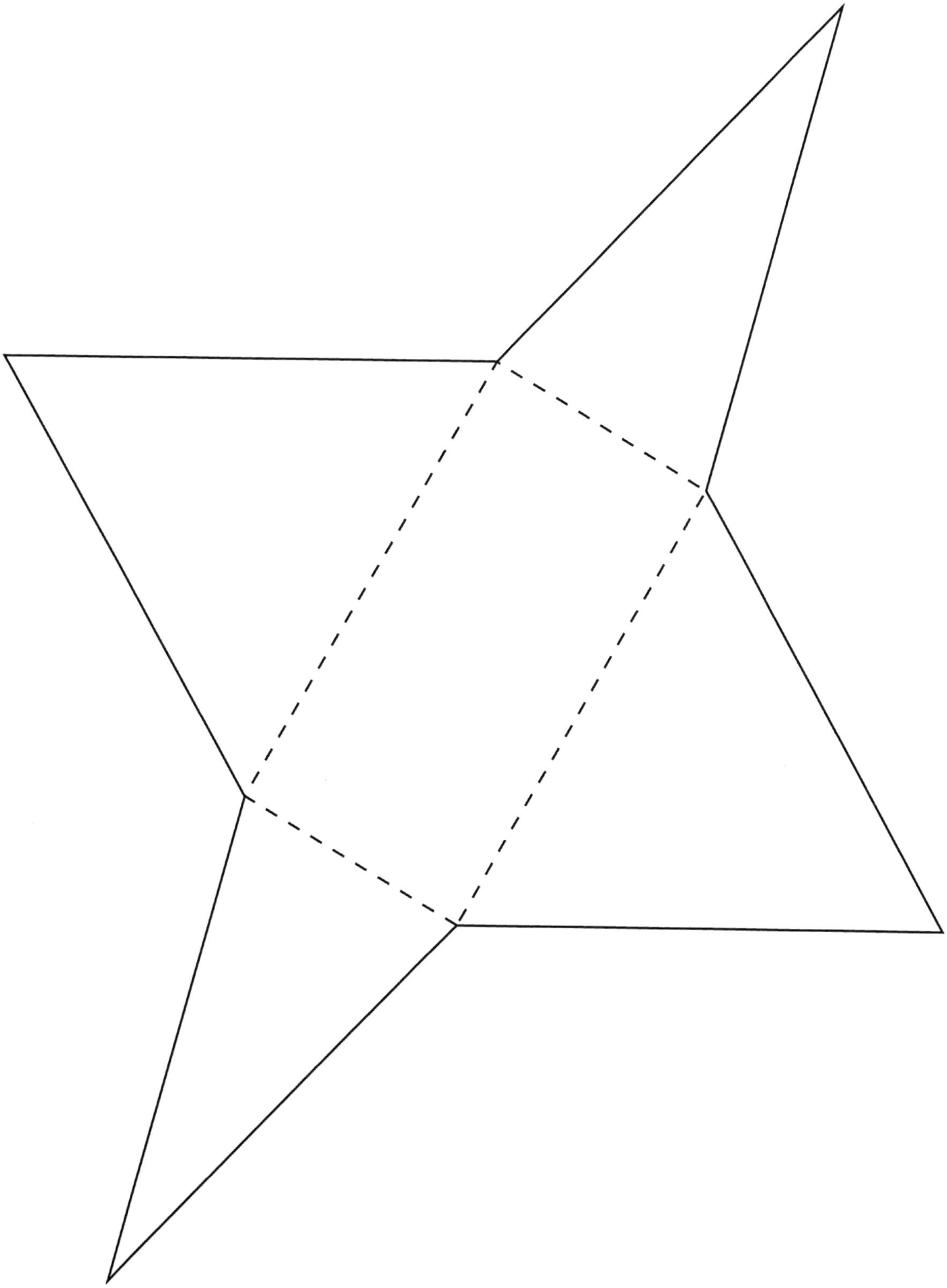

Name ____________________ Date ________________

Master 3.18

Net for Section 3.3 *Explore*

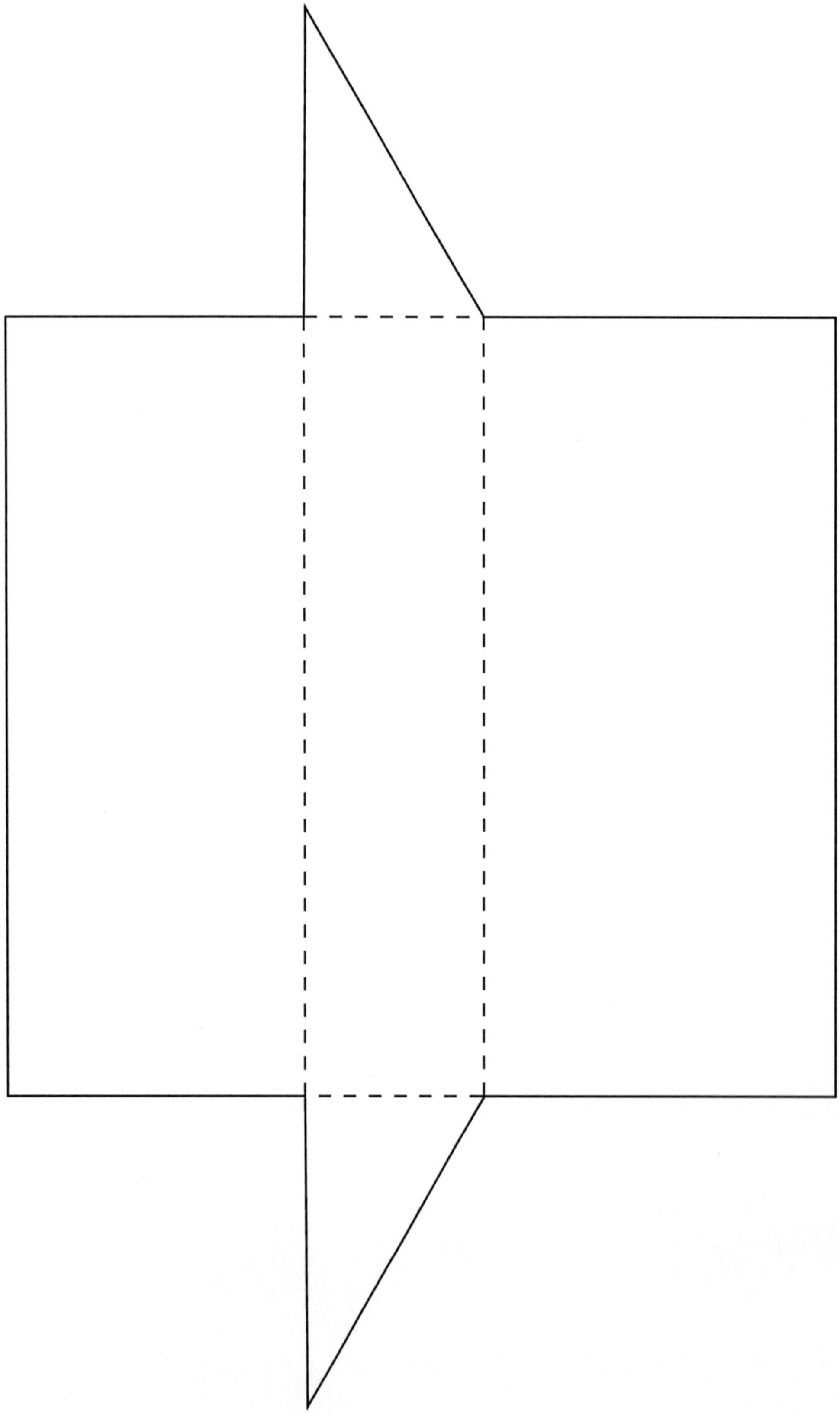

Name ____________________ Date ______________

Master 3.19

Net of Half an Icosahedron

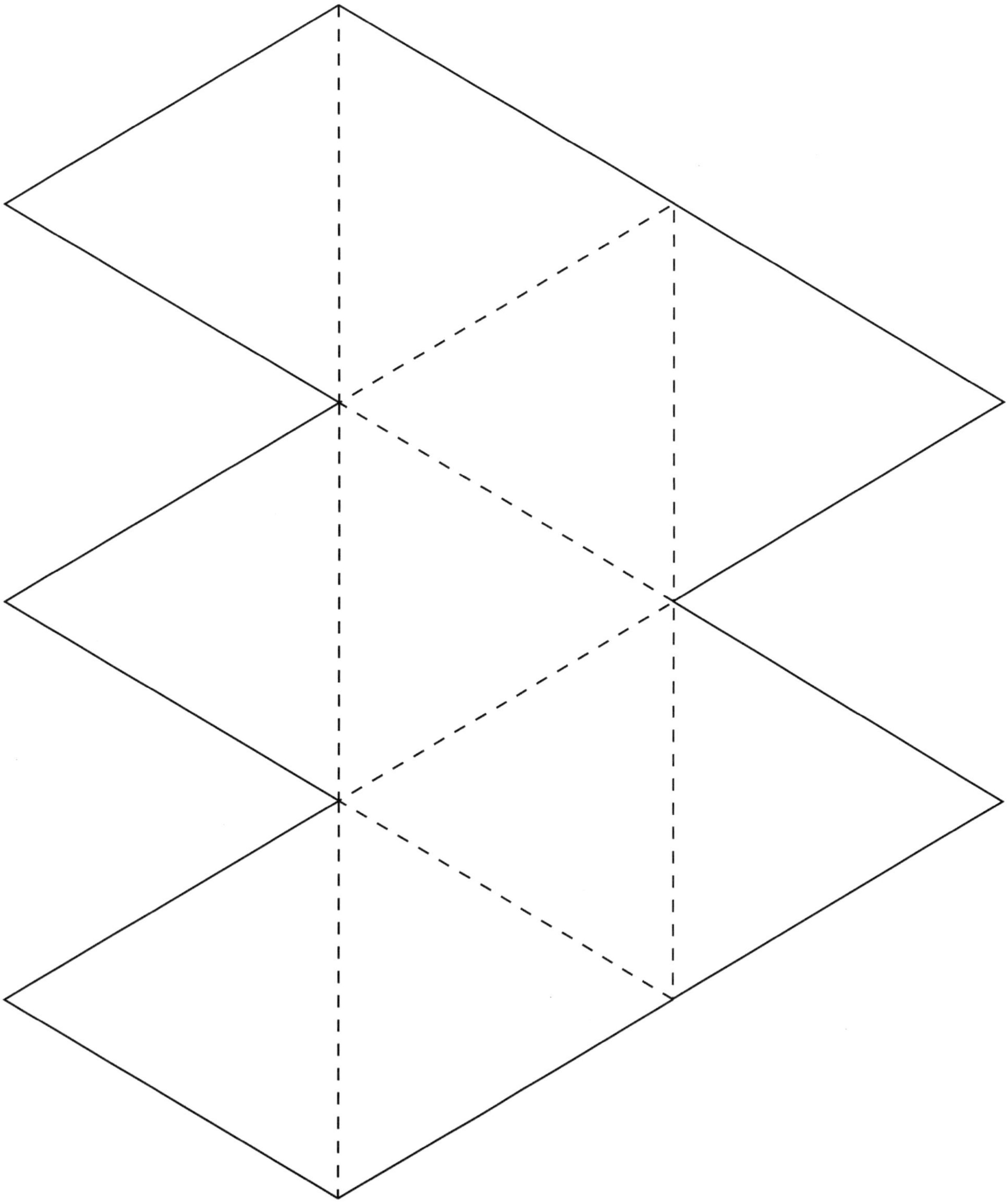

Name ____________________ Date ________________

Master 3.20

Net of a Frustum of a Square Pyramid

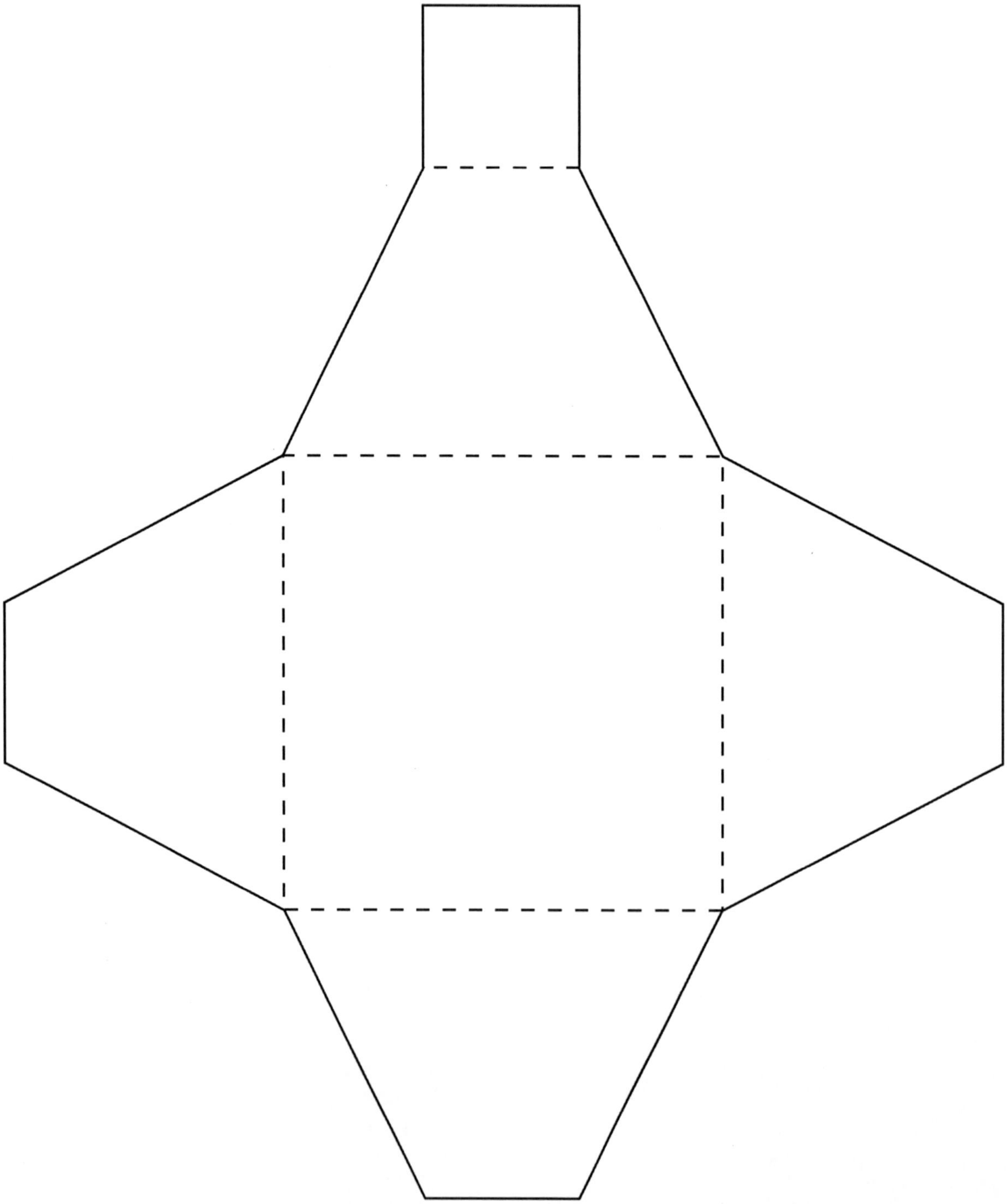

Name ____________________ Date ________________

Master 3.21

Net for Section 3.3, *Practice* Question 1

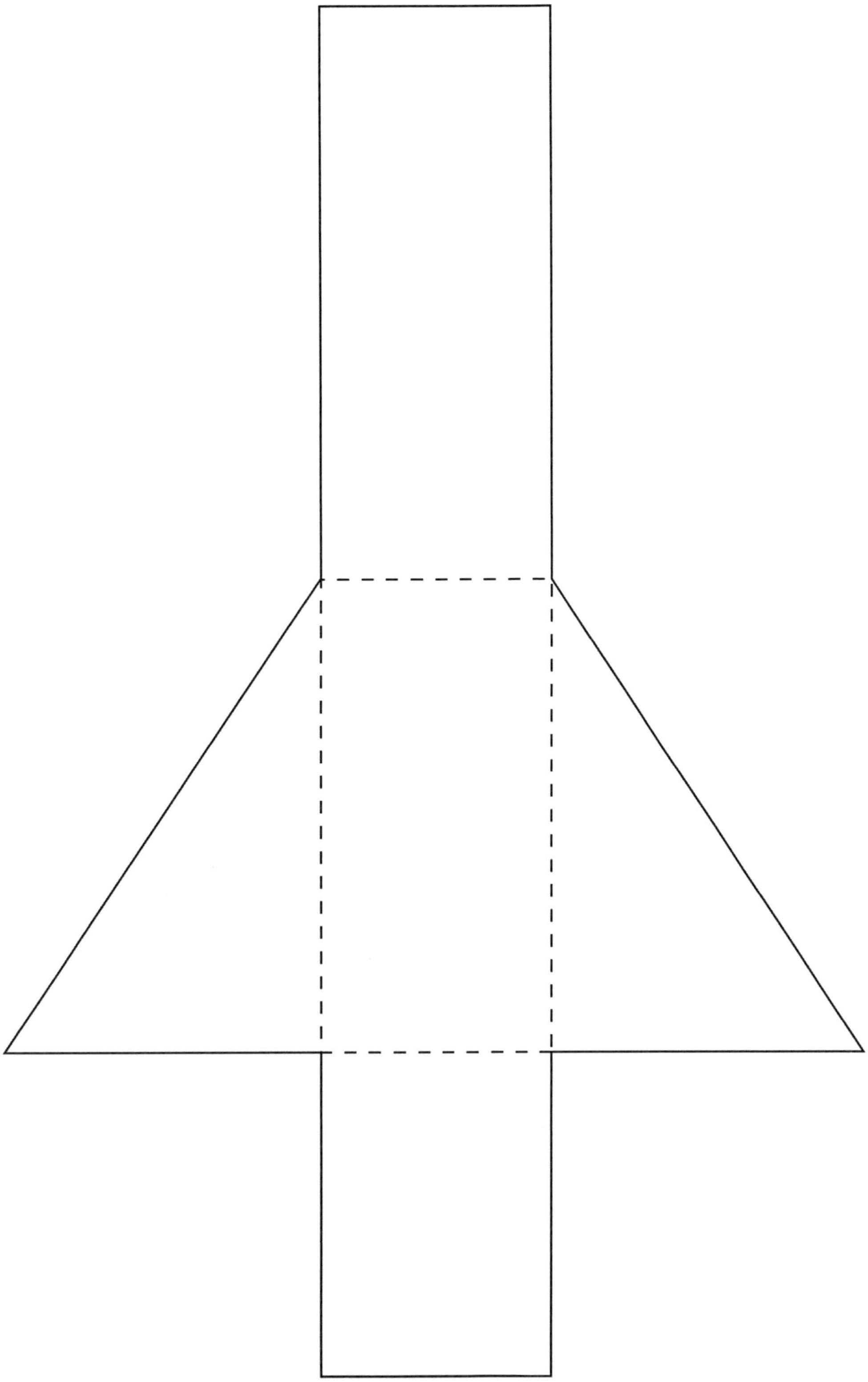

Name ____________________ Date ________________

Master 3.22

Net for Section 3.3, *Practice* Question 2

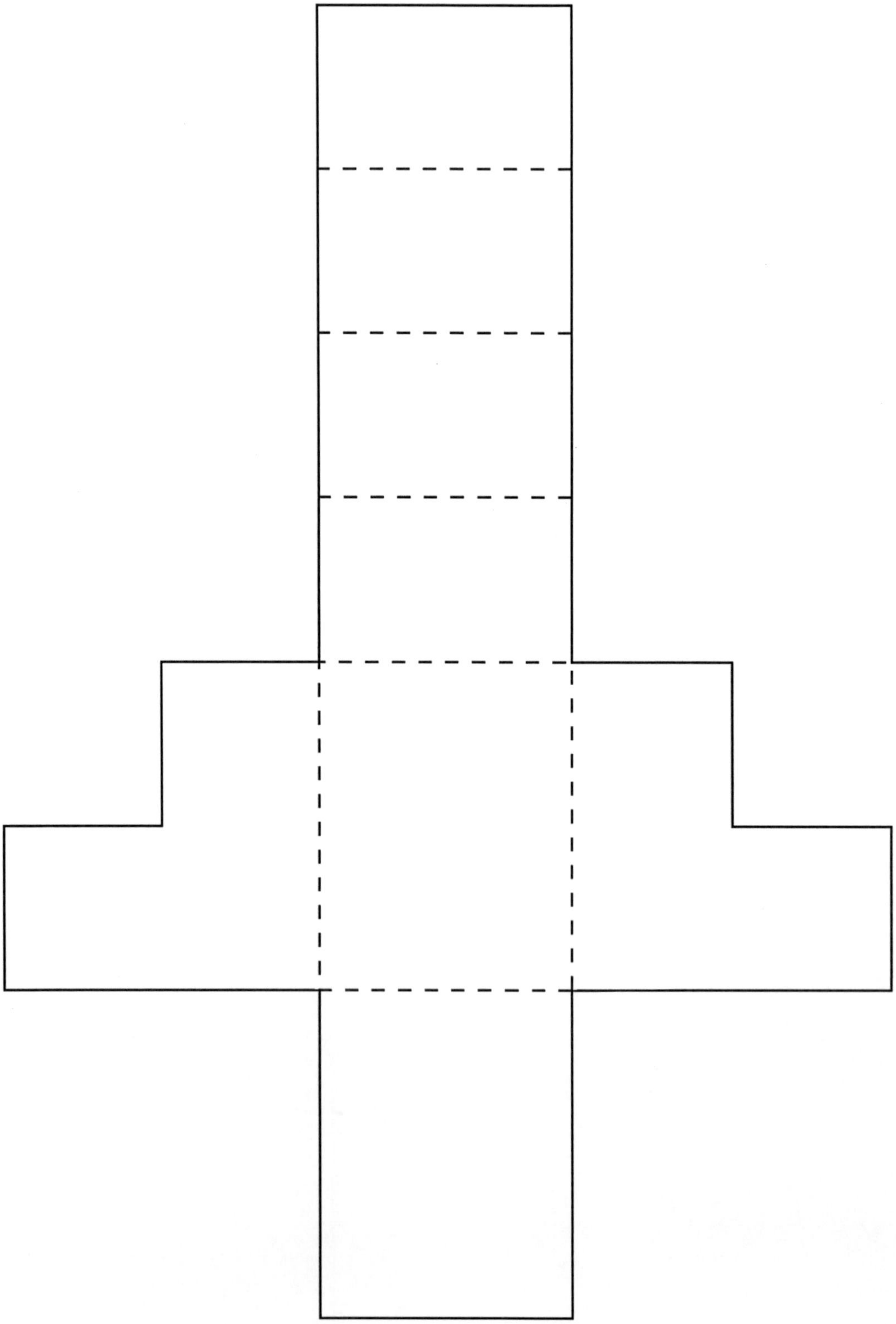

Name ____________________ Date ______________

Master 3.23

Net of Half a Regular Octahedron

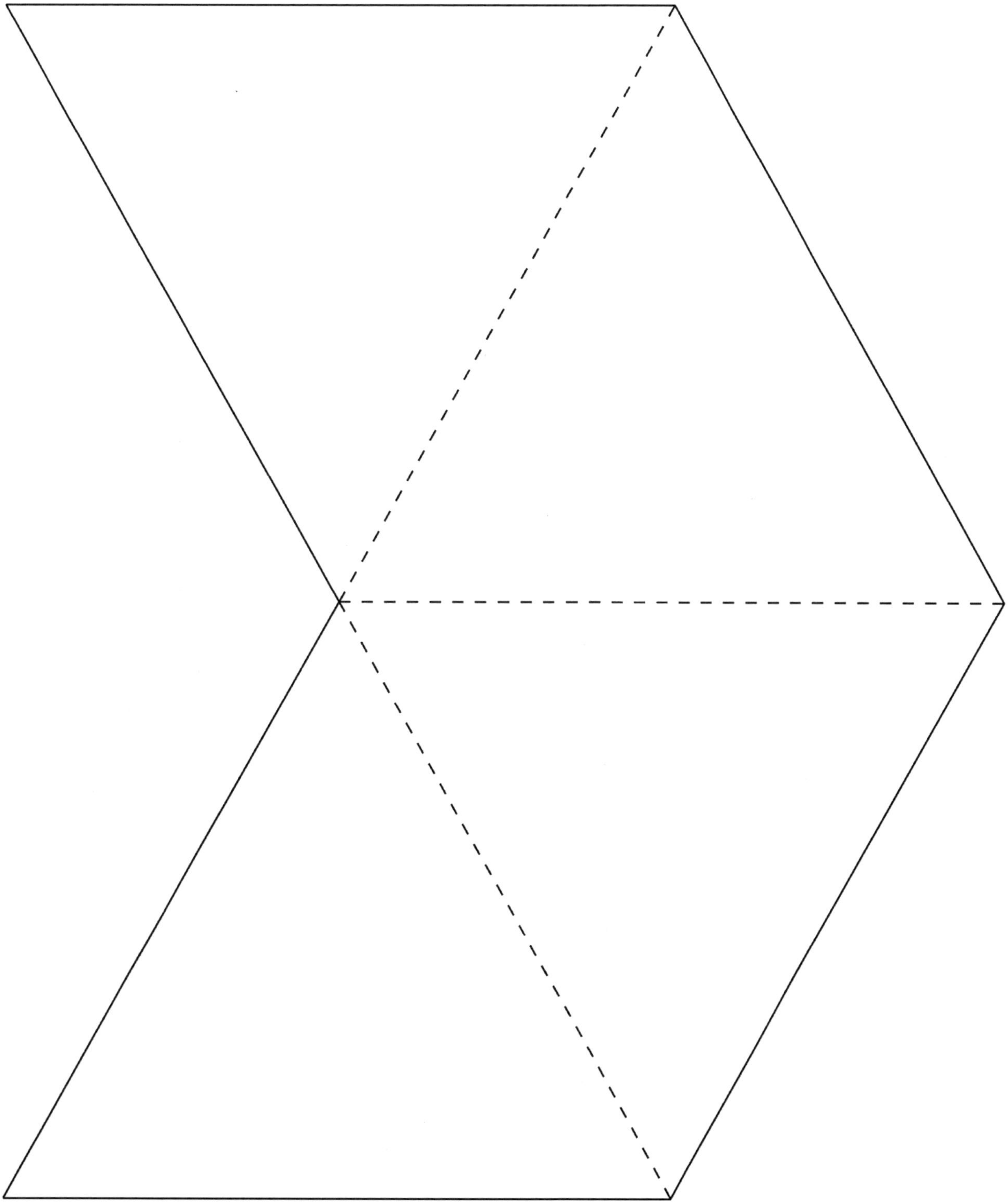

Name ____________________ Date ________________

Master 3.24

Net for Section 3.3, *Practice* Question 4a

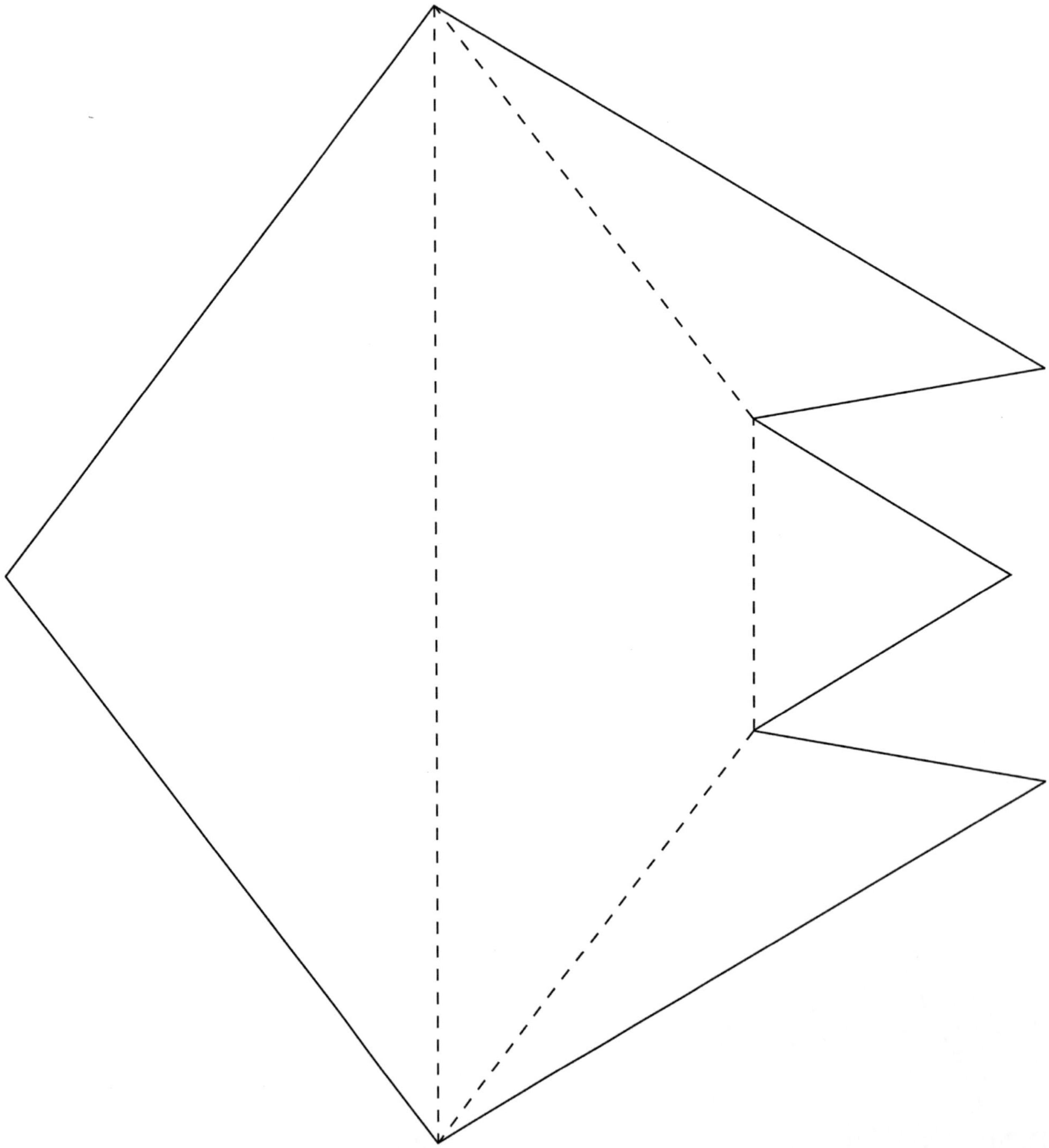

Name ____________________ Date ______________

Master 3.25

Net for Section 3.3, *Practice* Question 4b

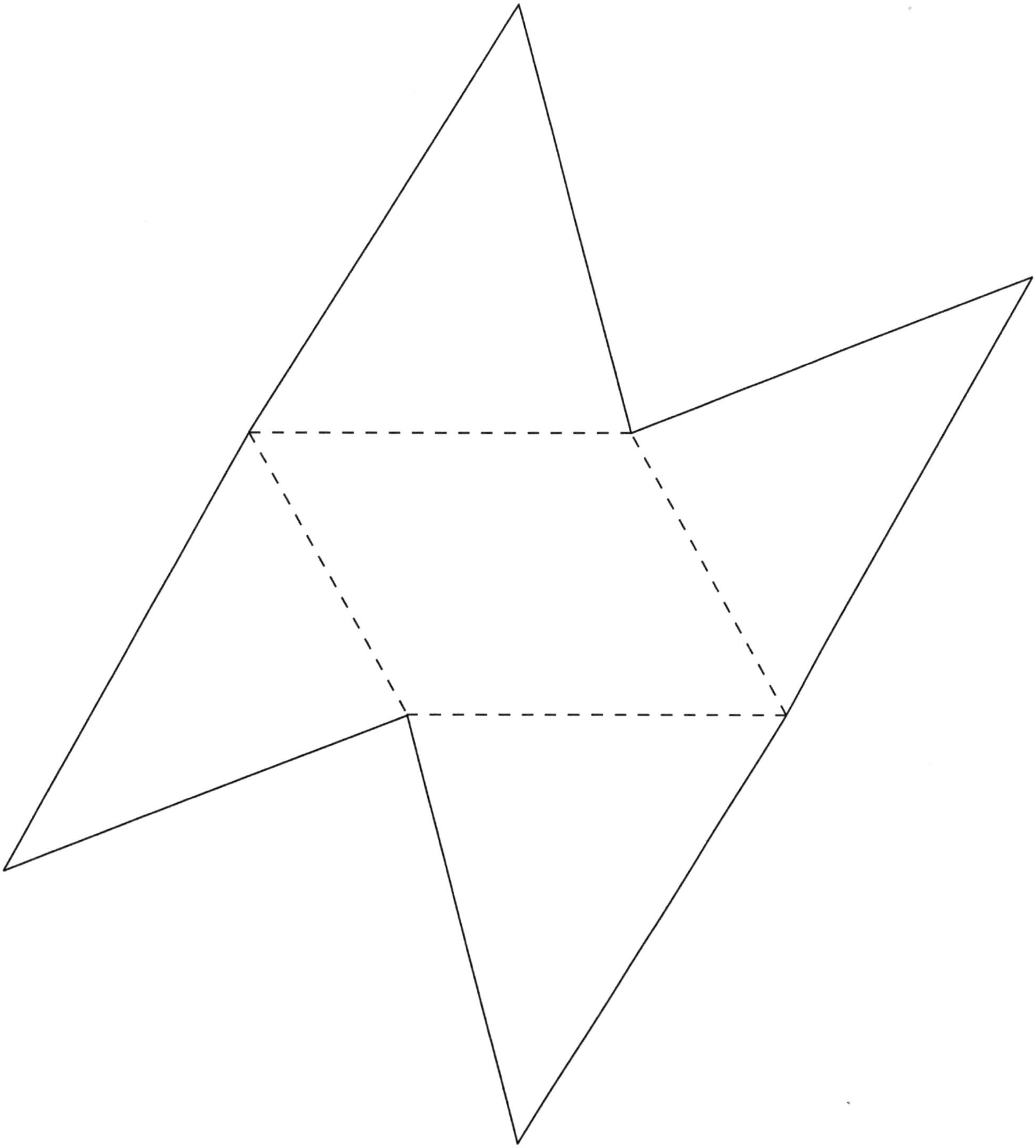

Name ____________________ Date ________________

Master 3.26

Net of Half a Regular Dodecahedron

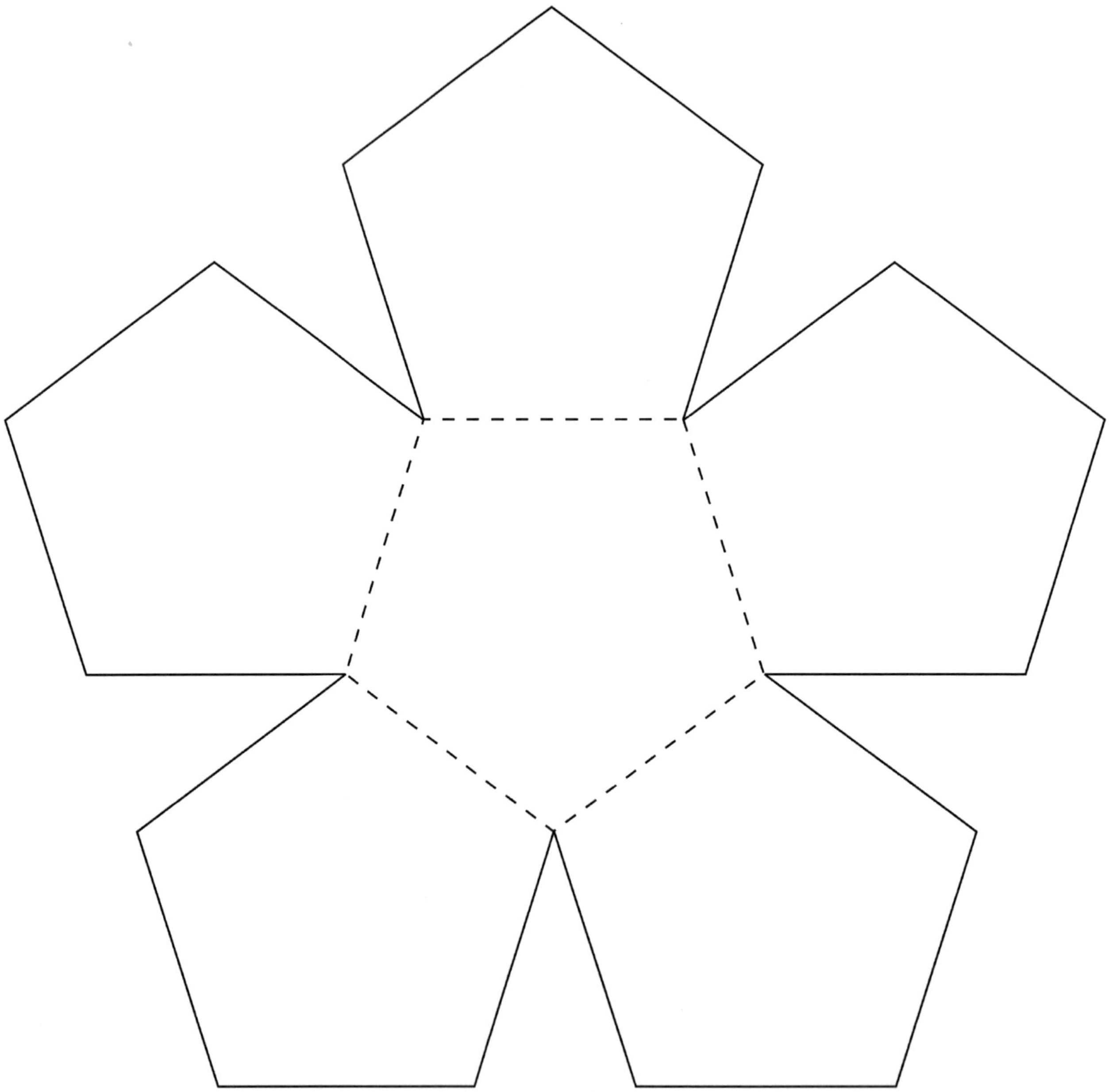

Name ____________________ Date ________________

Master 3.27

Net for Section 3.3, *Practice* Question 7

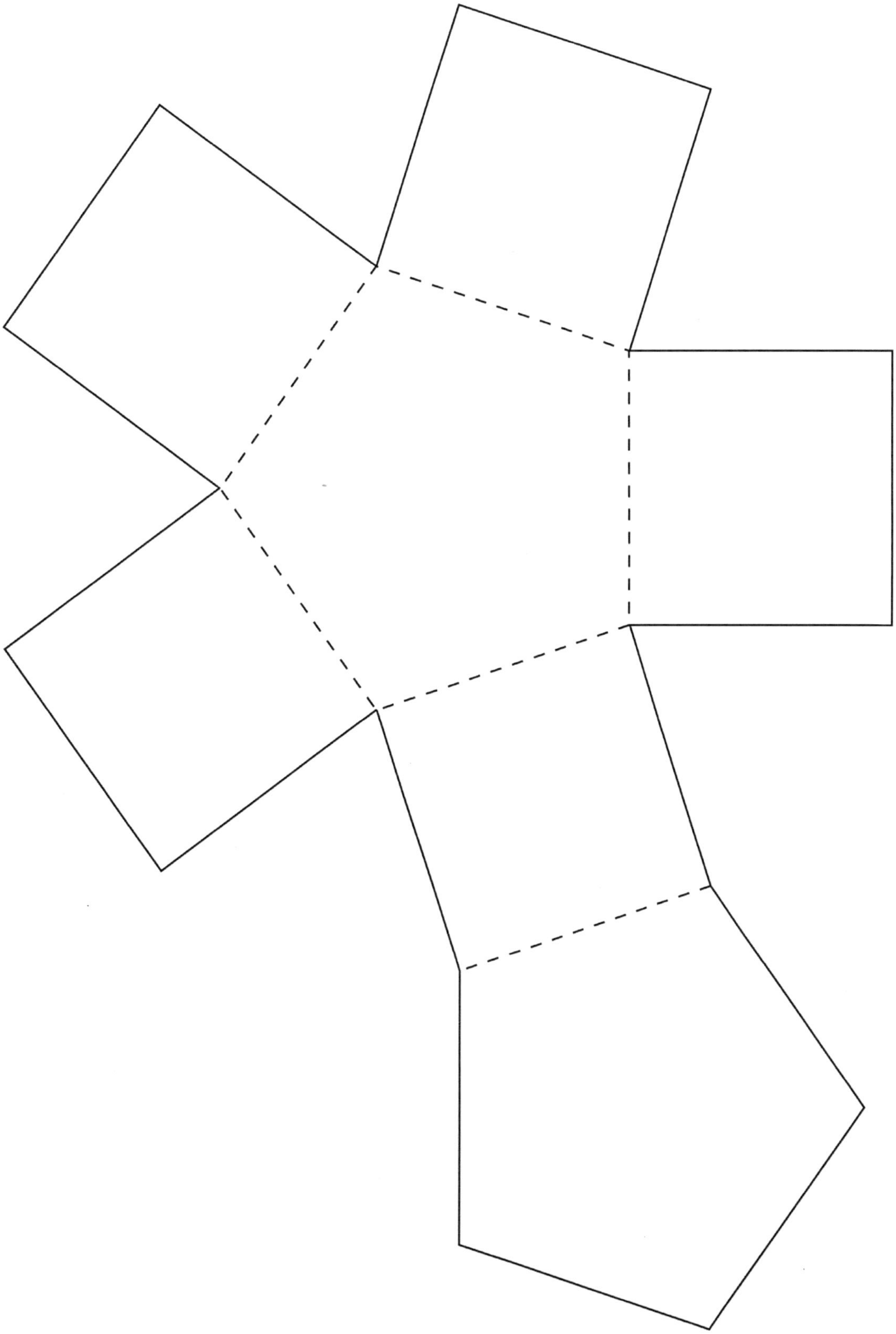

Name ____________________ Date ________________

Master 3.28

Net for Mid-Unit Review, Question 5

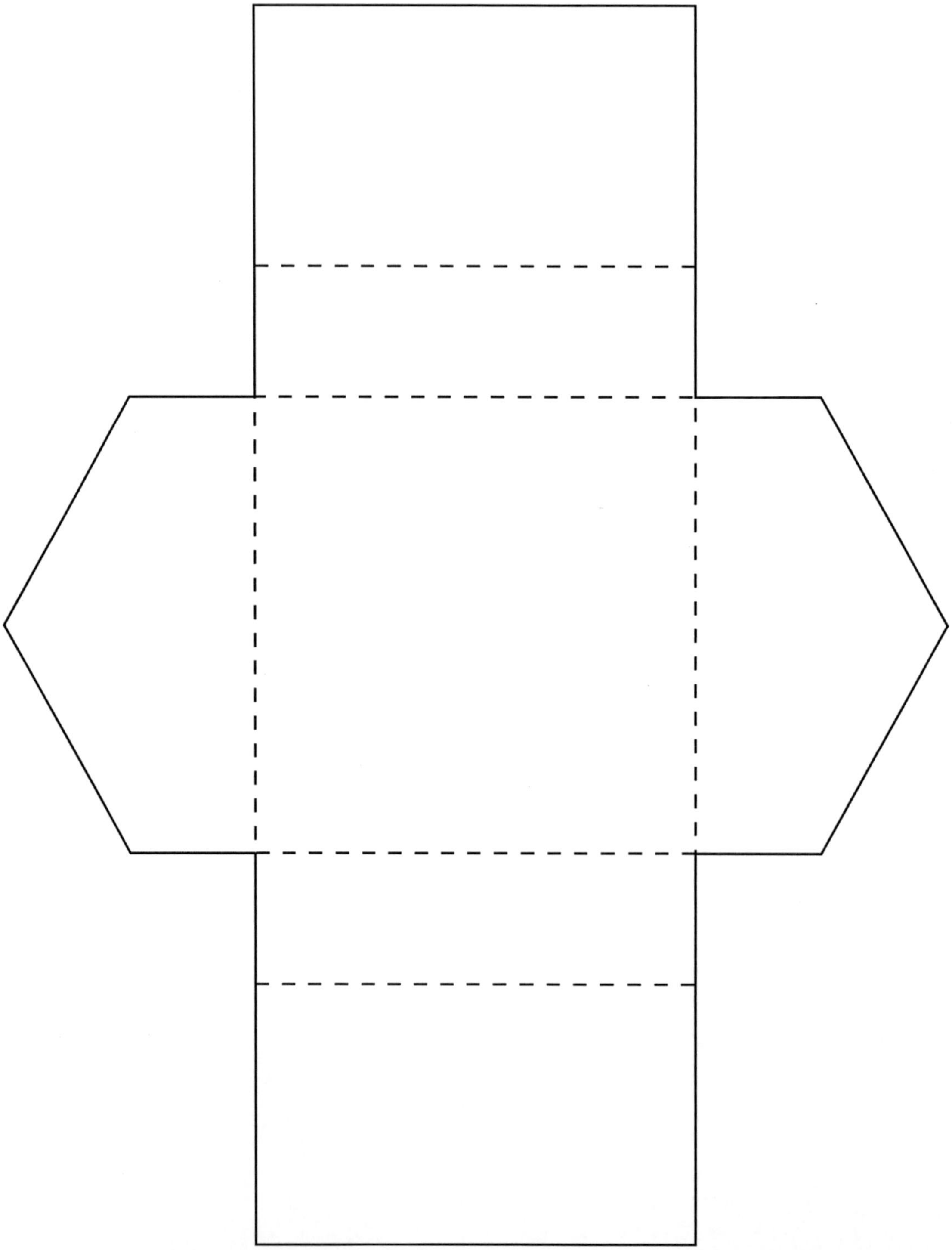

Name ______________________ Date ________________

Master 3.29

Net for Unit Review, Question 3

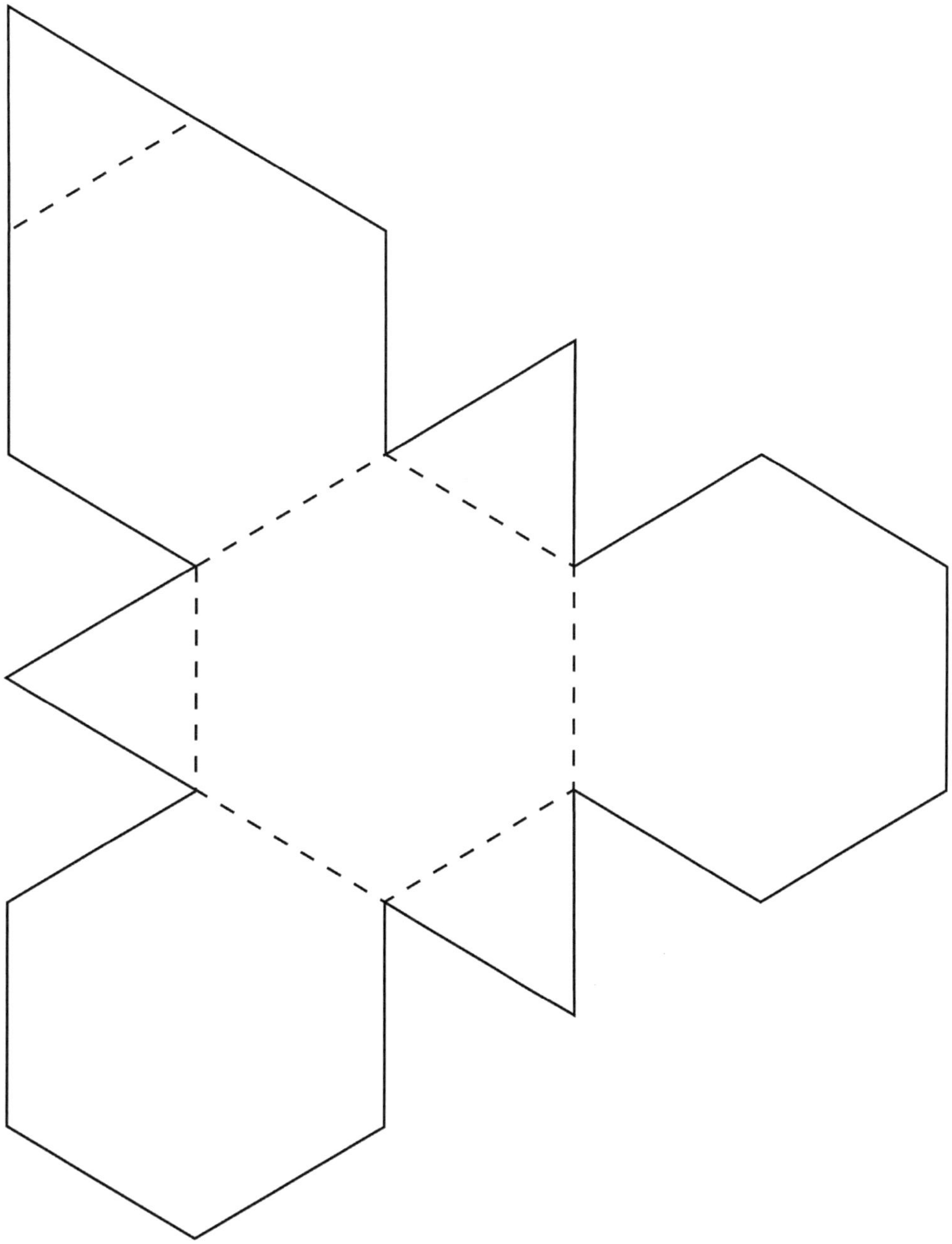

Name ____________________ Date ______________

Master 3.30

Net for Practice Test, Question 2

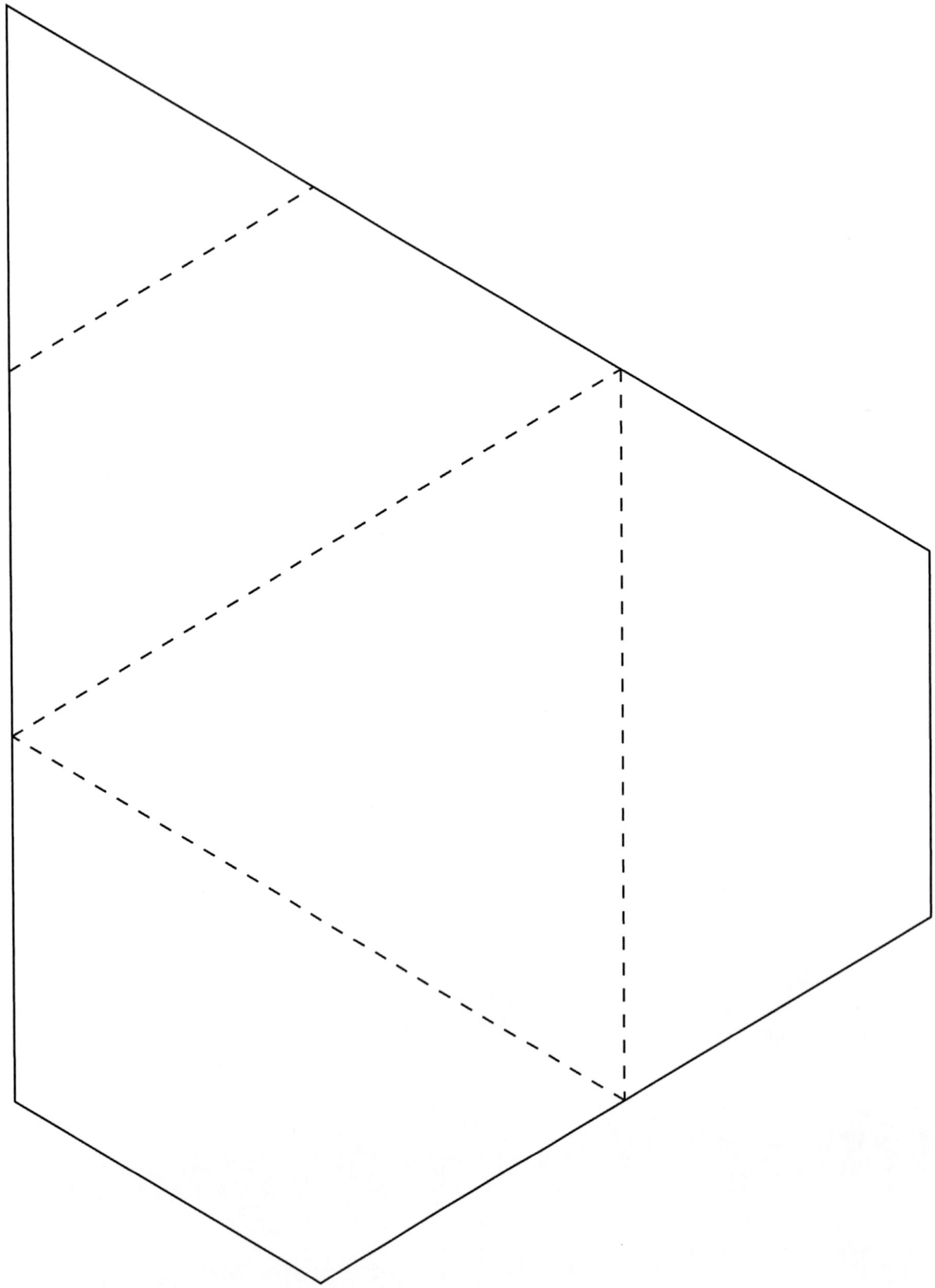

Name ____________________ Date _______________

Master 3.31a

Unit Test: Unit 3 Geometry and Measurement

1. Draw the front, top, and side views of each object.

a)

b)

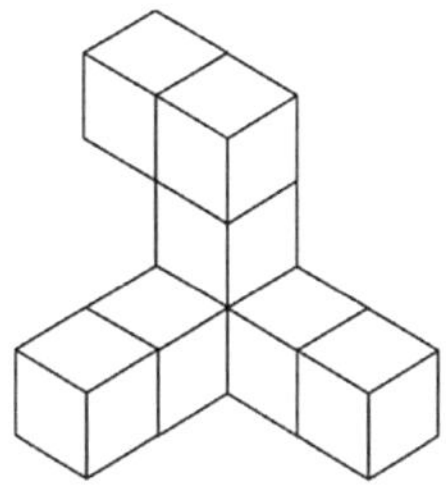

2. Fold a copy of this net.

a) Describe the object.

b) Suggest a name for it.

c) Sketch the object.

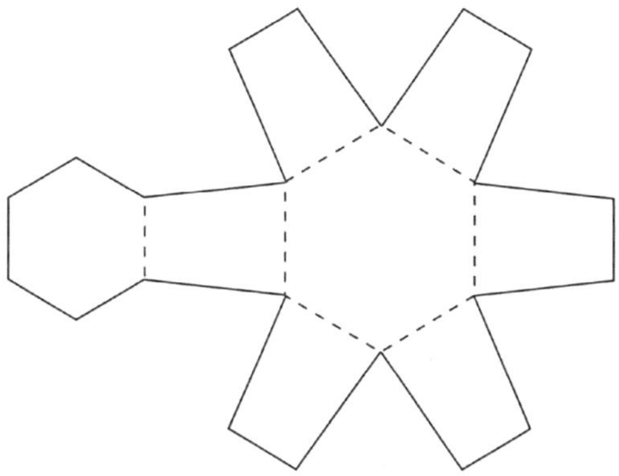

3. Jason has 36 m of fencing. Here are 3 different ways he can fence his pool:

a) He makes a square fence.

b) The length of the fence is twice its width.

c) Jason only needs fencing on three sides. The unfenced side is 8 m.

For each way above:

i) Find the dimensions of the region fenced.

ii) Find the area of the region fenced.

4. Calculate the surface area and volume of this rectangular prism.

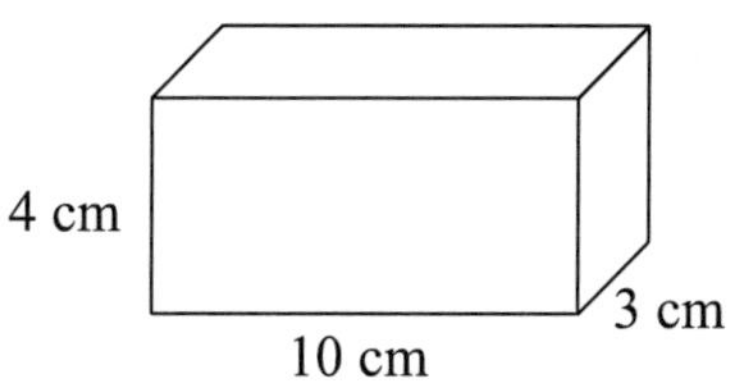

Name ____________________ Date ________________

Master 3.31b **Unit Test continued**

5. The drama club needs a plywood box with these dimensions: 70 cm by 40 cm by 50 cm. It will be used as a prop in a play.
   a) How much plywood is needed?
   b) Another box is built with each dimension twice as great.
   How much plywood is needed for this box?
   c) A sheet of plywood has area 2.4 m^2.
   How many sheets will be needed for both boxes?
   d) What assumptions do you make?

6. **a)** Sketch 3 different rectangular prisms with volume 27 cm^3.
   b) Which prism has the least surface area?

7. **a)** What is a variable?
   b) How are variables used in measurement formulas?
   Use examples in your explanation.

Name ______________________ Date ________________

Master 3.31c

Net for Unit Test, Question 2

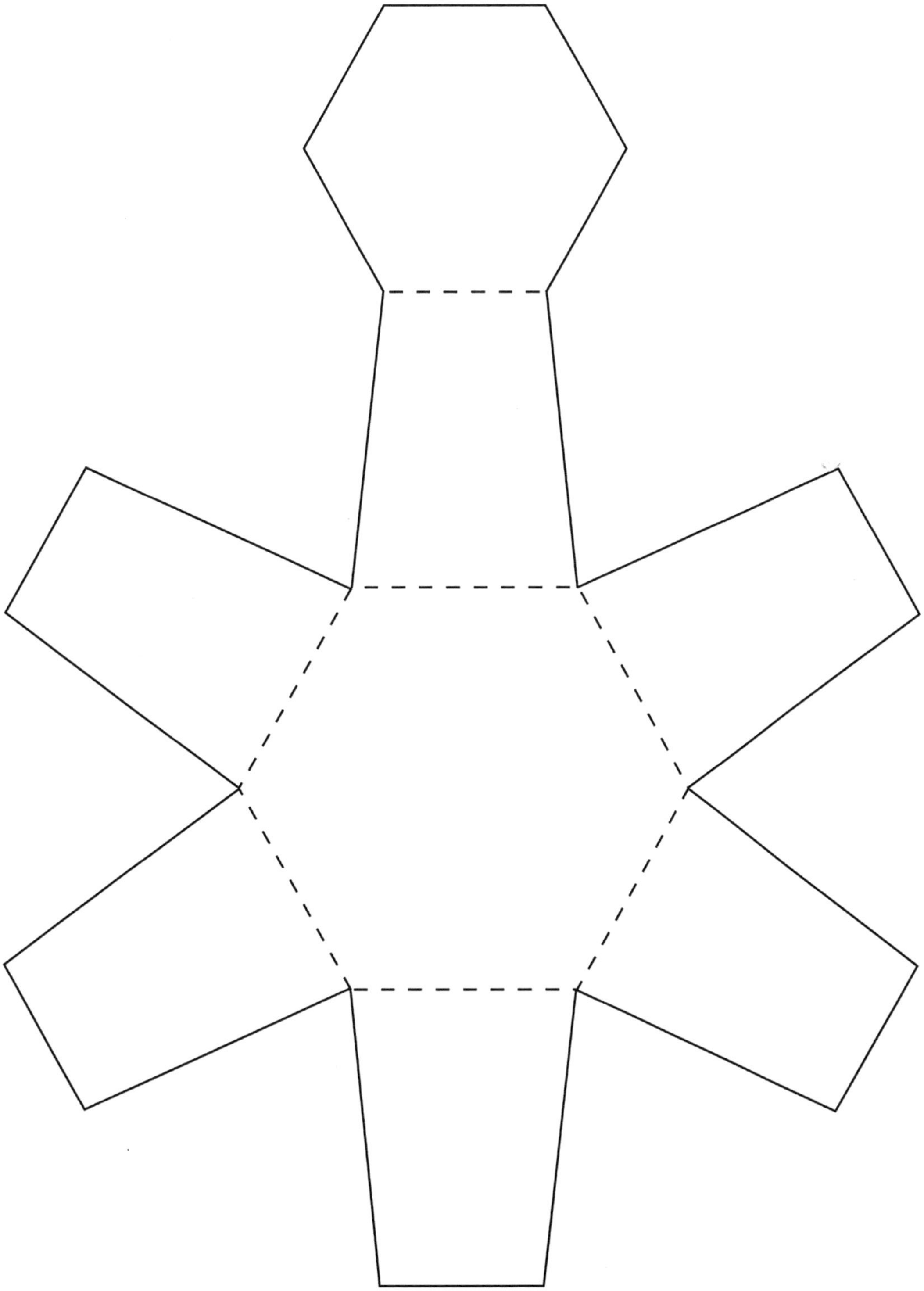

Name ____________________ Date ________________

Master 3.32 Sample Answers

Unit Test – Master 3.31

1. a) **front** **top** **right side** **left side**

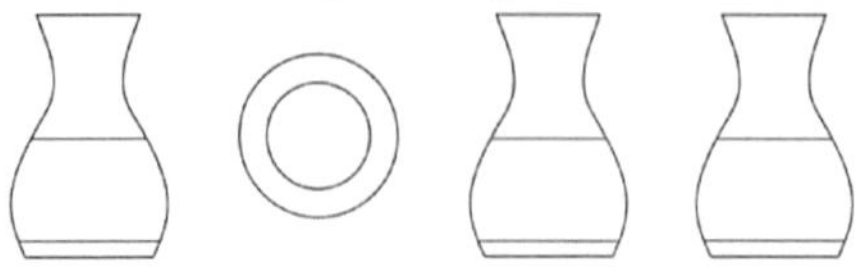

b) **front** **top** **right side** **left side**

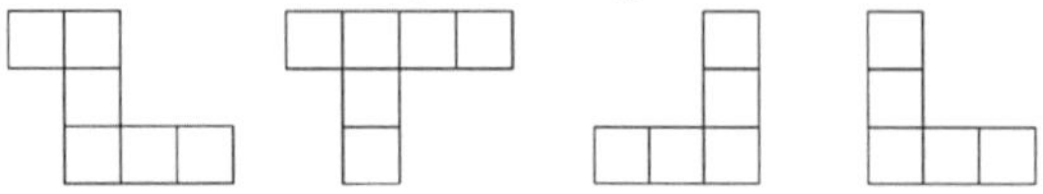

2. a) The object has 8 faces (2 faces are similar regular hexagons and 6 faces are congruent trapezoids).
It has 18 edges and 12 vertices.
The object is a hexagonal pyramid with its top cut off.

b) Frustum of a hexagonal pyramid

c)

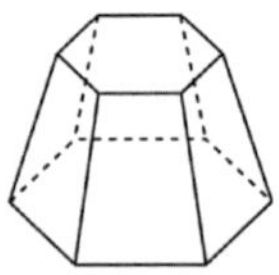

3. a) i) 9 m by 9 m **ii)** 81 m^2
b) i) 12 m by 6 m **ii)** 72 m^2
c) i) 14 m by 8 m **ii)** 112 m^2

4. $SA = 164\ cm^2$; $V = 120\ cm^3$

5. a) 16 600 cm^2 **b)** 66 400 cm^2 **c)** 4 sheets
d) Assume that all pieces can be used, and the faces of the boxes may be made from parts of sheets.

6. a) 1 cm by 1 cm by 27 cm, surface area: 110 cm^2;
1 cm by 3 cm by 9 cm, surface area: 78 cm^2;
3 cm by 3 cm by 3 cm, surface area: 54 cm^2
b) The prism that is a cube has the least surface area.

Prism	Dimensions	Surface Area
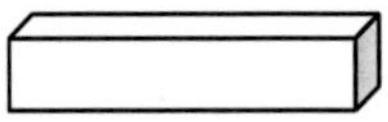	1 cm by 1 cm by 27 cm	110 cm^2
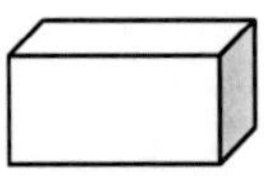	1 cm by 3 cm by 9 cm	78 cm^2
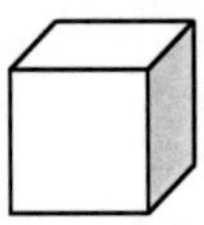	3 cm by 3 cm by 3 cm	54 cm^2

7. a) A variable is a letter that represents a number or different numbers.
b) Variables in measurement formulas represent dimensions, such as length, width, and height.
To make a formula easier to understand, we use a variable that is the first letter of the word it represents; for example: *l* for length; *w* for width; and *h* for height.
The volume of a rectangular prism is length × width × height. To write this using variables: $V = lwh$

Extra Practice Masters 3.33–3.39

Go to the CD-ROM to access editable versions of these Extra Practice Masters

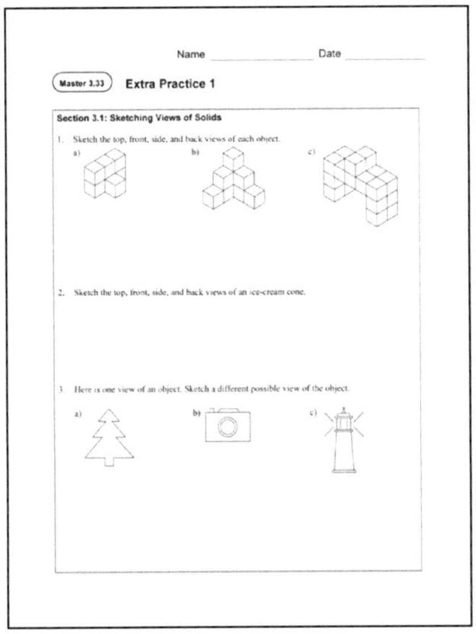

Name ____________ Date ____________

Master 3.33 **Extra Practice 1**

Section 3.1: Sketching Views of Solids

1. Sketch the top, front, side, and back views of each object.
a) b) c)

2. Sketch the top, front, side, and back views of an ice-cream cone.

3. Here is one view of an object. Sketch a different possible view of the object.
a) b) c)

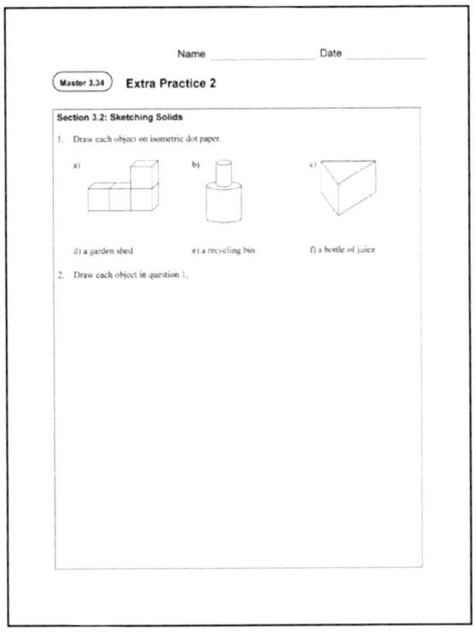

Name ____________ Date ____________

Master 3.34 **Extra Practice 2**

Section 3.2: Sketching Solids

1. Draw each object on isometric dot paper.
a) b) c)
d) a garden shed e) a recycling bin f) a bottle of juice

2. Draw each object in question 1.

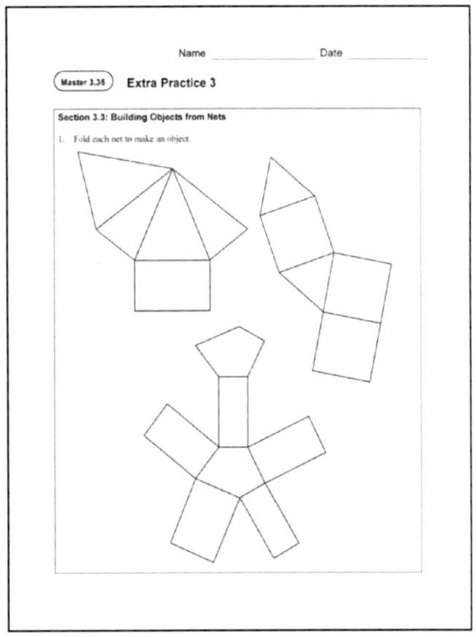

Name ____________ Date ____________

Master 3.35 **Extra Practice 3**

Section 3.3: Building Objects from Nets

1. Fold each net to make an object.

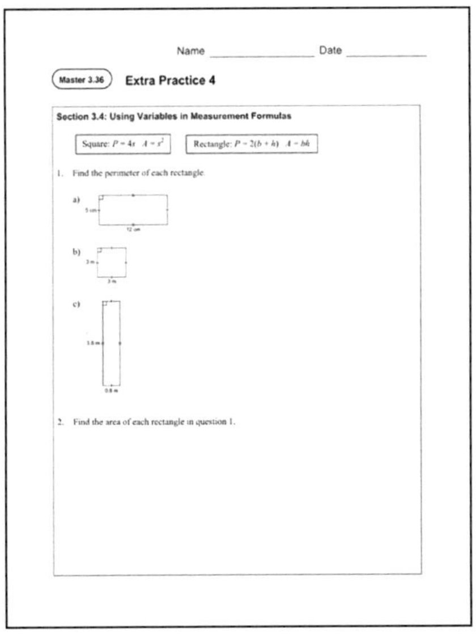

Name ____________ Date ____________

Master 3.36 **Extra Practice 4**

Section 3.4: Using Variables in Measurement Formulas

Square: $P = 4s$ $A = s^2$ Rectangle: $P = 2(b + h)$ $A = bh$

1. Find the perimeter of each rectangle.
a) 5 cm, 12 cm
b) 3 m, 3 m
c) 3.8 m, 0.8 m

2. Find the area of each rectangle in question 1.

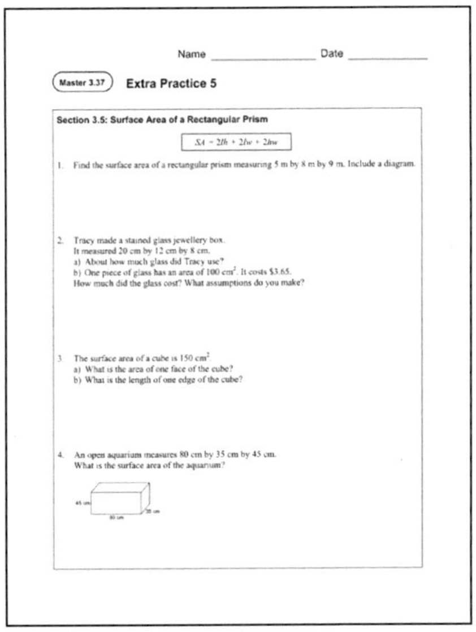

Name ____________ Date ____________

Master 3.37 **Extra Practice 5**

Section 3.5: Surface Area of a Rectangular Prism

$SA = 2lh + 2lw + 2hw$

1. Find the surface area of a rectangular prism measuring 5 m by 8 m by 9 m. Include a diagram.

2. Tracy made a stained glass jewellery box.
It measured 20 cm by 12 cm by 8 cm.
a) About how much glass did Tracy use?
b) One piece of glass has an area of 100 cm². It costs $3.65.
How much did the glass cost? What assumptions do you make?

3. The surface area of a cube is 150 cm².
a) What is the area of one face of the cube?
b) What is the length of one edge of the cube?

4. An open aquarium measures 80 cm by 35 cm by 45 cm.
What is the surface area of the aquarium?
45 cm, 80 cm, 35 cm

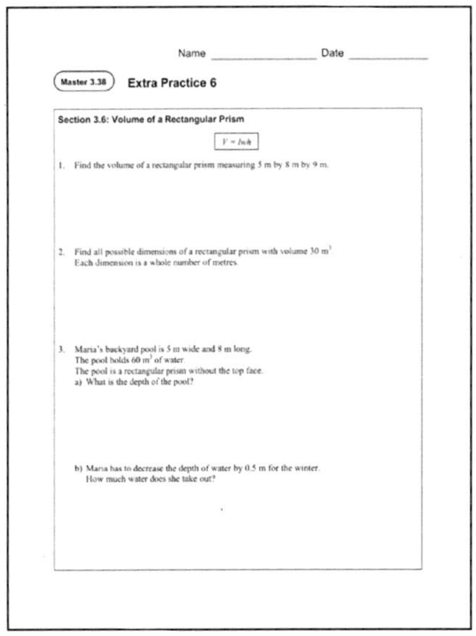

Name ____________ Date ____________

Master 3.38 **Extra Practice 6**

Section 3.6: Volume of a Rectangular Prism

$V = lwh$

1. Find the volume of a rectangular prism measuring 5 m by 8 m by 9 m.

2. Find all possible dimensions of a rectangular prism with volume 30 m³.
Each dimension is a whole number of metres.

3. Maria's backyard pool is 5 m wide and 8 m long.
The pool holds 60 m³ of water.
The pool is a rectangular prism without the top face.
a) What is the depth of the pool?

b) Maria has to decrease the depth of water by 0.5 m for the winter.
How much water does she take out?

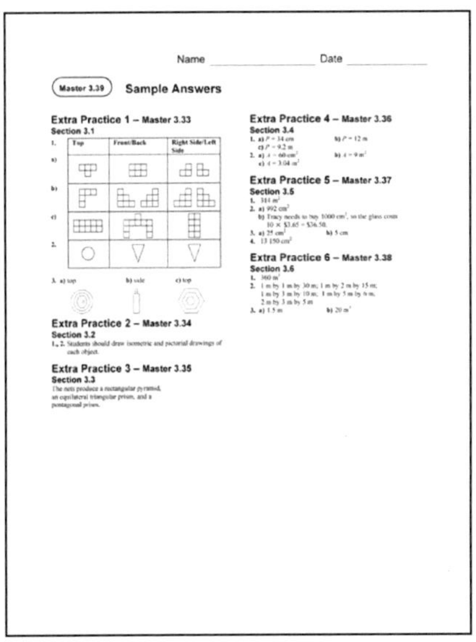

Name ____________ Date ____________

Master 3.39 **Sample Answers**

Extra Practice 1 – Master 3.33
Section 3.1

	Top	Front/Back	Right Side/Left Side
1. a)			
b)			
c)			
2.			

3. a) top b) side c) top

Extra Practice 2 – Master 3.34
Section 3.2
1., 2. Students should draw isometric and pictorial drawings of each object.

Extra Practice 3 – Master 3.35
Section 3.3
The nets produce a rectangular pyramid, an equilateral triangular prism, and a pentagonal prism.

Extra Practice 4 – Master 3.36
Section 3.4
1. a) $P = 34$ cm b) $P = 12$ m
c) $P = 9.2$ m
2. a) $A = 60$ cm² b) $A = 9$ m²
c) $A = 3.04$ m²

Extra Practice 5 – Master 3.37
Section 3.5
1. 314 m²
2. a) 992 cm²
b) Tracy needs to buy 1000 cm², so the glass costs 10 × $3.65 = $36.50.
3. a) 25 cm² b) 5 cm
4. 13 150 cm²

Extra Practice 6 – Master 3.38
Section 3.6
1. 360 m³
2. 1 m by 1 m by 30 m; 1 m by 2 m by 15 m; 1 m by 3 m by 10 m; 1 m by 5 m by 6 m; 2 m by 3 m by 5 m
3. a) 1.5 m b) 20 m³

Addison Wesley
Mathematics
Makes Sense

Program Authors

Jason Johnston
Bryn Keyes
Mary Doucette
Antonietta Lenjosek
Steve Thomas
Margaret Sinclair
Trevor Brown
Cathy Heideman
Don Jones
Michael Davis
Jennifer Paziuk
Ken Harper
Sharon Jeroski
Ray Appel
Laura Weatherhead
Betty Milne
Jim Mennie
Lynn Strangway

Printed and bound in Canada

10 17

PEARSON
Education Canada

ADDISON WESLEY

Ontario

Math Makes Sense 7

Ontario

Teacher Guide

Unit 4: Fractions and Decimals

PEARSON
Addison Wesley

UNIT 4

Fractions and Decimals

"(Students) can use their understanding of what the operations mean to give meaning to fraction computation. However, . . . a firm understanding of fractions is the most critical foundation for fraction computation."

John A. Van de Walle

FOCUS STRAND
Number Sense and Numeration

SUPPORTING STRANDS
Measurement
Patterning and Algebra

TIPS
Adolescent learners benefit from using a variety of manipulatives: area models, fraction strips, fraction circles, e-Tools.

Mathematics Background

What Are the Big Ideas?

- Equivalent fractions name the same number using different denominators.
- Algorithms for adding and subtracting fractions require common denominators.
- Estimation strategies for fractions focus on benchmarks such as one-half and one whole.
- A fraction is an indicated division, and this can be used to find a decimal representation.
- As for repeated addition of a whole number, repeated addition of a fraction can be represented as multiplication of the fraction by a whole number.

How Will the Concepts Develop?

Students use concrete models to develop the concept of equivalent fractions. These models remind students how to rename fractions. Students learn the advantages of expressing fractions using common denominators when comparing, adding, and subtracting.

Students develop an algorithm for adding and subtracting fractions by finding common denominators. They use estimation strategies to ensure the reasonableness of a solution.

In earlier grades, students learned multiplication as repeated addition. They extend this concept to fractions. By understanding that this concept is a shortcut, students will be able to develop an algorithm for multiplying and dividing fractions at a later grade.

Students use concrete materials to build area models that represent the multiplication and division of decimals. They employ different strategies to visualize the problems.

Why Are These Concepts Important?

Work with fractions establishes an understanding essential for subsequent topics related to algebra and proportional reasoning, such as skills related to percents, decimals, ratios, and rates. These skills are fundamental to all strands of mathematics, and to using mathematics in everyday life.

Decimals are encountered frequently in the use of money and the metric system. So, understanding the decimal system and the ability to compute with decimals are vital life skills.

Curriculum Overview

Cluster 1: Adding and Subtracting Fractions

Overall Expectations

- Understand and explain operations with fractions using manipulatives. (7m2)
- Use estimation to justify or assess the reasonableness of calculations. (7m5)
- Solve and explain multi-step problems involving simple fractions, ... (7m6)

Specific Expectations

- Demonstrate an understanding of operations with fractions using manipulatives. (7m17)
- Add and subtract fractions with simple denominators using concrete materials, drawings, and symbols. (7m18)
- Relate the repeated addition of fractions with simple denominators to the multiplication of a fraction by a whole number. (7m19)
- Solve problems involving fractions ... using the appropriate strategies and calculation methods. (7m26)

Launch

Section 4.1: Combining Fractions

Section 4.2: Adding Fractions Using Models

Section 4.3: Adding Fractions

Section 4.4: Subtracting Fractions Using Models

Section 4.5: Subtracting Fractions

Mid-Unit Review

Section 4.6: Exploring Repeated Addition

Cluster 2: Solving Problems

Overall Expectations

- Compare, order, and represent decimals ... (7m1)
- Demonstrate an understanding of the order of operations with brackets. (7m3)
- Use estimation to justify or assess the reasonableness of calculations. (7m5)
- Solve and explain multi-step problems involving simple fractions, decimals, ... (7m6)

Specific Expectations

- Compare and order decimals. (7m9)
- Demonstrate an understanding of the order of operations with brackets and apply the order of operations in evaluating expressions that involve whole numbers and decimals. (7m20)
- ... pose problems involving simple fractions, decimals, ..., and investigate solutions (7m23)
- Solve problems involving fractions and decimals using the appropriate strategies and calculation methods. (7m26)
- Solve problems that involve converting between fractions, decimals, ... (7m27)

Section 4.7: Multiplying Decimals

Section 4.8: Dividing Decimals

Section 4.9: Order of Operations with Decimals

Unit Review
Practice Test

Unit Problem
Publishing a Book

Curriculum across the Grades

Grade 6	Grade 7	Grade 8
Students compare, order, and represent relationships between decimals and ratios using concrete materials, drawings, and symbols. Students compare, order, and represent the relationships between fractions with unlike denominators using concrete materials and drawings. Students perform computations using appropriate techniques to solve problems involving fractions with unlike denominators and decimals. Students use estimation strategies to determine the reasonableness of solutions.	Students compare, order, and represent fractions and decimals. Students add and subtract fractions with simple denominators using concrete materials, drawings, and symbols. Students understand and relate the repeated addition of fractions to the multiplication of a fraction by a whole number. Students understand and apply the order of operations in evaluating expressions involving decimals. Students use estimation strategies to determine the reasonableness of solutions.	Students compare, order, and represent fractions and decimals. Students are proficient in operations with fractions. Students understand and apply the order of operations with expressions that involve fractions. Students solve and explain multi-step problems involving fractions and decimals.

Materials for This Unit

Have students cut out and colour fraction strips (Masters 4.22, 4.23), then laminate them for durability. Cut out and laminate the number lines (Masters 4.24, 4.25). Stick 2 lines together, then laminate to get number lines from 0 to 2. Cut out and laminate the game board and fraction cards (Masters 4.26, 4.27, 4.28) for the game *Shade One*.

Additional Activities

How Close Can You Get?

For Extra Practice (Appropriate for use after Skills You'll Need)
Materials: *How Close Can You Get?* (Master 4.5); a deck of playing cards; 3 counters; calculator (optional)

Playing this game reinforces the skills of comparing decimals; adding and subtracting decimals; and using mental math strategies.

The work students do: Students play in pairs. Four cards are turned face up to establish a target number. Students use four cards from their hand of six cards to make a number as close to the target number as possible. The difference between the target number and their number is their score for the round. The player with the lower score after 3 rounds wins.

Take It Further: Change the target number to include more decimal places. Students need two cards more than the number of digits in the target number.

Social/Kinesthetic/Logical
Partner Activity

Beat the Clock

For Extra Practice (Appropriate for use after Skills You'll Need)
Materials: *Beat the Clock* (Master 4.6); a deck of playing cards; watch or clock with a second hand; calculator (optional)

Playing this game reinforces the skills of estimation and operations with decimals.

The work students do: Students play in pairs. Four cards are arranged into a multiplication problem by one player. The other player has 20 s to estimate the product. The difference between the actual and estimated product is the player's score. Reverse roles. The player with the lower score after 3 rounds wins.

Take It Further: Change the problem to multiply a decimal with hundredths by a 2-digit whole number.

Spatial/Kinesthetic/Logical
Partner Activity

Fill It Up

For Extra Practice (Appropriate for use after Skills You'll Need)
Materials: *Fill It Up* (Master 4.7); isometric grid paper (PM 24); *Fill It Up* game cards (Master 4.18); Pattern Blocks

When students play this game, their spatial reasoning skills are enhanced.

The work students do: Students play in pairs. If a student draws a card with Pattern Blocks, she places those blocks on the game board and her score is the fraction associated with that block. If a student draws a card with a fraction, he places Pattern Blocks on the board that correspond with that fraction. Play continues until no more moves are possible. The player with the greater score wins.

Take It Further: Use the trapezoid or rhombus to represent 1.

Social/Kinesthetic/Logical
Partner Activity

Tic-Tac-Quo-tient

For Extra Practice (Appropriate for use after Skills You'll Need)
Materials: *Tic-Tac-Quo-tient* (Master 4.8); *Tic-Tac-Quo-tient* Game Board (Master 4.19); 36 2-colour counters; 2 coins; calculator (optional)

Playing this game uses the skills of estimation and dividing decimals by whole numbers.

The work students do: Students play in pairs. One student chooses a divisor and a dividend using the numbers at the bottom of the game board. That student covers the square on the board that matches the quotient. The other student then has a turn. Play alternates until one player lines up 3 counters in a row, in any direction.

Take It Further: Play the game so that the player who lines up 4 counters in a row wins.

Social/Kinesthetic/Logical
Partner Activity

Planning for Unit 4

Planning for Instruction

Suggested Unit time: About 4 weeks

Section	Time	Materials	Program Support
Launch, page 2	15–20 min	Magazines, newspapers (optional)	
Skills You'll Need, page 4	65–80 min	Pattern Blocks	PM 25: Pattern Blocks
4.1: Combining Fractions, page 8 Find equivalent fractions and add fractions.	80–100 min	fraction strips 30-cm ruler dot paper 2-cm grid transparency	PM 21: 2-cm Grid Paper PM 22: Square Dot Paper Master 4.20: Map for Section 4.1, *Explore* Masters 4.22, 4.23: Fraction Strips 1, 2 Master 4.20a: Divided Square transparency Master 4.9: Step-by-Step 1 Master 4.32: Extra Practice 1
Game: Join the Dots, page 11		dot paper	PM 22: Square Dot Paper
4.2: Adding Fractions Using Models, page 12 Add fractions using circles or fraction strips.	80–100 min	analog clocks number lines fraction strips	Masters 4.22, 4.23: Fraction Strips 1, 2 Masters 4.24, 4.25: Number Lines 1, 2 Master 4.10: Step-by-Step 2 Master 4.33: Extra Practice 2
4.3: Adding Fractions, page 16 Add fractions using symbols.	80–100 min	0.5-cm grid paper	PM 14: 0.5-cm Grid Paper Master 4.11: Step-by-Step 3 Master 4.34: Extra Practice 3
4.4: Subtracting Fractions Using Models, page 20 Subtract fractions using fraction strips and number lines.	80–100 min	fraction strips number lines	Masters 4.22, 4.23: Fraction Strips 1, 2 Masters 4.24, 4.25: Number Lines 1, 2 Master 4.12: Step-by-Step 4 Master 4.35: Extra Practice 4
4.5: Subtracting Fractions, page 24 Subtract fractions using symbols.	80–100 min	number cards 1 to 6 fraction strips number lines	Masters 4.22, 4.23: Fraction Strips 1, 2 Masters 4.24, 4.25: Number Lines 1, 2 Master 4.13: Step-by-Step 5 Master 4.36: Extra Practice 5
Game: Shade One, page 27		game board coloured markers set of 42 fraction cards	Master 4.26: *Shade One* Game Board Masters 4.24, 4.25: Number Lines 1, 2
Mid-Unit Review, page 28		fraction strips number lines analog clocks or fraction circles	Masters 4.22, 4.23: Fraction Strips 1, 2 Masters 4.24, 4.25: Number Lines 1, 2
4.6: Exploring Repeated Addition, page 29 Multiply a fraction by a whole number.	80–100 min	0.5-cm grid paper fraction strips	PM 14: 0.5-cm Grid Paper Masters 4.22, 4.23: Fraction Strips 1, 2 Master 4.14: Step-by-Step 6 Master 4.37: Extra Practice 6
Technology: Fractions to Decimals, page 32		calculator	Masters 4.29: Fractions to Decimal Table
4.7: Multiplying Decimals, page 33 Multiply decimals with tenths.	80–100 min	Base Ten Blocks 0.5-cm grid paper, ruler	PM 14: 0.5-cm Grid Paper Master 4.15: Step-by-Step 7 Master 4.38: Extra Practice 7
4.8: Dividing Decimals, page 37 Divide decimals with tenths.	80–100 min	Base Ten Blocks 0.5-cm grid paper	Master 4.16: Step-by-Step 8 Master 4.39: Extra Practice 8 PM 14: 0.5-cm Grid Paper
4.9: Order of Operations with Decimals, page 42 Use the order of operations to evaluate expressions.	80–100 min		Master 4.17: Step-by-Step 9 Master 4.40: Extra Practice 9
Reading and Writing in Math: Writing a Math Journal Entry, p. 44			

Section	Time	Materials	Program Support
Unit Review, page 46		number lines fraction strips 0.5-cm grid paper	PM 14: 0.5-cm Grid Paper Masters 4.22, 4.23: Fraction Strips 1, 2 Masters 4.24, 4.25: Number Lines 1, 2 Extra Practice: Student Book page 441
Practice Test, page 49		fraction strips number lines 0.5-cm grid paper	PM 14: 0.5-cm Grid Paper Masters 4.22, 4.23: Fraction Strips 1, 2 Masters 4.24, 4.25: Number Lines 1, 2
Unit Problem: Publishing a Book, page 50	40–50 min	sketch paper	

etext online tutorial

This web-based tutorial uses voice, animation, and an optional quiz to present each core lesson, so that students can review content with a new approach.

Planning for Assessment

Purpose	Tools and Process	Recording and Reporting
Diagnostic	*Unit Launch* Question; conference; scaffold problems throughout the unit	 PM 8: Conference Prompts
Formative	*Explore* – Ongoing Assessment: Observe and Listen	Master 4.2 Ongoing Observations: Fractions and Decimals PM 1: Inquiry Process Check List PM 6: Observation Record 1 PM 7: Observation Record 2 PM 8: Conference Prompts PM 2: Self-Assessment PM 3: Self-Assessment: Problem Solving PM 9: Work Sample Records
Summative	*Unit Review* *Unit Problem* – Performance Assessment Unit Test Review assessment records; add unit results to ongoing records	Master 4.1 Unit Rubric: Fractions and Decimals Master 4.3 Performance Assessment Rubric: Publishing a Book Master 4.4 Unit Summary: Fractions and Decimals PM 10: Summary Class Records: Strands PM 11: Summary Class Records: Achievement Categories PM 12: Summary Record: Individual
Learning Skills/ Mathematical Disposition	Observe and record throughout the unit	PM 4: Learning Skills Check List PM 5: Mathematical Dispositions and Learning Skills

Program Masters (PM) are in the *Grade 7 Planning and Program Masters* module.
Extra Practice Masters are on the CD-ROM and are printed in reduced format on page 89 of this module.

SECTION ORGANIZER

15–20 min

Curriculum Focus: Activate prior learning about comparing and ordering fractions, and operations with decimals.

Teacher Materials

Optional

- magazines or newspapers that have several advertisements on one page
- travel section of newspaper, local newspaper of community events

Vocabulary: like and unlike denominators, tenths, hundredths, thousandths

ASSUMED PRIOR KNOWLEDGE

- ☑ Students can add and subtract fractions with the same or related denominators using manipulatives.
- ☑ Students can multiply whole numbers by 0.1, 0.01, and 0.001.
- ☑ Students can perform operations with decimals.
- ☑ Students can compare and order decimals.

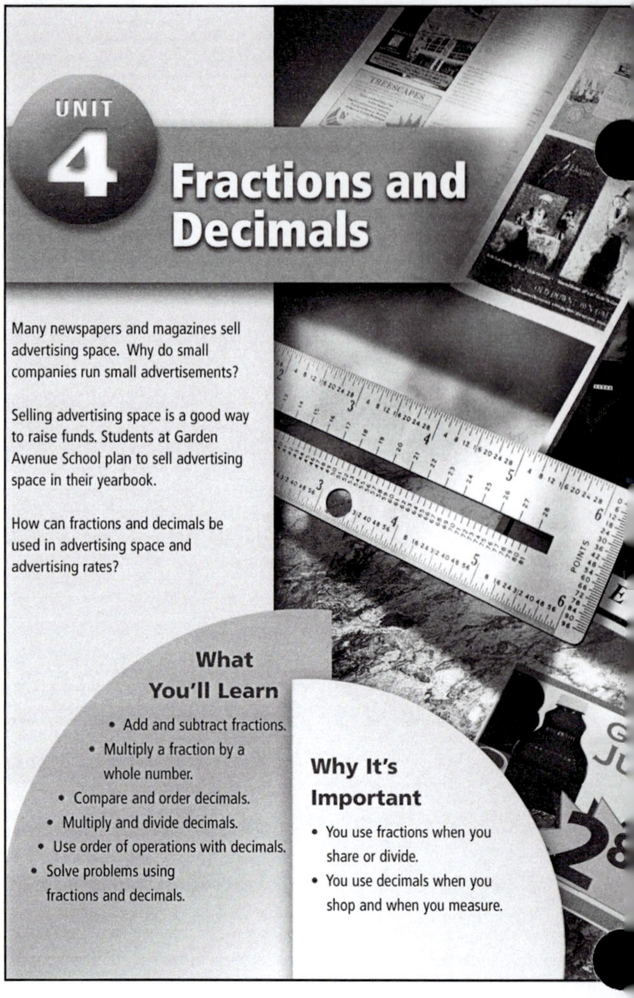

UNIT 4 Fractions and Decimals

Many newspapers and magazines sell advertising space. Why do small companies run small advertisements?

Selling advertising space is a good way to raise funds. Students at Garden Avenue School plan to sell advertising space in their yearbook.

How can fractions and decimals be used in advertising space and advertising rates?

What You'll Learn

- Add and subtract fractions.
- Multiply a fraction by a whole number.
- Compare and order decimals.
- Multiply and divide decimals.
- Use order of operations with decimals.
- Solve problems using fractions and decimals.

Why It's Important

- You use fractions when you share or divide.
- You use decimals when you shop and when you measure.

ACTIVATE PRIOR LEARNING

Engage students in a discussion about advertising.

Ask:

- Why do newspapers and magazines sell advertising space? (*To make money to produce their publication and keep subscription rates to customers lower*)
- Why do businesses and companies advertise? (*To let people know of their products and services*)
- How do publishers decide how much to charge for an advertisement? (*Size of advertisement, place in publication, number of words, amount of colour used*)

As a class, read the text on page 114 of the Student Book.

Show students a newspaper or magazine page with advertisements. Ask:

- About what fraction of this page is covered by this advertisement? (*One-half*)
- What would a smaller fraction be? (*One-quarter, one-eighth*)
- What would the page look like if the advertisement covered one-quarter? One-eighth?

Discuss the question on page 114.

Students may suggest that advertisements are usually $\frac{1}{2}$, $\frac{1}{4}$, $\frac{1}{8}$ of a page. Decimals are used in the cost of an advertisement, in dollars.

Key Words

- fraction strips
- equivalent fractions
- related denominators
- unrelated denominators
- common denominator
- lowest common denominator
- unit fraction
- terminating decimal
- repeating decimal

FROM THE LIBRARY

Math Games for Middle School: Challenges and Skill-Builders for Students at Every Level by Mario Salvadori, Joseph P. Wright. Chicago Review Press, 1998.
ISBN: 1556522886
This book invites youngsters to sharpen their math skills.
The authors discuss different aspects of math, including fractions, and provide detailed explanations and step-by-step examples. Each chapter contains "Math Camps," short exercises designed to reinforce concepts introduced in each section. Comprehensive answers are also included in the back of the book.

Tic-Tac-Toe Math: Grades 5-8 by Dave Clark. Dale Seymour Publications, 1997.
ISBN: 086651547X
These fun, reproducible problems in a tic-tac-toe game format are perfect for warm-ups. The problems cover topics, such as money, fractions, decimals, algebra, and more. Students practice problem-solving techniques such as guess-and-check, look for a pattern, and work backward.

REACHING ALL LEARNERS

Some students will benefit from using the virtual manipulatives on the e-Tools CD-ROM.
The appropriate e-Tools to use for this unit are *Fractions, Place-Value Blocks.*

DIAGNOSTIC ASSESSMENT

What to Look For	What to Do
✔ Students can add and subtract fractions with the same or related denominators using manipulatives. ✔ Students can multiply whole numbers by 0.1, 0.01, and 0.001. ✔ Students can perform operations with decimals. ✔ Students can compare and order decimals.	***Extra Support:*** Students who have difficulty adding and subtracting fractions may need a different type of manipulative to understand the operations. Try Pattern Blocks, Cuisenaire rods, fraction strips, fraction circles, or household items that have several sub-parts like egg cartons, or measuring cups. Students who have difficulty with operations with decimals may benefit from the use of Base Ten Blocks, tenths and hundredths circles, or metre sticks. Estimating first with whole numbers and writing the decimals in a place-value chart for addition and subtraction may also be helpful. Students need to understand the importance of place value for ordering decimals. The use of models should help students visualize how the decimals relate.

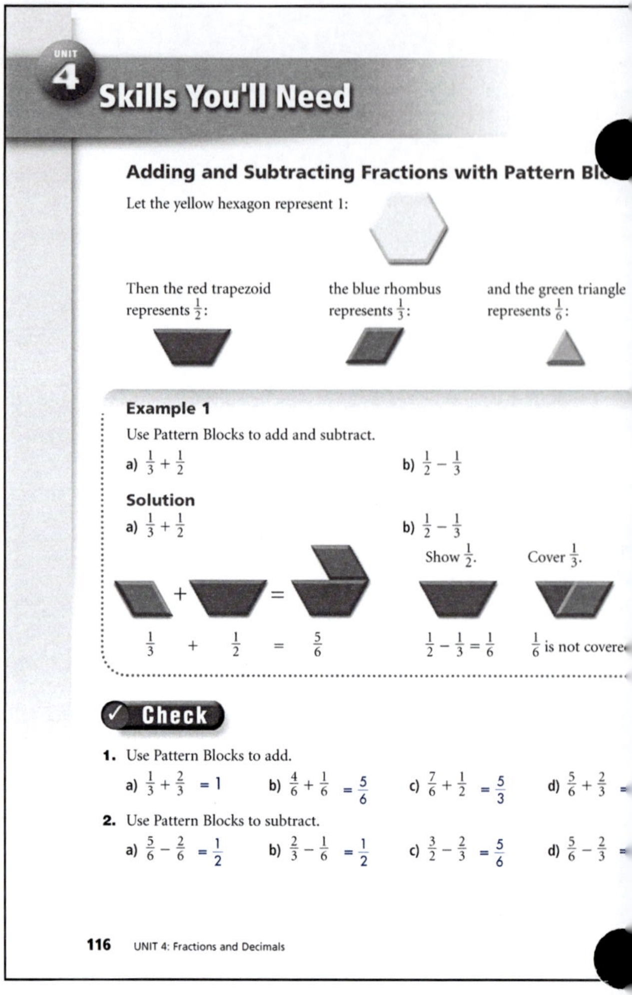

UNIT 4

Skills You'll Need

Adding and Subtracting Fractions with Pattern Bl

Let the yellow hexagon represent 1:

Then the red trapezoid represents $\frac{1}{2}$: the blue rhombus represents $\frac{1}{3}$: and the green triangle represents $\frac{1}{6}$:

Example 1

Use Pattern Blocks to add and subtract.

a) $\frac{1}{3} + \frac{1}{2}$ b) $\frac{1}{2} - \frac{1}{3}$

Solution

a) $\frac{1}{3} + \frac{1}{2}$

$\frac{1}{3} + \frac{1}{2} = \frac{5}{6}$

b) $\frac{1}{2} - \frac{1}{3}$

Show $\frac{1}{2}$. Cover $\frac{1}{3}$.

$\frac{1}{2} - \frac{1}{3} = \frac{1}{6}$ $\frac{1}{6}$ is not covere

✓ Check

1. Use Pattern Blocks to add.

a) $\frac{1}{3} + \frac{2}{3} = 1$ b) $\frac{4}{6} + \frac{1}{6} = \frac{5}{6}$ c) $\frac{7}{6} + \frac{1}{2} = \frac{5}{3}$ d) $\frac{5}{6} + \frac{2}{3} =$

2. Use Pattern Blocks to subtract.

a) $\frac{5}{6} - \frac{2}{6} = \frac{1}{2}$ b) $\frac{2}{3} - \frac{1}{6} = \frac{1}{2}$ c) $\frac{3}{2} - \frac{2}{3} = \frac{5}{6}$ d) $\frac{5}{6} - \frac{2}{3} =$

116 UNIT 4: Fractions and Decimals

SECTION ORGANIZER — 65–80 min

Skills in Review

- Using concrete models to add and subtract fractions
- Multiplying by 0.1, 0.01, and 0.001
- Adding, subtracting, multiplying, and dividing decimals
- Comparing and ordering decimals

Student Materials

- Pattern Blocks (PM 25)

Optional

- Base Ten Blocks
- calculators
- 12 by 12 Multiplication Chart (PM 15)

Alternative Example 1

Add: $\frac{1}{3} + \frac{1}{6}$

Solution

Use Pattern Blocks. Let the yellow hexagon represent 1.

The blue rhombus is $\frac{1}{3}$. The green triangle is $\frac{1}{6}$.

Placed side by side, these blocks cover one red trapezoid, which is $\frac{1}{2}$. So, $\frac{1}{3} + \frac{1}{6} = \frac{1}{2}$.

Adding and Subtracting Fractions with Pattern Blocks

Have students justify the relationships of the hexagon with the trapezoid, rhombus, and triangle.

Ask:

- How would the fractional relationships change if the blue rhombus was 1 whole? *(The hexagon: 3 wholes; the triangle: $\frac{1}{2}$; the trapezoid: $\frac{3}{2}$ or $1\frac{1}{2}$)*

For extra practice, have students play *Fill It Up*.

Common Misconceptions

➤ Students do not understand the meaning of the denominator.

How to Help: Demonstrate that the denominator describes how many equal parts fit into the whole. Use the hexagon as the whole and show how many of other figure covers the whole. The number of figures used to make the whole is the denominator.

➤ Students are unable to use Pattern Blocks to model the subtraction of fractions.

How to Help: Instead of describing subtraction as "covering," talk about "what is missing" or "what is the difference between the two." Model both fractions using Pattern Blocks. Have students use trial and error to find the missing fraction. Show how subtraction can be written as addition: $\frac{1}{2} - \frac{1}{3} = \frac{1}{6}$; or $\frac{1}{2} = \frac{1}{6} + \frac{1}{3}$.

Multiplying by 0.1, 0.01, and 0.001

We can use patterns to multiply by 0.1, 0.01, and 0.001.
We can show products on a place-value chart.

	Thousands	Hundreds	Tens	Ones	Tenths	Hundredths	Thousandths
24 × 100	2	4	0	0			
24 × 10		2	4	0			
24 × 1			2	4			
24 × 0.1				2	4		
24 × 0.01				0	2	4	
24 × 0.001				0	0	2	4

On the chart:
- To multiply by 0.1, move each digit 1 place to the right.
- To multiply by 0.01, move each digit 2 places to the right.
- To multiply by 0.001, move each digit 3 places to the right.

To get the product:
- Move the decimal point 1 place to the left.
- Move the decimal point 2 places to the left.
- Move the decimal point 3 places to the left.

Example 2

Multiply.
a) 372 × 0.1 b) 56 × 0.01 c) 41 × 0.001

Solution

Mark the decimal point in the whole number.
a) 372. × 0.1 = 37.2 The decimal point moves 1 place to the left.
b) 56. × 0.01 = 0.56 The decimal point moves 2 places to the left.
c) 41. × 0.001 = 0.041 Write zeros as placeholders. Then move the decimal point 3 places to the left.

✓ Check

3. Multiply.
a) 5 × 0.1 = 0.5 b) 98 × 0.1 = 9.8 c) 124 × 0.1 = 12.4
d) 326 × 0.01 = 3.26 e) 72 × 0.01 = 0.72 f) 6 × 0.01 = 0.06
g) 56 × 0.001 = 0.056 h) 276 × 0.001 = 0.276 i) 8 × 0.001 = 0.008

Alternative Example 2

Multiply.
a) 78 × 0.1 **b)** 952 × 0.001 **c)** 248 × 0.01

Solution

a) 78 × 0.1
Mark the decimal point in the whole number: 78.
Move the decimal point 1 place to the left: 7.8
78 × 0.1 = 7.8

b) 952 × 0.001
Mark the decimal point in the whole number: 952.
Move the decimal point 3 places to the left: 0.952
952 × 0.001 = 0.952

c) 248 × 0.01
Mark the decimal point in the whole number: 248.
Move the decimal point 2 places to the left: 2.48
248 × 0.01 = 2.48

Multiplying by 0.1, 0.01, and 0.001

Discuss the place value of each digit in 485.203. Emphasize the patterns in value from column to column, going from left to right and right to left.

Encourage students to use Base Ten Blocks to model the questions in *Example 2* and explain why each solution makes sense. Help students see that multiplying by powers of 10 is a skill to master using mental math strategies.

For extra practice, have students play *Fill It Up*.

Common Misconceptions

➤ Students believe that multiplication always produces a product that is greater than either of the numbers that are multiplied.

How to Help: Use Base Ten Blocks. Model 24 × 0.1 using 24 rods. Guide students to see that 10 rods are 1 flat (1 whole), and 20 rods are 2 wholes. The 4 rods left over represent 4 tenths. Write 2 wholes and 4 tenths as 2.4. Compare 2.4 to the original factor of 24. Students may want to model other products for reinforcement.

➤ Students move the decimal point in the wrong direction.

How to Help: Students should use what they know to rediscover the pattern. Think of 5 × 0.1. Have students write the products: 5 × 100 = 500, 5 × 10 = 50, 5 × 1 = 5. Be sure students see the pattern of how the decimal point moves, thus resulting in a lesser product. So, 5 × 0.1 = 0.5

Alternative Example 3

Evaluate.

a) 5.62 ÷ 5 **b)** 46.2 − 19.7 **c)** 16.8 × 7

Solution

a) Divide: 5.62 ÷ 5

Use short division.

$$5\overline{\smash{)}5.6^{1}2^{2}0}$$
$$\quad 1.1\,2\,4$$

b) Subtract: 46.2 − 19.7

To subtract the tenths, trade 1 whole for 10 tenths.

$$\begin{array}{r} \overset{5\,1}{46.2} \\ -\,19.7 \\ \hline .5 \end{array} \qquad \begin{array}{r} \overset{3\,15\,1}{\not{4}\not{6}.2} \\ -\,19.7 \\ \hline 26.5 \end{array}$$

c) Multiply: 16.8 × 7

Multiply without regard to the decimal point.

$$\begin{array}{r} 168 \\ \times\quad 7 \\ \hline 1176 \end{array}$$

The factors have a total of one decimal place; so, the product has one decimal place.

The product is 117.6.

Operations with Decimals

Example 3

Evaluate.

a) 82.34 + 4.7 **b)** 79.1 − 43.8 **c)** 426.31 × 2 **d)** 9.47 ÷ 2

Solution

a) 82.34 + 4.7

Add the hundredths.

Add the tenths: 10 tenths = 1 whole

Add the ones. Add the tens.

Estimate: 80 + 5 = 85

$$\begin{array}{r} \overset{1}{8}2.34 \\ +\;4.7 \\ \hline 87.04 \end{array}$$

b) 79.1 − 43.8

To subtract the tenths, trade 1 whole for 10 tenths.

Subtract the ones. Subtract the tens.

Estimate: 80 − 40 = 40

$$\begin{array}{r} \overset{8\,11}{79.1} \\ -\,43.8 \\ \hline 35.3 \end{array}$$

c) 426.31 × 2

Ignore the decimal point.

Multiply as you would with whole numbers.

Place the decimal point in the answer by estimation:

426.31 × 2 is about 400 × 2 = 800

So, 426.31 × 2 = 852.62

Estimate: 400 × 2 = 800

$$\begin{array}{r} 426.31 \\ \times\quad 2 \\ \hline 852.62 \end{array}$$

d) 9.47 ÷ 2

Use short division.

Divide 9 ones by 2. There is 1 whole left.

Trade 1 whole for 10 tenths.

Divide 14 tenths by 2.

Divide 7 hundredths by 2. There is 1 hundredth left.

Trade 1 hundredth for 10 thousandths. Divide 10 thousandths by 2.

So, 9.47 ÷ 2 = 4.735

Estimate: 10 ÷ 2 = 5

$$2\overline{\smash{)}9.^{1}47^{1}0}$$
$$\quad 4.\,73\,5$$

✓ Check

4. Evaluate.

a) 12.3 + 3.5 = 15.8 **b)** 21.41 − 13.8 = 7.61 **c)** 31.47 × 4 = 125.88 **d)** 7.44 ÷ 2 = 3.72

e) 182.34 × 7 = 1276.38 **f)** 52.103 + 71.81 = 123.913 **g)** 49.35 ÷ 3 = 16.45 **h)** 138.97 × 6 = 833.82

118 UNIT 4: Fractions and Decimals

Operations with Decimals

Have students use models, such as Base Ten Blocks or money, to "act out" the multiplication and division examples. Use repeated addition and subtraction strategies with the models.

For extra practice, have students play *Beat the Clock* or *Tic-Tac-Quo-tient*.

Common Misconceptions

➤ Students do not understand the importance of place-value columns when adding or subtracting, using paper and pencil.

How to Help: Use Base Ten Blocks to show the meaning of each column. Encourage students to write the problem on grid paper. Use the squares to line up the place-value columns. Mark the decimal point on the vertical grid line between the ones and tenths column.

➤ Students do not know multiplication and division facts.

How to Help: Emphasize strategies, not speed. Use arrays to model multiplication facts. Show students how to use facts they know to build facts they do not know. Remind students, for any fact they do not know, to use repeated addition to find the product. Provide students with a 12 by 12 multiplication chart (PM 15).

➤ Students cannot build mental models of the division process.

How to Help: Present the problem in a context to show how division means sharing or creating equal groups. Money is a context students usually understand. Use Base Ten Blocks to model the dividend. Begin from the ones column and show the process using short division.

Comparing and Ordering Decimals

Here are two ways to order these decimals from least to greatest: 1.84, 2.10, 1.80, 1.89

➢ Use a number line.

Mark each decimal on a number line in hundredths from 1.75 to 2.15.
1.84 is between 1.80 and 1.85, but closer to 1.85.
1.89 is between 1.85 and 1.90, but closer to 1.90.

➢ Use place value.

1.84, 2.10, 1.80, 1.89
In the ones place, the least digit is 1.
Three decimals have 1 as a ones digit.
Compare these 3 decimals: 1.84, 1.80, 1.89
In the tenths place, each decimal has the digit 8.
So, look in the hundredths place:
The least hundredths digit is 0; so, 1.80 is the least decimal.
The next hundredths digit is 4; so, 1.84 is the next largest decimal.
The next hundredths digit is 9; so, 1.89 is the next largest decimal.

So, from least to greatest: 1.80, 1.84, 1.89, 2.10

Example 4

Compare each pair of decimals. Place > or < between each pair.

a) 0.5 and 0.08 **b)** 47.305 and 47.5

Solution

a) 0.5 and 0.08
Both decimals have 0 ones.
In the tenths place, 5 > 0
So, 0.5 > 0.08

b) 47.305 and 47.5
Both decimals have 4 tens and 7 ones.
In the tenths place, 3 < 5
So, 47.305 < 47.5

✓ Check

5. Order the numbers in each set from least to greatest.
a) 7.32, 4.116, 3.79, 4.12, 3.1 **b)** 4.4, 0.62, 2.591, 0.65, 4.15
c) 1.25, 3.62, 1.43, 2.81, 2.55 **d)** 3.669, 1.752, 3.68, 2.67, 1.8

a) 3.1, 3.79, 4.116, 4.12, 7.32 b) 0.62, 0.65, 2.591, 4.15, 4.4
c) 1.25, 1.43, 2.55, 2.81, 3.62 d) 1.752, 1.8, 2.67, 3.669, 3.68

Alternative Example 4

Compare each pair of decimals. Place > or < between each pair.

a) 0.1 and 0.07 **b)** 165.43 and 165.9

Solution

a) 0.1 and 0.07
Both decimals have 0 ones.
In the tenths place, 1 > 0
So, 0.1 > 0.07

b) 165.43 and 165.9
Both decimals have 1 hundred.
Both decimals have 6 tens.
Both decimals have 5 ones.
In the tenths place, 4 < 9
So, 165.43 < 165.9

Comparing and Ordering Decimals

Discuss with students the meaning of each column to the right of the decimal point (tenths, hundredths, thousandths). Illustrate a number line divided into tenths and hundredths. Demonstrate how Base Ten Blocks can be used to show tenths, hundredths, and thousandths. Encourage students to use grid paper where they can align the numbers in each place-value column for ease of comparison. Invite students to use any or all of these strategies when following the examples and completing *Practice* questions.

For extra practice, have students play *How Close Can You Get?*

Common Misconceptions

➤ Students do not understand the decimal symbol.

How to Help: Connect decimal notation to fraction terminology by using fraction names, such as 0.01 is one-hundredth, 0.1 is one-tenth.

➤ Students do not understand the relative sizes of the decimal columns.

How to Help: Refer to a place-value chart. Use a calculator to ensure students see that, as they move from left to right, the value of the column becomes ten times smaller, or one-tenth the size. This strategy employs the skills reviewed in *Multiplying by 0.1, 0.01, and 0.001.*

➤ Students assume a number with more digits is a larger number.

How to Help: A visual model helps students understand the decimal system. Use Base Ten Blocks or money to model decimals.

Combining Fractions

SECTION ORGANIZER (80–100 min)

Curriculum Focus: Find equivalent fractions and add fractions. (7m17, 7m18)

Teacher Materials
- Divided Square transparency (Master 4.20a)
- Map for Section 4.1, *Explore* transparency (Master 4.20)
- overhead projector markers
- 2-cm grid transparency (PM 21)

Student Materials
- Map for Section 4.1 (Master 4.20)
- 30-cm ruler
- fraction strips (Masters 4.22 and 4.23)
- dot paper (PM 22)

Optional
- 2-cm grid transparency
- coloured tiles or paper squares (64 squares, 8 colours)
- Step-by-Step 1 (Master 4.9)
- Extra Practice 1 (Master 4.32)

Vocabulary: fraction strips, equivalent fractions

Assessment: Master 4.2 Ongoing Observations: Fractions and Decimals

Key Math Learnings
1. Equivalent fractions describe the same amount relative to the whole, but use different denominators.
2. Equivalent fractions are helpful when comparing, describing, and manipulating fractions.
3. Concrete models can be used to represent the addition and subtraction of fractions.

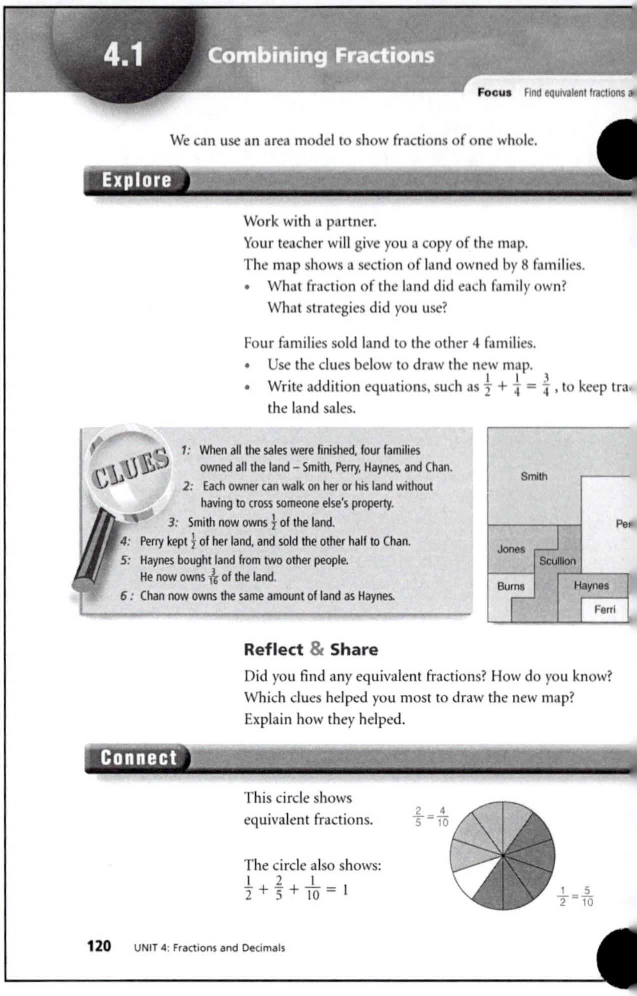
4.1 Combining Fractions

Focus Find equivalent fractions a

We can use an area model to show fractions of one whole.

Explore

Work with a partner.
Your teacher will give you a copy of the map.
The map shows a section of land owned by 8 families.
- What fraction of the land did each family own? What strategies did you use?

Four families sold land to the other 4 families.
- Use the clues below to draw the new map.
- Write addition equations, such as $\frac{1}{2} + \frac{1}{4} = \frac{3}{4}$, to keep tra the land sales.

CLUES
1: When all the sales were finished, four families owned all the land – Smith, Perry, Haynes, and Chan.
2: Each owner can walk on her or his land without having to cross someone else's property.
3: Smith now owns $\frac{1}{2}$ of the land.
4: Perry kept $\frac{1}{2}$ of her land, and sold the other half to Chan.
5: Haynes bought land from two other people. He now owns $\frac{3}{16}$ of the land.
6: Chan now owns the same amount of land as Haynes.

Reflect & Share

Did you find any equivalent fractions? How do you know?
Which clues helped you most to draw the new map?
Explain how they helped.

Connect

This circle shows equivalent fractions.

The circle also shows:
$\frac{1}{2} + \frac{2}{5} + \frac{1}{10} = 1$

120 UNIT 4: Fractions and Decimals

BEFORE — Get Started

Display the transparency of the Divided Square (Master 4.20a).

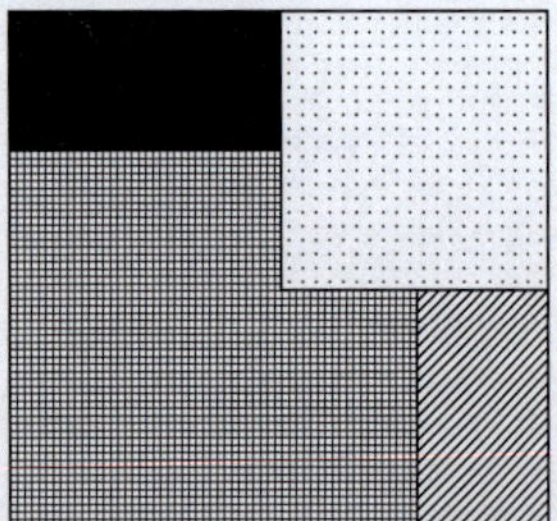

Ask:
- Which fractional part can you identify immediately? (*The dotted figure, which is a square, is* $\frac{1}{4}$ *of the whole square.*)
- How can you visually rearrange the grid-square figure to more easily name its fractional part? (*Imagine dividing the square in half. The section of the grid-square figure that extends to the right of the halfway line can be repositioned along the top of the grid-square figure. This grid-square figure is* $\frac{1}{2}$ *of the square.*)
- What fractional part of the square is each other figure? Explain. ($\frac{1}{8}$, $\frac{1}{8}$; *each is* $\frac{1}{2}$ *the size of the dotted figure.* $\frac{1}{2}$ *of* $\frac{1}{4}$ *is* $\frac{1}{8}$.)
- Why do you not automatically recognize these fractions in this square? (*The half doesn't look like one-half. There's not a grid dividing the square into smaller pieces.*)

Distribute copies of Master 4.20. Read the *Explore* together. Have students work in pairs to find a solution that satisfies all the clues.

DURING — Explore

Ongoing Assessment: Observe and Listen

As students work on the map, ask:
- Which section of the map is easiest to describe as a fraction? (*Perry's is* $\frac{1}{4}$.) Which is next easiest? (*Chan's is* $\frac{1}{16}$.)

This strip represents 1 whole.

You can model fractions with strips of paper called **fraction strips**.

Here are more fraction strips and some equivalent fractions they show.

$\frac{1}{4} = \frac{2}{8}$

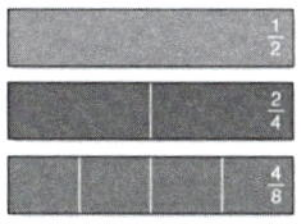

$\frac{1}{2} = \frac{2}{4} = \frac{4}{8}$

To add $\frac{1}{4} + \frac{1}{2}$, estimate first.
You know that $\frac{1}{2} + \frac{1}{2} = 1$. Since $\frac{1}{4} < \frac{1}{2}$, then $\frac{1}{4} + \frac{1}{2} < 1$
Use fraction strips to add. Align the strips for $\frac{1}{4}$ and $\frac{1}{2}$.
Find a single strip that has the same length as the two strips.
There are 2 single strips: $\frac{6}{8}$ and $\frac{3}{4}$.
So, $\frac{1}{4} + \frac{1}{2} = \frac{6}{8}$
And, $\frac{1}{4} + \frac{1}{2} = \frac{3}{4}$
$\frac{3}{4}$ and $\frac{6}{8}$ are **equivalent fractions**.
They represent the same amount.

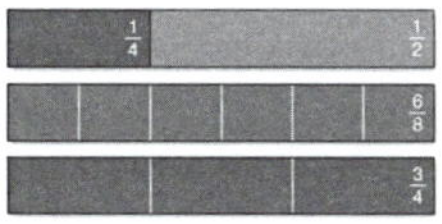

Example

Use fraction strips to add.
$\frac{1}{3} + \frac{2}{4}$

Estimate: $\frac{1}{3} < \frac{1}{2}$; $\frac{2}{4} = \frac{1}{2}$
So, $\frac{1}{3} + \frac{2}{4} < 1$

Solution

$\frac{1}{3} + \frac{2}{4}$

Use the $\frac{1}{3}$- and $\frac{2}{4}$-fraction strips.
These strips align with the $\frac{5}{6}$-strip.
$\frac{1}{3} + \frac{2}{4} = \frac{5}{6}$

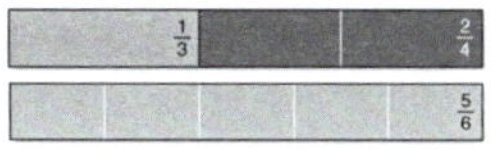

4.1 Combining Fractions **121**

REACHING ALL LEARNERS

Alternative Explore

Materials: fraction strips or fraction circles
Students use fraction strips or fraction circles to discover all the ways they can make $\frac{3}{4}$. They record all possible combinations, using addition and equations.

Early Finishers

Have students extend the *Explore* to the following situation. After all the sales, Smith still wants more land. She buys: $\frac{1}{2}$ of Parry's land; $\frac{1}{2}$ of Haynes' land; and $\frac{1}{2}$ of Chan's land. What fraction does each landowner have now? (*Smith has $\frac{3}{4}$; Haynes has $\frac{3}{32}$; Perry has $\frac{1}{16}$; Chan has $\frac{3}{32}$.*)

Common Misconceptions

➤ Students confuse equivalence with congruence.
How to Help: Guide students to understand that congruence is related to shape and size, and equivalence is related to value. Have students re-create the map using coloured tiles or squares of paper. Students count how many squares they need in total (*64*) and how many are needed for each piece of land. They move the tiles around to show that the quantities are equivalent even though the shapes are different.

ESL Strategies

ESL students benefit from having pictures associated with key words. Provide ESL students with a photocopy of the lesson for them to add drawings to link key words to a visual cue.

- How can you use what you know to find out what you don't know? (*Divide the map into 64 equal squares, then see if I can recognize any fractional parts.*)
- How can a ruler help? (*I measure to be sure the grid sections are equal.*)
- What equivalent fractions do you see? ($\frac{1}{2} = \frac{2}{4} = \frac{4}{8} = \frac{8}{16} = \frac{16}{32}$)

Provide students who are having difficulty with a 2-cm grid transparency or square tiles.

As students use clues to draw the new map, ask:

- How are you keeping track of your work? (*I use different colours. I use equations.*)

If necessary, discuss possible solutions for Clue 3. (*Smith could buy one-half from Perry.*) Seek explanations why each is possible. Encourage students to look at other clues to eliminate possibilities.

AFTER — Connect

What you might see:

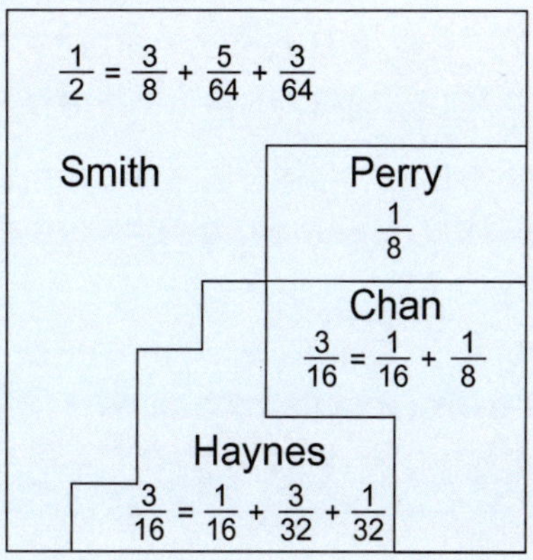

Invite students to share their solutions and strategies.

Ask:

- Does the strategy used by this group seem reasonable?
- Does anyone have a different strategy or solution?

Number Strategies

1 km = 1000 m
1 m = 1000 mm
So, 1 km = 1000 × 1000 mm
= 1 000 000 mm
Divide.
1 000 000 ÷ 25 = 40 000

Assignment Guidelines

If your students do not have time to complete all the *Practice* questions on page 122, these questions provide minimum curriculum coverage: 1, 2, 4, 6, 7, 8, *Reflect*
To assess the 4 Achievement Chart categories listed in the curriculum document, have students complete these *Practice* questions:
Communication: 2
Understanding concepts: 4
Application: 6
Problem Solving: 8

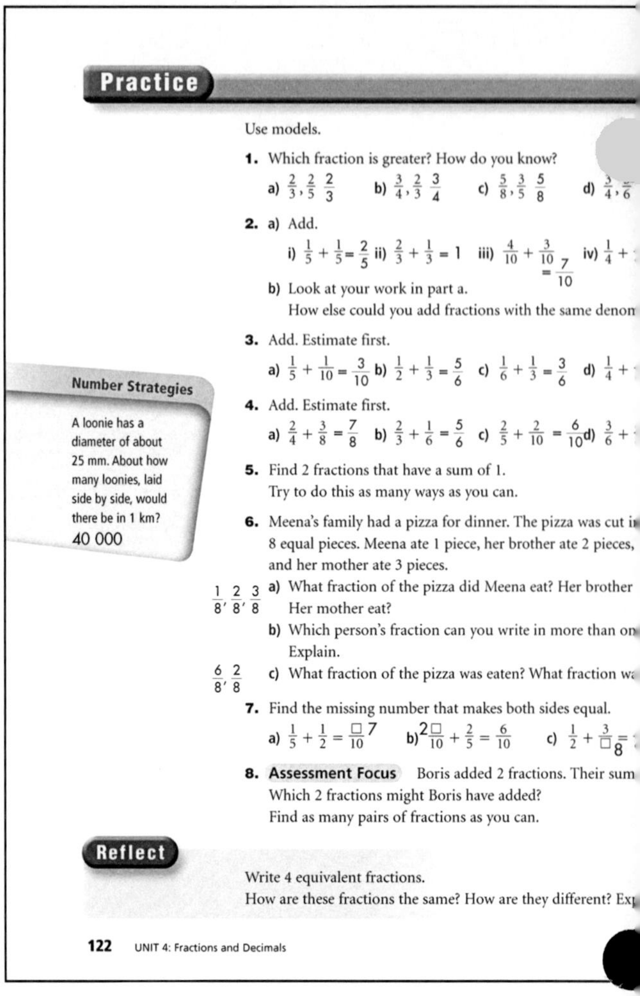
Practice

Use models.

1. Which fraction is greater? How do you know?
a) $\frac{2}{3}, \frac{2}{5}$ $\frac{2}{3}$ b) $\frac{3}{4}, \frac{2}{3}$ $\frac{3}{4}$ c) $\frac{5}{8}, \frac{3}{5}$ $\frac{5}{8}$ d) $\frac{3}{4}, \frac{}{6}$

2. a) Add.
i) $\frac{1}{5} + \frac{1}{5} = \frac{2}{5}$ ii) $\frac{2}{3} + \frac{1}{3} = 1$ iii) $\frac{4}{10} + \frac{3}{10} = \frac{7}{10}$ iv) $\frac{1}{4} +$
b) Look at your work in part a.
How else could you add fractions with the same denom

3. Add. Estimate first.
a) $\frac{1}{5} + \frac{1}{10} = \frac{3}{10}$ b) $\frac{1}{2} + \frac{1}{3} = \frac{5}{6}$ c) $\frac{1}{6} + \frac{1}{3} = \frac{3}{6}$ d) $\frac{1}{4} +$

4. Add. Estimate first.
a) $\frac{2}{4} + \frac{3}{8} = \frac{7}{8}$ b) $\frac{2}{3} + \frac{1}{6} = \frac{5}{6}$ c) $\frac{2}{5} + \frac{2}{10} = \frac{6}{10}$ d) $\frac{3}{6} +$

Number Strategies

A loonie has a diameter of about 25 mm. About how many loonies, laid side by side, would there be in 1 km?
40 000

5. Find 2 fractions that have a sum of 1.
Try to do this as many ways as you can.

6. Meena's family had a pizza for dinner. The pizza was cut in 8 equal pieces. Meena ate 1 piece, her brother ate 2 pieces, and her mother ate 3 pieces.
$\frac{1}{8}, \frac{2}{8}, \frac{3}{8}$ a) What fraction of the pizza did Meena eat? Her brother Her mother eat?
b) Which person's fraction can you write in more than on Explain.
$\frac{6}{8}, \frac{2}{8}$ c) What fraction of the pizza was eaten? What fraction wa

7. Find the missing number that makes both sides equal.
a) $\frac{1}{5} + \frac{1}{2} = \frac{\square 7}{10}$ b) $\frac{\square 2}{10} + \frac{2}{5} = \frac{6}{10}$ c) $\frac{1}{2} + \frac{3}{\square 8} =$

8. Assessment Focus Boris added 2 fractions. Their sum
Which 2 fractions might Boris have added?
Find as many pairs of fractions as you can.

Reflect

Write 4 equivalent fractions.
How are these fractions the same? How are they different? Ex

122 UNIT 4: Fractions and Decimals

Ensure students with different solutions or strategies share them with the class.

Record the equivalent fractions students find. Record the addition equations. Discuss strategies for finding equivalent fractions.

(Someone might suggest finding common denominators. This skill is developed formally in Section 4.3.)

Use the examples in *Connect* to demonstrate how fraction strips model: equivalent fractions; combining fractions; and adding fractions.

Distribute fraction strips (Masters 4.22, 4.23) to students, and have them model the examples in the Student Book.

Practice

Encourage students to use fraction strips.

Assessment Focus, Question 8

Students show the addition equations for $\frac{5}{6}$ when the fractions that are added have denominator 6. Students can then rename any fraction as an equivalent fraction.

There is an infinite number of pairs of fractions that Boris could have added.

Students will commonly name fractions with denominators 6, 3, and 2.

Students who need extra support to complete the Assessment Focus question may benefit from Step-by-Step 1 (Master 4.9).

Join the Dots

YOU WILL NEED

Square dot paper

NUMBER OF PLAYERS

2 or more

GOAL OF THE GAME

To write the greatest number of equivalent fractions

HOW TO PLAY THE GAME:

1. Use dot paper. Mark an array of 49 dots.

2. Take turns to join 2 dots.
3. The player who completes a square claims that square by writing her initials in it.
4. Continue playing until all squares are claimed.
5. Each player writes the squares he has as a fraction of the whole.
6. The winner is the player who can write the greatest number of equivalent fractions for her share.

What if you used a square array of 81 dots. How would this affect the game?

Game: Join the Dots 123

Sample Answers

1. In each pair, the greater fraction has the longer fraction strip.

2. b) Add the numerators. Keep the same denominator.

5. There is no limit to the number of pairs of fractions with a sum of 1. For example, $\frac{3}{10} + \frac{7}{10} = 1$; $\frac{5}{10} + \frac{1}{2} = 1$; $\frac{1}{3} + \frac{2}{3} = 1$

6. b) Meena's brother's fraction is $\frac{2}{8}$. It can be written as $\frac{1}{4}$.

8. There are many pairs of fractions that Boris could have added. For example, $\frac{1}{6} + \frac{4}{6}$; $\frac{1}{2} + \frac{1}{3}$

REFLECT: $\frac{1}{2}, \frac{2}{4}, \frac{5}{10}, \frac{6}{12}$

These fractions are the same because they represent the same number. These fractions are different because they show their value using different numbers in the numerators and denominators.

ASSESSMENT FOR LEARNING

What to Look For	What to Do
Understanding concepts ✔ Students understand how to compare fractions and write equivalent fractions. ***Applying procedures*** ✔ Students can use concrete models to compare fractions and to add fractions with simple denominators. ***Communicating*** ✔ Students can explain why fractions are equivalent.	***Extra Support:*** Students who have difficulty finding equivalent fractions may benefit from working with Cuisenaire rods (see the notes on page 14). Students can use Step-by-Step 1 (Master 4.9) to complete question 8. ***Extra Practice:*** Students can play the *Join the Dots* game in the Student Book to practise writing equivalent fractions. Students can complete Extra Practice 1 (Master 4.32). ***Extension:*** Students can modify the additional activities *Tic-Tac-Quo-tient* or *Beat the Clock* to add fractions with simple denominators.

Recording and Reporting

Master 4.2 Ongoing Observations: Fractions and Decimals

SECTION 4.2

Adding Fractions Using Models

SECTION ORGANIZER (80–100 min)

Curriculum Focus: Add fractions using circles or fraction strips. (7m2, 7m17, 7m18)

Teacher Materials
- analog clock

Optional
- analog clock on overhead transparency
- transparency fraction strips and number lines

Student Materials
- fraction strips (Masters 4.22, 4.23)
- number lines (Masters 4.24, 4.25)

Optional
- fraction circles (Master 4.21)
- 10 by 10 multiplication chart (PM 15)
- Step-by-Step 2 (Master 4.10)
- Extra Practice 2 (Master 4.33)

Vocabulary: related denominators, unrelated denominators

Assessment: Master 4.2 Ongoing Observations: Fractions and Decimals

Key Math Learning

Models, such as fractions strips, number lines, and clocks can be used to add fractions.

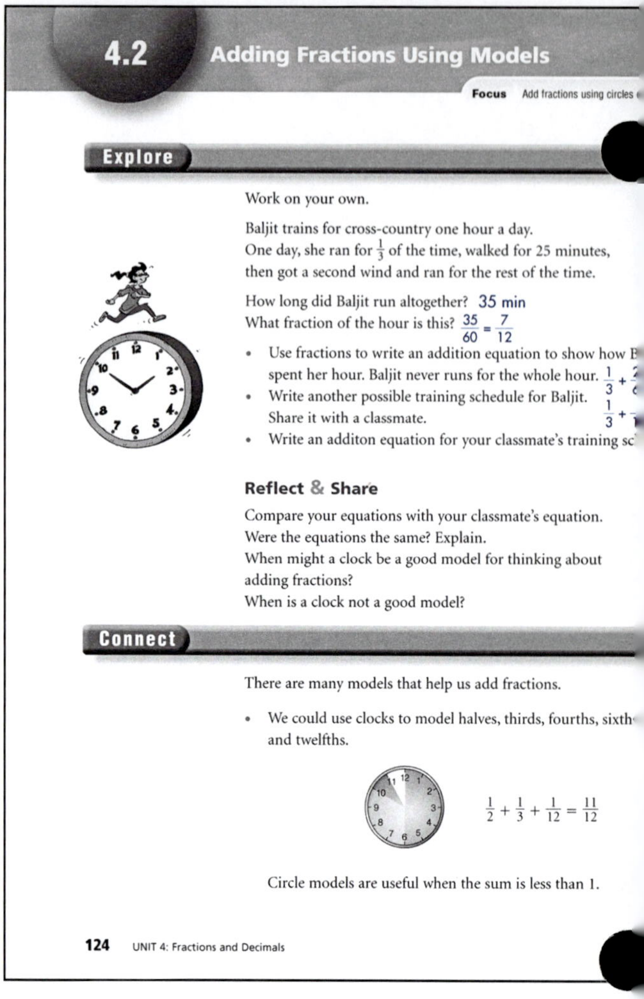

4.2 Adding Fractions Using Models

Focus Add fractions using circles

Explore

Work on your own.

Baljit trains for cross-country one hour a day.
One day, she ran for $\frac{1}{3}$ of the time, walked for 25 minutes, then got a second wind and ran for the rest of the time.

How long did Baljit run altogether? 35 min
What fraction of the hour is this? $\frac{35}{60} = \frac{7}{12}$

- Use fractions to write an addition equation to show how B spent her hour. Baljit never runs for the whole hour.
- Write another possible training schedule for Baljit. Share it with a classmate.
- Write an additon equation for your classmate's training sc

Reflect & Share

Compare your equations with your classmate's equation.
Were the equations the same? Explain.
When might a clock be a good model for thinking about adding fractions?
When is a clock not a good model?

Connect

There are many models that help us add fractions.

- We could use clocks to model halves, thirds, fourths, sixth and twelfths.

$\frac{1}{2} + \frac{1}{3} + \frac{1}{12} = \frac{11}{12}$

Circle models are useful when the sum is less than 1.

124 UNIT 4: Fractions and Decimals

BEFORE Get Started

Use an analog clock or an overhead transparency of one. Review how the minute and hour markings represent $\frac{1}{60}$ and $\frac{1}{12}$ of an hour, respectively. Ask:

- How many minutes is $\frac{3}{4}$ of an hour? (*45 min*)
- How can we write 45 min as a different fraction of 1 hour? ($\frac{45}{60}$)
- What fraction of an hour is 20 min? ($\frac{20}{60} = \frac{1}{3}$)

Leave the clock on display for students to refer to during *Explore.*

Ensure students understand the problem in *Explore.*

DURING Explore

Ongoing Assessment: Observe and Listen

As students work individually on the *Explore,* ask:

- How can the schedule be written entirely in minutes? (*20 min, 25 min, 15 min*)
- How can each time in minutes be written as a fraction of one hour? (*Express the time in minutes as a fraction with denominator 60.*)
- How can the clock model be used to write equivalent fractions for these fractions? (*Multiples of 5 minutes can be written as equivalent fractions with denominators 12, 6, 4, 3, or 2:* $\frac{20}{60} = \frac{4}{12} = \frac{2}{6} = \frac{1}{3}$; $\frac{25}{60} = \frac{5}{12}$; $\frac{15}{60} = \frac{3}{12} = \frac{1}{4}$)

Have students check that their equations account for the full hour. Provide students who have difficulty with fractions of an hour a fraction circle for twelfths (Master 4.21).

As students compare equations written for their classmate's training schedule, ask:

- When the sum is greater than 1, we could use fraction strips and a number line.

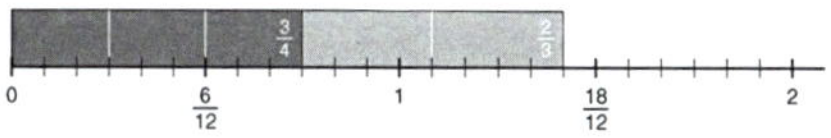

$\frac{3}{4} + \frac{2}{3} = \frac{17}{12}$

Example

Add. $\frac{1}{2} + \frac{4}{5}$

Estimate:
$\frac{4}{5}$ is close to 1; so, $\frac{1}{2} + \frac{4}{5} > 1$

Solution

$\frac{1}{2} + \frac{4}{5}$

Place both strips end-to-end on the halves line.

The right end of the $\frac{4}{5}$-strip does not line up with a fraction on the halves line.

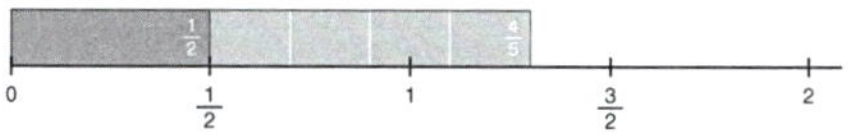

Place both strips on the fifths line.

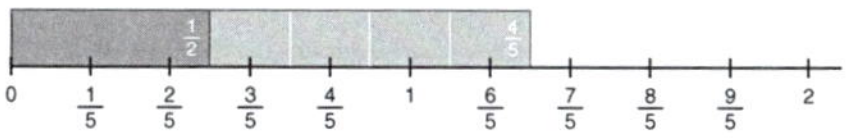

The right end of the $\frac{4}{5}$-strip does not line up with a fraction on the fifths line.

Find a line on which to place both strips so the end of the $\frac{4}{5}$-strip lines up with a fraction.

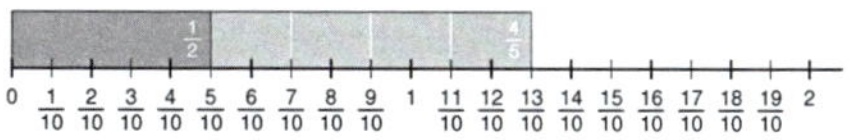

The end of the $\frac{4}{5}$-strip lines up with a fraction on the tenths line.

The strips end at $\frac{13}{10}$.

So, $\frac{1}{2} + \frac{4}{5} = \frac{13}{10}$

4.2 Adding Fractions Using Models **125**

REACHING ALL LEARNERS

Alternative Explore

Materials: fraction strips or fraction circles

Students use fraction strips or fraction circles to find 3 fractions that have a sum of 1. They record all possible sums.

Early Finishers

Have students create a training schedule for $1\frac{1}{4}$ h.

Common Misconceptions

➤ Students have difficulty writing time in minutes as a fraction of one hour, and vice versa.

How to Help: Have students colour a fraction circle for each time and matching fraction. Suggest students create a chart of minutes and fractions of an hour. They use as many equivalent fractions as possible, each time. The times in the minute column could increase by increments of 5 min.

ESL Strategies

On a photocopy of the lesson, have an ESL student highlight words he does not understand. During the *Explore*, this student could work with a partner to help him understand these words. For example, if training for cross-country is not understood, the partner could explain about practising for a sport and what "second wind" means.

- What do you notice about the equations when you compare them? (*The fractions are different but equivalent. The order the fractions are added is different.*)
- Does the order of the fractions matter for addition? (*No,* $\frac{1}{3} + \frac{5}{12} + \frac{1}{4} = \frac{5}{12} + \frac{1}{3} + \frac{1}{4} = \frac{1}{4} + \frac{1}{3} + \frac{5}{12}$*, and so on*)

AFTER — Connect

Have a volunteer write an addition equation for another training schedule on the board. Have another student write the same equation that uses equivalent fractions;
for example, $\frac{1}{2} + \frac{1}{6} + \frac{1}{3} = 1$; $\frac{6}{12} + \frac{2}{12} + \frac{4}{12} = 1$

Have students explain how the equations are the same.

A clock is a good model when the fractions that are added have denominators 2, 3, 4, 5, 6, 12, or 60 (that is, factors of 60).

A clock is not a good model when the fractions that are added have denominators that are not factors of 60 (for example, denominator 8).

Use *Connect* to ensure students understand what to do when the fractions have a sum greater than 1. Rewrite the addition equations using equivalent fractions related to the models:
$\frac{1}{2} + \frac{1}{3} + \frac{1}{12} = \frac{6}{12} + \frac{4}{12} + \frac{1}{12} = \frac{11}{12}$ and
$\frac{3}{4} + \frac{2}{3} = \frac{9}{12} + \frac{8}{12} = \frac{17}{12}$

Students may observe the relationship between the answer and the sum of the numerators of the equivalent fractions.

Model the *Example* so students understand how to choose the correct fraction strip.

Distribute copies of number lines (Masters 4.24, 4.25) so students can model the *Example* as you review it.

Sample Answers

6. a) The greater denominator is a multiple of the lesser denominator. The greater denominator tells the number line used to get the answer. The fraction with the lesser denominator has an equivalent fraction that uses the greater denominator. The numerator of the answer is the sum of the numerators when the fractions have the same denominator.
   b) The greater denominator is a multiple of the lesser denominator. The lesser denominator is a factor of the greater denominator.
8. a) The product of the two denominators tells the number line to use. Each fraction in the question has an equivalent fraction with the same denominator as the answer. The answer is the sum of the numerators of the equivalent fractions.
   b) Each denominator is not a multiple or a factor of the other.
   c) Use a number line that is labelled with the product of the unrelated denominators.
10. Since the total amount of liquid is $\frac{14}{8}$ cups, which is less than 2 cups, the jug will hold the punch.
13. Student can use a model to represent a pitcher that is $\frac{1}{2}$ full and a pitcher that is $\frac{3}{4}$ full. The extra $\frac{1}{4}$ is the added $\frac{1}{2}$ cup. So four $\frac{1}{4}$s or four $\frac{1}{2}$ cups make a full pitcher, which is 2 cups.

Calculator Skills

Remind students of the relationships for seconds, minutes, hours, and days. This is a calculator exercise so students should not round until the end. The order of operations is division from left to right: 1 000 000 ÷ 60 ÷ 60 ÷ 24 = 11.6.

Practice

Use models.

1. Write 2 equivalent fractions for each fraction shown.

a)  $\frac{3}{4}, \frac{9}{12}$

b)  $\frac{1}{3}, \frac{4}{12}$

2. Add.
   a) $\frac{2}{4}+\frac{3}{4}=\frac{5}{4}$ b) $\frac{8}{10}+\frac{9}{10}=\frac{17}{10}$ c) $\frac{3}{5}+\frac{4}{5}=\frac{7}{5}$ d) $\frac{7}{8}+\frac{7}{8}=\frac{14}{8}$
3. Find 2 fractions with a sum of $\frac{3}{2}$. For example: $\frac{1}{2}+\frac{2}{2}$; $\frac{1}{6}+\frac{4}{3}$; $\frac{1}{4}+\frac{5}{4}$
   Try to do this as many ways as you can.
   Record each way you find.
4. Add. Estimate first.
   a) $\frac{7}{8}+\frac{1}{2}=\frac{11}{8}$ b) $\frac{7}{10}+\frac{3}{5}=\frac{13}{10}$ c) $\frac{1}{2}+\frac{3}{4}=\frac{5}{4}$ d) $\frac{5}{6}+\frac{2}{3}=\frac{9}{6}$
5. Add. Estimate first.
   a) $\frac{3}{8}+\frac{3}{4}=\frac{9}{8}$ b) $\frac{4}{4}+\frac{1}{2}=\frac{6}{4}$ or $\frac{3}{2}$ c) $\frac{2}{2}+\frac{4}{6}=\frac{10}{6}$ or $\frac{5}{3}$ d) $\frac{1}{2}+\frac{9}{10}=$
6. Use your answers to questions 4 and 5.
   a) Look at the denominators in each part, and the number line you used to get the answer. What patterns do you see?
   b) The denominators in each part of questions 4 and 5 are **related denominators**.
   Why do you think they have this name?
7. Add.
   a) $\frac{1}{2}+\frac{2}{3}=\frac{7}{6}$ b) $\frac{1}{2}+\frac{2}{5}=\frac{9}{10}$ c) $\frac{1}{3}+\frac{3}{4}=\frac{13}{12}$ d) $\frac{2}{2}+\frac{3}{5}=$ or $\frac{8}{5}$
8. Look at your answers to question 7.
   a) Look at the denominators in each part, and the number line you used to get the answer. What patterns do you see?
   b) The denominators in each part of question 7 are called **unrelated denominators**.
   Why do you think they have this name?
   c) When you add 2 fractions with unrelated denominators, how do you decide which number line to use?

Calculator Skills

How many days are there in one million seconds?
About 12 days

126 UNIT 4: Fractions and Decimals

If you have Cuisenaire rods, they can be used instead of fraction strips to add fractions. There are 10 Cuisenaire rods. The following table shows each colour of rod and its length.

Colour	Length
Orange	10 cm
Blue	9 cm
Brown	8 cm
Black	7 cm
Dark Green	6 cm
Yellow	5 cm
Purple	4 cm
Light Green	3 cm
Red	2 cm
White	1 cm

When the orange rod represents 1, then the blue rod is $\frac{9}{10}$, the brown rod is $\frac{8}{10}$, and so on, to the white rod is $\frac{1}{10}$.

When the blue rod represents 1, then the dark green rod is $\frac{2}{3}$, the light green rod is $\frac{1}{3}$, and the white rod is $\frac{1}{9}$.

When the dark green rod represents 1, then the yellow rod is $\frac{5}{6}$, the purple rod is $\frac{4}{6}$, and so on, to the white rod is $\frac{1}{6}$.

Practice

Encourage students to use fraction strips, number lines, or fraction circles. Some students may need a 10 by 10 Multiplication Chart (PM 15) to help find equivalent fractions and identify related denominators.

Assessment Focus: Question 11

Students may use guess and check. If they use only number lines and fraction strips, the least sum greater than 1 is $\frac{13}{12}$. For a level 4 response, students may use equivalent fractions and get a sum such as $\frac{16}{15}$.

Students who need extra support to complete the Assessment Focus question may benefit from Step-by-Step 2 (Master 4.10).

9. One day Ryan ran for 30 min, rested for 20 min, and then ran for another 45 min. Use fractions of one hour. Write an addition equation that represents his training session. $\frac{1}{2} + \frac{1}{3} + \frac{3}{4} = \frac{19}{12}$

10. A jug holds 2 cups of liquid. A recipe for punch is $\frac{1}{2}$ cup of orange juice, $\frac{1}{4}$ cup of raspberry juice, $\frac{3}{8}$ cup of grapefruit juice, and $\frac{5}{8}$ cup of lemonade. Is the jug big enough for the punch? Explain.

11. **Assessment Focus** Use any of the digits 1, 2, 3, 4, 5, 6 only once. Copy and complete. Replace each □ with a number.

$\frac{□}{□} + \frac{□}{□}$ $\frac{3}{4} + \frac{5}{6} = \frac{19}{12}$; $\frac{3}{5} + \frac{2}{4} = \frac{11}{10}$; $\frac{3}{6} + \frac{5}{4} = \frac{7}{4}$

a) Find as many sums as you can that are between 1 and 2.

b) Find the least sum that is greater than 1.

Show your work. $\frac{5}{6} + \frac{1}{4} = \frac{13}{12}$ or $1\frac{1}{12}$

12. Abey and Anoki are eating chocolate bars. The bars are the same size. Abey has $\frac{3}{4}$ left. Anoki has $\frac{7}{8}$ left. How much chocolate is left altogether? $\frac{13}{8}$

Take It Further

13. A pitcher of juice is half empty. After $\frac{1}{2}$ cup of juice is added, the pitcher is $\frac{3}{4}$ full. How much juice does the pitcher hold when it is full? Show your thinking. 2 cups

14. Which number line would you need to add each pair of fractions? Explain.

a) $\frac{1}{3} + \frac{1}{8}$ b) $\frac{1}{3} + \frac{1}{5}$ c) $\frac{1}{4} + \frac{1}{5}$ d) $\frac{1}{4} + \frac{1}{6}$

Reflect

Which strategies do you use to add 2 fractions? Include 3 different examples in your answer.

4.2 Adding Fractions Using Models **127**

14. a) Thirds and eighths are unrelated. So, their equivalent fractions have denominator $3 \times 8 = 24$.

b) Thirds and fifths are unrelated. So, their equivalent fractions have denominator $3 \times 5 = 15$.

c) Fourths and fifths are unrelated. So, their equivalent fractions have denominator $4 \times 5 = 20$.

d) Fourths and sixths have a common denominator 12. So, their equivalent fractions have denominator 12.

REFLECT: When the denominators are the same, I use fraction strips and a number line with the same denominator; for example, $\frac{4}{5} + \frac{3}{5} = \frac{7}{5}$.
When the denominators are related, I use fraction strips on a number line that matches the greater denominator; for example, $\frac{7}{8} + \frac{1}{4} = \frac{9}{8}$.
When the denominators are not related, I multiply the denominators, and use a fraction strip labelled for the product; for example, $\frac{3}{4} + \frac{2}{3} = \frac{17}{12}$.

Assignment Guidelines

If your students do not have time to complete all the *Practice* questions on pages 126, 127, these questions provide minimum curriculum coverage: 4, 6, 7, 8, 10, 11, *Reflect*

To assess the 4 Achievement Chart categories listed in the curriculum document, have students complete these *Practice* questions:

Understanding concepts: 4, 7
Communication: 8
Application: 10
Problem Solving: 11

ASSESSMENT FOR LEARNING

What to Look For

Understanding concepts

✔ Students understand how to use models to show the addition of fractions.

Applying procedures

✔ Students can choose the correct number line for adding fractions with different denominators.

Problem solving

✔ Students choose appropriate strategies to solve a problem.

Communicating

✔ Students can explain why their answer is appropriate.

What to Do

Extra Support: Pair a student who has difficulty choosing the correct number line with a capable student.
Students can use Step-by-Step 2 (Master 4.10) to complete question 11.

Extra Practice: Have students check their answers by using a different model to calculate each sum.
Students can complete Extra Practice 2 (Master 4.33).

Extension: Students can find the greatest sum less than 1 in question 11.

Recording and Reporting

Master 4.2 Ongoing Observations: Fractions and Decimals

Adding Fractions

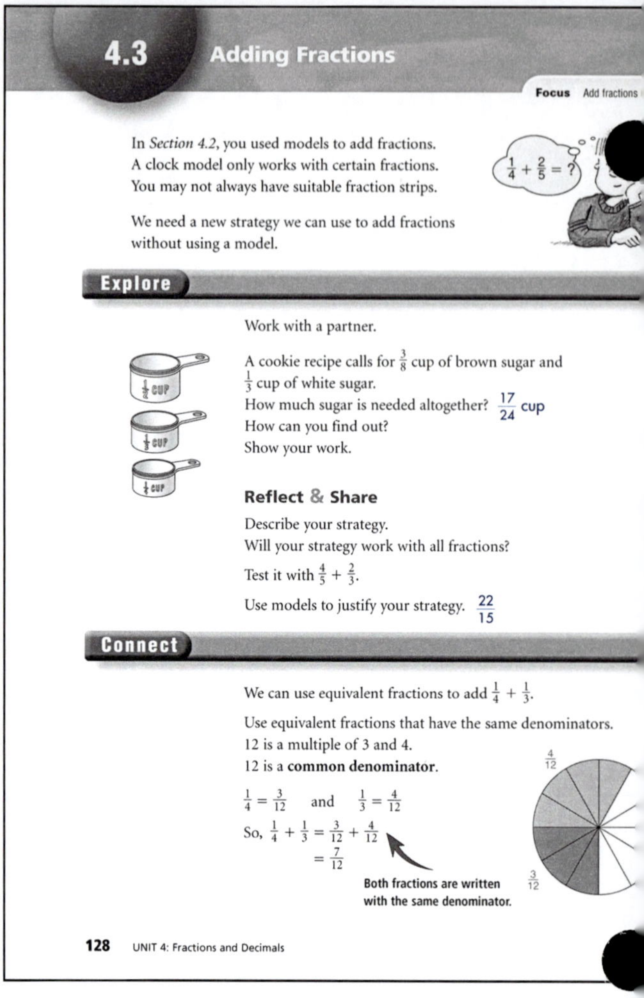

4.3 Adding Fractions

Focus Add fractions

In *Section 4.2*, you used models to add fractions.
A clock model only works with certain fractions.
You may not always have suitable fraction strips.

We need a new strategy we can use to add fractions without using a model.

Explore

Work with a partner.

A cookie recipe calls for $\frac{3}{8}$ cup of brown sugar and $\frac{1}{3}$ cup of white sugar.
How much sugar is needed altogether? $\frac{17}{24}$ cup
How can you find out?
Show your work.

Reflect & Share

Describe your strategy.
Will your strategy work with all fractions?
Test it with $\frac{4}{5}+\frac{2}{3}$.
Use models to justify your strategy. $\frac{22}{15}$

Connect

We can use equivalent fractions to add $\frac{1}{4}+\frac{1}{3}$.

Use equivalent fractions that have the same denominators.
12 is a multiple of 3 and 4.
12 is a **common denominator**.

$\frac{1}{4}=\frac{3}{12}$ and $\frac{1}{3}=\frac{4}{12}$

So, $\frac{1}{4}+\frac{1}{3}=\frac{3}{12}+\frac{4}{12}$
$=\frac{7}{12}$

Both fractions are written with the same denominator.

128 UNIT 4: Fractions and Decimals

SECTION ORGANIZER	80–100 min

Curriculum Focus: Add fractions using symbols. (7m18)
Teacher Materials
- fraction strips (Masters 4.22, 4.23)

Student Materials
- 0.5-cm grid paper (PM 14)

Optional
- fraction strips (Masters 4.22, 4.23)
- number lines (Masters 4.24, 4.25)
- fraction circles (Master 4.21)
- 12 by 12 multiplication chart (PM 15)
- Step-by-Step 3 (Master 4.11)
- Extra Practice 3 (Master 4.34)

Vocabulary: common denominator, lowest common denominator, unit fraction
Assessment: Master 4.2 Ongoing Observations: Fractions and Decimals

Key Math Learning

Fractions can be added using equivalent fractions with common denominators.

BEFORE Get Started

Have a volunteer review how to add fractions using fraction strips and number lines. Tell students that they will now try to add fractions without these models.

Ensure students understand the problem in the *Explore* is to find a strategy that does not require any models.

Encourage students to estimate the sum before they calculate.

DURING Explore

Ongoing Assessment: Observe and Listen

As students work in pairs, ask:

- What is an estimate of the sum: $\frac{3}{8}+\frac{1}{3}$?
  (*I estimate the sum is between $\frac{1}{2}$ and 1.*)
  How did you get that estimate?
  (*$\frac{3}{8}$ is less than $\frac{1}{2}$. $\frac{1}{3}$ is less than $\frac{1}{2}$. So, when I add two numbers that are less than $\frac{1}{2}$, I get a sum less than 1. Also, $\frac{3}{8}$ is greater than $\frac{1}{4}$, and $\frac{1}{3}$ is greater than $\frac{1}{4}$, so when I add two numbers that are greater than $\frac{1}{4}$, I get a sum that is greater than $\frac{1}{2}$.*)
- What would you need to add $\frac{3}{8}$ and $\frac{1}{3}$ with models? (*I'd need a number line for 24ths.*)
- Since you don't have that number line, what can you do instead? (*I can write equivalent fractions with the same denominator.*)
- How can the sum be written as an addition equation?
  (*$\frac{3}{8}=\frac{9}{24}$; $\frac{1}{3}=\frac{3}{24}$; so, $\frac{3}{8}+\frac{1}{3}=\frac{9}{24}+\frac{8}{24}=\frac{17}{24}$*)
- How is the denominator of the sum related to the denominator of the fractions you added? (*The denominator of the sum is the number I get when I multiply the denominators of the fractions I add.*)
- When the denominators are the same, how can you add the fractions?
  (*I add the numerators, 9 twenty-fourths plus 8 twenty-fourths is 17 twenty-fourths.*)

A fraction is in simplest form when the numerator and [d]enominator have no [co]mmon factors.

Look at the pattern in the equivalent fractions below.

$\frac{1}{4} \xrightarrow{\times 3} = \frac{3}{12}$ (numerator ×3, denominator ×3) $\frac{1}{3} = \frac{4}{12}$ (numerator ×4, denominator ×4)

So, to get an equivalent fraction, multiply numerator and denominator by the same number.

We may also get equivalent fractions by dividing.
For example, $\frac{8}{10}$ can be written $\frac{8 \div 2}{10 \div 2} = \frac{4}{5}$ This fraction is in simplest form.

Example 1

Add. $\frac{5}{6} + \frac{2}{9}$

Solution

$\frac{5}{6} + \frac{2}{9}$
The common denominator is a multiple of 6 and 9.
List the multiples of 6: 6, 12, **18**, 24, …
List the multiples of 9: 9, **18**, 27, 36, …
18 is the lowest common multiple of 6 and 9.
So, choose 18 as the common denominator.

Estimate:
$\frac{5}{6}$ is close to 1; $\frac{2}{9} < \frac{1}{2}$
So, $\frac{5}{6} + \frac{2}{9}$ is less than $1\frac{1}{2}$.

$\frac{5}{6} = \frac{15}{18}$ (×3, ×3) $\frac{2}{9} = \frac{4}{18}$ (×2, ×2) We say that 18 is the lowest common denominator.

$\frac{5}{6} + \frac{2}{9} = \frac{15}{18} + \frac{4}{18}$
$= \frac{19}{18}$ We can write $\frac{19}{18}$ as a mixed number: $1\frac{1}{18}$

Example 2

Add. $\frac{1}{2} + \frac{2}{3} + \frac{3}{4}$

Solution

$\frac{1}{2} + \frac{2}{3} + \frac{3}{4}$
2 is a multiple of 4.
So, the common denominator is a multiple of 3 and 4.
List the multiples of 3: 3, 6, 9, **12**, 15, 18, …
List the multiples of 4: 4, 8, **12**, 16, 20, 24, …
12 is the lowest common multiple of 3 and 4.

Estimate:
$\frac{2}{3} > \frac{1}{2}$ and $\frac{3}{4} > \frac{1}{2}$
So, $\frac{1}{2} + \frac{2}{3} + \frac{3}{4}$ is greater than $1\frac{1}{2}$.

4.3 Adding Fractions 129

REACHING ALL LEARNERS

Early Finishers

Have students work in pairs. They make up questions like those in *Practice* question 2, then trade with a partner to complete each other's sentence.

Common Misconceptions

➤ Students add the denominators as well as the numerators.
How to Help: Students should use models to reinforce the concept of adding fractions. Also, have them read the sum aloud; for example, nine-twelfths plus four-twelfths is thirteen-twelfths, and relate this to 9 + 4 = 13.

➤ Students always multiply the two denominators to find a common denominator, rather than finding the lowest common denominator.
How to Help: Review students' work with the lowest common multiple. Help students see that although they can add with any common denominator, using the lowest common denominator may avoid having to write the sum in lowest terms.

- How could you test that strategy with the sum: $\frac{4}{5} + \frac{2}{3}$? (*I write each fraction with a denominator 15, because 5 × 3 = 15. $\frac{4}{5} = \frac{12}{15}$; $\frac{2}{3} = \frac{10}{15}$; so, $\frac{4}{5} + \frac{2}{3} = \frac{12}{15} + \frac{10}{15} = \frac{22}{15}$*)
- How can you use a model to show this sum? (*I use a rectangle. I draw a 3 by 5 rectangle on grid paper. It has 15 squares, so each square is $\frac{1}{15}$. Four-fifths is 12 squares, so I shade in 12 squares. I draw another 3 by 5 rectangle. Two-thirds is 10 squares, so I shade in 10 squares. Altogether, I have shaded 10 + 12 = 22 squares, so the sum is $\frac{22}{15}$.*)

Have students with clear strategies for the *Explore* model these for the class.

AFTER Connect

Review the use of equivalent fractions to add, and the two methods to find equivalent fractions.

Ask students for another model that could illustrate $\frac{1}{3} = \frac{4}{12}$ and $\frac{1}{4} = \frac{3}{12}$. Students may suggest a rectangle drawn on grid paper with an area of 12 square units.

When you review multiplying numerator and denominator to get equivalent fractions, ask:

- What other numbers could we multiply by to get equivalent fractions?
  (*We could multiply the top and bottom of $\frac{1}{4}$ by 6 to get $\frac{6}{24}$; and the top and bottom of $\frac{1}{3}$ by 8 to get $\frac{8}{24}$.*)
- Why did we not do this?
  (*We always choose numbers that give the lowest common multiple; 24 is a greater common multiple than 12.*)

Review the *Examples* in *Connect*. Ensure students understand how estimating before calculating can indicate whether the calculated sum is "in the ball park." Point out the sums that are written as mixed numbers. It is *not* appropriate

Sample Answers

7. $\frac{3}{4} + \frac{4}{5}$ is greater. I used common denominators to find each sum: $\frac{3}{2}$ and $\frac{31}{20}$. Then I had to write these fractions with a common denominator of 20: $\frac{30}{20}$ and $\frac{31}{20}$.

11. Statement b is true because the fractions have a sum of 1. Statement a is false because the fractions have a sum greater than 1.

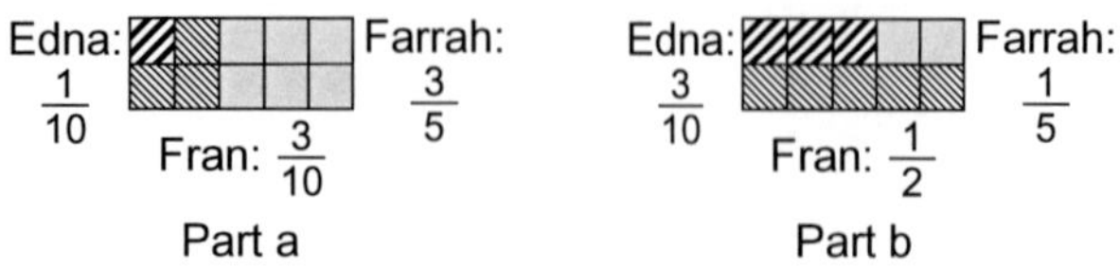

In part a, if Edna ate $\frac{1}{10}$, and Farrah ate $\frac{3}{5}$, then only $\frac{3}{10}$ remain for Fran.

12. I started with a sum of 3 fractions with the same denominator. I chose numerators so I could write equivalent fractions for 2 of the fractions: for example, $\frac{5}{10} + \frac{2}{10} + \frac{3}{10} = \frac{1}{2} + \frac{1}{5} + \frac{3}{10}$; $\frac{1}{4} + \frac{1}{3} + \frac{5}{12}$; $\frac{1}{5} + \frac{1}{3} + \frac{7}{15}$, and so on.

13. Add the whole numbers: 2 + 1 = 3. Write the fractions with a common denominator of 12: $\frac{1}{4} + \frac{\square}{3} = \frac{3}{12} + \frac{\square}{12} = \frac{7}{12}$. Then, 3 plus "what" equals 7? The answer is 4: $\frac{4}{12} = \frac{1}{3}$; so, $\square$ = 1.

Mental Math

Students should look for factors that have a product of 10 (2 × 5), or 100 (4 × 25), or multiples of 10 (6 × 5 = 30).

For example, 5 × 27 × 2 = 5 × 2 × 27 = 10 × 27 = 270

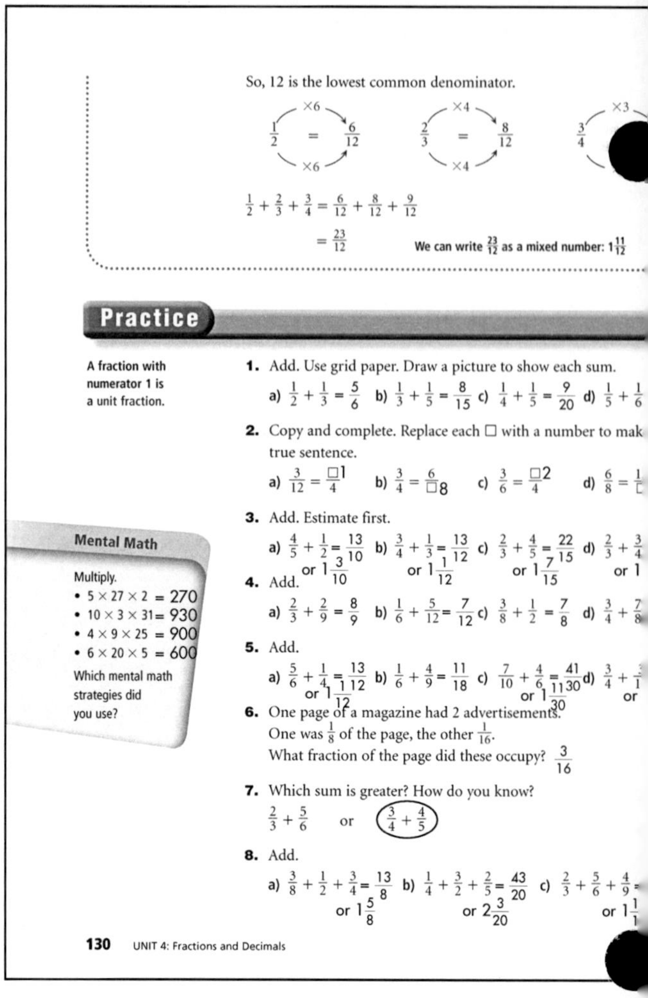

So, 12 is the lowest common denominator.

$\frac{1}{2} = \frac{6}{12}$ (×6) $\frac{2}{3} = \frac{8}{12}$ (×4) $\frac{3}{4}$ (×3)

$\frac{1}{2} + \frac{2}{3} + \frac{3}{4} = \frac{6}{12} + \frac{8}{12} + \frac{9}{12}$

$= \frac{23}{12}$ We can write $\frac{23}{12}$ as a mixed number: $1\frac{11}{12}$

Practice

A fraction with numerator 1 is a unit fraction.

1. Add. Use grid paper. Draw a picture to show each sum.
   a) $\frac{1}{2} + \frac{1}{3} = \frac{5}{6}$ b) $\frac{1}{3} + \frac{1}{5} = \frac{8}{15}$ c) $\frac{1}{4} + \frac{1}{5} = \frac{9}{20}$ d) $\frac{1}{5} + \frac{1}{6}$
2. Copy and complete. Replace each □ with a number to mak[e a] true sentence.
   a) $\frac{3}{12} = \frac{\square}{4}$ 1 b) $\frac{3}{4} = \frac{6}{\square}$ 8 c) $\frac{3}{6} = \frac{\square}{4}$ 2 d) $\frac{6}{8} = \frac{1}{\square}$
3. Add. Estimate first.
   a) $\frac{4}{5} + \frac{1}{2} = \frac{13}{10}$ or $1\frac{3}{10}$ b) $\frac{3}{4} + \frac{1}{3} = \frac{13}{12}$ or $1\frac{1}{12}$ c) $\frac{2}{3} + \frac{4}{5} = \frac{22}{15}$ or $1\frac{7}{15}$ d) $\frac{2}{3} + \frac{3}{4}$ or 1
4. Add.
   a) $\frac{2}{3} + \frac{2}{9} = \frac{8}{9}$ b) $\frac{1}{6} + \frac{5}{12} = \frac{7}{12}$ c) $\frac{3}{8} + \frac{1}{2} = \frac{7}{8}$ d) $\frac{3}{4} + \frac{7}{8}$
5. Add.
   a) $\frac{5}{6} + \frac{1}{4} = \frac{13}{12}$ or $1\frac{1}{12}$ b) $\frac{1}{6} + \frac{4}{9} = \frac{11}{18}$ c) $\frac{7}{10} + \frac{4}{6} = \frac{41}{30}$ or $1\frac{11}{30}$ d) $\frac{3}{4} + \frac{}{1}$ or
6. One page of a magazine had 2 advertisements. One was $\frac{1}{8}$ of the page, the other $\frac{1}{16}$. What fraction of the page did these occupy? $\frac{3}{16}$
7. Which sum is greater? How do you know?
   $\frac{2}{3} + \frac{5}{6}$ or $\frac{3}{4} + \frac{4}{5}$ (circled)
8. Add.
   a) $\frac{3}{8} + \frac{1}{2} + \frac{3}{4} = \frac{13}{8}$ or $1\frac{5}{8}$ b) $\frac{1}{4} + \frac{3}{2} + \frac{2}{5} = \frac{43}{20}$ or $2\frac{3}{20}$ c) $\frac{2}{3} + \frac{5}{6} + \frac{4}{9} =$ or $1\frac{1}{1}$

Mental Math

Multiply.
- 5 × 27 × 2 = 270
- 10 × 3 × 31 = 930
- 4 × 9 × 25 = 900
- 6 × 20 × 5 = 600

Which mental math strategies did you use?

130 UNIT 4: Fractions and Decimals

at this time to teach an algorithm for writing an improper fraction as a mixed number. For example, for $\frac{19}{18}$, students should think, "$\frac{18}{18}$ is 1 whole, so $\frac{19}{18}$ is 1 whole and one-eighteenth: $1\frac{1}{18}$."

Practice

Students who have difficulty adding fractions may still need to use fraction strips or another model. Encourage students to write the sums in simplest form.

Question 9 involves adding mixed numbers. There is no guided example to illustrate this. If you think your students may need an example, adapt a question in *Practice*, or make up a sum of mixed numbers, and review the method on the board.

For question 6, students could use a rectangle with area 16 square units, drawn on 1-cm grid paper, to illustrate the answer.

Assessment Focus: Question 11

Students show that the sum of fractions in part a is greater than 1. This sum can be modelled with 2 fraction circles. Students could colour fraction circles or draw rectangles on grid paper.

To add 2 mixed numbers:
Add the whole numbers.
Add the fractions.
Write the sum as a mixed number.

9. Add.

a) $1\frac{1}{6} + 2\frac{1}{2} = 3\frac{4}{6}$ or $3\frac{2}{3}$ b) $3\frac{1}{3} + 1\frac{1}{2} = 4\frac{5}{6}$ c) $4\frac{1}{6} + 2\frac{3}{8} = 6\frac{13}{24}$

10. A recipe for punch calls for $2\frac{2}{3}$ cups of fruit concentrate and $6\frac{3}{4}$ cups of water. $2\frac{2}{3} + 6\frac{3}{4} = 9\frac{5}{12}$
How many cups of punch will the recipe make?

11. Assessment Focus Three people shared a pie.
Which statement is true? Can both statements be true?
Use diagrams to show your thinking.

a) Edna ate $\frac{1}{10}$, Farrah ate $\frac{3}{5}$, and Fran ate $\frac{1}{2}$. False

b) Edna ate $\frac{3}{10}$, Farrah ate $\frac{1}{5}$, and Fran ate $\frac{1}{2}$. True

Take It Further

12. $\frac{1}{2} + \frac{1}{3} + \frac{1}{6} = 1$

Find 3 other fractions with different denominators that add to 1.
Explain your strategy. $\frac{1}{2} + \frac{1}{5} + \frac{3}{10}$; $\frac{1}{4} + \frac{1}{3} + \frac{5}{12}$; $\frac{1}{5} + \frac{1}{3} + \frac{7}{15}$

13. Copy this sum. Replace □ with the correct digit.

$2\frac{1}{4} + 1\frac{\square 1}{3} = 3\frac{7}{12}$

Explain your strategy.

Reflect

When you add fractions, and the denominators are different, how do you add?
Give 2 different examples. Use pictures to show your thinking.

4.3 Adding Fractions 131

REFLECT: I added $\frac{2}{3} + \frac{3}{4}$.
I used a common denominator of 12, because $3 \times 4 = 12$.
$\frac{2}{3} + \frac{3}{4} = \frac{8}{12} + \frac{9}{12} = \frac{17}{12}$

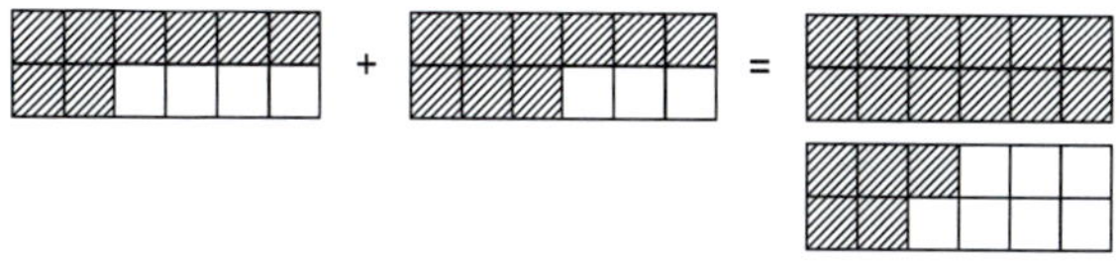

I added $\frac{4}{5} + \frac{7}{8}$.
I used a common denominator of 40, because $5 \times 8 = 40$.
The picture is similar to that above, with each rectangle divided in 40 equal parts.

Assignment Guidelines

If your students do not have time to complete all the *Practice* questions on pages 130, 131, these questions provide minimum curriculum coverage: 3, 5, 7, 9, 11, 12, *Reflect*
To assess the 4 Achievement Chart categories listed in the curriculum document, have students complete these *Practice* questions:
Understanding Concepts: 3, 5, 9
Communication: 7
Application: 11
Problem Solving: 12

ASSESSMENT FOR LEARNING

What to Look For

Understanding concepts
✔ Students understand how to add fractions with symbols.

Applying procedures
✔ Students can find a common denominator.

Communicating
✔ Students can explain the solutions using diagrams.

What to Do

Extra Support: Students who have difficulty may continue to use models. Use Step-by-Step 3 (Master 4.11) for question 11.
Extra Practice: Students could play a game to practise finding a common denominator. They need a deck of number cards, comprising 4 each of the numbers; 2, 3, 4, 5, 6, 8, 10, 12. Students play in pairs. One student deals all the cards. Each student turns over a card. The first person to correctly state the lowest common multiple of the numbers on the cards wins those cards. The game ends when one person has all the cards.
Students can complete Extra Practice 3 (Master 4.34).

Extension: Students could create and answer other addition questions that use denominators that are not based on fraction strips or clocks; for example, include denominators 7, 9, and 11.

Recording and Reporting
Master 4.2 Ongoing Observations: Fractions and Decimals

Subtracting Fractions Using Models

SECTION ORGANIZER (80–100 min)

Curriculum Focus: Subtract fractions using fraction strips and number lines. (7m17, 7m18)

Teacher Materials
- fraction strips and number lines (Masters 4.22, 4.23, 4.24, 4.25)

Optional
- overhead transparencies of fraction strips

Student Materials
- fraction strips (Masters 4.22, 4.23)
- number lines (Masters 4.24, 4.25)

Optional
- Step-by-Step 4 (Master 4.12)
- Extra Practice 4 (Master 4.35)

Assessment: Master 4.2 Ongoing Observations: Fractions and Decimals

Key Math Learning

Models such as fraction strips, number lines, and fraction circles can be used to subtract fractions.

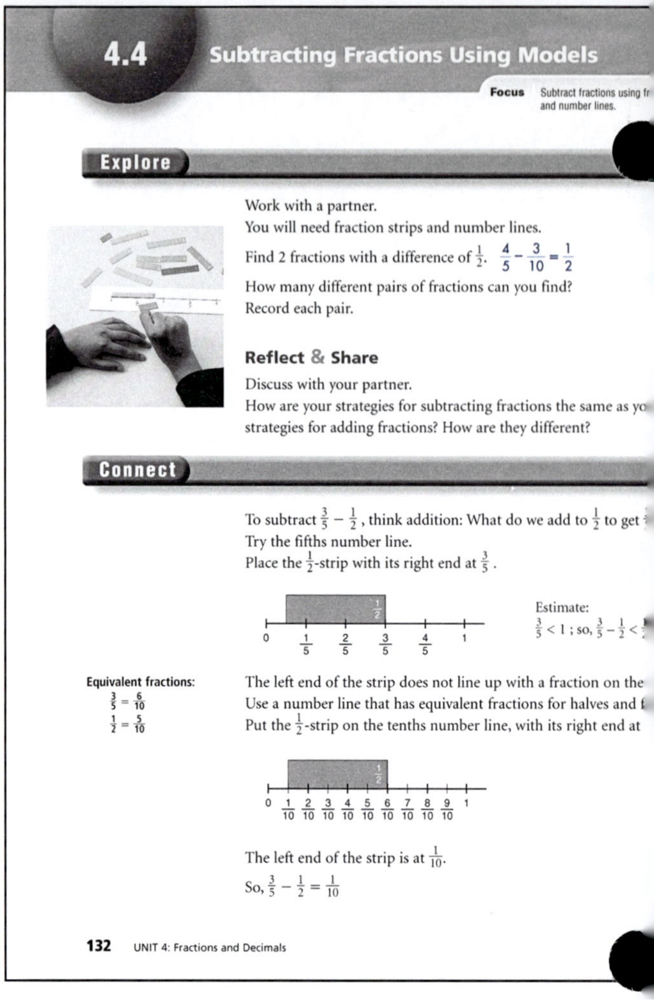

4.4 Subtracting Fractions Using Models

Focus Subtract fractions using fr
and number lines.

Explore

Work with a partner.
You will need fraction strips and number lines.
Find 2 fractions with a difference of $\frac{1}{2}$. $\frac{4}{5} - \frac{3}{10} = \frac{1}{2}$
How many different pairs of fractions can you find?
Record each pair.

Reflect & Share

Discuss with your partner.
How are your strategies for subtracting fractions the same as yo
strategies for adding fractions? How are they different?

Connect

To subtract $\frac{3}{5} - \frac{1}{2}$, think addition: What do we add to $\frac{1}{2}$ to get
Try the fifths number line.
Place the $\frac{1}{2}$-strip with its right end at $\frac{3}{5}$.

Estimate:
$\frac{3}{5} < 1$; so, $\frac{3}{5} - \frac{1}{2} <$

Equivalent fractions:
$\frac{3}{5} = \frac{6}{10}$
$\frac{1}{2} = \frac{5}{10}$

The left end of the strip does not line up with a fraction on the
Use a number line that has equivalent fractions for halves and
Put the $\frac{1}{2}$-strip on the tenths number line, with its right end at

The left end of the strip is at $\frac{1}{10}$.
So, $\frac{3}{5} - \frac{1}{2} = \frac{1}{10}$

132 UNIT 4: Fractions and Decimals

BEFORE — Get Started

On the overhead projector, model how the fraction strips can be used to subtract two fractions. Show the $\frac{4}{5}$-strip above the $\frac{3}{10}$-strip, with the strips aligned at the left. Show how the $\frac{1}{2}$- or $\frac{5}{10}$-strip is used to show the difference.

Ask:
- How much greater is $\frac{4}{5}$ than $\frac{3}{10}$? (*$\frac{5}{10} = \frac{1}{2}$*)
- How can we write these strips as a subtraction equation? (*$\frac{4}{5} - \frac{3}{10} = \frac{5}{10}$; or $\frac{4}{5} - \frac{3}{10} = \frac{1}{2}$*)

Make sure students understand they are to find more pairs of fractions that have this difference.

DURING — Explore

Ongoing Assessment: Observe and Listen

As students find pair of fractions, ask:
- Which pairs of fractions are easiest to find? (*A pair with one fraction of 1 and an equivalent fraction equal to $\frac{1}{2}$, such as: $1 - \frac{1}{2}$; $1 - \frac{3}{6}$; also, pairs with the same denominator, such as: $\frac{6}{10} - \frac{1}{10}$, $\frac{7}{8} - \frac{3}{8}$.*)
- Which pairs of fractions are more difficult to find? (*Pairs with different denominators*)
- Are other pairs of fractions possible if you use a different model? (*I used a clock model to find pairs with denominator 12, such as: $\frac{11}{12} - \frac{5}{12}$.*)
- How did you use what you learned about adding two fractions to subtract two fractions? (*I used a number line. I put a fraction strip greater than $\frac{1}{2}$ on the line. Then I tried to find a fraction strip that left $\frac{1}{2}$ of the first strip uncovered when I placed the second fraction on top of the first fraction.*)

Example

Use fraction strips and number lines to subtract.

a) $\frac{6}{5} - \frac{4}{5}$ b) $\frac{5}{8} - \frac{1}{4}$

Solution

a) $\frac{6}{5} - \frac{4}{5}$

Estimate:
$\frac{6}{5} > 1$, $\frac{4}{5} < 1$;
so, $\frac{6}{5} - \frac{4}{5} < 1$

Think addition.
What do we add to $\frac{4}{5}$ to get $\frac{6}{5}$?
Use the fifths number line because both denominators are 5.
Place the $\frac{4}{5}$-strip on the fifths number line with its right end at $\frac{6}{5}$.

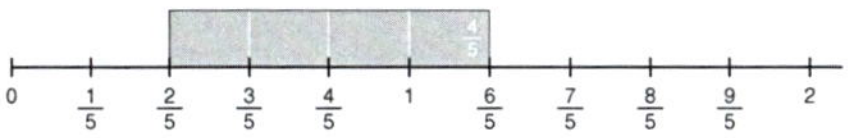

The left end of the strip is at $\frac{2}{5}$.

So, $\frac{6}{5} - \frac{4}{5} = \frac{2}{5}$

b) $\frac{5}{8} - \frac{1}{4}$

Estimate:
$\frac{5}{8}$ is between $\frac{1}{2}$ and 1,
$\frac{1}{4} < \frac{1}{2}$; so, $\frac{5}{8} - \frac{1}{4} < \frac{1}{2}$

Think addition.
What do we add to $\frac{1}{4}$ to get $\frac{5}{8}$?

Use a number line that shows equivalent fractions for eighths and fourths.
That is, use the eighths number line.
Place the $\frac{1}{4}$-strip on the eighths number line with its right end at $\frac{5}{8}$.

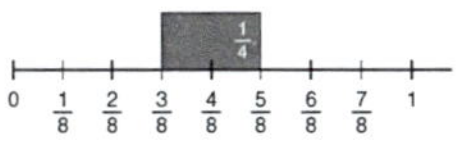

The left end of the strip is at $\frac{3}{8}$.

So, $\frac{5}{8} - \frac{1}{4} = \frac{3}{8}$

4.4 Subtracting Fractions Using Models **133**

REACHING ALL LEARNERS

Alternative Explore

Have students use analog clocks or fraction circles to find pairs of fractions with a difference of $\frac{1}{3}$.

Early Finishers

Have students look for pairs of fractions with a difference of $1\frac{1}{4}$.

Common Misconceptions

➤ Students do not know which number line to use when the fractions have different denominators.

How to Help: Remind students to find the lowest common multiple of the two denominators.

➤ Students do not know which fraction strip to use, and where to place it on the number line.

How to Help: Give students much practice with fractions with the same denominator. Make sure students understand that the first fraction in the subtraction statement is greater, then find that fraction on the line. Students then place the strip for the second fraction to the left of this fraction; that is, toward 0 on the line.

ESL Strategies

Students from other countries may have learned different strategies for adding and subtracting fractions. Give these students an opportunity to share these strategies with the class.

- How is this different from adding two fractions? (*When I add, I put two fraction strips next to each other. When I subtract, I put one strip on top of another.*)

AFTER Connect

Have students write their results on the board. Review these results and have volunteers illustrate how they know each difference is $\frac{1}{2}$. Review the illustration and *Example* in *Connect*. If necessary, remind students of the "think addition" strategy for subtracting whole numbers. For example: to find 12 – 5, think, "What do I add to 5 to get 12?"

Review how to use Cuisenaire rods to subtract the fractions in *Connect*.

For $\frac{3}{5} - \frac{1}{2}$, use the orange rod as one whole ($\frac{10}{10}$). On top of the orange rod, place the dark green rod ($\frac{6}{10}$ or $\frac{3}{5}$) to align with the orange rod at the left.

On top of the dark green rod, place the yellow rod ($\frac{5}{10}$ or $\frac{1}{2}$) to align with the other rods at the left.

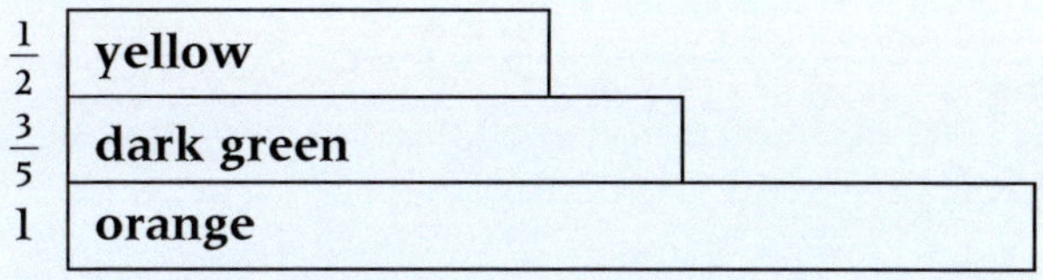

$\frac{3}{5} - \frac{1}{2}$ is the difference between a dark green rod and a yellow rod. This is one white rod, or $\frac{1}{10}$.

So, $\frac{3}{5} - \frac{1}{2} = \frac{1}{10}$.

For $\frac{6}{5} - \frac{4}{5}$, use the yellow rod as one whole ($\frac{5}{5}$).

Then the dark green rod is $\frac{6}{5}$.

And the purple rod is $\frac{4}{5}$.

Align the purple rod, the dark green rod, and the yellow rod at the left.

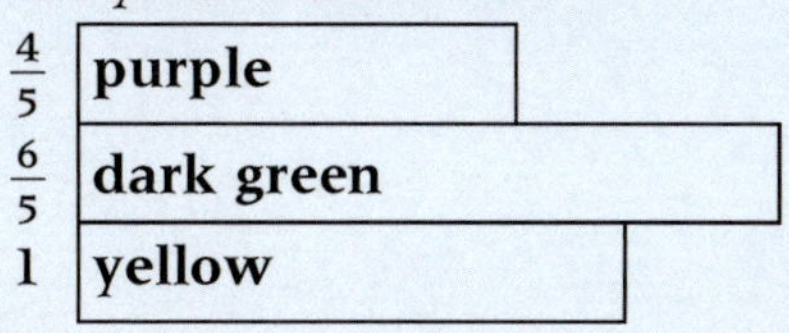

Sample Answers

2. a) Subtract the numerators; leave the denominator the same.
   b) For example: $\frac{8}{10} - \frac{3}{10} = \frac{5}{10}$; $\frac{7}{8} - \frac{2}{8} = \frac{5}{8}$; $\frac{5}{6} - \frac{1}{6} = \frac{4}{6}$

10. Spencer does not have enough, because $\frac{2}{3}$ is less than $\frac{3}{4}$. Spencer needs the difference of $\frac{3}{4}$ and $\frac{2}{3}$: $\frac{3}{4} - \frac{2}{3} = \frac{1}{12}$. Spencer needs $\frac{1}{12}$ cup more.

12. a) Kelly used more than $\frac{1}{2}$ of a tank because she used the difference: $\frac{3}{4} - \frac{1}{8} = \frac{6}{8} - \frac{1}{8} = \frac{5}{8}$. Kelly used $\frac{5}{8}$ of a tank, and $\frac{5}{8}$ is greater than $\frac{4}{8}$, or $\frac{1}{2}$.
    b) Kelly used $\frac{1}{8}$ of a tank more than $\frac{1}{2}$ of a tank, because $\frac{1}{2} + \frac{1}{8} = \frac{4}{8} + \frac{1}{8} = \frac{5}{8}$.

13. a) $\frac{5}{6} - \frac{1}{6} = \frac{4}{6}$, which is greater than $\frac{1}{2}$
    b) I could subtract. Or, I could estimate. For part i, both $\frac{5}{6}$ and $\frac{2}{3}$ are between $\frac{1}{2}$ and 1, so when they are subtracted, the answer is less than $\frac{1}{2}$. For part ii, $\frac{5}{6}$ is between $\frac{1}{2}$ and 1, so when $\frac{1}{2}$ is subtracted, the answer is less than $\frac{1}{2}$.

Number Strategies

Students need to remember how to write decimals between zero and one using digits.

22.23 − 0.8 = 21.43;
94.43 + 0.09 = 94.52;
48.425 + 0.36 = 48.785;
48.425 + 0.036 = 48.461

Practice

Use models.

1. Subtract.
   a) $\frac{3}{4} - \frac{2}{4} = \frac{1}{4}$ b) $\frac{4}{5} - \frac{1}{5} = \frac{3}{5}$ c) $\frac{2}{3} - \frac{1}{3} = \frac{1}{3}$ d) $\frac{5}{8} - \frac{3}{8} = \frac{2}{8}$ or $\frac{1}{4}$
2. a) Write a rule you could use to subtract fractions with like denominators without using number lines or fraction strips.
   b) Write 3 subtraction questions with like denominators.
   Use your rule to subtract the fractions.
   Use fraction strips and number lines to check your answers.
3. Write the subtraction equation that each number line and fraction strip represent.

a)

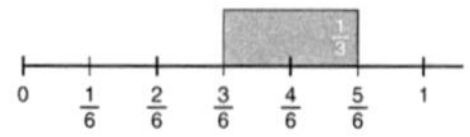

$\frac{5}{6} - \frac{1}{3} = \frac{3}{6}$ or $\frac{1}{2}$

b)

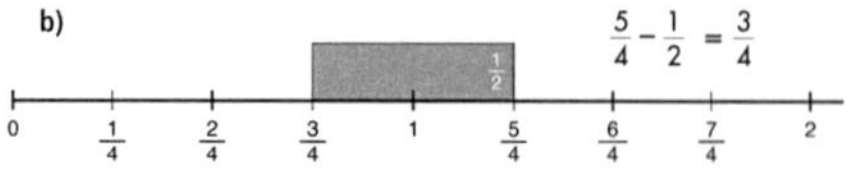

$\frac{5}{4} - \frac{1}{2} = \frac{3}{4}$

c)

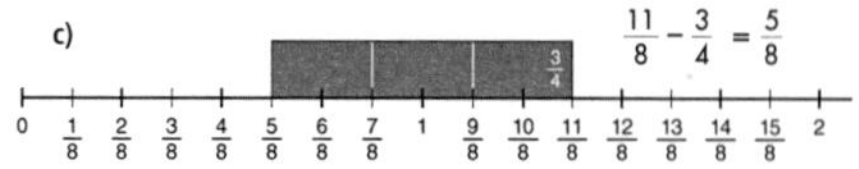

$\frac{11}{8} - \frac{3}{4} = \frac{5}{8}$

Number Strategies

Find:
- 8 tenths less than 22.23 21.43
- 9 hundredths more than 94.43 94.52
- 36 hundredths more than 48.425 48.785
- 36 thousandths more than 48.425 48.461

4. Subtract. Estimate first.
   a) $\frac{3}{8} - \frac{1}{4} = \frac{1}{8}$ b) $\frac{5}{6} - \frac{2}{3} = \frac{1}{6}$ c) $\frac{5}{4} - \frac{1}{2} = \frac{3}{4}$ d) $\frac{7}{10} - \frac{3}{5} = \frac{1}{10}$
5. Subtract. Estimate first.
   a) $\frac{3}{4} - \frac{1}{2} = \frac{1}{4}$ b) $\frac{3}{4} - \frac{3}{8} = \frac{3}{8}$ c) $\frac{2}{3} - \frac{1}{6} = \frac{3}{6}$ or $\frac{1}{2}$ d) $\frac{5}{6} - \frac{1}{2} = \frac{2}{6}$ or $\frac{1}{3}$
6. Aaron has $\frac{2}{3}$ cup of raisins. He gives Raj $\frac{1}{2}$ cup. How much does Aaron have left? $\frac{1}{6}$ cup
7. Subtract.
   a) $\frac{2}{3} - \frac{1}{4} = \frac{5}{12}$ b) $\frac{5}{3} - \frac{1}{2} = \frac{7}{6}$ or $1\frac{1}{6}$ c) $\frac{1}{2} - \frac{1}{5} = \frac{3}{10}$ d) $\frac{3}{2} - \frac{1}{3} = \frac{7}{6}$ or $1\frac{1}{6}$

134 UNIT 4: Fractions and Decimals

$\frac{6}{5} - \frac{4}{5}$ is the difference between a dark green rod and a purple rod. This is 1 red rod, or $\frac{2}{5}$.

So, $\frac{6}{5} - \frac{4}{5} = \frac{2}{5}$

For $\frac{5}{8} - \frac{1}{4}$, use the brown rod as one whole ($\frac{8}{8}$).

Then the yellow rod is $\frac{5}{8}$.

And the red rod is $\frac{1}{4}$, or $\frac{2}{8}$.

Align the red rod, the yellow rod, and the brown rod at the left.

$\frac{5}{8} - \frac{1}{4}$ is the difference between a yellow rod and a red rod. This is 1 light green rod, or $\frac{3}{8}$.

So, $\frac{5}{8} - \frac{1}{4} = \frac{3}{8}$

Practice

Encourage students to use models and number lines to complete the questions.

Assessment Focus: Question 12

Students may use benchmarks and reasoning to answer part a. They know $\frac{3}{4} = \frac{1}{2} + \frac{1}{4}$, and $\frac{1}{8} < \frac{1}{4}$, so Kelly must have used more than $\frac{1}{2}$ of a tank.

8. Subtract.

a) $\frac{11}{8} - \frac{3}{4} = \frac{5}{8}$ b) $\frac{3}{2} - \frac{2}{3} = \frac{5}{6}$ c) $\frac{9}{5} - \frac{3}{2} = \frac{3}{10}$ d) $\frac{5}{3} - \frac{5}{6} = \frac{5}{6}$

9. Subtract.

a) $2 - \frac{1}{2} = 1\frac{1}{2}$ b) $1 - \frac{3}{5} = \frac{2}{5}$ c) $2 - \frac{5}{4} = \frac{3}{4}$ d) $1 - \frac{2}{3} = \frac{1}{3}$

10. A cookie recipe calls for $\frac{3}{4}$ cup of chocolate chips.
Spencer has $\frac{2}{3}$ cup. Does he have enough? No
If your answer is yes, explain.
If your answer is no, how much more does Spencer need? $\frac{1}{12}$ cup more

11. Copy and replace each □ with a number, to make each statement correct.
Try to do this more than one way.

a) $\frac{3}{4} - \frac{□}{□} = \frac{1}{4}$ b) $\frac{□}{□} - \frac{1}{5} = \frac{3}{5}$ c) $\frac{□}{6} - \frac{2}{□} = \frac{1}{6}$

a) $\frac{2}{4}$ or $\frac{1}{2}$
b) $\frac{4}{5}$ or $\frac{8}{10}$
c) 3 (or 5); 6 (or 3)

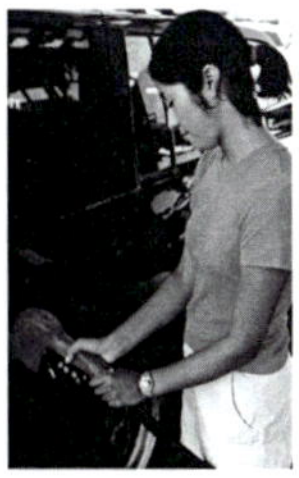

12. **Assessment Focus** Kelly had $\frac{3}{4}$ of a tank of gas at the beginning of the week.
At the end of the week, Kelly had $\frac{1}{8}$ of a tank left.

a) Did Kelly use more or less than $\frac{1}{2}$ of a tank? Explain. More

b) How much more or less than $\frac{1}{2}$ of a tank did Kelly use? $\frac{1}{8}$

13. a) Which of these differences is greater than $\frac{1}{2}$?
How do you know?

i) $\frac{5}{6} - \frac{2}{3}$ ii) $\frac{5}{6} - \frac{1}{2}$ iii) $\frac{5}{6} - \frac{1}{6}$ (circled)

b) Explain how you found your answers to part a.
Which other way can you find the fractions with a difference greater than $\frac{1}{2}$? Explain.

Reflect

Which pairs of fractions can you *not* subtract using the number lines and fraction strips you have? Give 3 examples.

REFLECT: The number lines have denominators 2, 3, 4, 5, 6, 8, 10, and 12. The fraction strips have denominators 2, 3, 4, 5, 6, 8, and 10. I cannot use fraction strips and number lines to subtract two fractions with denominators that are different, and that have a common denominator that is not one of the numbers above. For example, for $\frac{1}{3} - \frac{1}{5}$: I would need a fifteenths number line; for $\frac{1}{3} - \frac{1}{8}$: I would need a twenty-fourths number line; for $\frac{1}{5} - \frac{1}{8}$: I would need a fortieths number line.

Assignment Guidelines

If your students do not have time to complete all the *Practice* questions on pages 134, 135, these questions provide minimum curriculum coverage: 2, 3, 5, 7, 9, 10, 12, *Reflect*
To assess the 4 Achievement Chart categories listed in the curriculum document, have students complete these *Practice* questions:
Communication: 2
Understanding Concepts: 5
Application: 10
Problem Solving: 12

ASSESSMENT FOR LEARNING

What to Look For	What to Do
Understanding concepts ✔ Students understand how to subtract fractions using models. ***Applying procedures*** ✔ Students can choose correct equivalent models to subtract fractions with different denominators. ***Communicating*** ✔ Students can explain their reasoning using appropriate language.	***Extra Support:*** Have students use Cuisenaire rods to subtract fractions with the same denominator. Students can continue to use Step-by-Step 4 (Master 4.12) to complete question 12. ***Extra Practice:*** Have students roll two number cubes to get a numerator and a denominator for one fraction. They repeat a roll of the number cubes to get a second fraction. Students then subtract the lesser fraction from the greater fraction. Students can complete Extra Practice 4 (Master 4.35). ***Extension:*** Students use a clock model to make up a subtraction word problem. They then solve the problem. Students exchange problems with a classmate, and solve each other's problem.

Recording and Reporting
Master 4.2 Ongoing Observations: Fractions and Decimals

Subtracting Fractions

SECTION ORGANIZER (80–100 min)

Curriculum Focus: Subtract fractions using symbols. (7m18)

Teacher Materials
- fraction strips (Masters 4.22, 4.23)

Student Materials
- number cards 1 to 6
- number lines (Masters 4.24, 4.25)
- fraction strips (Masters 4.22, 4.23)

Optional
- 12 by 12 multiplication chart (PM 15)
- Step-by-Step 5 (Master 4.13)
- Extra Practice 5 (Master 4.36)
- *Shade One* game board and cards (Masters 4.26, 4.27, 4.28)

Assessment: Master 4.2 Ongoing Observations: Fractions and Decimals

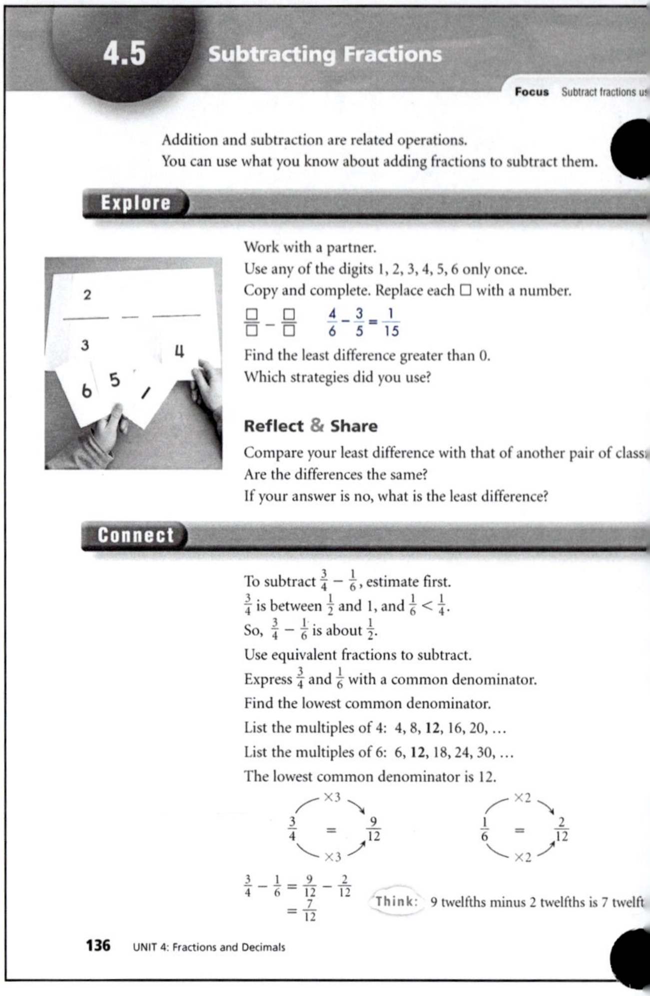

4.5 Subtracting Fractions

Focus Subtract fractions us

Addition and subtraction are related operations.
You can use what you know about adding fractions to subtract them.

Explore

Work with a partner.
Use any of the digits 1, 2, 3, 4, 5, 6 only once.
Copy and complete. Replace each □ with a number.

$\frac{\square}{\square} - \frac{\square}{\square}$ $\quad \frac{4}{6} - \frac{3}{5} = \frac{1}{15}$

Find the least difference greater than 0.
Which strategies did you use?

Reflect & Share

Compare your least difference with that of another pair of class
Are the differences the same?
If your answer is no, what is the least difference?

Connect

To subtract $\frac{3}{4} - \frac{1}{6}$, estimate first.
$\frac{3}{4}$ is between $\frac{1}{2}$ and 1, and $\frac{1}{6} < \frac{1}{4}$.
So, $\frac{3}{4} - \frac{1}{6}$ is about $\frac{1}{2}$.
Use equivalent fractions to subtract.
Express $\frac{3}{4}$ and $\frac{1}{6}$ with a common denominator.
Find the lowest common denominator.
List the multiples of 4: 4, 8, **12**, 16, 20, …
List the multiples of 6: 6, **12**, 18, 24, 30, …
The lowest common denominator is 12.

$\frac{3}{4} = \frac{9}{12}$ (×3) $\qquad \frac{1}{6} = \frac{2}{12}$ (×2)

$\frac{3}{4} - \frac{1}{6} = \frac{9}{12} - \frac{2}{12}$
$= \frac{7}{12}$

Think: 9 twelfths minus 2 twelfths is 7 twelft

136 UNIT 4: Fractions and Decimals

Key Math Learning

Fractions can be subtracted by using equivalent fractions with common denominators. Use the same strategies as those for adding fractions.

BEFORE Get Started

If you do not have number cards, distribute index cards and markers to students. Have them write the numbers 1 to 6 on the cards. Have students draw two fraction bars and a subtraction sign, as shown in the photo on page 136.

Introduce the *Explore*. Students may remember a similar question from Section 4.2, *Practice* question 11. Suggest they consider using similar strategies in *Explore*. Students can use number lines and fraction strips to subtract.

DURING Explore

Ongoing Assessment: Observe and Listen

As students work in pairs, ask:
- What strategies are you using?
  (*Guess and check: I try different pairs of fractions, each of which is less than 1.*)
- How can you use what you know about adding fractions to help you subtract?
  (*I can use equivalent fractions to get common denominators when I don't have a number line to subtract.*)
- What strategy are you using?
  (*I want my answer to have the greatest possible denominator and the least possible numerator. So, I'm trying to get an answer with a numerator of 1, and a denominator of 6 × 5 = 30.*)

Example

Subtract.

a) $\frac{3}{4} - \frac{5}{8}$ b) $\frac{3}{2} - \frac{2}{5}$

Solution

a) $\frac{3}{4} - \frac{5}{8}$

Since 8 is a multiple of 4, use 8 as the lowest common denominator.

Estimate: Both $\frac{3}{4}$ and $\frac{5}{8}$ are between $\frac{1}{2}$ and 1; so, $\frac{3}{4} - \frac{5}{8} < \frac{1}{2}$

$$\frac{3}{4} \xrightarrow{\times 2} \frac{6}{8}$$

$$\frac{3}{4} - \frac{5}{8} = \frac{6}{8} - \frac{5}{8} = \frac{1}{8}$$

b) $\frac{3}{2} - \frac{2}{5}$

Estimate: $\frac{2}{5} < \frac{1}{2}$; so, $\frac{3}{2} - \frac{2}{5} > 1$

List the multiples of 2:
2, 4, 6, 8, **10**, 12, …
List the multiples of 5:
5, **10**, 15, 20, …
The lowest common denominator is 10.
Write each fraction with a denominator of 10.

$$\frac{3}{2} \xrightarrow{\times 5} \frac{15}{10} \qquad \frac{2}{5} \xrightarrow{\times 2} \frac{4}{10}$$

$$\frac{3}{2} - \frac{2}{5} = \frac{15}{10} - \frac{4}{10} = \frac{11}{10}$$

We can write $\frac{11}{10}$ as the mixed number $1\frac{1}{10}$.

Practice

1. Subtract.
   a) $\frac{4}{5} - \frac{2}{5} = \frac{2}{5}$ b) $\frac{2}{3} - \frac{1}{3} = \frac{1}{3}$ c) $\frac{7}{9} - \frac{4}{9} = \frac{3}{9}$ or $\frac{1}{3}$ d) $\frac{5}{7} - \frac{3}{7} = \frac{2}{7}$
2. Subtract. Estimate first.
   a) $\frac{5}{8} - \frac{1}{2} = \frac{1}{8}$ b) $\frac{4}{9} - \frac{1}{3} = \frac{1}{9}$ c) $\frac{3}{2} - \frac{4}{10} = \frac{11}{10}$ or $1\frac{1}{10}$ d) $\frac{5}{3} - \frac{5}{6} = \frac{5}{6}$

4.5 Subtracting Fractions **137**

REACHING ALL LEARNERS

Alternative Explore

Have students apply what they learned about adding fractions without number lines or fraction strips to subtract these fractions: $\frac{3}{5} - \frac{1}{4}$, $\frac{3}{5} - \frac{1}{3}$, $\frac{3}{4} - \frac{1}{5}$. Students explain their strategies.

Early Finishers

Have students use the cards and diagram from *Explore* to find the greatest difference that is less than 1.

Common Misconceptions

- Students multiply the two denominators to find the lowest common multiple.

How to Help: Remind students of their work with prime factors. The lowest common multiple contains the prime factors of each denominator. For example, for denominators $8 = \mathbf{2} \times \mathbf{2} \times 2$ and $12 = \mathbf{2} \times \mathbf{2} \times 3$, the LCM is $\mathbf{2} \times \mathbf{2} \times 2 \times 3 = 24$.

- What other strategies are there?
  (*I wrote all the possible fractions, then listed them in order from least to greatest: $\frac{1}{6}, \frac{1}{5}, \frac{1}{4}, \frac{1}{3}, \frac{2}{6}, \frac{2}{5}, \frac{1}{2}, \frac{2}{4}, \frac{3}{6}, \frac{3}{5}, \frac{2}{3}, \frac{4}{6}, \frac{3}{4}, \frac{4}{5}, \frac{5}{6}$. I then picked two fractions that are close together, such as $\frac{5}{6} - \frac{3}{4} = \frac{10}{12} - \frac{9}{12} = \frac{1}{12}$. I did this until I found the least answer: $\frac{2}{5} - \frac{1}{3} = \frac{6}{15} - \frac{5}{15} = \frac{1}{15}$.*)

AFTER Connect

Review students' answers and strategies.
If students used only number lines and fraction strips, the least difference is: $\frac{5}{6} - \frac{3}{4} = \frac{1}{12}$.
If students can apply what they know about addition, the least difference is:
$\frac{4}{6} - \frac{3}{5} = \frac{1}{15}$.
Review the examples in *Connect*. Ask students which other common denominators they could use to subtract: $\frac{3}{4} - \frac{1}{6}$.
They could continue the list of multiples of 4 and 6 and use 24, 36, 48, and so on; the multiples of 12. Complete the subtraction using 24 as the common denominator:

$$\frac{3}{4} = \frac{18}{24} \text{ and } \frac{1}{6} = \frac{4}{24}$$

$$\frac{3}{4} - \frac{1}{6} = \frac{18}{24} - \frac{4}{24} = \frac{14}{24} = \frac{7}{12}$$

Students should notice that when the common denominator is not the least common denominator, the difference is not in simplest form and we need an extra step at the end of the solution to write the answer in simplest form.

For part a of the *Example*, have students use Cuisenaire rods to check. The brown rod represents one whole ($\frac{8}{8}$). The dark green rod represents $\frac{3}{4}$ ($\frac{6}{8}$). The yellow rod represents $\frac{5}{8}$. Then $\frac{3}{4} - \frac{5}{8}$ is the difference between the dark green rod and the yellow rod, which is the white rod, $\frac{1}{8}$.

Sample Answers

7. a) Terri; she bikes $3\frac{3}{4}$ h the next Saturday, and Sam bikes only $3\frac{1}{2}$ h.
   b) $\frac{1}{4}$ h
   c) I need to know how to add and subtract fractions.
8. Walnuts; $\frac{1}{12}$
9. $1 - \frac{1}{4}, \frac{7}{8} - \frac{1}{8}, \frac{10}{12} - \frac{1}{12}, \frac{5}{6} - \frac{1}{12}, \frac{11}{12} - \frac{2}{12}, \frac{11}{12} - \frac{1}{6}$, and many others
10. The other fraction must be between $\frac{1}{2}$ and $\frac{3}{4}$.

REFLECT: For $\frac{3}{5} - \frac{1}{3}$, I find the common denominator by multiplying: $5 \times 3 = 15$. The denominators have no common factors, so 15 is the lowest common denominator. I write each fraction as an equivalent fraction with denominator 15.
$\frac{3}{5} - \frac{1}{3} = \frac{9}{15} - \frac{5}{15} = \frac{4}{15}$. For $\frac{3}{5} - \frac{1}{15}$, the common denominator is 15 because 5 is a factor of 15.
I write a fraction equivalent to $\frac{3}{5}$ with denominator 15:
$\frac{3}{5} - \frac{1}{15} = \frac{9}{15} - \frac{1}{15} = \frac{8}{15}$

Calculator Skills

Students write each question a different way.
$18 + 27 = 20 + 27 - 2 = 45$
$118 - 85 = 120 - 2 - 70 - 15 = 33$
$18 \times 27 = 20 \times 27 - 2 \times 27 = 486$
$225 \div 8 = 225 \div 4 \div 2 = 28.125$

3. Subtract.
   a) $\frac{5}{6} - \frac{2}{9} = \frac{11}{18}$ b) $\frac{5}{6} - \frac{2}{4} = \frac{4}{12}$ or $\frac{1}{3}$ c) $\frac{5}{8} - \frac{3}{12} = \frac{9}{24}$ or $\frac{3}{8}$ d) $\frac{7}{10} - \frac{4}{15} = \frac{13}{30}$
4. Subtract. Estimate first.
   a) $\frac{3}{4} - \frac{2}{3} = \frac{1}{12}$ b) $\frac{5}{2} - \frac{3}{4} = \frac{7}{4}$ or $1\frac{3}{4}$ c) $\frac{4}{5} - \frac{2}{3} = \frac{2}{15}$ d) $\frac{5}{4} - \frac{4}{5} = \frac{9}{20}$
5. Subtract.
   a) $\frac{4}{6} - \frac{1}{2} = \frac{1}{6}$ b) $\frac{5}{3} - \frac{3}{4} = \frac{11}{12}$ c) $\frac{7}{2} - \frac{3}{2} = \frac{4}{2}$ or 2 d) $\frac{5}{6} - \frac{3}{4} = \frac{1}{12}$

To subtract 2 mixed numbers: Subtract the whole numbers. Subtract the fractions. Write the difference as a mixed number.

6. Subtract.
   a) $5\frac{5}{7} - 1\frac{2}{7} = 4\frac{3}{7}$ b) $3\frac{4}{9} - 2\frac{1}{6} = 1\frac{5}{18}$ c) $4\frac{3}{10} - 2\frac{1}{5} = 2\frac{1}{10}$ d) $4\frac{3}{5} - 2\frac{1}{2} = 2\frac{1}{10}$
7. **Assessment Focus** Terri biked $2\frac{1}{4}$ h on Sunday.
   Terri increased the time she biked by $\frac{1}{4}$ h every day.
   Sam biked $\frac{1}{2}$ h on Sunday.
   Sam increased the time he biked by $\frac{1}{2}$ h every day.
   a) Who will bike longer the next Saturday? Explain. Terri
   b) For how much longer will this person bike? $\frac{1}{4}$ h
   c) What did you need to know about fractions to answer these questions?

Calculator Skills

Suppose the [8] key on your calculator is broken. How would you use your calculator to find each answer?
- 18 + 27
- 118 − 85
- 18 × 27
- 225 ÷ 8

- $20 + 27 - 2 = 45$
- $120 - 2 - 70 - 15 = 33$
- $20 \times 27 - 2 \times 27 = 486$
- $225 \div 4 \div 2 = 28.125$

8. A recipe calls for $\frac{3}{4}$ cup of walnuts and $\frac{2}{3}$ cup of pecans.
   Which type of nut is used more in the recipe? How much more? $\frac{1}{12}$
   Walnuts
9. Write as many different subtraction questions as you can where the answer is $\frac{3}{4}$.
10. The difference of 2 fractions is $\frac{1}{2}$.
    The lesser fraction is between 0 and $\frac{1}{4}$.
    What do you know about the other fraction?
    Must be between $\frac{1}{2}$ and $\frac{3}{4}$

Reflect

When you subtract fractions, and the denominators are different, how do you subtract? Give 2 different examples.
Explain your steps.

138 UNIT 4: Fractions and Decimals

All the examples can be modelled with fraction strips and number lines. Here is an additional example that cannot be modelled that way:
$\frac{7}{8} - \frac{2}{5}$

Ask:
- How do you estimate this difference?
  (*$\frac{7}{8}$ is almost 1, $\frac{2}{5}$ is almost $\frac{1}{2}$; so, $\frac{7}{8} - \frac{2}{5}$ is about $1 - \frac{1}{2} = \frac{1}{2}$.*)
- What is the lowest common denominator? (*40*) How do you know?
  (*I listed the multiples of 8 and 5 and found the first multiple that is the same in both lists.*)
- What are the equivalent fractions with this denominator? (*$\frac{7}{8} = \frac{35}{40}; \frac{2}{5} = \frac{16}{40}$*)
- What is the difference of these fractions? (*$\frac{35}{40} - \frac{16}{40} = \frac{19}{40}$*)
- Is this in simplest form? (*Yes*) How do you know?
  (*The numerator and denominator have no common factors.*)

Practice

Students may still need fraction strips and number lines. Encourage students to use these to check their answers.

Assessment Focus: Question 7

Students add $\frac{1}{4}$ six times to $2\frac{1}{4}$, and they add $\frac{1}{2}$ six times to $\frac{1}{2}$. They then compare the fractions, and subtract to find how much greater one is than the other.

Game

Shade One

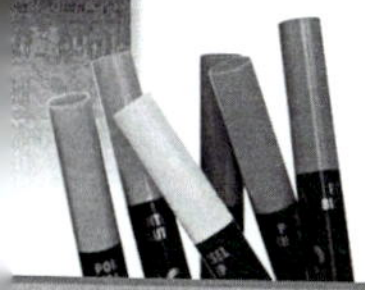

YOU WILL NEED

One gameboard; coloured markers; 1 set of 42 fraction cards

NUMBER OF PLAYERS

2 or more

GOAL OF THE GAME

To shade 1 whole on each fraction strip

HOW TO PLAY THE GAME:

1. Each player chooses a different colour marker.
2. Place the set of fraction cards face down.
3. Player A turns over a card. This is his *target fraction*.
4. Player A could shade the target fraction on one fraction strip, or share the fraction among several fraction strips. However, the total fraction shaded must equal the target fraction.

For example: If your target fraction is $\frac{3}{4}$, you could shade from 0 to $\frac{3}{4}$ on the fourths strip, or 0 to $\frac{6}{8}$ on the eighths strip. Or you could shade several fractions that add up to $\frac{3}{4}$. For example, you could shade $\frac{3}{12}$, $\frac{2}{8}$, and $\frac{1}{4}$; or you could shade $\frac{2}{5}$, $\frac{1}{10}$, and $\frac{1}{4}$.

5. Player B turns over the next fraction card. He repeats *Step 4* for his fraction.
6. Play continues with players taking turns to shade the target fraction. If there is not enough of a fraction strip left, and it is impossible to shade the target fraction, that player forfeits his turn. When a player is not able to shade any more fractions, the game is over.
7. The player who shades to complete 1 whole gets 1 point.
8. The person with the most points wins.

Game: Shade One **139**

Assignment Guidelines

If your students do not have time to complete all the *Practice* questions on pages 137, 138, these questions provide minimum curriculum coverage: 2, 3, 4, 7, 9, *Reflect*

To assess the 4 Achievement Chart categories listed in the curriculum document, have students complete these *Practice* questions:

Understanding Concepts: 3

Application: 7

Problem Solving: 9

Communication: *Reflect*

ASSESSMENT FOR LEARNING

What to Look For	What to Do
Understanding concepts ✔ Students understand how to subtract fractions using symbols.	***Extra Support:*** Students who have difficulty could continue to use models, and use a 12 by 12 Multiplication Chart (PM 15) to find the lowest common denominator. Students can use Step-by-Step 5 (Master 4.13) to complete question 7.
Applying procedures ✔ Students can find the lowest common denominator.	***Extra Practice:*** Have students play the *Shade One* Game (Masters 4.26, 4.27, 4.28). Students can complete Extra Practice 5 (Master 4.36).
Communicating ✔ Students can explain the strategies they used to solve problems.	***Extension:*** Students could create and answer other subtraction questions that cannot be solved using fraction strips, number lines, or clocks.

Recording and Reporting

Master 4.2 Ongoing Observations: Fractions and Decimals

SECTION ORGANIZER

Student Materials

- fraction strips (Masters 4.22, 4.23)
- number lines (Masters 4.24, 4.25)
- analog clocks or fraction circles

Assessment: Master 4.2 Ongoing Observations: Fractions and Decimals

Mid-Unit Review

LESSON

4.1 **1.** Add. Use fraction strips to help you.

a) $\frac{2}{3} + \frac{1}{6} = \frac{5}{6}$ b) $\frac{2}{4} + \frac{1}{3} = \frac{10}{12}$, or $\frac{5}{6}$

c) $\frac{2}{8} + \frac{2}{4} = \frac{6}{8}$, or $\frac{3}{4}$ d) $\frac{2}{10} + \frac{3}{5} = \frac{8}{10}$, or $\frac{4}{5}$

4.2 **2.** We know that $\frac{1}{2} + \frac{4}{5} = \frac{13}{10}$. Use this result to find each sum.

a) $1\frac{1}{2} + \frac{4}{5} = 1\frac{13}{10}$ or $2\frac{3}{10}$ b) $5\frac{1}{2} + 2\frac{4}{5} = 7\frac{13}{10}$ or $8\frac{3}{10}$

3. Use models to add.

a) $\frac{4}{5} + \frac{3}{5} = \frac{7}{5}$ b) $\frac{2}{3} + \frac{1}{2} = \frac{7}{6}$, or $1\frac{1}{6}$

c) $\frac{1}{2} + \frac{5}{6} = \frac{8}{6}$, or $1\frac{1}{3}$ d) $\frac{3}{2} + \frac{1}{3} = \frac{11}{6}$, or $1\frac{5}{6}$

4.3 **4.** Add. Estimate first.

$\frac{19}{12}$, or $1\frac{7}{12}$ a) $\frac{3}{4} + \frac{5}{6}$ b) $\frac{3}{2} + \frac{2}{3} = \frac{13}{6}$, or $2\frac{1}{6}$

$\frac{11}{10}$, or $1\frac{1}{10}$ c) $\frac{7}{10} + \frac{2}{5}$ d) $\frac{5}{9} + \frac{5}{6} = \frac{25}{18}$, or $1\frac{7}{18}$

5. Add.

a) $\frac{2}{5} + \frac{3}{2} + \frac{3}{10} = \frac{22}{10} = \frac{11}{5} = 2\frac{1}{5}$

b) $\frac{3}{8} + \frac{3}{4} + \frac{1}{2} = \frac{13}{8} = 1\frac{5}{8}$

c) $\frac{1}{3} + \frac{5}{6} + \frac{2}{9} = \frac{25}{18} = 1\frac{7}{18}$

6. Add.

a) $2\frac{1}{3} + 3\frac{1}{3} = 5\frac{2}{3}$

b) $2\frac{1}{4} + 1\frac{1}{3} = 3\frac{7}{12}$

c) $1\frac{3}{4} + 3\frac{3}{8} = 4\frac{9}{8}$, or $5\frac{1}{8}$

4.4 **7.** Use models to subtract.

a) $\frac{7}{8} - \frac{3}{4} = \frac{1}{8}$ b) $\frac{3}{2} - \frac{3}{5} = \frac{9}{10}$

c) $\frac{4}{3} - \frac{5}{6} = \frac{3}{6}$, or $\frac{1}{2}$ d) $\frac{11}{6} - \frac{2}{3} = \frac{7}{6}$, or $1\frac{1}{6}$

8. Peter put $\frac{4}{5}$ cup of chocolate chips into his cookie batter. Samantha put $\frac{7}{8}$ cup into hers. Whose batter contains more chips? How do you know?

Samantha's b

9. Alex delivered flyers to $\frac{1}{4}$ of her route on Saturday morning. She delivered to $\frac{2}{3}$ of the route Saturday afternoon, and the remainder on Sunday.

a) What fraction of her route Alex deliver on Saturday?

b) What fraction did she delive on Sunday?

4.5 **10.** Subtract. Estimate first.

$\frac{13}{10}$, or $1\frac{3}{10}$ a) $\frac{3}{2} - \frac{1}{5}$ b) $\frac{7}{6} - \frac{2}{3} =$

$\frac{13}{12}$, or $1\frac{1}{12}$ c) $\frac{11}{6} - \frac{3}{4}$ d) $\frac{13}{10} - \frac{3}{5} =$

11. We know that $\frac{9}{8} - \frac{1}{4} = \frac{7}{8}$. Use this result to find each difference.

Explain how you did this.

a) $\frac{12}{8} - \frac{1}{4} = \frac{10}{8} = \frac{5}{4} = 1\frac{1}{4}$ b) $\frac{5}{8} - \frac{1}{4} =$

12. Subtract.

a) $3\frac{5}{8} - 2\frac{3}{8} = 1\frac{2}{8} = 1\frac{1}{4}$ b) $2\frac{1}{2} - 1\frac{1}{4}$

140 UNIT 4: Fractions and Decimals

Assignment Guidelines

To assess the 4 Achievement Chart categories listed in the curriculum document, have students complete these questions:

Understanding Concepts: 4, 10

Application: 8

Problem Solving: 9

Communication: 11

Sample Solutions

2. If students know the sum of the fraction parts of two mixed numbers, they need only to add this fraction to the sum of the whole numbers parts of the mixed numbers, to get the sum of the mixed numbers.

4. Possible estimates are:

   a) Since $\frac{3}{4}$ is between $\frac{1}{2}$ and 1, and $\frac{5}{6}$ is less than 1, but close to 1, then, $\frac{3}{4} + \frac{5}{6}$ is about $1\frac{1}{2}$.

   b) Since $\frac{2}{3}$ is between $\frac{1}{2}$ and 1, and $\frac{3}{2}$ is $1\frac{1}{2}$, then, $\frac{3}{2} + \frac{2}{3}$ is between 2 and $2\frac{1}{2}$.

   c) Since $\frac{7}{10}$ is between $\frac{1}{2}$ and 1, and $\frac{2}{5}$ is less than $\frac{1}{2}$, then, $\frac{7}{10} + \frac{2}{5}$ is about 1.

   d) Since $\frac{5}{9}$ is a little more than $\frac{1}{2}$, and $\frac{5}{6}$ is a little less than 1, then, $\frac{5}{9} + \frac{5}{6}$ is about $1\frac{1}{2}$.

8. Students could compare fraction strips or find a common denominator for $\frac{4}{5}$ and $\frac{7}{8}$. Since 5 and 8 have no common factors, the lowest common denominator is $8 \times 5 = 40$. Write $\frac{4}{5}$ with denominator 40, by multiplying numerator and denominator by 8: $\frac{4}{5} = \frac{32}{40}$. Write $\frac{7}{8}$ with denominator 40, by multiplying numerator and denominator by 5: $\frac{7}{8} = \frac{35}{40}$. Since $\frac{35}{40} > \frac{32}{40}$, then $\frac{7}{8} > \frac{4}{5}$, and Samantha's batter contains more chocolate chips.

10. Possible estimates are:

    a) Since $\frac{3}{2}$ is $1\frac{1}{2}$, and $\frac{1}{5}$ is less than $\frac{1}{2}$, then, $\frac{3}{2} - \frac{1}{5}$ is between 1 and $1\frac{1}{2}$.

    b) Since $\frac{7}{6}$ is a little more than 1, and $\frac{2}{3}$ is between $\frac{1}{2}$ and 1, then, $\frac{7}{6} - \frac{2}{3}$ is about $\frac{1}{2}$.

    c) Since $\frac{11}{6}$ is almost 2, and $\frac{3}{4}$ is between $\frac{1}{2}$ and 1, then, $\frac{11}{6} - \frac{3}{4}$ is between 1 and $1\frac{1}{2}$.

    d) Since $\frac{13}{10}$ is between 1 and $1\frac{1}{2}$, and $\frac{3}{5}$ is greater than $\frac{1}{2}$, then, $\frac{13}{10} - \frac{3}{5}$ is between $\frac{1}{2}$ and 1.

11. a) Since $\frac{9}{8} - \frac{1}{4} = \frac{7}{8}$, and $\frac{12}{8}$ is $\frac{3}{8}$ more than $\frac{9}{8}$, then, $\frac{12}{8} - \frac{1}{4}$ is $\frac{3}{8}$ more than $\frac{7}{8}$, which is $\frac{10}{8} = \frac{5}{4} = 1\frac{1}{4}$.

    b) Since $\frac{9}{8} - \frac{1}{4} = \frac{7}{8}$, and $\frac{5}{8}$ is $\frac{4}{8}$ less than $\frac{9}{8}$, then, $\frac{5}{8} - \frac{1}{4}$ is $\frac{4}{8}$ less than $\frac{7}{8}$, which is $\frac{3}{8}$.

4.6 Exploring Repeated Addition

Focus Multiply a fraction by a whole number.

How many ways can you find this sum?
2 + 2 + 2 + 2 + 2 + 2 + 2 + 2 + 2
You can use the same strategies in *Explore*.

Explore

Work with a partner.
Jan takes $\frac{3}{4}$ h to walk to her music lesson.
Jan has a music lesson once a week, for 9 weeks.
How much time does Jan spend walking to her music lessons? $\frac{27}{4} = 6\frac{3}{4}$

Reflect & Share

Compare your strategy for solving the problem with that of another pair of classmates.
Did you get the same answers?
If not, who is correct? Explain.

Connect

$\frac{1}{5} + \frac{1}{5} + \frac{1}{5} + \frac{1}{5} = \frac{4}{5}$
All the fractions added are $\frac{1}{5}$.
Repeated addition can be written as multiplication.
$\frac{1}{5} + \frac{1}{5} + \frac{1}{5} + \frac{1}{5} = 4 \times \frac{1}{5} = \frac{4}{5}$
We can show this as a picture.

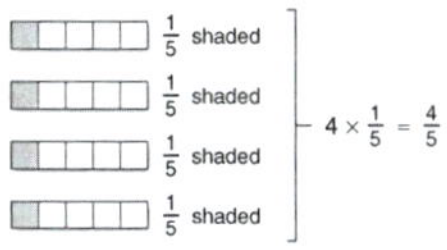

Similarly: $\frac{3}{4} + \frac{3}{4} + \frac{3}{4} + \frac{3}{4} + \frac{3}{4}$
$= 5 \times \frac{3}{4}$
$= \frac{15}{4}$
We can show this as a picture.

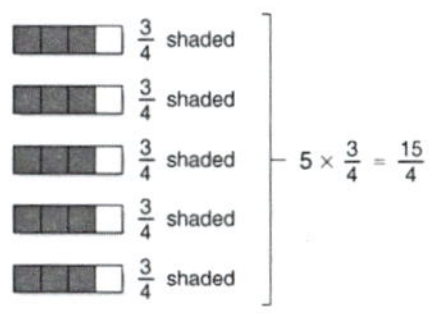

4.6 Exploring Repeated Addition 141

Exploring Repeated Addition

SECTION ORGANIZER (80–100 min)

Curriculum Focus: Multiply a fraction by a whole number. (7m17, 7m19)

Teacher Materials
- fraction strips (Masters 4.22, 4.23)

Student Materials
- fraction strips (Masters 4.22, 4.23)
- 0.5-cm grid paper (PM 14)

Optional
- Step-by-Step 6 (Master 4.14)
- Extra Practice 6 (Master 4.37)

Assessment: Master 4.2 Ongoing Observations: Fractions and Decimals

Key Math Learning

The repeated addition of fractions can be illustrated as a product in a similar way to the repeated addition of whole numbers.

Number Strategies

To divide by 10, move the decimal point one place to the left. Since dividing by 10 is the same as multiplying by 0.1, the answers in each row are equal.

BEFORE — Get Started

Have students share their strategies for finding the sum of repeated whole numbers. Some will do the addition as it is, others may look for groupings of 10 (5 twos) and 4 more twos, or write it as $9 \times 2 = 18$. Provide fraction strips and grid paper.

DURING — Explore

Ongoing Assessment: Observe and Listen

As students work in pairs, ask:
- Which strategy did you use? (*I added* $\frac{3}{4} + \frac{3}{4} + \frac{3}{4} + \frac{3}{4} + \frac{3}{4} + \frac{3}{4} + \frac{3}{4} + \frac{3}{4} + \frac{3}{4} = \frac{27}{4} = 6\frac{3}{4}$.)
- What other strategy could you have used? (*I know that* $\frac{3}{4} + \frac{3}{4} = 1\frac{1}{2}$. *So, eight* $\frac{3}{4}$*s will be* $1\frac{1}{2} + 1\frac{1}{2} + 1\frac{1}{2} + 1\frac{1}{2} = 6$; *and one more* $\frac{3}{4}$ *makes* $6\frac{3}{4}$.)
- How does your strategy relate to adding repeated whole numbers? (*The sum of nine* $\frac{3}{4}$*s is the same as 9 times* $\frac{3}{4}$, *which is* $\frac{27}{4} = 6\frac{3}{4}$.)

AFTER — Connect

Have students share their strategies with the class. Review the examples in *Connect*, reinforcing that repeated addition is the same as multiplying the whole number and the numerator of the fraction. The denominator is not affected.

For *Example 2*, review that $3 \times 5 = 5 \times 3 = 15$. This property is true for any numbers, so $\frac{3}{5} \times 5 = 5 \times \frac{3}{5}$.

Use Cuisenaire rods to model the products in the *Examples* in *Connect*.

REACHING ALL LEARNERS

Early Finishers

Have students make up another problem similar to question 9, and solve it. Students trade problems with a classmate, then solve the classmate's problem, and compare solutions. Students may need to edit their problems and/or solutions after other students have tried them.

Common Misconceptions

➤ Students erroneously multiply the denominator by the whole number.

How to Help: Encourage students to read the problem aloud; for example, 4 times three-fifths is twelve-fifths. Alternatively, have students write the product as a sum of fractions first.

Sample Answers

6. a) i)

ii)

b) The products are equal. The numerator and whole number are interchanged. $5 \times \frac{3}{8} = 3 \times \frac{5}{8} = \frac{15}{8}$

7. $\frac{9}{4}$ cups $= 2\frac{1}{4}$ cups

8. a)

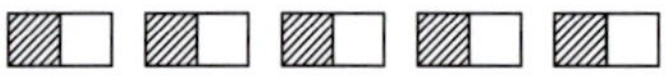

$\frac{5}{2}$ or $2\frac{1}{2}$

Example 1

Use multiplication to find this sum.

$\frac{3}{8} + \frac{3}{8} + \frac{3}{8} + \frac{3}{8} + \frac{3}{8} + \frac{3}{8} + \frac{3}{8} + \frac{3}{8} + \frac{3}{8}$

Solution

$\frac{3}{8} + \frac{3}{8} + \frac{3}{8} + \frac{3}{8} + \frac{3}{8} + \frac{3}{8} + \frac{3}{8} + \frac{3}{8} + \frac{3}{8} = 9 \times \frac{3}{8}$

$= \frac{27}{8}$

Think: 9 times 3 eighths is 27 eighths.

Example 2

Multiply.

a) $\frac{3}{5} \times 5$ b) $7 \times \frac{5}{6}$

Solution

a) $\frac{3}{5} \times 5 = \frac{15}{5}$

$= 3$

Think: $\frac{15}{5}$ means $15 \div 5$, which is 3.

b) $7 \times \frac{5}{6} = \frac{35}{6}$

Think: 7 times 5 sixths is 35 sixths.

Practice

1. Write each repeated addition as a multiplication question.

a) $\frac{1}{4} + \frac{1}{4} + \frac{1}{4} = 3 \times \frac{1}{4}$

b) $\frac{2}{7} + \frac{2}{7} + \frac{2}{7} + \frac{2}{7} + \frac{2}{7} = 5 \times \frac{2}{7}$

c) $\frac{3}{10} + \frac{3}{10} + \frac{3}{10} + \frac{3}{10} = 4 \times \frac{3}{10}$

2. Write each multiplication question as repeated addition. Draw a picture to show each answer.

a) $5 \times \frac{1}{8}$ $\frac{1}{8} + \frac{1}{8} + \frac{1}{8} + \frac{1}{8} + \frac{1}{8}$

b) $\frac{2}{5} \times 3$ $\frac{2}{5} + \frac{2}{5} + \frac{2}{5}$

c) $4 \times \frac{5}{12}$ $\frac{5}{12} + \frac{5}{12} + \frac{5}{12}$

3. Multiply. Draw a picture to show each answer.

a) $3 \times \frac{4}{7} = \frac{12}{7}$ b) $5 \times \frac{1}{12} = \frac{5}{12}$ c) $\frac{2}{15} \times 10 = \frac{20}{15}$

d) $4 \times \frac{9}{4} = \frac{36}{4}$ or 9 e) $\frac{2}{5} \times 7 = \frac{14}{5}$ f) $9 \times \frac{1}{2} = \frac{9}{2}$

142 UNIT 4: Fractions and Decimals

For *Example 1*, since the denominator is 8, use the rod that is 8 cm long, the brown rod, to represent one whole. Then $\frac{3}{8}$ is represented by the light green rod.

Place 9 light green rods in a line.

Beneath these rods, place as many brown rods as needed to find the total of the fractions represented by the light green rods.

We need 4 brown rods. The light green rods align to show 3 wholes and $\frac{3}{8}$. The sum $\frac{27}{8}$ can be written as $3\frac{3}{8}$.

For *Example 2a*, use the yellow rod to represent one whole, and the light green rod to represent $\frac{3}{5}$. Align the green rods. Align the yellow rods. Three yellow rods align with 5 green rods to show that $\frac{3}{5} \times 5 = 3$.

For *Example 2b*, use the dark green rod to represent one whole and the yellow rod to represent $\frac{5}{6}$. The rods illustrate that $\frac{35}{6}$ can be written as $5\frac{5}{6}$.

Practice

Provide 0.5-cm grid paper (PM 14) for students to record their pictures.

Assessment Focus, Question 8

Students can represent $5 \times \frac{1}{2}$ as 5 congruent rectangles, with $\frac{1}{2}$ of each rectangle shaded. For $\frac{1}{2} \times 5$, students know it is $2\frac{1}{2}$ (from part a), so they can interpret $\frac{1}{2} \times 5$ as $\frac{1}{2}$ of 5, and draw a set of 5 objects, with $2\frac{1}{2}$ of them shaded.

4. Multiply.

a) $3 \times \frac{4}{5} = \frac{12}{5}$ b) $5 \times \frac{7}{10} = \frac{35}{10} = \frac{7}{2}$ c) $\frac{5}{6} \times 6 = \frac{30}{6} = 5$

d) $\frac{1}{2} \times 5 = \frac{5}{2}$ e) $12 \times \frac{7}{12} = \frac{84}{12} = 7$ f) $\frac{2}{3} \times 9 = \frac{18}{3} = 6$

5. It takes $\frac{2}{3}$ h to pick all the apples on one tree at Springwater Farms. There are 24 trees.
How long will it take to pick all the apples? 16 h
Show your work.

Number Strategies

Calculate each answer.

$6000 \div 10 = 6000 \times 0.1 = 600$
$600 \div 10 = 600 \times 0.1 = 60$
$60 \div 10 = 60 \times 0.1 = 6$
$6 \div 10 = 6 \times 0.1 = 0.6$

What patterns do you see in the questions and answers?

6. a) Draw a picture to show each product. What is each answer?
i) $4 \times \frac{3}{10} = \frac{12}{10}$ ii) $3 \times \frac{4}{10} = \frac{12}{10}$
b) How are the questions in part a related?
Write 2 more questions like these.
Find each product. What do you notice?

7. A cookie recipe calls for $\frac{3}{4}$ cup of oatmeal.
How much oatmeal is needed to make 3 batches of cookies?
$\frac{9}{4}$ cups $= 2\frac{1}{4}$ cups

8. **Assessment Focus**
a) Draw a picture to show $5 \times \frac{1}{2}$.
b) What meaning can you give to $\frac{1}{2} \times 5$?
Draw a picture to show your thinking.

Take It Further

9. Jacob takes $\frac{3}{4}$ h to fill one shelf at the supermarket.
Henry can fill the shelves in half Jacob's time.
There are 15 shelves. Henry and Jacob work together.
How long will it take to fill the shelves? Justify your answer.

Reflect

Draw a picture to show why $4 \times \frac{2}{5}$ is the same as $\frac{2}{5} + \frac{2}{5} + \frac{2}{5} + \frac{2}{5}$.
Explain your picture.
Draw a different picture to show the same answer.

4.6 Exploring Repeated Addition 143

b) $\frac{1}{2} \times 5$ is equal to $5 \times \frac{1}{2} = 2\frac{1}{2}$. So, $\frac{1}{2} \times 5$ is $2\frac{1}{2}$. Since $\frac{1}{2}$ of 5 is $2\frac{1}{2}$, then $\frac{1}{2} \times 5$ means $\frac{1}{2}$ of 5. I have 5 cookies. I give my friend half of the cookies. My friend has $2\frac{1}{2}$ cookies.

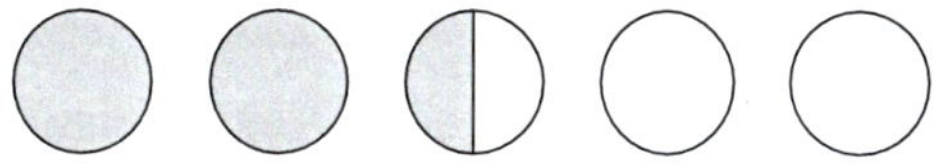

9. Jacob fills 1 shelf in $\frac{3}{4}$ h. Henry fills 2 shelves in $\frac{3}{4}$ h. So, together they fill 3 shelves in $\frac{3}{4}$ h. They have 15 shelves to fill. Since $15 = 3 \times 5$, they will take $5 \times \frac{3}{4}$ h $= \frac{15}{4}$ h $= 3\frac{3}{4}$ h.

REFLECT:

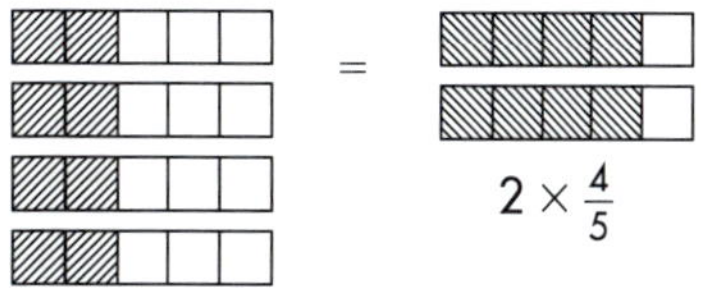

$4 \times \frac{2}{5} = 2 \times \frac{4}{5} = \frac{8}{5}$ because we multiply the whole number and numerator to get the total number of fifths.

Assignment Guidelines

If your students do not have time to complete all the *Practice* questions, these questions provide the minimum curriculum coverage: 1, 2, 3, 5, 6, 8, 9, *Reflect*
To assess the 4 Achievement Chart categories in the curriculum document, have students complete these questions:
Understanding Concepts: 3
Application: 5
Communication: 6
Problem Solving: 9

ASSESSMENT FOR LEARNING

What to Look For	What to Do
Understanding concepts ✔ Students understand that the repeated addition of a fraction is the same as the product of a whole number (which is the number of fractions) and the fraction. ***Applying procedures*** ✔ Student can apply what they know about the product of whole numbers to the product of a fraction and a whole number. ***Problem solving*** ✔ Students can use the product of a fraction and a whole number to solve problems.	***Extra Support:*** Have students continue to draw diagrams or use fraction strips to model each question. Students can use Step-by-Step 6 (Master 4.14) to complete question 8. ***Extra Practice:*** Have students work in pairs, with grid paper and 3 number cubes labelled 1 to 6, 3 to 8, and 5 to 10. One student rolls the cubes, and uses the 3 numbers to write a fraction and a whole number. The other student multiplies the fraction and whole number, then draws a picture to illustrate the product. Students take turns to roll the cubes. Students can complete Extra Practice 6 (Master 4.37). ***Extension:*** Have students choose 3 different numbers between 0 and 10. They use these numbers to write as many different multiplication questions as they can, and find each product.

Recording and Reporting
Master 4.2 Ongoing Observations: Fractions and Decimals

Fractions to Decimals

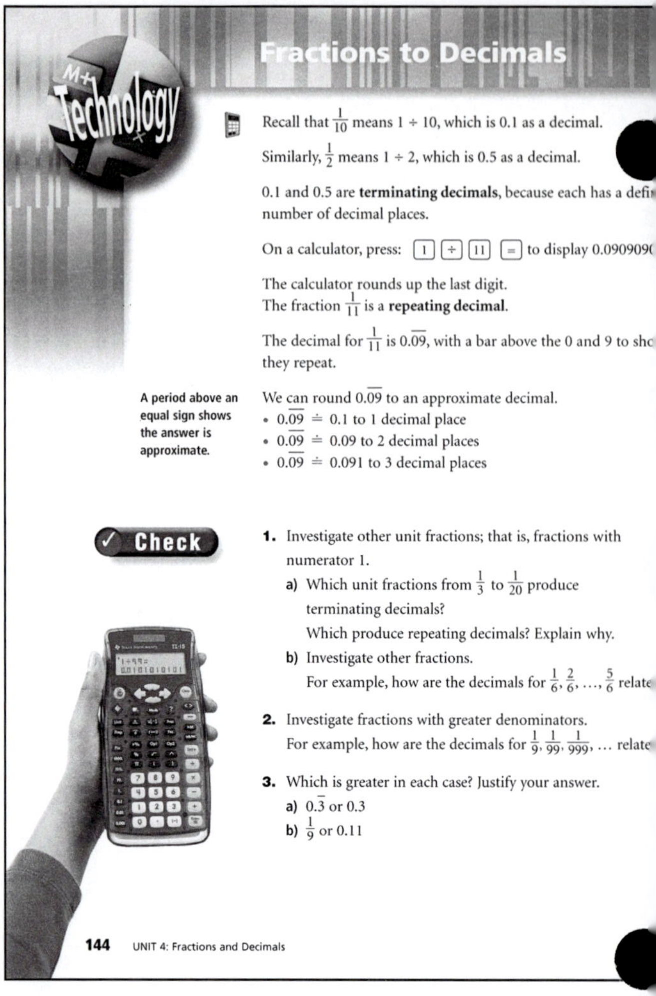
Fractions to Decimals

Recall that $\frac{1}{10}$ means $1 \div 10$, which is 0.1 as a decimal.

Similarly, $\frac{1}{2}$ means $1 \div 2$, which is 0.5 as a decimal.

0.1 and 0.5 are **terminating decimals**, because each has a defi
number of decimal places.

On a calculator, press: [1] [÷] [11] [=] to display 0.090909

The calculator rounds up the last digit.
The fraction $\frac{1}{11}$ is a **repeating decimal**.

The decimal for $\frac{1}{11}$ is $0.\overline{09}$, with a bar above the 0 and 9 to sho
they repeat.

A period above an equal sign shows the answer is approximate.

We can round $0.\overline{09}$ to an approximate decimal.
- $0.\overline{09} \doteq 0.1$ to 1 decimal place
- $0.\overline{09} \doteq 0.09$ to 2 decimal places
- $0.\overline{09} \doteq 0.091$ to 3 decimal places

✓ Check

1. Investigate other unit fractions; that is, fractions with numerator 1.
   a) Which unit fractions from $\frac{1}{3}$ to $\frac{1}{20}$ produce terminating decimals?
   Which produce repeating decimals? Explain why.
   b) Investigate other fractions.
   For example, how are the decimals for $\frac{1}{6}, \frac{2}{6}, \dots, \frac{5}{6}$ relate
2. Investigate fractions with greater denominators.
   For example, how are the decimals for $\frac{1}{9}, \frac{1}{99}, \frac{1}{999}, \dots$ relate
3. Which is greater in each case? Justify your answer.
   a) $0.\overline{3}$ or 0.3
   b) $\frac{1}{9}$ or 0.11

144 UNIT 4: Fractions and Decimals

SECTION ORGANIZER

Curriculum Focus: Develop calculator skills to convert a fraction to a decimal. (7m9, 7m23, 7m27)

Teacher Materials
- calculator

Optional
- overhead calculator

Student Materials
- calculator
- Fractions to Decimals table (Master 4.29)

Vocabulary: terminating decimal, repeating decimal

Assessment: Master 4.2 Ongoing Observations: Fractions and Decimals

Key Math Learning

Any fraction can be written as a decimal. Some decimals terminate; others repeat.

Distribute copies of Fractions to Decimals table (Master 4.29) for students to record their answers to question 1.

Students may use different types of calculators. As you review repeating decimals, with the decimal form of a fraction such as $\frac{1}{11}$, ensure students know if their calculators truncate and show 0.090909090, or if their calculators round to get the last digit in the display and show 0.090909091.

Review these rules for rounding decimals.

- If the digit that follows what is to be the final digit is 5 or greater, then round up what will be the final digit, and delete all following digits.
- If the digit that follows what is to be the final digit is less than 5, then delete all following digits.

Note that the calculator displays are too short to show how decimals for fractions with these denominators repeat: 7, 13, 14, 17, 19

Sample Answers

1. a) Terminating: $\frac{1}{4}, \frac{1}{5}, \frac{1}{8}, \frac{1}{10}, \frac{1}{16}, \frac{1}{20}$; all others are repeating.
   b) All are repeating decimals except $\frac{3}{6}$. Also, the decimal for $\frac{2}{6}$ is two times the decimal for $\frac{1}{6}$, and so on.
2. $0.\overline{1}$, $0.\overline{01}$, $0.\overline{001}$; as the number of 9s increases in the denominator, so does the number of 0s in the repeating part of the decimal.
3. a) $0.\overline{3} = 0.3333333 \dots$; this is greater than 0.3, which can be written as 0.3000000
   b) $\frac{1}{9} = 0.1111111 \dots$; this is greater than 0.11, which can be written as 0.11000000

Multiplying Decimals

4.7 Multiplying Decimals

Focus Multiply decimals with tenths.

To multiply 2 whole numbers, we can use Base Ten Blocks.
This picture shows the product
$20 \times 16 = 100 + 100 + 60 + 60$
$= 320$

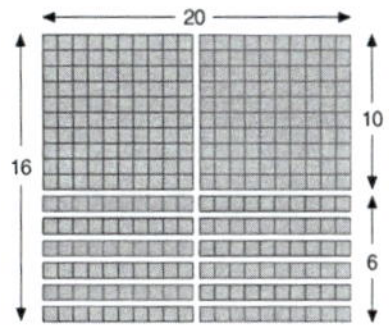

We can also use Base Ten Blocks to multiply a decimal and a whole number.

The flat represents 1. The rod represents 0.1. The small cube represents 0.01.

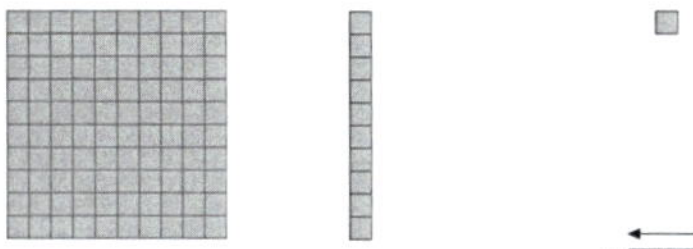

This picture shows the product
$2 \times 1.6 = 1 + 1 + 0.6 + 0.6$
$= 3.2$

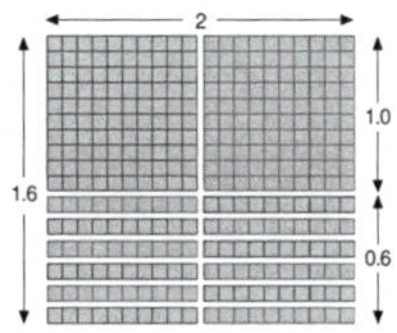

In *Explore*, you will use Base Ten Blocks to multiply 2 decimals.

Explore

Work with a partner.
A rectangular tabletop measures 2.4 m by 1.8 m. $2.4 \times 1.8 = 4.32$
Use Base Ten Blocks to find the area of the tabletop.
Record your work on grid paper.

Reflect & Share

Compare your answer with that of another pair of classmates.
Did you draw the same picture? Explain.
Did you get the same area? Explain.

4.7 Multiplying Decimals 145

SECTION ORGANIZER (80–100 min)

Curriculum Focus: Multiply decimals with tenths. (7m26)

Teacher Materials
- Base Ten Blocks
- 0.5-cm chart paper

Student Materials
- Base Ten Blocks
- 0.5-cm grid paper (PM 14)
- ruler

Optional
- Step-by-Step 7 (Master 4.15)
- Extra Practice 7 (Master 4.38)

Assessment: Master 4.2 Ongoing Observations: Fractions and Decimals

Key Math Learning

Base Ten Blocks and the area model used for multiplying whole numbers can also be used to multiply decimals.

BEFORE Get Started

Review how to use Base Ten Blocks to multiply whole numbers and to record this on 0.5-cm grid paper. Model this on large grid chart paper that students can refer to. Students need to understand the change in values of the flat, rod, and small cube. Encourage students to use a ruler to produce neat diagrams.

DURING Explore

Ongoing Assessment: Observe and Listen

As students work in pairs, ask:
- How do you find the area of a rectangle? (*I use the formula* $A = lw$*.*)
- What is an estimate of the area? ($2\ m \times 2\ m = 4\ m^2$)
- What product do the Base Ten Blocks show if you were multiplying whole numbers? ($24 \times 18 = 100 + 100 + 80 + 80 + 40 + 32 = 432$)
- What product do the Base Ten Blocks show if you are multiplying decimals? ($2.4 \times 1.8 = 1 + 1 + 0.8 + 0.8 + 0.4 + 0.32 = 4.32$)
- How does your estimate compare with your answer? (*The estimate was 4 and the answer is 4.32. These numbers are so close so our answer is probably correct.*)
- How could you find the area using what you know about whole number multiplication? (*Multiply the decimals as though they were whole numbers, then use the estimate to place the decimal point.*)

As students compare Base Ten Blocks and grid paper calculations, they should only have differences in the orientation of the blocks or grid. Any place value or numerical differences from 4.32 m^2 should be resolved. Were the flats, rods, and small cubes assigned the correct values? Were all pieces counted?

REACHING ALL LEARNERS

Early Finishers

Have students use their results from *Practice* questions 12 and 13 to multiply 1.32×2.1 and 4.01×0.89.

Common Misconceptions

➤ Students confuse the multiplication of decimals with the addition of decimals, and write the question as a product with the decimal points in place. They then place the decimal point in the product below the decimal points in the numbers that are multiplied.

How to Help: Guide students to always estimate the product to place the decimal point.

Connect

A rectangular park measures 1.7 km by 2.5 km.
Here are 2 ways to find the area of the park.

➢ Use Base Ten Blocks.

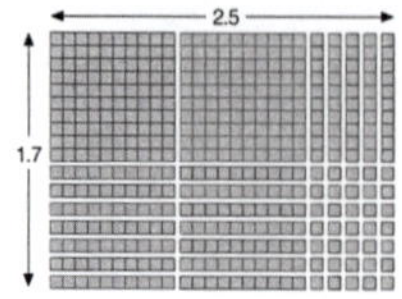

There are 2 flats: $2 \times 1 = 2$
There are 19 rods: $19 \times 0.1 = 1.9$
There are 35 small cubes: $35 \times 0.01 = 0.35$
The total area is $2 + 1.9 + 0.35 = 4.25$
The area of the park is 4.25 km^2.

➢ Use the method for multiplying 2 whole numbers.
The area, in square kilometres, is 1.7×2.5.
Multiply: 17×25

$$\begin{array}{r} 17 \\ \times\ 25 \\ \hline 85 \\ 340 \\ \hline 425 \end{array}$$

Estimate to place the decimal point in the answer.
1.7×2.5 is about $2 \times 3 = 6$
So, the product is 4.25.
The area of the park is 4.25 km^2.

Example 1

Multiply. 5.8×9.7

Solution

5.8×9.7
Multiply: 58×97

$$\begin{array}{r} 58 \\ \times\ 97 \\ \hline 406 \\ 5220 \\ \hline 5626 \end{array}$$

Estimate to place the decimal point.
5.8×9.7 is about $6 \times 10 = 60$.
So, the product is 56.26.

146 UNIT 4: Fractions and Decimals

AFTER Connect

Have students compare their pictures on grid paper. Different orientations that produce the same product illustrate $2.4 \times 1.8 = 1.8 \times 2.4$. This is the commutative property of multiplication. Introduce this term if you think your students would benefit from knowing the terminology.

Have students use Base Ten Blocks to model the area of the park in *Connect*. Encourage students to share how this relates to whole number multiplication.

There is a limit to the products that can be displayed using Base Ten Blocks or grid paper. For a product such as that in *Example 1*, students would need 45 flats, 107 rods, and 56 small cubes.
That is, 9.7×5.8
$= 9 \times 5 + 9 \times 0.8 + 5 \times 0.7 + 0.7 \times 0.8$
= 45 ones + 72 tenths + 35 tenths + 56 hundredths
= 45 ones + 107 tenths + 56 hundredths.

Similarly, to show this product on 0.5-cm grid paper, you would need 97 squares by 58 squares, which is 97×0.5 cm by 58×0.5 cm = 48.5 cm by 29 cm.

This is one reason why we use long multiplication to multiply two decimals.

As you review *Example 2b,* have students model it with Base Ten Blocks and draw it on 0.5-cm grid paper.

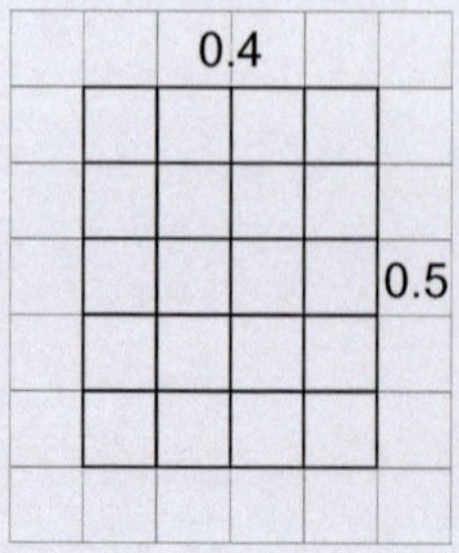

Each small square represents 0.01, or one-hundredth.
There are 20 small squares, or 20 hundredths.
So, $0.5 \times 0.4 = 0.20$

Example 2

Multiply.

a) 0.9×6.8 b) 0.5×0.4

Solution

a) 0.9×6.8

Multiply: 9×68

$$\begin{array}{r} 68 \\ \times\ 9 \\ \hline 612 \end{array}$$

Estimate to place the decimal point.

0.9×6.8 is about $1 \times 7 = 7$.

So, the product is 6.12.

b) 0.5×0.4

Multiply: $5 \times 4 = 20$

Estimate to place the decimal point.

0.5×0.4 is about $1 \times 0.4 = 0.4$.

So, the product is 0.20.

Practice

1. Write a multiplication equation for each picture.
Each small square represents 0.01.

a) 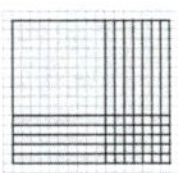 $1.7 \times 1.5 = 2.55$

b) 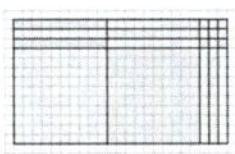 $2.3 \times 1.3 = 2.99$

2. Use Base Ten Blocks to find each product.
a) $2.6 \times 1.5 = 3.9$ b) $1.4 \times 2.8 = 3.92$ c) $2.7 \times 1.6 = 4.32$

3. Use Base Ten Blocks to find each product.
Record your work on grid paper.
a) $2.3 \times 0.4 = 0.92$ b) $0.6 \times 1.9 = 1.14$ c) $0.8 \times 0.7 = 0.56$

4. Multiply: $36 \times 24 = 864$
Use this to find each product. Explain your work.
a) $36 \times 2.4 = 86.4$ b) $3.6 \times 24 = 86.4$ c) $3.6 \times 2.4 = 8.64$

5. Multiply.
a) $4.2 \times 3.7 = 15.54$ b) $8.9 \times 0.3 = 2.67$ c) $0.6 \times 0.9 = 0.54$

4.7 Multiplying Decimals 147

Sample Answers

8. a) i) 11.34 ii) 2.94 iii) 0.40
b) The total number of decimal places in the question is equal to the number of decimal places in the answer.
Find the total number of decimal places in the question, then use this number in the answer by counting places from right to left.

9. 0.4×0.9 or 0.2×1.8 or 0.1×3.6 or 0.6×0.6 or 0.5×0.72, and so on

11. I did not have enough Base Ten Blocks, so I used a sheet of grid paper. I drew a rectangle that was 34 squares long and 27 squares wide. Each small square represents 0.01 m^2.
A 10 by 10 square represents 1 m^2. The area is 9.18 m^2.
I also multiplied: 34×27, then estimated the answer to place the decimal point: 3.4×2.7 is about $3 \times 3 = 9$.
The second strategy is better because drawing a rectangle and counting squares took me longer to do.

12. a) i) 25.44 ii) 2.88 iii) 0.24
b) If both decimals in the question are greater than 1, then the product is greater than both numbers. If one decimal in the question is greater than 1 and the other decimal is between 0 and 1, then the product is between the two given decimals. If both decimals are between 0 and 1, then the product is less than both these decimals.

13. The side length of one small square on grid paper represents 0.1. When I multiply 0.1 by 0.1, I get the area of the square as 0.01. So, when I multiply a decimal with tenths by a decimal with tenths, I get a decimal with hundredths.

If time permits, review this strategy for multiplying whole numbers:

$$\begin{aligned} 51 \times 25 &= (50 + 1) \times (20 + 5) \\ &= (50 \times 20) + (50 \times 5) + (1 \times 20) + (1 \times 5) \\ &= 1000 + 250 + 20 + 5 \\ &= 1275 \end{aligned}$$

Then, apply the strategy to multiplying decimals:

$$\begin{aligned} 5.1 \times 2.5 &= (5 + 0.1) \times (2 + 0.5) \\ &= (5 \times 2) + (5 \times 0.5) + (0.1 \times 2) + (0.1 \times 0.5) \\ &= 10 + 2.5 + 0.2 + 0.05 \\ &= 12.75 \end{aligned}$$

Practice

Students could use calculators only to check their answers. Students need 0.5-cm grid paper (PM 14) to illustrate the products in question 3.

For question 9, students may first want to find factors of 36, then decide how to write the factors as decimals, so their product is 0.36.

Question 10 illustrates an important relationship: to multiply by a unit fraction, divide by the denominator. For example, to multiply by $\frac{1}{2}$, divide by 2; to multiply by $\frac{1}{10}$, divide by 10.

Assessment Focus: Question 11

Since the numbers may be too large to permit the practical use of Base Ten Blocks, students can sketch a diagram on grid paper to show the area model.

REFLECT: I multiplied: 4.8×3.6.
I used long multiplication of whole numbers to find that
$48 \times 36 = 1728$.
Then I estimated to place the decimal point.
4.8×3.6 is about $5 \times 4 = 20$.
So, I put the decimal point after the 7 to get 17.28.

Calculator Skills

Students can refer to the work they did for *Technology: Fractions to Decimals*, page 144, or use a calculator to express the fractions as decimals to compare them.

Assignment Guidelines

If your students do not have time to complete all the *Practice* questions on pages 147, 148, these questions provide minimum curriculum coverage: 3, 5, 7, 9, 11, 12, *Reflect*
To assess the 4 Achievement Chart categories listed in the curriculum document, have students complete these *Practice* questions:
Understanding Concepts: 3
Application: 7
Problem Solving: 9
Communication: 12

---

6. Carla drives 7.6 km to work. She drives the same distance hom
How many kilometres does Carla drive in a 5-day workweek? 76 km

7. A rectangular plot of land measures 30.5 m by 5.3 m.
What is the area of the plot? $A = 161.65\ m^2$

8. a) Multiply.
i) $6.3 \times 1.8 = 11.34$ ii) $4.2 \times 0.7 = 2.94$ iii) $0.8 \times 0.5 =$
b) Look at the questions and products in part a. What patterns do you see in the numbers of decimal places in the question and the product? How could you use this pattern to place the decimal point in a product without estimating?

Calculator Skills

Which is greater in each pair?
0.3 or $\frac{1}{3}$ 0.4 or $\frac{1}{4}$
0.7 or $\frac{2}{3}$ 0.09 or $\frac{1}{11}$
Justify your answer.

9. The product of 2 decimals is 0.36.
What might the decimals be? Find as many answers as possible

10. Recall that dividing by 10 is the same as multiplying by 0.1.
Multiply to find:
a) $\frac{1}{10}$ of 25.2 = 2.52 b) $\frac{2}{10}$ of 37.3 = 7.46 c) $\frac{6}{10}$ of 58.7 = 35.2

11. Assessment Focus An area rug is rectangular.
Its dimensions are 3.4 m by 2.7 m.
Show different strategies you can use to find the area of the rug. Which strategy is best? Justify your answer.
$A = 9.18\ m^2$

12. a) Find each product.
i) $4.8 \times 5.3 = 25.44$ ii) $4.8 \times 0.6 = 2.88$ iii) $0.4 \times 0.6 = 0$
b) When you multiply 2 decimals, how does the product compare with the numbers you multiplied?
Explain your reasoning.

Take It Further

13. Explain why the sum of the number of digits to the right of the decimal point in the factors of a product equals the number of digits to the right of the decimal point in the product.

Reflect

When you multiply 2 decimals, how do you know where to place th decimal point in the product? Use examples to explain.

148 UNIT 4: Fractions and Decimals

ASSESSMENT FOR LEARNING

What to Look For	What to Do
Understanding concepts ✔ Students understand how to multiply decimals. ***Applying procedures*** ✔ Students can use estimation to place the decimal point correctly in a product. ***Communicating*** ✔ Students can use pictures and whole number multiplication to explain decimal multiplication.	***Extra Support:*** Students who have difficulty placing the decimal point may need to continue to use Base Ten Blocks for multiplication. Students who do not know the multiplication facts up to 12×12 could make and use a multiplication chart. Students can use Step-by-Step 7 (Master 4.15) to complete question 11. ***Extra Practice:*** Students can complete Extra Practice 7 (Master 4.38) ***Extension:*** Have students make up and solve word problems similar to *Practice* questions 6 and 7.

Recording and Reporting
Master 4.2 Ongoing Observations: Fractions and Decimals

4.8 Dividing Decimals

Focus Divide decimals with tenths.

Recall that we can use the same Base Ten Blocks to multiply:
14 × 18 = 252 and 1.4 × 1.8 = 2.52

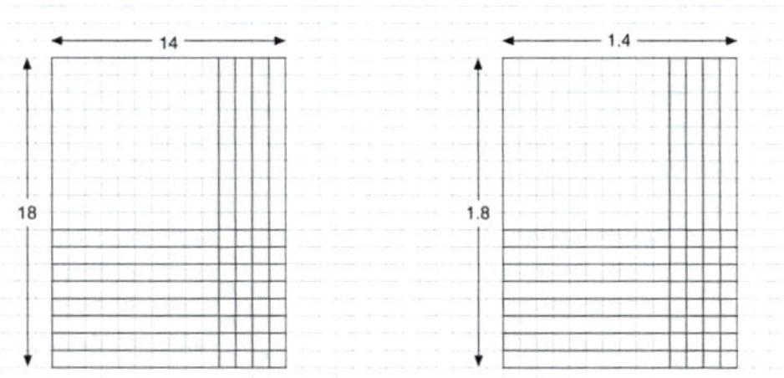

The only difference is the values we assign to the flat, the rod, and the small cube.

In a similar way, we can divide 2 decimals by thinking about whole numbers instead.

So, 252 ÷ 18 = 14 and 2.52 ÷ 1.8 = 1.4

To divide 2 decimals, ignore the decimal points.
Divide as you would whole numbers, then estimate to place the decimal point in the answer.

Explore

Work with a partner.
Mark bought 19.5 m of fabric to make costumes for a play.
Each costume needs 2.6 m of fabric.
How many costumes can Mark make? 7
How much material is left over? 1.3 m
Show your work.

Reflect & Share

How did you use division of whole numbers to find your answer?

4.8 Dividing Decimals 149

SECTION 4.8

Dividing Decimals

SECTION ORGANIZER (80–100 min)

Curriculum Focus: Divide decimals with tenths. (7m26)
Teacher Materials
- Base Ten Blocks
- 0.5-cm grid paper (PM 14)

Student Materials
Optional
- Base Ten Blocks
- 0.5-cm grid paper
- Step-by-Step 8 (Master 4.16)
- Extra Practice 8 (Master 4.39)

Assessment: Master 4.2 Ongoing Observations: Fractions and Decimals

Key Math Learning

Multiplication is the inverse of division. So, Base Ten Blocks and the area model can be used to illustrate the division of decimals.

BEFORE Get Started

Students may want to see how Base Ten Blocks or grid paper can be used to divide: 2.52 ÷ 1.8

On the grid chart paper, draw one side of a rectangle that is 1.8 units long. This will be modelled with 18 small squares. Draw an arrangement of large squares (one large square is 10 small squares by 10 small squares); rods (one rod is 1 small square by 10 small squares); and small squares to make a rectangle with an area of 2.52.

The second side of the rectangle (that is, the side that is not equal to 1.8) is then the quotient of the division question:
2.52 ÷ 1.8 = 1.4. This model is not intuitive and some students may have difficulty drawing the rectangle.

That is why this lesson uses long division instead of the area model to find a quotient.

DURING Explore

Ongoing Assessment: Observe and Listen

As students work in pairs, ask:
- Why would you choose to use division?
  (I need to find how many lengths of 2.6 m are in 19.5 m. It is easier to divide by 2.6 than to do repeated subtractions of 2.6 from 19.5.)
- What is an estimate of the number of costumes? *(I rounded both numbers to numbers that I know division facts for: 19.5 ÷ 2.6 is about 21 ÷ 3, which is 7.)*
- What is the long division answer? *(7.5)*
- Can Mark round this answer?
  (If I round up, the answer is 8, but I know there is not enough material to make 8 costumes. So, I round down to 7. Mark can make 7 costumes and he will have some material left over.)

REACHING ALL LEARNERS

Early Finishers

Have students use grid paper or Base Ten Blocks to complete the divisions.

Common Misconceptions

➤ Students do not know how to estimate a possible quotient for each step in the long division process.

How to Help: In the *Example, part b*: 252 ÷ 47; have students round the dividend and divisor to "friendly numbers": 250 ÷ 50; then, they can ignore the zeros and divide 25 by 5 to get 5. If this estimate does not work, students can try the numbers that are 1 more than and 1 less than this number.

ESL Strategies

To help with the vocabulary of division, students could complete a division question and then use arrows to label each part: divisor, dividend, and quotient.

Math Link

Have students suggest different items that may be measured with each unit: for example, the length of an eyelash in millimetres; the thickness of a hair in micrometres. The symbol for micrometres is μm.

Connect

Jan bought 18.9 m of framing to make picture frames.
Each picture needs 1.8 m of frame.
How many frames can Jan make?
How much framing material is left over?

When you divide 2 numbers, the answer is the quotient.

To divide: 18.9 ÷ 1.8, ignore the decimal points.
Find 189 ÷ 18, then estimate.

```
   10.5
18)189.0
   180
     9 0
     9 0
       0
```

189 ÷ 18 = 10.5
Estimate to place the decimal point correctly.
18.9 ÷ 1.8 is about 20 ÷ 2, which is 10.
So, 18.9 ÷ 1.8 is 10.5.

Jan can make 10 frames.
10 frames use 10 × 1.8 m = 18 m.
So, the framing material left is 18.9 m – 18 m = 0.9 m.

Sometimes when we divide 2 decimals, the quotient is not a terminating decimal.

Example

Divide.

a) 12.5 ÷ 0.6 b) 25.2 ÷ 4.7

Solution

a) 12.5 ÷ 0.6

```
6 |125.⁵0²0²0
   20. 8 3 3
```

Think: Use short division to find 125 ÷ 6.

If we continue to divide, the 3 in the quotient repeats.
So, 125 ÷ 6 = $20.8\overline{3}$
To estimate: 12.5 ÷ 0.6 is about 13 ÷ 1 = 13.
So, the quotient is $20.8\overline{3}$.

150 UNIT 4: Fractions and Decimals

- What did you do to find how much material is leftover?
  (*I multiplied 2.6 by 7 to get 18.2, then I subtracted: 19.5 − 18.2 = 1.3, to get 1.3 m of material left over.*)

AFTER Connect

Review how to divide two decimals, by ignoring the decimal points, dividing whole numbers, then estimating to place the decimal point.

An alternative strategy is to multiply both divisor and dividend by 10, to get the whole number question: 189 ÷ 18.

You could write the division as a fraction: $\frac{18.9}{1.8}$, then write an equivalent fraction by multiplying numerator and denominator by 10.

$$\frac{18.9}{1.8} \xrightarrow{\times 10} = \frac{189}{18}$$

(× 10 applied to both numerator and denominator)

As you review the long division, remind students that instead of using a remainder, we mark a decimal point in the dividend and write zeros after it—as many zeros as we need.

The *Example part a* reviews short division and illustrates what to do when the quotient is a repeating decimal.

If necessary, explain the process for each step of the short division.

➤ 6 doesn't go into 1.

➤ 6 into 12 is 2.

➤ 6 doesn't go into 5. Write 0 in the quotient.

➤ Mark a decimal point and write a zero in the dividend. Mark a decimal point in the quotient.

➤ Move the 5 (which is 5 units) to the tenths place, where it becomes 50 tenths.

➤ 6 into 50 is 8 with 2 left over.

b) 25.2 ÷ 4.7   **Think:** Use long division to find 252 ÷ 47.

```
     5.36
47)252.00
   235
    17 0
    14 1
     2 90
     2 82
        8
```

There is 1 decimal place in each number in the question. Continue to divide until there are 2 decimal places in the quotient. That is, calculate the quotient to 1 more decimal place than in the question. Then, round the quotient to 1 decimal place.

Round the quotient to 5.4.
To estimate: 25.2 ÷ 4.7 is about 25 ÷ 5 = 5.
So, the quotient is approximately 5.4.

Practice

1. Look at each division equation on the left. Estimate each quotient on the right.

a) 234 ÷ 13 = 18	23.4 ÷ 1.3 = 18
b) 133 ÷ 7 = 19	13.3 ÷ 7 = 1.9
c) 714 ÷ 34 = 21	71.4 ÷ 3.4 = 21
d) 450 ÷ 18 = 25	4.5 ÷ 1.8 = 2.5
e) 51 ÷ 17 = 3	5.1 ÷ 1.7 = 3

Number Strategies

A rectangular prism has dimensions 6 cm by 4 cm by 8 cm. Find the surface area and volume of this rectangular prism. $SA = 208\ m^2$ $V = 192\ m^3$

2. Choose the correct quotient for each division question. Explain how you know.

Question	Possible Quotients		
a) 5.95 ÷ 3.5	17	(1.7)	0.17
b) 195.3 ÷ 6.2	315	(31.5)	3.15
c) 31.32 ÷ 1.8	174	(17.4)	1.74
d) 1.44 ÷ 0.12	(12)	1.2	0.12

3. Divide.
a) 8.7 ÷ 0.3 = 29 b) 2.24 ÷ 0.7 = 3.2 c) 10.3 ÷ 0.6 = $17.\bar{6}$

4. Divide.
a) 10.92 ÷ 0.6 = 18.2 b) 30.42 ÷ 1.3 = 23.4 c) 18.56 ÷ 5.8 = 3.2

4.8 Dividing Decimals 151

Number Strategies

Students review the formulas for finding the surface area and volume of a prism, from Unit 3, page 106. $SA = 208\ m^2$ and $V = 192\ m^3$

Sample Answers

1. a) 23.4 ÷ 1.3 = 18 b) 13.3 ÷ 7 = 1.9
   c) 71.4 ÷ 3.4 = 21 d) 4.5 ÷ 1.8 = 2.5
   e) 5.1 ÷ 7.1 = 3
2. a) 5.95 ÷ 3.5 is about 6 ÷ 3, which is 2; 1.7 is closest to 2.
   b) 195.3 ÷ 6.2 is about 200 ÷ 5, which is 40; 31.5 is closest to 40.
   c) 31.32 ÷ 1.8 is about 30 ÷ 2, which is 15; 17.4 is closest to 15.
   d) 1.44 ÷ 0.12 is about 14 ÷ 1, which is 14; 12 is closest to 14.
7. 1.2 ÷ 10 , 3.6 ÷ 30, 0.36 ÷ 3, 2.4 ÷ 20, and so on.
8. a) No; she needs 12 × 0.85 m = 10.2 m
   b) If partial pieces can be put together then she needs 0.5 m, or she needs a whole 0.85-m piece if not.
9. 21.5 m
10. 237 ÷ 7 is about 210 ÷ 7, which is 30.
    So, 237 ÷ 7 is about 33.857.
    a) 237 ÷ 0.7 is about 237 ÷ 1, which is 237.
       The closest answer is 338.57.
    b) 2.37 ÷ 7 is about 2 ÷ 7, or $\frac{2}{7}$, which is a bit less

➤ Move the 2 to the hundredths place, where it becomes 20 hundredths.

➤ 6 into 20 is 3 with 2 left over.

➤ Move the 2 to the thousandths place, where it becomes 20 thousandths.

➤ 6 into 20 is 3 with 2 left over.

This process continues indefinitely, so we know the quotient is a repeating decimal.

The *Example part b* illustrates what to do when the quotient appears not to repeat.

If time and interest permit, have students continue the division to verify that it does not appear to repeat.

Practice

Students may want to use calculators. They need the practice with long division and estimation so calculator use should be discouraged.

As students complete question 1, have them explain how they wrote the quotients.
For example, in *part a*, 23.4 ÷ 1.3 rounds to 20 ÷ 1 = 20, so the quotient is 18. In *part b*, 13.7 ÷ 7 rounds to 14 ÷ 7 = 2, so the quotient is 1.9.

For question 7, students could find a division statement with whole numbers that has a quotient of 12, then decide how to write the dividend and divisor as decimals so the quotient is 0.12.

Assessment Focus: Question 8

Students can estimate and divide to determine if Alex has enough fabric. Since the quotient is less than 12, Alex will need more. Students use multiplication and subtraction to calculate the extra amount needed. Students need to organize their work clearly.

than $\frac{1}{2}$, or 0.5. The closest answer is 0.338 57.

c) 23.7 ÷ 7 is about 21 ÷ 7, which is 3.
The closest answer is 3.3857.

d) 2370 ÷ 70 is the same as 237 ÷ 7, which is 33.857, as above.

11. 0.125 g yeast, 1.875 L milk, 2.5 g salt, 7.5 g butter, 2 kg flour, 0.4 kg sugar, 85 g cardamom

12. 2.5 ÷ 0.4 = 6.25; in 6 days, Jack will drink 6 ÷ 0.4 L, or 2.4 L. He will drink the rest on day 7. So, he takes 7 days to drink the juice.

REFLECT: I divided: 18.9 ÷ 4.2.
I used long division of whole numbers to find that
189 ÷ 42 = 4.5.
I estimated to check that the decimal point was in the correct place.
18.9 ÷ 4.2 is about 20 ÷ 4 = 5.
Since 4.5 is close to 5, then 4.5 is the quotient.

Math Link

Measurement

The prefixes in units of length less than 1 m show fractions or decimals of 1 m.

One decimetre is $\frac{1}{10}$ or 0.1 m.

One centimetre is $\frac{1}{100}$ or 0.01 m.

One millimetre is $\frac{1}{1000}$ or 0.001 m.

One micrometre is $\frac{1}{1\,000\,000}$ or 0.000 001 m.

5. Divide. Round the quotient to the nearest tenth.
a) 172.5 ÷ 2.6 = 66.3 b) 21.68 ÷ 3.4 = 6.4 c) 92.8 ÷ 8.2 = 11.3

6. Divide. Round to the nearest tenth where necessary.
a) 7.3 ÷ 0.4 = 18.25 b) 1.98 ÷ 1.3 = 1.5 c) 426.8 ÷ 3.7 = 115.4

7. The quotient of 2 decimals is 0.12. What might the decimals be? Write as many different possible decimal pairs as you can.

8. **Assessment Focus** Alex finds a remnant of landscaping fabric at a garden store.
The fabric is the standard width, with length 9.7 m.
Alex needs twelve 0.85-m pieces for a garden patio.
a) Will Alex have more fabric than she needs? No
If so, how much more?
b) Will Alex need more fabric? If so, how much more?

9. The area of a rectangular lawn is 120.4 m^2.
The width is 5.6 m. What is the length? 21.5 m

10. The question 237 ÷ 7 does not have an exact quotient.
The first five digits of the quotient are 33857. The decimal point has been omitted. Use only this information and estimation.
Write an approximate quotient for each question.
Justify each answer.
a) 237 ÷ 0.7 b) 2.37 ÷ 7 c) 23.7 ÷ 7 d) 2370 ÷ 70

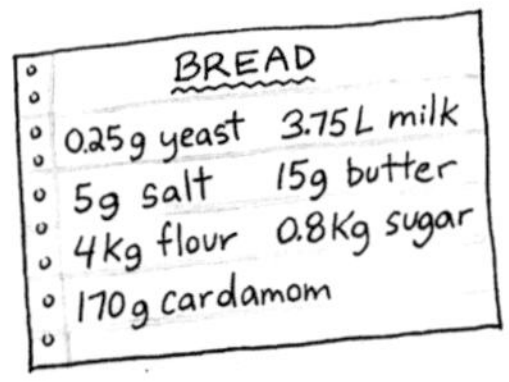

11. Here is a recipe for bread.
Sam wants to make one-half the amount.
Find how much of each ingredient Sam needs.

12. Jack has 2.5 L of juice.
Each day, he drinks 0.4 L.
How many days will it take Jack to drink the juice? 7 days
Justify your answer.

Reflect

Explain how you decide where to place the decimal point when you divide 2 decimals. Use an example in your explanation.

152 UNIT 4: Fractions and Decimals

Assignment Guidelines

If your students do not have time to complete all the *Practice* questions on pages 151, 152, these questions provide minimum curriculum coverage: 2, 4, 6, 7, 8, 9, *Reflect*

To assess the 4 Achievement Chart categories listed in the curriculum document, have students complete these *Practice* questions:
Communication: 2
Understanding Concepts: 6
Problem Solving: 7
Application: 9

ASSESSMENT FOR LEARNING

What to Look For

Understanding concepts

✔ Students understand how to divide decimals.

Applying procedures

✔ Students can use estimation to place the decimal point in a quotient.

Problem solving

✔ Students can choose and organize the correct operations to solve a problem with decimals.

Communicating

✔ Students can present their solutions in an organized form.

What to Do

Extra Support: Students struggling with long division may need a calculator. Encourage them to use the calculator to divide whole numbers and then estimate to place the decimal point rather than using the calculator to answer the question. Students can use Step-by-Step 8 (Master 4.16) to complete question 8.

Extra Practice: Students can complete Extra Practice 8 (Master 4.39).

Extension: Have students make up and solve word problems similar to *Practice* questions 8, 9, 11, and 12.

Recording and Reporting

Master 4.2 Ongoing Observations: Fractions and Decimals

Advertising Sales Representative

Advertising Sales Representative

Magazines and newspapers make money by selling advertising space.

The advertising sales representative contacts companies whose products might be of interest to readers. She offers to sell them various sizes of advertisement space at different rates. When talking about ads smaller than a full page, the sales rep uses fractions to describe them. It's much simpler to talk about a $\frac{2}{3}$-page ad instead of a 0.666 667 page ad!

The sales rep tries to sell combinations of ads that can fill pages, with no space left over. A sales rep has sold two $\frac{1}{4}$-page ads and one $\frac{1}{6}$-page ad. She wants to know the possible combinations of ad sizes she can sell to fill the page. What might they be?

The World of Work: Advertising Sales Representative 153

Sample Solution

The sales rep has sold :

$\frac{1}{4} + \frac{1}{4} + \frac{1}{6} = \frac{1}{2} + \frac{1}{6} = \frac{3}{6} + \frac{1}{6} = \frac{4}{6} = \frac{2}{3}$ of a page of ads.

She needs to sell $\frac{1}{3}$ more. This can be $\frac{1}{6} + \frac{1}{6}$, or $\frac{1}{4} + \frac{1}{12}$, or $\frac{1}{5} + \frac{2}{15}$, and so on.

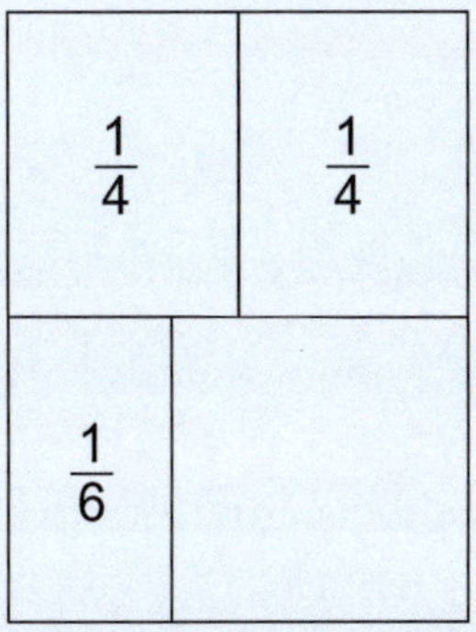

Have students suggest other careers or times in daily life that require the use of operations with fractions.

Trades: Because of our import and export to the United States, we still use Imperial units. Length measurements are $\frac{1}{2}$, $\frac{1}{4}$, $\frac{1}{8}$, $\frac{1}{16}$ of an inch and multiples of these are used in building and carpentry trades, so these tradespeople must be able to operate with fractions to build accurately. The measures of the tools and their components, such as drill bits, are given in Imperial units.

Order of Operations with Decimals

SECTION ORGANIZER 80–100 min

Curriculum Focus: Use the order of operations to evaluate expressions. (7m20)
Student Materials
Optional
- Extra Practice 9 (Master 4.40)
- Step-by-Step 9 (Master 4.17)

Assessment: Master 4.2 Ongoing Observations: Fractions and Decimals

Key Math Learning
The order of operations for whole numbers can be applied to decimals.

4.9 Order of Operations with Decimals

Focus Use the order of operations to evaluate expressions.

We use a base ten, or decimal, number system.
Every whole number is also a decimal.
So, we use the same order of operations for decimals as for whole numbers.

Explore

Work on your own.
Evaluate this expression: $6 \times (15.9 + 36.4) \div 4$
Explain each step.

Reflect & Share

Compare your solution and answer with that of a classmate.
If your answers are different, who has the correct answer?

Connect

Here is the order of operations.
- Do the operations in brackets first.
- Then divide and multiply, in order, from left to right.
- Then add and subtract, in order, from left to right.

Example Evaluate. $12.4 - (4.7 + 1) + 2.4 \times 3 - 4.8 \div 2$

Solution
$12.4 - (4.7 + 1) + 2.4 \times 3 - 4.8 \div 2$ Calculate in brackets.
$= 12.4 - 5.7 + 2.4 \times 3 - 4.8 \div 2$ Multiply and divide from left to rig
$= 12.4 - 5.7 + 7.2 - 2.4$ Add and subtract from left to right.
$= 6.7 + 7.2 - 2.4$
$= 13.9 - 2.4$
$= 11.5$

154 UNIT 4: Fractions and Decimals

BEFORE Get Started

Review the order of operations for whole numbers.

DURING Explore

Ongoing Assessment: Observe and Listen

As students work on their own, ask:
- How could you write an estimate for this question using whole numbers? *($6 \times (16 + 36) \div 4 = 6 \times 52 \div 4 = 6 \times 50 \div 4 = 300 \div 4 = 75$)*
- What is the order of operations with whole numbers? (*Do the operations in brackets, then divide and multiply in order, from left to right, then add and subtract in order, from left to right.*) (*Answer: 78.45*)

AFTER Connect

Have a volunteer write the solution from *Explore* on the board and review the order of operations as this is done. If the example in *Connect* has too many steps for some students, do a simpler example first taken from *Practice* question 1 or 2.

Practice

As students practise, watch for those who want to do all the work mentally or with a calculator. Remind students that good mathematical communication means showing the steps, as modelled in the examples.

Assessment Focus: Question 7

Students need to show all the steps clearly.

Practice

1. Evaluate.
   a) 3.4 + 4 × 7 = 31.4
   b) 14 − 2.2 × 5 = 3
   c) 8 − 3.6 ÷ 2 = 6.2
2. Evaluate.
   a) 7.4 − 3 + 2.3 × 4 = 13.6
   b) 4.6 + 5.1 − 3.2 ÷ 2 = 8.1
   c) 16.4 − (10.8 − 3.1) = 8.7
   d) 23 × 6.2 + 4 = 146.6
   e) 81.2 − (35.8 + 2.1) = 43.3
   f) 85.7 ÷ 0.4 × 7 = 1499.74
3. Evaluate.
   a) 46.78 − 6.1 × 2.3 = 32.75
   b) 75.06 × (3.45 − 1.2) = 168.885
   c) (98.5 + 7) ÷ 2.5 = 42.2
   d) 9.0023 × 5.1 − 4.32 × 6
   e) 8.3 + 46.2 ÷ 1.4 = 41.3
   f) 70.56 − 32.8 ÷ 4.1 = 62.56

   3. d) = 19.99173
4. Evaluate.
   a) 3.2 + 5.6 × 7.2 ÷ 2.4 − 9.3 = 10.7
   b) 8.5 × 7 − 6.3 ÷ 9 + 10.6 = 69.4
   c) 1.35 + (5 × 4.9 ÷ 0.7) − 2.7 × 2.1 = 30.68
   d) (4.7 − 3.1) × 5 − 7.5 ÷ 2.5 = 5
5. Evaluate.
   a) 164.5 ÷ 7 × 10 + 7.2 = 242.2
   b) 73.8 × (3.2 + 6.8) − 14.1 ÷ 0.2 = 667.5
6. The cross-country team members ran timed circuits. Here are their times: 15.8 min, 12.5 min, 18.0 min, 14.2 min, 13.9 min, 16.0 min, 16.2 min, 17.5 min, 16.3 min, 15.6 min. Find the mean time. 15.6 min

7. **Assessment Focus**
   Evaluate. Show all steps.
   0.38 + 16.2 × (2.1 + 4) + 21 ÷ 3.5 = 105.2

Number Sense

A number cube has faces labelled 1 to 6. The cube is rolled 75 times. About how many times will the number 3 show?

Approximately 12 or 13

The mean time is the sum of the times divided by the number of times.

Reflect

Explain why the brackets are unnecessary in this expression:
(4.2 × 3.8) − (15.25 ÷ 6.1)
Find the answer. Show each step.

4.9 Order of Operations with Decimals 155

REACHING ALL LEARNERS

Common Misconceptions

➤ Students do the operations in the order in which they appear, rather than following the order of operations.

How to Help: Have students put brackets around the numbers that are multiplied and divided. Then remind them to do the operations in brackets first.

REFLECT: Multiplying and dividing are done in order, from left to right, before subtraction, so the brackets are not needed:
4.2 × 3.8 − 15.25 ÷ 6.1 = 15.96 − 2.5 = 13.46

Number Sense

The probability that the number 3 shows on one roll is $\frac{1}{6}$.
An estimated number of times 3 might show in 75 rolls is $75 \times \frac{1}{6}$, which is approximately 12 or 13.

Assignment Guidelines

If your students do not have time to complete all the *Practice* questions on page 155, these questions provide minimum curriculum coverage: 2, 4, 6, 7, Reflect

To assess the 4 Achievement Chart categories listed in the curriculum document, have students complete these questions:
Understanding Concepts: 4
Application: 6
Communication: *Reflect*

ASSESSMENT FOR LEARNING

What to Look For	What to Do
Understanding concepts ✔ Students can use the order of operations with decimals. ***Communicating*** ✔ Students can show all steps in a clear, well-organized solution.	***Extra Support:*** Students who struggle with whole number operations could use a calculator, but only to check their work. Students can use Step-by-Step 9 (Master 4.17) to complete question 7. ***Extra Practice:*** Students can complete Extra Practice 9 (Master 4.40). ***Extension:*** Have students make up and solve a word problem that requires the use of the order of operations to solve it.

Recording and Reporting
Master 4.2 Ongoing Observations: Fractions and Decimals

Writing a Math Journal Entry

SECTION ORGANIZER

Vocabulary: dot jots, logical order, journal

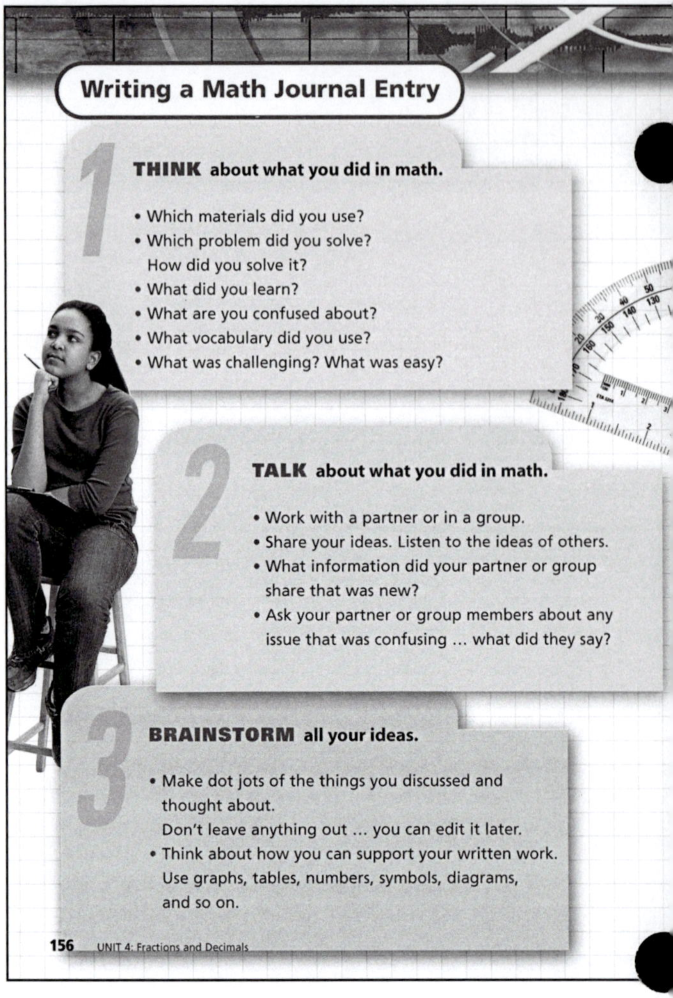
Writing a Math Journal Entry

1 **THINK** about what you did in math.

- Which materials did you use?
- Which problem did you solve? How did you solve it?
- What did you learn?
- What are you confused about?
- What vocabulary did you use?
- What was challenging? What was easy?

2 **TALK** about what you did in math.

- Work with a partner or in a group.
- Share your ideas. Listen to the ideas of others.
- What information did your partner or group share that was new?
- Ask your partner or group members about any issue that was confusing ... what did they say?

3 **BRAINSTORM** all your ideas.

- Make dot jots of the things you discussed and thought about. Don't leave anything out ... you can edit it later.
- Think about how you can support your written work. Use graphs, tables, numbers, symbols, diagrams, and so on.

156 UNIT 4: Fractions and Decimals

A **Math Journal** is a summary of *general* observations, ideas, and conclusions that arise from a *group* of problems or an investigation.

The Math Journal provides a way for students to develop big ideas and generalizations that connect math concepts and procedures from individual problems, problem sets, or investigations. It is a place to record trends, patterns, and relationships; to ask questions; to set goals; and to make personal hypotheses that may be investigated later. A teacher can use the journal as an indication of a student's understanding.

Although journals can be used to reflect on a student's daily performance in class, journal entries are generally best completed upon finishing a math investigation. The journal tends to be more formal than a notebook, and requires more revision and editing.

Discuss the attributes of acceptable journals frequently throughout the year. Regularly show students exemplary journals.

Steps 1 to 3 are important if students are to achieve quality math journal entries. Encourage students to clarify and organize their ideas, and to discuss them with their peers before putting them in writing.

Although capturing ideas in a written record is an important skill, it should not be overemphasized or used as the only evidence of reflective thinking. Students who have difficulty writing may need extra support and explicit instructions to improve this skill. These students should be given every opportunity to express their ideas both orally and visually. Mathematical thinking is important and students should be encouraged to demonstrate their thinking in many different ways. Teachers may often have to separate language skills from the understanding of mathematics.

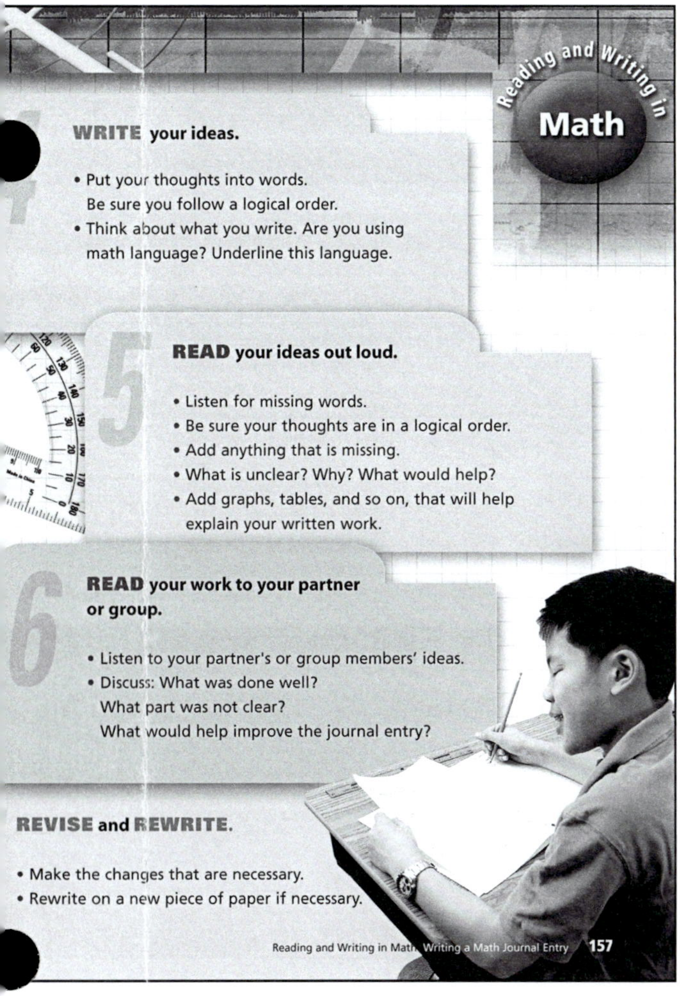
Reading and Writing in Math

WRITE your ideas.

- Put your thoughts into words. Be sure you follow a logical order.
- Think about what you write. Are you using math language? Underline this language.

5 **READ your ideas out loud.**

- Listen for missing words.
- Be sure your thoughts are in a logical order.
- Add anything that is missing.
- What is unclear? Why? What would help?
- Add graphs, tables, and so on, that will help explain your written work.

6 **READ your work to your partner or group.**

- Listen to your partner's or group members' ideas.
- Discuss: What was done well? What part was not clear? What would help improve the journal entry?

REVISE and REWRITE.

- Make the changes that are necessary.
- Rewrite on a new piece of paper if necessary.

Reading and Writing in Math: Writing a Math Journal Entry 157

REACHING ALL LEARNERS

ESL Strategies

Work directly with ESL students during Steps 4, 5 and 6. Have ESL students create pictures, charts, and numbers, then explain them orally instead of in writing. Reduce the amount of writing that is expected. Allow graphic organizers to replace the need for sentences and paragraphs.

Pair ESL students with students whose first language is English and have these strong English speakers assist with writing in English.

BEFORE

Discuss with students the purpose of a Math Journal. Have volunteers read aloud the 7-step process. Model your expectations by working through a collaborative journal entry. Follow each step.

DURING

It is useful to organize the dot jots in Step 3 in a logical order by colour coding, numbering, or cutting and sorting. Step 4 becomes much easier if the list of ideas is already organized. Logical order may need to be clarified. Depending on the topic, ideas might be ordered by:

- Time (for example, order of procedures)
- Importance
- Spatial order (for example, a description of a visual pattern)
- Cause and effect (for example, strategy and results)
- Generalization (for example, general statement followed by supporting evidence)
- Compare and contrast (for example, similarities and differences)
- Classification (for example, headings and subheadings)

Graphic organizers are helpful in developing logical order. Sometimes these can replace the need for writing sentences and paragraphs (for example, timelines, flow charts, Venn diagrams, T-charts, cross-classification charts or tables). Coordinate the use of these organizers with those used in other subjects.

AFTER

Suggest students exchange journals with a classmate. Students can comment on each of the 7 steps, and make suggestions as to where improvement is needed.

SECTION ORGANIZER

Student Materials
- fraction strips (Masters 4.22, 4.23)
- number lines (Masters 4.24, 4.25)
- 0.5-cm grid paper (PM 14)

Optional
- 12 by 12 multiplication chart (PM 15)

Vocabulary: partially related denominators

Assessment: Master 4.2 Ongoing Observations: Fractions and Decimals

Correlation of Extra Practice questions on page 441:

Section	Questions
4.2	4
4.3	1, 2, 5, 7, 9
Technology	3
4.4	6
4.5	8
4.6	10, 11, 12
4.7	13, 15, 17
4.8	14, 16
4.9	18

Assignment Guidelines

To assess the 4 Achievement Chart categories listed in the curriculum document, use these questions:
Understanding Concepts: 6; Problem Solving: 11;
Application: 12; Communication: 15

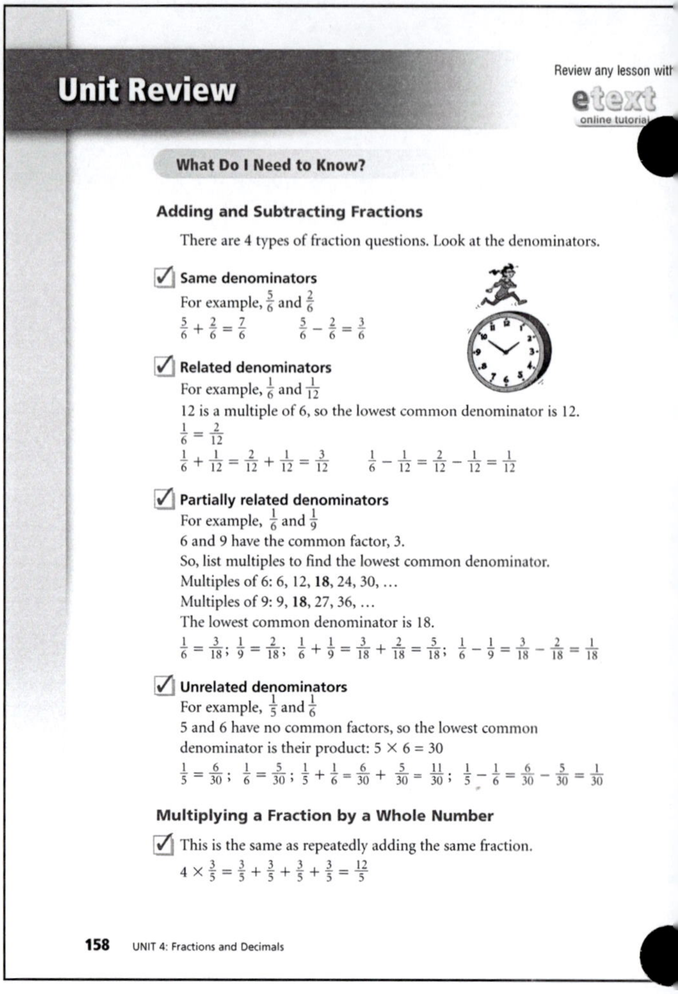

Unit Review

Review any lesson with etext online tutorial

What Do I Need to Know?

Adding and Subtracting Fractions

There are 4 types of fraction questions. Look at the denominators.

✓ **Same denominators**
For example, $\frac{5}{6}$ and $\frac{2}{6}$
$\frac{5}{6} + \frac{2}{6} = \frac{7}{6}$ $\frac{5}{6} - \frac{2}{6} = \frac{3}{6}$

✓ **Related denominators**
For example, $\frac{1}{6}$ and $\frac{1}{12}$
12 is a multiple of 6, so the lowest common denominator is 12.
$\frac{1}{6} = \frac{2}{12}$
$\frac{1}{6} + \frac{1}{12} = \frac{2}{12} + \frac{1}{12} = \frac{3}{12}$ $\frac{1}{6} - \frac{1}{12} = \frac{2}{12} - \frac{1}{12} = \frac{1}{12}$

✓ **Partially related denominators**
For example, $\frac{1}{6}$ and $\frac{1}{9}$
6 and 9 have the common factor, 3.
So, list multiples to find the lowest common denominator.
Multiples of 6: 6, 12, **18**, 24, 30, …
Multiples of 9: 9, **18**, 27, 36, …
The lowest common denominator is 18.
$\frac{1}{6} = \frac{3}{18}$; $\frac{1}{9} = \frac{2}{18}$; $\frac{1}{6} + \frac{1}{9} = \frac{3}{18} + \frac{2}{18} = \frac{5}{18}$; $\frac{1}{6} - \frac{1}{9} = \frac{3}{18} - \frac{2}{18} = \frac{1}{18}$

✓ **Unrelated denominators**
For example, $\frac{1}{5}$ and $\frac{1}{6}$
5 and 6 have no common factors, so the lowest common denominator is their product: $5 \times 6 = 30$
$\frac{1}{5} = \frac{6}{30}$; $\frac{1}{6} = \frac{5}{30}$; $\frac{1}{5} + \frac{1}{6} = \frac{6}{30} + \frac{5}{30} = \frac{11}{30}$; $\frac{1}{5} - \frac{1}{6} = \frac{6}{30} - \frac{5}{30} = \frac{1}{30}$

Multiplying a Fraction by a Whole Number

✓ This is the same as repeatedly adding the same fraction.
$4 \times \frac{3}{5} = \frac{3}{5} + \frac{3}{5} + \frac{3}{5} + \frac{3}{5} = \frac{12}{5}$

158 UNIT 4: Fractions and Decimals

If students have done a math journal entry for pages 156, 157, have them share what they learned in this unit. Use a mind map to help organize the topics.

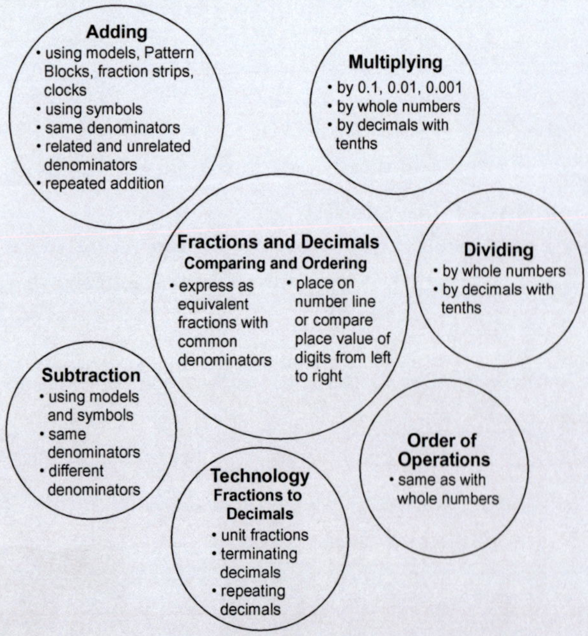

The term **partially related denominators** is introduced for fractions whose denominators have common factors. Another example is denominators of 6 and 8, which have a common factor of 2. If students have been comparing prime factors of the given denominators to find the lowest common denominator, then this concept will not be new.

Practice

As students work through the review, use the Ongoing Observations master to watch students' performance on those questions with which they have had difficulty. Encourage students to try questions without looking at previous examples. When they do have difficulty, have them review the question from the indicated section, then try the question again.

Encourage students to show all their work in their solutions to the question. Here are some sample solutions.

What Should I Be Able to Do?

For extra practice, go to page 441.

LESSON

4.1 **1.** Which fraction is greater? How do you know?
a) $\frac{2}{5}, \frac{2}{6}$ $\frac{2}{5}$ b) $\frac{3}{10}, \frac{1}{2}$ $\frac{1}{2}$
c) $\frac{4}{8}, \frac{3}{6}$ $\frac{4}{8} = \frac{3}{6}$ d) $\frac{7}{2}, \frac{7}{3}$ $\frac{7}{2}$

2. Add.
a) $\frac{2}{3} + \frac{1}{6} = \frac{5}{6}$ b) $\frac{3}{4} + \frac{2}{8} = \frac{8}{8} = 1$
c) $\frac{1}{4} + \frac{3}{6} = \frac{9}{12}$ or $\frac{3}{4}$ d) $\frac{1}{10} + \frac{3}{5} = \frac{7}{10}$

3. Find 2 fractions that add to $\frac{5}{8}$. Find as many pairs of fractions as you can.

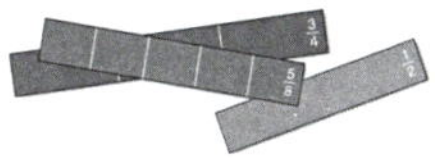

4.2 **4.** Add.
a) $\frac{2}{3} + \frac{5}{6}$ b) $\frac{1}{2} + \frac{3}{4}$
c) $\frac{1}{2} + \frac{9}{10}$ d) $\frac{8}{8} + \frac{1}{4}$

5. Adam eats $\frac{3}{10}$ of a pizza. Julie eats $\frac{2}{5}$ of the pizza.
a) How much of the pizza is eaten? $= \frac{7}{10}$
b) How much is left? $= \frac{3}{10}$

4.3 **6.** Add. Draw a picture to show each sum.
a) $\frac{1}{3} + \frac{2}{5} = \frac{11}{15}$ b) $\frac{1}{2} + \frac{3}{8} = \frac{7}{8}$
c) $\frac{2}{3} + \frac{3}{10} = \frac{29}{30}$ d) $\frac{3}{5} + \frac{1}{4} = \frac{17}{20}$

7. Add.
a) $\frac{2}{5} + \frac{5}{6} = 1\frac{7}{30}$ b) $\frac{1}{4} + \frac{2}{5} = \frac{13}{20}$
c) $\frac{3}{10} + \frac{5}{6} = 1\frac{2}{15}$ d) $\frac{3}{8} + \frac{2}{3} = 1\frac{1}{24}$

8. Add.
a) $6\frac{1}{3} + 2\frac{1}{3}$ $8\frac{2}{3}$ b) $1\frac{5}{12} + 2\frac{1}{6} = 3\frac{7}{12}$
c) $2\frac{3}{10} + 3\frac{1}{5}$ $5\frac{1}{2}$ d) $5\frac{1}{4} + 2\frac{2}{5} = 7\frac{13}{20}$

9. Add.
a) $\frac{2}{3} + \frac{3}{4} + \frac{3}{8} = 1\frac{19}{24}$
b) $\frac{5}{2} + \frac{1}{3} + \frac{2}{5} = 3\frac{7}{30}$
c) $\frac{7}{10} + \frac{3}{4} + \frac{5}{8} = 2\frac{3}{40}$

4.4 **10.** Subtract.
a) $\frac{1}{2} - \frac{1}{3} = \frac{1}{6}$ b) $\frac{7}{10} - \frac{2}{5} = \frac{3}{10}$
c) $\frac{3}{4} - \frac{1}{8} = \frac{5}{8}$ d) $\frac{5}{6} - \frac{1}{3} = \frac{3}{6}$ or $\frac{1}{2}$

11. Find 2 fractions with a difference of $\frac{1}{4}$. Find as many pairs of fractions as you can. Remember to use fractions with different denominators.

4.5 **12.** Ali drank $\frac{3}{4}$ cup of water. Brad drank $\frac{2}{3}$ cup of water.
a) Who drank more water? Ali
b) How much more water did he drink? $= \frac{1}{12}$ cup more

Unit Review **159**

Sample Solutions

1. a) $\frac{1}{5}$ is greater than $\frac{1}{6}$, so $\frac{2}{5}$ is greater than $\frac{2}{6}$.
b) $\frac{1}{2}$ is $\frac{5}{10}$, and $\frac{3}{10}$ is less than $\frac{5}{10}$, so $\frac{3}{10}$ is less than $\frac{1}{2}$.
c) $\frac{4}{8}$ is $\frac{1}{2}$ and $\frac{3}{6}$ is $\frac{1}{2}$, so $\frac{4}{8} = \frac{3}{6}$.
d) $\frac{1}{2}$ is greater than $\frac{1}{3}$, so $\frac{7}{2}$ is greater than $\frac{7}{3}$.

3. Possible answers: $\frac{1}{8} + \frac{4}{8}$; $\frac{1}{8} + \frac{1}{2}$; $\frac{2}{8} + \frac{3}{8}$; $\frac{1}{4} + \frac{3}{8}$

4. a) $\frac{9}{6} = \frac{3}{2} = 1\frac{1}{2}$ b) $\frac{5}{4} = 1\frac{1}{4}$ c) $\frac{14}{10} = \frac{7}{5} = 1\frac{2}{5}$ d) $1\frac{1}{4}$

6. a) $\frac{11}{15}$

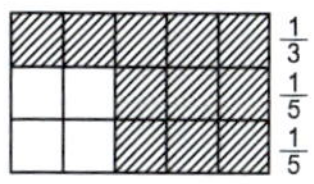

b) $\frac{7}{8}$

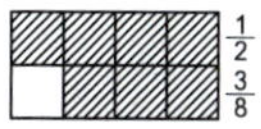

c) $\frac{29}{30}$

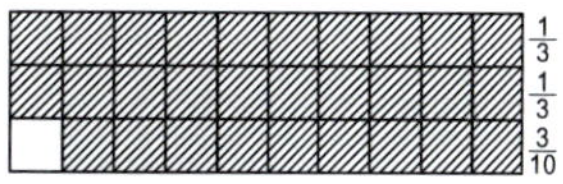

d) $\frac{17}{20}$

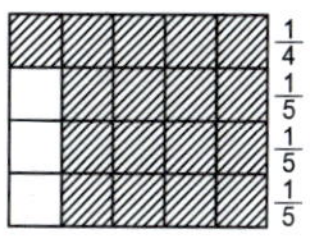

7. a) $\frac{37}{30} = 1\frac{7}{30}$ b) $\frac{13}{20}$
c) $\frac{34}{30} = \frac{17}{15} = 1\frac{2}{15}$ d) $\frac{25}{24} = 1\frac{1}{24}$

8. a) $8\frac{2}{3}$ b) $3\frac{7}{12}$ c) $5\frac{5}{10} = 5\frac{1}{2}$ d) $7\frac{13}{20}$

9. a) $\frac{43}{24} = 1\frac{19}{24}$ b) $\frac{97}{30} = 3\frac{7}{30}$ c) $\frac{83}{40} = 2\frac{3}{40}$

Question 5

a) The amount of pizza that is eaten is $\frac{3}{10} + \frac{2}{5}$.
Write $\frac{2}{5}$ as $\frac{4}{10}$: $\frac{3}{10} + \frac{2}{5} = \frac{3}{10} + \frac{4}{10} = \frac{7}{10}$
$\frac{7}{10}$ of the pizza is eaten.

b) There are $\frac{10}{10}$ in 1 whole pizza. $\frac{7}{10}$ are eaten.
So, $\frac{3}{10}$ are left.

Question 9

c) $\frac{7}{10} + \frac{3}{4} + \frac{5}{8}$
4 is a factor of 8.
The lowest common denominator is the lowest common multiple of 8 and 10.
Multiples of 8: 8, 16, 24, 32, 40, 48, 56, 64, …
Multiples of 10: 10, 20, 30, 40, …
The lowest common multiple is 40.
Write each fraction with denominator 40.
$\frac{7}{10} = \frac{28}{40}$ (multiplying top and bottom by 4)
$\frac{3}{4} = \frac{30}{40}$ (multiplying top and bottom by 10)
$\frac{5}{8} = \frac{25}{40}$ (multiplying top and bottom by 5)
$\frac{7}{10} + \frac{3}{4} + \frac{5}{8} = \frac{28}{40} + \frac{30}{40} + \frac{25}{40} = \frac{83}{40}$
$\frac{40}{40}$ is 1 whole, $\frac{80}{40}$ is 2 wholes, so $\frac{83}{40} = 2\frac{3}{40}$

Question 11

I used fraction strips and number lines.
I placed the $\frac{1}{4}$-strip on different lines, then read the fraction on the number line at each end of the strip.
On the $\frac{1}{4}$-line: $1 - \frac{3}{4}, \frac{3}{4} - \frac{2}{4}, \frac{2}{4} - \frac{1}{4}$
On the $\frac{1}{8}$-line: $1 - \frac{6}{8}, \frac{7}{8} - \frac{5}{8}, \frac{6}{8} - \frac{4}{8}, \frac{5}{8} - \frac{3}{8}, \frac{4}{8} - \frac{2}{8}, \frac{3}{8} - \frac{1}{8}$
I wrote these fractions in simplest form, when I could: $1 - \frac{3}{4}, \frac{3}{4} - \frac{1}{2}, \frac{1}{2} - \frac{1}{4}$
On the $\frac{1}{12}$-line: $1 - \frac{9}{12}, \frac{11}{12} - \frac{8}{12}, \frac{10}{12} - \frac{7}{12}, \frac{9}{12} - \frac{6}{12}, \frac{8}{12} - \frac{5}{12}, \frac{7}{12} - \frac{4}{12}, \frac{6}{12} - \frac{3}{12}, \frac{5}{12} - \frac{2}{12}, \frac{4}{12} - \frac{1}{12}$
I wrote these fractions in simplest form, when I could:
$1 - \frac{3}{4}, \frac{11}{12} - \frac{2}{3}, \frac{5}{6} - \frac{7}{12}, \frac{3}{4} - \frac{1}{2}, \frac{2}{3} - \frac{5}{12}, \frac{7}{12} - \frac{1}{3}, \frac{1}{2} - \frac{1}{4}, \frac{5}{12} - \frac{1}{6}, \frac{1}{3} - \frac{1}{12}$

Question 12

a) The strip for $\frac{3}{4}$ is longer than the strip for $\frac{2}{3}$, so $\frac{3}{4}$ is greater than $\frac{2}{3}$. So, Ali drank more water.

10. a) $\frac{1}{6}$ b) $\frac{3}{10}$ c) $\frac{5}{8}$ d) $\frac{3}{6} = \frac{1}{2}$

11. Possible combinations: $\frac{3}{4} - \frac{2}{4}$; $\frac{3}{4} - \frac{1}{2}$; $\frac{1}{2} - \frac{1}{4}$; $\frac{1}{3} - \frac{1}{12}$

13. a) $\frac{5}{10} = \frac{1}{2}$ b) $\frac{9}{6} = \frac{3}{2} = 1\frac{1}{2}$

c) $\frac{27}{20} = 1\frac{7}{20}$ d) $\frac{19}{12} = 1\frac{7}{12}$

14. a) $1\frac{5}{8}$ b) $2\frac{2}{15}$ c) $6\frac{1}{6}$ d) $\frac{11}{20}$

15. a) $\frac{7}{4}$

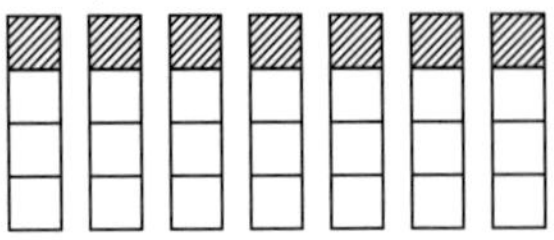

b) $\frac{24}{8} = 3$

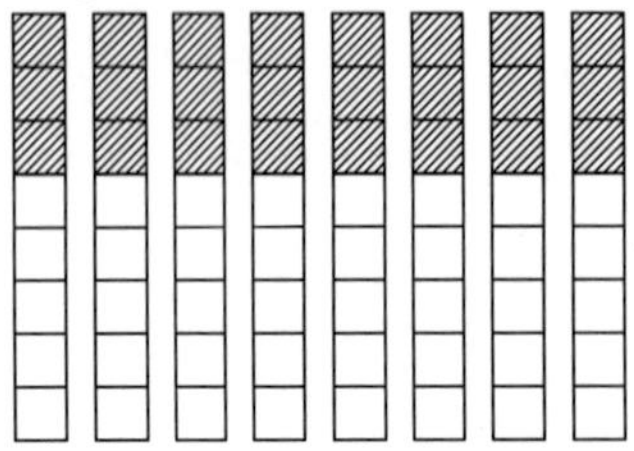

c) $\frac{42}{10} = \frac{21}{5} = 4\frac{1}{5}$

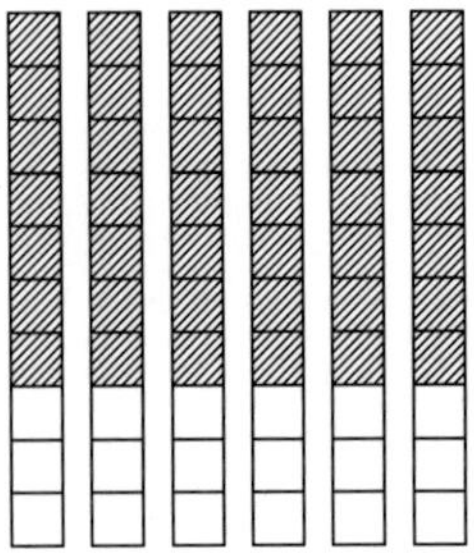

d) $\frac{20}{5} = 4$

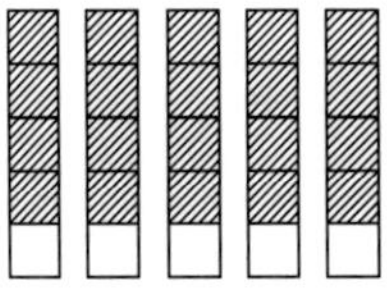

LESSON

13. Subtract.

a) $\frac{9}{10} - \frac{2}{5} = \frac{1}{2}$ b) $\frac{7}{3} - \frac{5}{6} = 1\frac{1}{2}$

c) $\frac{8}{5} - \frac{1}{4} = 1\frac{7}{20}$ d) $\frac{9}{4} - \frac{2}{3} = 1\frac{7}{12}$

14. Subtract.

a) $3\frac{3}{4} - 2\frac{1}{8} = 1\frac{5}{8}$ b) $4\frac{4}{5} - 2\frac{2}{3} = 2\frac{2}{15}$

c) $9\frac{1}{2} - 3\frac{1}{3} = 6\frac{1}{6}$ d) $6\frac{3}{4} - 6\frac{1}{5} = \frac{11}{20}$

4.6 **15.** Multiply. Draw a picture to show each answer.

a) $\frac{1}{4} \times 7 = \frac{7}{4}$ b) $8 \times \frac{3}{8} = 3$

c) $6 \times \frac{7}{10} = 4\frac{1}{5}$ d) $\frac{4}{5} \times 5 = 4$

16. Sasha had 16 tomatoes in his vegetable garden. He gave: Samira $\frac{1}{8}$ of the tomatoes; Sielen $\frac{1}{8}$ of the tomatoes; and Amina $\frac{1}{4}$ of the tomatoes.

a) What fraction of the tomatoes did Sasha have left? $= \frac{1}{2}$

b) How many tomatoes did Sasha have left? 8 tomatoes

17. Orit spends $\frac{1}{4}$ of her day at school, $\frac{1}{12}$ of her day playing soccer, and $\frac{1}{3}$ of her day sleeping. How many hours are left in Orit's day? 8 h

4.7 **18.** A rectangular park has dimensions 2.8 km by 1.9 km. What is the area of the park? $A = 5.32\ km^2$

4.8 **19.** Nuri has 10.8 L of water. He pours 1.5 L into each of several plastic bottles.

a) How many bottles can Nuri fill? 7 bottles

b) How much water is left over? 0.3 L

20. Delia works at the library after school. She earns $7.50/h. She usually works 15 h a week.

a) What does Delia earn in a week? $112.50 Use estimation to check your answer.

b) One week Delia only works $\frac{1}{2}$ the hours she usually works. What are her earnings that week? $56.25

4.9 **21.** Mr. Statler took his class to the local library 4 times last year. One student had a pedometer. She measured the trip as 1.7 km each way. How far did the students walk back and forth to the library during the year? 13.6 km

22. Evaluate.

a) $5.3 + 5.1 \div 3 = 7$

b) $12.6 \times (1.5 + 2.5) = 50.4$

c) $68.9 - 32.7 \times 2 = 3.5$

23. Evaluate.

a) $5.9 + 3.7 \times 2.8 - 1.5 \div 0.5 = 13.26$

b) $3.4 \times 1.9 \div 1.7 + 7.2 \div 1.2 = 9.8$

160 UNIT 4: Fractions and Decimals

b) Subtract: $\frac{3}{4} - \frac{2}{3}$ to find how much more water Ali drank.
The lowest common denominator is 12.
$\frac{3}{4} = \frac{9}{12}$ and $\frac{2}{3} = \frac{8}{12}$
$\frac{3}{4} - \frac{2}{3} = \frac{9}{12} - \frac{8}{12} = \frac{1}{12}$
So, Ali drank $\frac{1}{12}$ cup more than Brad.

Question 16

$\frac{1}{8}$ of 16 is 2; $\frac{1}{8}$ of 16 is 2; $\frac{1}{4}$ of 16 is 4.
So, Sasha gave away 2 + 2 + 4, or 8 tomatoes.
So, Sasha has 8 tomatoes left.
Sasha has $\frac{8}{16}$, or $\frac{1}{2}$ of his tomatoes left.

Question 17

There are 24 h in one day.
$\frac{1}{4}$ of 24 is $\frac{1}{4} \times 24 = 6$
$\frac{1}{12}$ of 24 is $\frac{1}{12} \times 24 = 2$
$\frac{1}{3}$ of 24 is $\frac{1}{3} \times 24 = 8$
Orit spends 6 + 2 + 8, or 16 h at school, playing soccer, or sleeping.
There are 24 – 16, or 8 h left in Orit's day.

Question 19

a) Divide: $10.8 \div 1.5$ to find how many bottles Nuri can fill.
Round and estimate: $12 \div 2 = 6$
Write each number as a whole number, then divide.

```
      7.2
15)108.0
   105
     30
     30
      0
```

So, $10.8 \div 1.5 = 7.2$; this is close to the estimate.
Nuri can fill 7 bottles.

b) The volume in the bottles is 7×1.5 L = 10.5 L
The volume left over is 10.8 L – 10.5 L = 0.3 L

Question 23

a) $5.9 + 3.7 \times 2.8 - 1.5 \div 0.5$
Multiply first: $3.7 \times 2.8 = 10.36$
$5.9 + 10.36 - 1.5 \div 0.5$
Divide next: $1.5 \div 0.5 = 3$
$5.9 + 10.36 - 3$
Add next: $5.9 + 10.36 = 16.26$
Then subtract: $16.26 - 3 = 13.26$

Practice Test

1. Add or subtract.
   a) $\frac{5}{4}+\frac{3}{8}=1\frac{5}{8}$ b) $\frac{3}{2}-\frac{3}{5}=\frac{9}{10}$ c) $\frac{11}{12}-\frac{2}{3}=\frac{1}{4}$ d) $\frac{4}{9}+\frac{7}{6}=1\frac{11}{8}$

$\frac{1}{5}+\frac{2}{5}$, $\frac{1}{10}+\frac{1}{2}$, $\frac{3}{10}+\frac{3}{10}$, $\frac{2}{5}-\frac{1}{5}$, $\frac{3}{10}-\frac{1}{10}$, $\frac{1}{2}-\frac{3}{10}$

2. a) Find three pairs of fractions that have a sum of $\frac{3}{5}$.
   b) Find three pairs of fractions that have a difference of $\frac{1}{5}$.
3. Add or subtract.
   a) $6\frac{3}{8}-2\frac{1}{5}=4\frac{7}{40}$ b) $4\frac{1}{4}+2\frac{2}{3}=6\frac{11}{12}$
4. Lana does yard work. The table shows the approximate time for each job.

Job	Time
Mow small lawn	$\frac{1}{2}$ h
Mow large lawn	$\frac{3}{4}$ h
Mow lawn/tidy yard	$1\frac{1}{2}$ h
Plant annuals	$2\frac{1}{2}$ h

For one Saturday, Lana has these jobs:
– mow 3 small lawns
– mow 1 large lawn
– mow lawn/tidy yard in 2 places
– plant annuals in 1 place

Lana needs travel time between jobs, and a break for lunch. Do you think she will be able to do all the jobs? Justify your answer.

5. a) Evaluate.
   i) $\frac{3}{4}+\frac{3}{4}+\frac{3}{4}+\frac{3}{4}+\frac{3}{4}+\frac{3}{4}$ $4\frac{1}{2}=4.5$ ii) $7\times\frac{2}{3}$ $\frac{14}{3}=4.\overline{6}$ iii) $\frac{7}{8}\times 8=7$
   b) Convert each answer in part a to a decimal.
   c) Order the decimals from least to greatest. $= 4.5, 4.\overline{6}, 7.0$
6. A 6-kg bag of fertilizer covers a rectangular area of 2.5 m by 5.0 m.
   a) How many bags of fertilizer are needed for a rectangular lawn measuring 7.5 m by 10.2 m? 7 bags
   b) A 6-kg bag of fertilizer costs $15.50. How much does it cost to fertilize the lawn? $108.50
7. Evaluate. Explain each step.
   $12.4\times(2.9+4.6)+23.7\div 2.4=102.875$

Practice Test 161

SECTION ORGANIZER

Student Materials
- fraction strips (Masters 4.22, 4.23)
- number lines (Masters 4.24, 4.25)
- 0.5-cm grid paper (PM 14)

Optional
- 12 by 12 multiplication chart (PM 15)

Assessment: Master 4.2 Ongoing Observations: Fractions and Decimals

Assignment Guidelines

To assess the 4 Achievement Chart categories listed in the curriculum document, use these test questions:
Understanding Concepts: 1
Application: 4
Problem Solving: 6
Communication: 7

Sample Solutions

1. a) $\frac{5}{4}+\frac{3}{8}=\frac{10}{8}+\frac{3}{8}=\frac{13}{8}$, or $1\frac{5}{8}$
   b) $\frac{3}{2}-\frac{3}{5}=\frac{15}{10}-\frac{6}{10}=\frac{9}{10}$
   c) $\frac{11}{12}-\frac{2}{3}=\frac{11}{12}-\frac{8}{12}=\frac{3}{12}=\frac{1}{4}$
   d) $\frac{4}{9}+\frac{7}{6}=\frac{16}{36}+\frac{42}{36}=\frac{58}{36}=\frac{29}{18}$, or $1\frac{11}{18}$

4. Mow 3 small lawns: $3\times\frac{1}{2}=\frac{3}{2}$ or $1\frac{1}{2}$
   Mow 1 large lawn: $\frac{3}{4}$
   Mow lawn/tidy yard in 2 places: $1\frac{1}{2}+1\frac{1}{2}=3$
   Plant annuals in 1 place: $2\frac{1}{2}$
   Total time working: $1\frac{1}{2}+\frac{3}{4}+3+2\frac{1}{2}=6+\frac{1}{2}+\frac{1}{2}+\frac{3}{4}$
   $=6+1+\frac{3}{4}=7\frac{3}{4}$
   Lana probably cannot do all the jobs. She works in 7 different places. Allow $\frac{1}{2}$ h travelling time; that's $6\times\frac{1}{2}$ h $= 3$ h.
   Allow $\frac{1}{2}$ h for lunch: $\frac{1}{2}$. So, that's $7\frac{3}{4}+3\frac{1}{2}=11\frac{1}{4}$
   $11\frac{1}{4}$ h is a long working day.

6. a) The area of the lawn: 7.5 m × 10.2 m = 76.5 m^2
   One bag of fertilizer covers: 2.5 m × 5.0 m = 12.5 m^2
   The number of bags needed: 76.5 ÷ 12.5 = 6.12
   So, 7 bags of fertilizer are needed.
   b) The cost is 7 × $15.50 = $108.50
7. 12.4 × (2.9 + 4.6) + 23.7 ÷ 2.4
   Do brackets first, so add: 2.9 + 4.6 = 7.5
   Then multiply: 12.4 × 7.5 = 93
   Then divide: 23.7 ÷ 2.4 = 9.875
   Then add: 93 + 9.875 = 102.875

Publishing a Book

SECTION ORGANIZER 40–50 min

Teacher Materials
- magazines or other material with advertisement layouts

Student Grouping: 2 or 3

Student Materials
- sketch paper

Optional
- fraction strips (Masters 4.22, 4.23)
- Performance Assessment Rubric: Publishing a Book (Master 4.3)

Assessment: Masters 4.3 Performance Assessment Rubric: Publishing a Book, 4.4 Unit Summary: Fractions and Decimals

Unit Problem Publishing a Book

The students at Garden Avenue School are preparing a special b
for the school's 100th anniversary. They finance the book by se
advertising space to sponsors.

The students sold the following space:

Full page	$\frac{1}{2}$ page	$\frac{1}{3}$ page	$\frac{1}{4}$ page	$\frac{1}{6}$ page	$\frac{1}{8}$ page
1	1	1	3	4	5

All the advertisements are to fit at the back of the book.

Sam asks: "How many pages do we need for the advertisements?"
Mara asks: "Will the advertisements fill the pages?"
Kathleen asks: "Is there more than one way to arrange these advertisements?"
Can you think of other questions students might ask?

1. Find the total advertising space needed. $3\frac{7}{8}$
2. Sketch the pages to find how the advertisements can be placed. Use grid paper if it helps.

Sample Solution

Other possible questions:
- Who designs the ads?
- Do the ads need colour?
- How do we enlarge or reduce the ads to fit the purchased space?

1. Total advertising space $= 1 + \frac{1}{2} + \frac{1}{3} + 3 \times \frac{1}{4} + 4 \times \frac{1}{6} + 5 \times \frac{1}{8}$
$= \frac{24}{24} + \frac{12}{24} + \frac{8}{24} + \frac{18}{24} + \frac{16}{24} + \frac{15}{24} = \frac{93}{24} = 3\frac{21}{24} = 3\frac{7}{8}$

(*Solution continues below right*)

Explain that students will work in groups of 2 or 3 to complete all 7 questions. Invite volunteers to read aloud each question. Ensure students understand what they are expected to do. Remind students to show their work.

Have a volunteer read the *Check List*. Remind students that they should use the *Check List* to assess their work before handing it in. You may also wish to provide students with copies of the Performance Assessment Rubric: Publishing a Book (Master 4.3) so they will know how their performance will be assessed.

As students work on the *Unit Problem*, circulate to answer questions, to provide help with interpreting the questions, and to record notes on observations. Encourage students to use the skills they developed in this unit.

As students discuss different arrangements for question 3, listen and watch for those students whose arrangements do not satisfy all the criteria, and if they can correct the arrangements. Listen for mathematical language.

(Sample Solution, continued)

2. One possible layout for the pages:

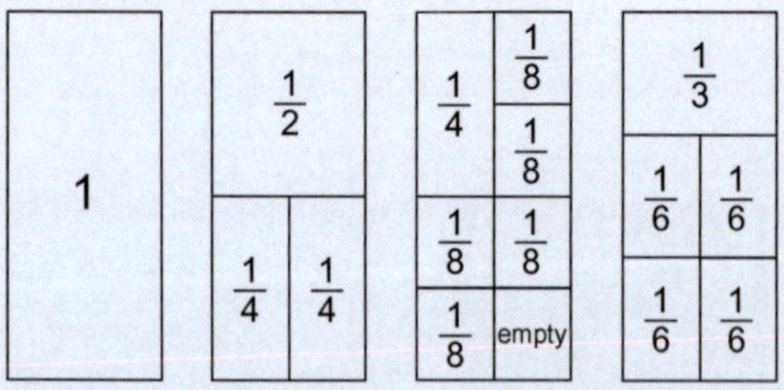

3. There are many different possible layouts. Students may try to put different sizes of ads together. Most students will use rectangles but some may try layouts like the map in Section 4.1, *Explore*.
4. Since the total advertising space is $3\frac{7}{8}$ pages, 4 pages will be needed. $\frac{1}{8}$ of a page is left over for more ads, since $4 - 3\frac{7}{8} = \frac{1}{8}$.
5. Other things to consider are: the costs that will be incurred to collect and organize the material that will go in the book; advertising the sale of the book; phone calls to contributors; payment for articles contributed; use of photographs that may need editing/cropping/repair.

3. Compare your group's sketch with those of other groups. When you made your sketch, what decisions did you make about the shape of each advertisement? Did other groups make the same decisions? Explain.

4. What are the fewest pages needed to display the advertisements? Will there be room for any other advertisements? Explain.

5. What else might students need to consider as they prepare the layout for the book?

Here are the fees for the advertisements.

Size	Full page	$\frac{1}{2}$ page	$\frac{1}{3}$ page	$\frac{1}{4}$ page	$\frac{1}{6}$ page	$\frac{1}{8}$ page
Cost ($)	500	360	250	200	150	100

6. How much money will students get from the advertisers?

7. Students will do the layout on computer. The cost to copy and bind 500 books is $4750. Use the income from question 6.
   a) What do the students have to charge per book so they do not incur a loss? Justify your answer.
   b) The students cannot print fewer than 500 books. What if they can sell only 350 books? What do the students have to charge per book so they do not incur a loss? Justify your answer.
   c) What if the students decide to charge $5 per book? How many books do the students need to sell so they do not incur a loss? Justify your answer.

Check List

Your work should show:

✓ all calculations in detail
✓ diagrams of the layout for the advertisements
✓ a clear explanation of how you prepared the layout
✓ a clear explanation of how students do not incur losses

Reflect on the Unit

Choose one operation with fractions and a different operation with decimals. Write an example that illustrates how to carry out each operation.

6. Income from advertisers: $500 + $360 + $250 + $200 × 3 + $150 × 4 + $100 × 5 = $2810

7. a) Cost per book: (Cost to copy and bind − Income from advertisers) ÷ number of books = ($4750 − $2810) ÷ 500 = $3.88. This assumes all books are purchased.

b) Charge per book = (Cost to copy and bind − Income from advertisers) ÷ number of books sold = ($4750 − $2810) ÷ 350 = $5.54

c) Number of books to sell to break even = (Cost to copy and bind − Income from advertisers) ÷ price per book = ($4750 − $2810) ÷ $5 = 388 books

REFLECT ON THE UNIT:

Fraction addition: If the denominators are different, express the fractions as equivalent fractions with common denominators. Add the numerators. Express the answer as an equivalent fraction in simplest form.

$\frac{4}{5} + \frac{2}{3} = \frac{12}{15} + \frac{10}{15} = \frac{22}{15} = 1\frac{7}{15}$

Decimal multiplication: Estimate using whole numbers. Multiply the numbers without the decimal point, then place the decimal point to match the estimated value.

To multiply 30.25 × 4.2; estimate: 30 × 4 = 120

Multiply: 3025 × 42

```
   3025
 ×   42
   6050
 121000
 127050
```

The estimate is 120, so place the decimal point after the 7.

30.25 × 4.2 = 127.05

ASSESSMENT FOR LEARNING

What to Look For

Understanding concepts

✔ Students understand how to calculate total advertising space using fraction addition, and multiplication.

Applying procedures

✔ Students can choose the correct operations and sequence of steps to avoid a loss.

Problem solving

✔ Students can create an appropriate layout that uses the fewest pages.

Communicating

✔ Students can explain and justify the choices they made for a layout.

What to Do

Extra Support: Students may need pieces of paper that represent the size and number of the ads to help with the addition of the fractions of advertising space, and the layout of these advertisements. Have magazines or other books that contain advertisements as samples for students to look at.

Recording and Reporting

Master 4.3 Performance Assessment Rubric: Publishing a Book
Master 4.4 Unit Summary: Fractions and Decimals

Units 1–4

SECTION ORGANIZER

Student Materials
- fraction strips (Masters 4.22, 4.23)
- number lines (Masters 4.24, 4.25)
- 0.5-cm grid paper (PM 14)
- Net for Question 10, page 165 (Master CR 1.1)

Optional
- calculators

Units 1–4 **Cumulative Review**

UNIT 1

1. Find the number that is:
- a factor of 1000
- not a factor of 100 40
- a multiple of 5
- has fewer than 3 digits

Explain how you found the number.

2. A rectangular pen is built with 60 m of fencing.
The length of each side of the pen is a whole number of metres.
a) Which dimensions are possible? Make an organized list of your answers.
b) What are the dimensions of the pen with the greatest area? Explain. 15 m by 15 m

3. The number 49 is a perfect square. It can be written as 7^2.
Some numbers that are not perfect squares can be written as the sum of a perfect square and a prime number.
For example: $21 = 4^2 + 5$
a) Find all the numbers between 40 and 50 that can be written this way.
b) Which numbers in part a can be written more than one way? Show each new way.

4. Write the next 3 terms in each pattern. Describe each pattern.
a) 49, 36, 25, 16, . . . 9, 4, 1
b) 3, 7, 15, 31, . . . 63, 127, 255
c) 6, 36, 216, 1296, . . . 7776, 46 656, 279 936

UNIT 2

5. Write each ratio in simplest form.

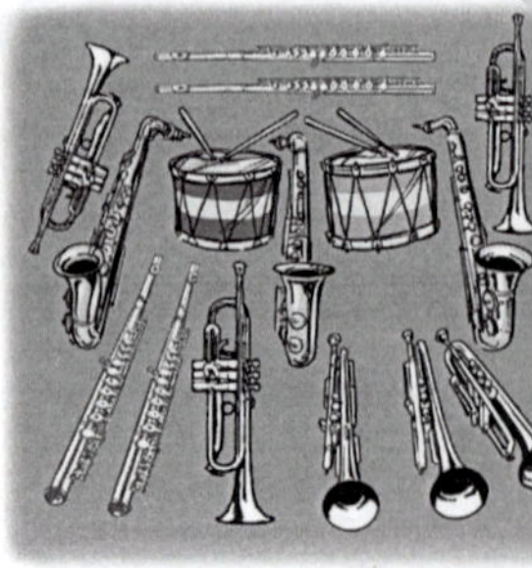

a) saxophones to trumpets 3:6 or 1:2
b) drums to flutes 2:4 or 1:2
c) saxophones to total number of instruments 3:15 or 1:5

6. The ratio of the number of hits to the times at bat for three baseball players is:
Irina, 3:5; Juana, 2:3; Carla, 3:4
a) Who has the best record? Carla
b) Who had the least success? Irina
Explain your answers.

7. The ratio of boys to girls in the sailing club is 4:5.
a) There are 15 girls in the club. How many boys are in the club? 12 boys
b) What if 3 boys leave the club? What is the new ratio of girls to boys? 9:15 = 3:5

164 Units 1–4

Sample Solutions

1. The factors of 1000 are: 1, 2, 4, 5, 10, 20, 25, 40, 50, 100, 200, 250, 500, 1000
The factors of 100 are: 1, 2, 4, 5, 10, 20, 25, 50, 100
The 2-digit number that is a factor of 1000 and not a factor of 100 is 40. 40 is a multiple of 5. So, the number is 40.
2. a) 1 m by 29 m, 2 m by 28 m, 3 m by 27 m, ..., 29 m by 1 m
b) A square pen with dimensions 15 m by 15 m has the greatest area. The area is 225 m^2.

(*Solutions continues below.*)

(*Sample Solutions, continued*)

3. a) The first few prime numbers are 1, 2, 3, 5, 7, 11, 13, 17, 19. The numbers between 40 and 50 that can be written as the sum of a perfect square and a prime number are:
$41 = 6^2 + 5$
$43 = 6^2 + 7$
$47 = 6^2 + 11$
$42 = 5^2 + 17$
$44 = 5^2 + 19$
$46 = 3^2 + 37$
$48 = 5^2 + 23$
b) $47 = 4^2 + 31$
4. a) 9, 4, 1; start at 7^2, reduce the base by 1 each time.
b) 63, 127, 255; start at 3, double the number and add 1 each time.
c) 7776, 46 656, 279 936; start at 6, multiply by 6 each time.
5. a) saxophones to trumpets: 3:6, or 1:2
b) drums to flutes: 2:4, or 1:2
c) saxophones to total number of instruments: 3:15, or 1:5
6. I compared the equivalent ratios. Irina, 3:5 = 36:60; Juana, 2:3 = 40:60; Carla, 3:4 = 45:60.
a) Carla has the best record because she has the greatest number of hits, 45, for the same number of at bats.
b) Irina had the least success because she has the least number of hits, 36, for the same number of at bats.
7. a) 4:5 = (4×3):(5×3) = 12:15
There are 12 boys in the club.
b) If 3 boys leave the club, the new ratio of boys to girls is: (12 − 3):15 = 9:15 = 3:5.
8. a) Back view of an envelope
b) Side view of a picnic table
c) Front view of a microwave oven
9. a) $SA = 2lh + 2lw + 2hw$
$= 2(4 \times 1) + 2(4 \times 2) + 2(2 \times 1) = 8 + 16 + 4 = 28$
The surface area of the rectangular prism is 28 cm^2.
b) $SA = 2lh + 2lw + 2hw$
$= 2(5.5 \times 3.5) + 2(5.5 \times 4.5) + 2(4.5 \times 3.5)$
$= 38.5 + 49.5 + 31.5 = 119.5$
The surface area of the rectangular prism is 119.5 cm^2.
c) $SA = 2lh + 2lw + 2hw$
$= 2(0.3 \times 0.3) + 2(0.3 \times 0.3) + 2(0.3 \times 0.3)$
$= 3 \times 0.18 = 0.54$
The surface area of the rectangular prism is 0.54 m^2.
10. a) The object is a square prism with a square pyramid on top.
b)

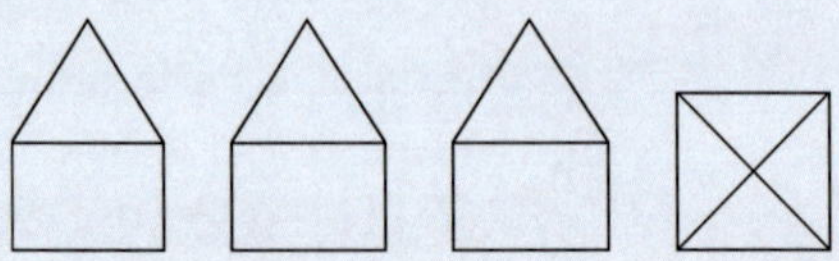

UNIT 3

8. Identify the view (front, back, side, or top) and the object on each sign. Then draw a different view of that object.

a) Post office
Back view

b) Picnic area
Side view

c) Microwave oven
Front view

9. Find the surface area of each rectangular prism.

a)

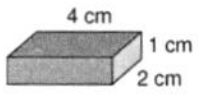

$SA = 28 \text{ cm}^2$

b)

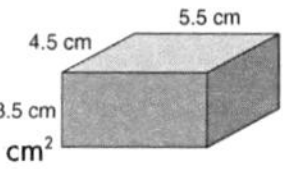

$SA = 119.5 \text{ cm}^2$

c)

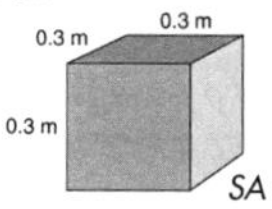

$SA = 0.54 \text{ m}^2$

10. Use a large copy of this net.

a) Fold the net to make an object.
b) Sketch the front, back, side, and top view of the object.

front view back view side view top view

11. Use fraction strips, number lines, or another model to add or subtract.

a) $\frac{3}{8} + \frac{3}{2} = \frac{15}{8}$ b) $\frac{2}{3} + \frac{1}{4} = \frac{11}{12}$
c) $\frac{7}{5} - \frac{1}{2} = \frac{9}{10}$ d) $\frac{11}{6} - \frac{4}{3} = \frac{1}{2}$

12. Skylar and Riley work together on a project.
Skylar does $\frac{3}{10}$ of the work.
Riley does $\frac{2}{5}$ of the work.
a) Who does more work? How much more does this person do? Riley $\frac{1}{10}$ more
b) What fraction of the project has yet to be done? $\frac{3}{10}$

13. Multiply. Draw a picture to show each answer.

a) $4 \times \frac{5}{8} = 2\frac{1}{2}$ b) $\frac{3}{5} \times 5 = 3$
c) $3 \times \frac{3}{10} = \frac{9}{10}$ d) $5 \times \frac{5}{4} = 6\frac{1}{4}$

14. Multiply.
Record your work on grid paper.
a) $3.5 \times 2.1 = 7.35$ b) $0.8 \times 1.2 = 0.96$

15. The area of a rectangle is 7.35 m^2.
The width is 2.1 m.
What is the length? $l = 3.5$ m

16. Evaluate.
a) $1.25 + 3.6 \times 2.4 \div 1.2 = 8.45$
b) $10.5 \div 1.5 - 2.8 \times 0.3 = 6.16$
c) $10.1 - 4.5 \div 0.5 + 7.5 = 8.6$
d) $(10.1 - 4.5) \div (0.5 + 7.5) = 0.7$
Why are the answers to parts c and d different?

Cumulative Review 165

11. a) $\frac{15}{8}$ or $1\frac{7}{8}$ **b)** $\frac{11}{12}$ **c)** $\frac{9}{10}$ **d)** $\frac{3}{6} = \frac{1}{2}$

12. a) I compare equivalent fractions: Skylar: $\frac{3}{10}$, Riley: $\frac{2}{5} = \frac{4}{10}$
$\frac{3}{10} < \frac{4}{10}$, so Riley does more work than Skylar
$\frac{4}{10} - \frac{3}{10} = \frac{1}{10}$; Riley does $\frac{1}{10}$ more work than Skylar.

b) $\frac{3}{10} + \frac{4}{10} = \frac{7}{10}$; There is still $\frac{10}{10} - \frac{7}{10} = \frac{3}{10}$ of the project yet to be done.

13. a)

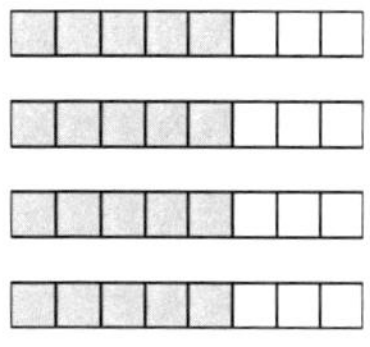

$\frac{5}{8}$ shaded
$\frac{5}{8}$ shaded
$\frac{5}{8}$ shaded
$\frac{5}{8}$ shaded

$4 \times \frac{5}{8} = \frac{20}{8} = \frac{10}{4} = \frac{5}{2} = 2\frac{1}{2}$

b)

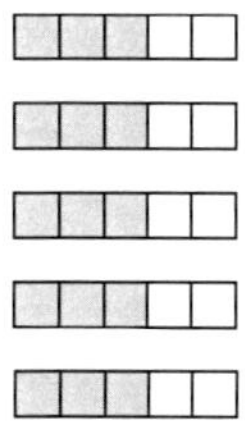

$\frac{3}{5}$ shaded
$\frac{3}{5}$ shaded
$\frac{3}{5}$ shaded
$\frac{3}{5}$ shaded
$\frac{3}{5}$ shaded

$5 \times \frac{3}{5} = \frac{15}{5} = 3$

c)

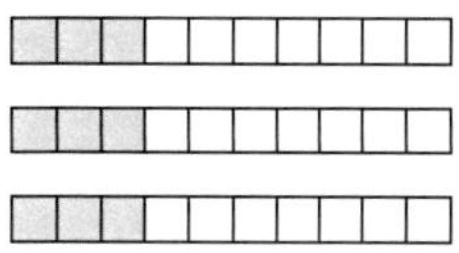

$\frac{3}{10}$ shaded
$\frac{3}{10}$ shaded
$\frac{3}{10}$ shaded

$3 \times \frac{3}{10} = \frac{9}{10}$

d)

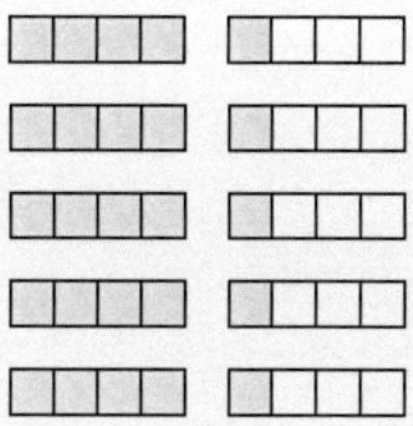

$\frac{5}{4}$ shaded
$\frac{5}{4}$ shaded
$\frac{5}{4}$ shaded
$\frac{5}{4}$ shaded
$\frac{5}{4}$ shaded

$5 \times \frac{5}{4} = \frac{25}{4} = 6\frac{1}{4}$

14. a) Here are the Base Ten Blocks:
There are 6 flats: $6 \times 1 = 6$
There are 13 rods: $13 \times 0.1 = 1.3$
There are 5 small cubes: $5 \times 0.01 = 0.05$
The total area is $6 + 1.3 + 0.05 = 7.35$.

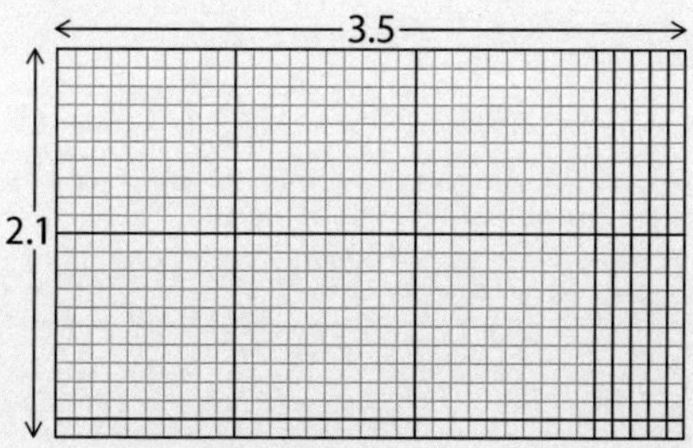

b) There are 8 rods: $8 \times 0.1 = 0.8$
There are 16 small cubes: $16 \times 0.01 = 0.16$
The total area is $0.8 + 0.16 = 0.96$.

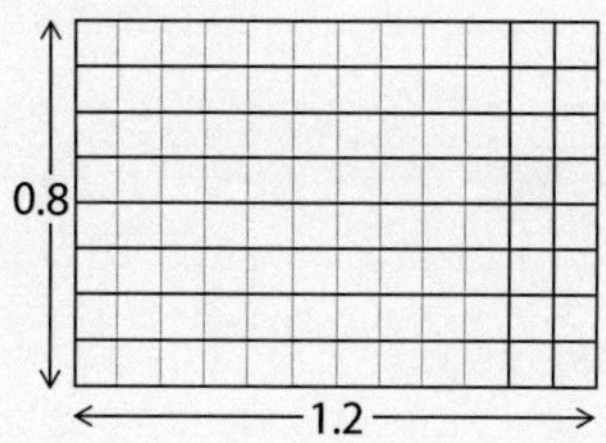

15. $A = lw$
$l = 7.35 \div 2.1 = 3.5$. So, the length is 3.5 m.

16. a) 8.45 **b)** 6.16 **c)** 8.6 **d)** 0.7
The answers are different in part c and d because the order of operations is different.

Evaluating Student Learning: Preparing to Report: Unit 4 Fractions and Decimals

This unit provides an opportunity to report on the **Number Sense and Numeration** strand. *Master 4.4: Unit Summary: Fractions and Decimals* provides a comprehensive format for recording and summarizing evidence collected.

Here is an example of a completed summary chart for this Unit:

Strand: *Number Sense and Numeration*	**Problem solving**	**Understanding of concepts**	**Application of mathematical procedures**	**Communication**	***Overall***
Ongoing Observations	4	4	4	3	4
Work samples or portfolios; conferences	3	4	4	3	3/4
Unit Review	4	3	4	4	4
Unit Test	4	4	4	3	4
Unit Problem *Publishing a Book*	3	4	4	4	4
Achievement Level for reporting					4

Recording	**How to Report**
Ongoing Observations	Use *Master 4.2 Ongoing Observations: Fractions and Decimals* to determine the most consistent level achieved in each category. Enter it in the chart. Choose to summarize by achievement category, or simply to enter an overall level. Observations from late in the Unit should be most heavily weighted.
Portfolios or collections of work samples; conferences or interviews	Use *Master 4.1 Unit Rubric: Fractions and Decimals* to guide evaluation of collections of work and information gathered in conferences. Teachers may choose to focus particular attention on the Assessment Focus questions. Work from late in the unit should be most heavily weighted.
Unit Review	*Master 4.1 Unit Rubric: Fractions and Decimals* may be helpful in determining levels of achievement. #2, 4, 7, 10, 13, 15, and 22 provide evidence of Understanding of concepts; #5, 12, 18, and 19 provide evidence of Application of mathematical procedures; #3, 11, 16, 17, 20, and 21 provide evidence of Problem solving; #1, 6, and 15 provide evidence of Communication.
Unit Test	*Master 4.1 Unit Rubric: Fractions and Decimals* may be helpful in determining levels of achievement. #1 provides evidence of Understanding of concepts; #4 provides evidence of Application of mathematical procedures; #6 provides evidence of Problem solving; #7 provides evidence of Communication.
Unit performance task	Use *Master 4.3 Performance Assessment Rubric: Publishing a Book.* The *Unit Problem* offers a snapshot of students' achievement. In particular, it shows their ability to synthesize and apply what they have learned.
Student Self-Assessment	Note students' perceptions of their own progress. This may take the form of an oral or written comment, or a self-rating.
Comments	Analyse the pattern of achievement to identify strengths and needs. In some cases, specific actions may need to be planned to support the learner.

Learning Skills	**Ongoing Records**
PM 4: Learning Skills Check List Use to record and report throughout a reporting period, rather than for each unit and/or strand.	*PM 10: Summary Class Records: Strands;* *PM 11: Summary Class Records: Achievement Categories;* *PM 12: Summary Record: Individual* Use to record and report evaluations of student achievement over several clusters, a reporting period, or a school year. These can also be used in place of the Unit Summary.

Name ____________________ Date ________________

Master 4.1

Unit Rubric: Fractions and Decimals

	Level 1	Level 2	Level 3	Level 4
Problem solving • chooses and carries out a range of strategies to solve multi-step problems involving fractions and decimals, and assesses the reasonableness of the result	with assistance, chooses and carries out a limited range of appropriate strategies, including estimation, rarely resulting in an accurate solution	with limited assistance, chooses and carries out appropriate strategies, including estimation, that frequently result in an accurate solution	chooses and carries out appropriate strategies, including estimation, that usually result in an accurate solution	chooses and carries out appropriate strategies, including estimation; may offer an innovative approach; results in accurate solution
Understanding of concepts • shows understanding by using concrete materials, drawings, and symbols to demonstrate, explain, and/or justify choice of method for: – operations with fractions – relating repeated addition to multiplication by a whole number – order of operations	shows little understanding; may be unable to demonstrate, explain or justify choice of method for: – operations with fractions – relating repeated addition to multiplication by a whole number – order of operations	shows some understanding; partially able to demonstrate, explain, and justify choice of method for: – operations with fractions – relating repeated addition to multiplication by a whole number – order of operations	shows understanding; able to clearly and appropriately demonstrate, explain, and justify choice of method for: – operations with fractions – relating repeated addition to multiplication by a whole number – order of operations	shows thorough understanding; able to accurately and effectively demonstrate, explain, and justify choice of method for: – operations with fractions – relating repeated addition to multiplication by a whole number – order of operations
Application of mathematical procedures • accurately uses concrete materials, drawings, and symbols to: – add and subtract fractions with simple denominators – multiply a fraction by a whole number – apply order of operations – compare and order decimals – multiply and divide decimals	limited accuracy; major errors or omissions in: – adding and subtracting fractions – multiplying a fraction by a whole number – applying order of operations – comparing and ordering decimals – multiplying and dividing decimals	somewhat accurate; several minor errors or omissions in: – adding and subtracting fractions – multiplying a fraction by a whole number – applying order of operations – comparing and ordering decimals – multiplying and dividing decimals	generally accurate; few minor errors or omissions in: – adding and subtracting fractions – multiplying a fraction by a whole number – applying order of operations – comparing and ordering decimals – multiplying and dividing decimals	accurate and precise; no errors in: – adding and subtracting fractions – multiplying a fraction by a whole number – applying order of operations – comparing and ordering decimals – multiplying and dividing decimals
Communication • explains reasoning and procedures clearly	unable to explain reasoning and procedures clearly	partially explains reasoning and procedures	explains reasoning and procedures clearly	explains reasoning and procedures clearly, precisely, and confidently
• presents calculations clearly, including appropriate symbols	presents calculations with little clarity; rarely uses appropriate symbols	presents calculations with some clarity; uses some appropriate symbols	presents calculations clearly and precisely; uses appropriate symbols	presents calculations clearly and precisely; uses a range of appropriate symbols

Name ____________________ Date ________________

Master 4.2

Ongoing Observations: Fractions and Decimals

The behaviours described under each heading are examples; they are not intended to be an exhaustive list of all that might be observed. More detailed descriptions are provided in each lesson under *Assessment for Learning*.

STUDENT ACHIEVEMENT: Fractions and Decimals				
Student	**Problem solving** ▪ Chooses and carries out appropriate strategies to solve multi-step problems and check results (estimates)	**Understanding of concepts** ▪ Explains and demonstrates operations with fractions ▪ Justifies methods	**Application of mathematical procedures** ▪ Adds and subtracts fractions ▪ Multiplies fractions by a whole number ▪ Multiplies and divides decimals	**Communication** ▪ Explains reasoning clearly ▪ Presents work clearly

Level 1 – very limited; Level 2 – somewhat or limited; Level 3 – satisfactory; Level 4 – thorough

Name ____________________ Date ______________

Master 4.3

Performance Assessment Rubric: Publishing a Book

	Level 1	Level 2	Level 3	Level 4
Problem solving • chooses appropriate strategies to solve multi-step problems involving fractions and decimals, and checks reasonableness of solutions	uses few simple strategies to solve multi-step problems involving decimals; limited success	uses some appropriate strategies to solve multi-step problems involving decimals; some success	uses appropriate strategies to solve multi-step problems involving decimals; successful	uses innovative and appropriate strategies to solve multi-step problems involving decimals; successful and effective
Understanding of concepts • shows understanding of fractions and decimals by giving appropriate explanations and justifications of: – layout chosen (shape of ads) (#3) – fewest pages needed and space remaining (#4) – other considerations in preparing layout (#5) – how students can avoid losses (#7)	shows very limited understanding by giving few appropriate explanations or justifications of strategies, procedures, and results	shows limited understanding by giving some appropriate but incomplete explanations and justifications of strategies, procedures, and results	shows understanding by giving appropriate explanations and justifications of strategies, procedures, and results	shows thorough understanding by giving appropriate and complete explanations and justifications of strategies, procedures, and results using all relevant concepts related to decimals
Application of mathematical procedures • adds and subtracts fractions • multiplies a fraction by a whole number • multiplies and divides decimals	limited accuracy; major errors or omissions in: – adding and subtracting fractions – multiplying a fraction by a whole number – multiplying and dividing decimals	somewhat accurate; several minor errors or omissions in: – adding and subtracting fractions – multiplying a fraction by a whole number – multiplying and dividing decimals	generally accurate; few minor errors or omissions in: – adding and subtracting fractions – multiplying a fraction by a whole number – multiplying and dividing decimals	accurate and precise; with no errors or omissions in: – adding and subtracting fractions – multiplying a fraction by a whole number – multiplying and dividing decimals
Communication • explains reasoning clearly, using appropriate mathematical terminology	explains reasoning unclearly and imprecisely, using few mathematical terms	explains reasoning with some clarity, using some appropriate mathematical terms	explains reasoning clearly and precisely, using appropriate mathematical terms	explains reasoning clearly, precisely, and confidently, using a range of appropriate mathematical terminology
• presents work, including diagrams, clearly	presents work with little clarity	presents work with some clarity	presents work clearly	presents work clearly and precisely

Name ____________________ Date ______________

Master 4.4

Unit Summary: Fractions and Decimals

Review assessment records to determine the most consistent achievement levels for the assessments conducted. Some cells may be blank. *Overall* achievement levels may be recorded in each row, rather than identifying levels for each achievement category.

	Most Consistent Level of Achievement*				
Strand: *Number Sense and Numeration*	**Problem Solving**	**Understanding of concepts**	**Application of mathematical procedures**	**Communication**	***Overall***
Ongoing Observations					
Work samples or portfolios; conferences					
Unit Review					
Practice Test					
Unit Problem: Publishing a Book					
Achievement Level for reporting					

* Use Ontario Achievement Levels 1, 2, 3, 4

Self-Assessment:

Comments: (Strengths, Needs, Next Steps)

Name ____________________ Date ________________

Master 4.5

Additional Activity 1: How Close Can You Get?

Work with a partner.

Materials: a deck of playing cards; 3 counters; calculator (optional)

How to Play:
Use the cards Ace (to represent 1) to 9 from a deck of cards.
Shuffle these cards.

1. Find the target number. Deal four cards and arrange them as shown:

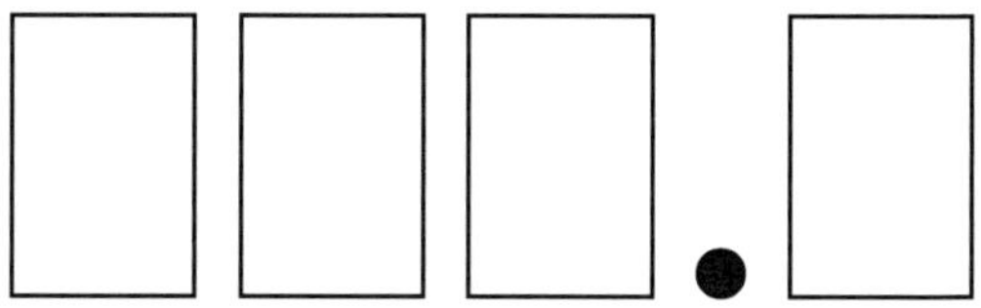

   Use a counter as the decimal point.
2. Deal 6 cards to each player.
3. Choose any 4 cards to create a number as close to the target number as possible.
   Use a counter to show the decimal point.
   The number can be greater than or less than the target number.
4. Find and record the difference between the two numbers.
   The difference is your score for that round.
5. Shuffle the cards, create a new target number, and play another round.
6. The winner has the lower score after 3 rounds.

Take It Further:
Change the target number arrangement. Move the decimal point so the number has 2 decimal places.
Always deal 2 more cards than the number of digits in the target number.

Name ____________________ Date ________________

Master 4.6

Additional Activity 2: Beat the Clock

Work with a partner.

Materials: a deck of playing cards; watch or clock with a second hand; calculator (optional)

How to Play:

1. Copy this format on a piece of paper. It shows a decimal with hundredths multiplied by a 1-digit whole number.

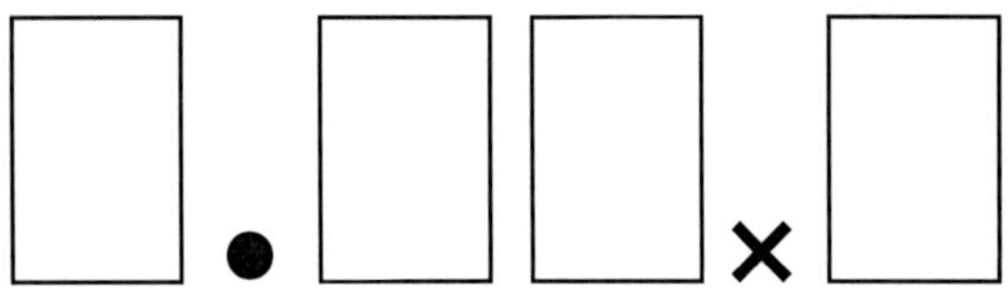

2. Use the cards Ace (to represent 1) to 9 from a deck of cards.
3. Shuffle these cards.
   Player A takes the top 4 cards.
   She places the cards, in any order she likes, in the format above.
4. Player A shows Player B the problem and starts timing.
   Player B has 20 seconds to estimate a product.
   Player B cannot use pencil and paper or a calculator.
   Player A calculates the answer, using pencil and paper.
   Both players check the answer with a calculator.
5. Player B records his estimate and the product. The difference between these numbers is Player B's score.
6. Trade roles. Repeat *Steps 3* to *5*.
7. The winner has the lower score after 3 rounds.

Take It Further:
Change the format to multiply a decimal with hundredths by a 2-digit whole number.
In *Step 3*, take the top 5 cards.

Name ____________________ Date ________________

Master 4.7

Additional Activity 3: Fill It Up

Work with a partner.

Materials: *Fill It Up* game cards (Master 4.18); Pattern Blocks; isometric grid paper (PM 24)

How to Play:

1. Mix up the game cards and place the cards face down. The yellow hexagon represents 1 whole. The isometric paper is the game board.
2. Turn over a card. Place the appropriate Pattern Block(s) on the game board. Record the fraction on the scoresheet. For example,
   - If your card shows a rhombus and a triangle:
     Place a rhombus and a triangle anywhere on the isometric paper.
     Record $\frac{1}{3} + \frac{1}{6} = \frac{1}{2}$ as your score.
   - If your card shows $\frac{1}{2}$:
     Place a rhombus and a triangle, or a trapezoid, anywhere on the board.
     Record $\frac{1}{2}$ as your score.
3. Put the card at the bottom of the pile. Take turns.
4. If a player cannot make a move, he or she forfeits the turn.
   Play continues until no more moves are possible.
5. Each player adds the fractions she recorded. The greater sum wins.

Take It Further:
Play the game again. This time, use the trapezoid or rhombus to represent 1.

Name ____________________ Date ______________

Master 4.8

Additional Activity 4: Tic-Tac-Quo-tient

Work with a partner.

Materials: *Tic-Tac-Quo-tient* Game Board (Master 4.19); 36 two-colour counters; 2 coins; calculator (optional)

How to Play:

1. Each player chooses a colour for her counter.

2. Player A places a coin on a divisor and a coin on a dividend; for example, she places a coin on divisor 4 and a coin on dividend 6.
   She says, "How many times does 4 go into 6?"
   She places her counter on the matching quotient, 1.5.

3. Player B creates a new quotient by changing either the divisor or the dividend.
   He can only change one.
   For example, he moves the divisor coin to 8. He says, "How many times does 8 go into 6?"
   He places his counter on the quotient, 0.75.
   The space must be unoccupied.

4. If there is more than one square with the correct quotient, the player may choose either square.
   He does not place a counter on each square.

5. The winner is the first person to get 3 counters in a row, in any direction.

Take It Further:
Play the game again.
The winner is the first person to get 4 counters in a row.

Name ____________________ Date ________________

Master 4.9

Step-by-Step 1

Section 4.1, Question 8

Step 1 The numerator of the sum is 5.
Write two whole numbers with a sum of 5.

$\square + \square = 5$

Step 2 Use *Step 1* to write the numerators of possible fractions Boris added.

$\frac{\ }{6} + \frac{\ }{6} = \frac{5}{6}$

Step 3 Repeat *Steps 1* and *2* using two different whole numbers.

$\square + \square = 5$

Step 4 Are there any other pairs of whole numbers that add to 5?
How do you know?

Step 5 Look at the fractions that are added in *Step 2*.
Can any of them be renamed as an equivalent fraction?

$\frac{\ }{6} = \frac{\ }{\ }$ $\frac{\ }{6} = \frac{\ }{\ }$

Step 6 Write pairs of fractions that have a sum $\frac{5}{6}$.

$\frac{\ }{6} + \frac{\ }{6} = \frac{5}{6}$ $\frac{\ }{6} + \frac{\ }{\ } = \frac{5}{6}$

$\frac{\ }{\ } + \frac{\ }{6} = \frac{5}{6}$ $\frac{\ }{\ } + \frac{\ }{\ } = \frac{5}{6}$

Step 7 Review your work. Suppose you started with a fraction equivalent to $\frac{5}{6}$.

Could you get different fractions with a sum equivalent to $\frac{5}{6}$?

Name ____________________ Date ______________

Master 4.10

Step-by-Step 2

Section 4.2, Question 11

Step 1 Write all possible fractions with each denominator.
Each fraction should be less than 1.

$\frac{}{2}$

$\frac{}{3}$ $\frac{}{3}$

$\frac{}{4}$ $\frac{}{4}$ $\frac{}{4}$

$\frac{}{5}$ $\frac{}{5}$ $\frac{}{5}$ $\frac{}{5}$

$\frac{}{6}$ $\frac{}{6}$ $\frac{}{6}$ $\frac{}{6}$ $\frac{}{6}$

Step 2 Use fraction strips to order the fractions from *Step 1,* from least to greatest.

____

Step 3 Choose 2 fractions that you think have a sum between 1 and 2.
Use number lines to check.
How many different sums can you find?

____

____

Step 4 Order the sums from least to greatest.

____

Step 5 Which is the least sum that is greater than 1?

Name ____________________ Date ________________

Master 4.11

Step-by-Step 3

Section 4.3, Question 11

Step 1 Shade $\frac{1}{10}$ of this pie blue.

Shade $\frac{3}{5}$ of this pie green.

Shade $\frac{1}{2}$ of this pie red.

What do you notice?

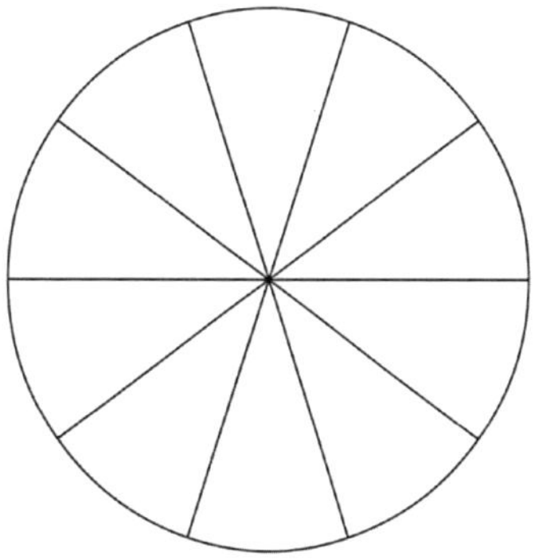

____

Step 2 Shade $\frac{3}{10}$ of this pie blue.

Shade $\frac{1}{5}$ of this pie green.

Shade $\frac{1}{2}$ of this pie red.

What do you notice?

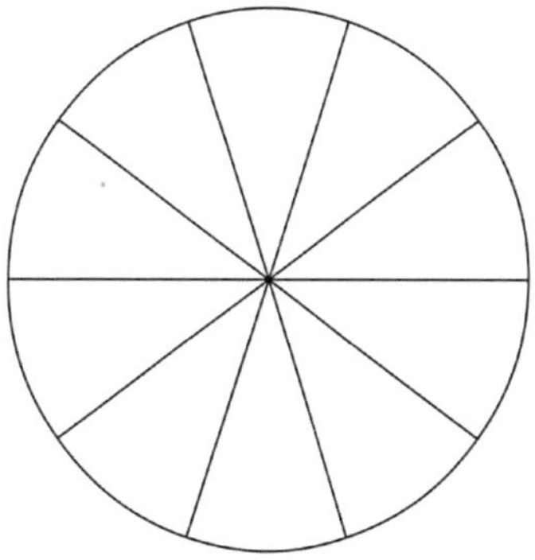

____

Step 3 Use the diagrams in *Steps 1* and *2*.
Which statement about the pies is true?
Explain how you know.

____

____

Name ____________________ Date ______________

Master 4.12 Step-by-Step 4

Section 4.4, Question 12

Step 1 Shade this strip to show $\frac{3}{4}$.

Step 2 Shade this strip to show $\frac{1}{8}$.

Step 3 Compare the diagrams in *Steps 1* and *2*.

Did Kelly use more or less than $\frac{1}{2}$ of a tank of gas?

____

How do you know?

____

Step 4 Shade this strip to show the amount of gas Kelly used.

Step 5 Shade this strip to show $\frac{1}{2}$.

Step 6 Compare the diagrams in *Steps 4* and *5*.

How much more or how much less than $\frac{1}{2}$ of a tank did Kelly use? ______________

How do you know?

____

Name ____________________ Date ________________

Master 4.13

Step-by-Step 5

Section 4.5, Question 7

Step 1 Complete this table for each person's bike riding time during the week.

Keep adding $\frac{1}{4}$ to Terri's time.

Keep adding $\frac{1}{2}$ to Sam's time.

	Sun	Mon	Tues	Wed	Thurs	Fri	Sat
Terri	$2\frac{1}{4}$						
Sam	$\frac{1}{2}$						

Step 2 Use the table. Who will bike longer on Saturday? ____________________

Step 3 Find the difference between Terri's time and Sam's time on Saturday.

____

Step 4 What did you need to know about fractions to do *Steps 1, 2,* and *3?*

____

____

Name ____________________ Date ______________

Master 4.14

Step-by-Step 6

Section 4.6, Question 8

Step 1 Shade this diagram to show $5 \times \frac{1}{2}$.

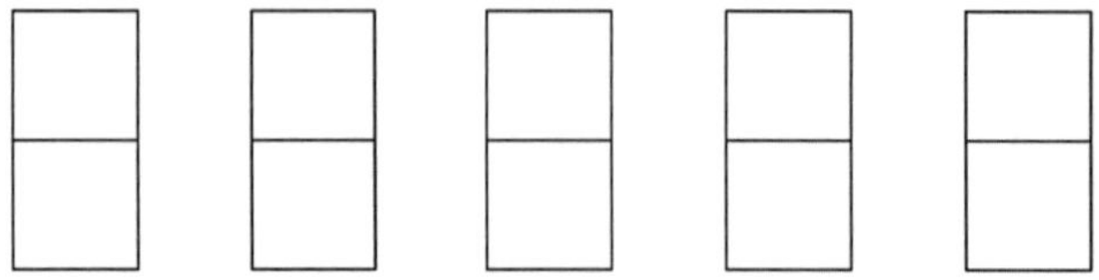

Step 2 What is $5 \times \frac{1}{2}$? ____________________

Step 3 What is $\frac{1}{2} \times 5$? ____________________

Step 4 Shade this diagram to show $\frac{1}{2} \times 5$.

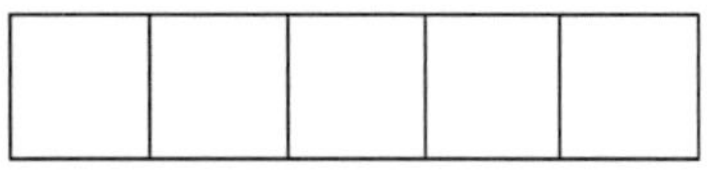

Name ____________________ Date ________________

Master 4.15

Step-by-Step 7

Section 4.7, Question 11

Step 1 Write the dimensions of the area rug on this rectangle.

Step 2 Estimate the area of the rug.

Step 3 Use Base Ten Blocks to model 3.4 × 2.7. Sketch the blocks on grid paper.

Step 4 Use the grid paper sketch to find 3.4 × 2.7.

Step 5 How does your answer in *Step 4* compare with your estimate in *Step 2*?

____

Step 6 Use long multiplication to find 34 × 27.

Step 7 Use your estimate in *Step 2* to place the decimal point in your answer in *Step 6*, to get the product of 3.4 × 2.7. ____________________

Step 8 Compare your answers in *Steps 4* and *7*. Which method did you prefer? Why?

____

____

Step 9 What is the area of the rug?

Name ____________________ Date ______________

Master 4.16

Step-by-Step 8

Section 4.8, Question 8

Step 1 Alex needs twelve 0.85-m pieces of fabric.
Multiply: 0.85×12

How much fabric does Alex need in total? ______________________________

Step 2 Alex buys 9.7 m of fabric.
Does she have enough? ______________________________
How can you use your answer in *Step 1* to find out?

____

Step 3 Does Alex have more fabric than she needs? ______________________________
How do you know?

____

Step 4 Does Alex need more fabric? ______________________________

How much more? ______________________________

Name ____________________ Date ______________

Master 4.17

Step-by-Step 9

Section 4.9, Question 7

$$0.38 + 16.2 \times (2.1 + 4) + 21 \div 3.5$$

Step 1 Add in brackets first.

____

Step 2 Multiply next.

____

Step 3 Divide next.

____

Step 4 Add twice.

____

Step 5 What is the answer? ______________________________

Name ____________________ Date _______________

Master 4.18 *Fill It Up* Game Cards

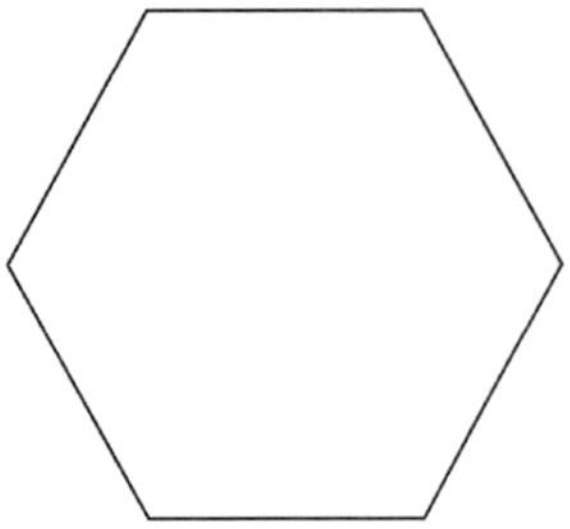	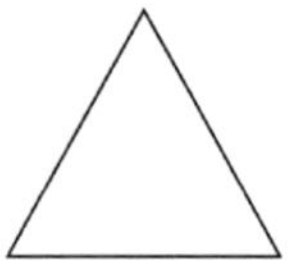		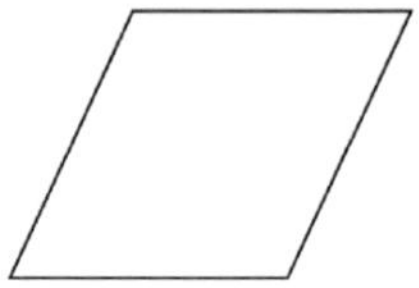
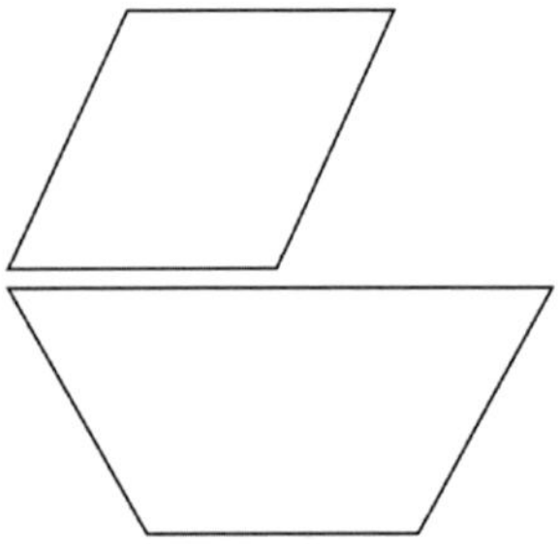	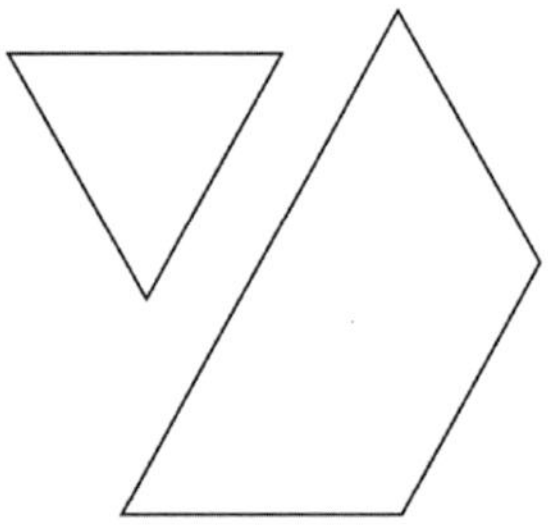	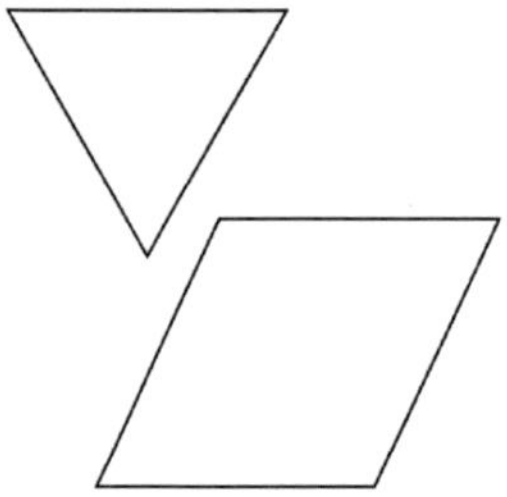	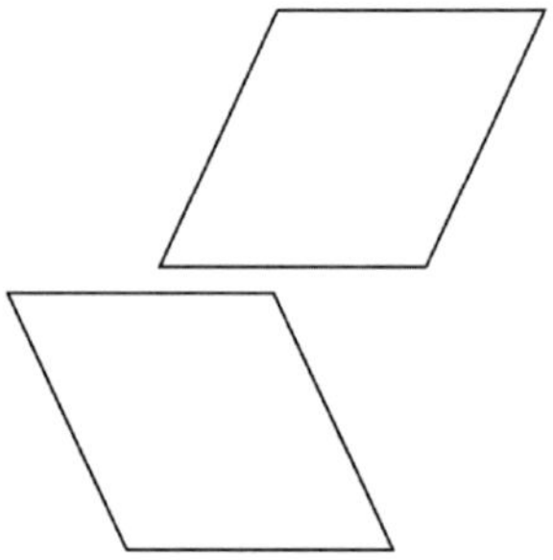
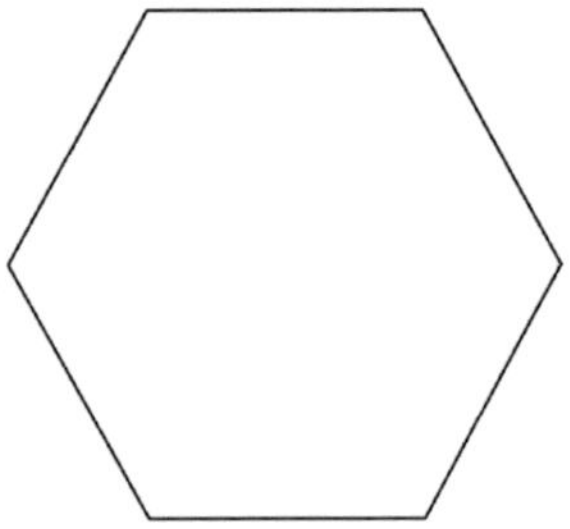	$\frac{2}{6}$	$\frac{3}{6}$	$\frac{4}{6}$
$\frac{5}{6}$	$\frac{1}{3}$	$\frac{2}{3}$	$\frac{1}{2}$

Name ____________________ Date ________________

Master 4.19

Tic-Tac-Quo-tient Game Board

5	3.5	2.5	0.8	0.5	3
2.5	0.25	1.4	0.375	0.75	0.2
1	0.4	2	0.875	1.5	1.8
0.125	1.125	4.5	1	0.5	2.25
4	1.75	0.25	1.25	0.5	1.2
0.75	2	0.6	1.5	0.625	1.6

2	4
5	8

Divisor

1	**2**	**3**	**4**	**5**
6	**7**	**8**	**9**	**10**

Dividend

Name ____________________ Date ____________________

Master 4.20

Map for Section 4.1, *Explore*

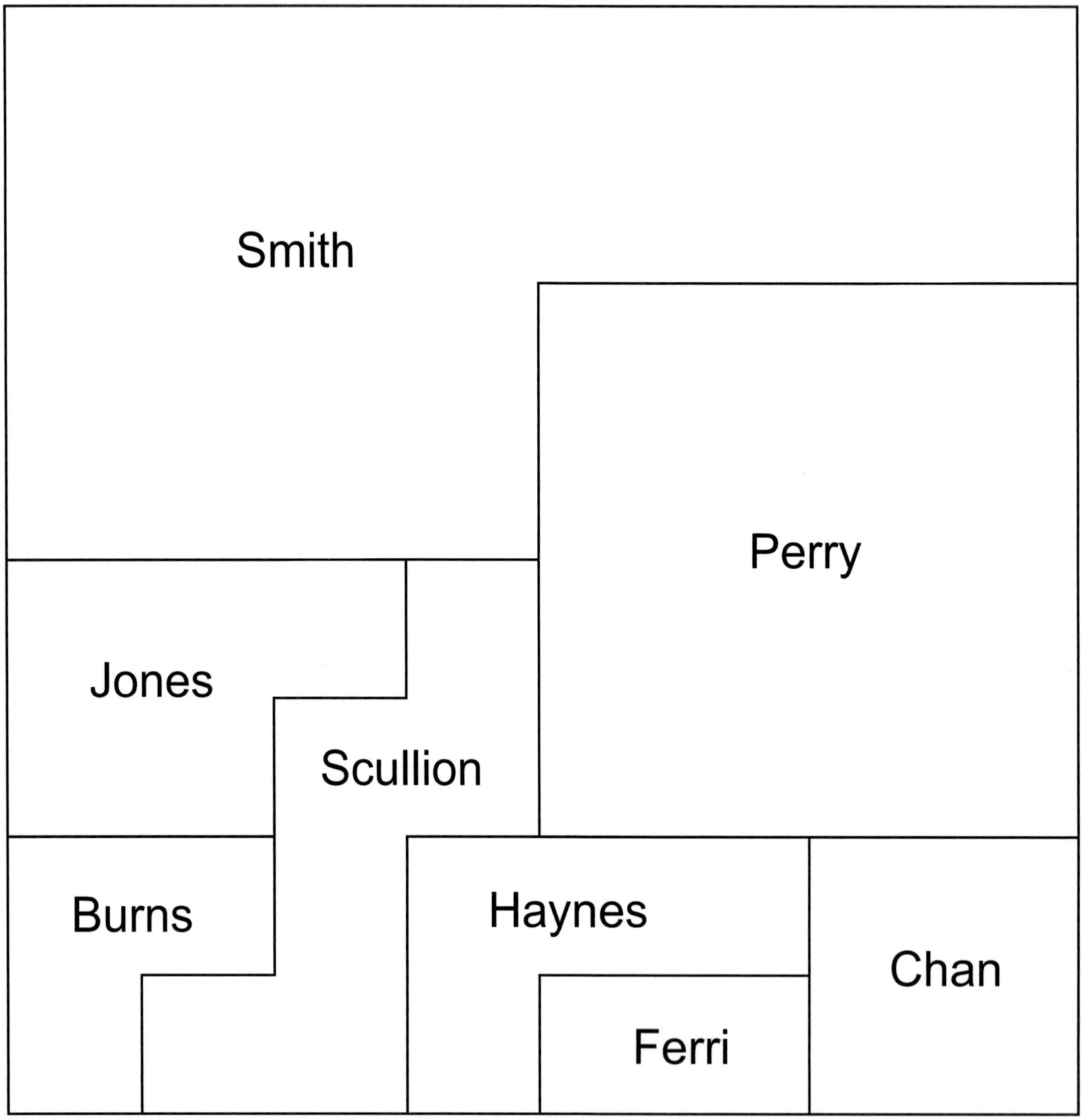

Name ____________________ Date _______________

Master 4.20a

The Divided Square

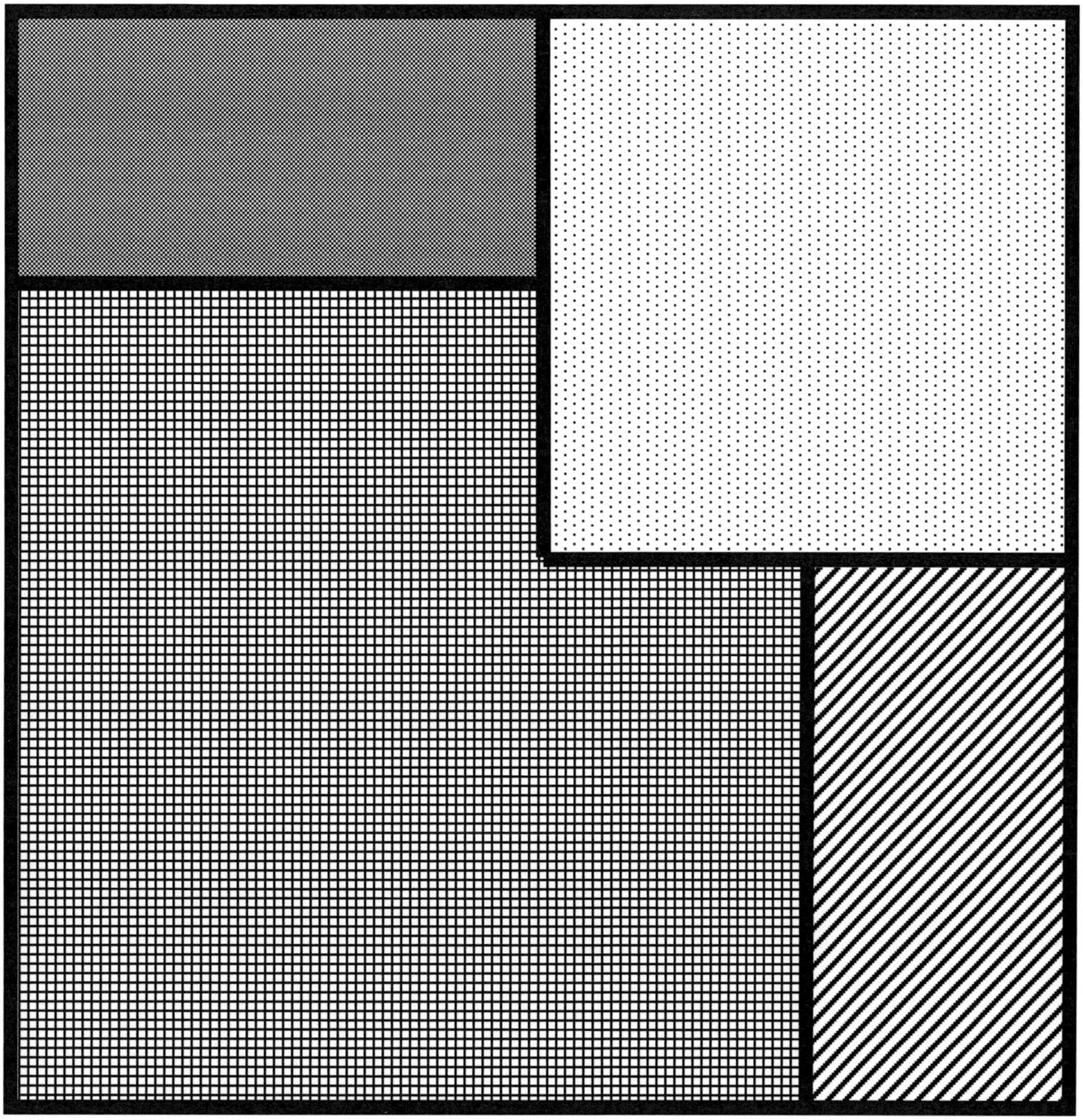

Name ____________________ Date ________________

Master 4.21

Fraction Circles (12ths, 10ths, 8ths, 6ths)

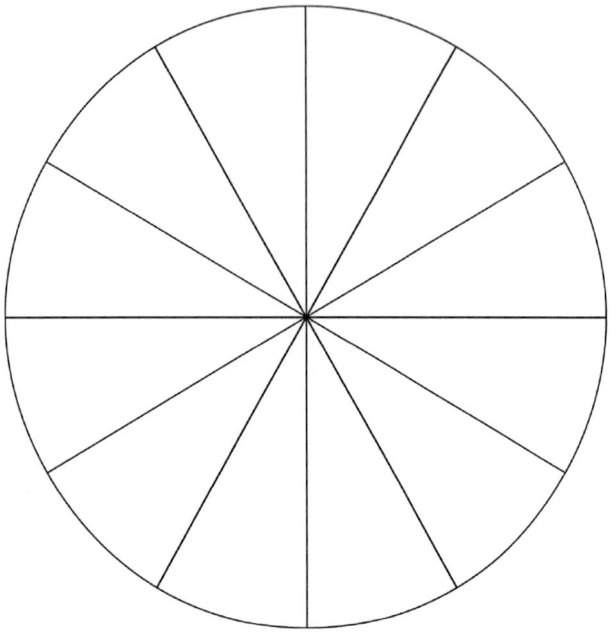

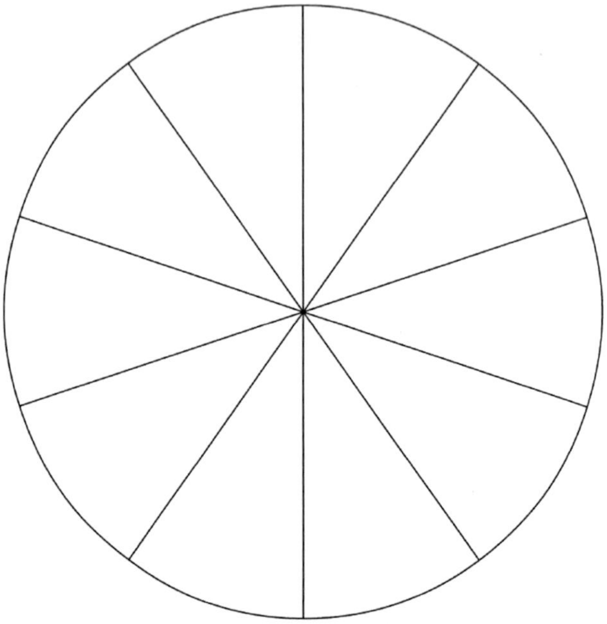

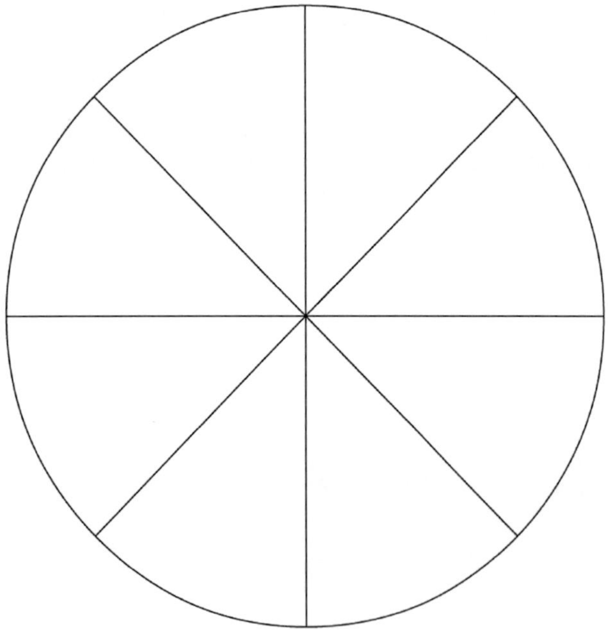

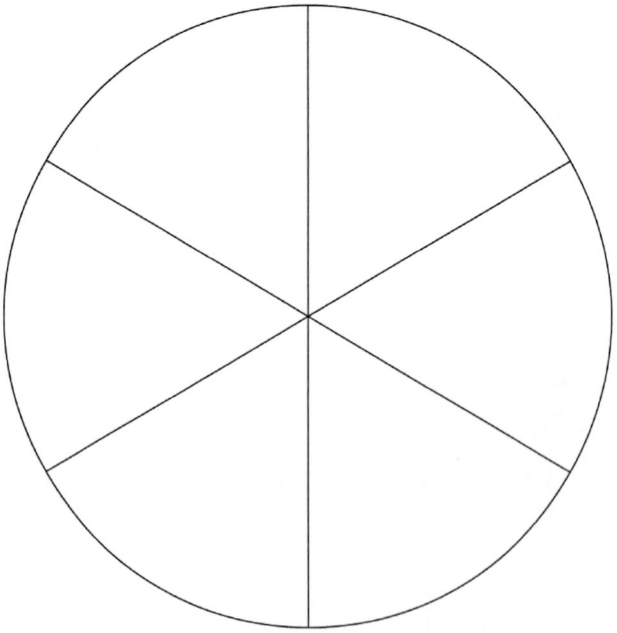

Name ____________________ Date ________________

Master 4.22

Fraction Strips 1

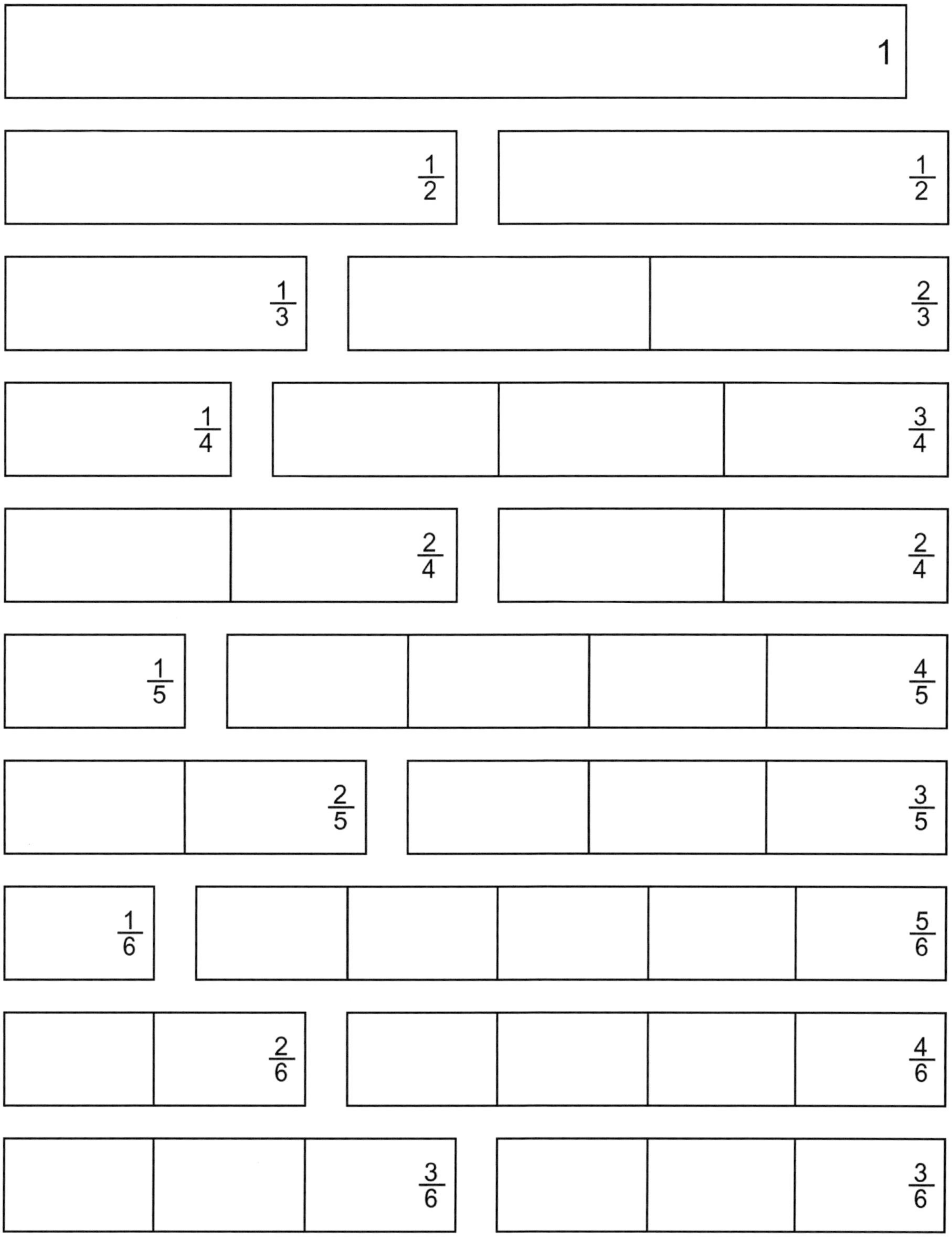

Name ____________________ Date ______________

Fraction Strips 2

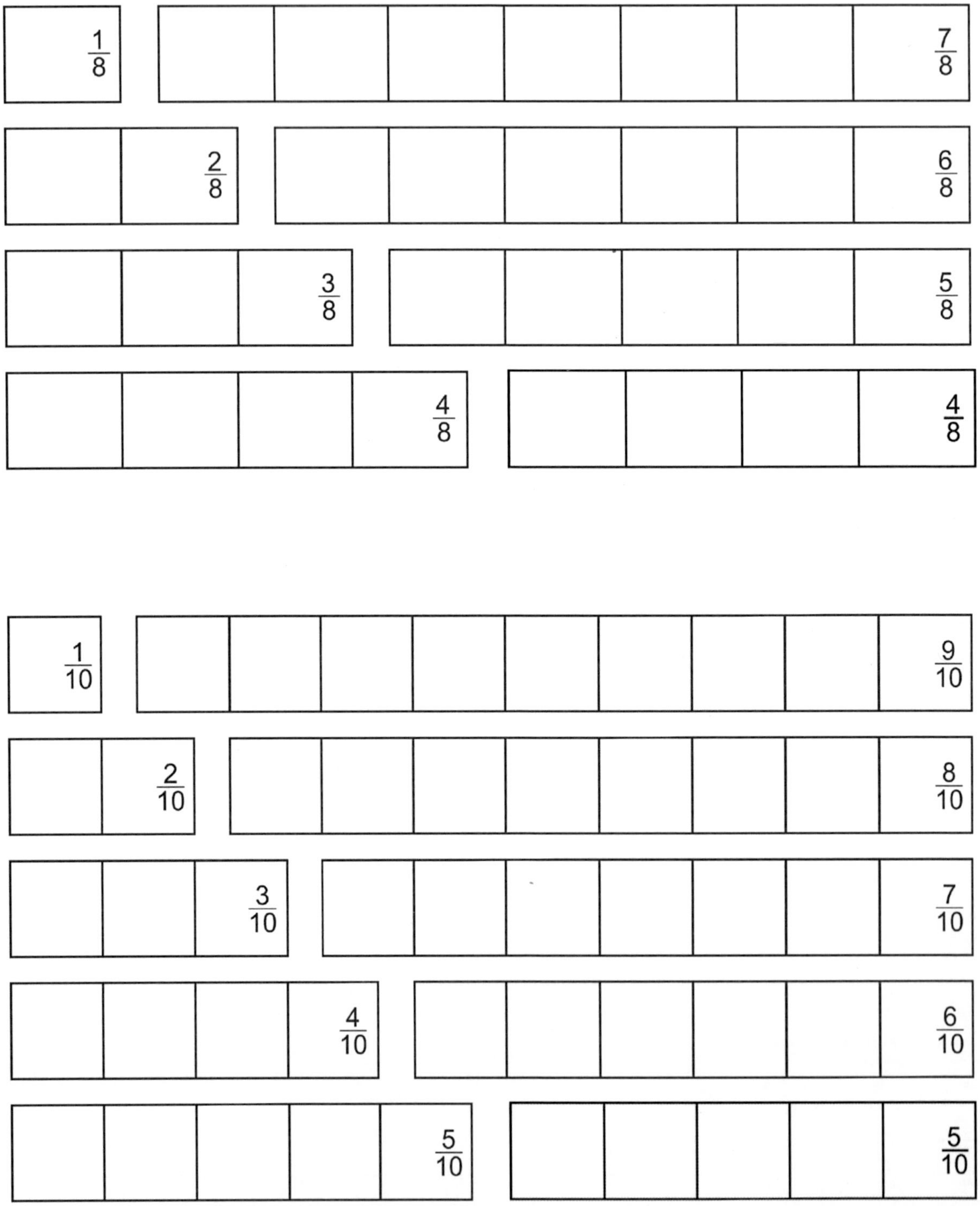

Name ____________________ Date _______________

Master 4.24

Number Lines 1

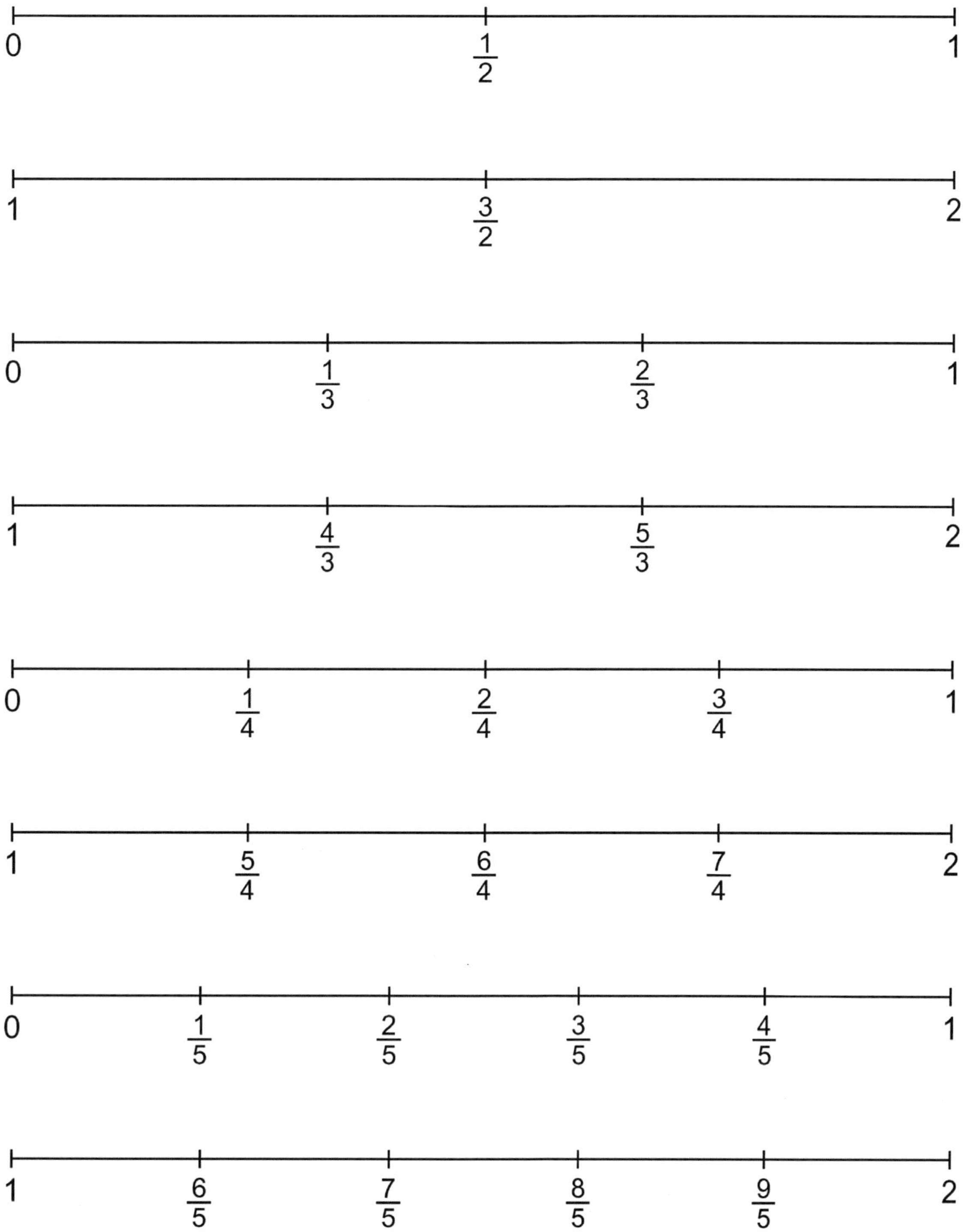

Name ____________________ Date ______________

Master 4.25

Number Lines 2

0 $\frac{1}{6}$ $\frac{2}{6}$ $\frac{3}{6}$ $\frac{4}{6}$ $\frac{5}{6}$ 1

1 $\frac{7}{6}$ $\frac{8}{6}$ $\frac{9}{6}$ $\frac{10}{6}$ $\frac{11}{6}$ 2

0 $\frac{1}{8}$ $\frac{2}{8}$ $\frac{3}{8}$ $\frac{4}{8}$ $\frac{5}{8}$ $\frac{6}{8}$ $\frac{7}{8}$ 1

1 $\frac{9}{8}$ $\frac{10}{8}$ $\frac{11}{8}$ $\frac{12}{8}$ $\frac{13}{8}$ $\frac{14}{8}$ $\frac{15}{8}$ 2

0 $\frac{1}{10}$ $\frac{2}{10}$ $\frac{3}{10}$ $\frac{4}{10}$ $\frac{5}{10}$ $\frac{6}{10}$ $\frac{7}{10}$ $\frac{8}{10}$ $\frac{9}{10}$ 1

1 $\frac{11}{10}$ $\frac{12}{10}$ $\frac{13}{10}$ $\frac{14}{10}$ $\frac{15}{10}$ $\frac{16}{10}$ $\frac{17}{10}$ $\frac{18}{10}$ $\frac{19}{10}$ 2

0 $\frac{1}{12}$ $\frac{2}{12}$ $\frac{3}{12}$ $\frac{4}{12}$ $\frac{5}{12}$ $\frac{6}{12}$ $\frac{7}{12}$ $\frac{8}{12}$ $\frac{9}{12}$ $\frac{10}{12}$ $\frac{11}{12}$ 1

1 $\frac{13}{12}$ $\frac{14}{12}$ $\frac{15}{12}$ $\frac{16}{12}$ $\frac{17}{12}$ $\frac{18}{12}$ $\frac{19}{12}$ $\frac{20}{12}$ $\frac{21}{12}$ $\frac{22}{12}$ $\frac{23}{12}$ 2

Name ____________________ Date ________________

Master 4.26

Shade One Game Board

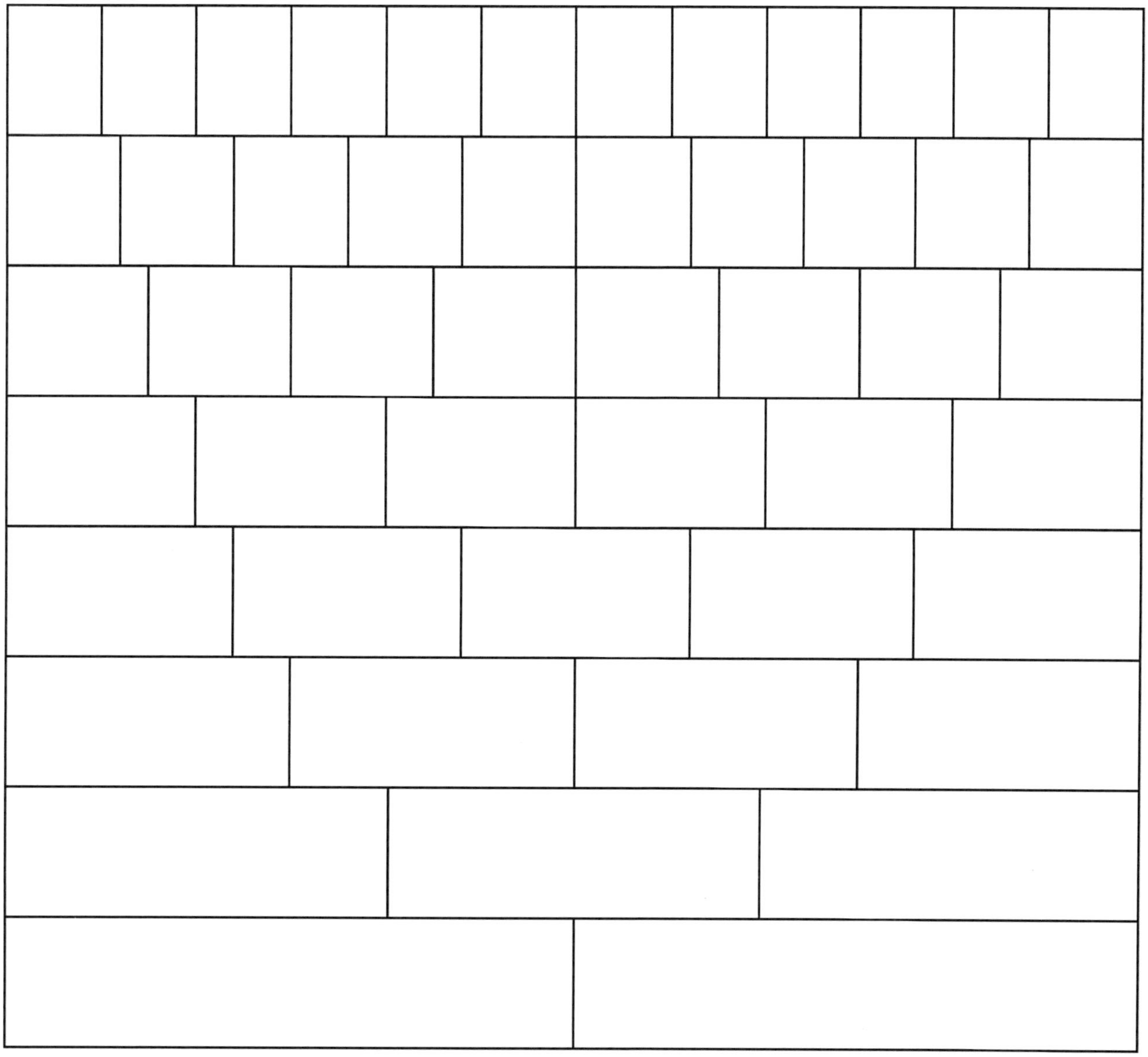

Name ____________________ Date ________________

Master 4.27

Shade One Game Cards 1

$\frac{4}{5}$	$\frac{2}{12}$	$\frac{1}{12}$
$\frac{4}{6}$	$\frac{3}{4}$	$\frac{2}{3}$
$\frac{4}{8}$	$\frac{3}{5}$	$\frac{2}{4}$
$\frac{4}{10}$	$\frac{3}{6}$	$\frac{2}{5}$
$\frac{4}{12}$	$\frac{3}{8}$	$\frac{2}{6}$
$\frac{5}{6}$	$\frac{3}{10}$	$\frac{2}{8}$
$\frac{5}{8}$	$\frac{3}{12}$	$\frac{2}{10}$

Name ____________________ Date ________________

Master 4.28

Shade One Game Cards 2

$\frac{1}{2}$	$\frac{7}{12}$	$\frac{5}{10}$
$\frac{1}{3}$	$\frac{8}{10}$	$\frac{5}{12}$
$\frac{1}{4}$	$\frac{8}{12}$	$\frac{6}{8}$
$\frac{1}{5}$	$\frac{9}{10}$	$\frac{6}{10}$
$\frac{1}{6}$	$\frac{9}{12}$	$\frac{6}{12}$
$\frac{1}{8}$	$\frac{10}{12}$	$\frac{7}{8}$
$\frac{1}{10}$	$\frac{11}{12}$	$\frac{7}{10}$

Name ____________________ Date ______________

Master 4.29

Fractions to Decimals

1. a) Record your results in this table.

Unit Fraction	Decimal Form	Terminating (T), or Repeating (R)	Unit Fraction	Decimal Form	Terminating (T), or Repeating (R)
$\frac{1}{2}$	0.5		$\frac{1}{11}$		
$\frac{1}{3}$			$\frac{1}{12}$		
$\frac{1}{4}$			$\frac{1}{13}$		
$\frac{1}{5}$			$\frac{1}{14}$		
$\frac{1}{6}$			$\frac{1}{15}$		
$\frac{1}{7}$			$\frac{1}{16}$		
$\frac{1}{8}$			$\frac{1}{17}$		
$\frac{1}{9}$			$\frac{1}{18}$		
$\frac{1}{10}$			$\frac{1}{19}$		
			$\frac{1}{20}$		

b) Fraction family name: ______________________________

Family members: ______________________________

Decimal forms: ______________________________

Patterns or observations: ______________________________

____

____

Name ____________________ Date ________________

Master 4.30a

Unit Test: Unit 4 Fractions and Decimals

1. Add or subtract.

a) $\frac{1}{4} + \frac{5}{12}$ **b)** $\frac{3}{5} - \frac{1}{10}$ **c)** $\frac{2}{3} + \frac{3}{5}$ **d)** $\frac{5}{9} - \frac{1}{4}$

2. Add or subtract.

a) $3\frac{2}{3} + 4\frac{1}{5}$ **b)** $5\frac{3}{4} - 2\frac{2}{9}$

3. In an election for school council, one-quarter of the students voted for Alanna, one-fifth voted for Barry, and one-third voted for Cristina. What fraction of students did not vote? What assumptions did you make?

Name ____________________ Date ______________

Master 4.30b

Unit Test continued

4. **a)** Find a fraction between $\frac{1}{5}$ and $\frac{1}{4}$.

b) Find two fractions between $\frac{1}{3}$ and $\frac{1}{2}$.

5. Find.

a) $\frac{2}{3} + \frac{2}{3} + \frac{2}{3} + \frac{2}{3} + \frac{2}{3}$ **b)** $5 \times \frac{4}{5}$ **c)** $\frac{3}{4} \times 8$

6. **a)** Use a calculator. Convert each fraction to a decimal.

$\frac{2}{3}$, $\frac{15}{19}$, $\frac{5}{7}$, $\frac{13}{15}$, $\frac{11}{13}$

b) Order the fractions from greatest to least.

Name ____________________ Date ______________

Master 4.30c **Unit Test continued**

7. A 2-L can of paint covers a rectangular area 6.3 m by 3.0 m.
   a) How many cans of paint are needed for an area 8.5 m by 9.2 m?
   b) A 2-L can of paint costs $16.45.
   How much does it cost to paint the area in part a?

8. A company that services furnaces charges $25 for a house call, plus $42.50 an hour for labour. One family's bill was $88.75. How long was the service call?

9. Evaluate. Explain each step.
   18 ÷ (3.4 – 1.9) + 15.2 × 3.7

Name ____________________ Date ______________

Master 4.31

Sample Answers

Unit Test – Master 4.30

1. **a)** $\frac{8}{12}$, or $\frac{2}{3}$ **b)** $\frac{5}{10}$, or $\frac{1}{2}$

   c) $\frac{19}{15}$, or $1\frac{4}{15}$ **d)** $\frac{11}{36}$

2. **a)** $7\frac{13}{15}$ **b)** $3\frac{19}{36}$

3. $\frac{13}{60}$ of the students did not vote.

   Answers will vary. Possible assumptions:
   - All students were eligible to vote.
   - No ballots were spoiled and so discounted.

4. Answers will vary. Sample answers:

   a) $\frac{9}{40}$ **b)** $\frac{9}{24}$, or $\frac{3}{8}$ and $\frac{11}{24}$

5. **a)** $\frac{10}{3}$, or $3\frac{1}{3}$ **b)** 4 **c)** 6

6. **a)** Approximately 0.666 666 667; 0.789 473 684; 0.714 285 714; 0.866 666 667; 0.846 153 846

   b) $\frac{13}{15}, \frac{11}{13}, \frac{15}{19}, \frac{5}{7}, \frac{2}{3}$

7. **a)** 5 cans **b)** $82.25

8. 1.5 h

9. 68.24
   Start by subtracting what is enclosed in brackets:
   $3.4 - 1.9 = 1.5$
   $18 \div 1.5 + 15.2 \times 3.7$
   Multiply and divide from left to right:
   $18 \div 1.5 = 12.0$, $15.2 \times 3.7 = 56.24$
   Add: $12.0 + 56.24 = 68.24$

Extra Practice Masters 4.32–4.41

Go to the CD-ROM to access editable versions of these Extra Practice Masters.

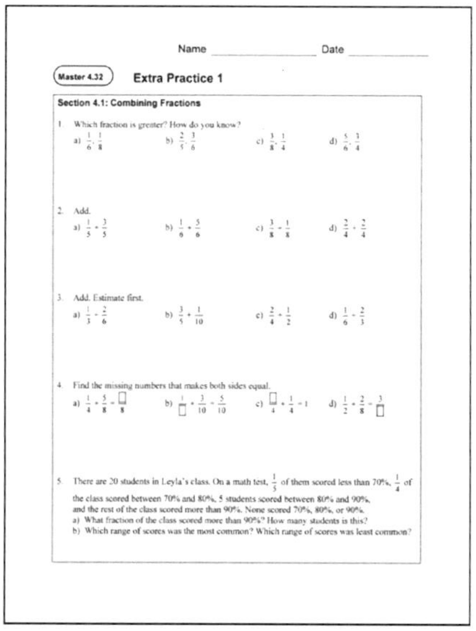

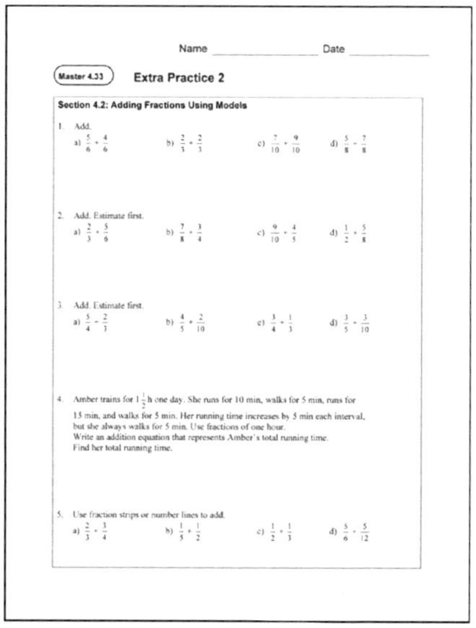

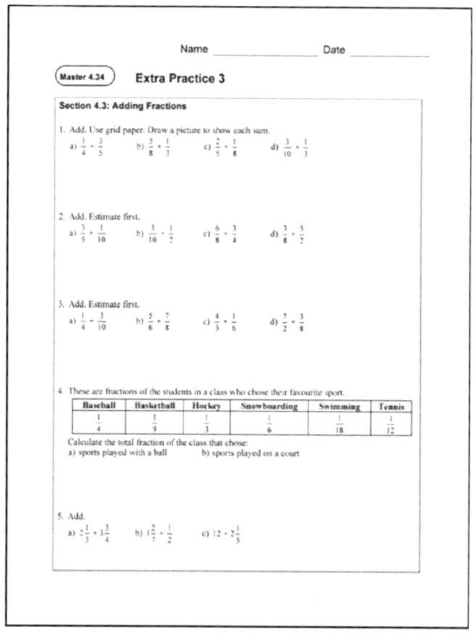

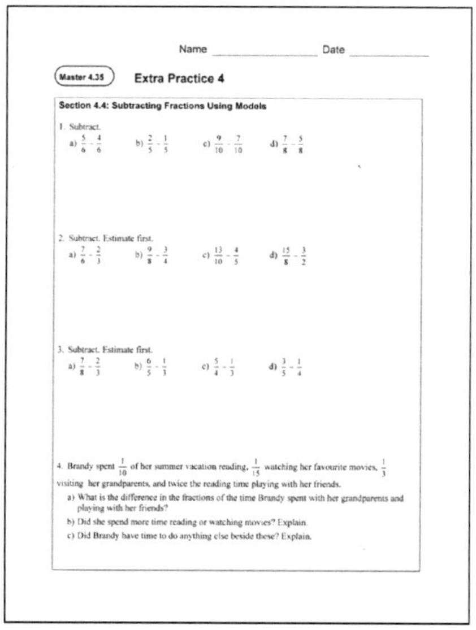

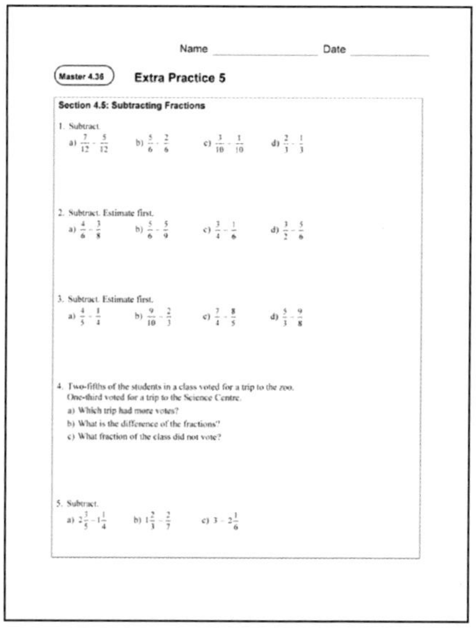

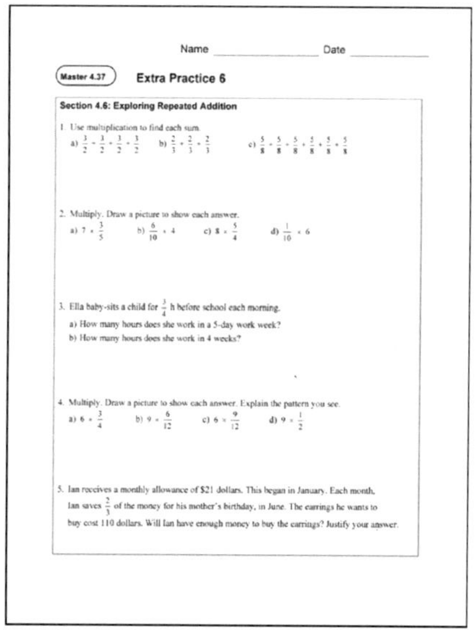

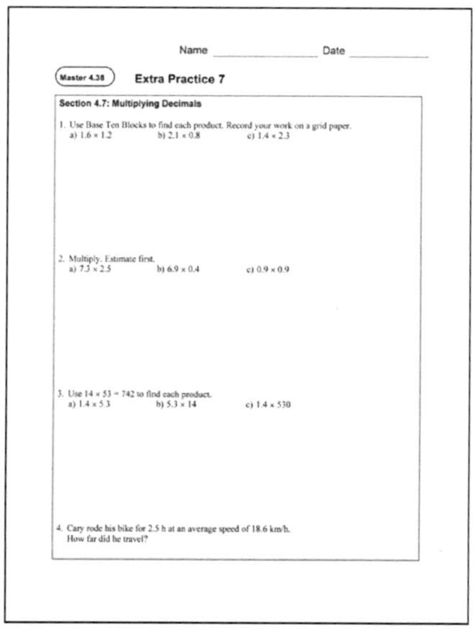

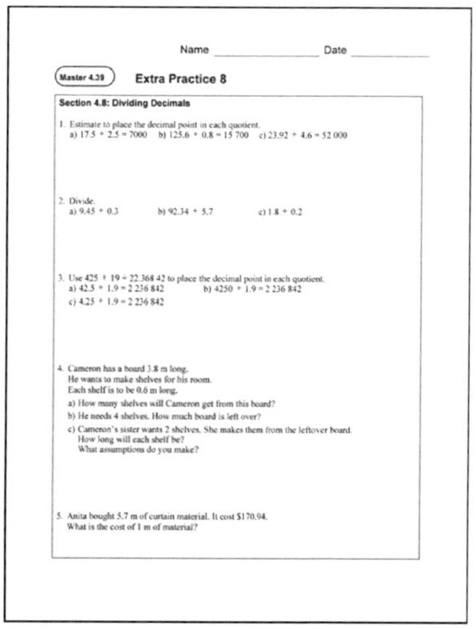

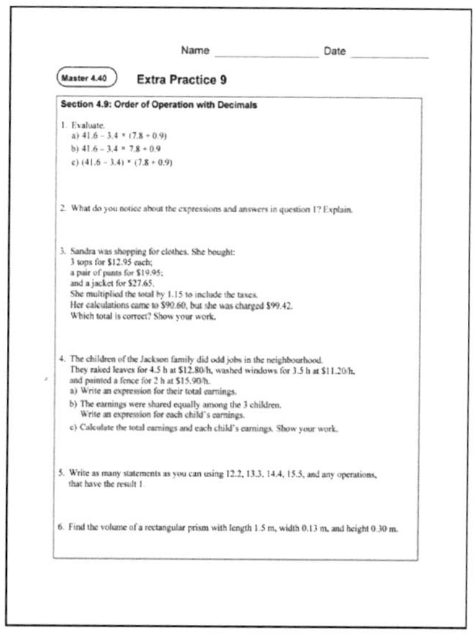

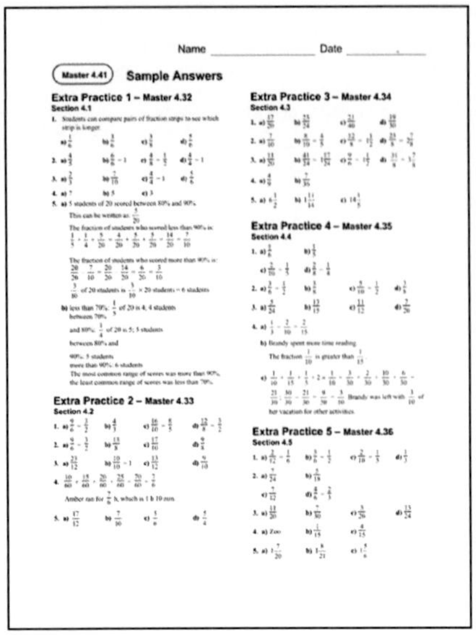

Name ______________ Date ______________

Master 4.41 **Sample Answers**

Extra Practice 1 – Master 4.32
Section 4.1

Extra Practice 2 – Master 4.33
Section 4.2

Extra Practice 3 – Master 4.34
Section 4.3

Extra Practice 4 – Master 4.35
Section 4.4

Extra Practice 5 – Master 4.36
Section 4.5

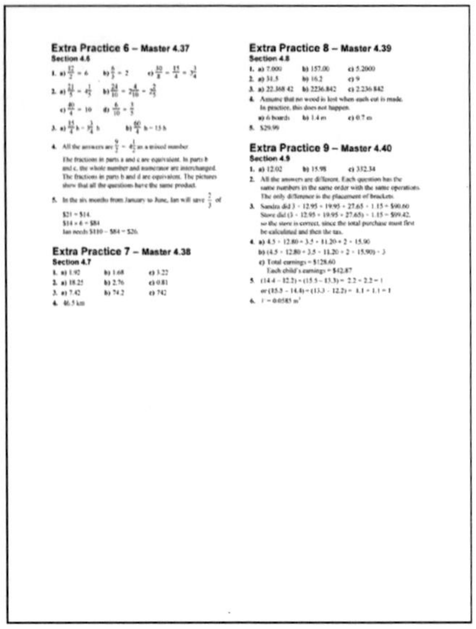

Extra Practice 6 – Master 4.37
Section 4.6

Extra Practice 7 – Master 4.38
Section 4.7

Extra Practice 8 – Master 4.39
Section 4.8

Extra Practice 9 – Master 4.40
Section 4.9

Name ____________________ Date ______________

Master CR1.1

Net for Question 10, page 165

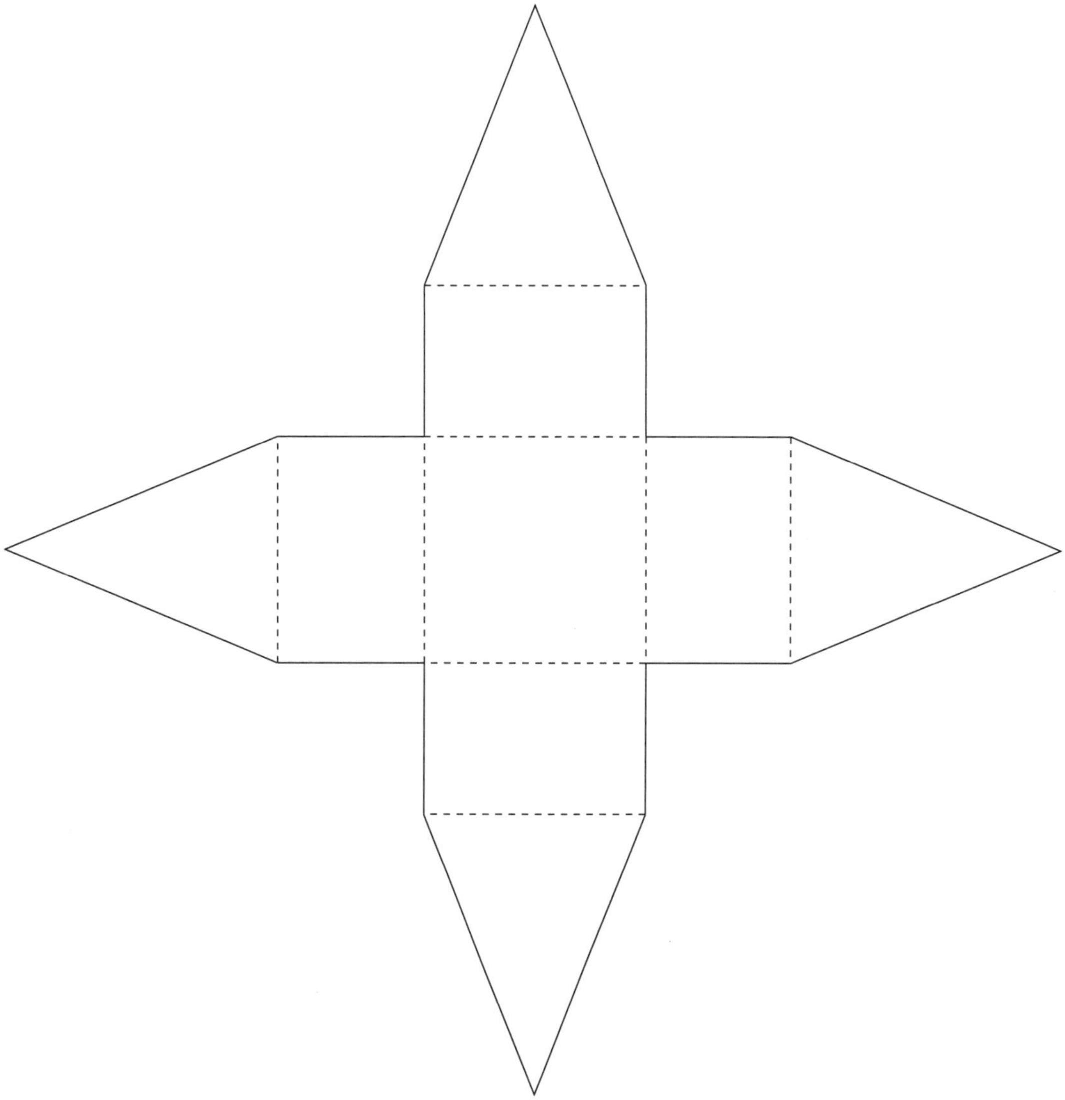

Addison Wesley

Mathematics Makes Sense

Program Authors

Jason Johnston
Bryn Keyes
Mary Doucette
Antonietta Lenjosek
Steve Thomas
Margaret Sinclair
Trevor Brown
Cathy Heideman
Don Jones
Michael Davis
Jennifer Paziuk
Ken Harper
Sharon Jeroski
Ray Appel
Laura Weatherhead
Betty Milne
Jim Mennie
Lynn Strangway

Printed and bound in Canada

10 17

PEARSON
Education Canada

ADDISON WESLEY

Ontario

Math Makes Sense 7

Ontario Teacher Guide

Unit 5: Data Management

PEARSON
Addison Wesley

UNIT 5

Data Management

"The emphasis or goal of our instruction should be to help children see that graphs and charts tell about information, that different types of representation tell different things about the same data. The value of having students actually construct their own graphs is not so much that they learn the techniques but that they are personally invested in the data and that they learn how a graph conveys information."

John A. Van de Walle

FOCUS STRAND
Data Management and Probability

SUPPORTING STRAND
Number Sense and Numeration

TIPS
Adolescent learners benefit from using graphic organizers and technology that depict relationships among key concepts.

Mathematics Background

What Are the Big Ideas?

- A database is an organized collection of data. Data that are collected directly or first-hand are called primary data. Data that are not collected first-hand are called secondary data.
- Data may be biased or unbiased. Unbiased data are preferred because they provide information that is typical of the population.
- Data can be organized and displayed in many ways.
- Sometimes, people or organizations use graphs to distort information and to mislead.
- Data may show a pattern or trend, and may be used to make predictions.
- The mean, median, and mode of a set of data are measures of central tendency.
- Spreadsheets can be used to record and graph data in a variety of ways.

How Will the Concepts Develop?

Students review the mean, median, and mode of a set of data. They learn when each measure of central tendency best describes data.

Students collect primary data by conducting surveys and experiments. They learn to use databases to obtain secondary data.

Students record and organize collected data on tally charts and stem-and-leaf plots. They display data on frequency tables, bar graphs, pictographs, and line graphs.

Students use technology, such as *Fathom* and *AppleWorks*, to investigate scatter plots, and record and graph data.

Students interpret and describe data presented on charts, tables, and graphs, and solve related problems. They identify and describe trends in graphs.

Students learn the importance of an unbiased survey. They understand that graphs can be drawn to mislead and to create a false impression.

Why Are These Concepts Important?

In this age of information technology, it is important for students to understand how information is processed and translated into usable knowledge, and how data are used to make predictions and decisions.

Graphs and data are used in advertising, opinion polls, population trends, and other everyday situations. A knowledge of data management is necessary if students are to become intelligent consumers who can make informed decisions.

Curriculum Overview

Cluster 1: Collecting and Organizing Data

Overall Expectations
- Systematically collect, organize, and analyse data. (7m81)
- Recognize the different levels of data collection. (7m82)
- Use computer applications to examine and interpret data in a variety of ways. (7m83)
- Construct graphic organizers using computer applications. (7m85)
- Interpret displays of data and present the information using mathematical terms. (7m86)

Specific Expectations
- Demonstrate the pervasive use of data ... (7m89)
- Collect and organize data on tally charts and stem-and-leaf plots, and display data on frequency tables, using primary data and secondary data. (7m91)
- Understand how tally charts and frequency tables can be used to record data. (7m92)
- Understand the difference between a spreadsheet and database. (7m93)
- Search databases for information and interpret the numerical data. (7m94)
- Identify and describe trends in graphs. (7m96)
- Describe in their own words information presented on tally charts, stem-and-leaf plots, and frequency tables. (7m97)
- Use conventional symbols, titles, and labels when displaying data. (7m98)
- Analyse bias in data-collection methods. (7m99)
- Read and report information about data presented on graphs, and solve problems. (7m100)
- Display data on bar graphs, pictographs, and circle graphs, with and without the help of technology. (7m102)
- Explore with technology to find the best presentation of data. (7m105)

Cluster 2: Analysing Data

Overall Expectations
- Systematically collect, organize, and analyse data. (7m81)
- Develop an appreciation for statistical methods as powerful means of decision making. (7m84)
- Evaluate data and make conclusions from the analysis of data. (7m87)

Specific Expectations
- Understand the impact that statistical methods have on decision making. (7m90)
- Understand that each measure of central tendency gives different information about the data. (7m95)
- Describe data using calculations of mean, median, and mode. (7m101)
- Make inferences and convincing arguments that are based on data analysis. (7m103)
- Evaluate arguments that are based on data analysis. (7m104)

Launch

Section 5.1: Collecting Data

Technology: Using Databases to Find Data

Section 5.2: Recording Data

Section 5.3: Stem-and-Leaf Plots

Mid-Unit Review

Technology: Using *Fathom* to Investigate Scatter Plots

Section 5.4: Line Graphs

Technology: Using Spreadsheets to Record and Graph Data

Section 5.5: Applications of Mean, Median and Mode

Section 5.6: Evaluating Data Analysis

Unit Review
Practice Test

Unit Problem
Organizing a Winter Carnival

Curriculum across the Grades

Grade 6	Grade 7	Grade 8
Students design surveys, then organize data and record data on spreadsheets or tally charts. They use computer applications to examine data, then select the type of graph that best represents the data. Students evaluate and explore how data were collected and how the results represent the population. They explain how the choice of intervals affects the appearance of data. Students calculate the median of a set of data. Students construct line graphs, bar graphs, and scatter plots both by hand and by using computer applications. They make inferences and convincing arguments based on the analysis of tables, charts, and graphs. Students recognize that different types of graphs can present the same data differently.	Students collect and organize data on tally charts and stem-and-leaf plots, and display data on frequency tables, using primary and secondary data. They search databases for information and interpret the numerical data. Students display data on bar graphs, pictographs, and circle graphs, with and without the help of technology. They explore with technology to find the best presentation of data. Students make inferences and convincing arguments based on data analysis. They identify and describe trends in graphs and describe in their own words information presented on tally charts, stem-and-leaf plots, and frequency tables. They read and report information about data presented on graphs, and use the information to solve problems. Students describe data using calculations of mean, median, and mode. They analyse bias in data-collection methods.	Students collect primary data using both a whole population and a sample, organize the data on tally charts and stem-and-leaf plots, and display the data on frequency tables. They manipulate and present data using spreadsheets, search databases for information, then solve problems. Students display data on line graphs, comparative bar graphs, circle graphs, and histograms, with and without the help of technology. They explore with technology to find the best presentation of data. Students discuss trends in graphs and the quantitative information presented on tally charts, stem-and-leaf plots, frequency tables, and/or graphs. They read and report information presented on graphs and use the information to solve problems. Students assess bias in data-collection methods. They determine the effect on a measure of central tendency of adding or removing a value.

Materials for This Unit

Students have to research, using newspapers and magazines. Collect these items that contain tables and/or graphs of data, and survey results.

Additional Activities

Triple M–An "Average" Game

For Extra Practice (Appropriate for use after Skills You'll Need)
Materials: *Triple M—An "Average" Game* (Master 5.5); a deck of cards or number cards (1 to 13); number cube labelled 1 to 6, calculator (optional)

Playing this game reinforces the skills of calculating mean, median, and mode.

The work students do: Students work in groups of 3 or 4. One player rolls the number cube, then adds 1 to the number rolled. Each player is dealt this number of cards. Each player records the value of each of her cards (a joker is assigned the value of one of the cards already in the hand) as a number. Each player calculates the mean, median, and mode of the numbers in his hand, rounding each average to the nearest whole number. If there is no mode, student records a 0. Students calculate their score for the round by adding their mean, median, and mode.

Students continue to play more rounds until all cards have been used. The player with the highest score wins.

Take It Further: Students use two decks of cards and two number cubes. One player rolls the number cubes, then adds the two numbers rolled. Each player is dealt this number of cards.

Mathematical/Social
Group Activity

Connecting Lines

For Extra Practice (Appropriate for use after Section 5.4)
Materials: *Connecting Lines* (Master 5.6), a deck of cards with the jokers removed (Ace = 1, Jack = 11, Queen = 12, King = 13), 2 number cubes labelled 1 to 6, 1-cm grid paper (PM 20), rulers, calculator

Playing this game reinforces the skills of plotting points on a coordinate grid, calculating the range, and comparing ratios.

The work students do: Students work in groups of 3 or 4. Students roll number cubes and draw cards to plot points on a coordinate grid, with the horizontal axis labelled "Dice Number" and the vertical axis labelled "Card Number." When all the cards have been used, students use a ruler to connect all the dots, from right to left, on the grid paper. Each player calculates both the horizontal range and the vertical range. Each player writes the ratio of the vertical range to the horizontal range. The winner is the player with the greatest ratio.

Take It Further: Each player describes the trends in his graph, then describes a situation that could be represented by the graph.

Logical/Mathematical/Visual
Group Activity

Planning for Unit 5

Planning for Instruction

Suggested Unit time: About 3 weeks

Section	Time	Materials	Program Support
Launch, page 2	15–20 min		
Skills You'll Need, page 4	15–20 min	calculators	
5.1: Collecting Data, page 5 Analyse data collection and possible bias.	80–100 min	2-column charts	PM 17: 2-Column Chart Master 5.7: Step-by-Step 1 Master 5.15: Extra Practice 1
Technology: Using Databases to Find Data, page 8 Search databases for information.	40–50 min	computers (E-STAT website)	
5.2: Recording Data, page 10 Record data in tables, bar graphs, and pictographs.	80–100 min	novels, 0.5-cm grid paper, number cubes (labelled 1 to 6), atlases or almanacs, rulers 2-column charts (optional) 3-column charts (optional)	PM 14: 0.5-cm Grid Paper PM 17: 2-Column Chart PM 18: 3-Column Chart Master 5.8: Step-by-Step 2 Master 5.16: Extra Practice 2
5.3: Stem-and-Leaf Plots, page 15 Display data on a stem-and-leaf plot.	80–100 min	metre sticks tape measures newspapers or the Internet	Master 5.9: Step-by-Step 3 Master 5.17: Extra Practice 3
Mid-Unit Review, page 20		2-column charts 3-column charts atlases or databases 0.5-cm grid paper	PM 14: 0.5-cm Grid Paper PM 17: 2-Column Chart PM 18: 3-Column Chart
Technology: Using *Fathom* to Investigate Scatter Plots, page 21 Identify trends in scatter plots.	40–50 min	computers with *Fathom*	
5.4: Line Graphs, page 24 Display data using line graphs and describe trends.	80–100 min	1-cm grid paper, rulers, databases such as *Environment Canada* 3-column charts (optional)	PM 20: 1-cm Grid Paper PM 18: 3-Column Chart Master 5.10: Step-by-Step 4 Master 5.18: Extra Practice 4
Technology: Using Spreadsheets to Record and Graph Data, page 29 Display data on graphs using spreadsheets.	40–50 min	computers with *AppleWorks*	
5.5: Applications of Mean, Median, and Mode, page 34 Understand which measure of central tendency best describes a set of data.	80–100 min	calculators	Master 5.11: Step-by-Step 5 Master 5.19: Extra Practice 5
5.6: Evaluating Data Analysis, page 38 Examine how data can be misleading.	80–100 min	0.5-cm grid paper, rulers newspapers, magazines, or the Internet	PM 14: 0.5-cm Grid Paper Master 5.12: Step-by-Step 6 Master 5.20: Extra Practice 6
Reading and Writing in Math, page 42			

Section	Time	Materials	Program Support
Unit Review, page 44		0.5-cm grid paper, calculators, rulers	PM 14: 0.5-cm Grid Paper Extra Practice: Student Book page 442
Practice Test, page 47		0.5-cm grid paper	PM 14: 0.5-cm Grid Paper
Unit Problem: Organizing a Winter Carnival, page 48	80–100 min	0.5-cm grid paper, 3-column charts, calculators, rulers	PM 14: 0.5-cm Grid Paper PM 18: 3-Column Chart

etext online tutorial

This web-based tutorial uses voice, animation, and an optional quiz to present each core lesson, so that students can review content with a new approach.

Planning for Assessment

Purpose	Tools and Process	Recording and Reporting
Diagnostic	*Unit Launch* Question; conference; scaffold problems throughout the unit	PM 8: Conference Prompts
Formative	*Explore* – Ongoing Assessment: Observe and Listen	Master 5.2 Ongoing Observations: Data Management PM 1: Inquiry Process Check List PM 6: Observation Record 1 PM 7: Observation Record 2 PM 8: Conference Prompts PM 2: Self-Assessment PM 3: Self-Assessment: Problem Solving PM 9: Work Sample Records
Summative	*Unit Review* *Unit Problem* – Performance Assessment Unit Test Review assessment records; add unit results to ongoing records	Master 5.1 Unit Rubric: Data Management Master 5.3 Performance Assessment Rubric: Organize a Winter Carnival Master 5.4 Unit Summary: Data Management PM 10: Summary Class Records: Strands PM 11: Summary Class Records: Achievement Categories PM 12: Summary Record: Individual
Learning Skills/Mathematical Disposition	Observe and record throughout the unit	PM 4: Learning Skills Check List PM 5: Mathematical Dispositions and Learning Skills

Program Masters (PM) are in the *Grade 7 Planning and Program Masters* module.
Extra Practice Masters are on the CD-ROM and are printed in reduced format on page 67 of this module.

SECTION ORGANIZER

15–20 min

Curriculum Focus: Activate prior learning about collecting, displaying, and analysing data.
Vocabulary: survey, tally chart, data, graph

ASSUMED PRIOR KNOWLEDGE

- ☑ Students can interpret data on a tally chart, a circle graph, a pictograph, and a bar graph.
- ☑ Students can draw simple bar graphs and pictographs.
- ☑ Students can ask questions about graphs, then answer their own questions.

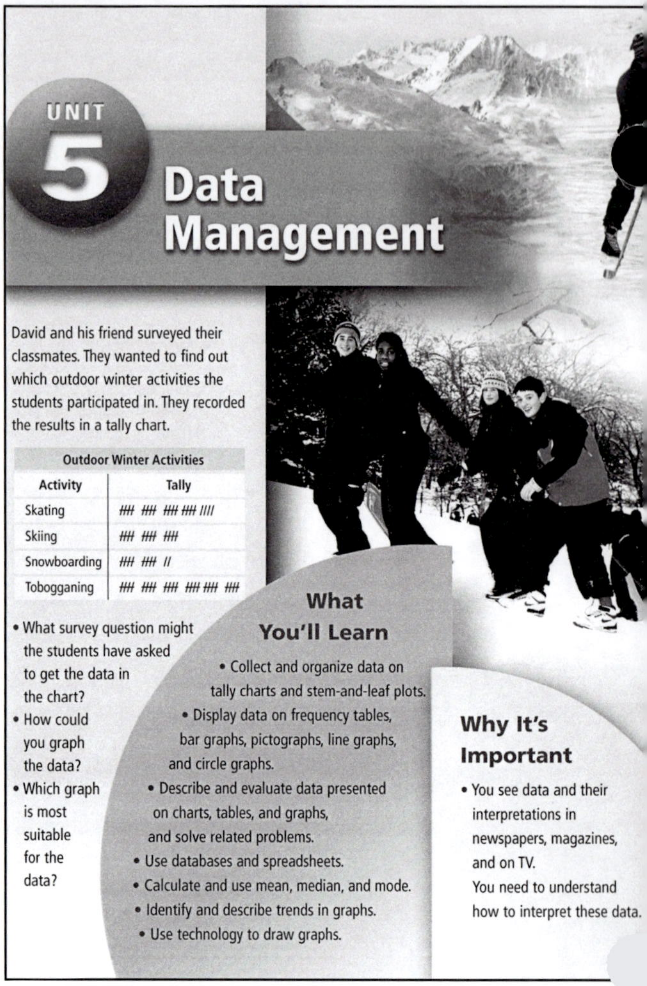

UNIT 5
Data Management

David and his friend surveyed their classmates. They wanted to find out which outdoor winter activities the students participated in. They recorded the results in a tally chart.

Outdoor Winter Activities

Activity	Tally
Skating	𝍸 𝍸 𝍸 𝍸 ||||
Skiing	𝍸 𝍸 𝍸
Snowboarding	𝍸 𝍸 ||
Tobogganing	𝍸 𝍸 𝍸 𝍸 𝍸 𝍸

- What survey question might the students have asked to get the data in the chart?
- How could you graph the data?
- Which graph is most suitable for the data?

What You'll Learn

- Collect and organize data on tally charts and stem-and-leaf plots.
- Display data on frequency tables, bar graphs, pictographs, line graphs, and circle graphs.
- Describe and evaluate data presented on charts, tables, and graphs, and solve related problems.
- Use databases and spreadsheets.
- Calculate and use mean, median, and mode.
- Identify and describe trends in graphs.
- Use technology to draw graphs.

Why It's Important

- You see data and their interpretations in newspapers, magazines, and on TV. You need to understand how to interpret these data.

ACTIVATE PRIOR LEARNING

Engage students in a discussion about which outdoor winter activities they participate in. Ask:

- What is your favourite outdoor winter activity? (*Skiing*)
- About how many times did you ski last year? (*Almost every weekend during the winter months*)

Invite students to examine the tally chart in the Student Book.

Ask questions, such as:

- How many students did David and his friend survey? (*81*) How do you know? (*I added all the tally marks.*)
- Which outdoor winter activity do the greatest number of students participate in? (*Tobogganing*) How do you know? (*It has the greatest number of tally marks.*)
- What survey question might the students have asked to get the data in the chart? (*What is your favourite outdoor winter activity? Skating _____ Skiing _____ Snowboarding _____ Tobogganing _____*)
- How could you graph the data? (*We could use a bar graph or a pictograph.*)
- Which graph is most suitable for the data? (*Both a bar graph and a pictograph are suitable. In a bar graph, the tallest or longest bar would represent the favourite activity. In a pictograph, the activity with the greatest number of pictures would represent the favourite activity. A circle graph could be used but it may be difficult to divide the circle into 4 sections to represent the numbers on the tally chart.*)

Tell students that, in this unit, they will learn more about collecting, organizing, displaying, and analysing data. They will use databases and spreadsheets, and they will use technology to draw graphs. At the end of the unit, students will demonstrate what they have learned by organizing a winter carnival.

Key Words

- mean
- median
- mode
- primary data
- secondary data
- biased
- database
- fields
- Statistics Canada (Stats Can)
- frequency table
- stem-and-leaf plot
- cluster
- trend
- line graph
- spreadsheet

FROM THE LIBRARY

Yesterday's Sports, Today's Math by Don Fraser and Joan Gideon. Dale Seymour Publications, 1997
ISBN: 1572322004
Students discover math through sports as they investigate scoring patterns, averages, records, and other statistics. The starting point is the sports page of the newspaper. Explorations based on real-world data teach students number sense while they build math skills, understanding, and communication.

REACHING ALL LEARNERS

Some students may benefit from using the virtual manipulatives on the e-Tools CD-ROM.
The e-Tool appropriate for this unit is *Spreadsheet/Data/Grapher*.

DIAGNOSTIC ASSESSMENT

What to Look For	What to Do
✔ Students can interpret data on a tally chart, a circle graph, a pictograph, and a bar graph. ✔ Students can draw simple bar graphs and pictographs. ✔ Students can ask questions about a graph, then answer their own questions.	***Extra Support:*** Students who have difficulty interpreting data should be given very simple charts or graphs to work with to build confidence. Work on this skill during Sections 5.1 and 5.2. Students who have difficulty drawing bar graphs and pictographs should first become comfortable drawing graphs with a scale (or key) of 1 square (or picture) to 1 item. Work on this skill during Section 5.2.

SECTION ORGANIZER

15–20 min

Skills in Review: Calculating mean, median, and mode

Student Materials

- calculators

Vocabulary: mean, median, mode

Technology: e-tools

Alternative Example 1

Calculate the mean, median, and mode of these numbers:
87, 90, 66, 58, 100, 99, 87, 96, 100

Solution

There are 9 numbers in the set.

- Mean: $\frac{87 + 90 + 66 + 58 + 100 + 99 + 87 + 96 + 100}{9} = \frac{783}{9}$
  $= 87$
- For the median, arrange the numbers in order, beginning with the least number. The median is the middle number, or the 5th number.
  58, 66, 87, 87, **90**, 96, 99, 100, 100
  The median is 90.
- The mode is the number that occurs most often. In this case, there are two modes, 87 and 100.

UNIT 5

Skills You'll Need

Calculating Mean, Median, and Mode

For any set of numbers:

- The **mean** is the sum of all the numbers divided by the number of numbers.
- The **median** is the middle number when the numbers are arranged in order. When there is an even number of numbers, the median is the mean of the two middle numbers. Half the numbers are above the median and half are below.
- The **mode** is the number that occurs most often. There may be more than one mode. There may be no mode.

Example

Calculate the mean, median, and mode of these numbers:
7, 13, 10, 12, 14, 8, 9, 7, 11, 6

Solution

There are 10 numbers in the set.

- For the mean, add the numbers, then divide by 10.
  Mean: $\frac{7 + 13 + 10 + 12 + 14 + 8 + 9 + 7 + 11 + 6}{10} = \frac{97}{10}$
  $= 9.7$
- For the median, arrange the numbers in order, beginning with the least number. The median is the middle number. Since there are 10 numbers, the median is the mean of the two middle numbers. For 10 numbers in order, the first middle number is $\frac{10}{2} = 5$, or the 5th number. The next middle number is the 6th number.
  6, 7, 7, 8, 9, 10, 11, 12, 13, 14
  Median: $\frac{9 + 10}{2} = \frac{19}{2}$, or 9.5
- The mode is the number that occurs most often. The mode is 7.

✓ Check

1. Calculate the mean, median, and mode for the numbers in each set.
   5.125; 5; 9 and 5 **a)** 3, 9, 5, 8, 2, 0, 9, 5 **b)** 25, 24, 55, 30, 44, 21, 17, 19, 21 28.4; 24; 2
   14.5; 15; 16 **c)** 14, 18, 16, 12, 11, 16 **d)** 76, 81, 50, 64, 67, 69, 72, 94, 81, 76
   73; 74; 76 and 8

168 UNIT 5: Data Management

Calculating Mean, Median, and Mode

Discuss with students the meanings of the terms **mean, median,** and **mode.** Remind students that these are measures of central tendency. Ask:

- How do you find the middle number when there is an odd number of data?
  (*I add 1 to the number of data, then divide by 2 to get the position of the middle number. For example, if the number of data is 13, the position of the middle number is* $\frac{13+1}{2} = \frac{14}{2} = 7$*. The middle number is the 7th number.*)

For extra practice, have students play *Triple M—An "Average" Game.*

Common Misconceptions

➤ Students do not order the numbers before finding the median.

How to Help: Encourage students to order the numbers, beginning with the least number, before finding any of the mean, median, and mode. Students should then count the numbers to ensure that the numbers they have written match those in the text.

➤ Students give two medians when there is an even number of data.

How to Help: Tell students that there can only be one median. When there is an even number of data, students should find the mean of the two middle numbers. For example, if the two middle numbers are 7 and 11, the median is $\frac{7 + 11}{2} = \frac{18}{2} = 9$.

➤ When students use a calculator to find the mean, they forget to press [=] before dividing, thus they divide only the last number entered.

How to Help: Have students insert brackets around the sum, and key in the brackets as they calculate.

5.1 Collecting Data

Focus Analyse data collection and possible bias.

Electronic games are popular among Grade 7 students.
Which electronic game do you think Grade 7 students in your class like to play?
How could you find out?

Explore

Work in a group.
Which electronic game is most popular in your class?
Conduct a survey to find out.
What survey question will you ask? Record your results.

Reflect & Share

Compare your results with those of another group.
How did the survey question affect the results?

Connect

Mia wanted to find out the favourite singer of her classmates.
She conducted a survey. She asked this question:

"Who is your favourite singer: Bryan Adams ____, Susan Aglukark ____, Celine Dion ____, Sam Roberts ____, Shania Twain ____, or Other ____?"

Mia recorded the results in a tally chart.

Singer	Number of Students
Bryan Adams	~~||||~~
Susan Aglukark	~~||||~~
Celine Dion	~~||||~~ ||
Sam Roberts	|||
Shania Twain	||
Other	~~||||~~ ~~||||~~ |

Mia concluded that Celine Dion was the most popular singer of those named.
However, if all the votes in the "Other" category were for the same person, then that person would be the most popular.

The word "data" is plural. So, we say "The data are ..." A single piece of information is called "datum."

Since Mia collected the data herself, they are called **primary data**.
Data that are found from the library or using the Internet are called **secondary data**.

5.1 Collecting Data 169

Collecting Data

SECTION ORGANIZER (80-100 min)

Curriculum Focus: Analyse data collection and possible bias. (7m89, 7m91, 7m99)

Student Materials
- 2-column charts (PM 17)

Optional
- Step-by-Step 1 (Master 5.7)
- Extra Practice 1 (Master 5.15)

Vocabulary: primary data, secondary data, biased

Assessment: Master 5.2 Ongoing Observations: Data Management

Key Math Learnings

1. Data that are collected directly or first-hand are primary data. Data that are not collected first-hand are secondary data.
2. A survey is used to collect primary data.
3. A question that might persuade a person to answer a certain way is biased. Survey questions must be unbiased to ensure data are collected in a fair way.

Number Strategies

Students should see that the pattern rule for the first pattern is: Start at 0.75. Multiply by 2 each time.
The pattern rule for the second pattern is: Start at 96. Multiply by 2 each time.

BEFORE Get Started

Invite students to discuss the electronic games they like to play. Ask:

- How could we find out which electronic game students in the class most like to play?
  (*We could conduct a survey.*)
- What survey question could you ask?
  (*What is your favourite electronic game?*)
- How could you record the results?
  (*I could use a tally chart.*)

Present *Explore.* Invite students to work in groups of 3 or 4. Ensure students understand that it is a good idea to give a list of choices with a question, to limit the number of possible answers. The last choice is usually "Other" to include those answers that are not common. Suggest students who have difficulty coming up with choices look through department store flyers for some ideas. Provide each group with a 2-column chart to record the results of their survey.

DURING Explore

Ongoing Assessment: Observe and Listen

Ask students work, ask questions, such as:

- What survey question did you ask?
  (*What is your favourite electronic game: World Cup Soccer, NHL Hockey, Super Mario, Harry Potter, Shrek, or Other?*)
- Why did you include "Other" as a possible answer?
  (*For those classmates whose favourite games were not included in my list of possible answers*)
- What were the results of your survey?
  (*NHL Hockey was the favourite electronic game.*)
- How did your results compare with those of another group?
  (*Our results were different because we listed different possible answers. The other group did not list NHL Hockey as a possible answer.*)

REACHING ALL LEARNERS

Early Finishers

Use the idea in *Explore.* Have students suggest what they would do to find out the most popular game in the school and in Ontario. What survey methods could they use?

Common Misconceptions

➤Students ask an incomplete question when conducting a survey, such as: "What is your favourite ice-cream flavour, chocolate, strawberry, or vanilla?"

How to Help: Tell students that they are leading people to answer chocolate, strawberry, or vanilla. Many people will have a different favourite flavour. Encourage students to include "Other" so that those people whose favourite flavours are not listed have a possible response.

ESL Strategies

Give students 2 index cards, one labelled "primary data" and the other labelled "secondary data." Students draw pictures on each card to represent different ways of collecting each type of data. For example, on the "secondary data" card, students draw an encyclopedia, a computer, and a newspaper. On the "primary data" card, students draw a clipboard, a person knocking on a door, and a person using the phone.

It is important that a survey is conducted and data are collected in a fair way. Sometimes, the way a question is asked or written might persuade a person to answer a certain way. This type of question is **biased**. A survey question must be unbiased. That is, the question must not lead a person toward a particular answer.

Example

How is each survey question biased?
Rewrite the question so it is unbiased.

a) "Many students are bored at the end of August.
Should the school year be longer?
Yes ______ No ______"

b) "Some people get sick after visiting patients in a hospital.
Do you think patients in a hospital should have visitors?
Yes ______ No ______ No Opinion ______"

Solution

a) The question includes a statement about how some students feel.
This may encourage more people to answer "Yes."
An unbiased survey question is:
"The school year is 10 months long. Should it be longer?
Yes ______ No ______"

b) The question includes a statement that may encourage people to answer "No."
An unbiased survey question is:
"Should patients in a hospital have visitors?
Yes ______ No ______ No Opinion ______"

Practice

1. Are primary data or secondary data collected in each situation?
How do you know?
Secondary a) Elly used an encyclopedia to find the area of each continent.
Primary b) Jason read the thermometer to find the outside temperature.
Secondary c) Jane looked in the newspaper to see which NHL team won the game.

Sample Answers

1. a) Secondary data; an encyclopedia contains information already collected by other people.
   b) Primary data; Jason read the thermometer himself.
   c) Secondary data; Jane did not watch the hockey game herself.

AFTER Connect

Invite students to share the results of their surveys with the class.

Use *Connect* to introduce the terms **primary data, secondary data,** and **biased**. Have students give examples of situations where primary data and secondary data would be used. Discuss different ways of collecting primary data, such as by telephone, by canvassing door-to-door, and by observing situations.

Ask:

- Would you use primary or secondary data to find the favourite novel of Grade 7 students in Canada? Explain.
  (*I would use secondary data because I can't survey all Grade 7 students in Canada.*)

Ensure students understand the importance of an unbiased question when conducting a survey. Reinforce the idea that a survey question must not lead a person to a particular answer. Ask:

- What is an example of a biased survey question? (*Skateboarding can be dangerous. Should children be allowed to skateboard?*)
- Why is this question biased?
  (*It includes a statement that may encourage people to answer "No."*)
- How can you rewrite the question so that it is unbiased?
  (*Should children be allowed to skateboard?
  Yes ___ No ___ No opinion ___*)

Practice

Assessment Focus: Question 6

Students should write unbiased questions that would help the person decide what style or make of shoes to stock. Since the shoe store is local, students should suggest surveying people of all ages in the area.

2. Would you use primary or secondary data in each case? Explain.
   a) To find the favourite car model in Canada Secondary
   b) To find the favourite juice of Grade 7 students in your school
   c) To find the favourite song of Grade 7 students in Ontario Primary
   d) To find the most popular type of transport used by students in your school Secondary Primary
3. Biased data are unreliable. Yet, sometimes people use biased data. Why do people use biased data?
4. Think of a survey you could conduct in your school.
   a) Write a biased survey question.
   b) Write an unbiased survey question.
5. Comment on each survey question. If it is biased, write an unbiased question. Biased
   a) "Sugar is bad for your teeth. Should children eat candy? Yes ______ No ______ No Opinion ______"
   b) "Children prefer snowboarding to skiing. Biased Which do you think is more fun? Snowboarding ______ Skiing ______"
6. **Assessment Focus** Suppose a person intends to open a shoe store in the local mall. The person is unsure of the style or make of shoes to stock. What questions should the person ask to make the best decision? Explain what role a survey might play in the decision.
7. a) Predict the favourite hobby or pastime of your classmates.
   b) Write a survey question you could ask to find out. Explain how you know your question is unbiased.
   c) Conduct the survey. Tally the results.
   d) How did your prediction compare with your results?

Number Strategies

How are these two patterns related?
- 0.75, 1.5, 3, 6, . . .
- 96, 192, 384, 768, . . .

ach pattern, a term is
ained by multiplying the
vious term by 2.

Reflect

Why is it important that a survey question is unbiased?

5.1 Collecting Data 171

2. a) Secondary data; it is impossible to survey every Canadian who owns a car.
   b) Primary data; I can collect these data by surveying all the Grade 7 students in my school.
   c) Secondary data; I cannot survey all the Grade 7 students in Ontario by myself.
   d) Primary data; I can collect these data by surveying all the students in my school.
3. Biased data might be used to mislead people, to persuade people to believe claims that are untrue, or to influence a decision in favour of a certain point of view.
4. a) Some students think the food served in the cafeteria is tasteless. Do you like the food served in the cafeteria?
   Yes ___ No ___
   b) Do you like the food served in the cafeteria?
   Yes ___ No ___

(Answers continue on page 9.)

Assignment Guidelines

If your students do not have time to complete all the *Practice* questions on pages 170 and 171, these questions provide minimum curriculum coverage: 1, 3, 5, 6, *Reflect*
To assess the 4 Achievement Chart categories listed in the curriculum document, have students complete these *Practice* questions:
Understanding Concepts: 1
Communication: 3
Application: 5
Problem Solving: 6

ASSESSMENT FOR LEARNING

What to Look For

Understanding concepts

✔ Students understand that a survey is used to collect primary data.

Applying procedures

✔ Students can identify bias in a survey question and rewrite it as an unbiased question.

Communicating

✔ Students can explain the difference between primary and secondary data.

What to Do

Extra Support: Students who have difficulty distinguishing between primary and secondary data may benefit from asking themselves the question, "Am I collecting the data or has someone else already collected it for me?"
Students can use Step-by-Step 1 (Master 5.7) to complete question 6.

Extra Practice: Students name 3 situations in which primary data would be collected and 3 situations in which secondary data would be collected.
Students can complete Extra Practice 1 (Master 5.15).

Extension: Students conduct a survey using an unbiased question, then repeat the same survey using a biased question. Students compare the results of the two surveys.

Recording and Reporting

Master 5.2 Ongoing Observations: Data Management

Using Databases to Find Data

SECTION ORGANIZER 40–50 min

Curriculum Focus: Search databases for information. (7m93, 7m94)

Student Materials

- computers (E-STAT website)

Vocabulary: database, fields, Statistics Canada (Stats Can), CANSIM II, E-STAT

Using Databases to Find Data

Focus Search databases for information.

A **database** is an organized collection of data. Examples of databases include a telephone book, a dictionary, an encyclopedia, or a library catalogue.

A database is organized into **fields**. Each field contains specific information. In a library database, a book may be stored with information in each of these fields: title, author, publisher, subject, ISBN (international standard book number), or Dewey decimal number.

Statistics Canada (Stats Can) is the federal government department that collects, analyses, and stores data about Canada and Canadians. Two of its Internet databases are **CANSIM II** (**Can**adian **S**ocio-economic **I**nformation **M**anagement System) and **E-STAT**.

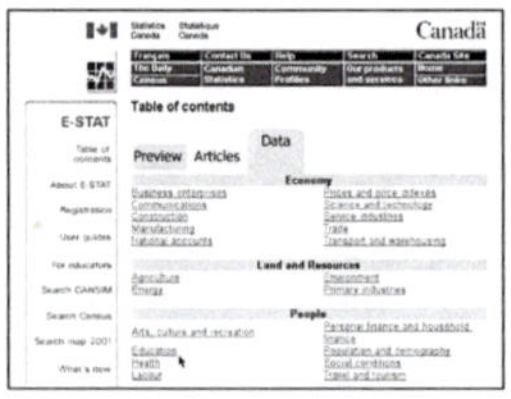

Stats Can charges a fee for some of its data on CANSIM II.
E-STAT is a free database for teachers and students. Your teacher will give you the website addresses for these databases.

To use E-STAT to find data on school attendance for 15- to 24-year-olds, follow these steps:

1. Open the E-STAT Website.
   You may be asked for your username and password. Ask your teacher for these.
2. Click the "Data" tab. Click "Education," as shown above left.
3. Under Census databases, click "Enrolment," as shown below left.

172 UNIT 5: Data Management

Key Math Learning

Databases can be used to find information.

Research Topic: Occupations at the Time of the 1911 Census

Source: Statistics Canada (E-STAT)

Selected occupations, Canada: 1911 Census

Occupation	Males	Females
Bridge and gate tenders	436	2
Char-workers	12	4700
Launderers and laundresses	588	282
Hotel keepers	3102	848
Undertakers	43	0
Gardeners	469	18
Coachmen and grooms	418	0
Sailors and seamen	16 347	0
Match makers	72	178
Nurses	124	5476
Stenographers and typists	1603	9754
Actors and theatrical employees	2410	432
Musicians and teachers of music	2001	3574
Hucksters and peddlers	3135	113
Total	**30 760**	**25 377**

Things we know from looking at the data:

- The greatest number of males were sailors and seamen.
- The greatest number of females were stenographers and typists.
- No females were undertakers, coachmen and grooms, or sailors and seamen.

4. Under 2001 Census of Population (Provinces, Census Divisions, Municipalities), click "2001 School Attendance, Education, Field of Study, Highest Level of Schooling and Earnings," as shown below left.

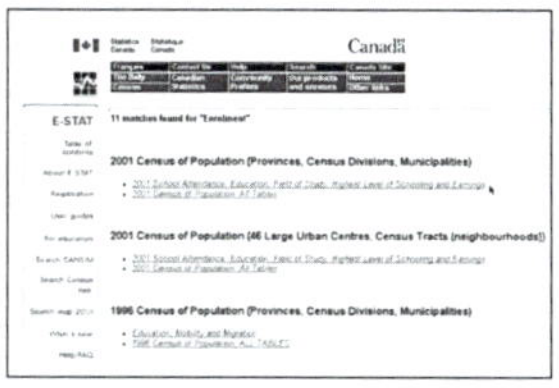

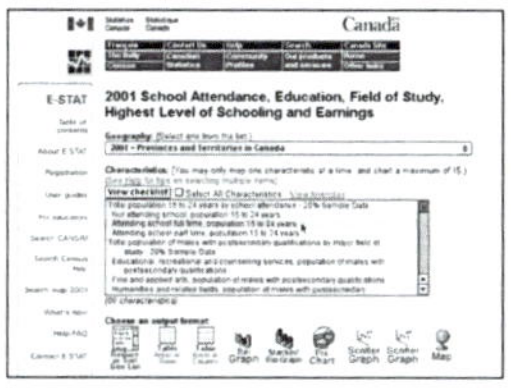

5. Click "Attending school, full time, population 15 to 24 years," as shown above right.

6. Choose an output format. For data in a table arranged in rows, click "Table Areas as Rows," as shown below left. The data are displayed as shown below right.

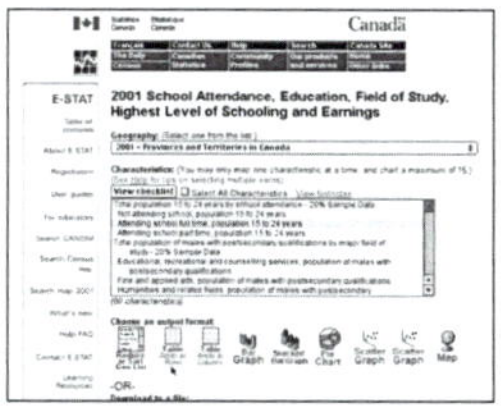

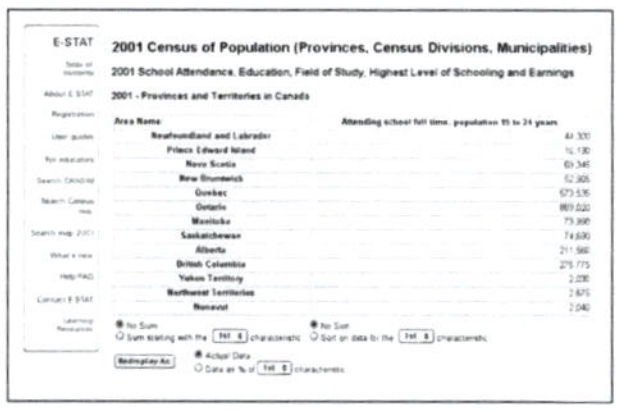

Check

1. Use E-STAT or another database.
   Research one of the topics below. Print your data.
   Be sure to state your source.
   - The number of Canadians who had a particular type of occupation at the time of the 1911 Census
   - The top 10 movies of the year
   - The top 10 music CDs of the year
   - A topic of your choice

   Write 3 things you know from looking at the data.

REACHING ALL LEARNERS

Early Finishers

Have students search different databases for the same information, such as the top 10 movies of 2003, then compare their findings.

Common Misconceptions

➤ Students think Statistics Canada is the only database available to them.

How to Help: Tell students that there is a database in the school library. Have students go to the library and find all books by a certain author, or all books on a specific topic.

(Sample Answers for Section 5.1 page 171, continued)

5. a) This is a biased question because it includes a statement that may encourage people to answer "No." An unbiased survey question is: "Do you think children should eat candy?
Yes ___ No ___ No opinion ___"

b) This is a biased question because it includes a statement about how some children feel. This may encourage more people to answer "Snowboarding." An unbiased survey question is: "Which do you think is more fun? Snowboarding __ Skiing __"

6. Some possible survey questions are:
"Which make of shoe do you prefer?
Nike ___ Adidas ___ Nine West ___ Rockport ___ Other ___"
"What style of shoe do you wear most often?
Sandal ___ Dress shoe ___ Athletic shoe ___ Casual shoe ___ Boot ___ Other ___"
This survey would collect information about the shoes worn by people in the community. Since these people are most likely to shop in the store, these data could be used to help decide how to stock the new store.

7. a) Reading

b) "What is your favourite hobby? Watching TV ___
Reading ___ Playing sports ___
Playing on the computer ___ Other ___"
This is an unbiased question because it contains generalized choices and contains the choice "Other."

c)

Hobby	Number of Students
Watching TV	////
Reading	~~////~~ ////
Playing sports	~~////~~ //
Playing on the computer	~~////~~
Other	//

d) My prediction was correct. Most of my classmates prefer to read.

REFLECT: It is important that a survey question is unbiased so that the data collected provide accurate information that may be used to help make decisions.

Recording Data

SECTION ORGANIZER (80–100 min)

Curriculum Focus: Record data in tables, bar graphs, and pictographs. (7m91, 7m92, 7m97, 7m98, 7m100, 7m102)

Student Materials
- novels
- 0.5-cm grid paper (PM 14)
- number cubes, labelled 1 to 6
- atlases or almanacs
- rulers

Optional
- 2-column charts (PM 17)
- 3-column charts (PM 18)
- Step-by-Step 2 (Master 5.8)
- Extra Practice 2 (Master 5.16)

Vocabulary: frequency table

Assessment: Master 5.2 Ongoing Observations: Data Management

Key Math Learnings

1. Data can be organized in a tally chart or frequency table.
2. Data can be displayed on a bar graph or pictograph.
3. A double-bar graph is used to display 2 related sets of data at the same time.

Number Strategies

For $\frac{1}{2} + \frac{2}{3}$, students could use fraction strips or number lines.
For $\frac{3}{4} + \frac{4}{5}$ and $\frac{5}{6} + \frac{6}{7}$, students should find a common denominator.

5.2 Recording Data

Focus Record data in tables, bar graphs, and pictographs.

Explore

Work on your own.
Use a novel you are currently reading.
Open it to any page.

➢ Count the number of letters in each of the first 50 words.
Record your data in a tally chart.

Number of Letters	Tally of Number of Words
1	
2	
3	
4	

➢ Graph your data. Justify your choice of graph.
➢ Which is the most common length of word?
➢ Who might be interested in these data?

Reflect & Share

Compare your most common length of word with that of a classmate. Should the lengths be the same? Explain.

Connect

Data can be organized in a tally chart or **frequency table**.
A frequency table is a tally chart with an extra column.

Andrew recorded the different birds that visited his feeder one morning.

Birds at the Feeder

Bird	Tally	Frequency
Blue jay	𝍸	5
Cardinal	////	4
Sparrow	𝍸 𝍸 𝍸 //	17
Robin	𝍸 𝍸 /	11
Chickadee	𝍸 //	7

174 UNIT 5: Data Management

BEFORE Get Started

Invite students to discuss the novels they are currently reading. Tell students we want to find the most common length of word in their novels. Ask:

- What do you think is the most common length of word in your novel? (*6 letters*)
- How could you find the most common length of word in your novel?
  (*I could count the number of letters in each of the words on any 2 pages to find the most common length. This would be typical of the entire novel.*)
- How could you keep track of the lengths of the words?
  (*I could use a tally chart with the headings "Number of letters" and "Number of words."*)
- Why wouldn't we find the lengths of all the words in the novel?
  (*It would take too long. We can get a good idea by using two pages.*)

Present *Explore.* If students do not have a novel in class, they can borrow a novel from the library or use one of their textbooks. Have 2-column charts and grid paper available.

DURING Explore

Ongoing Assessment: Observe and Listen

As students work, ask questions, such as:

- How many rows do you have in your tally chart?
  (*I have 10 rows because I found some long words with 9 and 10 letters.*)
- How will you find the total number of words with 5 letters?
  (*I will add the tally marks in the row for 5.*)
- What are some graphs you can use to display your data?
  (*I can use a bar graph or a pictograph.*)

To fill in the *Frequency* column, Andrew counted the tallies for each bird.
He graphed the data using a pictograph.
Andrew chose a key of 1 symbol represents 2 birds.

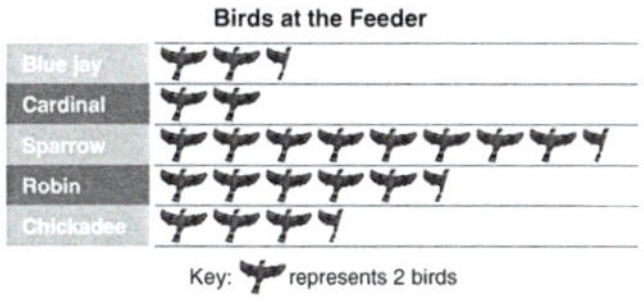

Example

a) Construct a bar graph of Andrew's data.
b) Compare the graph and tally chart.
How are they alike?

Solution

a) Construct a bar graph, below left.
One square represents 2 birds.

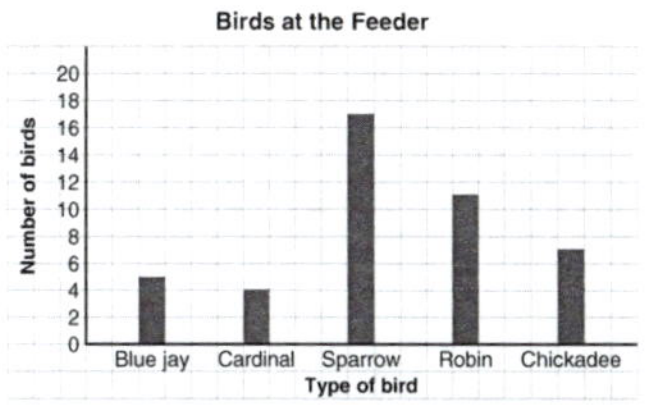

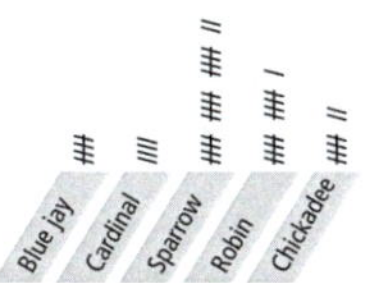

b) The longest bar on the bar graph represents the same bird as the longest row on the tally chart.
When we rotate the *Tally* column $\frac{1}{4}$ turn counterclockwise, above right, its shape matches that of the bar graph, above left.

5.2 Recording Data **175**

REACHING ALL LEARNERS

Alternative Explore

Write the first names of all the students in the class on the board. Students work alone. Students count the number of letters in each name, then record the data in a tally chart.

Students graph the data, then find the most common length of name.

Early Finishers

Have students count the number of letters in each of the next 50 words in their novel. They now have a total of 100 words. Students complete *Explore* with 100 words, then compare their findings with their original results.

Common Misconceptions

➤Students do not provide a key with a pictograph.
How to Help: Remind students that the key tells the reader what each symbol represents. Demonstrate that a pictograph without a key could be interpreted in many ways. For example, the reader could assume each symbol represents 1, or each symbol represents 5. The results would be quite different.

ESL Strategies

Students for whom English is a second language may be reading a novel that is below the Grade 7 level. Be sure these students share their results with the class to emphasize how these data might be used to determine the appropriate grade level for novels.

Remind students to use a ruler when drawing their bar graphs. Ensure students understand the importance of selecting an appropriate scale or key, of labelling the axes, and of giving the graph a title. Encourage students to use coloured pencils to make their graphs visually appealing.

- What information will the graph tell you?
(*It will tell me the most common length of word, as well as the lengths of the longest and shortest words.*)

AFTER Connect

Invite students to share their graphs and findings with the class.

Ask questions, such as:

- What was the most common length of word in your novel? (*5 letters*) How do you know?
(*Five letters had the greatest number of tally marks and the tallest bar on the bar graph.*)
- How can you be sure that you counted the number of letters in each of the first fifty words?
(*The total number of tally marks in the chart is 50.*)
- Why did you choose to draw a bar graph?
(*Because I knew that I could easily find the most common length of word by finding the tallest bar*)
- What scale did you use for your bar graph?
(*I used the scale 1 grid square represents 2 words.*)
- What other type of graph could you have drawn?
(*I could have drawn a pictograph. I would have used the key 1 book = 2 words.*)
- Who might be interested in these data?
(*People who determine the appropriate grade level for novels.*)
- Do you think a novel read by Grade 3 students would have the same most common length of word? (*No*) Explain.
(*Most students in Grade 3 would be reading easier novels, with shorter words. The most common word length would probably be 3 or 4 letters.*)

Sample Answers

1\. c) Most popular: Toronto Maple Leafs
Least popular: Montreal Canadiens and Ottawa Senators
The students surveyed live in Hamilton and Toronto is the closest city with an NHL team. Ottawa and Montreal would be rivals to Toronto in the east so they would not be very popular with people in Hamilton who are Toronto fans.

2\. b) If I were to roll the number cube 50 more times, I would expect the frequency for each number to be approximately the same. The probability of rolling each number is the same: 1 in 6. So, each number is likely to appear 8 or 9 times.

c) Our results are different because when a number cube is rolled 50 times, each number is likely to appear 8 or 9 times, but may appear more or fewer times.

d) I chose a bar graph because the heights of the bars make it easy to tell which number was rolled the most and which number was rolled the least.

3\. a) I think the question was "What is your main use of the Internet? Choose one of these options: E-mail __ Banking __ Shopping __ Games __ Music __ Education __ Research __" as this is the title of the pictograph.

c) If the key was changed to 1 symbol represents 1 person, there would be 10 times as many symbols. For example, there would be 80 symbols for *E-mail*. The graph would be too big to draw on a page, or the symbol would be too small. If the key was changed to 1 symbol represents 50 people, there would be very few symbols, with several part-symbols. For example, *Education* would have $\frac{3}{5}$ of a symbol. The graph would be more difficult to read.

Practice

Favourite Canadian Hockey Team		
Hockey Team	**Tally**	**Frequency**
Calgary Flames	~~IIII~~ III	8
Edmonton Oilers	~~IIII~~ I	6
Montreal Canadiens	~~IIII~~	5
Ottawa Senators	~~IIII~~	5
Toronto Maple Leafs	~~IIII~~ ~~IIII~~	10
Vancouver Canucks	~~IIII~~ I	6

Rolling a Number Cube		
Number	**Tally**	**Frequency**
1		
2		
3		

1\. The table shows the favourite Canadian hockey teams of some Grade 7 student[s at] Hamilton Junior High School.
a) Write the frequency of each team.
b) How many students were surveyed? 40 st
c) Which team is the most popular among the sample? The least popular? Give some possible reasons for these results.

2\. Work with a partner. You will need a number cube labelled 1 to 6.
a) Roll the number cube 50 times. Make a table. Record the frequency of each number.
b) Predict the results if you were to roll the number cube 50 more times. Justify your answer.
c) Compare your results with those of another pair of students. If they are different, explain why.
d) Graph your data. Justify your choice of graph.

3\. This pictograph displays the results of a survey.

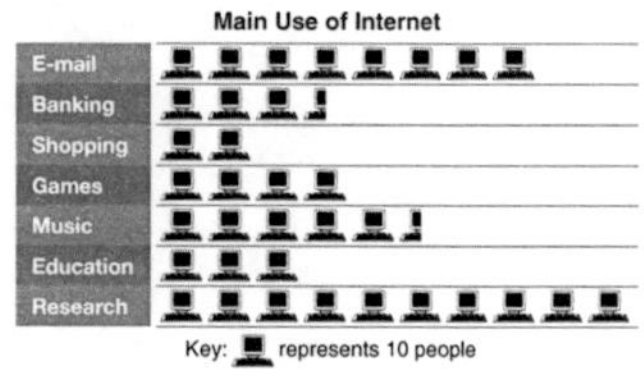

a) What do you think the survey question was? Explain.
360 people b) How many people were surveyed?
c) How would the pictograph change if [symbol] represented 1 person? 50 people?
d) Draw a bar graph to display these data.

- Should your most common word length be the same as that of your classmate? (*Since both of us are reading novels that are at a Grade 7 level, our most common word lengths should be close. They may not be the same.*)

Tell students that we can turn a tally chart into a frequency table by adding a third column, labelled "Frequency." The tally marks in each row are counted and the appropriate numbers are written in the "Frequency" column.

Review *Connect*. Discuss how when the *Tally* column is rotated $\frac{1}{4}$ turn counterclockwise, its shape matches that of a vertical bar graph. If a horizontal bar graph or pictograph were drawn, the shape of the *Tally* column, without any rotation, would match that of either of the 2 graphs. Have students compare the shapes of their graphs and tally charts from *Explore* to reinforce this feature.

Practice

Have 3-column chart paper (PM 18) available for questions 1, 2, 6, and 7. Have 2-column chart paper (PM 17) available for question 5. Questions 2, 3, 5, 6, and 7 require 0.5-cm grid paper (PM 14). Question 2 requires a number cube, labelled 1 to 6. Question 5 requires an atlas or an almanac.

Assessment Focus: Question 6

Students conduct a survey using an unbiased question, then record their data in a table and on a graph. Students draw conclusions from their survey, then write 3 other things they know from the graph. Students' answers will indicate their understanding of the data.

e) Is a bar graph better than a pictograph to display the data? Explain.
f) Write a question you could answer using the pictograph or bar graph. Answer the question.

ber Strategies

Add.
- $\frac{1}{2}+\frac{2}{3}=\frac{7}{16}$
- $\frac{3}{4}+\frac{4}{5}=\frac{31}{20}$
- $\frac{5}{6}+\frac{6}{7}=\frac{71}{42}$

4. This is a double-bar graph.

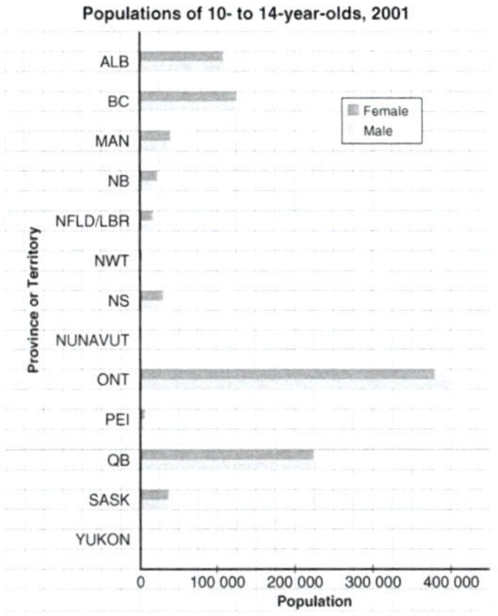

a) How is this bar graph different from the others in this lesson?
b) How does the female population compare with the male population?
c) Which province(s) have approximately the same number of 10- to 14-year-old females as males?
d) Here are the data for the 3 territories.

	Nunavut	Northwest Territories	Yukon
Females	1550	1725	1090
Males	1685	1785	1225

Why are there no bars on the graph for Nunavut and Yukon?
e) Could you use a pictograph to display the data in the double-bar graph? Explain.

5.2 Recording Data **177**

d)

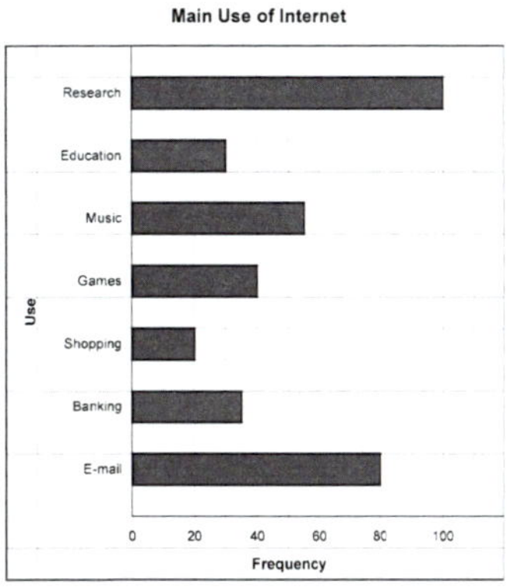

e) The bar graph and the pictograph are equally good for displaying data. It is easy to see the tallest or longest bar and it is easy to see the greatest number of symbols.
f) What do people least use the Internet for? (*Answer: Shopping*)

4. a) There are 2 bars for each province or territory and the bars are horizontal. Two sets of data are displayed on one graph.
b) In every province and territory, the female population is less than the male population.
c) Newfoundland/Labrador, Nova Scotia, and Prince Edward Island
d) The scale on the bar graph is 1 square represents 25 000 people. The data are too few to be displayed on the graph with this scale.
e) No, it would be difficult to show 2 sets of data at the same time on a pictograph. The range of the data is too large.

(*Answers continue below.*)

(*Sample Answers, continued*)

6. a) What do you spend the most money on? Books ___ Movies/Entertainment ___ Clothing ___ Food ___ Transportation ___ Other ___

b)

How My Classmates Spend Their Money		
Way Money Is Spent	**Tally**	**Frequency**
Books	~~////~~	5
Movies/Entertainment	~~////~~ ///	8
Clothing	~~////~~ /	6
Food	~~////~~ //	7
Transportation	//	2
Other	/	1

c) I chose a bar graph because it is easy to draw and I can tell how my classmates spend most of their money by looking at the lengths of the bars.

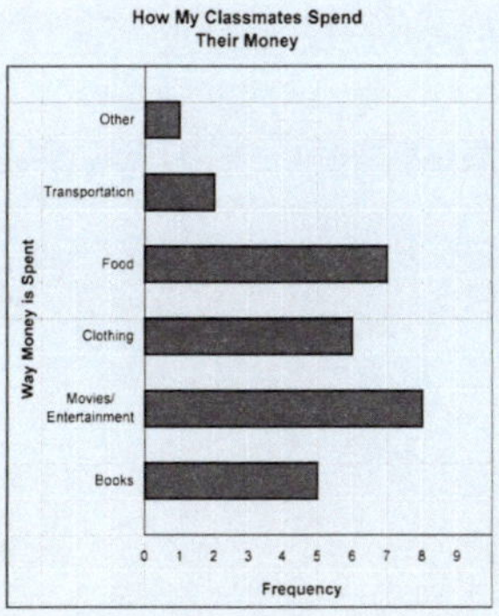

d) Most of my classmates spend most of their money on movies and entertainment.
e) Many classmates buy their own clothes. Few classmates spend money on transportation. The ways my classmates spend most of their money, from greatest to least popular, are movies/entertainment, food, clothing, books, transportation, other.

7. a)

Spelling Mistakes		
Number of Mistakes	**Tally**	**Frequency**
0 – 2	~~////~~ ~~////~~ /	11
3 – 5	~~////~~ ~~////~~ ~~////~~	15
6 – 8	~~////~~ ~~////~~ ~~////~~	15
9 – 11	~~////~~ ////	9
12 – 14	//	2
15 – 17	///	3
18 – 20	////	4

b) 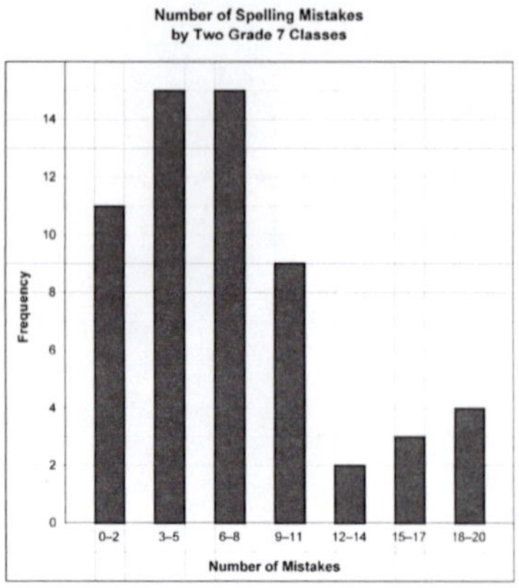

REFLECT: A pictograph is more appropriate than a bar graph when the data can be divided into equal parts that are easily represented by a symbol or half-symbol. For example, a set of data such as 100, 250, 300, and 750 can easily be represented by a symbol or half-symbol if 1 symbol represents 100. A bar graph is more appropriate if the data are very large and not easily divided into equal parts. For example, a set of data such as 657, 231, 429, and 573 cannot easily be represented by a symbol or a half-symbol.

Assignment Guidelines

These questions provide minimum curriculum coverage: 1, 2, 3, 6, 7, *Reflect*

To assess the 4 Achievement Chart categories, have students complete these *Practice* questions:

Understanding Concepts: 1; Problem Solving: 6;
Communication: 3; Application: 7

5. Use an atlas or an almanac.
a) Choose 5 cities in Canada.
b) Choose a recent year.
Find the population of each city in that year.
c) Record the data in a table.
d) Graph the data. Justify your choice of graph.
e) What do you know from looking at the data?

6. Assessment Focus
a) Suppose you want to find out how your classmates spend their money. Write a question you could use to survey your classmates.
b) Conduct the survey. Record the data in a frequency table.
c) Graph the data. Justify your choice of graph.
d) What do most of your classmates spend their money on?
e) Use the graph to write 3 other things you know about how your classmates spend their money.

Spelling Mistakes

4 7 9 2 1 0 6 5 8 10 7
3 2 12 8 11 3 4 8 4 5
8 15 9 6 2 1 0 17 19
16 3 11 5 10 7 3 7 1 9
10 3 5 8 6 13 8 2 4 6
18 19 5 20 0 1 8 10 3

The interval is 3 because the numbers of mistakes are counted in groups of 3.

7. Two classes of Grade 7 students took a spelling test. The number of words each student misspelled is recorded at the left.

Number of Mistakes	Tally	Frequency
0 – 2		
3 – 5		

a) Copy the frequency table. Continue the pattern of the intervals in the 1st column to 18–20.
Complete the 2nd and 3rd columns in the frequency table.
b) Graph the data.

Reflect

When is a pictograph more appropriate than a bar graph?
When is a bar graph more appropriate than a pictograph?
Give examples.

178 UNIT 5: Data Management

ASSESSMENT FOR LEARNING

What to Look For	What to Do
Understanding concepts ✔ Students understand how to organize data in a tally chart or frequency table.	***Extra Support:*** Students who have difficulty organizing data in a tally chart or frequency table may benefit from using 2- or 3-column chart paper to help them keep the data aligned. Students can use Step-by-Step 2 (Master 5.8) to complete question 6.
Applying procedures ✔ Students can display data on a bar graph or pictograph.	***Extra Practice:*** Have students display their data in *Explore* in a different way. For example, students who drew a bar graph could draw a pictograph. Students can complete Extra Practice 2 (Master 5.16).
Communicating ✔ Students can explain the difference between a horizontal bar graph, a vertical bar graph, and a double-bar graph.	***Extension:*** Have students repeat *Practice* question 5, this time choosing 2 different years, at least 10 years apart. Students draw graphs to display the 2 sets of data, then compare the populations of the 5 cities in the two years.

Recording and Reporting
Master 5.2 Ongoing Observations: Data Management

5.3 Stem-and-Leaf Plots

Focus Display data on a stem-and-leaf plot.

The data, and **stem-and-leaf plot**, show science test scores for a Grade 7 class.
How are the two displays related?
What can you see in the stem-and-leaf plot that you cannot see in the chart?

Science Test Scores

64	75	89	99	58	53	69
66	72	81	88	67	75	86
52	97	77	75	57	61	85
94	72	81	65	78	81	93

Science Test Scores

Stem	Leaf
5	2 3 7 8
6	1 4 5 6 7 9
7	2 2 5 5 5 7 8
8	1 1 1 5 6 8 9
9	3 4 7 9

This is a stem-and-leaf plot.

Explore

Work with a partner.
You will need a metre stick or a tape measure.
Measure each other's height in centimetres.
Write it on the board.
Use the data for the whole class.
Draw a stem-and-leaf plot to show the heights, in centimetres, of your classmates.

- Are any students the same height?
- Which is the shortest height? The tallest?
- What is the median height?
- What is the mode height?
- What else do you know from looking at the stem-and-leaf plot?

Reflect & Share

Compare your stem-and-leaf plot with that of another pair of classmates. Do your plots match?
If you answer no, how are they different?

5.3 Stem-and-Leaf Plots **179**

Stem-and-Leaf Plots

SECTION ORGANIZER (80–100 min)

Curriculum Focus: Display data on a stem-and-leaf plot. (7m91, 7m97, 7m98)

Student Materials
- metre sticks or measuring tapes
- sports sections of a newspaper or the Internet

Optional
- Step-by-Step 3 (Master 5.9)
- Extra Practice 3 (Master 5.17)

Vocabulary: stem-and-leaf plot

Assessment: Master 5.2 Ongoing Observations: Data Management

Key Math Learnings

1. Data can be organized in a stem-and-leaf plot. The stems are the digits that a set of data has in common. The leaves are always numbers from 0 to 9.
2. When data are displayed in a stem-and-leaf plot, the original data are visible and the range, the median, and the mode can be found from the plot.

Calculator Skills

Students could start with 2 numbers that have a product of 60, such as 6 and 10, then adjust the numbers as necessary until they find 2 numbers with a difference of 2.75 and a product of 60.125.

BEFORE Get Started

Invite students to examine the data showing science test scores on page 179 of the Student Book. Ask:

- Which test scores appear most often? (*75 and 81*) How do you know? (*I counted how many times each score appeared.*)

Tell students that the same data has been displayed on a **stem-and-leaf plot**. A stem-and-leaf plot is a way to organize data in numerical order.

Model how to draw the plot with a ruler, how to order the numbers, and how to write each number as a tens digit and a ones digit.

Ask:

- How does writing the data like this help you find the mode? (*I can count how many times the same ones digit is repeated in each row of leaves.*)
- What can you see in the stem-and-leaf plot that you cannot see in the chart? (*I can easily find the median, mode, and range of the data. I can see how many students scored in the 50s, 60s, 70s, 80s, or 90s. I can see the highest mark and the lowest mark.*)

Present *Explore.* Refer to the *Skills You'll Need* in this unit for students who need a review of the terms "median" and "mode." Tell students they will use a stem-and-leaf plot to display the heights of their classmates. Have students remove their shoes before measuring each other's height to ensure an accurate measurement. Students should round their heights to the nearest centimetre. When all heights have been listed on the board, students can begin to draw their stem-and-leaf plots.

REACHING ALL LEARNERS

Alternative Explore

Students find the highest daily temperature for their region or city for a two-week period. They draw a stem-and-leaf plot to display the data, then find the range of the highest daily temperatures, the median temperature, and the mode temperature. Students write anything else they know from looking at the plot.

Early Finishers

Have students repeat the steps of *Explore* but this time measure each other's arm span. Students then look for any relationships between arm span and height.

Common Misconceptions

➤Students use single digits for the stems when organizing data that are 3-digit numbers.

How to Help: Tell students that in a stem-and-leaf plot, the leaves are always numbers from 0 to 9. So, when the data are 3-digit numbers, the stems must have 2 digits.

Connect

Here are the numbers of books students in one Grade 7 class read in one year.
Each number is the number of books one student read.

Books Read in One Year							
23	19	43	12	16	18	31	17
15	23	27	18	13	16	24	10
16	15	29	25	33	42	20	24
17	38	36	11	26	31	32	19

We can make a stem-and-leaf plot from these data.

- The least number of books is 10. The greatest number is 43. Students read between 10 and 43 books. Write the tens digits 1 to 4 in a column. These are the **stems**.

Books Read in One Year	
Stem	Leaf
1	0 1 2 3 5 5 6 6 6 7 7 8 8 9 9
2	0 3 3 4 4 5 6 7 9
3	1 1 2 3 6 8
4	2 3

In a stem-and-leaf plot, the leaves are always numbers from 0 to 9.

- Start with the least number, 10. Write 0 as the **leaf** next to the stem, 1. Continue with the next greatest number, 11. Write 1 as the next leaf. Continue in this way. Record all the leaves in order from the least number to the greatest number.
- Write a title for the plot.

Example

Here are the heights, in centimetres, of the members of St. Mark's junior football team.

a) What is the range of the heights of the football players?
b) Draw a stem-and-leaf plot for the data.
c) What is the median height?
d) What is the mode height?

Heights of Football Players in Centimetres								
147	153	162	171	159	168	145	183	164
187	153	164	148	164	167	187	179	
148	190	188	173	155	177	176	189	192

DURING Explore

Ongoing Assessment: Observe and Listen

As student work, ensure they are ordering the numbers, both in the stems and in the leaves, from least to greatest, and that they give their plots a title.

Ask questions, such as:

- What are the stems in your plot? (*13, 14, 15, 16*)
- What are the leaves in your plot? (*The numbers from 0 to 9*)
- How can you check that all the heights of your classmates are in your stem-and-leaf plot? (*The total number of leaves should equal the total number of students in the class.*)
- Are any students the same height? (*Yes, three students have a height of 145 cm.*)
- Which is the shortest height? (*136 cm*) The tallest? (*160 cm*)
- What is the median height? (*146 cm*) The mode height? (*145 cm*)
- How did you find the median height? (*There are 27 heights, so the middle height is the 14th height, since* $\frac{27 + 1}{2} = 14$.)

AFTER Connect

Have students share their findings and stem-and-leaf plots with the class.

Here is a sample plot:

My Classmates' Heights (cm)	
Stem	Leaf
13	6 8 9 9
14	1 2 3 4 4 5 5 5 6 6 7 8 9 9
15	0 1 1 2 3 4 8 9
16	0

Ask:

- What else do you know from looking at the stem-and-leaf plot? (*We know the difference between the shortest and*

Solution

a) The least height is 145 cm.
The greatest height is 192 cm.
The range is 192 cm – 145 cm = 47 cm.

b) Each number has 3 digits, so the stem will be the hundreds and tens digits.
The leaf will be the ones digit.
The stems are from 14 to 19.
Start with the least number, 145.
Write the leaf, 5, next to the stem, 14.
Continue to write the leaves, from the least number to the greatest number.

Heights of Football Players in Centimetres

Stem	Leaf
14	5 7 8 8
15	3 3 5 9
16	2 4 4 4 7 8
17	1 3 6 7 9
18	3 7 7 8 9
19	0 2

c) There are 26 numbers.
This is an even number.
The median is the mean of the two middle numbers when the numbers are arranged in order.
For 26 numbers in order, the first middle number is $\frac{26}{2} = 13$, or the 13th number.
The next middle number is the 14th number.
Count the leaves, beginning at 5.
The 13th and 14th numbers are 167 and 168.
The median is: $\frac{167 + 168}{2} = 167.5$
The median height is 167.5 cm.

Heights of Football Players in Centimetres

Stem	Leaf
14	5 7 8 8
15	3 3 5 9
16	2 4 4 4 7 8
17	1 3 6 7 9
18	3 7 7 8 9
19	0 2

d) The mode is the number that occurs most often.
Leaf 4 occurs three times next to stem 16.
The mode is 164 cm.

The *Example* shows that, when the data are displayed in a stem-and-leaf plot, the range, the median, and the mode can be found from the plot.
When you organize data in a stem-and-leaf plot, the original data are visible. A frequency table only shows how many numbers are in each group, and not what the numbers are.

5.3 Stem-and-Leaf Plots **181**

Sample Answers

1. a) The stem-and-leaf plot shows the hours worked by part-time staff at a video store in one month.

2. a)

Masses in Kilograms	
Stem	**Leaf**
2	8 9
3	0 1 2 2 3 4 5 5 5 5 6 6 7 7 8 8 9
4	0 0 1 2 3 4 7 8 8
5	2 4

3. Data with a very narrow range; for example, data that are all 1-digit numbers or data that have only 1 stem. Also, data with a very wide range cannot be shown; for example, a data set such as 37, 294, 851, 1002, 22 654, 13 422, 620.

4. a) Sample response:

My Classmates' Strides	
Stem	**Leaf**
4	7 8 8 9
5	0 3 3 3 4 4 5 5 6 8 9
6	0 0 1 1 3 4 5 5 6 7 9
7	0 0 1 1 2 7

b) The shortest stride is 47 cm; the longest stride is 77 cm; the range is 30 cm; the mode is 53 cm; the median is 60 cm.

5. a) The manufacturer's claim may not be true because 13 of the 24 bags have a mass less than 50 g. But I would have to calculate the mean, median, and/or mode, then decide about the truth of the statement.

b) I could use a stem-and-leaf plot to find the median and the mode. The median is 49.85 g and the mode is 49.0 g. Both masses are less than 50 g, so the claim is not true.

the tallest height, the number of students with a height of 130 cm–139 cm, 140 cm–149 cm, 150 cm–159 cm, 160 cm–169 cm; and the order of the heights from shortest to tallest.)

- Does your plot look the same as that of another pair of classmates? (*Yes*) Why? (*We used the same data.*)
- How is a stem-and-leaf plot better than a frequency table or tally chart? (*It is easy to find the range, median, and mode; the data are ordered from least to greatest; and all the original data are still visible.*)

Review *Connect*. The *Example* is similar to the *Explore*, in that each number in the data has 3 digits, so each stem has 2 digits.

Practice

Have metre sticks available for question 4. Question 6 requires students to research the scores of the last 15 games of a basketball team. Students may use the Internet or newspapers to help them.

Assessment Focus: Question 6

Students could find the range, median, mode, highest score, or lowest score from looking at the plot. Students' work should include a stem-and-leaf plot drawn with a ruler, and it should have a title. The students' responses to part c should be complete sentences. This promotes better communication and understanding.

6. a) I chose my school's senior girls' basketball team.

b)

Points Scored in Last 15 Games	
Stem	**Leaf**
2	2 7 8 9
3	3 5 5 6
4	1 2 5 6 8
5	0 4

c) Three things I know from looking at the plot:

- The mode is 35 points.
- The median is 36 points; the eighth score is 36.
- The range is 32 points; 54 – 22 = 36.

REFLECT: It is easier to read data in a stem-and-leaf plot because the original data are visible; the data are arranged in order, from least to greatest; it is easy to find the least and greatest data values; the mode is easily seen; and the median is easily found.

Assignment Guidelines

These questions provide minimum curriculum coverage:
2, 3, 5, 6, *Reflect*

To assess the 4 Achievement Chart categories have students complete these *Practice* questions:

Understanding Concepts: 2; Application: 5;
Communication: 3; Problem Solving: 6

Practice

Hours Worked by Part-Time Staff at a Video Store in One Month

Stem	Leaf
9	1 6 9
10	2 5 6 8
11	0 3 4 4 4 7
12	0 1 2 2 5 6 6 8 9
13	2 3 5 6 7 7 7 7 8 9 9

1. a) What does this stem-and-leaf plot show?
b) How many part-time employees work at the video store? 33
c) What is the least number of hours worked? 91 h
The greatest number of hours worked? 139 h
d) What is the range of hours worked? 48 h
e) What is the median number of hours worked? 122 h
f) What is the mode number of hours worked? 137 h

2. The masses of parcels, in kilograms, are given.
a) Display the data in a stem-and-leaf plot.
b) Find the greatest mass. The least mass. Greatest mass: 54 kg Least mass: 28 kg
c) What is the range of masses? 26 kg
d) What is the median mass? 37 kg
e) What is the mode mass? 35 kg

Masses in Kilograms

28	32	40	36	31
40	48	35	38	34
43	35	41	36	52
37	47	29	42	35
33	39	32	48	37
38	30	35	44	54

3. Which type of data cannot be shown in a stem-and-leaf plot? Explain.

4. Work with a partner. Use a metre stick to measure each other's stride, to the nearest centimetre. Record the measures on the board. Use the measures for the whole class.
a) Make a stem-and-leaf plot.
b) What did you find out about the strides of your classmates? Write down as much as you can.

Calculator Skills

Find two numbers with a difference of 2.75 and a product of 60.125.

6.5 and 9.25

5. A food manufacturer claims:
"We guarantee an average of 50 g of peanuts per bag."
In 6 months, Devon found the masses of peanuts, in grams, in 24 bags. Look at the data.
a) Is the food manufacturer's claim true? No
b) How could you use a stem-and-leaf plot to justify your answer?

Masses of Peanuts in Grams

50.1, 49.9, 49.0, 48.9,
50.8, 50.3, 51.3, 49.8,
48.8, 49.0, 50.3, 51.2,
49.4, 49.0, 48.1, 49.6,
49.8, 51.3, 50.5, 50.7,
48.7, 51.0, 49.3, 52.5

182 UNIT 5: Data Management

ASSESSMENT FOR LEARNING

What to Look For

Understanding concepts

✔ Students understand how to find the range, median, and mode on a stem-and-leaf plot.

Applying procedures

✔ Students can organize data in a stem-and-leaf plot.

✔ Students can use a stem-and-leaf plot to draw conclusions about data.

Communicating

✔ Students can explain how a stem-and-leaf plot differs from a frequency table.

What to Do

Extra Support: Students who have difficulty organizing given data (2-digit numbers) on a stem-and-leaf plot may benefit from sorting the data by the tens digits, then organizing each group of data from least to greatest by looking at the ones digits.
Students can use Step-by-Step 3 (Master 5.9) to complete question 6.

Extra Practice: Students use a stem-and-leaf plot to find the median and mode for question 1, parts c and d of *Skills You'll Need*, page 168.
Students can complete Extra Practice 3 (Master 5.17).

Extension: Students explain how they would find the mean of a set of data, given only a stem-and-leaf plot. They find the mean of the data in *Practice* question 1.

Recording and Reporting

Master 5.2 Ongoing Observations: Data Management

Meteorologist

6. Assessment Focus

a) Collect data on the points scored by a basketball team in its last 15 games. The points could be from games played by your school team or a professional team.

b) Make a stem-and-leaf plot.

c) Write 3 things you know from looking at the plot.

Reflect

Explain why it is easier to read data in a stem-and-leaf plot than data in a table.

The World of Work

Meteorologist

A meteorologist is often a specialist. She uses data collection tools suitable for the weather condition being studied. The data collected are pooled nationally and internationally, and studied by a variety of meteorologists and others in related fields. The information and analysis produce severe weather alerts, which can save thousands of lives.

We may not experience surviving a tornado or a hurricane. But there are other weather conditions that are just as destructive. On January 6, 1998, a severe ice-storm hit Quebec, eastern Ontario, and northeastern U.S. Many people called it the largest ecological disaster in the history of Quebec. On February 6, 1998, Quebec was restored to some normalcy.

When was the last time you heard a "severe weather warning"? Was the prediction correct? What kinds of data management tools might have been used to predict this event?

The World of Work: Meteorologist 183

As a class, generate a list of careers that may involve data management.

Here are some careers that involve the study of data.

Statistician: A statistician collects, analyses, presents, and interprets numerical data.

Statisticians may apply their knowledge of statistical methods to a variety of subject areas, such as biology, economics, engineering, medicine, public health, psychology, marketing, education, and sports.

Actuary: An actuary is someone whose work is figuring risks, rates, and premiums for an insurance company. Actuaries collect and analyse data to estimate the probability and cost of the occurrence of an event such as death, sickness, injury, disability, or loss of property.

Economist: Economists conduct research, collect and analyse data, watch trends, and make forecasts about issues such as energy costs, inflation, interest rates, exchange rates, taxes, or employment levels.

Financial Analyst: Financial analysts work for businesses such as banks, insurance companies, and securities firms. They help these businesses make investment decisions by reading company financial statements and analysing commodity prices, sales, costs, expenses, and tax rates.

MID-UNIT REVIEW

SECTION ORGANIZER

Student Materials
- 3-column charts (PM 18)
- 2-column charts (PM 17)
- 0.5-cm grid paper (PM 14)
- atlases or databases

Assessment: Masters 5.1 Unit Rubric: Data Management, 5.4 Unit Summary: Data Management

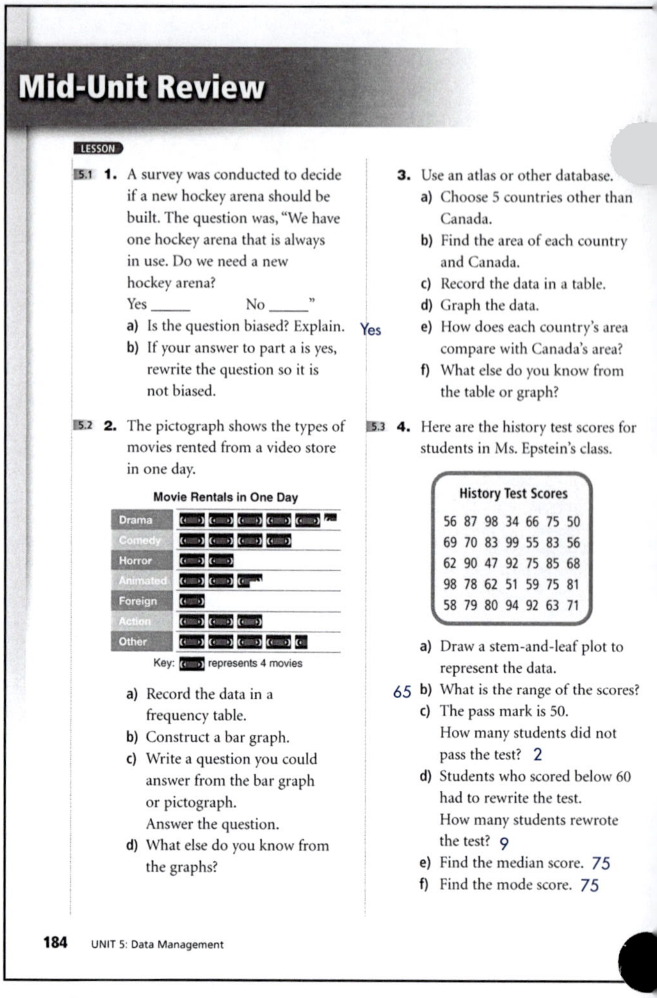

Mid-Unit Review

LESSON

5.1 **1.** A survey was conducted to decide if a new hockey arena should be built. The question was, "We have one hockey arena that is always in use. Do we need a new hockey arena?
Yes _____ No _____"
- a) Is the question biased? Explain. Yes
- b) If your answer to part a is yes, rewrite the question so it is not biased.

5.2 **2.** The pictograph shows the types of movies rented from a video store in one day.

Movie Rentals in One Day
Drama
Comedy
Horror
Animated
Foreign
Action
Other
Key: represents 4 movies

- a) Record the data in a frequency table.
- b) Construct a bar graph.
- c) Write a question you could answer from the bar graph or pictograph. Answer the question.
- d) What else do you know from the graphs?

3. Use an atlas or other database.
- a) Choose 5 countries other than Canada.
- b) Find the area of each country and Canada.
- c) Record the data in a table.
- d) Graph the data.
- e) How does each country's area compare with Canada's area?
- f) What else do you know from the table or graph?

5.3 **4.** Here are the history test scores for students in Ms. Epstein's class.

History Test Scores

56	87	98	34	66	75	50
69	70	83	99	55	83	56
62	90	47	92	75	85	68
98	78	62	51	59	75	81
58	79	80	94	92	63	71

- a) Draw a stem-and-leaf plot to represent the data.
- b) What is the range of the scores? 65
- c) The pass mark is 50. How many students did not pass the test? 2
- d) Students who scored below 60 had to rewrite the test. How many students rewrote the test? 9
- e) Find the median score. 75
- f) Find the mode score. 75

184 UNIT 5: Data Management

Sample Solutions

1. a) The question is biased because it includes a statement that may encourage people to answer "Yes."

b) "Do we need a new hockey arena? Yes ___ No ___"

2. a)

Movie Rentals in One Day		
Type of Movie	**Tally**	**Frequency**
Drama	~~////~~ ~~////~~ ~~////~~ ~~////~~ /	21
Comedy	~~////~~ ~~////~~ ~~////~~ /	16
Horror	~~////~~ ///	8
Animated	~~////~~ ~~////~~ /	11
Foreign	////	4
Action	~~////~~ ~~////~~ //	12
Other	~~////~~ ~~////~~ ~~////~~ ///	18

(*Solutions continue below.*)

(*Sample Solutions, continued*)

b)

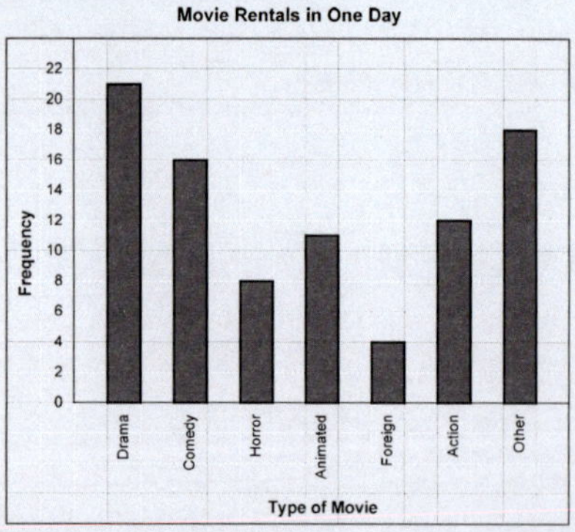

c) How many more drama movies were rented than horror movies? (*Answer: 21 − 8 = 13*)

d) More people rent comedy movies than horror movies. Ninety movies were rented that day.

3. a) I chose Egypt, South Africa, Mexico, Venezuela, and Spain.

b), c) For example,

Country	Area (km²)
Canada	9 984 670
Egypt	1 000 000
South Africa	1 227 200
Mexico	1 972 550
Venezuela	912 050
Spain	492 503

4. a)

History Test Scores	
Stem	**Leaf**
3	4
4	7
5	0 1 5 6 6 8 9
6	2 2 3 6 8 9
7	0 1 5 5 5 8 9
8	0 1 3 3 5 7
9	0 2 2 4 8 8 9

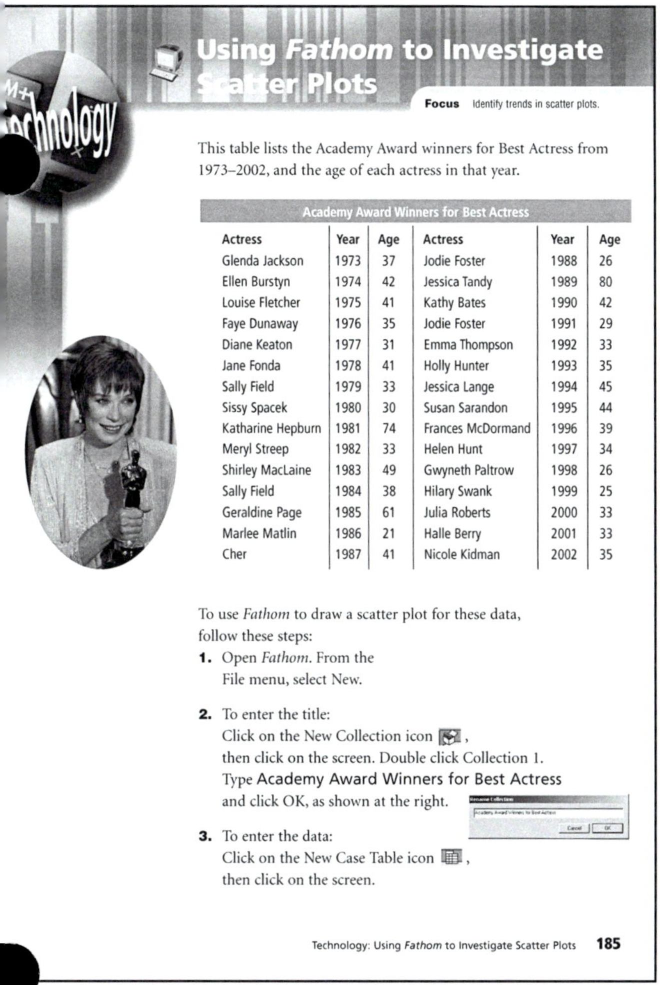

Using *Fathom* to Investigate Scatter Plots

Focus Identify trends in scatter plots.

This table lists the Academy Award winners for Best Actress from 1973–2002, and the age of each actress in that year.

Academy Award Winners for Best Actress

Actress	Year	Age	Actress	Year	Age
Glenda Jackson	1973	37	Jodie Foster	1988	26
Ellen Burstyn	1974	42	Jessica Tandy	1989	80
Louise Fletcher	1975	41	Kathy Bates	1990	42
Faye Dunaway	1976	35	Jodie Foster	1991	29
Diane Keaton	1977	31	Emma Thompson	1992	33
Jane Fonda	1978	41	Holly Hunter	1993	35
Sally Field	1979	33	Jessica Lange	1994	45
Sissy Spacek	1980	30	Susan Sarandon	1995	44
Katharine Hepburn	1981	74	Frances McDormand	1996	39
Meryl Streep	1982	33	Helen Hunt	1997	34
Shirley MacLaine	1983	49	Gwyneth Paltrow	1998	26
Sally Field	1984	38	Hilary Swank	1999	25
Geraldine Page	1985	61	Julia Roberts	2000	33
Marlee Matlin	1986	21	Halle Berry	2001	33
Cher	1987	41	Nicole Kidman	2002	35

To use *Fathom* to draw a scatter plot for these data, follow these steps:

1. Open *Fathom*. From the File menu, select New.
2. To enter the title:
   Click on the New Collection icon, then click on the screen. Double click Collection 1.
   Type Academy Award Winners for Best Actress and click OK, as shown at the right.
3. To enter the data:
   Click on the New Case Table icon, then click on the screen.

Technology: Using *Fathom* to Investigate Scatter Plots 185

Using *Fathom* to Investigate Scatter Plots

SECTION ORGANIZER

40–50 min

Curriculum Focus: Identify trends in scatter plots. (7m83, 7m85, 7m96)

Student Materials

- computers with *Fathom*

Vocabulary: cluster, trend

Key Math Learnings

1. Software, such as *Fathom*, can be used to draw a scatter plot for data.
2. From a scatter plot, we can see whether there is a pattern or trend in the data.

Tell students that *Fathom* is software that can be used to draw scatter plots. Students will use *Fathom* to create scatter plots, then analyse the scatter plots to look for trends in the data.

When students analyse the scatter plots, they should look for trends in the data. A trend is a general direction, or tendency of the data. If the data show an upward trend, the points tend to go up from left to right. For example, the more a person works, the more a person earns. If the data show a downward trend, the points tend to go down from left to right. For example, the more a person exercises, the more mass a person loses.

When most of the data are located in a certain interval, we say that the data are *clustered* around this interval.

Pair students so that a computer-literate student works with a student whose computer knowledge is limited.

(Sample Answers for Section 5.4, pages 191, 192, continued)

3. b) Round each number to the nearest whole number or integer.

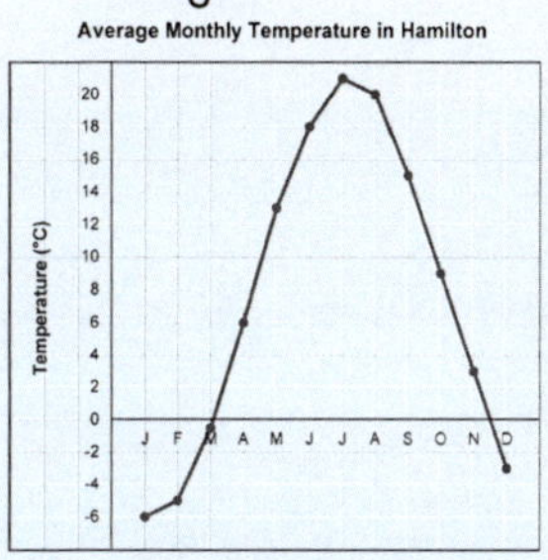

c)

Calgary, Average Monthly Temperature	
Month	**°C**
January	–8.9
February	–6.1
March	–1.9
April	4.6
May	9.8
June	13.8
July	16.2
August	15.6
September	10.8
October	5.4
November	–3.1
December	–7.4

REACHING ALL LEARNERS

Early Finishers

Have students research a topic of their choice using E-STAT or another database, then use *Fathom* to draw a scatter plot. Have them describe any trends they find.

ESL Strategies

Pair a student for whom English is a second language with a student for whom English is the first language. A student whose knowledge of English is poor may have very good computer skills.

Sample Solutions

1. There is an upward trend as the car accelerates and a downward trend as the car slows down, and comes to a stop. Points that are on the same horizontal line indicate that the car is maintaining the same speed (either 0 km/h or 100 km/h).
We know that it took 5 h for Emily to drive from Toronto to Cornwall. She stopped from 3:00 to 3:30. Her fastest speed was 100 km/h.
She maintained this speed for quite a while so she might have been using cruise control.

Emily's Drive to Cornwall

	Time	Speed in km per hour
1	12:00	0
2	12:30	70
3	1:00	85
4	1:30	100
5	2:00	100
6	2:30	100
7	3:00	0
8	3:30	0
9	4:00	100
10	4:30	65
11	5:00	0

Click on <new>; type Year, then press Enter. A new column appears to the right with the heading <new>. Click on the word <new>, type Age, then press Enter. Under the headings *Year* and *Age*, input the data from the table on page 185.

4. To graph the data:
Click on the New Graph icon, then click on the screen. Two axes appear.
Click on the column heading, *Year*, and drag it to the horizontal axis.
Click on the column heading, *Age*, and drag it to the vertical axis.
Fathom creates a scatter plot, as shown at the right.

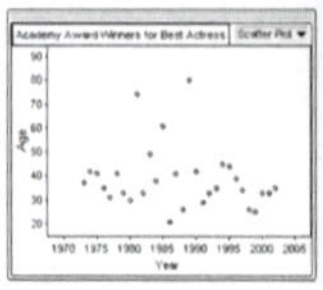

The range of the data is: 80 – 21, or 59 years.
However, most of the data are located between 31 and 42 years.
The data form a **cluster** between these ages.
This means that, from 1973 to 2002, most winners were between 31 and 42 years old.
There are two large sections without points — between 49 and 61 years, and between 61 and 74 years. These represent gaps in the data. From 1973 to 2002, none of the winners were between 49 and 61 years old, or between 61 and 74 years old.
From the scatter plot, we can see that there is no pattern or **trend** in the data.

Here is another example of data in a scatter plot:
Emidio works part-time as a waiter in a restaurant. The table and scatter plot on page 187 show the hours he worked each week for 12 weeks, and his earnings, in dollars, for each week.

From the scatter plot, the points show an **upward trend** from left to right. Emidio's earnings increase as time increases. That is, the more hours per week Emidio works, the more he earns.

186 UNIT 5: Data Management

(*Sample Answers for Section 5.4, pages 191, 192, continued*)

d)

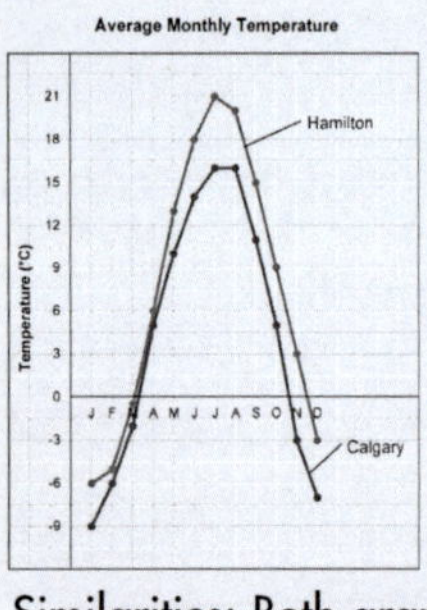

e) Similarities: Both graphs are shaped like a hill. Both graphs peak during the month of July. Both graphs rise to the right from January to July, then fall to the right from July to December. Differences: All the monthly average temperatures for Hamilton are higher than those for Calgary.

f) In Calgary, the average monthly temperatures are above 0°C from March to October and below 0°C from the end of October to early March. In Hamilton, average monthly temperatures are above 0°C from March to November and below 0°C from mid-November to early March. The cities are closest in temperature during March. The cities have the greatest difference in temperature during November.

4. a) Stopping distance depends on the speed at which a car is travelling, whether the pavement is wet or dry, and whether the road is paved or gravel.

b)

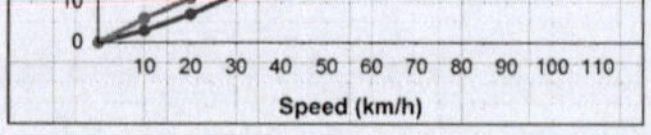

c) A line graph displays data over time and speed is measured in kilometres per hour.

d) Both graphs rise from left to right and they become steeper as the speed of the car increases. In both graphs, the faster the car is travelling, the greater the distance required to stop. The line graph for wet pavement is steeper and lies above the line graph for dry pavement, meaning that it takes a greater distance for a car to stop on wet pavement.

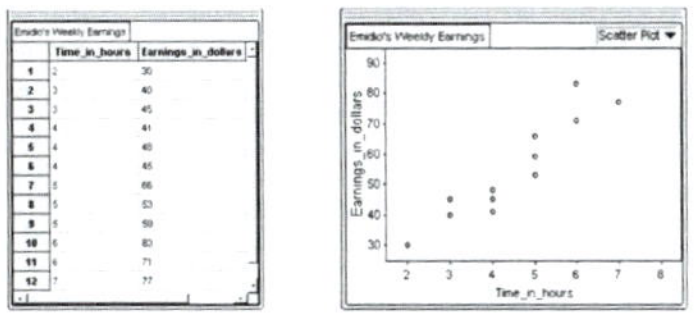

Here is a third example of data in a scatter plot:
Water is draining out of a swimming pool. The table and scatter plot show the volume of water, in litres, remaining in the pool at one-hour intervals.

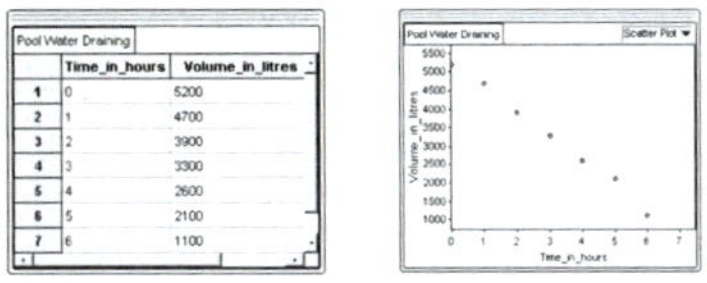

From the scatter plot, the points show a **downward trend** from left to right.
The volume of water in the pool decreases as time increases.
That is, the more hours the pool drains, the less water there is in it.

✓ Check

Time	Speed (km/h)
12 noon	0
12:30	70
1:00	85
1:30	100
2:00	100
2:30	100
3:00	0
3:30	0
4:00	100
4:30	65
5:00	0

1. Emily drove from Toronto to Cornwall.
   She left Toronto at 12 noon and arrived in Cornwall at 5 p.m.
   The table at the left shows the speed of the car recorded at different times during her trip.
   Use *Fathom* to draw a scatter plot to represent the data.
   Describe any trends.
   What do you know from looking at the graph?

Reflect

Describe 3 different types of scatter plots.
Provide an example for each type.

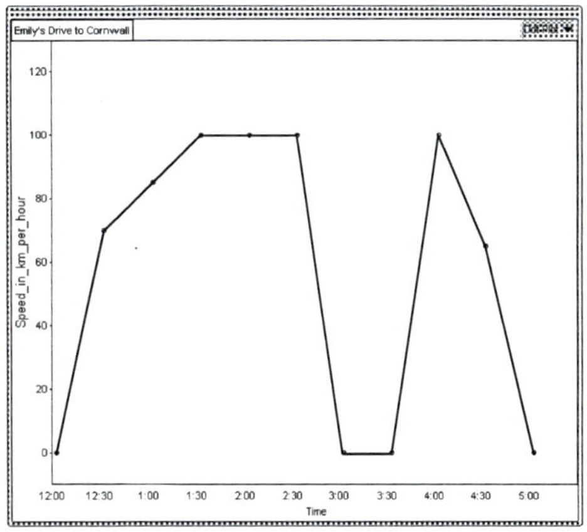

REFLECT:
- **i)** A scatter plot with an upward trend: this occurs when values along the vertical axis increase as values along the horizontal axis increase. An example is a hot air balloon rising.
- **ii)** A scatter plot with a downward trend: this occurs when values along the vertical axis decrease as values along the horizontal axis increase. An example is a plane landing.
- **iii)** A scatter plot where there is no apparent trend: the points on the graph have no pattern. This type of graph occurs if you plot an adult's height against her or his age.

(Sample Answers for Section 5.4, pages 191, 192, continued)

g) What is the stopping distance for a car travelling at 65 km/h on wet pavement? *(Answer: About 58 m)*

5. a) The yearly sales would be best represented by a line graph because the data are collected over time.

b)

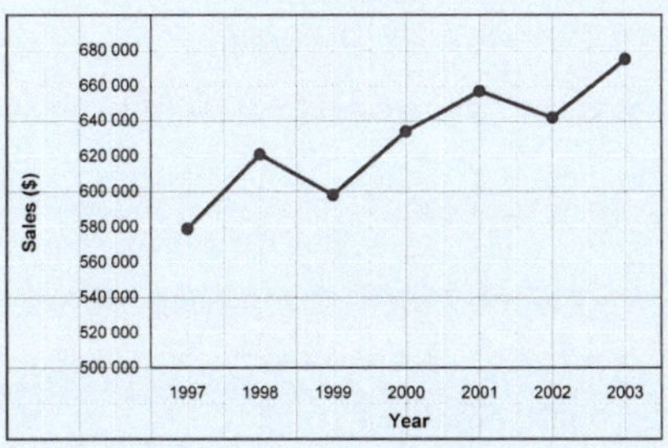

c) The yearly sales increase for a year or two, then drop off for a year before increasing again, but the trend is increasing sales.

d) A bar graph is suitable because the data are not measured over time. There are no shoe sizes between the given size values; for example, there is no such thing as a size $7\frac{3}{8}$ shoe.

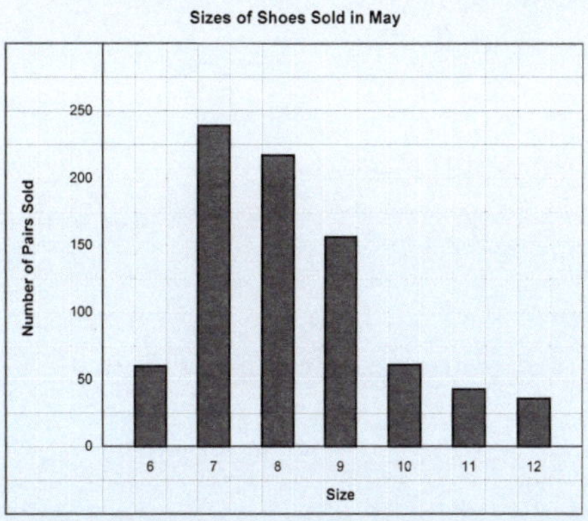

e) Yearly sales: Sales increased from 1997 to 1998, 1999 to 2001, and 2002 to 2003. The greatest yearly sales occurred in 2003, and the least yearly sales occurred in 1997.
Sizes of shoes sold in May: The most commonly sold shoe size is 7, followed by sizes 8, 9, 10, 6, 11, and 12. The least commonly sold shoe size is 12.

REFLECT: A line graph displays data over time. The graph may be extended to predict information into the future, assuming the same trends continue.

Line Graphs

SECTION ORGANIZER 80–100 min

Curriculum Focus: Display data using line graphs and describe trends. (7m96, 7m98)

Student Materials
- 1 cm grid paper (PM 20)
- databases, such as *Environment Canada*
- rulers

Optional
- 3-column charts (PM 18)
- Step-by-Step 4 (Master 5.10)
- Extra Practice 4 (Master 5.18)

Vocabulary: line graph

Assessment: Master 5.2 Ongoing Observations: Data Management

Key Math Learnings

1. A line graph displays data that change over time.
2. A line graph may show a trend, and may be used to make predictions.

5.4 Line Graphs

Focus Display data using line graphs and describe trends.

Explore

Work with a partner.
Madhu measured the mass of her pet guinea pig every 5 months, until it was 25 months old.
The data are shown at the left.

Age (months)	Mass (g)
5	200
10	350
15	480
20	510
25	520

- One person draws a bar graph. The other person draws a line graph.
- During which period did the guinea pig gain the most mass? Between 5 and 10 months
- What happened to the mass of the guinea pig after 15 months? Does this make sense? About 520 g
- Predict the mass of the guinea pig at 30 months.

Reflect & Share

Discuss with your partner which graph is better for displaying the data. Justify your answer.
Estimate the mass of the guinea pig at 18 months.
Which graph is better to make this estimate? Explain.

Connect

A **line graph** displays data that change over time.
The line graph on page 189 shows how Leah's height changes as she gets older.
From 2 to 13 years, each line segment goes up to the right.
This shows that Leah's height increases.
From 13 to 16 years, the line segments still go up to the right, but they are not as steep.
This shows that Leah's height increases, but at a slower rate than before.
From 16 years on, the line segments are horizontal.
This shows that Leah's height has stopped increasing.
She has stopped growing taller.

188 UNIT 5: Data Management

BEFORE Get Started

Review line graphs with the class. Remind students that line graphs are used to display data that change over time. Show students a line graph; for example, a graph of the outside temperature over a 24-h period. Tell students that the temperature does not suddenly increase or decrease from one plotted point to the next. The temperature changes continuously. This is why adjacent points are connected with a line segment.

Ensure students understand the importance of labelling the axes and giving the graph a title. Tell students to use a ruler when connecting the points. Remind students that it is important to choose an appropriate scale for each axis. They should keep the size of the grid paper in mind to be sure that all data fit on the graph.

Present *Explore.* Remind students that one person should draw the bar graph and the other person should draw the line graph.

DURING Explore

Ongoing Assessment: Observe and Listen

As students work, ask questions, such as:
- What does the horizontal axis represent? (*The age, in months, of the guinea pig*)
- What does the vertical axis represent? (*The mass, in grams, of the guinea pig*)
- What is the title of your graph? (*The Mass of Madhu's Guinea Pig*)
- What scale are you using for the horizontal axis of the line graph? (*I am using the scale 1 grid square represents 5 months.*) For the vertical axis? (*I am using the scale 1 grid square represents 50 g.*)

This symbol ⌇ on the vertical axis means that the numbers from 0 to 60 are not shown.

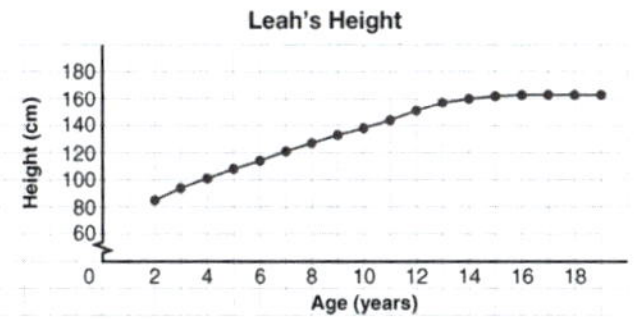

We can use this line graph to find values between data points. At $11\frac{1}{2}$ years, Leah was about 148 cm tall.

Example

a) Draw a line graph to display these data.
b) Use the graph. Describe any trends in Canada's population.
c) Use the graph. During which period did Canada's population increase the most? The least? How can you tell?
d) Estimate Canada's population in 2011. Explain how you used the graph to do this. What assumption did you make?

Canada's Population (to the nearest million)

Years	Number (millions)
1901	5
1911	7
1921	9
1931	10
1941	12
1951	14
1961	18
1971	22
1981	25
1991	28
2001	31

Solution

a) **Step 1.** Draw axes on grid paper. The horizontal axis represents time, in years. Use 1 square for each 10-year interval, starting in 1901. The vertical axis represents population, in millions. The greatest population to be graphed is 31 million. Make 35 the greatest number on the vertical scale. Use 1 square for every 5 million, starting at 0.
Step 2. Plot a point on the grid for each pair of entries in the table. Use a ruler to join adjacent points.
Step 3. Label the axes. Give the graph a title.

5.4 Line Graphs **189**

REACHING ALL LEARNERS

Early Finishers

Students state which of the following situations are better represented by a line graph.

- The length of a kitten as it grows (line graph)
- The number of students in each grade at an elementary school (bar graph)
- The school population over the last 10 years (line graph)
- The points scored by the school volleyball team in each of its last 12 games (bar graph)
- The height of a child from birth to adult (line graph)

Common Misconceptions

➤ Students have difficulty determining which of two line segments is steeper.

How to Help: Have students run their finger along each line segment, from left to right. Have them imagine they are walking up a hill, then ask themselves, "Which hill would be more difficult to climb?"

➤ Students believe that a prediction they make using a line graph is accurate.

How to Help: Remind students that their prediction is only an estimate of a future value, based on a trend in the data. If this trend changes, then the prediction might be wrong.

- How are the bar graph and the line graph similar?
  (*They have the same horizontal and vertical axes, the axes have the same units, the graphs have the same title, and they display the same data.*)
- How are the bar graph and the line graph different?
  (*On the bar graph, the masses are represented by bars; the longer the bar, the greater the mass. On the line graph, the masses are represented by points on the graph, and adjacent points are connected with a line segment.*)

AFTER Connect

Have students share their graphs and findings with the class.

What you might see:

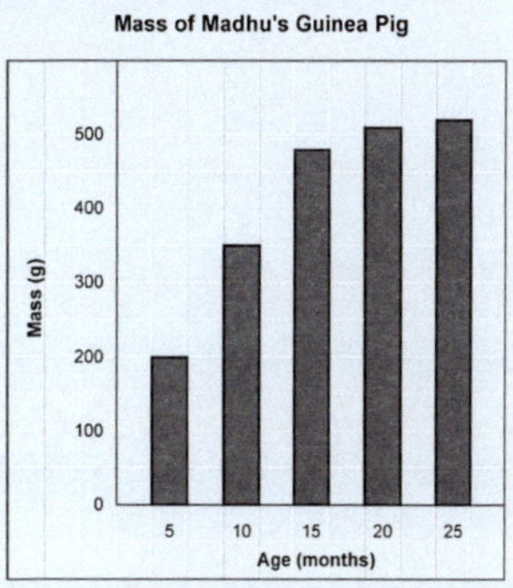

Sample Answers

1. a) Nathan's height, in centimetres, from age 8 to 16
   b) i) 125 cm   ii) 150 cm   iii) 180 cm
   c) Nathan grew the most from age 12 to 13 because the line segment from age 12 to 13 is the steepest line segment on the graph. Nathan grew the least from age 15 to 16 because this line segment is the least steep.
   d) 185 cm; Nathan is now growing very slowly so his height at age 18 won't be much different from his height at age 16.
   e) 185 cm; Nathan's height at age 50 will probably be the same as his height at age 18.
2. a) The average monthly rainfall, in centimetres, for Vancouver and Ottawa
   b)

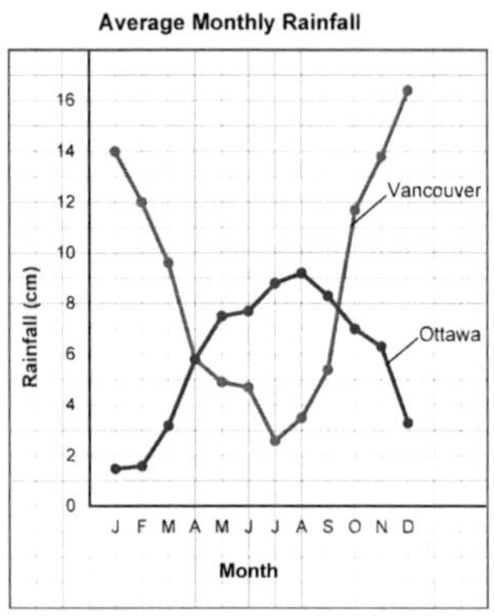

   c) Vancouver: Greatest increase in rain is from September to October—line segment is the steepest. December is the rainiest month—December is the highest point on the graph. July is the month with the least amount of rain—July is the lowest point on the graph.

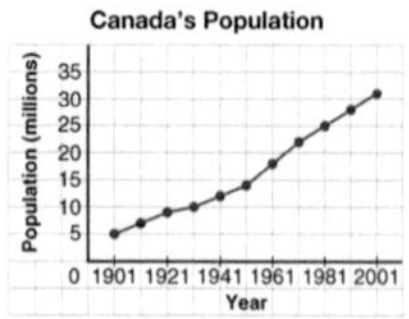

b) The graph goes up to the right.
This means that Canada's population increased from 1901 to 2001. In general, the line segments from 1951 to 2001 are steeper than the segments from 1901 to 1951.
This means that the population was increasing at a faster rate in the 2nd half of the century.

c) The period in which the line segment is the steepest represents the greatest increase in population. This happened from 1951 to 1971. From 1921 to 1931, the line segment is the least steep. This is when Canada's population had the least increase.

d) To predict Canada's population in 2011, extend the last line segment to 2011. From 2011 on the horizontal axis, draw a vertical line to the graph. From the graph, draw a horizontal line to the vertical axis. This line meets the axis at about 34 million. The population of Canada in 2011 will be approximately 34 million.
We assume that Canada's population will continue to grow at the same rate as it did from 1991 to 2001.

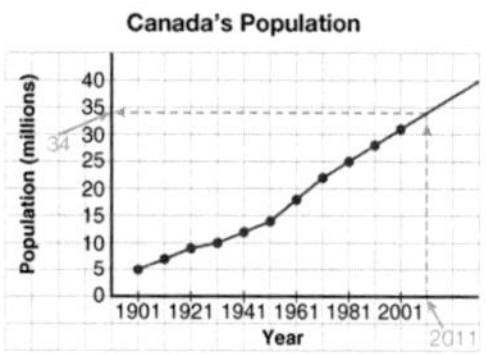

190 UNIT 5: Data Management

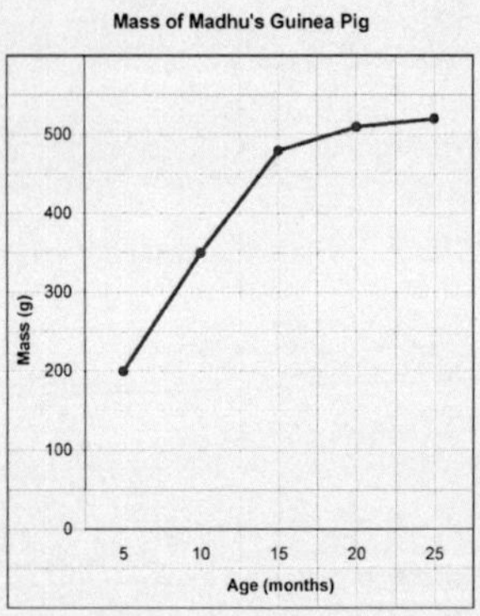

Ask:

- During which period did the guinea pig gain the most mass?
  (*Between 5 and 10 months*)
- How do we know this from the bar graph?
  (*We look for 2 bars next to each other that have the greatest difference in height.*)
  From the line graph?
  (*We look for the 2 points that are joined by the steepest segment.*)
- What happened to the mass of the guinea pig after 15 months?
  (*Its rate of growth decreased; its mass was not increasing as fast as it had before.*) Why?
  (*The guinea pig was close to full-grown.*)
- What do you think the mass of the guinea pig will be at 30 months?
  (*About 520 g*) Why? (*The mass didn't change much between 20 and 25 months, so I think it won't change at all between 25 and 30 months.*)
- What do you think the mass of the guinea pig was at 18 months? (*About 500 g*) Explain.
  (*I used the line graph. I found 18 on the horizontal axis, then drew a vertical line to the graph. From the graph, I drew a horizontal line to the vertical axis. The line meets the axis at about 500 g.*)
- Which graph is better for displaying the data? (*The line graph*) Why?
  (*The line graph can be used to find values between data points. It is also easier to see trends on a line graph.*)

We can use this line graph to find any trends in the data. For example, the steeper a line segment

Practice

Calculator Skills

Three consecutive 2-digit numbers have a product of 551 286.
What is the sum of the three numbers?
81 + 82 + 83 = 246

1. a) What does this line graph show?
   b) About how tall was Nathan at each age?
      i) 8 years 125 cm
      ii) 12 years 150 cm
      iii) 15 years 180 cm
   c) During which year did Nathan grow the most? The least? How does the graph show this?
   d) Predict Nathan's height at 18 years. Explain your reasoning.
   e) Predict Nathan's height at 50 years. Explain.

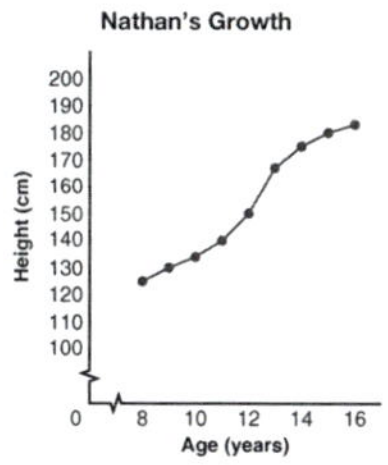

Average Monthly Rainfall (cm)

Month	Vancouver	Ottawa
January	14.0	1.5
February	12.0	1.6
March	9.6	3.2
April	5.8	5.8
May	4.9	7.5
June	4.7	7.7
July	2.6	8.8
August	3.5	9.2
September	5.4	8.3
October	11.7	7.0
November	13.8	6.3
December	16.4	3.3

2. a) What does this table show?
   b) Draw a line graph for each city on the same grid.
   c) Describe the trends in rainfall for the two cities. How do the line graphs illustrate these trends?
   d) In which month(s) do the line graphs cross? April and September
      What does this mean?
   e) What is the average annual rainfall for each city?
      Vancouver: 104.4 cm; Ottawa: 70.2 cm
3. a) Research your region on one of these topics:
      i) the average precipitation for each month
      ii) the maximum temperature for the first day of each month
      iii) the average temperature for each month
   b) Organize the data in a table. Draw a line graph.
   c) Repeat part a for a city or region in a different part of Canada.
   d) Draw a line graph to display these data on the same grid as in part b.
   e) How are the line graphs alike? How are they different?
   f) Write all that you know from looking at the graphs.

5.4 Line Graphs 191

Ottawa: Greatest increase in rain is from March to April—line segment is the steepest. August is the rainiest month—August is the highest point on the graph. January is the month with the least amount of rain—January is the lowest point on the graph.

d) The graphs cross in April and September. This means that the 2 cities have the same average rainfall at these times.

e) Vancouver: 104.4 cm; Ottawa: 70.2 cm

3. a) iii)

Hamilton, Average Monthly Temperature	
Month	**°C**
January	−6.0
February	−5.2
March	−0.3
April	6.3
May	12.9
June	18.0
July	20.8
August	19.8
September	15.5
October	9.1
November	3.3
December	−2.7

(*Sample Answers continue on page 21.*)

going up to the right, the faster the mass is increasing. If a line segment is horizontal, there is no increase in mass as time passes.

Review *Connect.* Ask students if they think the line graph for Leah's height would ever go down to the right. (*Probably not; Leah is not likely to get shorter. As people age, their spines compress and some elderly people are shorter by a few centimetres than they were in middle age.*)

Review the *Example.* For a social studies connection, ask students why Canada's population increased so much between 1951 and 1971. (There were many immigrants from Europe following the Second World War.)

Practice

Questions 2, 3, 4, and 5 require 1-cm grid paper. Have chart paper available for question 3.

Question 3 requires students to research information on weather in their region. When students research for question 3, they may find negative temperatures. Be prepared to show students how to extend their knowledge of plotting positive numbers to plotting negative numbers.

Assessment Focus: Question 5

Students should recognize that only one of the tables shows data that change over time and therefore, only the data in this table should be displayed on a line graph. Students draw a line graph, then describe any trends they see. Both graphs should include a title and axes labels.

Calculator Skills

Students could start with 3 consecutive numbers, such as 50, 51, and 52, then adjust the numbers as necessary until they get a product of 551 286. Students then calculate the sum of the 3 numbers.

Assignment Guidelines

If your students do not have time to complete all the *Practice* questions on pages 191 and 192, these questions provide minimum curriculum coverage: 1, 2, 4, 5, *Reflect*

To assess the 4 Achievement Chart categories listed in the curriculum document, have students complete these *Practice* questions:

Understanding Concepts: 1

Communication: 2

Application: 4

Problem Solving: 5

Stopping Distance for a Car

Speed (km/h)	Dry Pavement (m)	Wet Pavement (m)
0	0	0
10	3	6
20	7	11
30	12	17
40	16	26
50	23	38
60	30	50
70	38	64
80	49	78
90	60	97
100	72	120

4. a) What does stopping distance depend on?

b) On the same grid, draw a line graph for dry pavement and for wet pavement.

c) Why are line graphs suitable for these data?

d) Describe the trends in the graphs.

e) A car travels at 75 km/h on dry pavement. What is its stopping distance? About 45 m

f) A car takes 30 m to stop on wet pavement. How fast was it travelling? About 45 km/h

g) Write a question you could answer using the graph but not the table. Explain why you need the graph instead of the table.

5. Assessment Focus Nina owns a shoe store. These tables show data about the shoe store.

i)

Yearly Sales

Year	Sales ($)
1997	579 000
1998	621 000
1999	598 000
2000	634 000
2001	657 000
2002	642 000
2003	675 000

ii)

Sizes of Shoes Sold in May

Size	Number of Pairs Sold
6	60
7	239
8	217
9	156
10	61
11	43
12	36

a) Which data would be best represented with a line graph? Explain.

b) Draw a line graph for the table you chose in part a.

c) Describe the trends in the data.

d) Which type of graph would be suitable for the other table? Explain. Graph the data from the other table.

e) What do you know from looking at each graph?

Reflect

Why is a line graph the best type of graph to use to make predictions?

192 UNIT 5: Data Management

ASSESSMENT FOR LEARNING

What to Look For	What to Do
Understanding concepts ✔ Students understand that a line graph displays data that change over time. ***Applying procedures*** ✔ Students can draw a line graph that includes a title and appropriate labels. ***Communicating*** ✔ Students can identify and describe trends in a line graph, and use these trends to make predictions.	***Extra Support:*** Have students identify situations that provide data that change over time; for example, the height of a plant or the population of a city. Students can use Step-by-Step 4 (Master 5.10) to complete question 5. ***Extra Practice:*** Students can play the Additional Activity *Connecting Lines* (Master 5.6). Students can complete Extra Practice 4 (Master 5.18). ***Extension:*** Have students research a third region for *Practice* question 3, then draw a line graph to display these data on the same grid as the other 2 line graphs. Students write all they know from looking at the graphs and explain any points where 2 or 3 of the line graphs intersect.

Recording and Reporting

Master 5.2 Ongoing Observations: Data Management

Using Spreadsheets to Record and Graph Data

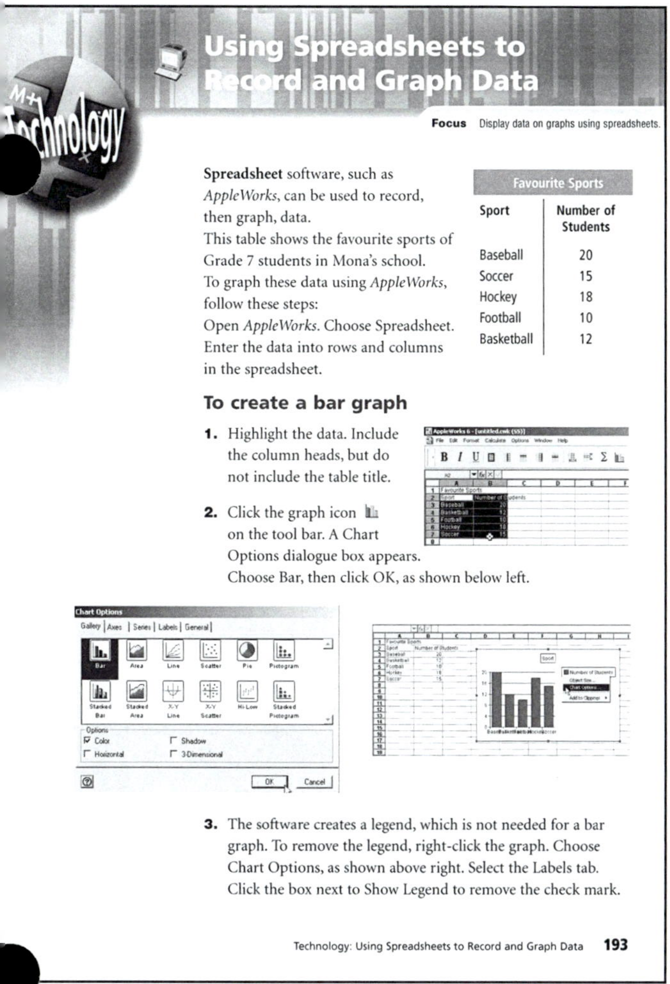
M+ Technology

Using Spreadsheets to Record and Graph Data

Focus Display data on graphs using spreadsheets.

Spreadsheet software, such as *AppleWorks*, can be used to record, then graph, data.
This table shows the favourite sports of Grade 7 students in Mona's school.
To graph these data using *AppleWorks*, follow these steps:
Open *AppleWorks*. Choose Spreadsheet. Enter the data into rows and columns in the spreadsheet.

Favourite Sports	
Sport	Number of Students
Baseball	20
Soccer	15
Hockey	18
Football	10
Basketball	12

To create a bar graph

1. Highlight the data. Include the column heads, but do not include the table title.
2. Click the graph icon on the tool bar. A Chart Options dialogue box appears. Choose Bar, then click OK, as shown below left.
3. The software creates a legend, which is not needed for a bar graph. To remove the legend, right-click the graph. Choose Chart Options, as shown above right. Select the Labels tab. Click the box next to Show Legend to remove the check mark.

Technology: Using Spreadsheets to Record and Graph Data 193

SECTION ORGANIZER (40–50 min)

Curriculum Focus: Display data on graphs using spreadsheets. (7m85, 7m93, 7m105)

Student Materials

- computers with *AppleWorks*

Vocabulary: spreadsheet

Key Math Learning

Spreadsheet software, such as *AppleWorks,* can be used to record, then graph, data.

Tell students they will use spreadsheet software to create bar graphs, circle graphs, and line graphs. They will enter data into the computer, then use the computer to create a graph. Students can use the graph to look for patterns or trends in the data, and to draw conclusions and make predictions.

Watch to ensure students understand and follow the directions carefully.

Invite volunteers to share their graphs and their findings.

Discuss using a computer to make graphs. Elicit from students that a computer can create a graph quickly, especially when a set of data is large.

Suggestions for Alternative Software

Commercial spreadsheets, such as *Microsoft Excel,* allow you to enter a set of data and create graphs.

General instructions for *Microsoft Excel:*

➤ To create a bar graph:

- Insert the data from the chart in the Student Book page 193 into a spreadsheet. Enter the sports in column 1. Enter the number of students in column 2.
- Highlight both columns.
- To insert a chart:
  Click on "Insert." Click on "Chart."
  This will open a window.
- To select the chart type:
  Click "Column."
  Click "Next."
  Click "Next" again.

REACHING ALL LEARNERS

Early Finishers

Have students use spreadsheet software to graph the data in *Practice* questions 4 and 5, page 192. Students can then compare the computer graphs with the graphs they drew.

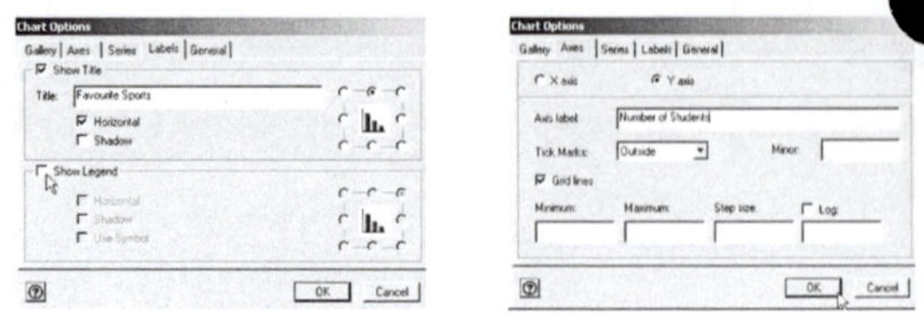

4. In the Title box, type **Favourite Sports**, as shown below left. To insert labels, click the Axes tab. Select X axis. Type **Sport**. Select Y axis. Type **Number of Students**, as shown below right. Then click OK.

Your graph should look like the one below.

To create a circle graph

1. Use the data on page 193.
Highlight the data as shown below left.
Do not include the column heads or title.

untitled 2.cwk (SS)

	A	B	C
1	Favourite Sports		
2	Sport	Number of Students	
3	Baseball	20	
4	Basketball	12	
5	Football	10	
6	Hockey	18	
7	Soccer	15	
8			

194 UNIT 5: Data Management

Sample Solutions

Step 4

The graph shows an upward trend. The average income increased from 1989 to 1992, from 1994 to 1995, and from 1997 to 1998. Each line segment for these years goes up to the right.
The average income decreased from 1992 to 1994, 1995 to 1997, and from 1998 to 1999. Each line segment for these years goes down to the right.
The average annual income had the greatest increase from 1997 to 1998. The line segment on the graph that shows this increase is the steepest segment that goes up to the right.
The average annual income had the greatest decrease from 1998 to 1999. The line segment that shows this decrease is the steepest segment that goes down to the right.
The graph shows that, overall, there is an upward trend in the average annual income of Canadian women.

The spreadsheet will plot column 1 on the horizontal axis, and column 2 on the vertical axis.

- Insert graph title and axis labels.
- Click "Finished" to close the window and create the graph.

➤ To create a circle graph, click on "Pie" instead of "Column."

➤ To create a line graph, click on "Line" instead of "Column."

(Sample Answers for Section 5.6, pages 204 and 205, continued)

5. a)

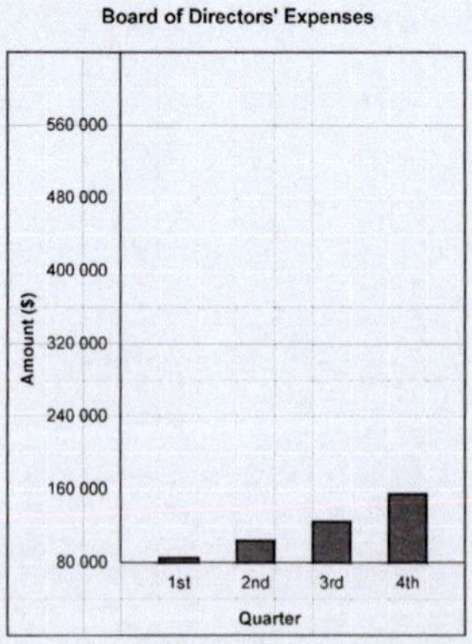

The scale on the vertical axis begins at 80 000; the scale is 1 square represents $40 000. The axis goes up to 560 000, so the bars are short and the difference in their heights appears to be small. The expenses appear to be low.

A spreadsheet program uses the term "pie" for a circle graph.

2. Click the graph icon on the tool bar.
A Chart Options dialogue box appears.
Choose Pie, then click OK, as shown bottom right, page 194.
The circle graph shows a legend at the right.
The legend shows what sport each sector represents.

3. To add a title, right-click the graph. Choose Chart Options.
Select the Labels tab. In the Title box, type Favourite Sports, as shown below left. Then click OK.
Your graph should look like the one below right.

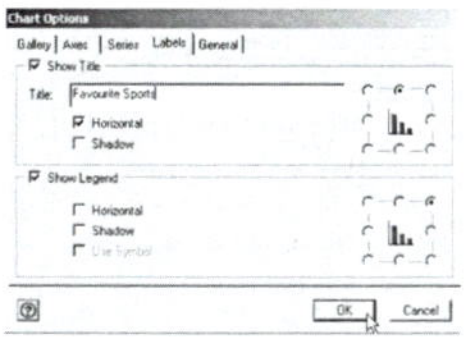

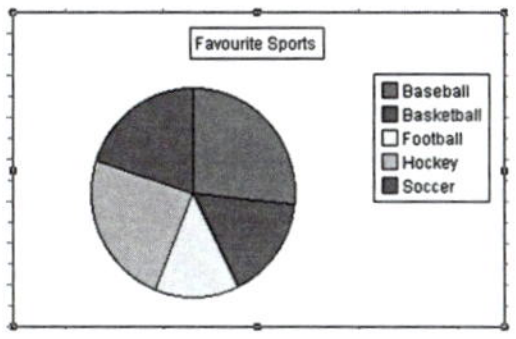

To create a line graph

These data came from the Statistics Canada website.

Average Annual Income of Canadian Women	
Year	Income ($)
1989	28 219
1990	29 050
1991	29 654
1992	30 903
1993	30 466
1994	30 274
1995	30 959
1996	30 606
1997	30 484
1998	32 553
1999	32 026

1. Enter the data into rows and columns in the spreadsheet.

2. Highlight the data.
Include the column heads, but do not include the table title.

3. Click the graph icon on the tool bar.
A Chart Options dialogue box appears.
Choose X-Y Line, then click OK, as shown below.

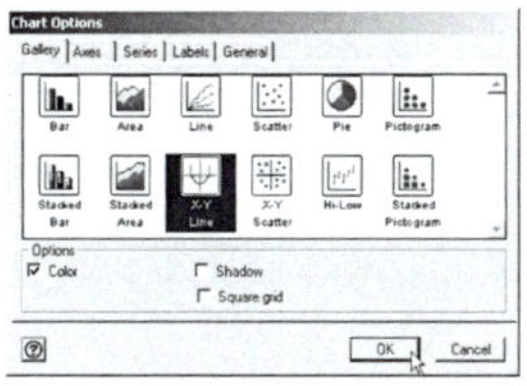

Technology: Using Spreadsheets to Record and Graph Data **195**

1. a)

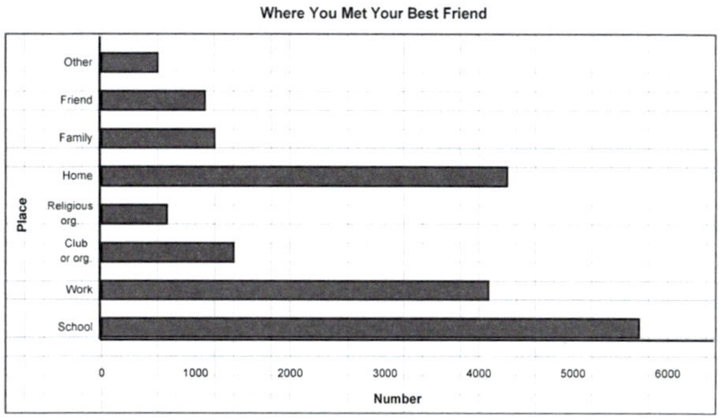

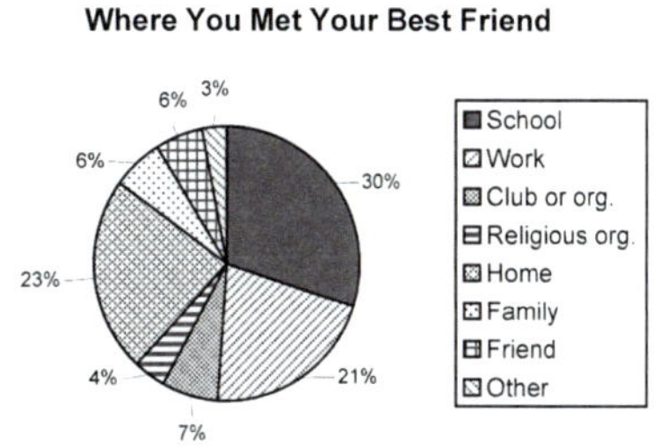

b) The bar graph represents the data better because it is easier to identify the number associated with each place. On the circle graph, though we can identify which place is represented by a larger or smaller sector, the corresponding number is not shown.

b)

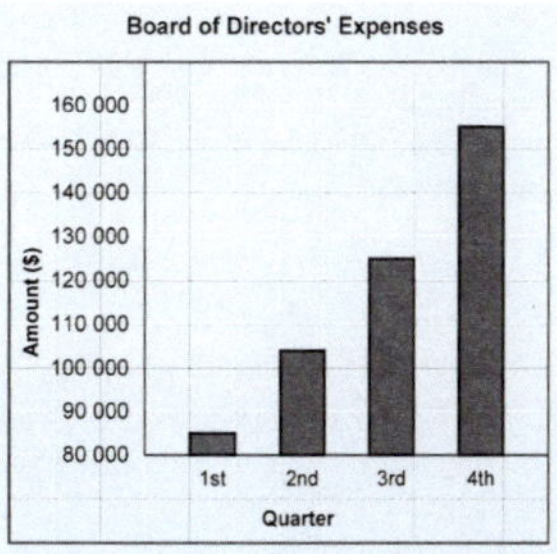

The scale on the vertical axis begins at 80 000; the scale is 1 square represents $10 000. The axis only goes up to 160 000, so the bars are tall and the difference in their heights appears to be great. The expenses appear to be high.

c)

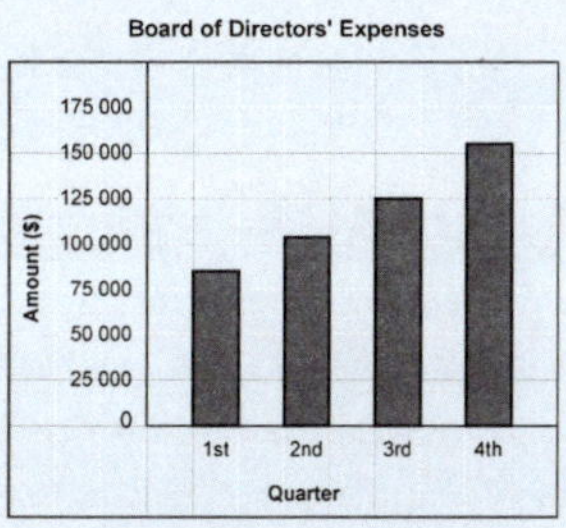

The scale on the vertical axis begins at 0; the scale is 1 square represents $25 000. The axis goes up to 175 000, and the bars are closer in heights, and each bar is drawn to scale of the amount it represents.

6. a) *Source*: Adapted from Statistics Canada website, http://www.statcan.ca/english/edu/power/ch9/linegraph/line.htm (date of extraction: November 2004)

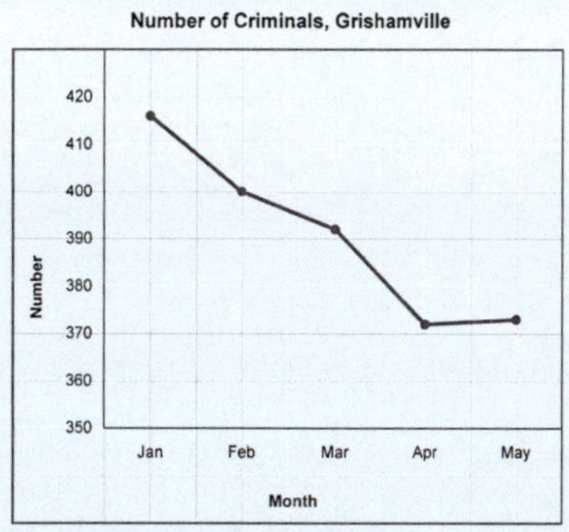

b) The graph might be used to make it appear that there is a large decrease in the number of criminals.

c) The scale on the vertical axis should start at 0. Reduce the scale to 1 square represents 50 people.

2.

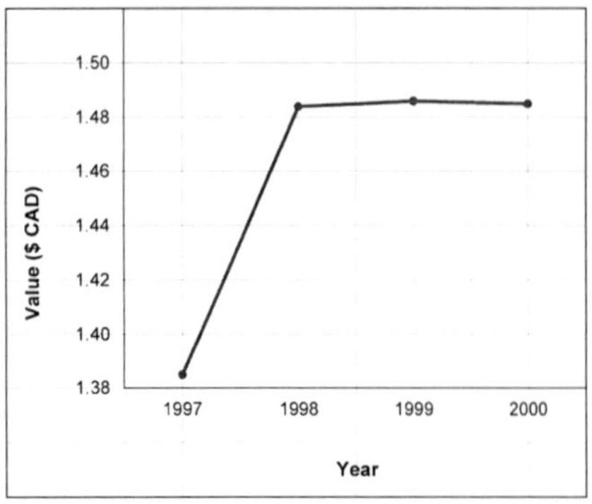

a) The average value of $1U.S. increases at a fast rate in the first year and then levels off.

b) Predicted values: 2002 – $1.486; 2003 – $1.485
I assumed the value of the dollar would not fluctuate much and would stay around $1.485.

c) The information could be found by phoning a bank; using the Internet and visiting the Statistics Canada website (do an Exchange Rate search); or visiting the Bank of Canada website (http://www.bankofcanada.ca) and using the average annual rates.
Actual value in 2002 was $1.570 and in 2003 was $1.401. My predictions were not very close. We cannot extend a trend in the graph to predict future values. Too many economic situations affect the value of the dollar.

4. The software creates a legend, which is not needed for a line graph. To remove the legend, right-click the graph. Choose Chart Options. Select the Labels tab.
Click the box next to Show Legend to remove the check mark.
In the Title box, type Average Annual Income of Canadian Women. Then click OK.
Your graph should look like the one below.

- What trend does the graph show? Explain.
- How often did the average income increase? Decrease? How can you tell this from the graph?
- When did the average annual income have the greatest increase? Greatest decrease?
- Write what else you know from the graph.

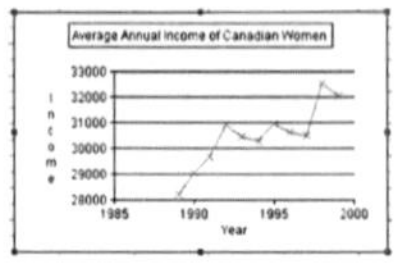

✓ Check

1. Think about where you met your best friend.
The table at the right lists the places where some Canadians met their best friends.
a) Use a spreadsheet to draw a bar graph and a circle graph.
b) Which graph represents the data better? Explain.

Place	Number
School	5700
Work	4100
Club or organization	1400
Religious organization	700
Home/neighbourhood	4300
Through family	1200
Through friend	1100
Other	600

2. Use a spreadsheet to draw a line graph for the data in the table at the left.
a) What trend does the graph show?
b) Predict the average value, in Canadian dollars, of $1U.S. in 2002 and in 2003.
What assumptions did you make?
c) Research to find the average value, in Canadian dollars, of $1U.S. in 2002 and 2003.
Where could you get this information?
How accurate was your prediction?

Average Value of $1U.S.

Year	Value in Canadian Dollars
1997	1.385
1998	1.484
1999	1.486
2000	1.485

d)

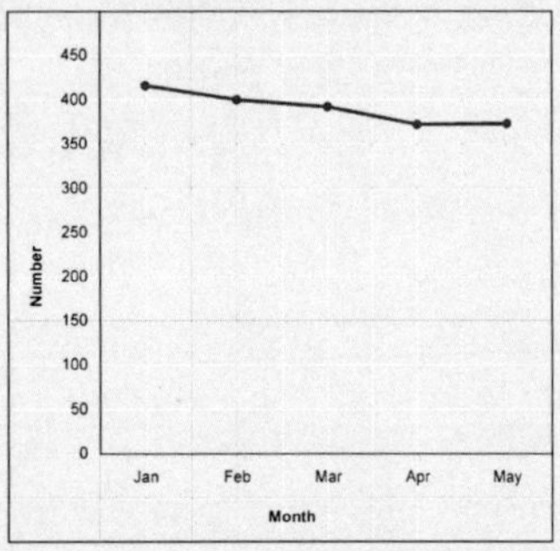

REFLECT: Ways in which a graph may be misleading:

- The scale on the vertical axis does not begin at 0.
- The scale on an axis is not given.
- The increments on one axis are not consistent.

(Sample Solutions for Practice Test, page 211, continued)

4. a)

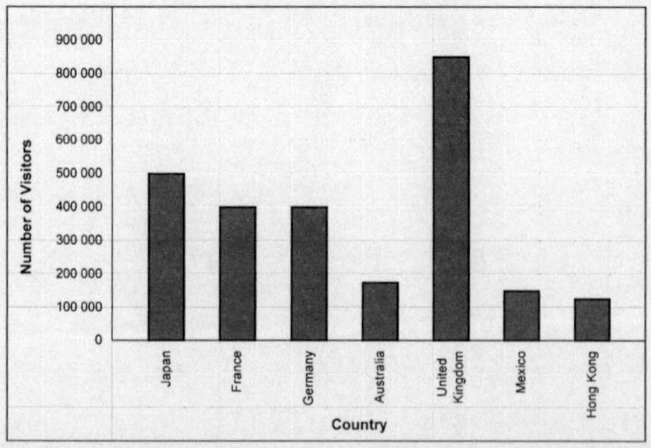

I chose a bar graph because the heights of the bars make it easy to compare the number of visitors that came from each country.

b) I would change the scale on the vertical axis. I would probably use increments of 2 000 000 because 15 000 000 is a very large number. The bar for the U.S. would be the tallest, more than 15 times as long as the bar for the United Kingdom.

3. The data below are from the Statistics Canada website.
   a) Use a spreadsheet.
   Create a graph to display the data.
   b) Which type of graph best represents the data? Explain.
   c) Which type of graph could not be used to represent the data? Explain.

Average Hours of Television Viewing per Week, Fall 2001	
Province	Adolescents 12–17 years
Newfoundland/Labrador	15.8
Prince Edward Island	12.4
Nova Scotia	14.1
New Brunswick	14.1
Quebec	14.5
Ontario	12.8
Manitoba	12.8
Saskatchewan	12.5
Alberta	13.3
British Columbia	10.9

Math Link

Your World

Newspapers often publish survey results. The headlines may be misleading.

Try to find headlines like these. Cut them out. Explain why they are misleading.

Why would newspapers do this?

3. a)

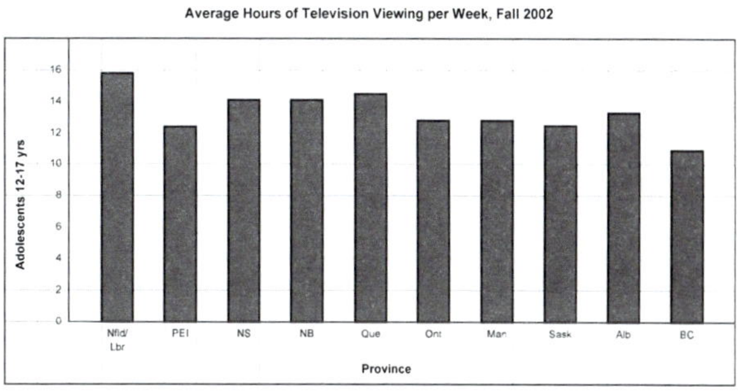

b) A bar graph (vertical or horizontal) best represents the data. A bar graph makes it easy to tell which province has the most average hours of television and which province has the least.

c) A line graph is not suitable because the graph does not represent data over time. A circle graph is not suitable because the data does not represent a part of a whole.

c)

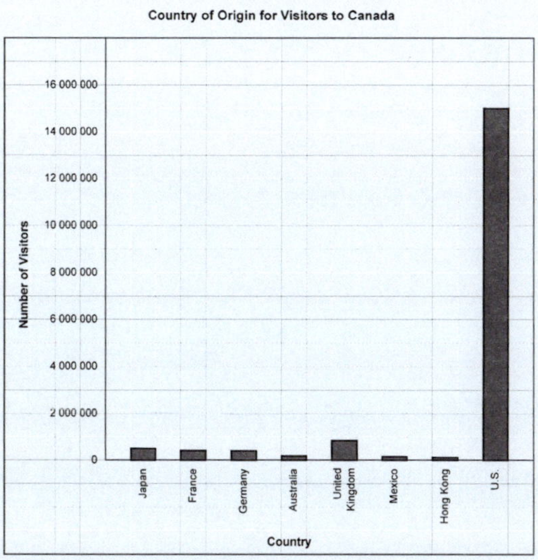

d) The graph in part a gives more information because it is easier to read the number of visitors for each country. The graph in part c is less accurate because the scale on the vertical axis is small. 1 to 2 000 000 is a much smaller scale than 1 to 100 000. Except for the bar for the U.S., all the other bars look about the same height.

Math Link

Misleading headlines are used in newspapers to create sensations and to attract readers. The more papers the owners of the newspaper can sell, the better.

Applications of Mean, Median, and Mode

SECTION ORGANIZER — 80–100 min

Curriculum Focus: Understand which measure of central tendency best describes a set of data. (7m95, 7m101)

Student Materials
- calculators

Optional
- Step-by-Step 5 (Master 5.11)
- Extra Practice 5 (Master 5.19)

Assessment: Master 5.2 Ongoing Observations: Data Management

Key Math Learnings

1. The mean, median, and mode are measures of central tendency. Each measure is an average.
2. Each measure of central tendency gives different information about the data. The choice of measure depends on the situation; one measure is often better than another as the best measure of central tendency.

5.5 Applications of Mean, Median, and Mode

Focus Understand which measure of central tendency best describes a set of data.

Explore

Work on your own.
Record on the board how many siblings you have.
Use the class data.
Find the mean, the median, and the mode.
Find the range.

The mean, median, and mode are measures of central tendency. Each measure is an average.

Reflect & Share

With a classmate, discuss which measure of central tendency best describes the average number of siblings.

Connect

A clothing store sold jeans in these sizes in one day:
28 30 28 26 30 32 28 32 26 28 34 38 36 30 34 32 30

To calculate the mean jeans size sold, add the sizes, then divide by the number of jeans sold.

$$\text{Mean} = \frac{28+30+28+26+30+32+28+32+26+28+34+38+36+30+34+32+30}{17}$$
$$= \frac{522}{17}$$
$$\doteq 30.7$$

The mean size is approximately 30.7.

When there is an odd number of data, to find the middle number: Add 1 to the number of data, then divide by 2. This gives the position of the middle number. For example: $\frac{17+1}{2} = \frac{18}{2} = 9$; the middle number is 9th.

To calculate the median, order the jeans sold from least size to greatest size. The middle number is the median.
There are 17 numbers. The middle number is 9th.
26, 26, 28, 28, 28, 28, 30, 30, 30, 30, 32, 32, 32, 34, 34, 36, 38
The median size is 30.

The mode is the number that occurs most often.
There are two numbers that occur most often.
They are 28 and 30. So, the mode sizes are 28 and 30.

In this situation, the mean, 30.7, is of little use.
The mean does not represent a size.

198 UNIT 5: Data Management

BEFORE — Get Started

Use *Skills You'll Need*, page 168, to review the meanings of the mean, median, and mode.

Ask:
- What is the mean of a set of numbers? (*It is the sum of all the numbers divided by the number of numbers.*)
- What is the median of a set of numbers? (*It is the middle number when the numbers are arranged in order.*) What if there is an even number of numbers? (*The median is the mean of the two middle numbers.*)
- What is the mode of a set of numbers? (*It is the number that occurs most often.*)
- Is there always only one mode? (*No, there may be more than one mode or there may be no mode.*)
- What is the range of a set of numbers? (*It is the difference between the greatest number and the least number.*)

Present *Explore*. Remind students they are to work on their own, using the class data.

DURING — Explore

Ongoing Assessment: Observe and Listen

An alternative method to collect the data is to have each student write the number of siblings he or she has on a small piece of paper. Collect the papers, then record the numbers on the board. Students should record all the numbers in their notebooks before beginning *Explore*. Encourage students to write the numbers in order from least to greatest to make finding the median and mode easier, and to help them keep track of the numbers.

Ask questions, such as:
- What is the mean number of siblings? (*2.2*)
- What is the median number of siblings? (*2*)

The median, 30, shows about one-half of the customers bought jeans of size 30 or smaller, and about one-half of the customers bought jeans of size 30 or larger.

The modes, 28 and 30, tell which sizes are purchased more often. The mode is most useful to the storeowner. He may use the mode to order extra stock of the most popular sizes.

Example

A bookstore has 15 books in its young adult section. There are 5 different prices. This table shows the number of books at each price.

a) Find the mean, median, and mode prices.
b) Which measure best represents the average price of a young adult book?
c) What is the range of the prices?

Young Adult Books

Price ($)	Number of Books
8.99	3
9.99	5
13.99	5
32.99	1
37.99	1

Solution

a) Mean price:

- Multiply each price by the total number of books at that price, then add the prices.
  $(8.99 \times 3) + (9.99 \times 5) + (13.99 \times 5) + 32.99 + 37.99 = 217.85$
- Divide the total price by the total number of books: 15
  $\frac{217.85}{15} \doteq 14.52$

The mean price per book is approximately $14.52.

Median price:
There are 15 books.
The table shows the books in order from least price to greatest price.
The median price is the 8th price. The 8th price is $9.99.
The median price is $9.99.

Mode price:
There are two mode prices. They are $9.99 and $13.99.

b) The mean price is not charged for any of the books.
Only two books cost more than the mean of $14.52.

There are two mode prices.
One mode, $9.99, is the same as the median price.

5.5 Applications of Mean, Median, and Mode **199**

REACHING ALL LEARNERS

Alternative Explore

Students work alone. They use the data in the table *Average Hours of Television Viewing per Week, Fall 2001* on page 197. Students find the mean, median, mode, and range of the data, then explain which measure of central tendency best represents the data.

Early Finishers

Have students organize the data from *Explore* in a frequency table, then graph the data, and justify their choice of graph.

Common Misconceptions

➤ Students think that the mean is the only "average" that exists.
How to Help: Remind students that all three of the mean, median, and mode are averages and that each provides valuable information in different situations. In common usage, "average" is usually the mean.

Number Strategies

Students should organize their work. For example, students could find all numbers with 2 digits with 0 as the first digit, then 2, and then 3. The answers will depend on the interpretation of the question. For example, some students may find all numbers with 2 digits that use a decimal point, while others may also include numbers that do not use the decimal point, such as 20 and 32.

- How did you find the median?
  (*I wrote all the numbers in order. There were 29 numbers. I crossed out a number at each end, at the same time, until I had only one number left. I crossed out the 1st and 29th together, then the 2nd and 28th, and so on. The number left is the median.*)
- What is the mode? (2)
- What is the range? (4)
- What measure of central tendency best describes the average number of siblings? (*The median and the mode*) Why?
  (*Both the median and mode are 2. In this situation, the mean, 2.2, is of little use. The mean does not represent a number of siblings.*)

AFTER Connect

Invite students to share their findings with the class. Ask:

- Why is it important to know if there is an odd or even number of data?
  (*If there is an odd number of data, the median is the middle number. If there is an even number of data, the median is the mean of the two middle numbers.*)

Review *Connect.* Explain to students that often the best measure of central tendency depends on the situation. In the *Example,* there are two modes, so the modes cannot best represent the data. Of these three measures, the mode is often the least useful.

Sample Answers

1. b) The median best describes Ira's race time because one-half of the races were at or below this time and one-half of the races were above this time.
   The mode also best describes Ira's race time because it is his best time and the time he got most often.
2. a) Math: Mean: 74.6, Median: 75, Mode: none
   Spelling: Mean: 77.3, Median: 81, Mode: 81
   History: Mean: 74.4, Median: 74, Mode: 74
   b) In each case, the mean is a decimal and is not a mark that Caitlin scored on any test. The median is the middle value in each ordered set of marks. One-half of Caitlin's marks lie at or above the median and one-half lie below. The mode is the mark that occurs most often in each set of data.
   c) Caitlin is best at spelling because the mean, median, and mode are highest for this subject. Caitlin is worst at history because it has the lowest mean, median, and mode.
3. a) Week 1: Mean: $825 Median: $800 Mode: none
   Week 2: Mean: $825 Median: $775 Mode: none
   b) Mean: $825 Median: $787.50 Mode: $600
   c) The means are the same. This makes sense because the means for Weeks 1 and 2 are the same. All the medians are different. To find the median for the two-week period, I had to find the mean of the fifth and sixth numbers. The median is not an amount that was actually earned. There is a mode when the earnings of the two weeks are combined because there is an amount of $600 in both weeks.
   (Answers continue below right.)

One-half the books cost less than the median price.
One-half cost more.
So, the median price, $9.99, best represents the average cost of a young adult book at the store.

c) For the range, subtract the lowest price from the highest:
$37.99 - 8.99 = 29.00$
The range of prices is $29.00.

Practice

1. Here are Ira's practice times, in seconds, for the 100-m backstroke: 122, 118, 123, 119, 118, 120, 118, 121, 119
   a) Find the mean, median, and mode of these data. Mean: 119.8 s; Median: 119 s; Mode: 118 s
   b) Of the mean, median, and mode, which do you think best describes Ira's race time? Explain.
   c) What is the range of these data? 5 s
2. Caitlin received these test marks in each subject.
   a) Find the mean, median, and mode for each subject.
   b) Explain what information each measure of central tendency gives.
   c) Which subject is Caitlin best at? Worst at? Explain your reasoning.

Caitlin's Marks

Math	85	69	92	55	68	75	78
Spelling	72	81	50	69	81	96	92
History	68	74	82	80	76	67	74

3. The table shows the tips earned by five waiters and waitresses during two weeks in December.
   a) Calculate the mean, median, and mode tips for each week.
   b) Calculate the mean, median, and mode tips for the two-week period.
   c) Compare your answers in parts a and b. Which are the same? Which are different? Explain why.
   d) Which measure of central tendency best represents the tips earned during the two weeks? Explain.

Weekly Tips Earned ($)

Waiter	Week 1	Week 2
James	1150	600
Kyrra	700	725
Tamara	800	775
Jacob	875	860
George	600	1165

200 UNIT 5: Data Management

Practice

Have calculators available for all questions.

Assessment Focus: Question 7

Most students will complete this question by adding 10 to each number, then finding the measures; and doubling each number, then finding the measures. Some students may be able to provide a logical argument as to how the measures are affected without having to do the math described above.

(Sample Answers, continued)

d) The median best represents the tips earned because one-half the tips earned are at or above the median and one-half are below.

4. b) 122 s; when there are 6 numbers in the ordered data set, the median is the mean of the 3rd and 4th numbers. The third number is 120 s. The fourth number must be 122 s to result in a mean of 121 s: $\frac{120 + 122}{2} = 121$
5. 21, 22, 25, 26, 26; Mean: $\frac{21 + 22 + 25 + 26 + 26}{5} = 24$, Median: 25
   There are many possible sets of 5 numbers, such as 18, 20, 25, 27, 30 or 13, 22, 25, 29, 31 or 12, 16, 25, 30, 37 or 10, 15, 25, 30, 40 or 8, 12, 25, 35, 40.
   In each set, 25 must be the third number so that the median is 25. Two numbers must be less than 25 and two numbers must be greater than 25. The sum of the 5 numbers must be 120, because $120 \div 5 = 24$, which is the mean. A number can occur more than once in a set.
6. a) Expression i, the mean is the sum of all the numbers divided by the number of numbers. In part ii, only the last product is divided by the number of numbers, 30.
   Mean: 395.3 g
   b) Yes, the mean mass, 395.3 g, is greater than the required mean mass of 395 g.

4. Jamal was training for a 400-m race.
His times, in seconds, for the first five races were:
120, 118, 138, 124, 118
a) Find the median and mode times. Median: 120 s; Mode: 118 s
b) Jamal wants his median time after 6 races to be 121 s.
What time must he get in his 6th race? Explain.

5. Find 5 numbers that have a mean of 24 and a median of 25.
Justify your answer.
How many different sets of 5 numbers can you find?
Show that each set has the mean and median stated.

6. A quality control inspector randomly selects boxes of crackers from the production line. She measures their masses. On one day she selects 30 boxes. The inspector records these data:
- 12 boxes: 405 g each
- 4 boxes: 385 g each
- 4 boxes: 395 g each
- 2 boxes: 380 g each
- 8 boxes: 390 g each

a) Which expression can be used to calculate the mean mass?
Use it to find the mean mass.
i) $\frac{(405 \times 12 + 395 \times 4 + 390 \times 8 + 385 \times 4 + 380 \times 2)}{30}$
ii) $405 \times 12 + 395 \times 4 + 390 \times 8 + 385 \times 4 + 380 \times 2 \div 30$
b) For the shipment of crackers to be acceptable, the mean mass must be at least 395 g. Is this shipment acceptable? Explain. Yes

Number Strategies

Use only the digits 0, 2, 3, and a decimal point.
Use each digit only once each time.
Make as many numbers with 2 digits as possible.
Find the sum of the numbers.

0.2 + 0.3 + 2.0 + 2.3 + 3.0 + 3.2 = 11.0

7. **Assessment Focus**
Use these data: 28, 30, 30, 31, 32, 33, 34, 35, 37, 38, 39, 41
a) Find the mean, median, and mode. Mean: 34; Median: 33.5; Mode: 30
b) What happens to the mean, median, and mode in each case?
i) Each number is increased by 10.
ii) Each number is doubled.
Explain the results.

Reflect

Use your answers from *Practice*. Describe a situation for each case.
a) The mean is the best measure of central tendency.
b) The median is the best measure of central tendency.
c) The mode is the best measure of central tendency.

5.5 Applications of Mean, Median, and Mode 201

7. b) i) 38, 40, 40, 41, 42, 43, 44, 45, 47, 48, 49, 51
Mean: 44 Median: 43.5 Mode: 40
Each of the mean, median, and mode is also increased by 10.
ii) 56, 60, 60, 62, 64, 66, 68, 70, 74, 76, 78, 82
Mean: 68 Median: 67 Mode: 60
Each of the mean, median, and mode is also doubled.

REFLECT:
a) The mean is the best measure of central tendency for quality control situations, such as the average mass of a shipment of crackers.
b) The median is the best measure of central tendency when looking at the average mark on a test. One-half the marks are at or above the median and one-half are below.
c) The mode is the best measure of central tendency when stocking a store. For example, in a shoe store, the mode is the shoe size sold most often.

Assignment Guidelines

If your students do not have time to complete all the *Practice* questions on pages 200 and 201, these questions provide minimum curriculum coverage: 2, 4, 6, 7, *Reflect*
To assess the 4 Achievement Chart categories listed in the curriculum document, have students complete these *Practice* questions:
Understanding Concepts: 2
Application: 4
Problem Solving: 5
Communication: 6

ASSESSMENT FOR LEARNING

What to Look For	What to Do
Understanding concepts ✔ Students understand how to find the mean, median, mode, and range for a set of data.	***Extra Support:*** Students having difficulty may benefit from working with data that are ordered from least to greatest. Students can use Step-by-Step 5 (Master 5.11) to complete question 7.
Applying procedures ✔ Students can solve problems using the mean, median, and mode.	***Extra Practice:*** Have students find the mean, median, and mode for data sets found in newspapers or magazines. Students can complete Extra Practice 5 (Master 5.19).
Communicating ✔ Students can explain which measure of central tendency best describes a set of data.	***Extension:*** Have students create and solve a problem for one situation they described in *Reflect*.

Recording and Reporting
Master 5.2 Ongoing Observations: Data Management

Evaluating Data Analysis

SECTION ORGANIZER (80–100 min)

Curriculum Focus: Examine how data can be misleading. (7m90, 7m103, 7m104)

Student Materials
- 0.5-cm grid paper (PM 14)
- newspapers, magazines, or the Internet
- rulers

Optional
- Step-by-Step 6 (Master 5.12)
- Extra Practice 6 (Master 5.20)

Assessment: Master 5.2 Ongoing Observations: Data Management

Key Math Learnings

1. A graph may be used to distort information and to mislead.
2. A graph that is misleading can be redrawn to accurately represent the data.

Mental Math

For 3.9 × 4.1, students could round each number to 4.
For 0.5 × 10.2, they could find one-half of 10.
For 1.1 × 11.1, students could multiply 1 × 11.
For 20.5 × 0.9, students could multiply 20 × 1.

5.6 Evaluating Data Analysis

Focus Examine how data can be misleading.

Explore

Work on your own.
What do the two graphs below show?
How are the graphs similar? How are they different?
Explain.

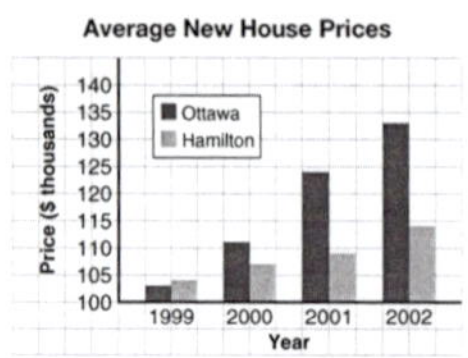

Reflect & Share

Discuss with a classmate:
What impression does each graph give? Explain.
Who may want to use each type of graph?

Connect

Sometimes, graphs are used to distort information and to mislead.
Look at these graphs.

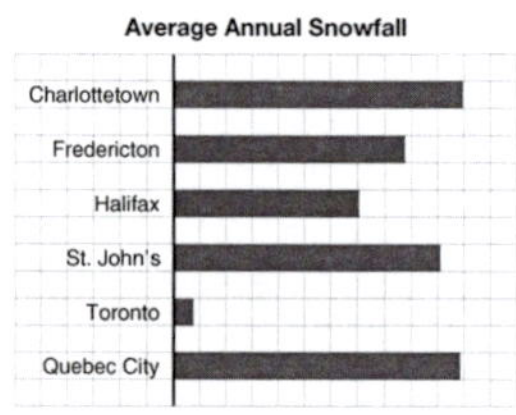

This bar graph is misleading.
It suggests that Quebec City has more than 10 times as much snow as Toronto.
This graph has no measurements of the depth of snow.

202 UNIT 5: Data Management

BEFORE — Get Started

Remind students of the bar graphs they have drawn, and the double-bar graph they interpreted on page 177. Discuss a possible different scale for the graph on page 177.

Ask:
- Suppose we could use a scale of 1 square to 10 000 people. What would the graph look like?
  (The bars would be much longer. For example, for Quebec, the numbers represented are approximately 220 000—we would need 22 squares to show these bars.)

Present *Explore.* Tell students they will investigate 2 different graphs that show the same data.

DURING — Explore

Ongoing Assessment: Observe and Listen

Ask questions, such as:
- What do the two graphs show? (*The average new house prices from 1999 to 2002*)
- How are the two graphs similar? (*Both of them are double-bar graphs and both sets of axes represent the same things.*)
- What does the horizontal axis on each graph represent? (*Time, in years, from 1999 to 2002*)
- What does the vertical axis on each graph represent? (*Price, in thousands of dollars*)
- What do you notice about the scale on the vertical axis of each graph? (*The scale for the graph on the left begins at 100 and is 1 square represents $5000. The scale for the graph on the right begins at 0 and is 1 square represents $25 000.*)

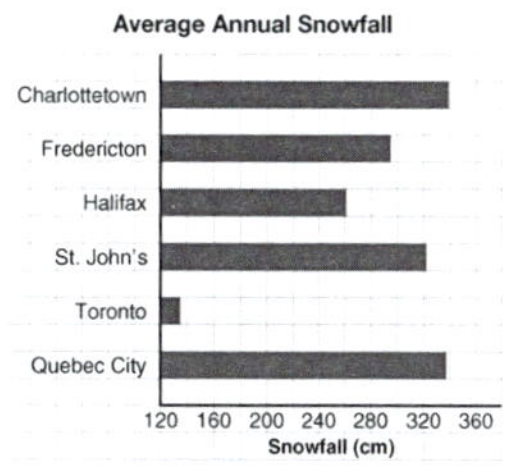

Visually, this graph suggests the same information as the first graph. However, the horizontal scale is labelled with the snowfall.

The scale shows that Toronto has about 135 cm of snow and Quebec City has about 335 cm.

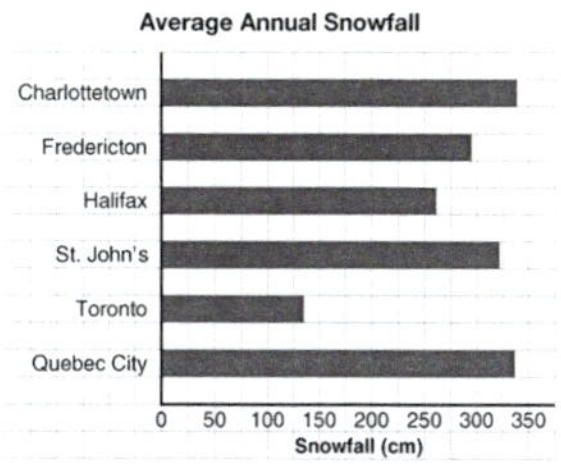

This graph accurately shows the data. The horizontal scale starts at 0.

The lengths of the bars are shown in the correct ratio. Quebec City has between 2 and 3 times as much snow as Toronto.

Example

This line graph is used to suggest that salaries have doubled in 6 years.

a) Why is this graph misleading?

b) Redraw the graph to show accurately how salaries have changed in 6 years.

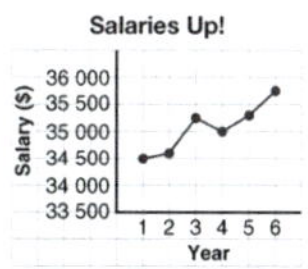

Solution

a) Use the vertical scale.
The salary in year 1 is about $34 500.
The salary in year 6 is about $35 750.
The increase in salary is: $35 750 − $34 500 = $1250
The salaries have increased by only $1250 in 6 years.

b) Make a table from the line graph.
Estimate each salary.

5.6 Evaluating Data Analysis 203

REACHING ALL LEARNERS

Alternative Explore

Students draw 2 different bar graphs for the data in the given table. Students tell how the graphs are similar and how they are different. They discuss what impression each graph gives.

Number of Students in Each Grade	
Grade	**Students**
4	52
5	58
6	55
7	62
8	54

Early Finishers

Have students use the data in one of the *Practice* questions on page 182 to draw a misleading graph and explain how and why the graph is misleading.

Common Misconceptions

➤When students draw an accurate graph, the scale on an axis is not consistent.

How to Help: When students have chosen a scale, for example, 1 square represents 25 people, have the students count by 25s, beginning at 0, up to the first multiple of 25 beyond the greatest number that is to be represented on the graph. As students count, they record the multiples on the axis, one multiple per grid square.

- How are the bars on the graph on the left different from the bars on the graph on the right?
  (*On the graph on the right, the bars in each pair are close in height. In the graph on the left, the difference between the heights of each pair of bars is much more obvious.*)
- How are the heights of the bars affected by the scale on the vertical axis?
  (*When the scale begins at 100 and the scale is 1 square represents $5000, the difference in heights of the bars in each pair is much greater than when the scale begins at 0 and the scale is 1 square represents $25 000.*)

AFTER Connect

Invite students to share their impressions with the class.

Ask questions, such as:

- What impression does the first graph give?
  (*The average new house prices in Ottawa are generally much higher than those in Hamilton.*)
- What impression does the second graph give?
  (*The average new house prices in the two cities are very similar.*)
- Who might want to use the first graph?
  (*A real estate company in Hamilton, trying to convince people to come to Hamilton to live*)
- Who might want to use the second graph?
  (*A company in Hamilton that is moving its office to Ottawa might use the graph to show its employees that new houses cost about the same in both cities.*)

Review the graphs and example in *Connect*.
Ask:

- What are some things you can do to draw a misleading graph?
  (*I can use a scale that does not begin at 0; I can use inappropriate intervals on the scale of the graph; I can omit some information, such as labels on an axis.*)

Sample Answers

1. The graph on the right is misleading because the vertical scale begins at 100 and not 0. The second graph suggests that Russ collected 3 times as many cans as Meg and twice as many cans as Vic.
2. a) The president of the company might choose the graph on the left because the profits appear to be increasing at a much faster rate.
   b) The rival company might use the graph on the right because the profits appear to be increasing at a much slower rate.
   c) $125 million; I assumed that the profits would continue to increase at the same rate as from March to April.
3. Some graphs display data in a misleading way to influence a decision in favour of a particular opinion or to try to illustrate, in a positive way, data that are not very impressive or favourable. A graph can be drawn to misrepresent data by: leaving out information on one or both axes; by starting a scale at a number besides 0; by using an inappropriate scale (for example, very large or very small intervals); or by using an inconsistent scale.
4. a) It gives the impression that Manufacturer A has almost 3 times the number of trucks on the road as Manufacturer D, about twice the number of trucks as Manufacturer C, and significantly more than Manufacturer B.
   b) Manufacturer B: 97.5 Manufacturer C: 96.5 Manufacturer D: 95.5
   c) No, there is not a great difference in the number of trucks still on the road for each manufacturer; the range is 3 trucks.

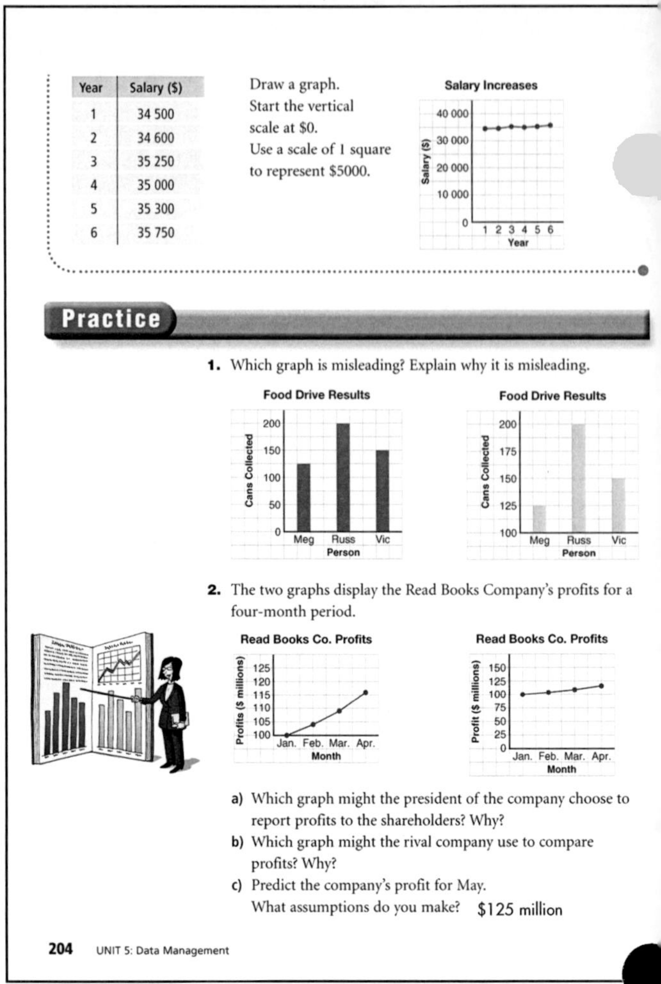

Year	Salary ($)
1	34 500
2	34 600
3	35 250
4	35 000
5	35 300
6	35 750

Draw a graph.
Start the vertical scale at $0.
Use a scale of 1 square to represent $5000.

Practice

1. Which graph is misleading? Explain why it is misleading.

2. The two graphs display the Read Books Company's profits for a four-month period.

a) Which graph might the president of the company choose to report profits to the shareholders? Why?
b) Which graph might the rival company use to compare profits? Why?
c) Predict the company's profit for May.
What assumptions do you make? $125 million

Have students think of situations where they could use a misleading graph. Make a list of students' ideas on the board.

Practice

Questions 4, 5, and 6 require 0.5-cm grid paper. Question 6 requires students to use newspapers, magazines, or the Internet.

Assessment Focus: Question 6

Students are able to redraw their graphs accurately; for example, by changing the scale, or by starting the scale at 0, or by including missing information.

3. Why do some graphs display data in a misleading way? Describe how a graph might be drawn to misrepresent data.

4. A graph similar to this is part of an advertisement for a truck manufacturer. With the graph, Manufacturer A says that more than 98 out of 100 of its trucks sold in the last 10 years are still on the road.

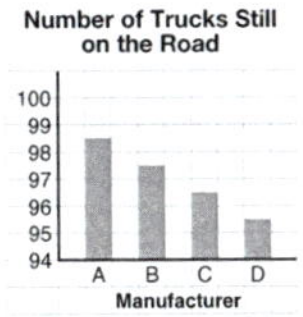

a) What impression does this graph give?
b) How many trucks, out of 100, are still on the road for Manufacturer B? C? D?
c) Do you think Manufacturer A's trucks are more dependable than the other manufacturers' trucks? Explain.
d) Redraw the graph to give an accurate representation of the data.

Mental Math

Estimate each product.
- 3.9 × 4.1 ≐ 16
- 0.5 × 10.2 ≐ 5
- 1.1 × 11.1 ≐ 11
- 20.5 × 0.9 ≐ 20

Board of Directors' Expenses

Quarter	Amount ($)
1st	85 000
2nd	104 000
3rd	125 000
4th	155 000

5. Draw a graph to display the data at the left in each way:
a) The directors want the expenses to look low.
b) The shareholders want to show the expenses are too high.
c) Draw an accurate representation of the data.
For each graph you draw, explain how it shows what you intended.

6. **Assessment Focus**
Use newspapers, magazines, or the Internet. Find a graph that creates a false impression.
a) Describe how the graph creates a false impression.
b) Why might the misleading graph be used?
c) How could the graph be changed to present the data more accurately?
d) Use your suggestions in part c to draw an accurate graph.

Reflect

Describe two ways in which a graph may be misleading.

5.6 Evaluating Data Analysis 205

d)

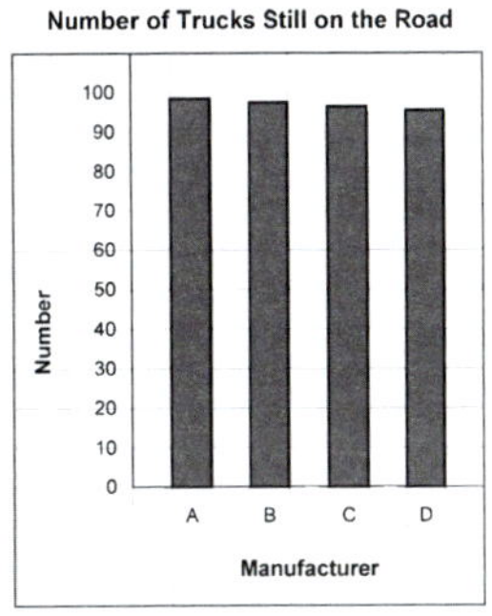

(Answers continue on page 30.)

Assignment Guidelines

If your students do not have time to complete all the *Practice* questions on pages 204 and 205, these questions provide minimum curriculum coverage: 1, 3, 5, 6, *Reflect*

To assess the 4 Achievement Chart categories listed in the curriculum document, have students complete these *Practice* questions:

Understanding Concepts: 1
Communication: 3
Application: 5
Problem Solving: 6

ASSESSMENT FOR LEARNING

What to Look For	What to Do
Understanding concepts ✔ Students can identify graphs that have been drawn to mislead or create a false impression.	***Extra Support:*** Students who have difficulty identifying a misleading graph should first look at the scale on each axis. Encourage students to take note of the starting number on each scale and the increments used. Students can use Step-by-Step 6 (Master 5.12) to complete question 6.
Applying procedures ✔ Students can redraw a misleading graph so that the data are displayed accurately.	***Extra Practice:*** Have students use the data in *Practice* question 3 of Section 5.2, page 176, to draw a misleading bar graph. Students tell who might use the graph and why. Students can complete Extra Practice 6 (Master 5.20).
Communicating ✔ Students can explain how a graph has been drawn to mislead.	***Extension:*** Students draw a misleading graph to represent a set of data, then show it to family members and neighbours. Students ask each person a question about the graph. Students record how many people were misled, an indication of the success of the graph.

Recording and Reporting
Master 5.2 Ongoing Observations: Data Management

Making a Study Sheet

SECTION ORGANIZER

Vocabulary:
- definitions
- colour code
- Word association

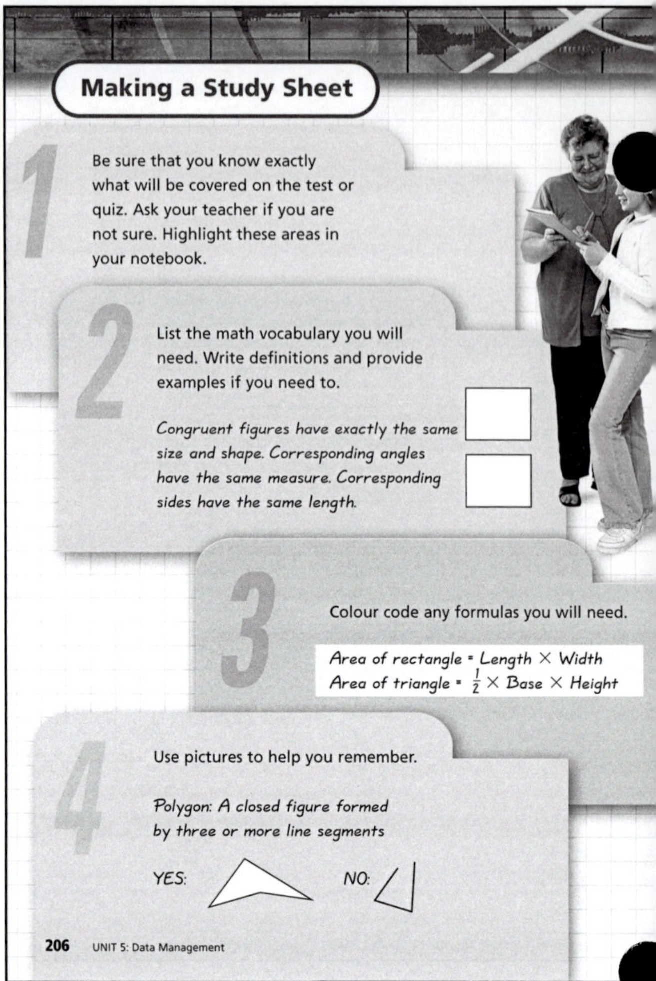
Making a Study Sheet

1 Be sure that you know exactly what will be covered on the test or quiz. Ask your teacher if you are not sure. Highlight these areas in your notebook.

2 List the math vocabulary you will need. Write definitions and provide examples if you need to.

Congruent figures have exactly the same size and shape. Corresponding angles have the same measure. Corresponding sides have the same length.

3 Colour code any formulas you will need.

Area of rectangle = Length × Width
Area of triangle = $\frac{1}{2}$ × Base × Height

4 Use pictures to help you remember.

Polygon: A closed figure formed by three or more line segments

YES: *NO:*

206 UNIT 5: Data Management

A **study sheet** is a brief synopsis of key concepts and procedures for quick reference.
The study sheet is a valuable reminder of important information for a test, quiz, or performance task. It is a memory aid. The math textbook, notebook, and journal are the primary sources of information for the study sheet. Study sheets are similar to "quick reference guides" that are used throughout the working world to help people remember important ideas or procedures. They typically fit onto a single page or card, or very small booklet.

BEFORE

- Ask students about any quick reference guides they have seen or where they might be useful in any subject or field. Provide professional examples if possible.
- Discuss with students the purpose of a study sheet.
- With students, read aloud the 6 points. After each, ask students to suggest why it is important and what examples from the current unit would apply.
- Model your expectations by working through a collaborative study sheet. Follow each step. For some topics, the points may be more obvious. Generate as many examples as possible from the class.
- In Step 1, collaboratively look back over the topic to determine what students think are the most important concepts and problems. Ask for reasons why. This can be done as a class or in small groups.
- The selection of content or data for the study sheet is important, but the final step is to organize the data into meaningful clusters for quick retrieval. Headings are useful (for example, *vocabulary, procedures, formulas, trouble questions,* or *clusters based on similar math concepts*). It is helpful for students to physically cut the data apart and assemble them in different ways to find an efficient and logical arrangement. The arrangement must make sense to them. The Teacher Guide Notes for *Reading and Writing in Math: Writing a Math Journal Entry,* Unit 4, pages 157, 167 have suggestions for organizing ideas.
- In subsequent study sheets, work collaboratively on fewer of the steps until most students are comfortable with the process.

Reading and Writing in Math

5

Copy out a sample problem. Include all necessary examples and discussion.

Sample Problem: You have a choice of recess times:
- *You may have 30 min a day for the next two weeks.*

OR

- *You may have 1 min of recess the 1st day, 2 min the 2nd day, 4 min the 3rd day, 8 min the 4th day, and so on, for the next two weeks. Which choice would give you more recess time in the 2 weeks? Explain your answer.*

Solution
This problem is about finding out which recess choice is better. The strategy I will use is to make a table.

Day	1	2	3
Choice 1 (min)	30	30	30
Total time (min)	30	60	90
Choice 2 (min)	1	2	4
Total time (min)	1	3	7

6

Use word association and patterns to help you remember.

A hexagon has six sides. (Both have an X.)
Octagon -- Octapus (Both have 8 sides/arms.)

Reading and Writing in Math: Making a Study Sheet 207

REACHING ALL LEARNERS

ESL Strategies

- ➤This is personal record for students and should be done in a manner that suits the needs of the learner, not the teacher. As such, the normal expectations of written language acuity will not be an issue. Instead, ESL students may need more support in reading and reviewing materials from the textbook, notebooks and journals.
- ➤Place more emphasis on vocabulary, using icons and images to provide the definitions.
- ➤Rhymes, mnemonics, humour, musical phrases, acronyms, and so on, are also useful in remembering disparate facts.

Creating a study sheet is a powerful review and study strategy. As a form of problem solving, it focuses on discerning important information from lesser details, capturing them as briefly as possible, while clustering and organizing them into a sensible format for easy retrieval. This decision-making process helps to consolidate long-term understanding. It is also a complex conceptual exercise that needs practice, support, and critical reflection. It is the creation, not the use of a study sheet that has long-term benefit. Using someone else's study sheet has only short-term impact.

DURING

- Students should make personal notes of problems that were challenging, include the correct solutions. It may be useful to note also what *not* to do; places where they went wrong.
- Stop periodically during the process to have students share their ideas with the group; both the selected key points and how they are represented. They should feel free to borrow ideas from peers.
- Bullets and phrases are more efficient than sentences and paragraphs. Icons and images may be even better. The intent is to capture ideas as briefly as possible, with enough detail to trigger the needed recollection. You may have to teach about leaving out unnecessary phrases, articles, adverbs, adjectives, and so on.
- Be selective in the use of sample problems. Students will often try to include more samples than needed. You may want to steer students toward Assessment Focus type problems. Reduce the words used in the problem and solutions.

AFTER

- Post some of the best examples in the room. If students are permitted to use study sheets on tests, they should be allowed to access the "best of" together.

SECTION ORGANIZER

Student Materials
- 0.5-cm grid paper (PM 14)
- calculators
- rulers

Assessment: Masters 5.1 Unit Rubric: Data Management, 5.4 Unit Summary: Data Management

Correlation of Extra Practice questions on page 442:

Section	Questions
5.2	1, 2
5.3	3, 5
5.4	1, 2
5.5	3, 4, 5

Sample Solutions

1. a) What is your favourite summer activity? Swimming ___ Baseball ___ Cycling ___ Soccer ___ Other ___
   b) Swimming is a great way to cool down. What is your favourite summer activity?
   The question includes a statement that may encourage people to answer "Swimming."
2. a) The data show the average weekly earnings in 2001 for various jobs in Canada.

(Solutions continue below.)

Unit Review

Review any lesson with etext online tutorial

What Do I Need to Know?

☑ **Primary data** are data you collect.

☑ **Secondary data** are found from databases on the Internet, or a library, or other sources.

☑ In a set of data:

The **mean** is the sum of numbers divided by the number of numbers in the set.

The **median** is the middle number, when there is an odd number of data in the set. When there is an even number of data, the median is the mean of the two middle numbers.

The **mode** is the number that occurs most often. A set of data can have no mode, one mode, or more than one mode.

What Should I Be Able to Do?

For extra practice, go to page 442.

LESSON

5.1 **1.** A recreation group wants to find out the favourite summer activity of teenagers in the town.
a) Write an unbiased survey question.
b) Write a biased survey question. Explain how it is biased.

5.2 5.5 **2.** The data in this table are from Statistics Canada.

Average Weekly Earnings in 2001

Job	Earnings ($)
Forestry	831
Mining	1153
Utilities	1000
Construction	800
Real Estate	612
Education	696
Health Care	584
Transportation	742

(Sample Solutions, continued)

b) **Average Weekly Earnings in 2001**

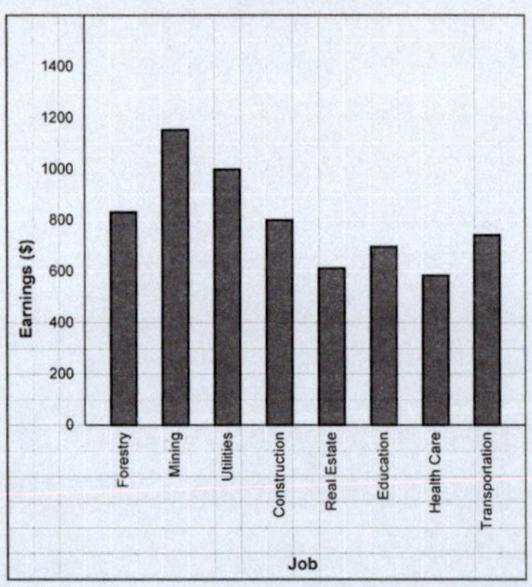

c) I chose a bar graph because the heights of the bars make it easy to tell which job has the highest average weekly earnings and which job has the lowest average weekly earnings. I could have used a pictograph but it would be very difficult to choose a key that would not require small fractions of a symbol. A line graph could not be used because the data are not measured over time.

d) Highest weekly earnings: Mining—it has the tallest bar. Lowest weekly earnings: Health Care—it has the shortest bar.

e) To calculate the average annual earnings, I would multiply the average weekly earnings by 52, the number of weeks in a year. To calculate the average monthly earnings, I would divide the average annual earnings by 12. To determine the average annual earnings by using the graph, I would multiply each number on the scale on the vertical axis by 52, then read the new length of each bar. To determine the average monthly earnings by using the graph, I would multiply the scale on the vertical axis by 52, then divide by 12. The lengths of the bars will not change because the ratios of the earnings remain the same.

f) The mean; this is how the average weekly earnings are calculated by Statistics Canada.

3. a) Frequency column: 17, 10, 9, 4, 20 b) 60 people
   c) Metro PD; it is the least favourite show of the 60 people surveyed.
   d) Reality Shock; according to the survey, it has the greatest number of viewers.

LESSON

a) What do the data show?
b) Draw a graph to display the data.
c) Explain your choice of graph. Could another type of graph have been used? Why?
d) Which job has the highest weekly earnings? The lowest weekly earnings? How is this shown in your graph?
e) How can the data be used to find the average annual earnings? The average monthly earnings? How might the graph be used to find these?
f) Which average: mean, median, or mode, do you think is shown in the table? Explain your answer.

5.5 **3.** Jacob collected the data in the table below. The table lists 5 TV shows that air on Sunday evenings. The survey question was "Which of these shows is your favourite? Everyone Loves Jordan___, Girl Meets World___, Lost in Time___, Metro PD___, Reality Shock___"

TV Show	Tally	Frequency
Everyone Loves Jordan	~~||||~~ ~~||||~~ ~~||||~~ ||	17
Girl Meets World	~~||||~~ ~~||||~~	10
Lost in Time	~~||||~~ ||||	9
Metro PD	||||	4
Reality Shock	~~||||~~ ~~||||~~ ~~||||~~ ~~||||~~	20

a) Write the frequency of each response.
b) How many people did Jacob survey? 60 people
c) Suppose you were a TV producer and had to take one show off the air. Which show would it be? Explain.
d) Suppose you were an advertiser. Which show would you advertise with? Why?
e) Display the data using:
i) a pictograph
ii) a bar graph

5.3 5.5 **4.** A quality control inspector measures the masses of boxes of raisins. He wants to know if the average mass of a box of raisins is 100 g. He randomly chooses boxes from the production department. The masses, in grams, are recorded below.

Masses of Boxes of Raisins in Grams
99.1, 101.7, 99.8, 98.9, 100.8, 100.3, 98.3, 100.0, 97.8, 97.6, 98.5, 101.7, 100.2, 100.2, 99.4, 100.3, 98.8, 102.0, 100.3, 98.0, 99.4, 99.0, 98.1, 101.8, 99.8, 101.3, 100.5, 100.7, 98.7, 100.3, 99.3, 102.5

a) Draw a stem-and-leaf plot.
b) What can you tell from the plot that you could not easily see from the data?
c) Will this shipment be approved? Explain. No
d) What is the median? 99.9 g
e) What is the mode? 100.3 g

e) i)

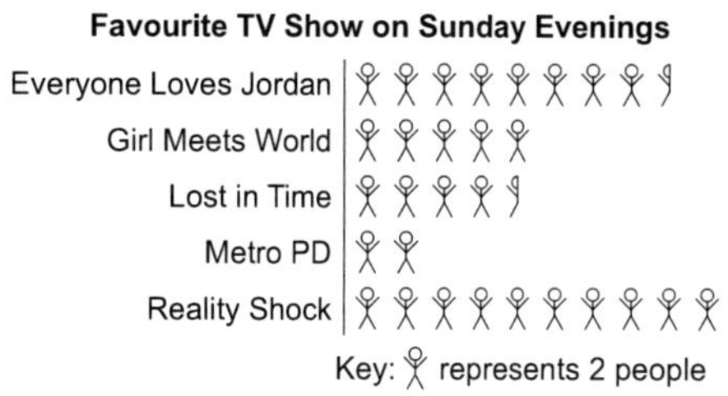

ii)

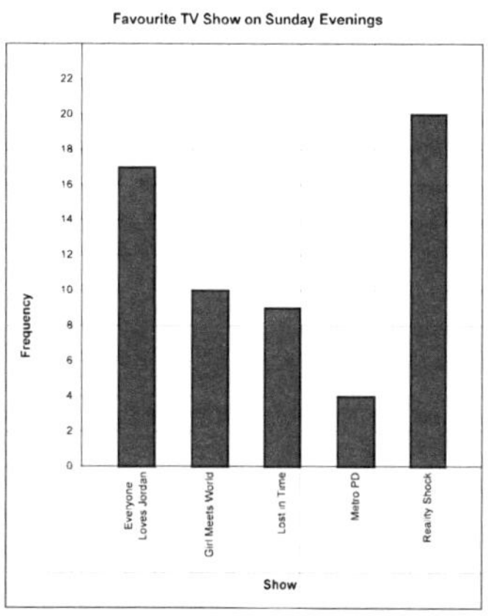

4. a)

Masses of Boxes of Raisins (g)	
Stem	**Leaf**
97.	6 8
98.	0 1 3 5 7 8 9
99.	0 1 3 4 4 8 8
100.	0 2 2 3 3 3 3 5 7 8
101.	3 7 7 8
102.	0 5

(Solutions continue below.)

(Sample Solutions, continued)

b) I can easily tell the range, the mode, the median, the greatest mass, and the least mass.

c) No, the mean mass is 99.8 g, which is less than the required mass of 100 g.

f) The shipment would be approved if the mode was used because the mode is greater than 100 g. The shipment would not be approved if the median was used because the median is less than 100 g.

5. a)

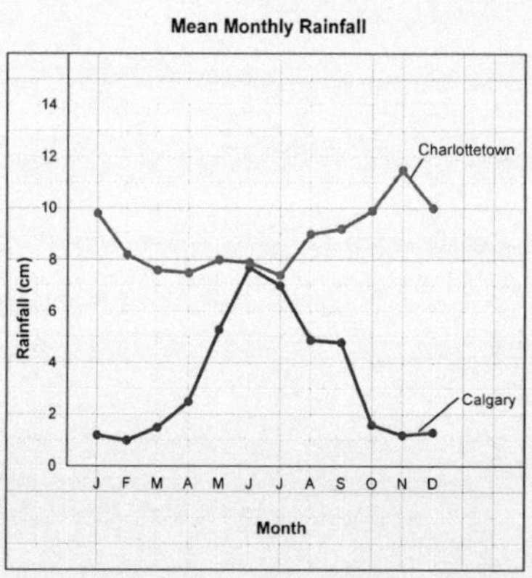

b) The graph for Calgary shows an upward trend from February to June and then a downward trend from June to November.
The graph for Charlottetown shows a downward trend from January to April, and from May to July, then an upward trend from July to November.

c) The graphs do not cross so this means that the mean monthly rainfall in Charlottetown is always greater than that in Calgary.

d) Calgary: 40 cm   Charlottetown: 106 cm
For each city, I added the mean monthly rainfalls to get the mean annual rainfall.

e) Calgary: 2.05 cm   Charlottetown: 8.6 cm

f) There is no mode monthly rainfall for Charlottetown. The mode monthly rainfall for Calgary is 1.2 cm. The range for Calgary is 6.7 cm and the range for Charlottetown is 4.1 cm.

6. a) Mode: the mode is the sweater size sold most often.
   b) Mean: The mean is $6.80. The mode is $5.00. The median is $6.00. Robbie should use the mean to convince his parents to increase his allowance as it has the greatest value.
   c) Median: the median is the middle number in the set of marks. One-half the marks are at or above the median, and one-half are below.
7. The mean is $62 667. The median is $50 000. There are two modes: $50 000 and $28 000.
   a) I would use the mean because it is the greatest number.
   b) I would use the lesser mode because it is the least number.

LESSON

f) Would the shipment be approved if the mode was used? If the median was used? Explain.

5.4 5.5 **5.** The mean monthly rainfalls for Calgary and Charlottetown are given.

Mean Monthly Rainfall (cm)

Month	Calgary	Charlottetown
January	1.2	9.8
February	1.0	8.2
March	1.5	7.6
April	2.5	7.5
May	5.3	8.0
June	7.7	7.9
July	7.0	7.4
August	4.9	9.0
September	4.8	9.2
October	1.6	9.9
November	1.2	11.5
December	1.3	10.0

a) Draw a line graph for each city on the same grid.
b) Describe each graph. Are there any trends? Explain.
c) Do the line graphs cross? What does this mean?
d) Determine the mean annual rainfall for each city. Explain your steps.
e) Determine the median monthly rainfall for each city.
f) What else do you know from the table or the graph?

5.5 **6.** In each case, which is most useful: the mean, median, or mode? Justify your answer.
a) A storeowner wants to kn which sweater sizes he shc order. Last week he sold 5 small, 15 medium, 6 large, and 2 X-large sweaters.
b) Five of Robbie's friends said their weekly allowances are: $5, $8, $10, $6, and $5. Robbie wants to convince his parents to increase his allowance.
c) Tina wants to know if her math mark was in the top half or bottom half of the class.

5.5 5.6 **7.** A small engineering company has an owner and 5 employees. This table shows their salaries.

Company Salaries

Position	Annual Salary ($)
Owner	130 000
Manager	90 000
2 Engineers	50 000
Receptionist	28 000
Secretary	28 000

Which measure of central tendency would you use to describe the average annual salary in each case?
a) You want to attract a new employee.
b) You want to suggest the company does not pay its employees well.

210 UNIT 5: Data Management

ASSESSMENT FOR LEARNING

What to Look For

Understanding of concepts

✔ **Question 4:** Student understands how to find the median and mode on a stem-and-leaf plot.

Application of mathematical procedures

✔ **Question 1:** Student can identify bias in a survey question and rewrite it as an unbiased question.
✔ **Question 3:** Student can display data on a bar graph and pictograph.
✔ **Question 4:** Student can organize data in a stem-and-leaf plot.

Communicating

✔ **Question 5:** Student can identify and describe trends in a line graph.
✔ **Question 6:** Student can explain which measure of central tendency is most useful in a particular situation.

Recording and Reporting

Master 5.1 Unit Rubric: Data Management
Master 5.4 Unit Summary: Data Management

Practice Test

1. a) Explain the difference between primary and secondary data.
   b) State if primary data or secondary data are used in each case. Justify your answers.
   Secondary i) Anna searched the Internet to find the top ten movies of the year.
   Primary ii) Rory phoned his friends to ask if they were coming to his party.

800-m Race Times
3:25, 3:07, 1:55, 3:11
2:41, 2:47, 3:04, 1:58
2:35, 3:25, 3:08, 2:53
2:29, 3:15, 2:55, 2:28
3:14, 2:47, 3:07, 2:39
2:39, 2:43, 3:19, 2:54
3:11, 2:59, 2:42, 2:57

2. Here are the times, in minutes and seconds, of 28 people who competed in an 800-m race.
   a) Display the data in a stem-and-leaf plot.
   b) What is the range of times for the race? 1 min 30 s
   c) Find the median time. 2 min 54.5 s
   d) Is there a mode time? If so, what is it? If not, explain how you know.
3. Parham received these marks on 7 math tests:
   91, 75, 95, 80, 83, 86, 68
   What mark will he need on his next test in each case? Justify each answer.
   a) The mean of his 8 tests is 84. 94
   b) The mode of his 8 tests is 86. 86
   c) The median of his 8 tests is 84. 85

Country of Origin for Visitors to Canada	
Country	Number of Visitors
Japan	500 000
France	400 000
Germany	400 000
Australia	175 000
United Kingdom	850 000
Mexico	150 000
Hong Kong	125 000

4. a) Graph the data at the left. Explain your choice of graph.
   b) In the year 2000, approximately 15 000 000 people visited Canada from the U.S. Suppose you want to add these data to your graph in part a. How would your graph change?
   c) Redraw the graph in part a. Include the data from part b.
   d) Compare the two graphs. Which graph gives you more information? Justify your answer.

Practice Test 211

SECTION ORGANIZER

Student Materials

- 0.5-cm grid paper (PM 14)

Assessment: Masters 5.1 Unit Rubric: Data Management, 5.4 Unit Summary: Data Management

TEACHING NOTE

For question 2, remind students that the leaves are from 0 to 9, so suggest they convert each time to seconds before making the stem-and-leaf plot.

Sample Solutions

1. a) Primary data are data you collect and secondary data are found from databases on the Internet, or a library, or other sources.
   b) i) Secondary data; Anna used the Internet to find the data.
      ii) Primary data: Rory collected the data himself by calling his friends.
2. a) Convert the times to seconds: 205, 187, 115, 191, 161, 167, 184, 118, 155, 205, 188, 173, 149, 195, 175, 148, 194, 167, 187, 159, 159, 163, 199, 174, 191, 179, 162, 177

800-m Race Times in Seconds	
Stem	Leaf
11	5 8
14	8 9
15	5 9 9
16	1 2 3 7 7
17	3 4 5 7 9
18	4 7 7 8
19	1 1 4 5 9
20	5 5

   b) 1 min 30 s c) 2 min 54.5 s
   d) There are 5 mode times: 2:39, 2:47, 3:07, 3:11, 3:25
3. a) 94; the sum of the 8 test marks must be $84 \times 8 = 672$. The sum of the given marks is 578; $672 - 578 = 94$.
   b) 86; the mode is the mark that occurs most often. For 86 to be the mode, 86 must occur twice since all other marks appear only once.
   c) If there are 8 marks, the median is the mean of the 4th and 5th marks. For the median to be 84, the mean of 83 and another mark must be 84. Parham needs 85 on his next test, because $\frac{83 + 85}{2} = 84$.

(Solutions continue on page 32)

Organizing a Winter Carnival

SECTION ORGANIZER (80–100 min)

Student Grouping: 4 or 5
Student Materials
- 3-column charts (PM 18)
- 0.5-cm grid paper (PM 14)
- calculators
- rulers

Assessment: Masters 5.3 Performance Assessment Rubric: Organizing a Winter Carnival, 5.4 Unit Summary: Data Management

Sample Solution

Part 1
- Our school has JK through to Grade 8. Because of the large number of students, the Grades 7s and 8s will have their own Winter Carnival Day.
- Indoor sports: basketball, volleyball, floor hockey
- Outdoor sports: skating, tobogganing, hockey, snow Frisbee, snow football
- Games: Chess, computer games, card games, trivia games
  Snacks: Popcorn (50¢), hotdogs ($1.00), pizza ($2.00 per slice), hot chocolate (50¢), juice (75¢), potato chips (50¢), donuts (75¢), fruit (50¢)
  (*Sample Solutions continue below.*)

Unit Problem **Organizing a Winter Carnival**

Your help is needed to organize a school Winter Carnival Day. Think about:
- the classes or grades that should participate
- which activities students would enjoy
- which snacks and drinks should be offered

You will collect, display, and analyse data.

Part 1

Brainstorm with your classmates. Keep a record of the ideas. Here are some topics you may want to discuss:
- Who will participate in Winter Carnival Day? Is it possible for all students in every grade in your school to participate? Are there special considerations for different age groups?
- What type of indoor and outdoor sports, games, and crafts do you think students in your school would enjoy?
- What types of snacks and drinks should be offered? How much will this cost?

After brainstorming, break into five groups. Each group will be responsible for collecting data and reporting on one of the following topics:
- Indoor sports
- Outdoor sports
- Games
- Crafts
- Snacks and drinks

212 UNIT 5: Data Management

Before students begin, brainstorm, as a class, which activities students would enjoy, which snacks and drinks could be offered, and who should participate. Divide the class into five groups, one for each of the listed topics. Encourage each group to share the work; for example, each group member could display the data in a different way.

(*Sample Solutions, continued*)

Part 2

We chose outdoor sports.
- Which outdoor sport would you like to participate in on Winter Carnival Day? Skating ___ Hockey ___ Tobogganing ___ Snow Frisbee ___ Snow Football ___ Other ___
  We avoided bias by not including a statement that might have encouraged people to answer in a certain way.

Favourite Outdoor Sports

Outdoor Sport	Number of Students	Frequency
Skating	~~||||~~ ~~||||~~ ~~||||~~ ~~||||~~ ~~||||~~ ////	29
Hockey	~~||||~~ ~~||||~~ ////	14
Tobogganing	~~||||~~ ~~||||~~ ~~||||~~ ~~||||~~ ~~||||~~ /	26
Snow Frisbee	~~||||~~ ~~||||~~ ~~||||~~ ////	19
Snow Football	~~||||~~ ~~||||~~ ///	13
Other	////	4

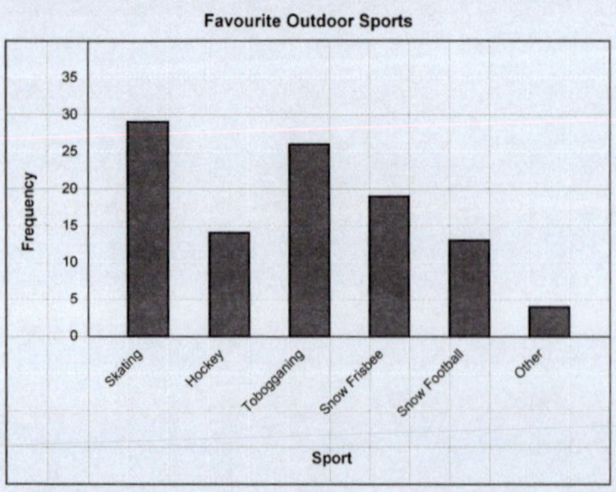

- We displayed our data in a frequency table and on a bar graph. The greatest number in the table and the tallest bar on the graph represent the most popular outdoor sport.

Part 2

Your group will collect, display, and analyse data related to your task.

- Write a survey question or questions related to your task. Explain how bias can be avoided when writing the question.
- Conduct the survey.
- Display the collected data in different ways. Justify your displays.
- Analyse the data. What decisions can be made about Winter Carnival Day from your results?
- Prepare a report of your findings.

Check List

Your work should include:

✓ your survey question and data collection plan

✓ at least two displays of your data

✓ justification for the procedures and displays you chose

✓ your analysis and recommendations

Part 3

Present the results of your group work to the rest of the class.

Reflect on the Unit

Describe the different types of graphs you drew. What can you tell about the data from each type of graph? Use examples to explain.

Unit Problem: Organizing a Winter Carnival 213

- The survey shows that skating is the most popular outdoor sport. Since we plan to offer 3 outdoor sports, we have decided on skating, tobogganing, and snow Frisbee. We will cancel any plans of offering snow football and hockey.
- The report should include all of the above and any other research, ideas, or observations that students used or came up with.

REFLECT ON THE UNIT: I drew line graphs, bar graphs, and pictographs. A bar graph displays data by using horizontal or vertical bars whose lengths are in the same ratio as the numbers they represent; that is, the greatest number has the longest bar and the least number has the shortest bar. A bar graph is useful for illustrating data that are not arranged in numerical order, such as TV shows. A pictograph uses a symbol to represent a certain number, and repetitions of the symbol illustrate the data. A pictograph is also useful for illustrating data that are not arranged in numerical order, such as hobbies. It is easy to determine the greatest and least frequency from both of these graphs. A line graph is used to display data that change over time, such as height and age, or temperature and time. A line graph often shows a trend and can be used to make predictions.

ASSESSMENT FOR LEARNING

What to Look For	What to Do
Understanding concepts ✔ Students understand how to collect and organize primary data on tally charts, and display data on frequency tables. ***Applying procedures*** ✔ Students can read and report information about data displayed on a graph. ***Communicating*** ✔ Students can describe, in their own words, information presented on frequency tables.	***Extra Support:*** Make the problem accessible. Some students may have difficulty choosing activities that are practical. Remind students to consider the location of their school (for example, are there tobogganing hills nearby?), the materials required to make certain crafts, how many people can participate at any one time, and so on. To prevent bias in their survey questions, tell students to avoid statements that might lead people toward a particular answer. Encourage students to include "Other" as a possible answer.

Recording and Reporting

Master 5.3 Performance Assessment Rubric: Organizing a Winter Carnival
Master 5.4 Unit Summary: Data Management

Evaluating Student Learning: Preparing to Report: Unit 5 Data Management

This unit provides an opportunity to report on the **Data Management and Probability** strand. *Master 5.4: Unit Summary: Data Management* provides a comprehensive format for recording and summarizing evidence collected.

Here is an example of a completed summary chart for this Unit:

Strand: *Data Management and Probability*	**Problem solving**	**Understanding of concepts**	**Application of mathematical procedures**	**Communication**	***Overall***
Ongoing Observations	2	3	2	3	2/3
Work samples or portfolios; conferences	2	3	3	3	3
Unit Review	3	3	3	3	3
Practice Test	2	3	2	3	2/3
Unit Problem Organizing a Winter Carnival	3	3	2	3	3
Achievement Level for reporting					3

Recording	How to Report
Ongoing Observations	Use *Master 5.2 Ongoing Observations: Data Management* to determine the most consistent level achieved in each category. Enter it in the chart. Choose to summarize by achievement category, or simply to enter an overall level. Observations from late in the Unit should be most heavily weighted.
Portfolios or collections of work samples; conferences or interviews	Use *Master 5.1 Unit Rubric: Data Management* to guide evaluation of collections of work and information gathered in conferences. Teachers may choose to focus particular attention on the Assessment Focus questions. Work from late in the unit should be most heavily weighted.
Unit Review	*Master 5.1 Unit Rubric: Data Management* may be helpful in determining levels of achievement. #4 provides evidence of Understanding concepts; #1, 3 and 5 provide evidence of Application of mathematical procedures; #2 and 7 provide evidence of Problem solving; #6 provides evidence of Communication.
Practice Test	*Master 5.1 Unit Rubric: Data Management* may be helpful in determining levels of achievement. #1 provides evidence of Understanding of concepts; #2 provides evidence of Application of mathematical procedures; #3 provides evidence of Problem solving; #4 provides evidence of Communication.
Unit Problem	Use *Master 5.3 Performance Assessment Rubric: Organizing a Winter Carnival.* The *Unit Problem* offers a snapshot of students' achievement. In particular, it shows their ability to synthesize and apply what they have learned.
Student Self-Assessment	Note students' perceptions of their own progress. This may take the form of an oral or written comment, or a self-rating.
Comments	Analyse the pattern of achievement to identify strengths and needs. In some cases, specific actions may need to be planned to support the learner.

Learning Skills	Ongoing Records
PM 4: Learning Skills Check List Use to record and report throughout a reporting period, rather than for each unit and/or strand.	*PM 10: Summary Class Records: Strands* *PM 11: Summary Class Records: Achievement Categories* *PM 12: Summary Record: Individual* Use to record and report evaluations of student achievement over several clusters, a reporting period, or a school year. These can also be used in place of the Unit Summary.

Name ____________________ Date ______________

Master 5.1

Unit Rubric: Data Management

	Level 1	Level 2	Level 3	Level 4
Problem solving • chooses and carries out a range of strategies to solve problems involving data collection, display, analysis, and interpretation	with assistance, chooses and carries out a limited range of appropriate strategies to solve problems that involve data and statistical methods	with limited assistance, chooses and carries out appropriate strategies to solve problems that involve data and statistical methods	chooses and carries out appropriate strategies to solve problems that involve data and statistical methods	chooses and carries out appropriate, often innovative, strategies to solve problems that involve data and statistical methods
Understanding of concepts • shows understanding by explaining, justifying, and evaluating: – methods of collecting, organizing, and displaying primary and secondary data – use of spreadsheets and databases – measures of central tendency – inferences, arguments, and conclusions based on data analysis	shows little understanding; may be unable to explain, justify, and evaluate: – methods of collecting, organizing, and displaying primary and secondary data – use of spreadsheets and databases – measures of central tendency – inferences, arguments, and conclusions based on data analysis	shows some understanding; partially able to explain, justify, and evaluate: – methods of collecting, organizing, and displaying primary and secondary data – use of spreadsheets and databases – measures of central tendency – inferences, arguments, and conclusions based on data analysis	shows understanding; able to clearly and appropriately explain, justify, and evaluate: – methods of collecting, organizing, and displaying primary and secondary data – use of spreadsheets and databases – measures of central tendency – inferences, arguments, and conclusions based on data analysis	shows thorough understanding; able to accurately and effectively explain, justify, and evaluate: – methods of collecting, organizing, and displaying primary and secondary data – use of spreadsheets and databases – measures of central tendency – inferences, arguments, and conclusions based on data analysis
Application of mathematical procedures • accurately: – constructs data displays – summarizes information presented in data displays (including trends) – calculates mean, median, mode	limited accuracy; major errors or omissions in: – constructing data displays – summarizing information presented in data displays – calculating mean, median, mode	somewhat accurate; several minor errors or omissions in: – constructing data displays – summarizing information presented in data displays – calculating mean, median, mode	generally accurate; few minor errors or omissions in: – constructing data displays – summarizing information presented in data displays – calculating mean, median, mode	accurate and precise; no errors in: – constructing data displays – summarizing information presented in data displays – calculating mean, median, mode
Communication • explains concepts, reasoning, and procedures clearly, using appropriate mathematical language (for example, mean, mode, bias)	unable to explain reasoning and procedures clearly	partially explains reasoning and procedures	explains reasoning and procedures clearly	explains reasoning and procedures clearly, precisely, and confidently
• presents work clearly including labels and symbols	presents work with little clarity; rarely uses appropriate labels or symbols	presents work with some clarity; uses some appropriate labels and symbols	presents work clearly and precisely; uses appropriate labels and symbols	presents work clearly and precisely; uses a range of appropriate labels and symbols

Name ____________________ Date ________________

Master 5.2

Ongoing Observations: Data Management

The behaviours described under each heading are examples; they are not intended to be an exhaustive list of all that might be observed. More detailed descriptions are provided in each lesson under *Assessment for Learning*.

STUDENT ACHIEVEMENT: Data Management				
Student	**Problem solving** ▪ Chooses and carries out appropriate strategies to solve problems and design investigations involving data	**Understanding of concepts** ▪ Explains and evaluates: – methods of collecting, organizing, displaying, and analysing data – inferences, arguments, and conclusions	**Application of mathematical procedures** ▪ Constructs data displays ▪ Summarizes information presented (for example, trends in graphs) ▪ Calculates mean, median, mode	**Communication** ▪ Explains concepts, reasoning, and procedures clearly ▪ Presents work clearly, including labels and symbols

Level 1 – very limited; Level 2 – somewhat or limited; Level 3 – satisfactory; Level 4 – thorough

Name ____________________ Date ______________

Master 5.3

Performance Assessment Rubric: Organizing a Winter Carnival

	Level 1	Level 2	Level 3	Level 4
Problem solving • chooses appropriate strategies to design a survey that provides useful, unbiased information for making decisions about a winter carnival	uses few simple strategies to design a survey; does not result in useful, unbiased information for making decisions about the winter carnival	uses some appropriate strategies to design a survey that provides somewhat useful, unbiased information for making decisions about the winter carnival	uses appropriate strategies to design a survey that provides useful, unbiased information for making decisions about the winter carnival	uses innovative and appropriate strategies to design a survey that provides useful and unbiased information for making decisions about the winter carnival
Understanding of concepts • shows understanding of data by: – explaining how to avoid bias – justifying the choice of data displays – making and supporting inferences and decisions	shows very limited understanding; may be unable to give appropriate explanations or justifications for: – explaining how to avoid bias – justifying the choice of data displays – making and supporting inferences and decisions	shows limited understanding by giving some appropriate but incomplete explanations or justifications for: – explaining how to avoid bias – justifying the choice of data displays – making and supporting inferences and decisions	shows understanding by giving appropriate explanations or justifications for: – explaining how to avoid bias – justifying the choice of data displays – making and supporting inferences and decisions	shows thorough understanding by giving appropriate and complete explanations or justifications for: – explaining how to avoid bias – justifying the choice of data displays – making and supporting inferences and decisions
Application of mathematical procedures • constructs data displays correctly (including titles, labels, symbols) – calculates measures of central tendency accurately – summarizes results accurately	limited accuracy; major errors or omissions in: – constructing data displays – calculating measures of central tendency – summarizing results	somewhat accurate; several minor errors or omissions in: – constructing data displays – calculating measures of central tendency – summarizing results	generally accurate; few minor errors or omissions in: – constructing data displays – calculating measures of central tendency – summarizing results	accurate and precise; no errors or omissions in: – constructing data displays – calculating measures of central tendency – summarizing results
Communication • explains reasoning clearly using appropriate mathematical terminology (for example, mean, median, mode, bias)	explains reasoning unclearly and imprecisely using few mathematical terms	explains reasoning with some clarity using some appropriate mathematical terms	explains reasoning clearly and precisely using appropriate mathematical terms	explains reasoning clearly, precisely, and confidently using a range of appropriate mathematical terminology
• presents work, including sketches, formulas, and calculations, clearly	presents work with little clarity	presents work with some clarity	presents work clearly	presents work clearly and precisely

Name ____________________ Date ______________

Master 5.4

Unit Summary: Data Management

Review assessment records to determine the most consistent achievement levels for the assessments conducted. Some cells may be blank. *Overall* achievement levels may be recorded in each row, rather than identifying levels for each achievement category.

	Most Consistent Level of Achievement*				
Strand: *Data Management and Probability*	**Problem Solving**	**Understanding of concepts**	**Application of mathematical procedures**	**Communication**	***Overall***
Ongoing Observations					
Work samples or portfolios; conferences					
Unit Review					
Unit Test					
Unit Problem: Organizing a Winter Carnival					
Achievement Level for reporting					

* Use Ontario Achievement Levels 1, 2, 3, 4

Self-Assessment:

Comments: (Strengths, Needs, Next Steps)

Name ____________________ Date ______________

Master 5.5

Additional Activity 1: Triple M—An "Average" Game

Work in groups of 3 or 4.

You will need a deck of cards or number cards (1 to 13), a number cube labelled 1 to 6, and a calculator (optional).

How to Play:

1. One player rolls the number cube.
   Add 1 to the number rolled.
   Deal this number of cards to each player.

2. Each player records the values of her cards.
   A player who has a joker may assign that card the value of any other card already in the hand.

3. Each player calculates the mean, median, and mode of the numbers recorded.
   Round each average to the nearest whole number.
   If there is no mode, record a 0.

4. Each player calculates his score for the round by adding the mean, median, and mode.

5. Play another round. Add your new scores to your previous scores.

6. Continue to play until all the cards have been used.
   The player with the highest score wins.

Take It Further: Use 2 decks of cards and 2 number cubes. One player rolls the number cubes, then adds the numbers rolled. Each player is dealt this number of cards.

Name ____________________ Date ______________

Master 5.6

Additional Activity 2: Connecting Lines

Work in groups of 3 or 4.

You will need a deck of cards with the jokers removed, 2 number cubes labelled 1 to 6, 1-cm grid paper, rulers, and a calculator.

How to Play:

1. Each player draws a horizontal axis and a vertical axis on grid paper. Draw the horizontal axis 3 grid squares from the bottom of the page. Label the axis "Dice Number." Draw the vertical axis 3 grid squares from the left of the page. Label the axis "Card Number." Label the horizontal axis from 0 to 12, and the vertical axis from 0 to 26.

2. Shuffle the cards and place them face down in a pile. Players take turns. Roll the number cubes and take one card. Add the numbers rolled. This is the number on the horizontal axis. The number on the vertical axis is the face value of the card (Ace = 1, Jack = 11, Queen = 12, and King = 13). Plot the point on the graph. For example, if you roll a total of 5 and the card is a King, you plot the point (5, 13) on your graph.

3. Play another round. This time, players roll one number cube and take 2 cards, adding the numbers on the 2 cards.

4. Continue to alternate rolling 2 number cubes and taking 1 card, with rolling 1 number cube and taking 2 cards. Play continues until all the cards have been used.

5. Make a line graph by using a ruler to connect all the points, from left to right, on the grid paper.

6. Calculate both the horizontal range and the vertical range of your graph.

7. Write the ratio of the vertical range to the horizontal range. For example, if the vertical range is 17 and the horizontal range is 9, the ratio is 17:9.

8. Use equivalent ratios. The player with the greatest ratio wins.

Take It Further: Describe the trends in your graph, then describe a situation that could be represented by the graph.

Name ____________________ Date _______________

Master 5.7

Step-by-Step 1

Section 5.1, Question 6

Step 1 Name as many different styles of shoes as you can.

____

Name as many different makes of shoes as you can.

____

Step 2 Write a question you could ask to find out what styles of shoes people wear.

____

Step 3 Write a question you could ask to find out what makes of shoes people buy.

____

Step 4 How can the questions you wrote in *Steps 2* and *3* be used to conduct a survey?

____

Step 5 What information will the survey provide to help a person stock her or his new shoe store?

____

Name ____________________ Date ______________

Master 5.8

Step-by-Step 2

Section 5.2, Question 6

Step 1 Write a question you could ask to find out how your classmates spend most of their money.

____

Step 2 Conduct the survey. Ask each classmate the survey question.

Step 3 Record the results in the frequency table below.

How My Classmates Spend Their Money		
Way Money Is Spent	**Tally**	**Frequency**

Step 4 How would you display the data? On a pictograph? On a bar graph? Why?

____

Display the data on the graph of your choice.

Step 5 Use your display. What do most of your classmates spend most of their money on?

____

Step 6 Write 3 other things you know about how your classmates spend most of their money.

i) What is the least money spent on? ____________________

ii) What is the second most popular way for your classmates to spend money? __________

iii) What do none of your classmates spend money on?

____

Name ____________________ Date ______________

Master 5.9

Step-by-Step 3

Section 5.3, Question 6

Step 1 Choose a basketball team. You may choose your school team or a professional team. Name the team.

____

Step 2 Write the number of points the team scored in each of its last 15 games.

____

Step 3 Write the scores in order from least to greatest.

____

Step 4 Make a stem-and-leaf plot. One-digit scores have stem 0.
Write the leaves in order from least to greatest.

Stem	Leaf

Step 5 What is the greatest number? ________________ The least number? ____________

What is the range? ______________________________

Which number(s) occurs most often? ______________________________

What is the mode? ______________________________

What is the middle number(s) of the data? ______________________________

What is the median? ______________________________

Name ____________________ Date ________________

Master 5.10 **Step-by-Step 4**

Section 5.4, Question 5

Step 1 Which table shows data that change over time? ____________________

Which data would be best represented with a line graph? ____________________

Step 2 Draw axes on grid paper. Label the horizontal axis *Time (year)*.
Choose a scale for the horizontal axis:
Let 1 square represent __________.
Write the years along the horizontal axis.

Step 3 Label the vertical axis *Sales ($)*.
Look at the greatest number in the second column.
Choose a scale for the vertical axis:
Let 1 square represent ____________.
Start at 0. Write the money along the vertical axis.

Step 4 Plot a point on the grid for each data pair in the table.
Use a ruler to join adjacent points.
Give the graph a title.

Step 5 Does the graph go up to the right or down to the right?

____

Does the graph have an upward trend or a downward trend?

____

What do you know from this graph?

____

Step 6 Draw a bar graph for the other table.
Draw a bar for each entry in the table.
Why is a bar graph better than a pictograph for these data?

____

What do you know from this graph?

____

Name ____________________ Date ______________

Master 5.11

Step-by-Step 5

Section 5.5, Question 7

Step 1 To calculate the mean: add the numbers, then divide by the number of numbers.

The mean is ____.

Step 2 To calculate the median: order the numbers from least to greatest.

____

The median is the mean of the two middle numbers.

What are the 2 middle numbers? ______________________________

Add them, then divide by 2 to find the median. ______________________

Step 3 Which number occurs most often? ________ This is the mode.

Step 4 Add 10 to each number. The new numbers are:

____

Follow *Steps 1* to *3* to find the mean, median, and mode of the new numbers.

____

Step 5 Compare the mean, median, and mode found in *Step 4* with those you found in *Steps 1* to *3*. How did increasing each number by 10 affect the mean, median, and mode?

____

Step 6 Multiply each number by 2. The new numbers are:

____

Step 7 Follow *Steps 1* to *3* to find the mean, median, and mode of the new numbers.

____

Step 8 Compare the mean, median, and mode found in *Step 6* with those you found in *Steps 1* to *3*. How did doubling each number affect the mean, median, and mode?

____

Name ____________________ Date ______________

Master 5.12

Step-by-Step 6

Section 5.6, Question 6

You will need newspapers, magazines, or the Internet.

Step 1 Find a graph that creates a false impression.
Look for a graph that has an axis labelled incorrectly or a graph that is not appropriate for the data.

Step 2 Describe how the data are distorted by the graph.

____

____

Step 3 What is the title of the graph? ______________________________

What are the units along the vertical axis? ______________________________

What are the units along the horizontal axis? ______________________________

How might these scales be used to influence a decision?

____

Who would benefit from the false impression given by the graph?

____

Step 4 How can you change the horizontal or vertical axis to display the data accurately? _____

Step 5 Decide on the type of graph that would best display the data.

Would it be a bar graph, a pictograph, or a line graph? ______________________________

Should the vertical scale begin at 0? ______________________________

What is an appropriate scale for each axis? ______________________________

Draw an accurate graph. Label each axis. ______________________________

Give the graph a title.

Name ____________________ Date ______________

Master 5.13a

Unit Test: Unit 5 Data Management

1. Grade 7 students completed 100 mental math questions in the weekly MAD MINUTE math test. The number of errors that each student made is recorded below.

2, 6, 8, 1, 0, 12, 18, 22, 14, 10, 4, 0, 20, 17, 25, 33, 24, 11, 6, 9, 13, 12, 5, 7, 16, 3, 0, 27, 28, 36, 22, 18, 10, 15, 6, 3, 20, 11, 9, 0, 5, 35, 0, 19, 34, 29, 2, 40, 26, 14, 4, 8, 23, 31, 42, 0, 30, 17, 26, 0

a) Complete the frequency table for these data.

Mad Minute Test Errors		
Number of Errors	**Tally**	**Frequency**
0 – 4		
5 – 9		
10 – 14		
15 – 19		
20 – 24		
25 – 29		
30 – 34		
35 – 39		
40 – 44		

b) How many students wrote the test? How do you know?

c) Which type of graph would best display the data in the table? Explain.

d) Draw the graph you selected in part c.

e) What else do you know by looking at your graph?

2. Here are the miniature golf scores for a grade 7 physical education class.

19, 33, 37, 24, 62, 41, 38, 48, 26, 36, 33, 40, 57, 29, 36, 22, 31, 18, 42, 49, 61, 35, 27, 36, 50, 34, 31, 40, 29, 53, 27, 35, 64, 58, 23

Name ____________________ Date ______________

Master 5.13b

Unit Test continued

a) Complete a stem-and-leaf plot for scores.

Stem	**Leaf**

b) What is the title for your stem-and-leaf plot?

c) What is the range of the scores?

d) Find the median score and mode score.

e) Which measure of central tendency best describes the average golf score? Explain.

3.

Yearly Sales of Lamps	
Year	**Sales ($)**
1995	341 000
1996	350 000
1997	356 000
1998	368 000
1999	373 000
2000	379 000
2001	389 000
2002	392 000
2003	399 000

a) Name two types of graphs that could be used to display the above data.
Which would be a better choice and why? Explain.

b) **i)** Draw a graph to display the data so that the yearly sales appear to be increasing dramatically.

ii) Explain how your graph shows this and how it might be used.

c) Draw an accurate representation of the data. Explain how your graph shows this.

d) Predict the yearly lamp sales for 2005. How did you use the graph to make this prediction?

Name ____________________ Date ______________

Master 5.13c **Unit Test continued**

4. A student received these marks on 7 math tests: 91%, 75%, 95%, 80%, 83%, 86%, and 68%. What mark will the student need on the 8th test to make each following statement true? Explain your thinking in each case.

a) The mean of the tests is 84%.

b) The mode of the tests is 86%.

c) The median of the tests is 84%.

5. **a)** **i)** Explain why this survey question might produce a biased response.
NHL hockey is boring. Do you think playing hockey is more fun than watching hockey?
Yes _____ No______

ii) Rewrite the survey question so it does not produce a biased response.

b) Are primary data or secondary data collected in each situation? How do you know?

i) A student used E-STAT to find the average wages of various occupations in Canada.

ii) A student measured the perimeter of a garden to find how much fencing would be needed.

Name ____________________ Date ______________

Master 5.14 Sample Answers

Unit Test – Master 5.13

1. a)

Mad Minute Test Errors		
Number of Errors	**Tally**	**Frequency**
0 – 4	𝍸 𝍸 ////	14
5 – 9	𝍸 𝍸	10
10 – 14	𝍸 ////	9
15 – 19	𝍸 //	7
20 – 24	𝍸 /	6
25 – 29	𝍸 /	6
30 – 34	////	4
35 – 39	//	2
40 – 44	//	2

b) 60; the sum of the frequency column is 60.

c) Bar graph; each interval is represented by a bar and the frequency is the height of the bar.

d)

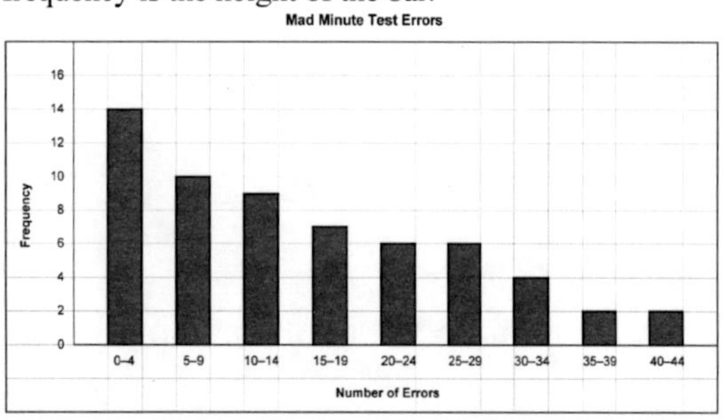

e) The same number of students had 20–24 errors as had 25–29 errors. Twice as many students had 0–4 errors as had 15–19 errors. The greatest number of students had between 0 and 4 errors. More than one-half of the students had less than 15 errors.

2. a), b)

Miniature Golf Scores	
Stem	**Leaf**
1	8 9
2	2 3 4 6 7 7 9 9
3	1 1 3 3 4 5 5 6 6 6 7 8
4	0 0 1 2 8 9
5	0 3 7 8
6	1 2 4

c) 46 **d)** Median: 36, Mode: 36

e) The median or the mode; these are equal. One-half of the scores are above 36 and one-half are below 36.

3. a) A bar graph and a line graph; the line graph is the better choice because the data change over time.

b) i)

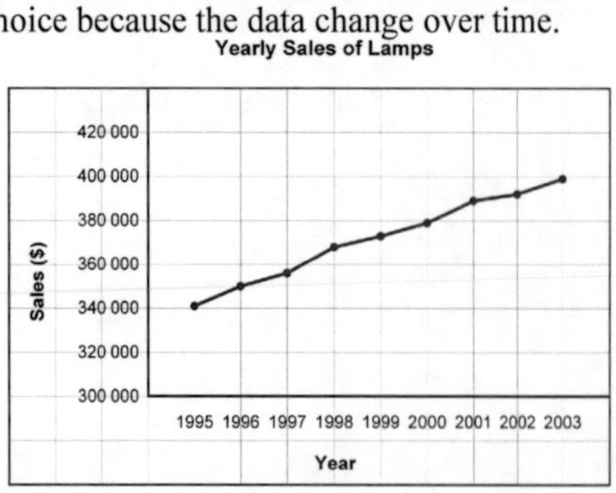

ii) I started the vertical axis at $300 000 instead of 0 to make it look like the sales are increasing at a fast rate. I also used a scale of 1 square represents $20 000. I used a horizontal scale of 1 square represents 1 year, to make the graph narrower. This also makes it look as though the sales are increasing faster. This graph might be used to impress investors, to attract employees, or to attract a possible buyer for the company.

c)

The vertical axis begins at 0, with a scale of 1 square represents $40 000. I used a horizontal scale of 2 squares represent 1 year. The yearly sales have a range of $58 000, which is a small increase over 8 years, compared with the starting sales of $341 000.

d) About $413 000; I used a ruler to extend the graph for 2 years. I assumed the sales would continue the trend for 2002 to 2003.

4. a) 94%; the total of the 8 tests, divided by 8, must be 84.

b) 86%; the mode is the mark that occurs most often. One mark is already 86%, so the student needs 86% on the next test so that 86% occurs most often.

c) 85%; the median of 8 marks is the mean of the 4th and 5th marks. The 4th mark is 83%. The 5th mark must be 85% because $\frac{83 + 85}{2} = 84$.

5. a) i) The question includes a statement that may encourage people to answer "Yes."

ii) Which do you think is more fun, playing hockey or watching hockey?

b) i) Secondary data; The student is using the Internet to collect data.

ii) Primary data; The student is collecting the data first hand.

Extra Practice Masters 5.15–5.21

Go to the CD-ROM to access editable versions of these Extra Practice Masters

Name ____________ Date ____________

Master 5.15 **Extra Practice 1**

Section 5.1: Collecting Data

1. Are primary data or secondary data collected in each situation? How do you know?
   a) Ben used a telephone book to find his friend's phone number.
   b) Tom asked a friend for her e-mail address.
   c) Claire found the population of each province in an atlas.
   d) Mr. Morris recorded his students' math test scores.

2. Comment on each survey question. If it is biased, write an unbiased question.
   a) Football players sometimes get injured. Do you think football is a dangerous sport?
   Yes ___ No ___

   b) White cars get dirty very quickly. Which car colour do you prefer?
   Black ___ White ___ Blue ___ Red ___ Other ___

3. a) Predict your classmates' favourite pet.

   b) Write a survey question you could ask to find out.
   Explain how you know your question is unbiased.

   c) Conduct the survey. Tally the results.

   d) How did your prediction compare with your results?

Name ____________ Date ____________

Master 5.16 **Extra Practice 2**

Section 5.2: Recording Data

1. The table shows the favourite Canadian football teams of some Grade 7 students at Mother Teresa Junior High School in Ottawa.

Favourite Canadian Football Team		
Football Team	Tally	Frequency
Hamilton Tiger-Cats	[illegible]	
Calgary Stampeders	[illegible]	
B.C. Lions	[illegible]	
Winnipeg Blue Bombers	[illegible]	
Edmonton Eskimos	[illegible]	
Saskatchewan Roughriders	[illegible]	
Montreal Alouettes	[illegible]	
Ottawa Renegades	[illegible]	
Toronto Argonauts	[illegible]	

a) Complete the frequency column.

b) How many students were surveyed? How do you know?

c) Which team is the most popular? The least popular?
Give some possible reasons for these results.

d) Graph your data. Justify your choice of graph.

e) Write a question you could answer using the graph or frequency table. Answer the question.

Name ____________ Date ____________

Master 5.17 **Extra Practice 3**

Section 5.3: Stem-and-Leaf Plots

1.

Daily Price, in Cents, of One Litre of Gas Over a Two-Month Period	
Stem	Leaf
56.	6 7 9
58.	2 4 5 5 6 7
62.	0 3 4 4 5 8 9
65.	0 1 3 3 5 6 7 9
67.	3 4 5 6 6 7 8 9
70.	0 3 4 6 7 7 8
73.	2 2 2 4 5 7 8 8
75.	1 3 4 4 4 6 7 8 9 9
76.	1 1 8 8

a) What does the stem-and-leaf plot show?

b) What is the lowest price? The highest price?

c) What is the range of the prices?

d) What is the median price? The mode price?

2. Angie recorded the masses, in kilograms, of fish caught on a fishing trip.
2.3, 5.0, 2.7, 0.9, 3.1, 3.8, 5.1, 4.4, 2.6, 3.2, 1.8, 2.5, 0.7, 1.2, 3.3, 1.5, 3.7, 0.8, 2.3, 3.9, 4.3, 4.7, 2.2, 3.9, 4.0, 2.1, 3.0, 1.1, 0.6, 3.9, 2.0, 4.7, 5.1, 4.6, 5.0, 3.4, 2.9, 4.1, 4.2, 3.5

a) Display the data in a stem-and-leaf plot.

b) How many fish were caught?

c) What is the greatest mass? The least mass?

d) What is the range of the masses? The median mass? The mode mass?

Name ____________ Date ____________

Master 5.18 **Extra Practice 4**

Section 5.4: Line Graphs

1. *Source:* Statistics Canada
The data in the table have been rounded to the nearest whole number.

Percent of Households With At Least One Regular Internet User		
Year	Newfoundland/ Labrador	British Columbia
1998	29	42
1999	35	48
2000	46	56
2001	50	65
2002	51	66

a) What does this table show?

b) Draw a line graph for each province on the same grid.

c) Describe the trends for the two provinces. How do the line graphs illustrate the trends?

d) How are the graphs similar? How are they different?

e) Predict the percent of households with at least one regular Internet user for each province in 2005. Explain your prediction.

Name ____________ Date ____________

Master 5.19 **Extra Practice 5**

Section 5.5: Applications of Mean, Median, and Mode

1. Here are a student's practice times, in seconds, for the 200-m backstroke:
215, 211, 222, 215, 212, 211, 218, 215, 220, 218, 216
   a) Find the mean, median, and mode of these data.
   b) Of the mean, median, and mode, which do you think best describes the race time? Explain.
   c) What is the range of these data?
   d) What time must the student get in the 12th practice so that the mean time is 215 s?
   Is this possible? Explain.

2. A quality control inspector randomly selects boxes of cereal from the production line.
She measures their masses. On one day she selects 40 boxes. The inspector records these data:
11 boxes: 415 g, 4 boxes: 418 g, 8 boxes: 420 g, 10 boxes: 422 g, 7 boxes: 430 g
   a) Write an expression that can be used to calculate the mean mass.
   b) Find the mean, median, and mode mass.
   c) For the shipment of cereal to be acceptable, the mean mass must be at least 420 g.
   Is this shipment acceptable? Explain.
   d) Suppose she selects 5 more boxes, each with the same mass. The mean mass of the 45 boxes is now 419.6 g. What is the mass of each of the 5 new boxes?

Name ____________ Date ____________

Master 5.20 **Extra Practice 6**

Section 5.6: Evaluating Data Analysis

1. Draw a graph to display the data in each way.

Northern City Snow Removal Budget	
Year	Amount ($)
1997	510 000
1998	515 000
1999	518 000
2000	521 000
2001	525 000
2002	530 000
2003	533 000
2004	535 000

a) Northern City Council wants to show it has substantially increased the snow removal budget. Explain how your graph shows this.

b) Northern City Taxpayers want to show the snow removal budget has hardly changed. Explain how your graph shows this.

Name ____________ Date ____________

Master 5.21 **Sample Answers**

Extra Practice 1 – Master 5.15
Section 5.1

1. a) Secondary data; Ben used a book to collect the data.
   b) Primary data; Tom collected the data herself.
   c) Secondary data; Claire used a book to collect the data.
   d) Primary data; Mr. Morris collected the data himself.
2. a) Biased; the question includes a statement that may encourage people to answer "Yes."
   Do you think football is a dangerous sport?
   Yes ___ *No* ___
   b) Biased; the question includes a statement that may influence people's answer.
   Which car colour do you prefer?
   Black ___ *White* ___ *Blue* ___ *Red* ___ *Other* ___
3. a) Hamster
   b) What is your favourite pet? Dog ___ Cat ___ Bird ___ Hamster ___ Fish ___ Other ___
   c)

Favourite Pet		
Pet	Tally	Frequency
Dog	//// //// /	11
Cat	//// /	6
Bird	//	2
Hamster	////	5
Fish	//	2
Other	/	1

   d) A dog is my classmates' favourite pet. This is not what I had predicted.

Extra Practice 2 – Master 5.16
Section 5.2

1. a) Frequency column: 8, 6, 10, 11, 9, 5, 2, 17, 7
   b) 75; the total of the numbers in the frequency column is 75.
   c) Most popular: Ottawa Renegades
   Least popular: Montreal Alouettes
   The school is located in Ottawa so the Ottawa team would be the favourite team. Montreal is the closest rival in the Eastern division, so it would be the least favourite team.
   d)

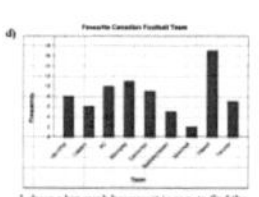

   I chose a bar graph because it is easy to find the favourite team by looking for the longest bar.
   e) Which team is twice as popular as the Saskatchewan Roughriders? (*Answer: The B.C. Lions*)

Extra Practice 3 – Master 5.17
Section 5.3

1. a) The daily price, in cents, of one litre of gas over a two-month period
   b) 56.6¢; 76.8¢ c) 20.2¢
   d) 67.75¢; 73.2¢ and 75.4¢
2. a)

Mass, in Kilograms, of Fish Caught	
Stem	Leaf
0.	6 7 8 9
1.	1 2 5 8
2.	0 1 2 3 3 5 6 7 9
3.	0 1 2 3 4 5 7 8 9 9 9
4.	0 1 2 3 4 6 7 7
5.	0 0 1 1

   b) 40 c) 5.1 kg; 0.6 kg
   d) 4.5 kg; 3.25 kg; 3.9 kg

Extra Practice 4 – Master 5.18
Section 5.4

1. a) The percent of households in Newfoundland/Labrador and British Columbia with at least one regular Internet user

Name ____________ Date ____________

   b)

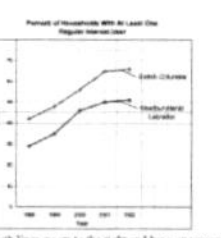

   c) Both lines go up to the right and have an upward trend. This means the percent of households with regular Internet users is increasing in both provinces.
   d) Both line graphs have an upward trend and both seem to level off between 2001 and 2002. The line graph for B.C. is above the line graph for Newfoundland/Labrador. This means that there is a higher percent of Internet users in B.C.
   e) Newfoundland/Labrador: about 54%
   B.C.: about 69%
   I extended the line for each province and I assumed the trends would remain the same.

Extra Practice 5 – Master 5.19
Section 5.5

1. a) Mean: approximately 215.7 s; median: 215 s; mode: 215 s
   b) Any of the measures would best describe the race time because all 3 are close in value.
   c) 11 s
   d) 207 s; it would be very difficult for the student to reduce her or his best time by 4 s.
2. a) [(11 × 415) + (8 × 420) + (10 × 422) + (7 × 430) + (4 × 418)] ÷ 40
   b) Mean: approximately 420.7 g; median: 420 g; mode: 415 g
   c) Yes, the mean mass is greater than 420 g.
   d) 411 g

Extra Practice 6 – Master 5.20
Section 5.6

1.

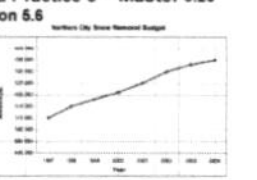

The vertical axis starts at $495 000 instead of 0. The scale on the vertical axis is 1 square represents $5000. This graph makes it look like the budget is increasing at a fast rate.

b)

The vertical axis starts at 0. The scale is 1 square represents $100 000. This graph makes it look like the budget is increasing very little.

Addison Wesley
Mathematics Makes Sense

Program Authors

Jason Johnston
Bryn Keyes
Mary Doucette
Antonietta Lenjosek
Steve Thomas
Margaret Sinclair
Trevor Brown
Cathy Heideman
Don Jones
Michael Davis
Jennifer Paziuk
Ken Harper
Sharon Jeroski
Ray Appel
Laura Weatherhead
Betty Milne
Jim Mennie
Lynn Strangway

Printed and bound in Canada

10 17

PEARSON
Education Canada

ADDISON WESLEY

Ontario

Math Makes Sense 7

Ontario

Teacher Guide

Unit 6: Measuring Perimeter and Area

PEARSON
Addison Wesley

UNIT 6

Measuring Perimeter and Area

"Before anything can be measured meaningfully, it is necessary to understand the attribute to be measured."

John A. Van de Walle

FOCUS STRANDS
Measurement
Patterning and Algebra

SUPPORTING STRANDS
Geometry
Number Sense and Numeration

TIPS
Adolescent learners require opportunities to progress through different representations (concrete to diagrams to symbolic). Use formulas only after students have personally developed them.

Mathematics Background

What Are the Big Ideas?

- Area formulas provide a method of measuring area by using only measures of length.
- Irregular figures can be subdivided to form smaller figures whose areas can be calculated by using formulas.

How Will the Concepts Develop?

Students use concrete materials and grid paper to make and record different parallelograms. They discover that the same formula is used to calculate the area of a parallelogram and the area of a rectangle.

Students understand that any two congruent triangles can be arranged to form a parallelogram. From this, students conclude that the area of a triangle is one-half the area of a parallelogram that has the same base and the same height.

Students use concrete materials to investigate the area of a trapezoid. They find the area of a trapezoid in different ways by combining different figures, then use this strategy to find the areas of other irregular figures. Students solve problems involving the estimation and calculation of the perimeter and area of irregular figures.

Why Are These Concepts Important?

Frequent exposure to the concepts of area and perimeter helps students develop an understanding of the measurement process. A solid foundation in area and perimeter is necessary for students to succeed with the concepts of volume and surface area.

The ability to measure is a life skill. We measure area and/or perimeter when we lay carpet, paint a wall, put baseboard around a room, wallpaper a room, build a fence, and so on. Measurement is pervasive in our lives and it is important that students not only learn the formulas, but understand how they are developed and why they work.

Curriculum Overview

Overall Expectations

- Demonstrate a verbal and written understanding of and ability to apply accurate measurement strategies that relate to their environment. (7m28)
- Identify relationships between and among measurement concepts. (7m29)
- Solve problems related to the calculation and comparison of the perimeter and the area of irregular two-dimensional shapes. (7m30)
- Identify the relationships between whole numbers and variables. (7m66)
- Identify, create, and solve simple algebraic equations. (7m68)

Specific Expectations

- Create definitions of measurement concepts. (7m32)
- Describe measurement concepts using appropriate measurement vocabulary. (7m33)
- Research and report on uses of measurement instruments in projects at home, in the workplace, and in the community. (7m34)
- Make increasingly more informed and accurate measurement estimations based on an understanding of formulas and the results of investigations. (7m35)
- Understand that irregular two-dimensional shapes can be decomposed into simple two-dimensional shapes to find the area and perimeter. (7m36)
- Estimate and calculate the perimeter and area of an irregular two-dimensional shape. (7m37)
- Develop the formula for finding the area of a trapezoid. (7m38)
- Estimate and calculate the area of a trapezoid, using a formula. (7m39)
- Draw a trapezoid given its area and/or perimeter. (7m40)
- Develop the formulas for finding the area of a parallelogram and the area of a triangle. (7m41)
- Interpret a variable as a symbol that may be replaced by a given set of numbers. (7m73)
- Evaluate simple algebraic expressions by substituting natural numbers for the variables. (7m76)

Launch

Section 6.1:
Area of a Parallelogram

Section 6.2:
Area of a Triangle

Mid-Unit Review

Section 6.3:
Area and Perimeter of a Trapezoid

Section 6.4:
Measuring Irregular Figures

Unit Review
Practice Test

Unit Problem
Designing a Patio

Curriculum across the Grades

Grade 6	Grade 7	Grade 8
Students select the most appropriate standard unit to measure the perimeter of irregular polygons. Students understand the relationships among the areas of a rectangle, a parallelogram, and a triangle, with the same base and the same height. Students estimate and calculate the areas of a parallelogram and a triangle, using word formulas.	Students create definitions of measurement concepts. They describe measurement concepts using appropriate measurement vocabulary. Students research and report on uses of measurement instruments in projects at home, in the workplace, and in the community. Students understand that irregular figures can be decomposed into simpler figures to find the area and perimeter. They estimate and calculate the perimeter and area of an irregular figure. Students develop algebraic formulas for finding the area of a parallelogram and the area of a triangle. Students develop a formula for finding the area of a trapezoid, and estimate and calculate the area of a trapezoid, using a formula. They draw a trapezoid given its area and/or perimeter.	Students research, describe, and report on uses of measurement in projects at home, in the workplace, and in the community that require precise measurements. Students measure the radius, diameter, and circumference of a circle. They investigate to find an approximate value for π. Students develop the formulas for the circumference and the area of a circle. They estimate and calculate the radius, diameter, circumference, and area of a circle. Students draw a circle given its area and/or circumference.

Additional Activities

Triangles and Parallelograms

For Extra Support (Appropriate for use after Section 6.2)
Materials: *Triangles and Parallelograms* (Master 6.5), deck of cards with face cards removed, 1-cm grid paper (PM 20), rulers, calculators

Playing this game reinforces the concept that the area of a triangle is one-half the area of a parallelogram with the same height and base.

The work students do: Students play with a partner. Students use a deck of cards to generate two numbers for the base and height of a parallelogram and triangle. Students draw the figures and find their areas. Students score points. Play continues until one player reaches 10 points.

Take It Further: Students calculate the perimeters of their figures.

Visual/Social/Logical
Partner Activity

Triangle Puzzle

For Extra Practice (Appropriate for use after Section 6.2.)
Materials: *Triangle Puzzle* (Master 6.6), paper, scissors, rulers, calculators

This activity reinforces students' understanding of the area of a triangle.

The work students do: Students work alone. Students measure and record the dimensions of a sheet of paper, then calculate its area. Students use a ruler to divide the paper into 8–10 triangles of different sizes. Students label each triangle, then calculate its area. Students record the areas in a table. Students add the areas of the triangles and compare the total area to the area of the sheet of paper. Students reflect upon their observations.

Take It Further: Students order the triangles from least to greatest area.

Kinesthetic/Mathematical
Individual Activity

Pattern Block Figures

For Extra Practice (Appropriate for use after Section 6.4)
Materials: *Pattern Block Figures* (Master 6.7), Pattern Blocks (PM 25), 1-cm grid paper (PM 20), rulers, calculators

This activity reinforces the skills of finding the area of an irregular figure.

The work students do: Students work alone. Students use at least 6 Pattern Blocks to make an irregular figure. Students copy their figures onto grid paper. They find the area of the irregular figure. Students should include a formula in words for the area of the irregular figure.

Take It Further: Students find the perimeter of the irregular figure.

Logical/Mathematical/Kinesthetic
Individual Activity

Rule the School

For Extension (Appropriate for use after Section 6.4)
Materials: *Rule the School* (Master 6.8), measuring tapes, calculators, 1-cm grid paper (PM 20), rulers

This activity extends and provides a real-life context for students' understanding of the area and perimeter of irregular figures.

The work students do: Students work in small groups. Students discuss strategies for measuring the area of ground the school covers and the perimeter of the school. Students use measuring tapes to measure the dimensions of the school, then sketch the school and label its dimensions. Students use calculators to find the approximate perimeter and area of the school.

Take It Further: Students make a scale drawing of the school on 1-cm grid paper.

Logical/Social/Spatial
Group Activity

Planning for Unit 6

Planning for Instruction

Suggested Unit time: About 2 weeks

Section	Time	Materials	Program Support
Launch, page 2	15–20 min		
Skills You'll Need, page 4	25–30 min	calculators (optional)	
6.1: Area of a Parallelogram, page 5 Use a formula to find the area of a parallelogram.	80–100 min	tangrams grid paper protractors rulers tracing paper	PM 26: Tangram PM 14: 0.5-cm Grid Paper PM 20: 1-cm Grid Paper Master 6.9: Step-by-Step 1 Master 6.17: Extra Practice 1
6.2: Area of a Triangle, page 9 Use a formula to find the area of a triangle.	80–100 min	rulers grid paper	PM 20: 1-cm Grid Paper Master 6.10: Step-by-Step 2 Master 6.17: Extra Practice 1
Mid-Unit Review, page 13		calculators	
6.3: Area and Perimeter of a Trapezoid, page 14 Use a formula to find the area of a trapezoid.	80–100 min	calculators scissors Figures for Explore rulers pieces of string pushpins (4 per student) grid paper isometric grid paper red Pattern Blocks	PM 20: 1-cm Grid Paper PM 24: Isometric Grid Paper PM 25: Pattern Blocks Master 6.13: Figures for Section 6.3, *Explore* Master 6.11: Step-by-Step 3 Master 6.18: Extra Practice 2
Reading and Writing in Math: Interpreting a Problem, page 20		calculators grid paper rulers	PM 14: 0.5-cm Grid Paper PM 20: 1-cm Grid Paper
6.4: Measuring Irregular Figures, page 22 Find the area and perimeter of an irregular figure.	80–100 min	overhead Pattern Blocks rulers calculators grid paper	PM 20: 1-cm Grid Paper Master 6.12: Step-by-Step 4 Master 6.18: Extra Practice 2
Game: Trapezoid Challenge, page 26		11 by 11 geoboards geobands number cubes labelled 1 to 6 square dot paper calculators 1-cm grid paper (optional)	PM 22: Square Dot Paper PM 20: 1-cm Grid Paper
Unit Review, page 27		1-cm grid paper calculators (optional) rulers (optional)	PM 20: 1-cm Grid Paper Extra Practice: Student Book page 443
Practice Test, page 29		rulers calculators 1-cm grid paper	PM 20: 1-cm Grid Paper
Unit Problem: Designing a Patio, page 30	80–100 min	calculators Patio Grid coloured pencils or markers rulers Pattern Blocks tangrams	Master 6.14: Patio Grid for Unit Problem PM 25: Pattern Blocks PM 26: Tangram

etext online tutorial

This web-based tutorial uses voice, animation, and an optional quiz to present each core lesson, so that students can review content with a new approach.

Planning for Assessment

Purpose	Tools and Process	Recording and Reporting
Diagnostic	*Unit Launch* Question; conference; scaffold problems throughout the unit	PM 8: Conference Prompts
Formative	*Explore* – Ongoing Assessment: Observe and Listen	Master 6.2: Ongoing Observations: Measuring Perimeter and Area PM 1: Inquiry Process Check List PM 6: Observation Record 1 PM 7: Observation Record 2 PM 8: Conference Prompts PM 2: Self-Assessment PM 3: Self-Assessment: Problem Solving PM 9: Work Sample Records
Summative	Unit Review *Unit Problem* – Performance Assessment Unit Test Review assessment records; add unit results to ongoing records	Master 6.1: Unit Rubric: Measuring Perimeter and Area Master 6.3: Performance Assessment Rubric: Designing a Patio Master 6.4: Unit Summary: Measuring Perimeter and Area PM 10: Summary Class Records: Strands PM 11: Summary Class Records: Achievement Categories PM 12: Summary Record: Individual
Learning Skills/ Mathematical Disposition	Observe and record throughout the unit	PM 4: Learning Skills Check List PM 5: Mathematical Dispositions and Learning Skills

Program Masters (PM) are in the *Grade 7 Planning and Program Masters* module.
Extra Practice Masters are on the CD-ROM and are printed in reduced format on page 51 of this module.

SECTION ORGANIZER

15–20 min

Curriculum Focus: Activate prior learning about perimeter and area.
Vocabulary: perimeter, area

ASSUMED PRIOR KNOWLEDGE

- ✓ Students understand the difference between perimeter and area.
- ✓ Students can calculate the perimeter and area of a square and a rectangle using formulas expressed in variables.
- ✓ Students can calculate the area of a parallelogram and the area of a triangle, using formulas expressed in words.

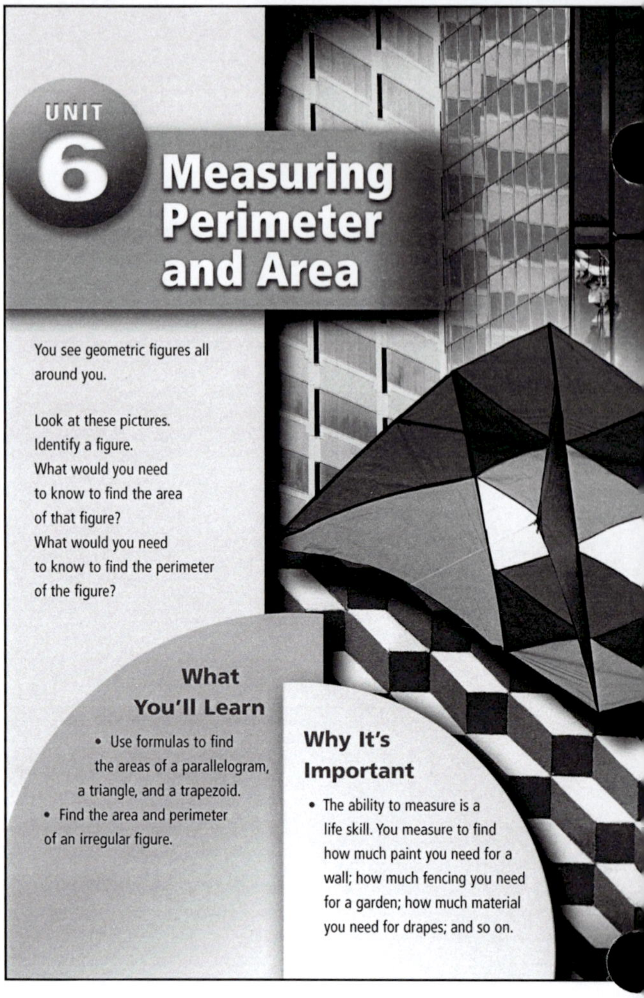

ACTIVATE PRIOR LEARNING

Have students look at the pictures on pages 214 and 215 of the Student Book and identify the geometric figures they contain. Remind students of the meanings of the terms **perimeter** and **area.** Perimeter is the distance around a figure and area is the amount of surface a figure covers. Perimeter is measured in units and area in square units. Ask questions, such as:

- Where have you seen geometric figures around you? (*In buildings, in plant pots, in road signs, and in wallpaper*)
- Name one figure you see in these pictures. (*A rectangle*) What would you need to know to find the area of the rectangle? (*I would need to know the length and the width of the rectangle because the area of a rectangle is* $A = b \times h$.) The perimeter of the rectangle? (*The length and width of the rectangle because the perimeter of a rectangle is* $P = 2(b + h)$.)
- What other figure do you see? (*A parallelogram*) What would you need to know to find the area of the parallelogram? (*I would need to know its base and height, because the area of a parallelogram is base × height.*) The perimeter of the parallelogram? (*I would need to know the side lengths because the perimeter is the sum of the 4 side lengths.*)

Tell students that, in this unit, they will investigate measuring perimeter and area. They will use formulas to find the areas of a parallelogram, a triangle, and a trapezoid. They will also find the area and perimeter of an irregular figure. At the end of the unit, students will use their understanding of measuring perimeter and area to design a patio for a large shopping centre.

Key Words

- perimeter
- area
- parallelogram
- triangle
- trapezoid

FROM THE LIBRARY

Math in the Real World of Architecture: Dimensions, Quantities, Shapes and Patterns by Shirley Cook. Incentive Publications, 1999
ISBN: 0865303428
This book provides students with a unique insight into how the art and science of architecture is built upon dimensions, quantities, shapes, and patterns. Activities cover topics such as perimeter, area, 2-D figures, and 3-D objects. Students learn how mathematical theorems and concepts can be used together to create plans for homes and buildings.

The Kids' Stuff Book of Math for the Middle Grades by Marjorie Frank. Incentive Publications, 1988
ISBN: 0865300127
These appealing, high-interest activities will challenge students' reasoning abilities while teaching the basics of the middle school math curriculum, including measurement, area, perimeter, and problem solving. Contains reproducible student activity pages.

REACHING ALL LEARNERS

Some students may benefit from using the virtual manipulatives on the e-Tools CD-ROM. The e-Tool appropriate for this unit is *Geometry Drawing*.

DIAGNOSTIC ASSESSMENT

What to Look For	What to Do
✔ Students understand the difference between perimeter and area.	***Extra Support:*** Students who have difficulty understanding the difference between area and perimeter should draw a figure. They use one colour for the perimeter and use the same colour to write the word "perimeter." Students use a different colour to shade the area and to write the word "area." *Work on this skill during Skills You'll Need.*
✔ Students can calculate the perimeter and area of a square and a rectangle using formulas expressed in variables.	Students who have difficulty calculating the perimeter and area using formulas expressed in variables should rewrite the formula in words before they use it. *Work on this skill during Skills You'll Need.*
✔ Students can calculate the areas of a parallelogram and a triangle using formulas expressed in words.	Students who have difficulty calculating the areas of a parallelogram and a triangle using formulas expressed in words should use figures drawn on grid paper, count squares and part squares, then relate the area to the base and height. *Work on this skill during Sections 6.1 and 6.2.*

SECTION ORGANIZER

25-30 min

Skills in Review: Calculating the perimeter and area of a rectangle.

Student Materials

- calculators (optional)

Vocabulary: perimeter, area

Alternative Example 1

A rectangular garden has dimensions 12.5 m by 6.0 m. Find the perimeter and area of the garden.

Solution

The garden is a rectangle.

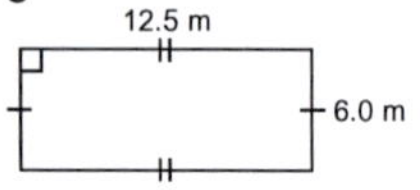

The perimeter of a rectangle is: $P = 2(b + h)$

Substitute $b = 12.5$ and $h = 6$.

$P = 2(12.5 + 6)$

$= 2 \times 18.5$

$= 37$

The perimeter is 37 m.

The area of a rectangle is: $A = bh$.

Substitute $b = 12.5$ and $h = 6$.

$A = 12.5 \times 6$

$= 75$

The area of the garden is 75 m^2.

UNIT 6

Skills You'll Need

Perimeter and Area of a Rectangle

Perimeter is the distance around a figure.

Area is the amount of surface a figure covers.

Example 1

a) Find the perimeter of each figure.

i)

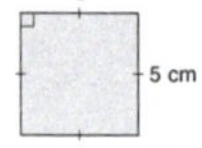

ii)

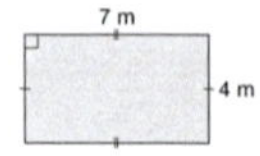

b) Find the area of each figure in part a.

Solution

a) i) The figure is a square.
The perimeter of a square is: $P = 4s$
Substitute $s = 5$.
$P = 4 \times 5$
$= 20$
The perimeter is 20 cm.

ii) The figure is a rectangle.
The perimeter of a rectangle is: $P = 2(b$
Substitute $b = 7$ and $h = 4$.
$P = 2(7 + 4)$
$= 2 \times 11$
$= 22$
The perimeter is 22 m.

b) i) The area of a square is: $A = s^2$
Substitute $s = 5$.
$A = 5^2$
$= 5 \times 5$
$= 25$
The area is 25 cm^2.

ii) The area of a rectangle is: $A = bh$
Substitute $b = 7$ and $h = 4$.
$A = 7 \times 4$
$= 28$
The area is 28 m^2.

✓ Check

1. Find the perimeter and area of each figure.

a)

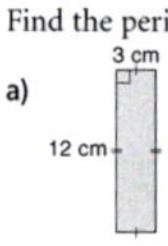

$P = 30$ cm
$A = 36$ cm^2

b)

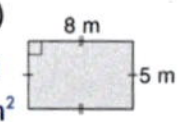

$P = 26$ m
$A = 40$ m^2

c)

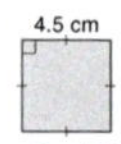

$P = 18$ cm
$A = 20.25$ cm^2

d)

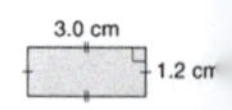

$P = 8.4$ cm
$A = 3.6$ cm^2

216 UNIT 6: Measuring Perimeter and Area

Perimeter and Area of a Rectangle

Remind students of the work they did in Unit 3, Section 3.4, on the algebraic representations of the formulas for perimeter and area of a rectangle and a square.

If it is necessary, have students draw the rectangles in the *Example* and *Check* on grid paper. They will need to use a scale of 1 cm (or 0.5 cm) to 1 m for the rectangle in *Example*, part b. They can count squares (and part squares as necessary) to find the area, and measure the sides to find the perimeter. Make sure students relate these results to the results obtained using the formulas.

Common Misconceptions

➤ Students report area and perimeter measures without the appropriate units.

How to Help: Remind students that it is important to indicate which unit has been used.

Ensure students understand that perimeter is measured in units and area is measured in square units. Have students use metre sticks to outline an area of 1 m^2 and relate it to the area of 1 cm^2 on 1-cm grid paper. This comparison illustrates the difference in the areas and the importance of using the correct units.

➤ Students misinterpret a power, such as 5^2, as 5×2.

How to Help: Remind students that the exponent 2 indicates how many 5s are multiplied; that is, 5^2 means 5×5.

➤ Students do not use the correct order of operations when evaluating the perimeter of a rectangle.

How to Help: Remind students that the operations in brackets are done first, and the number outside a bracket indicates multiplication. If it helps, have students write the multiplication sign:

$2(7 + 4) = 2 \times (7 + 4)$.

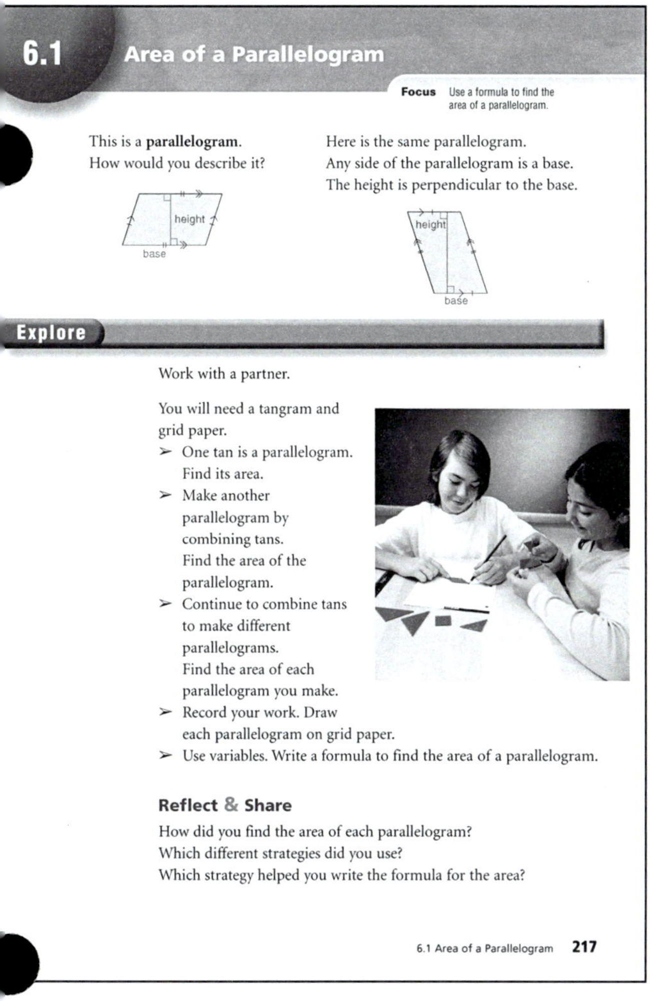
6.1 Area of a Parallelogram

Focus Use a formula to find the area of a parallelogram.

This is a **parallelogram**.
How would you describe it?

Here is the same parallelogram.
Any side of the parallelogram is a base.
The height is perpendicular to the base.

Explore

Work with a partner.

You will need a tangram and grid paper.

➢ One tan is a parallelogram. Find its area.
➢ Make another parallelogram by combining tans. Find the area of the parallelogram.
➢ Continue to combine tans to make different parallelograms. Find the area of each parallelogram you make.
➢ Record your work. Draw each parallelogram on grid paper.
➢ Use variables. Write a formula to find the area of a parallelogram.

Reflect & Share

How did you find the area of each parallelogram?
Which different strategies did you use?
Which strategy helped you write the formula for the area?

6.1 Area of a Parallelogram 217

Area of a Parallelogram

SECTION ORGANIZER (80–100 min)

Curriculum Focus: Use a formula to find the area of a parallelogram. (7m32, 7m33, 7m35, 7m41, 7m73, 7m76)

Student Materials
- tangram (PM 26)
- 0.5-cm grid paper (PM 14)
- 1-cm grid paper (PM 20)
- protractors
- rulers
- tracing paper

Optional
- Step-by-Step 1 (Master 6.9)
- Extra Practice 1 (Master 6.17)

Vocabulary: parallelogram

Assessment: Master 6.2 Ongoing Observations: Measuring Perimeter and Area

Key Math Learnings

1. The area of a parallelogram is equal to the area of a rectangle with the same height and base.
2. To find the area of a parallelogram, multiply its base by its height. The formula for the area is $A = bh$.

BEFORE Get Started

Invite students to examine the parallelograms on page 217 of the Student Book.

Ask:

- How would you describe a parallelogram? (*A parallelogram is a figure with 4 sides, and 2 pairs of opposite sides are equal and parallel.*)
- How could you show that these two parallelograms are congruent? (*I could use tracing paper to trace the parallelogram, then place the tracing on top of the other parallelogram and show that they coincide.*)

Ensure students understand that the base and height are perpendicular.

Present *Explore*. Distribute tangrams (PM 26) and 0.5-cm grid paper (PM 14) to pairs of students.

DURING Explore

Ongoing Assessment: Observe and Listen

As students work, ask questions, such as:

- How did you find the area of the tan that is a parallelogram? (*I drew the parallelogram on 0.5-cm grid paper, then counted whole squares and half squares. There were 28 whole squares and 8 half squares. Eight half squares = 4 whole squares. The area of the parallelogram is 28 + 4 = 32 grid squares.*)
- Did anyone use a different strategy to find the area of a parallelogram? Explain. (*I used the formula we learned in grade 6. The area of a parallelogram is base × height. I measured the base as 7.8 cm. The height is 3.4 cm. So, the area is 7.8 cm × 3.4 cm = 26.52 cm².*)
- How did you use variables to write the formula for the area? (*I know area = base × height, so I used A for area, b for base, and h for height; so, A = bh.*)

REACHING ALL LEARNERS

Alternative Explore

Materials: 1-cm grid paper (PM 20), rulers
Have students draw 4 different parallelograms on grid paper. They find the base, the height, and the area of each parallelogram. Students use their results to use variables to write a formula for the area of a parallelogram.

Early Finishers

Have students use the Internet or an encyclopedia to find flags of different countries that contain a parallelogram. Students find the area of each parallelogram they find.

Common Misconceptions

➤ Students use a side length as the height of a parallelogram.
How to Help: Tell students that the height of a parallelogram is the perpendicular distance from the base to the opposite side. The side length of a parallelogram is equal to the height only when the parallelogram is a square or a rectangle.

Mental Math

Students could use a calendar. Students could place a red counter on all Wednesdays in January and February. They could count on by 5s from January 14th and place a blue counter on all dates counted. Students find the next date that has both a red and a blue counter. Stronger math students may recognize that the lowest common multiple of 5 and 7 is 35, then count on 35 days, or 5 weeks, from January 14. Students should know that there are 31 days in January.

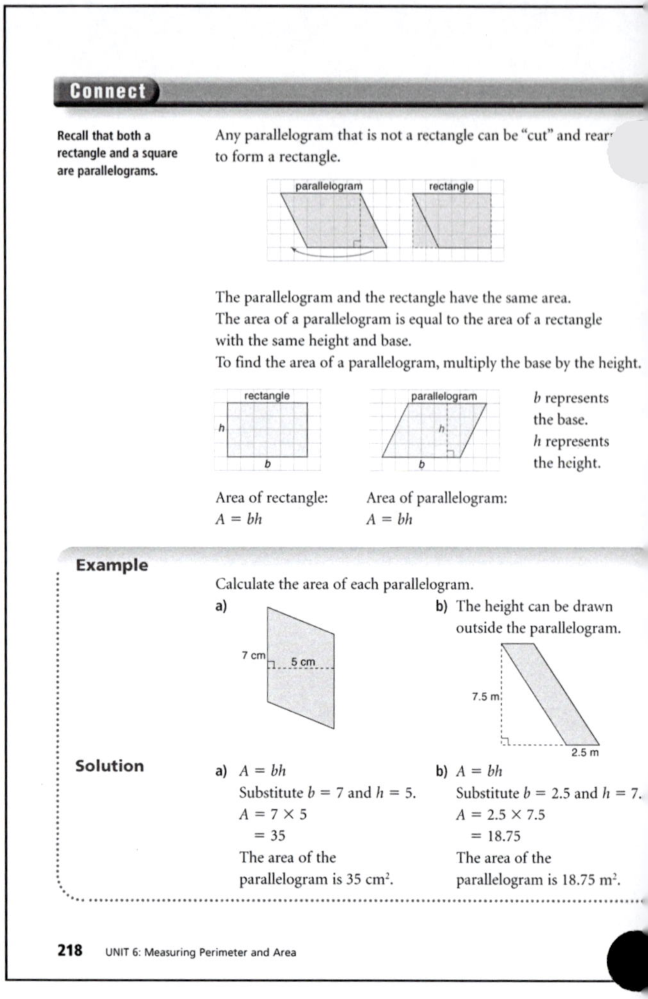

Connect

Recall that both a rectangle and a square are parallelograms.

Any parallelogram that is not a rectangle can be "cut" and rearr[anged] to form a rectangle.

The parallelogram and the rectangle have the same area.
The area of a parallelogram is equal to the area of a rectangle with the same height and base.
To find the area of a parallelogram, multiply the base by the height.

b represents the base.
h represents the height.

Area of rectangle: $A = bh$ Area of parallelogram: $A = bh$

Example

Calculate the area of each parallelogram.
a)
b) The height can be drawn outside the parallelogram.

Solution

a) $A = bh$
Substitute $b = 7$ and $h = 5$.
$A = 7 \times 5$
$= 35$
The area of the parallelogram is 35 cm².

b) $A = bh$
Substitute $b = 2.5$ and $h = 7.5$
$A = 2.5 \times 7.5$
$= 18.75$
The area of the parallelogram is 18.75 m².

218 UNIT 6: Measuring Perimeter and Area

AFTER Connect

Invite students to share their drawings and formulas with the class.

What you might see:

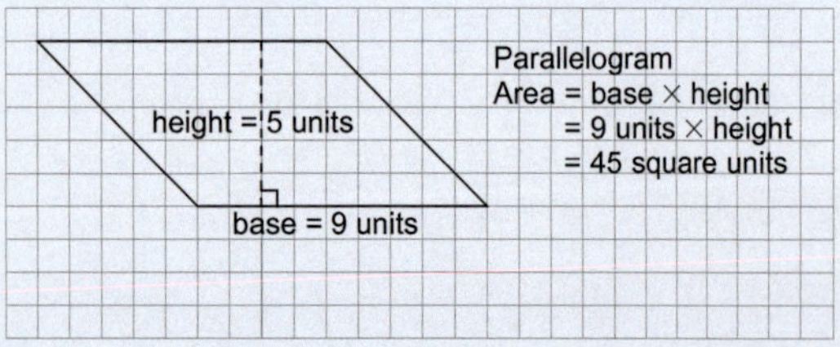

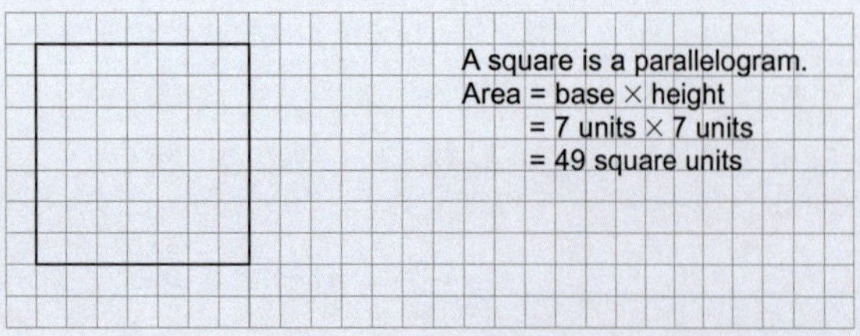

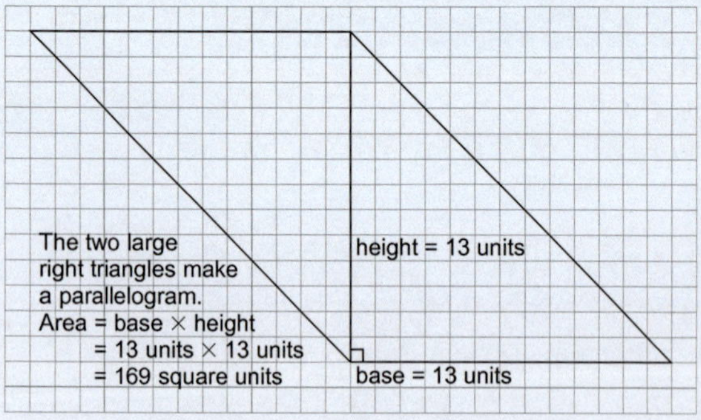

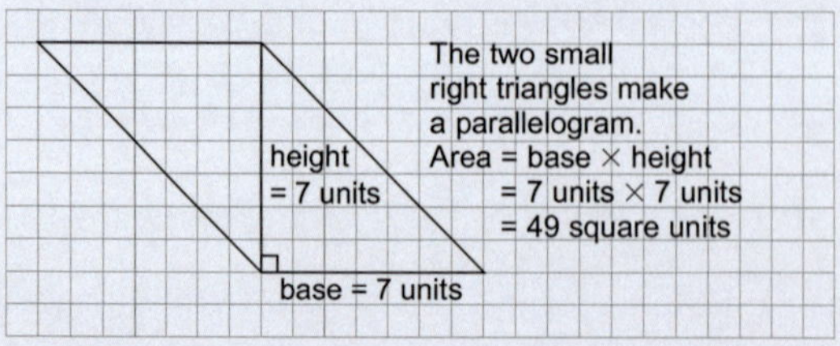

Practice

that you can use
tractor to draw
the height perpendicular
to the base.

The base of a
parallelogram is not
always horizontal.

1. Identify one base and height of each parallelogram.

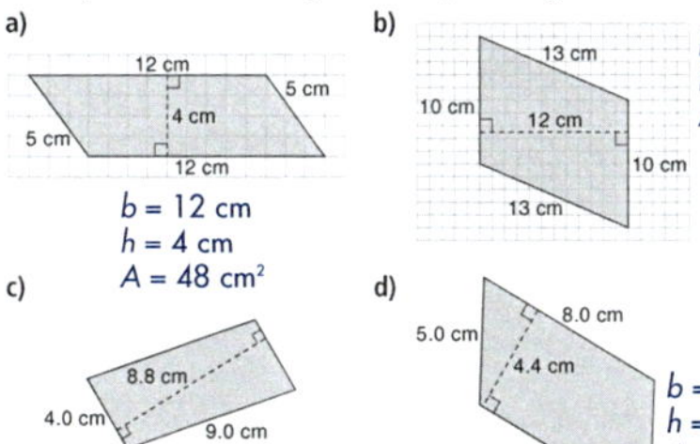

a) $b = 12$ cm, $h = 4$ cm, $A = 48$ cm²
b) $b = 10$ cm, $h = 12$ cm, $A = 120$ cm²
c) $b = 4.0$ cm, $h = 8.8$ cm, $A = 35.2$ cm²
d) $b = 8.0$ cm, $h = 4.4$ cm, $A = 35.2$ cm²

2. Find the area of each parallelogram in question 1.

3. a) On 1-cm grid paper, draw 3 different parallelograms with each base and height.
   i) base: 3 cm; height: 5 cm ii) base: 3.5 cm; height: 7.0 cm
   b) Find the area of each parallelogram you drew in part a. What do you notice? i) 15 cm² ii) 24.5 cm²

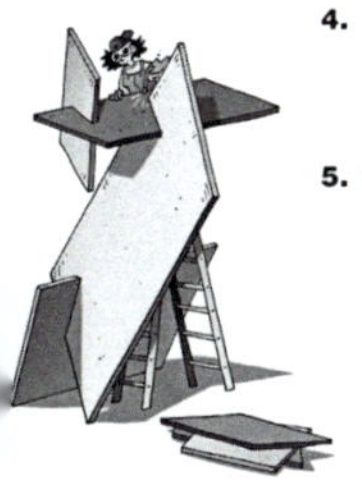

4. On 1-cm grid paper, draw as many different parallelograms as you can with each area.
   a) 10 cm² b) 18 cm² c) 28 cm²

5. **Assessment Focus** Use 1-cm grid paper.
   Draw a parallelogram, which is not a rectangle, with base 6 cm and height 4 cm.
   a) What is the area of the parallelogram? 24 cm²
   b) Change the base to draw a parallelogram with twice the area. What is the base? 12 cm
   c) Change the height to draw a parallelogram with twice the area. What is the height? 8 cm
   d) Change the base and height to draw a parallelogram with twice the area.
   How many different pairs of base and height can you find? Show your work.

6.1 Area of a Parallelogram 219

Assignment Guidelines

If your students do not have time to complete all the *Practice* questions on pages 219 and 220, these questions provide minimum curriculum coverage: 1, 2, 4, 5, 6, 8, *Reflect*
To assess the 4 Achievement Chart categories listed in the curriculum document, have students complete these *Practice* questions:
Understanding Concepts: 2; Application: 4; Communication: 8; Problem Solving: 7

Sample Answers

3. b) All parallelograms with the same base and height have the same area.

5. d) Twice the area is 24 cm² × 2 = 48 cm². The base and height must have a product of 48. For example, $b = 1$ cm, $h = 48$ cm; $b = 2$ cm, $h = 24$ cm; $b = 3$ cm, $h = 16$ cm; $b = 4$ cm, $h = 12$ cm; and so on. There are many different pairs of base and height possible. If base and height are not whole numbers of cm, then other answers are possible, such as $b = 0.5$ cm, $h = 96$ cm.

7. a) The base and height must have a product of 30; for example, $b = 1$ cm, $h = 30$ cm; $b = 2$ cm, $h = 15$ cm; and so on.

b) The base and height must have a product of 126; for example, $b = 1$ cm, $h = 126$ cm; $b = 2$ cm, $h = 63$ cm; and so on.

Review *Connect.* Suggest that students who have difficulty seeing the relationship between the parallelogram and the rectangle draw a parallelogram on grid paper, then cut off the right triangle and tape it to the other end of the parallelogram.

Use the examples in *Connect* to show students how to use the formula they developed to find the area of a parallelogram. In the *Example,* part b, the height is drawn outside the parallelogram. Have students practise drawing parallelograms like this on grid paper. Ask them how they know the height cannot be drawn inside the parallelogram.
(*The parallel sides between which the height is drawn do not align; that is, a line drawn perpendicular to one base will not meet the other base.*)

Practice

Questions 3, 4, 5, 7, and 9 require 1-cm grid paper (PM 20). Question 9 requires a ruler and tracing paper. Have protractors available for students who want to use them to draw the height of a parallelogram perpendicular to the base.

Assessment Focus: Question 5

Students understand that, as with a rectangle, doubling the length of either the base or the height of a parallelogram doubles its area. Ask students what happens if both the base and height are doubled (*the area is quadrupled*).

Students who need extra support to complete Assessment Focus questions may benefit from the Step-by-Step masters (Masters 6.9–6.12).

c) The base and height must have a product of 35; for example, $b = 1$ cm, $h = 35$ cm; $b = 2$ cm, $h = 17.5$ cm; and so on.

8. The base of both Figures A and B is 1 m. The height of Figure A equals the height of Figure B, which is the same as the height of the wall. So, both figures have the same area.

9. a) The two triangles have the same size and shape; they are congruent. I can trace one of the triangles, then place it over the other triangle to check that it fits exactly.

c) Since the two triangles are congruent, their areas are equal. Since the area of the parallelogram is 60 cm^2, the area of each triangle must be one-half of 60 cm^2, or 30 cm^2.

10. a) $14.4 \times 6.6 = 95.04$

b) $(14.4 + 5.6) \times 6.6 = 132$

c) The area of the gardens
= total area of the patio and gardens – the area of the patio
$= 132 - 95.04$
$= 36.96$

REFLECT: To find the area of a parallelogram, I need to know the measure of the height and the measure of the base. For example, using the formula $A = bh$, a parallelogram with base 4 cm and height 5 cm has an area of 4 cm $\times$ 5 cm = 20 cm^2.

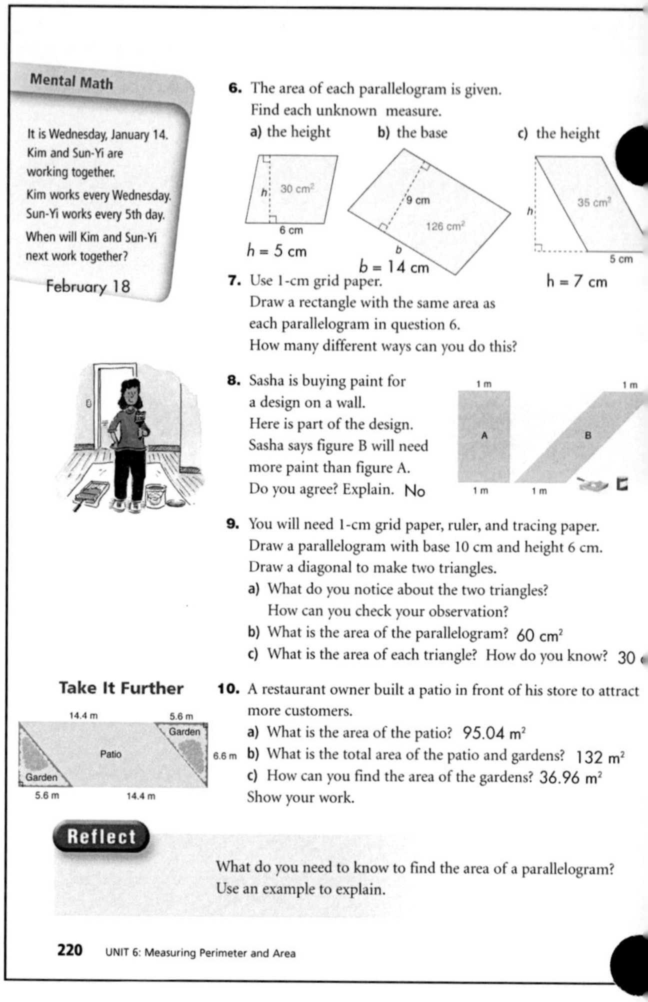

Mental Math

It is Wednesday, January 14. Kim and Sun-Yi are working together. Kim works every Wednesday. Sun-Yi works every 5th day. When will Kim and Sun-Yi next work together?

February 18

6. The area of each parallelogram is given. Find each unknown measure.
a) the height b) the base c) the height

$h = 5$ cm $b = 14$ cm $h = 7$ cm

7. Use 1-cm grid paper. Draw a rectangle with the same area as each parallelogram in question 6. How many different ways can you do this?

8. Sasha is buying paint for a design on a wall. Here is part of the design. Sasha says figure B will need more paint than figure A. Do you agree? Explain. No

9. You will need 1-cm grid paper, ruler, and tracing paper. Draw a parallelogram with base 10 cm and height 6 cm. Draw a diagonal to make two triangles.
a) What do you notice about the two triangles? How can you check your observation?
b) What is the area of the parallelogram? 60 cm^2
c) What is the area of each triangle? How do you know? 30

Take It Further

10. A restaurant owner built a patio in front of his store to attract more customers.
a) What is the area of the patio? 95.04 m^2
b) What is the total area of the patio and gardens? 132 m^2
c) How can you find the area of the gardens? 36.96 m^2 Show your work.

Reflect

What do you need to know to find the area of a parallelogram? Use an example to explain.

220 UNIT 6: Measuring Perimeter and Area

ASSESSMENT FOR LEARNING

What to Look For	What to Do
Understanding concepts ✔ Students understand that the area of a parallelogram is equal to the area of a rectangle with the same height and base.	***Extra Support:*** Students having difficulty may benefit from being given a drawing on grid paper of a rectangle and a parallelogram with the same base and height. Students count grid squares to see that the two figures have the same area. Students can use Step-by-Step 1 (Master 6.9) to complete question 5.
Applying procedures ✔ Students can use the formula $A = bh$ to find the area of a parallelogram.	***Extra Practice:*** Students draw a parallelogram with the same area as each of the rectangles in *Skills You'll Need*, question 1. Students can complete Extra Practice 1 (Master 6.17).
Problem solving ✔ Students can solve problems related to the areas of parallelograms.	***Extension:*** Have students change the base and height of the parallelogram in *Practice* question 5 to draw a parallelogram with 6 times the area. Students report their findings.

Recording and Reporting
Master 6.2 Ongoing Observations: Measuring Perimeter and Area

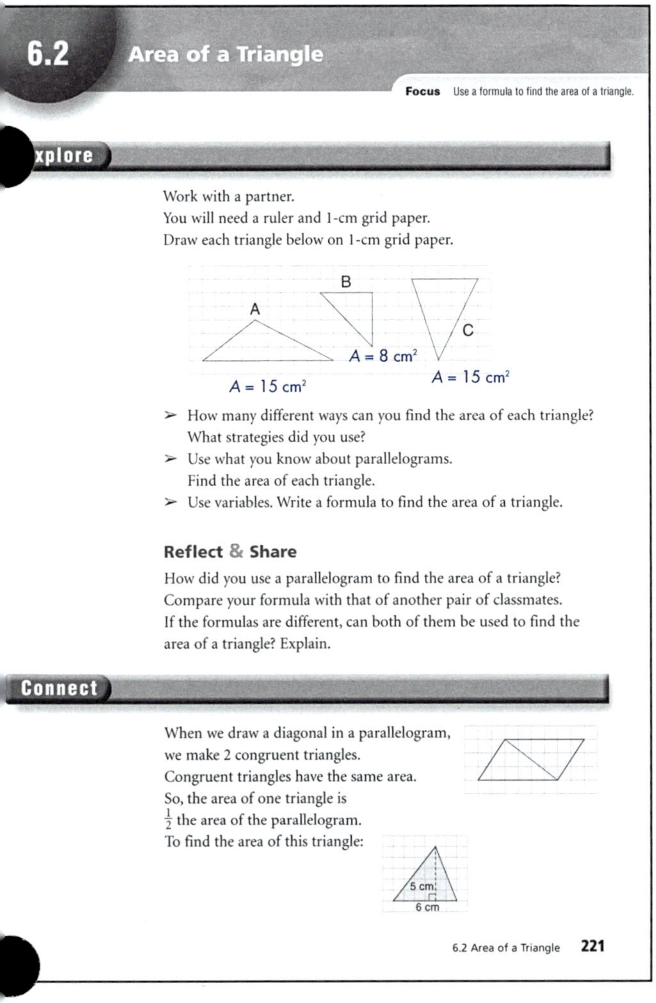
6.2 Area of a Triangle

Focus Use a formula to find the area of a triangle.

Explore

Work with a partner.
You will need a ruler and 1-cm grid paper.
Draw each triangle below on 1-cm grid paper.

A B C
A = 8 cm²
A = 15 cm²
A = 15 cm²

➢ How many different ways can you find the area of each triangle? What strategies did you use?
➢ Use what you know about parallelograms. Find the area of each triangle.
➢ Use variables. Write a formula to find the area of a triangle.

Reflect & Share

How did you use a parallelogram to find the area of a triangle?
Compare your formula with that of another pair of classmates.
If the formulas are different, can both of them be used to find the area of a triangle? Explain.

Connect

When we draw a diagonal in a parallelogram, we make 2 congruent triangles.
Congruent triangles have the same area.
So, the area of one triangle is $\frac{1}{2}$ the area of the parallelogram.
To find the area of this triangle:

5 cm
6 cm

6.2 Area of a Triangle 221

Area of a Triangle

SECTION ORGANIZER (80–100 min)

Curriculum Focus: Use a formula to find the area of a triangle. (7m34, 7m35, 7m41, 7m76)

Student Materials
- rulers
- 1-cm grid paper (PM 20)

Optional
- Step-by-Step 2 (Master 6.10)
- Extra Practice 2 (Master 6.18)

Vocabulary: triangle

Assessment: Master 6.2 Ongoing Observations: Measuring Perimeter and Area

Key Math Learnings

1. The area of a triangle is one-half the area of a parallelogram with the same base and same height.
2. The formula for the area of a triangle is $A = \frac{1}{2}bh$.

Math Link

Students will probably find that the kitchen and the workroom have the most measuring instruments. In the kitchen, students may find measuring spoons, measuring cups, an egg timer, and kitchen scales. In the workroom, students may find a carpenter's level, a measuring tape, a square, callipers, micrometers, and a stud finder. Students should give one example of what each tool measures.

BEFORE — Get Started

Review the types of triangles students should be familiar with.
Ask questions, such as:

- What is an acute triangle? (*A triangle in which each angle measures less than 90°*)
  A right triangle?
  (*A triangle that has one angle measuring 90°*)
  An obtuse triangle?
  (*A triangle with one angle greater than 90°*)
- What is an equilateral triangle?
  (*A triangle with three equal sides*) An isosceles triangle? (*A triangle with two equal sides*)
  A scalene triangle?
  (*A triangle with all sides different*)
- When are two triangles congruent?
  (*When they have the same size and shape, but not necessarily the same orientation*)

Present *Explore.* Distribute 1-cm grid paper to students. Ensure students understand they should use a ruler to draw the triangles.

DURING — Explore

Ongoing Assessment: Observe and Listen

For students who have difficulty, suggest they use two congruent triangles to make a figure for which they have an area formula.

As students work, ask questions, such as:

- How is the grid paper useful?
  (*I can find the area of each triangle by counting grid squares. I can count the number of whole squares, half squares, and part squares to get an estimate of the area.*)

REACHING ALL LEARNERS

Alternative Explore

Materials: 1-cm grid paper (PM 20), rulers

Have students draw one each of these triangles on grid paper: acute, scalene, isosceles, right, obtuse scalene. Students then find the area of each triangle, and use their results to write a formula for the area of a triangle, using variables.

Early Finishers

Have students find objects with triangular faces or look through magazines to find pictures containing triangles. Students measure, then find the area of each triangle.

Common Misconceptions

➤ Students forget to divide the product of base and height by 2 when finding the area of a triangle.

How to Help: Reinforce the idea that a triangle is one-half of a parallelogram. The area of a parallelogram is found by multiplying base times height. So, the area of a triangle is the area of the parallelogram divided by 2. Use paper triangles to demonstrate this idea.

➤ Students have difficulty recognizing the height of a triangle.

How to Help: Have students rotate the triangle until one base is parallel to the edge of the desk. Students draw a line segment from the opposite vertex to the base so that the line segment makes a 90° angle with the base. This is the height. The height may be a side of the triangle if the triangle is a right triangle.

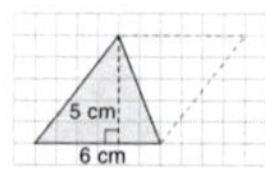

Complete a parallelogram on one side of the triangle.
The area of the parallelogram is:
A = base × height, or $A = bh$
So, $A = 6 \times 5$
$= 30$
The area of the parallelogram is 30 cm^2.
So, the area of the triangle is: $\frac{1}{2}$ of 30 cm^2 = 15 cm^2
We can write a formula for the area of a triangle.

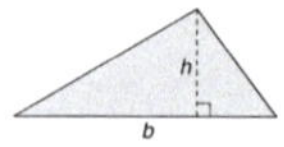

$A = \frac{1}{2}$ base × height
$A = \frac{1}{2}bh$
or $A = bh \div 2$
or $A = \frac{bh}{2}$

Example

Find the area of each triangle.

For an obtuse triangle, the height might be drawn outside the triangle.

a)
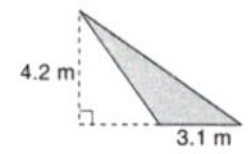

b)
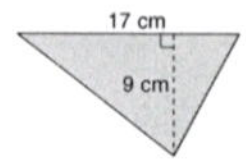

Solution

a) $A = \frac{bh}{2}$
Substitute $b = 3.1$ and $h = 4.2$.
$A = \frac{3.1 \times 4.2}{2}$
$A = 6.51$
The area is 6.51 m^2.

b) $A = \frac{bh}{2}$
Substitute $b = 17$ and $h = 9$.
$A = \frac{17 \times 9}{2}$
$A = \frac{153}{2}$
$= 76.5$
The area is 76.5 cm^2.

Practice

1. Identify one base and height of each triangle.

a)
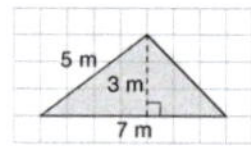

$b = 7$ m
$h = 3$ m
$A = 10.5\ m^2$

b)
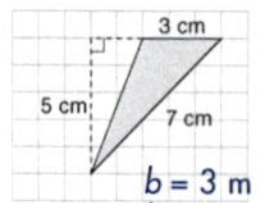

$b = 3$ m
$h = 5$ m
$A = 7.5$

- What is the area of Triangle B in grid squares? (*Triangle B covers 6 whole squares and 4 half squares. 4 half squares = 2 whole squares: the area of the triangle is 8 grid squares or 8 cm^2, as each grid square has area 1 cm^2.*)
- What other strategy can you use to find the area of triangle B?
(*Triangle B is a right-isosceles triangle. If I put two of these triangles together, I can make a square of side length 4 cm. The area of Triangle B is one-half the area of the square which is one-half of 16 cm^2. The area of Triangle B is 8 cm^2.*)
- What strategy can you use to find the area of Triangle A?
(*Triangle A is an obtuse triangle. I can put two of these triangles together to make a parallelogram. I know the area of a parallelogram is base times height. One base of the parallelogram is 10 cm and one height is 3 cm. The area is 30 cm^2. So, the area of each triangle is one-half the area of the parallelogram: $\frac{1}{2}$ of 30 cm^2 = 15 cm^2.*)
- What strategy did you use to find the area of Triangle C?
(*I remember the formula for the area of a triangle from grade 6. The area is one-half of the base times the height. The base is 5 cm, the height is 6 cm, so base × height is 30 cm^2, and one-half of this is 15 cm^2.*)
- How could you use variables to write that formula? (*I use b for base, h for height, and A for area; then $A = \frac{1}{2}bh$.*)

AFTER Connect

Invite volunteers to share their strategies and formulas.

Tell students that two congruent triangles can always be arranged to form a parallelogram with the same base and height as the triangle. Suggest students find and draw the three possible parallelograms for Triangle A in

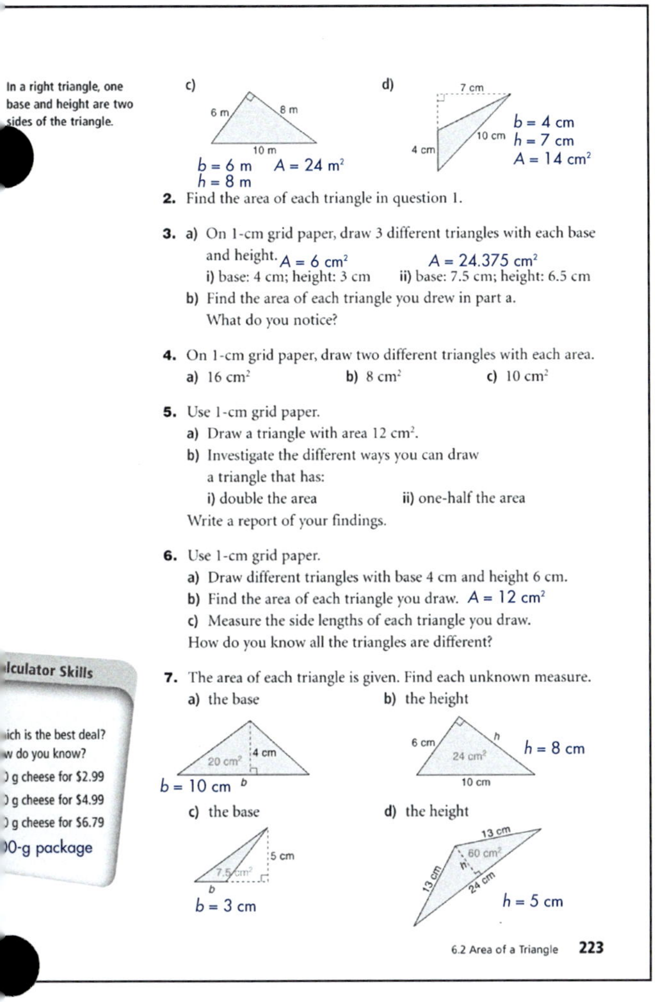

In a right triangle, one base and height are two sides of the triangle.

c) 6 m, 8 m, 10 m — $b = 6$ m, $h = 8$ m, $A = 24$ m^2

d) 7 cm, 10 cm, 4 cm — $b = 4$ cm, $h = 7$ cm, $A = 14$ cm^2

2. Find the area of each triangle in question 1.

3. **a)** On 1-cm grid paper, draw 3 different triangles with each base and height.
i) base: 4 cm; height: 3 cm $A = 6$ cm^2
ii) base: 7.5 cm; height: 6.5 cm $A = 24.375$ cm^2
b) Find the area of each triangle you drew in part a. What do you notice?

4. On 1-cm grid paper, draw two different triangles with each area.
a) 16 cm^2 **b)** 8 cm^2 **c)** 10 cm^2

5. Use 1-cm grid paper.
a) Draw a triangle with area 12 cm^2.
b) Investigate the different ways you can draw a triangle that has:
i) double the area ii) one-half the area
Write a report of your findings.

6. Use 1-cm grid paper.
a) Draw different triangles with base 4 cm and height 6 cm.
b) Find the area of each triangle you draw. $A = 12$ cm^2
c) Measure the side lengths of each triangle you draw. How do you know all the triangles are different?

Calculator Skills
Which is the best deal? How do you know?
…g cheese for \$2.99
…g cheese for \$4.99
…g cheese for \$6.79
…0-g package

7. The area of each triangle is given. Find each unknown measure.
a) the base — 20 cm^2, 4 cm — $b = 10$ cm
b) the height — 6 cm, 24 cm^2, 10 cm — $h = 8$ cm
c) the base — 7.5 cm^2, 5 cm — $b = 3$ cm
d) the height — 13 cm, 60 cm^2, 24 cm, 13 cm — $h = 5$ cm

6.2 Area of a Triangle 223

Calculator Skills

Students use a calculator to find the price per gram for each cheese.

Assignment Guidelines

If your students do not have time to complete all the *Practice* questions on pages 222, 223, and 224, these questions provide minimum curriculum coverage: 1, 2, 3, 5, 7, 9, *Reflect*

To assess the 4 Achievement Chart categories listed in the curriculum document, have students complete these *Practice* questions:

Understanding Concepts: 2; Application: 5; Communication: 8; Problem Solving: 9

Sample Answers

3. b) All triangles with the same base and height have the same area.

5. b) i) To double the area of the triangle, I can double the height or the base of the triangle.

ii) For example, to draw a triangle that has one-half the area, halve the height or the base of the triangle.

6. c) All the triangles are different because the triangles have different shapes.

8. To find its height, I double the area of the triangle, then divide by the length of the base. For example, if I know the area of a triangle is 20 cm^2 and its base is 5 cm, I first double the area: 20 cm^2 × 2 = 40 cm^2. I then divide 40 cm^2 by 5 cm to get 8 cm. The height of the triangle is 8 cm.

Explore. Each side of the triangle can be the base. Ask:

- How many different parallelograms are possible for a scalene triangle? (*3*)
  An isosceles triangle? (*2*)
  An equilateral triangle? (*1*)

Use the examples in *Connect* to show students how to use the formula they developed to find the area of a triangle. As with the parallelogram, have students practise drawing the height outside an obtuse triangle. Some students find this concept difficult and may need help and practice with it.

Practice

Questions 3, 4, 5, and 6 require 1-cm grid paper (PM 20). Students require a calculator for questions 9 and 10.

Assessment Focus: Question 9

Students should recognize that since the paint coverage is given in square metres, all areas should be calculated in square metres. Students should use the conversion 1 m = 100 cm to rewrite the dimensions of the window in metres. Students should find the area of the triangular-shaped attic wall, then subtract the area of the rectangular-shaped window to find the area to be painted. Students should find that 2 cans of paint are required.

9. a) I first convert the dimensions of the window to metres.
I know that 1 m = 100 cm. 150 cm = 1.5 m and
60 cm = 0.6 m; the window is 1.5 m by 0.6 m.
The area to be painted is the area of the triangular wall minus the area of the window.

$A = \frac{bh}{2} - bh$
$= \frac{4.2 \times 4.5}{2} - (1.5 \times 0.6)$
$= 9.45 - 0.9$
$= 8.55$

The area to be painted is 8.55 m^2.

b) One can covers 6.5 m^2. Two cans will cover $2 \times 6.5\ m^2 = 13\ m^2$, which is more than enough.

10. a) The total area is $46.36\ m^2 + 46.62\ m^2 = 92.98\ m^2$.

b) I convert the dimensions of a sheet of plywood to metres: the plywood is 2.4 m by 1.2 m. The area of a sheet of plywood is $2.4\ m \times 1.2\ m = 2.88\ m^2$.
I divide the total area of the roof by the area of a sheet of plywood to find the least number of sheets needed: $92.98 \div 2.88 \doteq 32.3$. About 33 sheets are needed.
Each sheet costs \$24.95, so 33 sheets will cost $\$24.95 \times 33 = \$823.35$. This assumes I can use pieces of a sheet to make a triangle. If I cannot do this, I shall need more than 33 sheets.

REFLECT: When a triangle and a parallelogram have the same base and height, the area of the triangle is one-half the area of the parallelogram. For example, if the area of the parallelogram is 30 cm^2, the area of the triangle is $\frac{1}{2} \times 30\ cm^2 = 15\ cm^2$.

Math Link

Your World

You use rulers and protractors to measure in the classroom.
Which measuring instruments do you have at home?
What do these instruments measure?
List all the instruments you can find.
Give an example of what each one measures.

8. When you know the area of a triangle, and its base, how can yo[u] find its height? Use an example to explain.

9. **Assessment Focus** The owner of a house paints this attic wall. There is a small rectangular window in the wall.
One litre of paint covers 6.5 m^2. 8.55 m^2
a) What is the area that is to be painted?
b) The paint comes in 1-L cans.
How many cans does the owner need? 2 cans
Explain your answer.

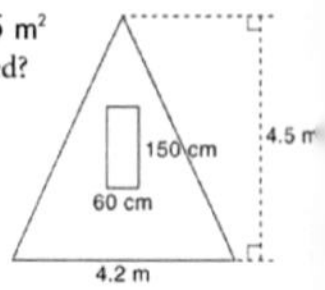

Take It Further

10. A local park has a pavilion to provide shelter.
The pavilion has a roof the shape of a rectangular pyramid.
a) What is the total area of all four parts of the roof? 92.98 [m²]
b) One sheet of plywood is 240 cm by 120 cm.
It costs \$24.95.
What is the least number of sheets of plywood needed to cover the roof? 33 sheets
What is the cost? \$823.35
Explain how you got your answer.

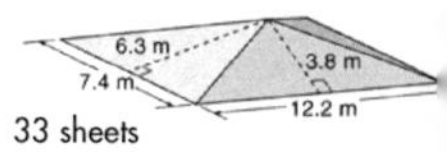

Reflect

A triangle and a parallelogram have the same base and height.
How are the areas of the triangle and parallelogram related?
Use an example to explain.

224 UNIT 6: Measuring Perimeter and Area

ASSESSMENT FOR LEARNING

What to Look For	What to Do
Understanding concepts ✔ Students understand that the area of a triangle is one-half the area of a parallelogram with the same base and height.	***Extra Support:*** Students can play the Additional Activity *Triangles and Parallelograms* (Master 6.5). Students can use Step-by-Step 2 (Master 6.10) to complete question 9.
Applying procedures ✔ Students can use the formula $A = \frac{1}{2}bh$ to find the area of a triangle.	***Extra Practice:*** Students can complete the Additional Activity *Triangle Puzzle* (Master 6.6). Students can complete Extra Practice 2 (Master 6.18).
Problem solving ✔ Students can solve problems related to the areas of triangles.	***Extension:*** Have students write problems similar to *Practice* question 9. Students trade problems with a classmate and solve each other's problems.

Recording and Reporting
Master 6.2 Ongoing Observations: Measuring Perimeter and Area

Mid-Unit Review

LESSON

6.1 **1.** Find the perimeter and area of each figure.

a) 5.0 m, 2.5 m — $P = 15$ m, $A = 12.5$ m^2

b) 3.4 m — $P = 13.6$ m, $A = 11.56$ m^2

2. Find the area of each parallelogram.

a) 2.4 cm, 2.0 cm, 3.5 cm — $A = 7.0$ cm^2

b) 2.3 cm, 4.0 cm, 2.5 cm — $A = 9.2$ cm^2

c) 2.0 cm, 3.0 cm, 1.5 cm — $A = 3.0$ cm^2

3. A parallelogram has height 45 cm and base 60 cm.

a) Find its area. $A = 2700$ cm^2

b) What is the base and height of a parallelogram with twice the area?

c) What is the base and height of a parallelogram with one-half the area?

6.2 **4.** Find the area of each triangle.

a) 6 cm, 4 cm — $A = 12$ cm^2

b) 3.5 cm, 2.0 cm, 3.2 cm, 2.3 cm — $A = 3.5$ cm^2

c) 2.2 m, 4.4 m, 2.0 m — $A = 2.2$ m^2

5. Po Ling is planning to pour a concrete patio beside her house. It has the shape of a triangle. The contractor charges $125.00 for each square metre of concrete poured.

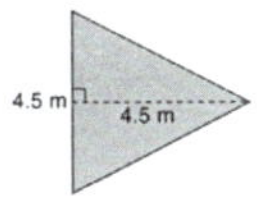

What will the contractor charge for the concrete?

Mid-Unit Review 225

SECTION ORGANIZER

Student Materials

- calculators

Assessment:

Masters 6.1 Unit Rubric: Measuring Perimeter and Area, 6.4 Unit Summary: Measuring Perimeter and Area

Sample Solutions

3. a) The formula for the area of a parallelogram is $A = bh$. Substitute $h = 45$ and $b = 60$.

$A = 45 \times 60 = 2700$

The area of the parallelogram is 2700 cm^2.

b) To find a parallelogram with double the area, I could either double the base or double the height. If I double the base, the parallelogram has height 45 cm and base 120 cm. Area = bh = 120 cm $\times$ 45 cm = 5400 cm^2, which is twice 2700 cm^2.

If I double the height, the parallelogram has height 90 cm and base 60 cm.

Area = bh = 60 cm $\times$ 90 cm = 5400 cm^2, which is twice 2700 cm^2.

c) To find a parallelogram with one-half the area, I could either halve the base or halve the height. If I halve the base, the parallelogram has height 45 cm and base 30 cm.

Area = bh = 30 cm $\times$ 45 cm = 1350 cm^2, which is one-half of 2700 cm^2.

If I halve the height, the parallelogram has height 22.5 cm and base 60 cm.

Area = bh = 60 cm $\times$ 22.5 cm = 1350 cm^2, which is one-half of 2700 cm^2.

Alternatively, for part a, I could double the area to get 5400 cm^2 and use two factors of this number as the base and height; for example, 54 cm and 100 cm.

Alternatively, for part b, I could halve the area to get 1350 cm^2, then use two factors of this number as the base and height; for example, 135 cm and 10 cm.

5. The area of the concrete patio $= \frac{1}{2}bh$

$= \frac{4.5 \times 4.5}{2}$

$= \frac{20.25}{2}$

$= 10.125$

The area of the patio is 10.125 m^2.

The contractor charges $125.00 for each square metre.

Po Ling will have to pay for 11 m^2 of concrete:

11 $\times$ $125.00 = $1375.

The contractor will charge $1375 for the concrete.

If the contractor charges for partial square metres, Po Ling will pay $125.00 $\times$ 10.125 = $1265.63.

Area and Perimeter of a Trapezoid

SECTION ORGANIZER — 80–100 min

Curriculum Focus: Use a formula to find the area of a trapezoid. (7m36, 7m37, 7m38, 7m39, 7m40)

Student Materials
- calculators
- scissors
- Figures for Section 6.3, *Explore* (Master 6.13)
- rulers
- pieces of string
- pushpins (4 per student)
- 1-cm grid paper (PM 20)
- isometric grid paper (PM 24)
- red Pattern Blocks (PM 25)

Optional
- Step-by-Step 3 (Master 6.11)
- Extra Practice 3 (Master 6.19)

Assessment: Master 6.2 Ongoing Observations: Measuring Perimeter and Area

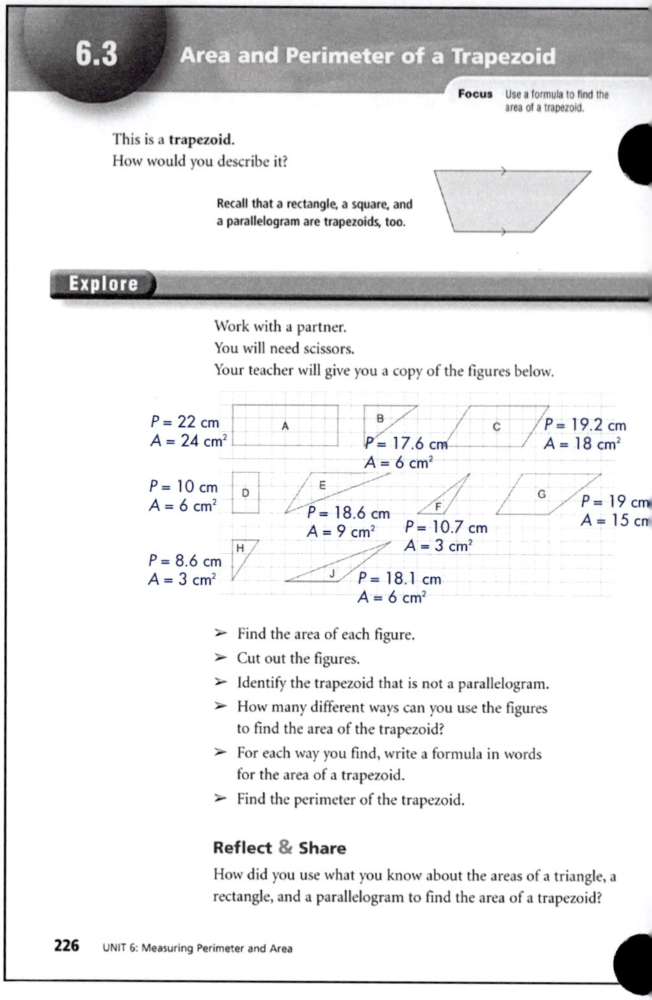

6.3 Area and Perimeter of a Trapezoid

Focus Use a formula to find the area of a trapezoid.

This is a **trapezoid**.
How would you describe it?

Recall that a rectangle, a square, and a parallelogram are trapezoids, too.

Explore

Work with a partner.
You will need scissors.
Your teacher will give you a copy of the figures below.

- Find the area of each figure.
- Cut out the figures.
- Identify the trapezoid that is not a parallelogram.
- How many different ways can you use the figures to find the area of the trapezoid?
- For each way you find, write a formula in words for the area of a trapezoid.
- Find the perimeter of the trapezoid.

Reflect & Share

How did you use what you know about the areas of a triangle, a rectangle, and a parallelogram to find the area of a trapezoid?

226 UNIT 6: Measuring Perimeter and Area

Key Math Learning

The area of a trapezoid can be found by dividing it into other figures, such as triangles, rectangles, and parallelograms.

Math Note

In this book, a trapezoid is defined as a quadrilateral with at least one pair of parallel sides. This is an inclusive definition, by which a square, a rectangle, a rhombus, and a parallelogram are trapezoids. A rectangle, a square, and a rhombus are also parallelograms.

BEFORE — Get Started

Invite students to look at the trapezoid on the top of page 226 of the Student Book.
Ask questions, such as:
- How would you describe it?
  (*The trapezoid has 4 sides and two sides are parallel.*)
- Why are rectangles, squares, and parallelograms also trapezoids?
  (*Each has 2 pairs of parallel sides. A trapezoid has one pair of parallel sides, so these figures are trapezoids.*)
- Which figures can you divide a trapezoid into? (*Rectangles, triangles, and parallelograms*)

Present *Explore*. Tell students they should use the areas of figures they know to help them find different formulas for the area of a trapezoid. Distribute copies of figures for Section 6.3, *Explore* (Master 6.13) to pairs of students.

DURING — Explore

Ongoing Assessment: Observe and Listen

Encourage students to use the formulas they have learned to find the areas of rectangles, parallelograms, and triangles rather than counting grid squares. Students can count grid squares to check the reasonableness of their calculations.

As students work, ask questions, such as:
- Which figures are rectangles?
  (*Figures A and D*)

Connect

We can find the area of a trapezoid by dividing it into other figures.
Here are 3 ways to find the area of this trapezoid.

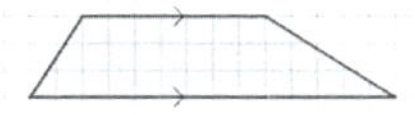

- Make 2 triangles and a rectangle.

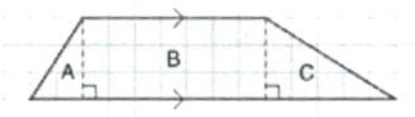

Area of trapezoid = area of triangle A + area of rectangle B + area of triangle C

- Make 1 triangle and a parallelogram.

Area of trapezoid = area of parallelogram D + area of triangle E

- Make 2 triangles.

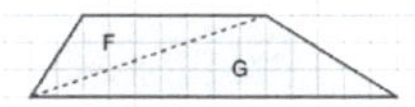

Area of trapezoid = area of triangle F + area of triangle G

Example

a) Estimate the area of this trapezoid.
b) Calculate the area to check your estimate.

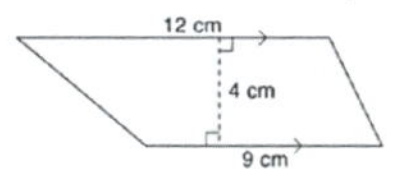

6.3 Area and Perimeter of a Trapezoid 227

REACHING ALL LEARNERS

Early Finishers

Have students check their answers to *Practice* questions 1 and 2 by using the method of *Practice* question 8.

Common Misconceptions

➤ Students divide a trapezoid into figures for which they do not know how to find the area.

How to Help: Remind students that they know how to find the areas of a square, a rectangle, a triangle, and a parallelogram. Encourage students to divide the trapezoid using only these figures. Ensure students understand that there should be no part of the trapezoid left over.

ESL Strategies

Encourage students for whom English is a second language to make index cards to help them remember the area formulas. For example, students could label one card "Triangle," draw and label a triangle, then write the formula for area, $A = \frac{1}{2}bh$. Students then make index cards for a rectangle, a parallelogram, and a trapezoid.

What is the formula for the area of a rectangle? (*$A = bh$*) What is the area of Figure A? (*24 cm^2*) Figure D? (*6 cm^2*)

- Which figures are triangles? (*Figures B, E, F, H, and J*) What is the formula for the area of a triangle? (*$A = \frac{1}{2}bh$*) What is the area of Figure B? (*6 cm^2*) Figure E? (*9 cm^2*) Figure F? (*3 cm^2*) Figure H? (*3 cm^2*) Figure J? (*6 cm^2*)
- Which of the remaining figures is a parallelogram? (*Figure C*) What is the formula for the area of a parallelogram? (*$A = bh$*) What is the area of Figure C? (*18 cm^2*)
- Which figure is a trapezoid and is not a parallelogram? (*Figure G*)
- How can you use the other figures to find the area of the trapezoid? (*I can make the trapezoid from Figures H, D, and B. The area of the trapezoid is the sum of the areas of these figures: $3 + 6 + 6 = 15$. The area of the trapezoid is 15 cm^2.*)
- How else can you use the other figures to find the area of the trapezoid? (*I can make the trapezoid from Figures E and J. The area of the trapezoid is the sum of the areas of these figures: $9 + 6 = 15$. The area of the trapezoid is 15 cm^2.*)
- Are there any other ways to find the area of the trapezoid? Explain. (*I can remove Figure F from Figure C to get the trapezoid: $18 - 3 = 15$, or I can remove Figures H and B from Figure A to get the trapezoid: $24 - 3 - 6 = 15$. The area of the trapezoid is 15 cm^2.*)
- How can you find the perimeter of the trapezoid? (*I can use a ruler to measure the length of each side, then add to find the perimeter.*)

AFTER Connect

Have students share the different ways they found the area of the trapezoid.

Ask:

- How did you use what you know about the areas of a triangle, a rectangle, and a parallelogram to find the area of a trapezoid?

Calculator Skills

To predict each product, students could round each number to the nearest ten, hundred, thousand, or ten thousand, then multiply. Estimates may be 100, 10 000, 1 000 000, and 100 000 000. Students use a calculator to check their predictions: 81, 9801, 998 001, 99 980 001. Students should see that the number of 9s and the number of 0s in the product starts at zero and increases by 1 each time. They use this pattern to predict the product of 99 999 × 99 999: 9 999 800 001.

Assignment Guidelines

If your students do not have time to complete all the *Practice* questions on pages 228, 229, and 230, these questions provide minimum curriculum coverage: 1, 2, 4, 6, 8, *Reflect*
To assess the 4 Achievement Chart categories listed in the curriculum document, have students complete these *Practice* questions:
Understanding Concepts: 4
Application: 6
Communication: 7
Problem Solving: 9

Sample Answers

5. b) I cannot find the perimeter of the first trapezoid because I do not know the lengths of all 4 sides. I can find the perimeter of the second trapezoid because the length of each side is given:
$P = 7.5\text{ m} + 6.5\text{ m} + 14.5\text{ m} + 7.5\text{ m} = 36.0\text{ m}$

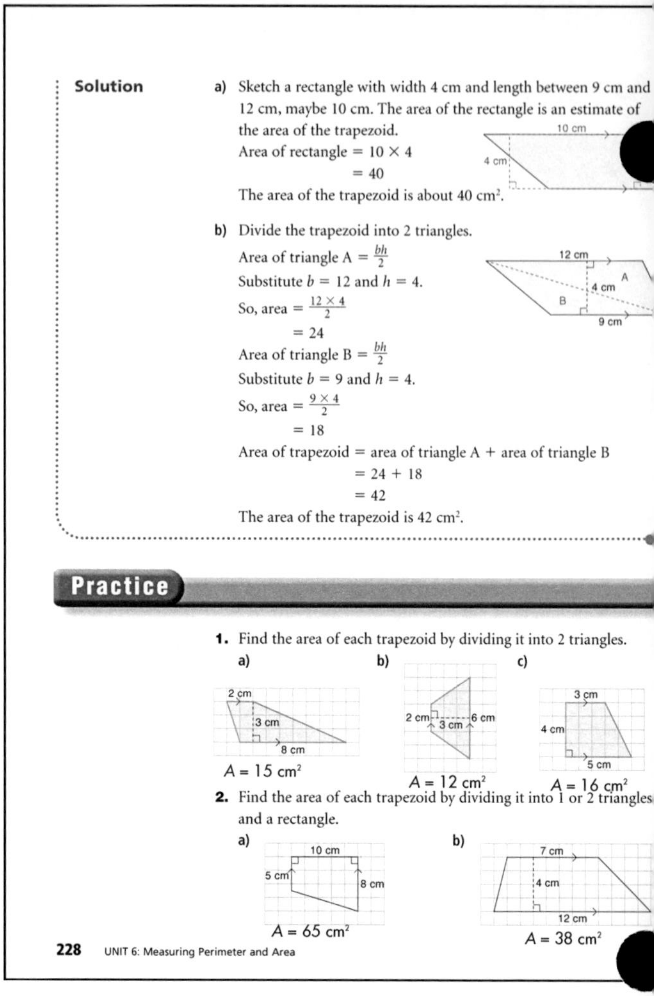

Solution

a) Sketch a rectangle with width 4 cm and length between 9 cm and 12 cm, maybe 10 cm. The area of the rectangle is an estimate of the area of the trapezoid.
Area of rectangle = 10 × 4
= 40
The area of the trapezoid is about 40 cm².

b) Divide the trapezoid into 2 triangles.
Area of triangle A = $\frac{bh}{2}$
Substitute $b = 12$ and $h = 4$.
So, area = $\frac{12 \times 4}{2}$
= 24
Area of triangle B = $\frac{bh}{2}$
Substitute $b = 9$ and $h = 4$.
So, area = $\frac{9 \times 4}{2}$
= 18
Area of trapezoid = area of triangle A + area of triangle B
= 24 + 18
= 42
The area of the trapezoid is 42 cm².

Practice

1. Find the area of each trapezoid by dividing it into 2 triangles.
a) A = 15 cm²
b) A = 12 cm²
c) A = 16 cm²

2. Find the area of each trapezoid by dividing it into 1 or 2 triangles and a rectangle.
a) A = 65 cm²
b) A = 38 cm²

228 UNIT 6: Measuring Perimeter and Area

(*I divided the trapezoid into other figures for which I knew the area, then found the sum of the areas. I also removed smaller figures from a larger figure, leaving the trapezoid. I then subtracted the areas of the smaller figures from the area of the larger figure to find the area of the trapezoid.*)

- What formula did you write to find the area of the trapezoid? (*Area of trapezoid = area of Figure H + area of Figure D + area of Figure B*)

Review *Connect*. You could also illustrate how to find the area by completing a rectangle in which the trapezoid fits, then subtracting the area of 2 triangles from the area of the rectangle.

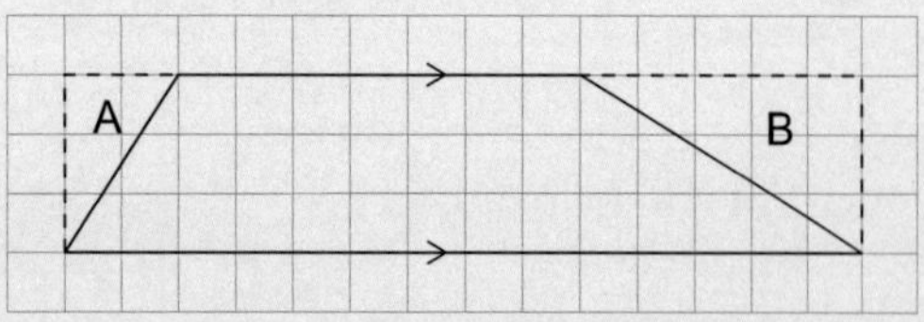

Area of trapezoid = area of rectangle – area of triangle A – area of triangle B

Practice

For question 7, each student requires a piece of string, 4 pushpins, a ruler, and 1-cm grid paper (PM 20). Question 8 requires 1-cm grid paper. Question 9 requires red Pattern Blocks (PM 25) and isometric grid paper (PM 24).

Assessment Focus: Question 8

Students should realize that a parallelogram can be divided into 2 congruent trapezoids, with the area of each trapezoid equal to one-half the area of the parallelogram. The area of the parallelogram can be calculated using the formula $A = bh$, so the area of each congruent trapezoid can be calculated using the formula $A = \frac{1}{2}bh$.

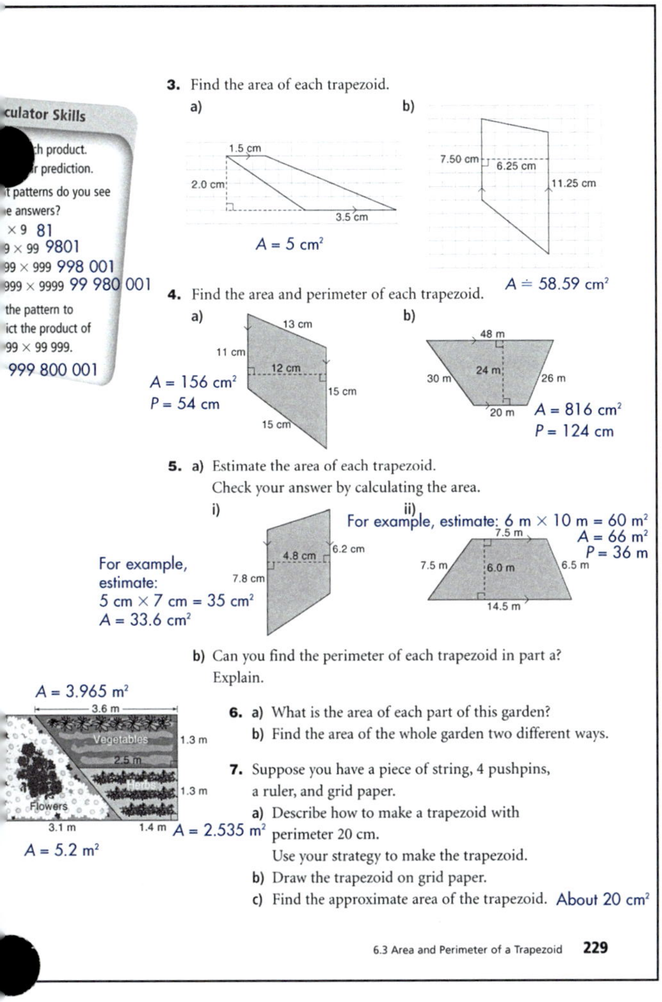

3. Find the area of each trapezoid.

a) $A = 5\ cm^2$

b) $A \doteq 58.59\ cm^2$

4. Find the area and perimeter of each trapezoid.

a) $A = 156\ cm^2$, $P = 54$ cm

b) $A = 816\ cm^2$, $P = 124$ cm

5. a) Estimate the area of each trapezoid. Check your answer by calculating the area.

i) For example, estimate: 5 cm × 7 cm = 35 cm^2; $A = 33.6\ cm^2$

ii) For example, estimate: 6 m × 10 m = 60 m^2; $A = 66\ m^2$; $P = 36$ m

b) Can you find the perimeter of each trapezoid in part a? Explain.

6. a) What is the area of each part of this garden? ($A = 3.965\ m^2$; $A = 2.535\ m^2$; $A = 5.2\ m^2$)

b) Find the area of the whole garden two different ways.

7. Suppose you have a piece of string, 4 pushpins, a ruler, and grid paper.

a) Describe how to make a trapezoid with perimeter 20 cm. Use your strategy to make the trapezoid.

b) Draw the trapezoid on grid paper.

c) Find the approximate area of the trapezoid. About 20 cm^2

6. b) To find the area of the whole garden, I can add the areas of the parts of the garden:

$5.2 + 3.965 + 2.535 = 11.7$

The area of the whole garden is 11.7 m^2.

The whole garden is rectangular.

I can also find the area of the whole garden by calculating the area of the rectangle. $A = bh$

$= (3.1 + 1.4) \times (1.3 + 1.3)$

$= 4.5 \times 2.6$

$= 11.7$

The area of the whole garden is 11.7 m^2.

7. a) I would cut a piece of string and tie a knot to make a loop with length 20 cm. I would place a piece of grid paper on corrugated cardboard or a cork tile. I would put pushpins in the paper to represent vertices of a trapezoid. I would put the pins on grid lines to make sure the two sides are parallel. I would loop the string around the pins, and move the pins along grid lines until the string was taut. I would then mark the position of each pin, remove the paper from the cardboard, and join the marks to make a trapezoid.

b)

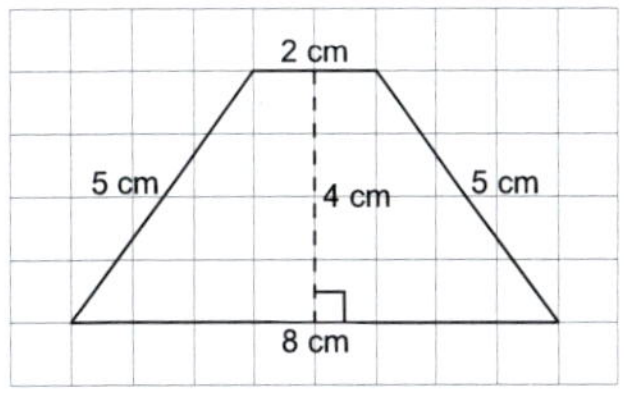

c) The area of my trapezoid is about 20 cm^2.

(Answers continue below.)

(Sample Answers, continued)

8. a) I can find the area of the parallelogram, then divide the area by 2 to find the area of each trapezoid. Since the trapezoids are congruent, the area of each trapezoid is one-half the area of the parallelogram.

b)

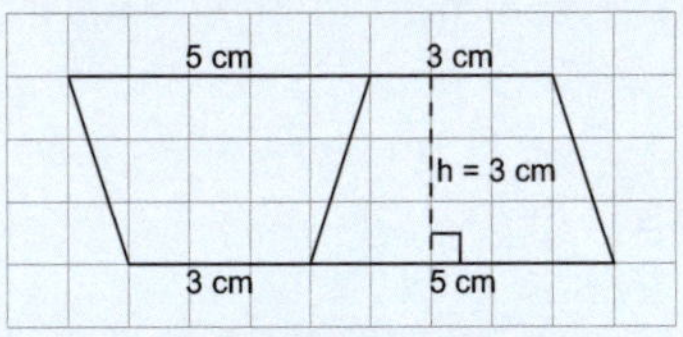

Area of parallelogram $= bh$

$= (3 + 5) \times 3$

$= 24$

The area of the parallelogram is 24 cm^2.

So, the area of one of the congruent trapezoids

$= \frac{1}{2}$ the area of the parallelogram

$= \frac{24}{2}$

$= 12$

The area of the trapezoid is 12 cm^2.

9. b) There are 24 tiles in my patio.

c) The area of each tile is 510 cm^2.

So, the area of 24 tiles is $510 \times 24 = 12\ 240$.

The area of my patio is 12 240 cm^2.

d) The completed patio would be larger than the area calculated because the tiles would not be right up against each other. There is a space for grout between the tiles. The strips of grout are approximately rectangular.I found the approximate area of the strips of grout between the tiles. Each strip has a height of 3 mm, or 0.3 cm. There are 26 smaller pieces.

The area of each smaller piece is

0.3 cm × 20 cm = 6 cm^2. The area of 26 of these is 6 cm^2 × 26 = 156 cm^2.

There are 11 larger strips of grout. The area of each larger strip is 0.3 cm × 40 cm = 12 cm^2. The area of 11 of these is 12 cm^2 × 11 = 132 cm^2. The total area covered by grout is 132 cm^2 + 156 cm^2 = 288 cm^2.

The patio will be larger by 288 cm^2.

10. I can place two congruent trapezoids side by side to form a parallelogram with the same height as the two trapezoids. I label the parallel sides *a* and *b*.

The height of the parallelogram is *h*.

The base of the parallelogram is *a* + *b*.

The area of the parallelogram is $(a + b) \times h$.

The area of the trapezoid is $\frac{(a + b) \times h}{2}$.

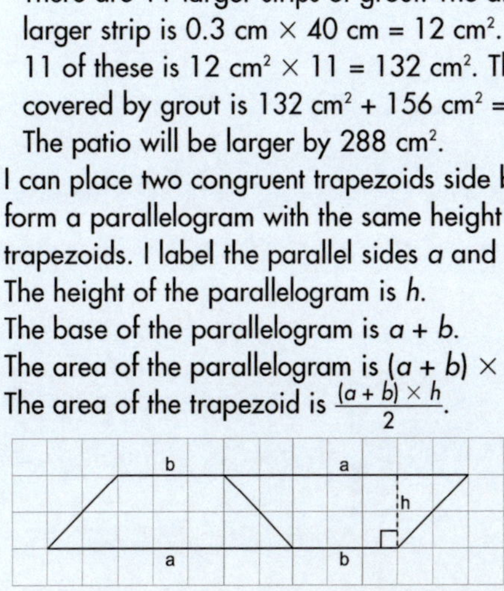

REFLECT: Squares, rectangles, and parallelograms are also trapezoids. To find the area of each of these figures, I can divide the figure into 2 triangles by drawing a diagonal. I can find the area of each triangle, then add to find the area of the original figure. For example, to find the area of this rectangle, I find the area of each triangle.

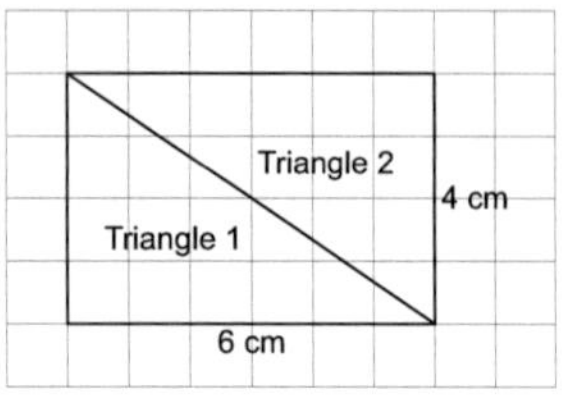

Area of triangle 1 $= \frac{bh}{2}$

$= \frac{6 \times 4}{2}$

$= \frac{24}{2}$

$= 12$

The area of triangle 1 is 12 cm^2.
The area of triangle 2 is also 12 cm^2 because the two triangles are congruent.

The area of the rectangle
= area of triangle 1 + area of triangle 2
= 12 + 12
= 24
The area of the rectangle is 24 cm^2.

8. Assessment Focus Two congruent trapezoids join to form a parallelogram.

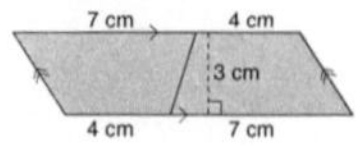

a) How can you use the area of the parallelogram to find the area of each trapezoid?
b) Use grid paper. Draw a trapezoid. Use the area of a parallelogram to find the area of your trapezoid. Show your work.

Take It Further

9. A patio is made with congruent brick tiles.

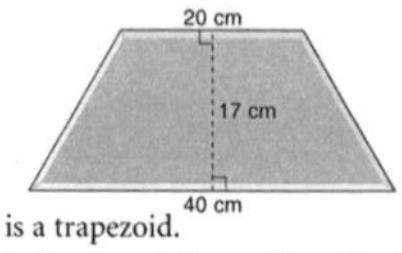

Each tile is a trapezoid.
a) What is the area of the top face of each tile? $A = 510$ cm^2
b) Use red Pattern Blocks on triangular grid paper. Sketch a patio that uses these trapezoid tiles. How many tiles are in your patio? 24 tiles
c) What is the area of your patio? 12 240 cm^2
d) When a patio is built, there is a 3-mm space between tiles for the grout. Would your completed patio be larger or smaller than the area you calculated in part c? Explain. How much larger or smaller would it be?

10. Use any of the methods you know to find the area of a trapezoid. Use variables. Write a formula for the area of a trapezoid.

Reflect

How can you use the strategies for finding the area of a trapezoid to find the areas of a square, rectangle, and parallelogram? Use examples to explain.

230 UNIT 6: Measuring Perimeter and Area

ASSESSMENT FOR LEARNING

What to Look For

Understanding concepts

✔ Students understand that the area of a trapezoid can be found by dividing it into other figures, such as triangles, rectangles, and parallelograms whose areas can be calculated.

Applying procedures

✔ Students can estimate, then use a formula to calculate the area of a trapezoid.

✔ Students can draw a trapezoid given its perimeter.

What to Do

Extra Support: Students who have difficulty dividing a trapezoid into smaller figures may benefit from copying the trapezoid onto grid paper. Students use a pencil and ruler to divide the trapezoid, find the area of each smaller figure, then add to find the area of the trapezoid.
Students can use Step-by-Step 3 (Master 6.11) to complete question 8.

Extra Practice: Students find the area of each trapezoid in *Practice* question 1 by dividing it into 1 or 2 triangles and a rectangle. Students can complete Extra Practice 3 (Master 6.19).

Extension: Challenge students to join 4 congruent trapezoids (2 rows of 2), then find the area of each trapezoid using the area of the parallelogram.

Recording and Reporting
Master 6.2 Ongoing Observations: Measuring Perimeter and Area

Measuring for Construction

Measuring for Construction

Before construction begins on a shopping mall, the site is precisely measured in different ways for different reasons. Measuring does not stop once construction begins. Initial measurements are checked and rechecked because estimates and plans sometimes change as the project continues.

The first "measurers" on the site are members of a survey team. The first thing they do is to verify the perimeter and area with an older, existing plan. In some cases, the last survey for the site might have been carried out 200 years before.

Most surveyors today have new, technology-based surveying tools. However, the team might use a transit (an angle-measuring device based on a telescope) and stadia (a graduated measuring rod). These measuring devices have been in use since the early 19th century. The survey team may have aerial or satellite photographs, EDM (Electronic Distance Measuring) equipment based on microwaves or lasers, or GPS (Global Positioning System) equipment.

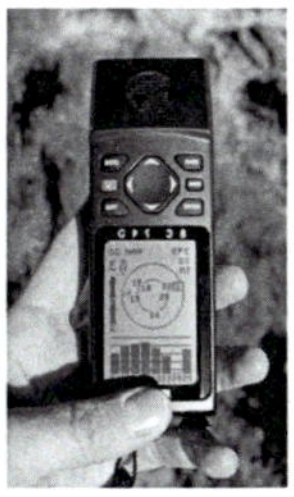

A construction project requires the services of many different suppliers and contractors. One company provides security fencing around the site. Another company lays asphalt for the roads and parking lots. A third company installs the flooring and carpets inside the mall. Some people work from the architect's blueprints to calculate how much to charge for their materials and labour. Other people will send an estimator to do her own measuring. Estimators use a variety of measuring tools: tape measure, trundle wheel, hand-held EDM, and so on. The estimators have to know how to use the measurements they collect.

Recently, a company introduced a digital measuring device. This device is wheeled around the perimeter of the region to calculate the area of the region. Why might this seem to be an impossible calculation? Can you explain how it might work?

The World of Work: Measuring for Construction 231

Here are some other careers that involve measuring.

Protective Service Occupations: This group includes workers who implement security measures, and provide protective services. They may be employed by police forces, security companies, hotels, stores, businesses, and industries. These workers may measure accident scene details such as skid marks, the location of vehicles involved, and the width of roads. They may also measure to determine how much wire is needed to install a security system.

Environmental Technologists: Environmental technologists ensure that we live in as clean an environment as possible.
This involves collecting information about the presence and effects of pollutants in our air, water and soil; developing and employing air, water or soil quality measurement plans; and using different laboratory techniques and instruments to prepare and analyse samples. Environmental technologists measure the perimeter and area of figures, and the volume of objects.

Land Surveyors: Land surveyors establish land, air space, and water boundaries. They write descriptions of land for deeds, leases, and other legal documents; define airspace for airports; and measure construction sites. Land surveyors often measure distances, perimeters, areas, and angles.

Interpreting a Problem

SECTION ORGANIZER

Curriculum Focus: Draw a trapezoid given its area. (7m40)

Student Materials

- calculators
- 1-cm grid paper (PM 20)
- 0.5-cm grid paper (PM 14)
- rulers

Assessment: Master 6.2 Ongoing Observations: Measuring Perimeter and Area

Sample Solutions

1. To draw a trapezoid (that is not a parallelogram) with area 30 cm^2: two congruent trapezoids join to form a parallelogram. If each trapezoid has area 30 cm^2, then the parallelogram has area 60 cm^2.
I drew a parallelogram with area 60 cm^2, then divided it into 2 congruent trapezoids.
I found two factors of 60: 15×4. I drew a parallelogram with base 15 cm and height 4 cm. I then chose a length for one base of the trapezoid, less than 15 cm. I chose 9 cm.
I marked a point on the top side of the parallelogram 9 cm from the left vertex, and a point on the bottom side of the parallelogram 9 cm from the right vertex. I joined these points

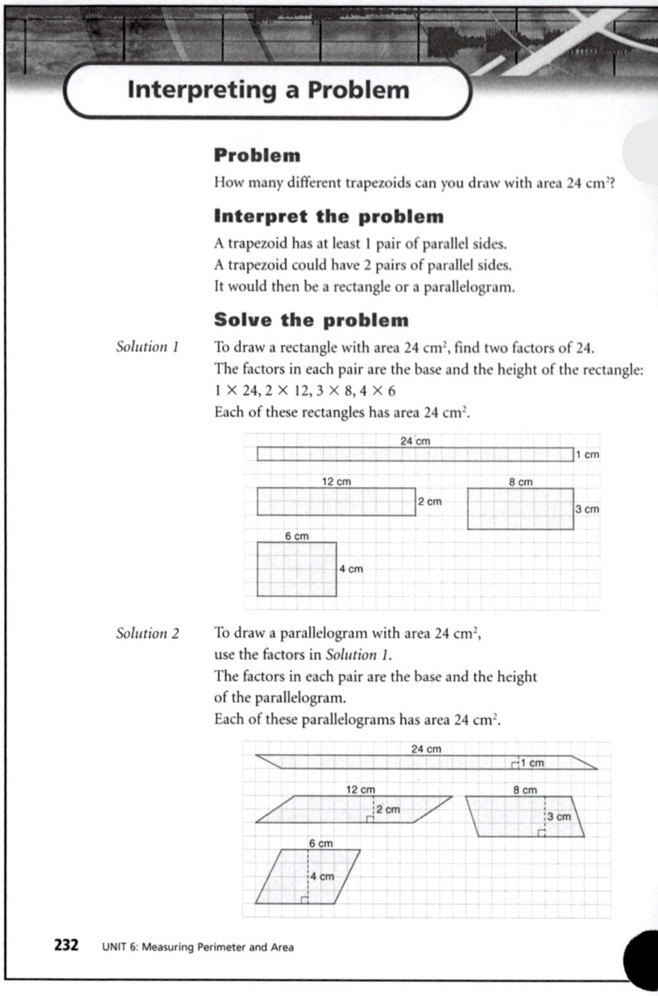

Interpreting a Problem

Problem

How many different trapezoids can you draw with area 24 cm^2?

Interpret the problem

A trapezoid has at least 1 pair of parallel sides.
A trapezoid could have 2 pairs of parallel sides.
It would then be a rectangle or a parallelogram.

Solve the problem

Solution 1 To draw a rectangle with area 24 cm^2, find two factors of 24.
The factors in each pair are the base and the height of the rectangle:
$1 \times 24, 2 \times 12, 3 \times 8, 4 \times 6$
Each of these rectangles has area 24 cm^2.

Solution 2 To draw a parallelogram with area 24 cm^2, use the factors in *Solution 1*.
The factors in each pair are the base and the height of the parallelogram.
Each of these parallelograms has area 24 cm^2.

232 UNIT 6: Measuring Perimeter and Area

This section addresses the curriculum requirement for drawing a trapezoid with a given area. Review the 4 steps of the problem-solving model with the students.

To produce further trapezoids with area 24 cm^2, students could draw rectangles and related parallelograms on 0.5-cm grid paper, which allows for dimensions such as 1.5 cm by 16 cm, 2.5 cm by 9.6 cm, and 7.5 cm by 3.2 cm.

Look back:

- For a parallelogram with base 8 cm and height 4 cm, the trapezoid would have area 16 cm^2, height 4 cm, and the sum of the lengths of the parallel sides is 8 cm.

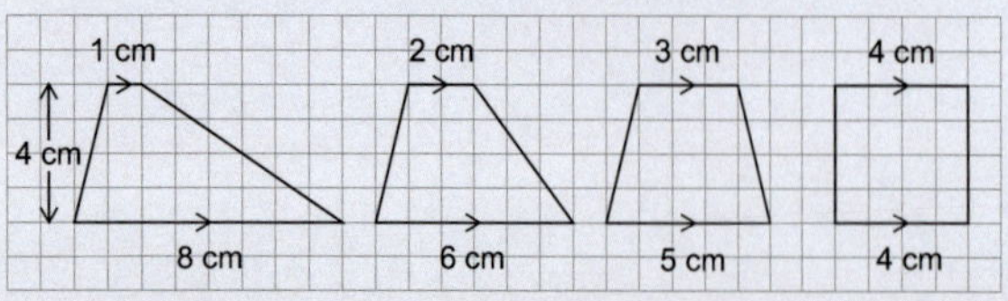

- The trapezoid has area 24 cm^2 and height 4 cm. The related parallelogram has area 48 cm^2 and base $\frac{48}{4} = 12$. So, the sum of the parallel sides of the trapezoid is 12 cm.
If the base is 5 cm, then the other parallel side is 7 cm.

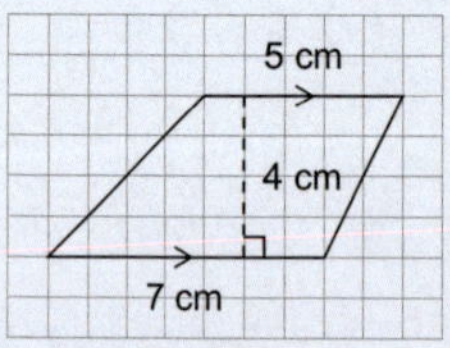

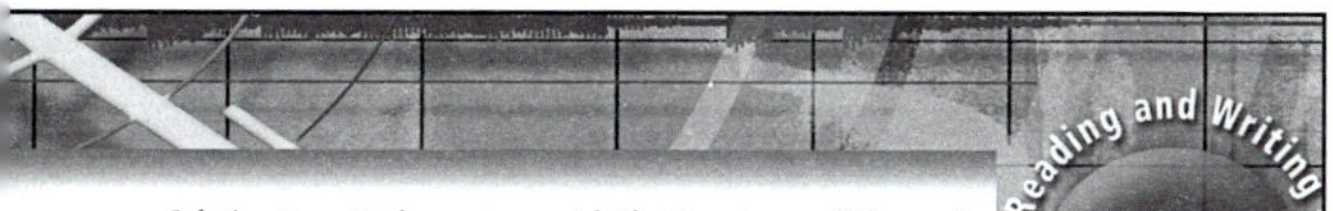

Solution 3 To draw a trapezoid (that is not a parallelogram) with area 24 cm²:
Two congruent trapezoids join to form a parallelogram. If each trapezoid has area 24 cm², then the parallelogram has area 48 cm².

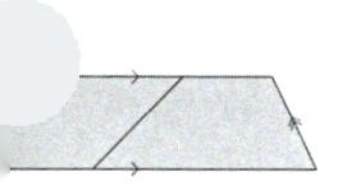

Work backward.
Draw a parallelogram with area 48 cm².
Divide it into 2 congruent trapezoids.
A parallelogram with area 48 cm² can have base 12 cm and height 4 cm.
Choose a length for one base of the trapezoid, less than 12 cm.
Choose 10 cm. Mark a point on the top side of the parallelogram 10 cm from the left vertex.

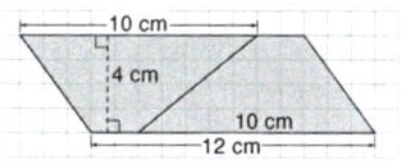

Mark a point on the bottom side of the parallelogram 10 cm from the right vertex.
Join these points to form two congruent trapezoids.
So, one trapezoid with area 24 cm² looks like this:

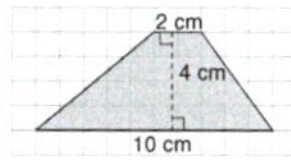

Look back

- What if we had chosen a parallelogram with base 8 cm and height 4 cm?
  What could the trapezoid look like?
- What if we had chosen 5 cm for one base of the trapezoid?
  What would the trapezoid look like?

Problems

1. Draw 3 different trapezoids with area 30 cm².
2. Think of other methods to find the area of a trapezoid.
   Use a different method to draw a trapezoid with area 20 cm².

Reflect

Choose an area for a trapezoid. Explain how to draw a trapezoid with that area. Include a diagram.

Reading and Writing in Math: Interpreting a Problem 233

to form 2 congruent trapezoids. So, one trapezoid with area 30 cm² looks like this:

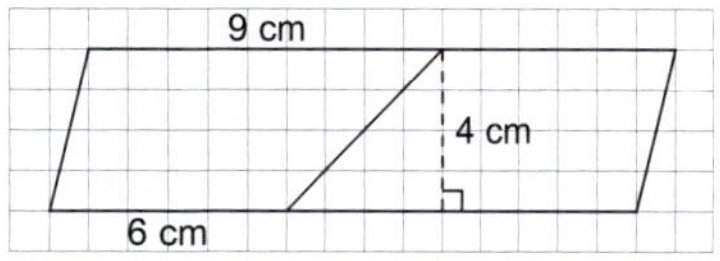

For a second trapezoid, I divided the base of the parallelogram into 2 parts: 5 cm and 10 cm. So, the trapezoid has parallel sides of lengths 5 cm and 10 cm, and height 4 cm.
For a third trapezoid, I divided the base of the parallelogram into 2 parts: 2 cm and 13 cm. So, the trapezoid has parallel sides of lengths 2 cm and 13 cm, and height 4 cm.

2. I can join 2 triangles to form a trapezoid as long as each triangle has the same height, and one side length in common. I chose a height of 4 cm. I then divided the required area into 2 parts, both of which are divisible by the height, 4 cm: 12 cm² and 8 cm². I drew a broken vertical line of length 4 cm; this is the height. For the first triangle, since $12 = \frac{1}{2}bh$, I know that the base times height must equal 24. Since the height is 4 cm, the base must be 6 cm. I drew a horizontal line 6 cm long perpendicular to the height. For the second triangle, since $8 = \frac{1}{2}bh$, I know that the base times height must equal 16. Since the height is 4 cm, the base must be 4 cm. I drew a horizontal line 4 cm long perpendicular to the height. I joined the top left point with the bottom right point, then joined the sides to form 2 triangles.

(*Solutions continue below.*)

(*Sample Solutions, continued*)
The area of the trapezoid formed
= the area of triangle 1 + the area of triangle 2
= 12 cm² + 8 cm²
= 20 cm²

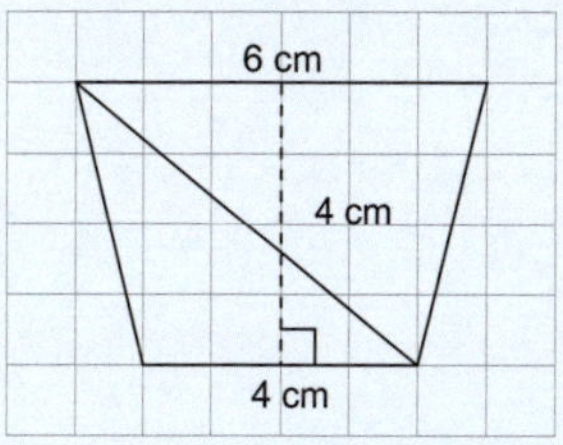

REFLECT: I chose an area of 15 cm². I drew a parallelogram with area 30 cm²: base 6 cm, height 5 cm. I divided each 6-cm side into 2 parts: 5 cm and 1 cm at the top, and 1 cm and 5 cm at the bottom. I joined the dividing points to form 2 trapezoids. Each trapezoid has area 15 cm².

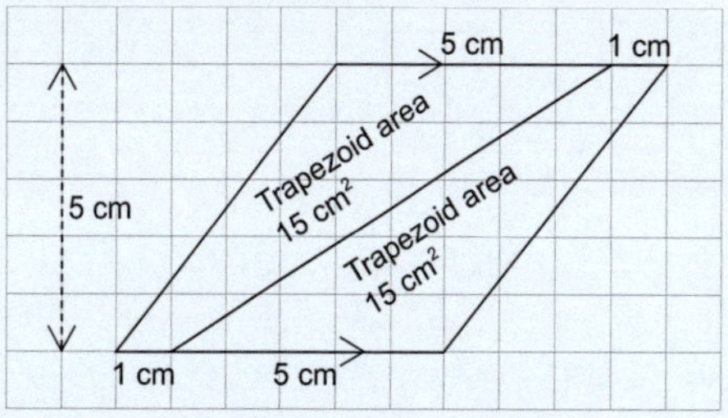

Measuring Irregular Figures

SECTION ORGANIZER (80–100 min)

Curriculum Focus: Find the area and perimeter of an irregular figure. (7m36, 7m37)

Teacher Materials
- overhead Pattern Blocks

Student Materials
- 1-cm grid paper (PM 20)
- calculators
- rulers

Optional
- Step-by-Step 4 (Master 6.12)
- Extra Practice 4 (Master 6.20)

Assessment: Master 6.2 Ongoing Observations: Measuring Perimeter and Area

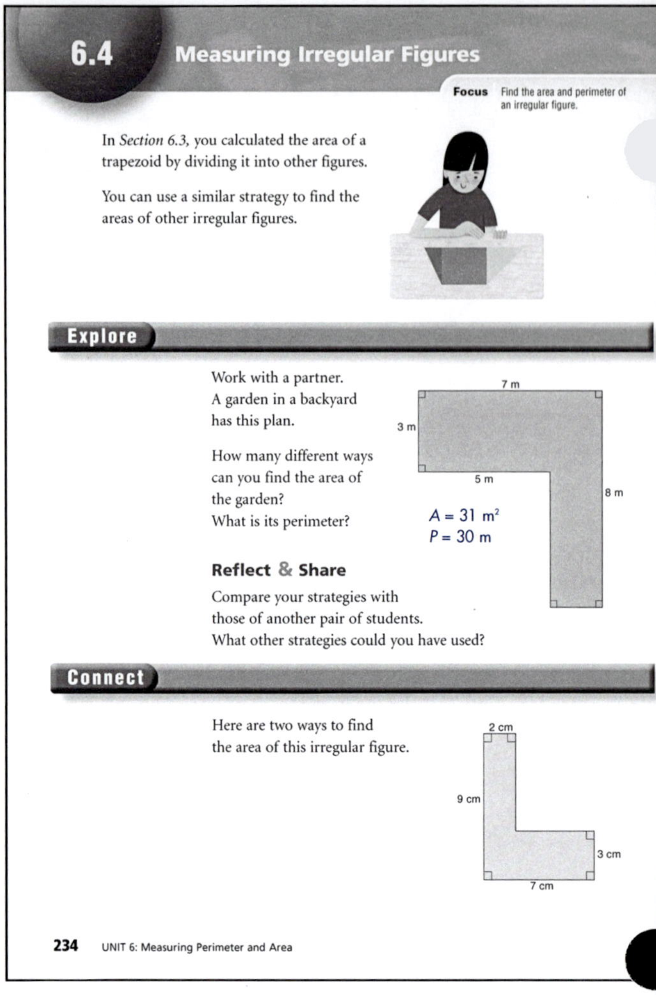
6.4 Measuring Irregular Figures

Focus Find the area and perimeter of an irregular figure.

In *Section 6.3*, you calculated the area of a trapezoid by dividing it into other figures.

You can use a similar strategy to find the areas of other irregular figures.

Explore

Work with a partner.
A garden in a backyard has this plan.

How many different ways can you find the area of the garden?
What is its perimeter?

Reflect & Share

Compare your strategies with those of another pair of students.
What other strategies could you have used?

Connect

Here are two ways to find the area of this irregular figure.

234 UNIT 6: Measuring Perimeter and Area

Key Math Learnings

1. The area of an irregular figure can be found by dividing it into smaller figures whose areas can be found.
2. The perimeter of an irregular figure can be found by adding its side lengths.

BEFORE Get Started

Remind students of the different ways they calculated the area of a trapezoid. Have a volunteer use overhead Pattern Blocks on the overhead projector to make an irregular figure. Trace around the blocks, then remove them.

Ask:
- Which blocks make up the figure? (*The orange square, 2 green triangles, and the blue rhombus*)
- How can we find the area of the figure? (*We can find the area of each block, then add the areas to get the area of the figure.*)
- How can we find the area of a rhombus? (*A rhombus is a parallelogram so we can use the formula $A = bh$.*)

Have another volunteer make a different irregular figure that uses a yellow hexagon.

Ask:
- How can we find the area of the yellow hexagon? (*The hexagon is made from two red trapezoids. We can find the area of the red trapezoid, then multiply the area by 2 to get the area of the yellow hexagon.*)

Present *Explore*. Students could draw the garden on grid paper to help them divide it into smaller figures.

DURING Explore

Ongoing Assessment: Observe and Listen

As students work, ask questions, such as:
- How did you find the area of the garden? (*I divided the garden into 2 rectangles with dimensions 7 m by 3 m and 2 m by 5 m. I found the area of each rectangle, then added the areas: $21\ m^2 + 10\ m^2 = 31\ m^2$.*)

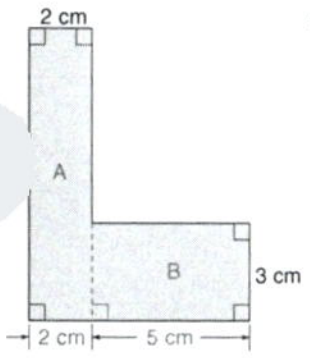

➢ Divide the figure into smaller figures whose areas you can find.
Rectangle A has length 9 cm and width 2 cm.
Area of rectangle A: 9 cm × 2 cm = 18 cm^2
Since the width of rectangle A is 2 cm,
the length of rectangle B is: 7 cm − 2 cm = 5 cm
Area of rectangle B: 3 cm × 5 cm = 15 cm^2
So, the area of the figure is: 18 cm^2 + 15 cm^2 = 33 cm^2

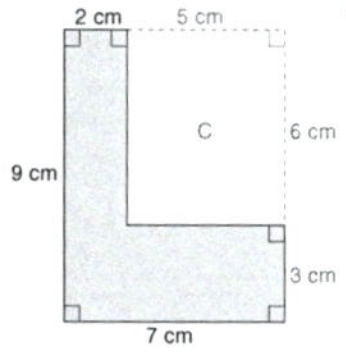

➢ Draw a rectangle around the figure.
The area of the large rectangle is: 9 cm × 7 cm = 63 cm^2
Figure C is a rectangle.
Its width is: 7 cm − 2 cm = 5 cm
Its length is: 9 cm − 3 cm = 6 cm
Area of rectangle C: 5 cm × 6 cm = 30 cm^2
So, the area of the figure is: 63 cm^2 − 30 cm^2 = 33 cm^2

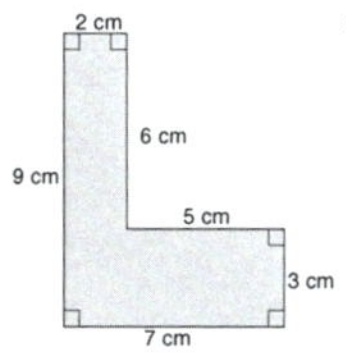

➢ To find the perimeter of the figure, add the side lengths.
Perimeter
= 2 cm + 6 cm + 5 cm + 3 cm + 7 cm + 9 cm
= 32 cm
The perimeter is 32 cm.

Example

Here is a plan of the back wall of a barn.

a) What is the area of the wall?
b) One can of paint covers 40 m^2. How many cans are needed to paint this wall?

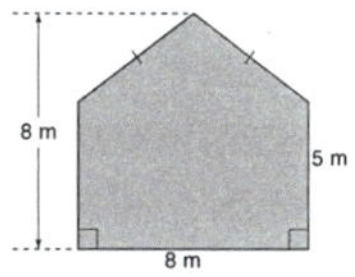

6.4 Measuring Irregular Figures 235

REACHING ALL LEARNERS

Alternative Explore

Materials: tangrams, 1-cm grid paper, rulers
Students use tans to make an irregular figure. Students trace their figure on grid paper, showing the individual tans. Students measure, then calculate the areas of the tans, then add to find the area of the irregular figure.

Early Finishers

Have students draw irregular figures, then find the area and perimeter of each figure.

Common Misconceptions

➤ Students divide an irregular figure into smaller figures that overlap.

How to Help: Show students, for example, that if they divide the backyard in *Explore* into 2 overlapping rectangles, they will get a greater area than the actual area because the area of the overlapping part has been counted twice. Ensure students understand that the smaller figures must not overlap, and that they must fit the irregular figure exactly.

- Did anyone use a different method? Explain. (*I divided the garden into 2 rectangles, but the dimensions of my rectangles were 5 m by 3 m and 2 m by 8 m. I found the area of each rectangle, then added the areas: 15 m² + 16 m² = 31 m².*)
- How else could you find the area of the garden? (*I draw a rectangle around the garden. It measures 7 m by 8 m. I subtract the area of the smaller rectangle, which is 5 m by 5 m, from the area of the larger rectangle to get the area of the garden: 56 m² – 25 m² = 31 m².*)
- What is the perimeter of the garden? (*30 m*) How do you know? (*I added the lengths of all the sides of the garden: 3 m + 7 m + 8 m + 2 m + 5 m + 5 m = 30 m.*)

AFTER Connect

Have volunteers share their strategies with the class.

What you might see:

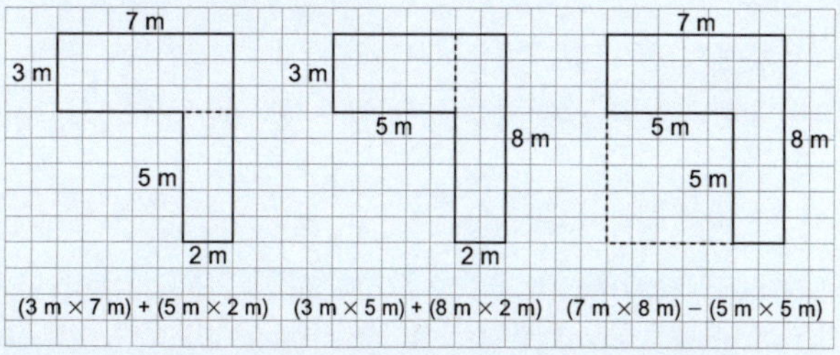

Ensure students understand how to subtract to find the dimensions of the smaller figures.

Work through the examples in *Connect*. Ensure students understand that no matter which strategy they use to find the area of an irregular figure, they should get the same answer each time.

Assignment Guidelines

If your students do not have time to complete all the *Practice* questions on pages 236 and 237, these questions provide minimum curriculum coverage: 1, 3, 5, 6, *Reflect*
To assess the 4 Achievement Chart categories listed in the curriculum document, have students complete these questions:
Understanding Concepts: 3; Problem Solving: 5;
Application: 6; Communication: *Reflect*

Sample Answers

3. a) I estimate the area to be about 38 m²: (8 × 6) – (5 × 2) = 38
   I estimate the perimeter to be about 38 m: 8 + 6 + 8 + 6 + 5 + 5 = 38
   c) My estimates are close to the actual values so my estimates are reasonable. The difference between the estimate and calculation of the perimeter is 0.4 m and the difference between the estimate and calculation of the area is 4.56 m².
4. a) I estimate the area to be about 2000 m² and the perimeter to be about 200 m.
   c) I could find the area by counting grid squares. Each grid square represents an area of 10 m × 10 m = 100 m². There are 22 squares. The total area = 22 × 100 m²
   = 2200 m²
   I can find the perimeter by counting units on each side. Each grid square has a length of 10 m.

(*Answers continue below, right*)

Solution

The wall is a rectangle with an isosceles triangle above it.

a) For the triangle:
The base, b, is 8 m.
The height, h, is 8 m − 5 m = 3 m.
Area = $\frac{bh}{2}$
Substitute $b = 8$ and $h = 3$.
Area = $\frac{8 \times 3}{2}$
= 12

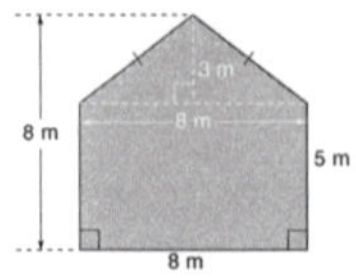

For the rectangle:
Area = bh
Substitute $b = 8$ and $h = 5$.
Area = 8 × 5
= 40
Area of wall = 40 m² + 12 m²
= 52 m²
The area of the wall is 52 m².

b) The area of the wall is 52 m².
One can of paint covers 40 m².
One can is not enough.
Two cans of paint are needed.

Practice

1. A living room in a home has the shape, below left.
What is the area of the living room? 24 m²

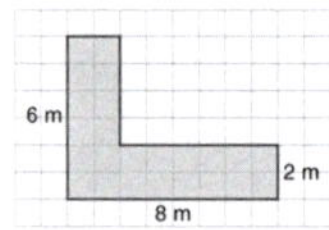

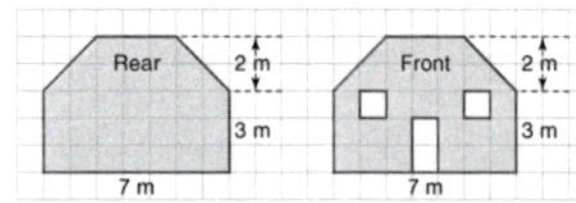

2. The rear and front walls of a shed are shown, above middle and right.
a) Find the area of the rear wall. 31 m²
b) Find the area of the front wall, excluding the windows and door. 27 m²

Practice

Questions 5 and 6 require 1-cm grid paper (PM 20) and rulers. Encourage students to draw the figures on grid paper, then label each smaller figure with a letter of the alphabet. This will make it easier for students to explain their strategies and to keep track of their work.

Assessment Focus: Question 6

Students realize that the areas of the 2 rectangles must have a sum of 30 m². Students divide 30 m² into 2 parts such that both areas are divisible by the width, 3 m. Students discover that the perimeter of the pools are the same. Students should also discover that it is impossible to draw an L-shaped swimming pool with the width of each arm 5 m; the only possible pool is rectangular, with dimensions 6 m by 5 m.

(*Sample Answers, continued*)

5. a)

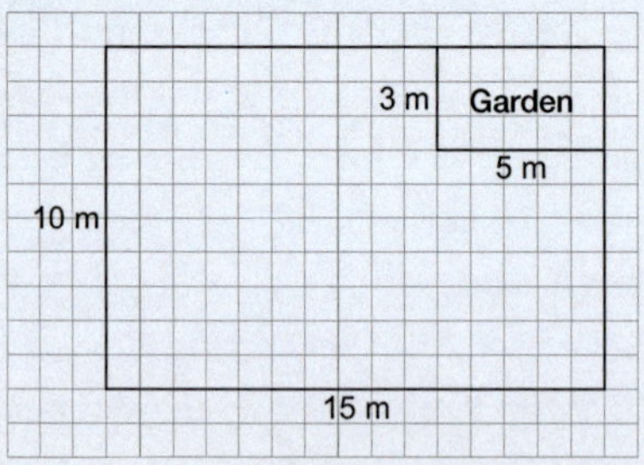

   c) The area of the garden will always be 15 m² and the area of the backyard will always be 150 m². To find the area of the backyard, excluding the garden, you are always subtracting the same numbers, no matter where the garden is placed.

6. a)

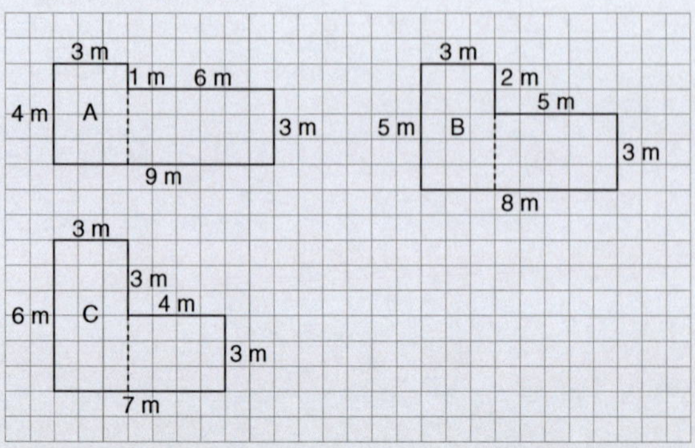

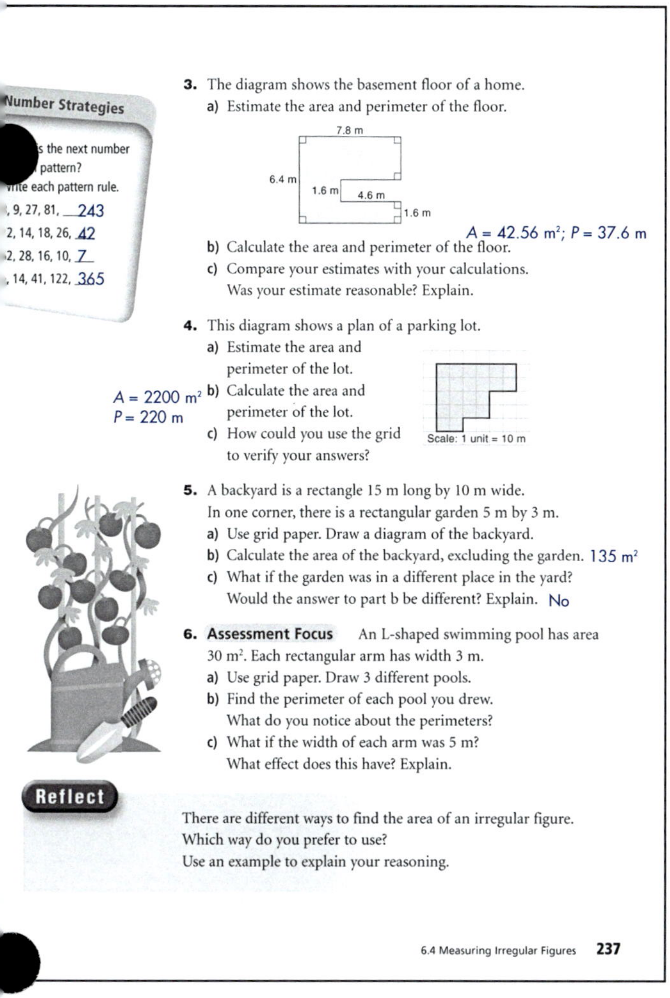
Number Strategies

...s the next number ... pattern?
...rite each pattern rule.

..., 9, 27, 81, 243
...2, 14, 18, 26, 42
...2, 28, 16, 10, 7
..., 14, 41, 122, 365

3. The diagram shows the basement floor of a home.
   a) Estimate the area and perimeter of the floor.

   b) Calculate the area and perimeter of the floor. $A = 42.56$ m²; $P = 37.6$ m
   c) Compare your estimates with your calculations. Was your estimate reasonable? Explain.

4. This diagram shows a plan of a parking lot.
   a) Estimate the area and perimeter of the lot.
   b) Calculate the area and perimeter of the lot. $A = 2200\ m^2$, $P = 220$ m
   c) How could you use the grid to verify your answers?

   Scale: 1 unit = 10 m

5. A backyard is a rectangle 15 m long by 10 m wide. In one corner, there is a rectangular garden 5 m by 3 m.
   a) Use grid paper. Draw a diagram of the backyard.
   b) Calculate the area of the backyard, excluding the garden. $135\ m^2$
   c) What if the garden was in a different place in the yard? Would the answer to part b be different? Explain. No

6. **Assessment Focus** An L-shaped swimming pool has area $30\ m^2$. Each rectangular arm has width 3 m.
   a) Use grid paper. Draw 3 different pools.
   b) Find the perimeter of each pool you drew. What do you notice about the perimeters?
   c) What if the width of each arm was 5 m? What effect does this have? Explain.

Reflect

There are different ways to find the area of an irregular figure. Which way do you prefer to use? Use an example to explain your reasoning.

6.4 Measuring Irregular Figures 237

6. b) Perimeter of Pool A: $3 + 4 + 9 + 3 + 6 + 1 = 26$
Perimeter of Pool B: $3 + 5 + 8 + 3 + 5 + 2 = 26$
Perimeter of Pool C: $6 + 7 + 3 + 4 + 3 + 3 = 26$
The perimeter of each pool is 26 m.

c) If the width of each arm was 5 m, it would be impossible to make an L-shaped pool. The pool would be rectangular, with dimensions 5 m by 6 m.

REFLECT: I prefer to divide the irregular figure into rectangles whenever possible. The calculation to find the area of a rectangle is easy: $A = bh$. I find the area of each rectangle, then add to find the total area. The calculations are more difficult when the figures are triangles or trapezoids. For example, to find the area of this irregular figure, I add the areas of the two rectangles.

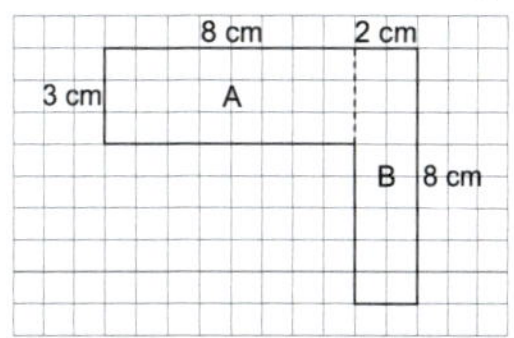

Area of rectangle A = bh = 8 cm × 3 cm = 24 cm²
Area of rectangle B = bh = 2 cm × 8 cm = 16 cm²

The total area = area of rectangle A + area of rectangle B
= 24 cm² + 16 cm² = 40 cm²

The area of the irregular figure is 40 cm².

Number Strategies

Students find the pattern rule for each pattern, then use the rule to find the next number in each pattern. The first pattern rule is: Start at 3. Multiply by 3 each time. The second pattern rule is: Start at 12. Add 2. Multiply the number added by 2 each time. The third pattern rule is: Start at 52. Subtract 24. Divide the number you subtract by 2 each time. The fourth pattern rule is: Start at 5. Add 9. Multiply the number you add by 3 each time.

ASSESSMENT FOR LEARNING

What to Look For

Understanding concepts

✔ Students understand that the area of an irregular figure can be found by dividing it into smaller figures whose areas can be found.

✔ Students understand that the perimeter of an irregular figure can be found by adding its side lengths.

Applying procedures

✔ Students can estimate and calculate the perimeter and area of irregular figures.

What to Do

Extra Support: Students who have difficulty dividing an irregular figure into smaller figures should continue to work with different L-shaped figures drawn on grid paper, until they feel confident enough to work with more complicated figures.
Students can use Step-by-Step 4 (Master 6.12) to complete question 6.

Extra Practice: Students can complete the Additional Activity *Pattern Block Figures* (Master 6.7).
Students can complete Extra Practice 4 (Master 6.20).

Extension: Have students write a formula in words for the area of each irregular figure calculated.
Students can complete the Additional Activity *Rule the School* (Master 6.8).

Recording and Reporting

Master 6.2 Ongoing Observations: Measuring Perimeter and Area

Trapezoid Challenge

SECTION ORGANIZER

Student Materials
- 11 by 11 geoboard
- geobands
- 3 number cubes labelled 1 to 6
- square dot paper (PM 22)
- calculators

Optional
- 1-cm grid paper (PM 20)

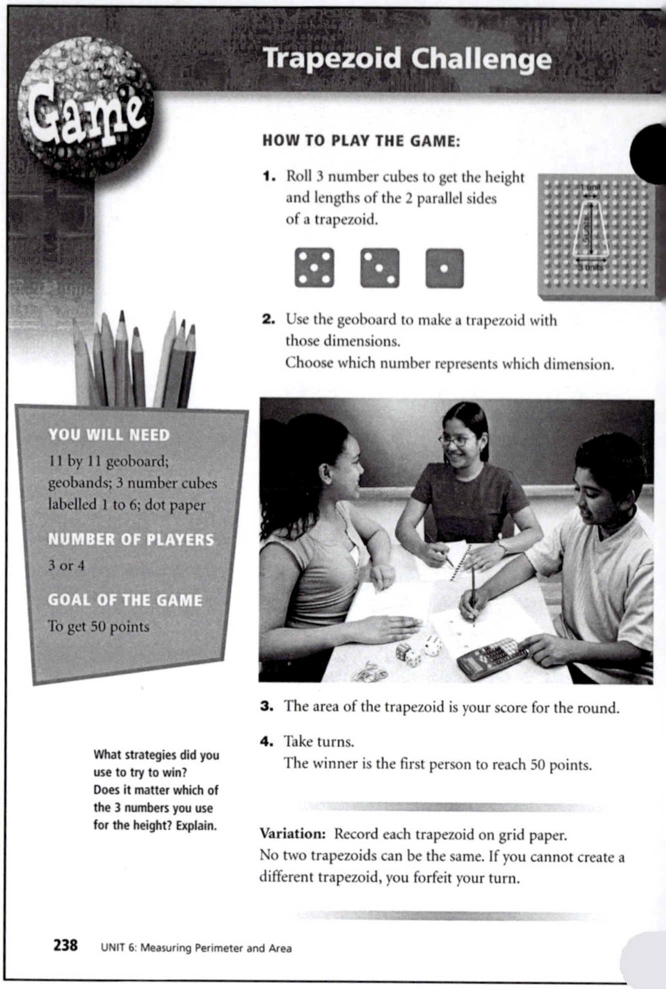

Trapezoid Challenge

Game

HOW TO PLAY THE GAME:

1. Roll 3 number cubes to get the height and lengths of the 2 parallel sides of a trapezoid.

2. Use the geoboard to make a trapezoid with those dimensions.
Choose which number represents which dimension.

YOU WILL NEED
11 by 11 geoboard; geobands; 3 number cubes labelled 1 to 6; dot paper

NUMBER OF PLAYERS
3 or 4

GOAL OF THE GAME
To get 50 points

3. The area of the trapezoid is your score for the round.

4. Take turns.
The winner is the first person to reach 50 points.

What strategies did you use to try to win? Does it matter which of the 3 numbers you use for the height? Explain.

Variation: Record each trapezoid on grid paper.
No two trapezoids can be the same. If you cannot create a different trapezoid, you forfeit your turn.

238 UNIT 6: Measuring Perimeter and Area

Arrange students into groups of 3 or 4. Invite a volunteer to read the game rules. Ensure students understand how the game is played. Encourage students to draw their trapezoids on dot paper to make it easier to calculate the areas.

As students play, ask questions such as:
- How will you try to be the first to get 50 points? (*By making trapezoids with greater areas than my opponents*)
- How did you find the area of your trapezoid? (*By dividing the trapezoid into 2 triangles, finding the area of each triangle, then adding*)
- Does it matter which of the 3 numbers you use for the height?
(*Yes. The height is used to calculate the area of both triangles so the greatest number should be used for the height.*)

After all students have played at least one game, ask questions, such as:

- What is the greatest area possible for a trapezoid? (*If the three numbers rolled are 6s, the area is 36 square units.*) What is the least area possible for a trapezoid? (*If the three numbers rolled are 1s, the area is 1 square unit.*)
- Did anyone use a different strategy to find the area of a trapezoid? Explain.
(*I used the formula I developed in the section on area and perimeter of a trapezoid:*
$A = \frac{1}{2}$ *(base 1 + base 2)* $\times$ *height. I find this formula easy to use.*)

Unit Review

Review any lesson with etext online tutorial

What Do I Need to Know?

✓ The *perimeter* of a figure is found by adding the lengths of its sides.

✓ **Area of a Parallelogram**
$A = bh$

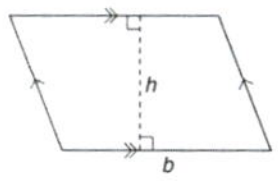

✓ **Area of a Triangle**
$A = \frac{bh}{2}$

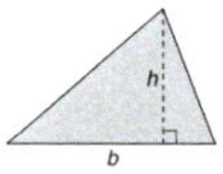

✓ **Area of a Trapezoid**
Divide the trapezoid into:

- Two triangles
- A parallelogram and a triangle
- A rectangle and 2 triangles

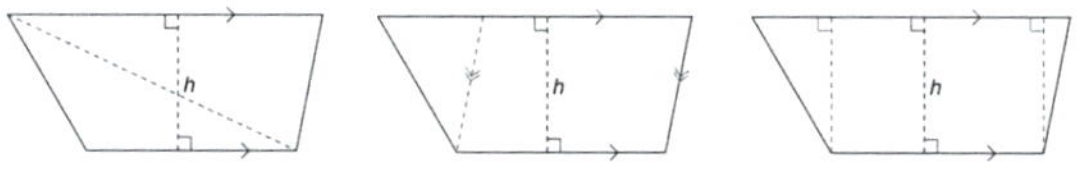

✓ **Area of an Irregular Figure**

- Divide the figure into figures whose area you can find, then add the areas.
- Or, draw a rectangle around the figure; subtract the areas of the newly formed figures from the area of the rectangle.

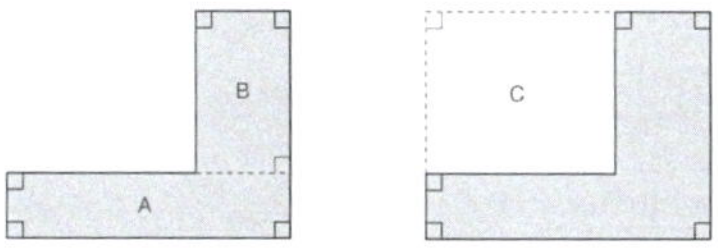

Unit Review 239

SECTION ORGANIZER

Student Materials
- calculators

Optional
- 1-cm grid paper (PM 20)
- rulers

Assessment: Masters 6.1 Unit Rubric: Measuring Perimeter and Area, 6.4 Unit Summary: Measuring Perimeter and Area

Sample Solutions

1. a) The formula for the area of a parallelogram is $A = bh$.
   I substituted $b = 4.0$ cm and $h = 1.7$ cm.
   b) The formula for the area of a triangle is $A = \frac{1}{2}bh$.
   I substituted $b = 2.8$ cm and $h = 2.1$ cm.
   c) The formula for the area of a triangle is $A = \frac{1}{2}bh$.
   I substituted $b = 2.5$ cm and $h = 2.5$ cm.
   d) The formula for the area of a parallelogram is $A = bh$.
   I substituted $b = 2.6$ cm and $h = 2.3$ cm.
2. a) I divided the trapezoid into 2 triangles: one with base 5 cm and height 12 cm, the other with base 26 cm and height 12 cm.
   $A = \frac{26 \times 12}{2} + \frac{5 \times 12}{2}$
   $= 156 + 30$
   $= 186$

(*Solutions continue below.*)

(*Sample Solutions, continued*)

2. b) $A = \frac{20.0 \times 30.0}{2} + \frac{55.0 \times 30.0}{2}$
   $= 300 + 825$
   $= 1125$
3. a) $P = 5 + 20 + 26 + 13 = 64$
   b) $P = 37.5 + 55.0 + 32.5 + 20.0 = 145$
4. I divided the trapezoid into 2 triangles. Triangle A has base 5 cm. Triangle B has base 26 cm. The total of their areas must be about 150 cm².
   Area = Area of triangle A + Area of triangle B
   $= \frac{1}{2}bh + \frac{1}{2}bh$
   $= (\frac{1}{2} \times 5 \times h) + (\frac{1}{2} \times 26 \times h)$
   $= (2.5 \times h) + (13 \times h)$
   Try $h = 10$
   $A = (2.5 \times 10) + (13 \times 10)$
   $= 25 + 130$
   $= 155$
   155 is close to 150, so I estimate the height of the trapezoid to be 10 cm.
5. a) $P = 4.2 + 3.0 + 8.2 + 3.2 + 12.4 + 6.2 = 37.2$
   A = area of rectangle A + area of rectangle B
   $= (12.4 \times 3.2) + (4.2 \times 3.0)$
   $= 39.68 + 12.6$
   $= 52.28$
   b) $P = 7.2 + 6.0 + 7.2 + 14.4 + 7.2 + 6.0 = 48$
   I divided the trapezoid into 2 triangles.
   Triangle A has base 14.4 m.
   Triangle B has base 7.2 m.
   A = area of rectangle + area of triangle A + area of triangle B
   $= (14.4 \times 7.2) + \frac{1}{2}(14.4 \times 4.8) + \frac{1}{2}(7.2 \times 4.8)$
   $= 103.68 + 34.56 + 17.28$
   $= 155.52$
6. a) The paved surface is rectangular. The formula for the area of a rectangle is $A = bh$.
   Substitute $b = 85$ m − 10 m − 8 m = 67 m, and $h = 16.5$ m.
   $A = (67 \times 16.5)$
   $= 1105.5$
   b) The perimeter of the grass area
   $= 85 + 50 + 8 + 16.5 + 67 + 16.5 + 10 + 50$
   $= 303$
   1 m of fencing costs \$35.50.
   So, 303 m of fencing costs \$35.50 × 303
   = \$10 756.50.

Correlation of Extra Practice questions on page 443:

Section	Questions
6.1	1, 2, 3, 4
6.2	5, 6, 7, 8
6.3	9
6.4	10

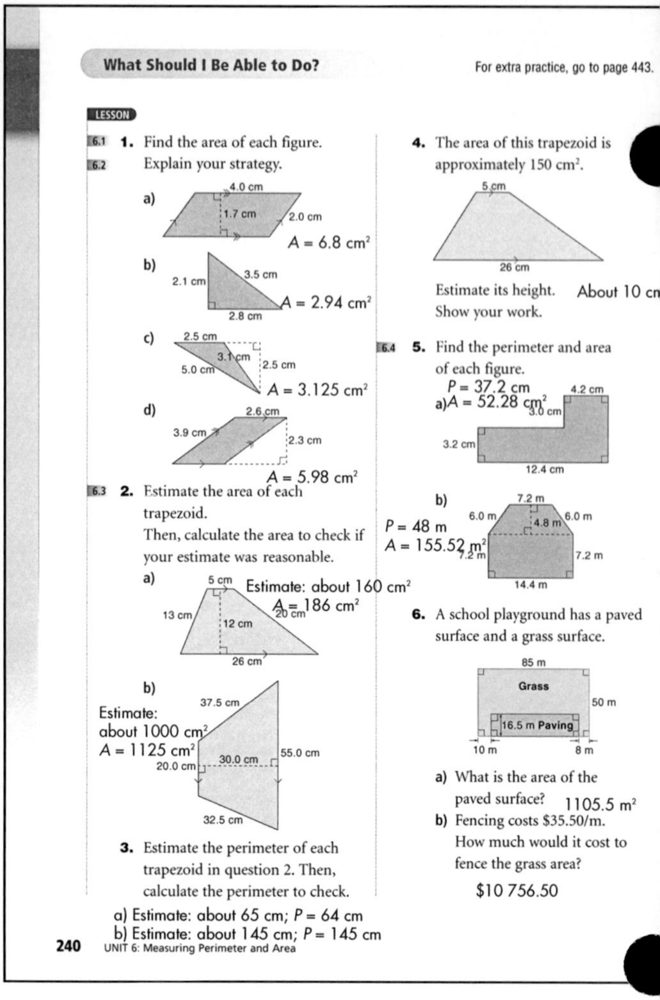

What Should I Be Able to Do?

For extra practice, go to page 443.

LESSON

6.1, 6.2 **1.** Find the area of each figure. Explain your strategy.

a) $A = 6.8\text{ cm}^2$

b) $A = 2.94\text{ cm}^2$

c) $A = 3.125\text{ cm}^2$

d) $A = 5.98\text{ cm}^2$

6.3 **2.** Estimate the area of each trapezoid. Then, calculate the area to check if your estimate was reasonable.

a) Estimate: about 160 cm^2; $A = 186\text{ cm}^2$

b) Estimate: about 1000 cm^2; $A = 1125\text{ cm}^2$

3. Estimate the perimeter of each trapezoid in question 2. Then, calculate the perimeter to check.

a) Estimate: about 65 cm; $P = 64$ cm

b) Estimate: about 145 cm; $P = 145$ cm

4. The area of this trapezoid is approximately 150 cm^2.

Estimate its height. Show your work. About 10 cm

6.4 **5.** Find the perimeter and area of each figure.

a) $P = 37.2$ cm; $A = 52.28\text{ cm}^2$

b) $P = 48$ m; $A = 155.52\text{ m}^2$

6. A school playground has a paved surface and a grass surface.

a) What is the area of the paved surface? 1105.5 m^2

b) Fencing costs \$35.50/m. How much would it cost to fence the grass area? \$10 756.50

ASSESSMENT FOR LEARNING

What to Look For

Understanding of concepts

✔ **Question 2:** Student understands that the area of a trapezoid can be found by dividing it into other figures, such as triangles, rectangles, and parallelograms.

Application of mathematical procedures

✔ **Question 1:** Student can use formulas to find the area of a parallelogram and the area of a triangle.

✔ **Question 5:** Student can calculate the perimeter and area of an irregular figure.

Communicating

✔ **Question 1:** Student can use mathematical language to describe a strategy for finding the area of a figure.

Problem solving

✔ **Questions 4 and 6:** Student can solve problems that involve the area and perimeter of trapezoids and irregular figures.

Recording and Reporting

Master 6.1 Unit Rubric: Measuring Perimeter and Area

Master 6.4 Unit Summary: Measuring Perimeter and Area

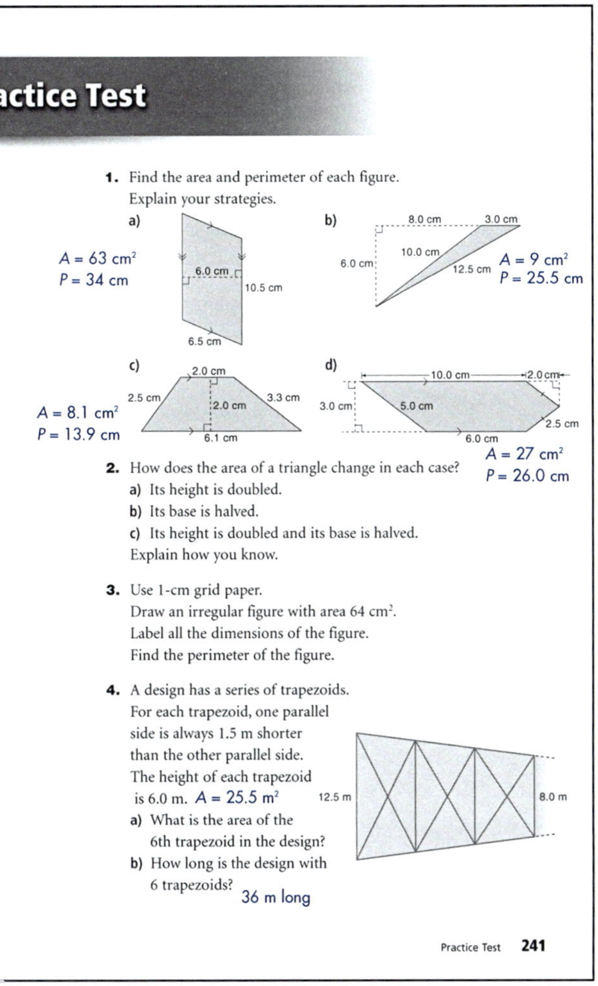

Practice Test

1. Find the area and perimeter of each figure.
Explain your strategies.

a) $A = 63$ cm^2, $P = 34$ cm (6.0 cm, 10.5 cm, 6.5 cm)

b) $A = 9$ cm^2, $P = 25.5$ cm (8.0 cm, 3.0 cm, 6.0 cm, 10.0 cm, 12.5 cm)

c) $A = 8.1$ cm^2, $P = 13.9$ cm (2.0 cm, 2.5 cm, 2.0 cm, 3.3 cm, 6.1 cm)

d) $A = 27$ cm^2, $P = 26.0$ cm (10.0 cm, 2.0 cm, 3.0 cm, 5.0 cm, 2.5 cm, 6.0 cm)

2. How does the area of a triangle change in each case?
a) Its height is doubled.
b) Its base is halved.
c) Its height is doubled and its base is halved.
Explain how you know.

3. Use 1-cm grid paper.
Draw an irregular figure with area 64 cm^2.
Label all the dimensions of the figure.
Find the perimeter of the figure.

4. A design has a series of trapezoids.
For each trapezoid, one parallel side is always 1.5 m shorter than the other parallel side.
The height of each trapezoid is 6.0 m. $A = 25.5$ m^2
a) What is the area of the 6th trapezoid in the design?
b) How long is the design with 6 trapezoids? 36 m long

(12.5 m, 8.0 m)

Practice Test 241

SECTION ORGANIZER

Student Materials

- rulers
- calculators
- 1-cm grid paper (PM 20)

Assessment: Masters 6.1 Unit Rubric: Measuring Perimeter and Area, 6.4 Unit Summary: Measuring Perimeter and Area

Assignment Guidelines

To assess the 4 Achievement Chart categories listed in the curriculum document, use these test questions:
Understanding Concepts: 1
Communication: 2
Application: 3
Problem Solving: 4

Sample Solutions

1. a) The formula for the area of a parallelogram is $A = bh$.
I substituted $b = 10.5$ cm and $h = 6.0$ cm.
b) The formula for the area of a triangle is $A = \frac{1}{2}bh$.
I substituted $b = 3.0$ cm and $h = 6.0$ cm.
c) I divided the trapezoid into 2 triangles.
Triangle A has base 6.1 cm.
Triangle B has base 2.0 cm.
A = area of triangle A + area of triangle B

(Solutions continue below.)

(Sample Solutions, continued)

d) I divided the irregular figure into 3 figures: a triangle with base 3.0 cm and height 4.0 cm; a rectangle with base 6.0 cm and height 3.0 cm; and a triangle with base 3.0 cm and height 2.0 cm. The area of the irregular figure is the sum of the areas of these smaller figures.

2. I will use a triangle with $b = 6$ cm and $h = 4$ cm as an example. The area of my original triangle is:
$A = \frac{1}{2}(6 \text{ cm} \times 4 \text{ cm}) = 12 \text{ cm}^2$.
a) If I double the height, $h = 8$ cm.
$A = \frac{1}{2}(6 \text{ cm} \times 8 \text{ cm}) = 24 \text{ cm}^2$
The area is doubled.
b) If I double the base, $b = 12$ cm.
$A = \frac{1}{2}(12 \text{ cm} \times 4 \text{ cm}) = 24 \text{ cm}^2$
The area is doubled.
c) If I double the height and halve the base, $h = 8$ cm and $b = 3$ cm.
$A = \frac{1}{2}(8 \text{ cm} \times 3 \text{ cm}) = 12 \text{ cm}^2$
The area stays the same.

3. $P = 4 + 2 + 2 + 2 + 2 + 2 + 4 + 2 + 6 + 2 + 2 + 2 + 4 + 2 + 4 + 2 + 4 + 2 + 4 + 2 = 56$

3.

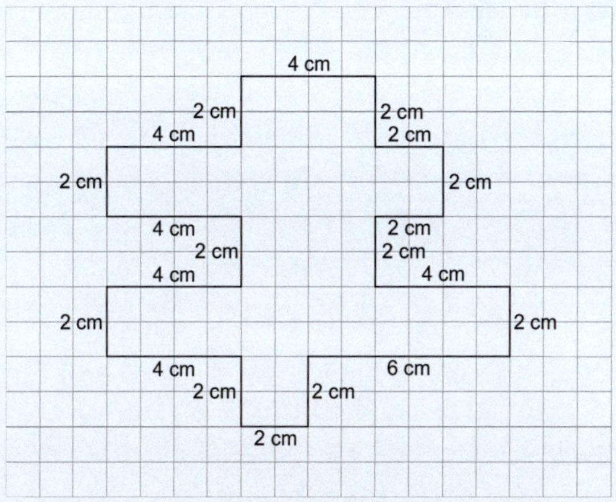

4. a) The lengths of the parallel sides are: 12.5 m, 11.0 m, 9.5 m, 8.0 m, 6.5 m, 5.0 m, 3.5 m
The 6th trapezoid will have one parallel side of length 5.0 m, one parallel side of length 3.5 m, and height 6.0 m. I divide the trapezoid into 2 triangles.
$A = \frac{1}{2}(5.0 \text{ cm} \times 6.0 \text{ cm}) + \frac{1}{2}(3.5 \text{ cm} \times 6.0 \text{ cm})$
$= 15 \text{ cm}^2 + 10.5 \text{ cm}^2 = 25.5 \text{ cm}^2$
b) Each trapezoid has a height of 6.0 cm. So, 6 trapezoids will have a height of 6×6.0 cm = 36 cm.

Designing a Patio

SECTION ORGANIZER (80–100 min)

Student Grouping: Individual

Student Materials
- calculators
- Patio Grid for Unit Problem (Master 6.14)
- coloured pencils or markers
- rulers

Optional
- Pattern Blocks (PM 25)
- tangrams (PM 26)

Assessment: Masters 6.3 Performance Assessment Rubric: Designing a Patio, 6.4 Unit Summary: Measuring Perimeter and Area

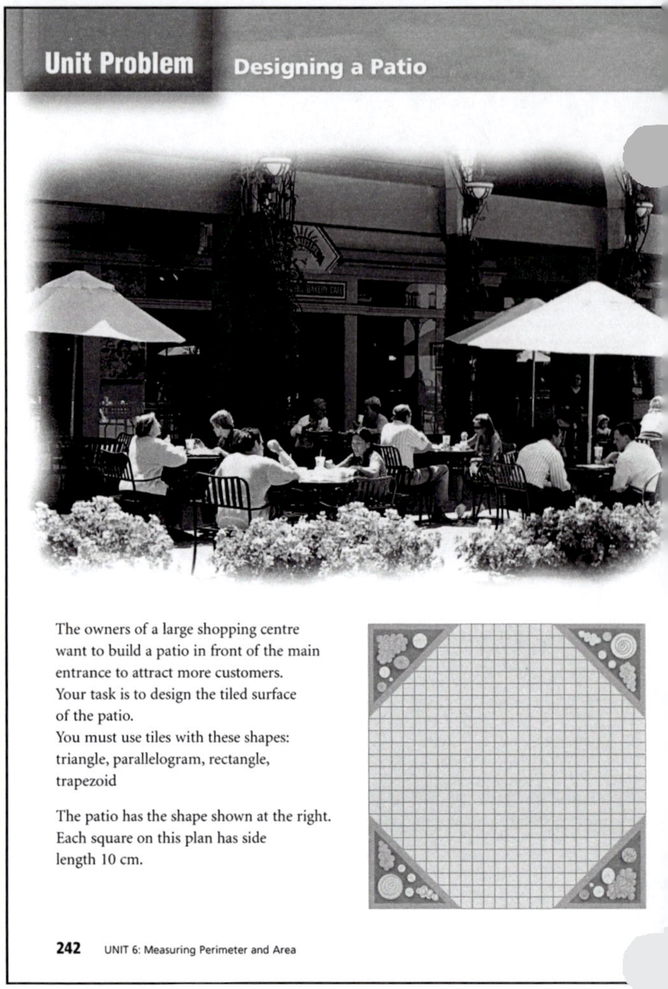
Unit Problem Designing a Patio

The owners of a large shopping centre want to build a patio in front of the main entrance to attract more customers.
Your task is to design the tiled surface of the patio.
You must use tiles with these shapes: triangle, parallelogram, rectangle, trapezoid

The patio has the shape shown at the right. Each square on this plan has side length 10 cm.

242 UNIT 6: Measuring Perimeter and Area

Sample Solution

This is my patio:

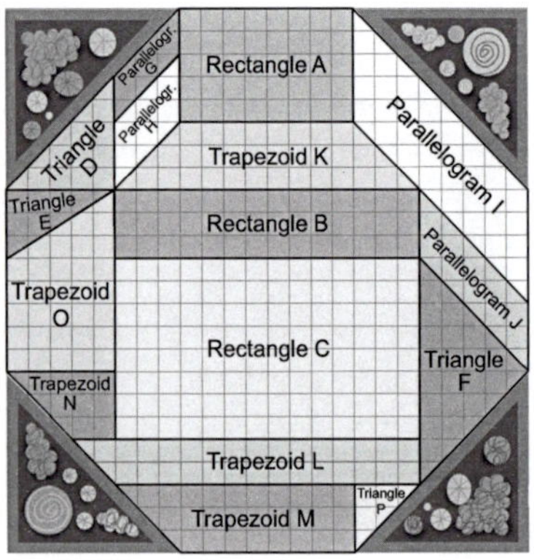

Have one student read the *Check List* aloud. Remind students that they should use the *Check List* to assess their work before handing it in. You may also wish to provide students with copies of Master 6.3 Performance Assessment Rubric: Designing a Patio so they will know how their work will be assessed.

Tell students that to check their work, they could compare the area of the patio grid, to the sum of the areas of the individual figures used to make their patio. The areas should be the same if all calculations are correct.

Encourage students to work with Pattern Blocks or tangram pieces to see how different figures can fit together. Encourage students to colour the different figures to make it easier to see the design and to make their work more attractive.

Reflect on the Unit

To find the area of a parallelogram, I need to know its base and height. For example, to find the area of a parallelogram with base 4 cm and height 2 cm, I substitute $b = 4$ and $h = 2$ into the formula $A = bh$.
$A = 4 \times 2 = 8$; the area of the parallelogram is 8 cm^2.
To find the area of a triangle, I need to know its base and height. For example, to find the area of a triangle with base 7 cm and height 3 cm, I substitute $b = 7$ and $h = 3$ into the formula $A = \frac{1}{2}bh$.
$A = \frac{7 \times 3}{2} = 10.5$; the area of the triangle is 10.5 cm^2.
To find the area of a trapezoid, I need to know the lengths of the parallel sides and the height. For example, to find the area of a trapezoid with height 2 cm and parallel sides 3 cm and 7cm, I divide the area into two triangles.
Area of upper triangle $= \frac{1}{2}(3 \times 2) = 3$; the area is 3 cm^2.
Area of lower triangle $= \frac{1}{2}(7 \times 2) = 7$; the area is 7 cm^2.
The area of the trapezoid = 3 cm^2 + 7 cm^2 = 10 cm^2.
Students' work should include art.

- You must include at least:
  3 triangles with different areas
  3 parallelograms with different areas
  3 rectangles with different areas
  3 trapezoids (that are not parallelograms) with different areas
- Use a formula to find the area of each tile.

Your teacher will give you a grid to draw your design.
Complete the design.
Colour the design if it helps to show the different figures.

Check List

Your work should show:

✓ the area of each different figure you used
✓ the formulas you used to calculate the areas
✓ a diagram of your design on grid paper
✓ an explanation of how you created the design

Reflect on the Unit

What do you need to know to find the area of a parallelogram, a triangle, and a trapezoid? Explain.
Include a diagram and an example to show how you found each area.

To find the area of each rectangle, I used the formula $A = bh$.
The areas of the rectangles are: Rectangle A: 4000 cm^2
Rectangle B: 4200 cm^2
Rectangle C: 11 200 cm^2
To find the area of each triangle, I used the formula $A = \frac{1}{2}bh$.
The areas of the triangles are: Triangle D: 1250 cm^2
Triangle E: 750 cm^2
Triangle F: 2500 cm^2
Triangle P: 450 cm^2
To find the area of each parallelogram, I used the formula $A = bh$.
The areas of the parallelograms are: Parallelogram G: 600 cm^2
Parallelogram H: 900 cm^2
Parallelogram I: 4000 cm^2
Parallelogram J: 1500 cm^2
To find the area of each trapezoid, I used the formula
$A = \frac{1}{2}(\text{base } 1 + \text{base } 2) \times h$.
The areas of the trapezoids are: Trapezoid K: 3300 cm^2
Trapezoid L: 3000 cm^2
Trapezoid M: 2850 cm^2
Trapezoid N: 1050 cm^2
Trapezoid O: 3250 cm^2
The sum of the areas of the different figures is 44 800 cm^2.
This is the same as the area of the blank patio grid.
To create the design, I drew a rectangle as my first figure. I then used sides or part sides of the rectangle as sides of other figures. I continued to follow this procedure until the patio was completely covered.

ASSESSMENT FOR LEARNING

What to Look For

Understanding concepts

✔ Students show understanding of perimeter and area by explaining the design and how it was developed.

Applying procedures

✔ Students accurately calculate the area of each figure, and of each tile.

Problem solving

✔ Students can choose appropriate strategies to design a patio.

Communicating

✔ Students present work clearly, including diagrams, formulas, and calculations.

What to Do

Extra Support: Make the problem accessible.
Encourage students to first build a design using Pattern Blocks or tangram pieces so they see how different figures fit together.

Encourage students to find the area of each figure in grid squares. Students then multiply their answers by 100 cm^2, the area of one grid square.

Encourage students to find the area of each rectangle, then each triangle, then each parallelogram, and then each trapezoid.

Recording and Reporting

Master 6.3 Performance Assessment Rubric: Designing a Patio
Master 6.4 Unit Summary: Measuring Perimeter and Area

Evaluating Student Learning: Preparing to Report: Unit 6 Measuring Perimeter and Area

This unit provides an opportunity to report on the **Measurement** and **Patterning and Algebra** strands. *Master 6.4: Unit Summary: Measuring Perimeter and Area* provides a comprehensive format for recording and summarizing evidence collected.

Here is an example of a completed summary chart for this Unit:

Strand: *Measurement/ Patterning and Algebra*	**Problem solving**	**Understanding of concepts**	**Application of mathematical procedures**	**Communication**	***Overall***
Ongoing Observations	2	2	1	2	2
Work samples or portfolios; conferences	3	2	2	3	2/3
Unit Review	3	3	2	3	3
Practice Test	3	3	3	2	3
Unit Problem Designing a Patio	3	3	3	3	3
Achievement Level for reporting					3

Recording	**How to Report**
Ongoing Observations	Use *Master 6.2 Ongoing Observations: Measuring Perimeter and Area* to determine the most consistent level achieved in each category. Enter it in the chart. Choose to summarize by achievement category, or simply to enter an overall level. Observations from late in the unit should be most heavily weighted.
Portfolios or collections of work samples; conferences or interviews	Use *Master 6.1 Unit Rubric: Measuring Perimeter and Area* to guide evaluation of collections of work and information gathered in conferences. Teachers may choose to focus particular attention on the Assessment Focus questions. Work from late in the unit should be most heavily weighted.
Unit Review	*Master 6.1 Unit Rubric: Measuring Perimeter and Area* may be helpful in determining levels of achievement. #1, 2, 3, and 5 provide evidence of Understanding of concepts; #4 provides evidence of Application of mathematical procedures; #6 provides evidence of Problem solving; #1 provides evidence of Communication.
Practice Test	*Master 6.1 Unit Rubric: Measuring Perimeter and Area* may be helpful in determining levels of achievement. #1 provides evidence of Understanding of concepts; #3 provides evidence of Application of mathematical procedures; #4 provides evidence of Problem solving; #2 provides evidence of Communication.
Unit Problem	Use *Master 6.3 Performance Assessment Rubric: Designing a Patio.* The *Unit Problem* offers a snapshot of students' achievement. In particular, it shows their ability to synthesize and apply what they have learned.
Student Self-Assessment	Note students' perceptions of their own progress. This may take the form of an oral or written comment, or a self-rating.
Comments	Analyse the pattern of achievement to identify strengths and needs. In some cases, specific actions may need to be planned to support the learner.

Learning Skills	**Ongoing Records**
PM 4: Learning Skills Check List Use to record and report throughout a reporting period, rather than for each unit and/or strand.	*PM 10: Summary Class Records: Strands* *PM 11: Summary Class Records: Achievement Categories* *PM 12: Summary Record: Individual* Use to record and report evaluations of student achievement over several clusters, a reporting period, or a school year. These can also be used in place of the Unit Summary.

Name ____________________ Date ______________

Master 6.1

Unit Rubric: Measuring Perimeter and Area

<table>
<tr><th></th><th>Level 1</th><th>Level 2</th><th>Level 3</th><th>Level 4</th></tr>
<tr><td>Problem solving
• chooses and carries out a range of strategies to solve problems involving perimeter and area (for example, using a formula, drawing a picture, using concrete objects, creating a diagram)</td><td>with assistance, chooses and carries out a limited range of appropriate strategies for problems involving perimeter and area, rarely resulting in an accurate solution</td><td>with limited assistance, chooses and carries out appropriate strategies for problems involving perimeter and area that frequently result in an accurate solution</td><td>chooses and carries out appropriate strategies for problems involving perimeter and area that usually result in an accurate solution</td><td>chooses and carries out appropriate strategies for problems involving perimeter and area; may offer an innovative approach; results in accurate solution</td></tr>
<tr><td>Understanding of concepts
• shows understanding by demonstrating and explaining:
– estimates of perimeter and area
– formulas for the area of a parallelogram, triangle, and trapezoid
– strategies for drawing a trapezoid, given its area and perimeter
– strategies for finding area and perimeter of irregular figures</td><td>shows little understanding; may be unable to demonstrate, explain, or justify choice of method for:
– estimating perimeter and area
– developing formulas for area of a parallelogram, triangle, and trapezoid
– drawing a trapezoid of given area and perimeter
– finding area and perimeter of irregular figures</td><td>shows some understanding; partially able to demonstrate, explain, and justify choice of method for:
– estimating perimeter and area
– developing formulas for area of a parallelogram, triangle, and trapezoid
– drawing a trapezoid of given area and perimeter
– finding area and perimeter of irregular figures</td><td>shows understanding; able to clearly and appropriately demonstrate, explain, and justify choice of method for:
– estimating perimeter and area
– developing formulas for area of a parallelogram, triangle, and trapezoid
– drawing a trapezoid of given area and perimeter
– finding area and perimeter of irregular figures</td><td>shows thorough understanding; able to accurately and effectively demonstrate, explain, and justify choice of method for:
– estimating perimeter and area
– developing formulas for area of a parallelogram, triangle, and trapezoid
– drawing a trapezoid of given area and perimeter
– finding area and perimeter of irregular figures</td></tr>
<tr><td>Application of mathematical procedures
• accurately calculates:
– area of parallelograms, triangles, and trapezoids
– perimeter and area of irregular figures</td><td>limited accuracy; major errors or omissions in calculating:
– area of parallelograms, triangles, and trapezoids
– perimeter and area of irregular figures</td><td>somewhat accurate; several minor errors or omissions in calculating:
– area of parallelograms, triangles, and trapezoids
– perimeter and area of irregular figures</td><td>generally accurate; few minor errors in calculating:
– area of parallelograms, triangles, and trapezoids
– perimeter and area of irregular figures</td><td>accurate and precise; no errors in calculating:
– area of parallelograms, triangles, and trapezoids
– perimeter and area of irregular figures</td></tr>
<tr><td>Communication
• explains concepts, reasoning, and procedures clearly, using appropriate mathematical language</td><td>unable to explain reasoning and procedures clearly</td><td>partially explains reasoning and procedures</td><td>explains reasoning and procedures clearly</td><td>explains reasoning and procedures clearly, precisely, and confidently</td></tr>
<tr><td>• presents work clearly, including appropriate formulas and symbols</td><td>presents calculations with little clarity; rarely uses appropriate symbols</td><td>presents calculations with some clarity; uses some appropriate symbols</td><td>presents calculations clearly and precisely; uses appropriate symbols</td><td>presents calculations clearly and precisely; uses a range of appropriate symbols</td></tr>
</table>

Name ____________________ Date ______________

Master 6.2

Ongoing Observations: Measuring Perimeter and Area

The behaviours described under each heading are examples; they are not intended to be an exhaustive list of all that might be observed. More detailed descriptions are provided in each lesson under *Assessment for Learning*.

STUDENT ACHIEVEMENT: Measuring Perimeter and Area				
Student	**Problem solving** ▪ Chooses and carries out appropriate strategies to solve problems involving area and perimeter	**Understanding of concepts** ▪ Explains and demonstrates: – formulas for area – strategies for finding perimeter and area of irregular figures	**Application of mathematical procedures** ▪ Calculates area of parallelograms, triangles, and trapezoids ▪ Calculates perimeter and area of irregular figures	**Communication** ▪ Explains concepts, reasoning, and procedures clearly ▪ Presents work clearly

Level 1 – very limited; Level 2 – somewhat or limited; Level 3 – satisfactory; Level 4 – thorough

Name ____________________ Date ______________

Master 6.3

Performance Assessment Rubric: Designing a Patio

	Level 1	Level 2	Level 3	Level 4
Problem solving • chooses appropriate strategies to design a patio to given specifications (perimeter and area; including specific figures); for example, estimating, using formulas, drawing a picture, using concrete objects, creating a diagram	uses few simple strategies to design a patio that incorporates the required figures; limited success	uses some appropriate strategies to design a patio that incorporates the required figures; some success	uses appropriate strategies to design a patio that incorporates the required figures; successful	uses innovative and appropriate strategies to design a patio that incorporates the required figures; successful and effective
Understanding of concepts • shows understanding of perimeter and area by explaining the design and how it was developed	shows very limited understanding; may be unable to give appropriate explanations or justifications	shows limited understanding by giving some appropriate but incomplete explanations or justifications	shows understanding by giving appropriate explanations or justifications	shows thorough understanding by giving appropriate and complete explanations or justifications, using all relevant concepts
Application of mathematical procedures • calculates the area of each figure, and of each tile • draws the design accurately on grid paper	limited accuracy; major errors or omissions in: – calculating areas – drawing an accurate diagram of the design	somewhat accurate; several minor errors or omissions in: – calculating areas – drawing an accurate diagram of the design	generally accurate; few minor errors in: – calculating areas – drawing an accurate diagram of the design	accurate and precise; with no errors in: – calculating areas – drawing an accurate diagram of the design
Communication • explains reasoning clearly, using appropriate mathematical terminology	explains reasoning unclearly and imprecisely, using few mathematical terms	explains reasoning with some clarity, using some appropriate mathematical terms	explains reasoning clearly and precisely, using appropriate mathematical terms	explains reasoning clearly, precisely, and confidently, using a range of appropriate mathematical terminology
• presents work clearly, including diagrams, formulas, and calculations	presents work with little clarity	presents work with some clarity	presents work clearly	presents work clearly and precisely

Name ____________________ Date ______________

Master 6.4

Unit Summary: Measuring Perimeter and Area

Review assessment records to determine the most consistent achievement levels for the assessments conducted. Some cells may be blank. *Overall* achievement levels may be recorded in each row, rather than identifying levels for each achievement category.

	Most Consistent Level of Achievement*				
Strand: *Measurement/ Patterning and Algebra*	**Problem Solving**	**Understanding of concepts**	**Application of mathematical procedures**	**Communication**	***Overall***
Ongoing Observations					
Work samples or portfolios; conferences					
Unit Review					
Practice Test					
Unit Problem: Designing a Patio					
Achievement Level for reporting					

* Use Ontario Achievement Levels, 1, 2, 3, 4

Self-Assessment:

Comments: (Strengths, Needs, Next Steps)

Name ____________________ Date ______________

Master 6.5

Additional Activity 1: Triangles and Parallelograms

Play with a partner.

You will need a deck of cards with the face cards removed, 1-cm grid paper, rulers, and a calculator.

How to Play:

1. Player A shuffles the cards.
   Place them face down in a pile.

2. Player A turns over 2 cards.
   The 2 numbers represent the base and height of a figure in centimetres.

3. Player A draws a parallelogram with these dimensions.
   Player B draws a triangle with these dimensions.
   Calculate the area of your figure.

4. Check each other's work.
   Is the area of the parallelogram twice the area of the triangle?

5. If both players are correct, score 1 point each.
   If only one player is correct, that player scores 2 points.
   If neither player is correct, no points are scored.

6. Player B turns over 2 cards.
   Player B draws a parallelogram.
   Player A draws a triangle.

7. Play continues until one player reaches 10 points.

Take It Further:
Play the game again.
This time, each player calculates the perimeter of her or his figure.
Both the area and perimeter calculations must be correct to score any points.

Name ____________________ Date ________________

Master 6.6

Additional Activity 2: Triangle Puzzle

Work on your own.

You will need a sheet of paper, a ruler, scissors, and a calculator.

- Measure and record the dimensions of a sheet of paper.
  Calculate its area.
- Use a ruler.
  Divide the paper into 8 or 10 triangles of different sizes.
- Label each triangle.
  Measure and record the dimensions of each triangle in centimetres.
  Calculate the area of each triangle in square centimetres.
  Record the areas in the table.

Triangle	**Area**

- Add the areas of the triangles.
  Compare the total area to the area of the sheet of paper.
  What do you notice?

Take It Further:
Order the triangles from least to greatest area.

Name ____________________ Date ______________

Master 6.7

Additional Activity 3: Pattern Block Figures

Work on your own.

You will need Pattern Blocks, 1-cm grid paper, a ruler, and a calculator.

- Use at least 6 Pattern Blocks.
  Make an irregular figure.
- Copy the figure onto grid paper.
- Find the area of the irregular figure.
- Write a formula in words for the area of the irregular figure.
- Tell how you found the area.
  Show all your work.

Take It Further:
Find the perimeter of the irregular figure.

Name ____________________ Date ________________

Master 6.8

Additional Activity 4: Rule the School

Work in a small group.

You will need measuring tapes, a calculator, a ruler, and 1-cm grid paper.

- Discuss strategies for measuring the area of ground the school covers and the perimeter of the school.
- Use measuring tapes.
  Measure the dimensions of the outside of the school.
- Make a sketch of the school.
  Label its dimensions.
- Use a calculator.
  Find the approximate area of the ground the school covers.
  Find the approximate perimeter of the school.

Take It Further:
Make a scale drawing of the school on 1-cm grid paper.

Name ____________________ Date _______________

Master 6.9

Step-by-Step 1

Section 6.1, Question 5

Use 1-cm grid paper.

Step 1 Draw a parallelogram with base 6 cm and height 4 cm.

Use the formula $A = bh$.

What is the area of the parallelogram? ____________________

Step 2 Twice the area is 48 cm^2.

The height is 4 cm.

What do you have to multiply 4 by to get 48? __________

What is the base when the parallelogram has area 48 cm^2? ______

Draw the parallelogram.

Step 3 Twice the area is 48 cm^2.

The base is 6 cm.

What do you have to multiply 6 by to get 48? ___________

What is the height when the parallelogram has area 48 cm^2? ______

Draw the parallelogram.

Step 4 The base and height must have a product of 48.

List pairs of factors of 48.

____

What other dimensions could a parallelogram with twice the area have?

____

Draw the parallelograms.

How many different pairs of base and height can you find?

____

Name ____________________ Date ______________

Master 6.10 **Step-by-Step 2**

Section 6.2, Question 9

Use the picture on page 224.

Step 1 Use the formula $A = \frac{bh}{2}$.

What is the area of the triangular wall? ______

Step 2 Convert the dimensions of the window to metres.

1 m = 100 cm

So, 150 cm = ______ m and 60 cm = ______ m

Use the dimensions in metres and the formula $A = bh$.

What is the area of the rectangular window? ______

Step 3 Subtract the area of the window from the area of the triangular wall.

____

What is the area that is to be painted? ______________________________

Step 4 One litre of paint covers 6.5 m^2.

Divide the area to be painted by 6.5.

____

How many litres of paint are needed? ______________________________

Step 5 Paint comes in 1-L cans. How many cans does the owner need?

____

Explain.

____

____

Name ____________________ Date _______________

Master 6.11

Step-by-Step 3

Section 6.3, Question 8

Use the picture on Student Book page 230.

Step 1 What is the height of the parallelogram? ____________

What is the base of the parallelogram? ____________

Use the formula $A = bh$.

Find the area of the parallelogram. ____________

Step 2 The trapezoids are congruent.

How does the area of one trapezoid compare to the area of the parallelogram? ____________

Use the area from *Step 1*.

What is the area of each trapezoid? ____________

Step 3 Draw a trapezoid on grid paper.

Draw a second congruent trapezoid to form a parallelogram.

To find the base of the parallelogram, add the lengths of the parallel sides of one trapezoid. ____________

What is the height of the parallelogram? ____________

Use the formula to find the area of the parallelogram. ____________

Step 4 Find one-half of the area in *Step 3*. ____________

What is the area of the trapezoid you drew? ____________

Name ____________________ Date ______________

Master 6.12

Step-by-Step 4

Section 6.4, Question 6

Step 1 Use grid paper. Let one side of each grid square represent 1 m.

Draw 2 rectangles, each with width 3 m, so they form an L-shaped pool with area 30 m^2.

Step 2 Repeat *Step 1* twice to draw 2 more different pools.

Measure and record the side lengths of each pool.

What is the perimeter of Pool 1? __________

Pool 2? __________

Pool 3? __________

What do you notice about the perimeters?

____

Step 3 Draw 2 rectangles, each with width 5 m, so that their total area is 30 m^2.

Can you put these rectangles together to make an L-shape? _______

Explain. ____

Step 4 Draw 2 different rectangles, each with width 5 m, so that their total area is 30 m^2.

Can you put these rectangles together to make an L-shape? _______

Explain. ____

Name ____________________ Date _______________

Master 6.13

Figures for Section 6.3, *Explore*

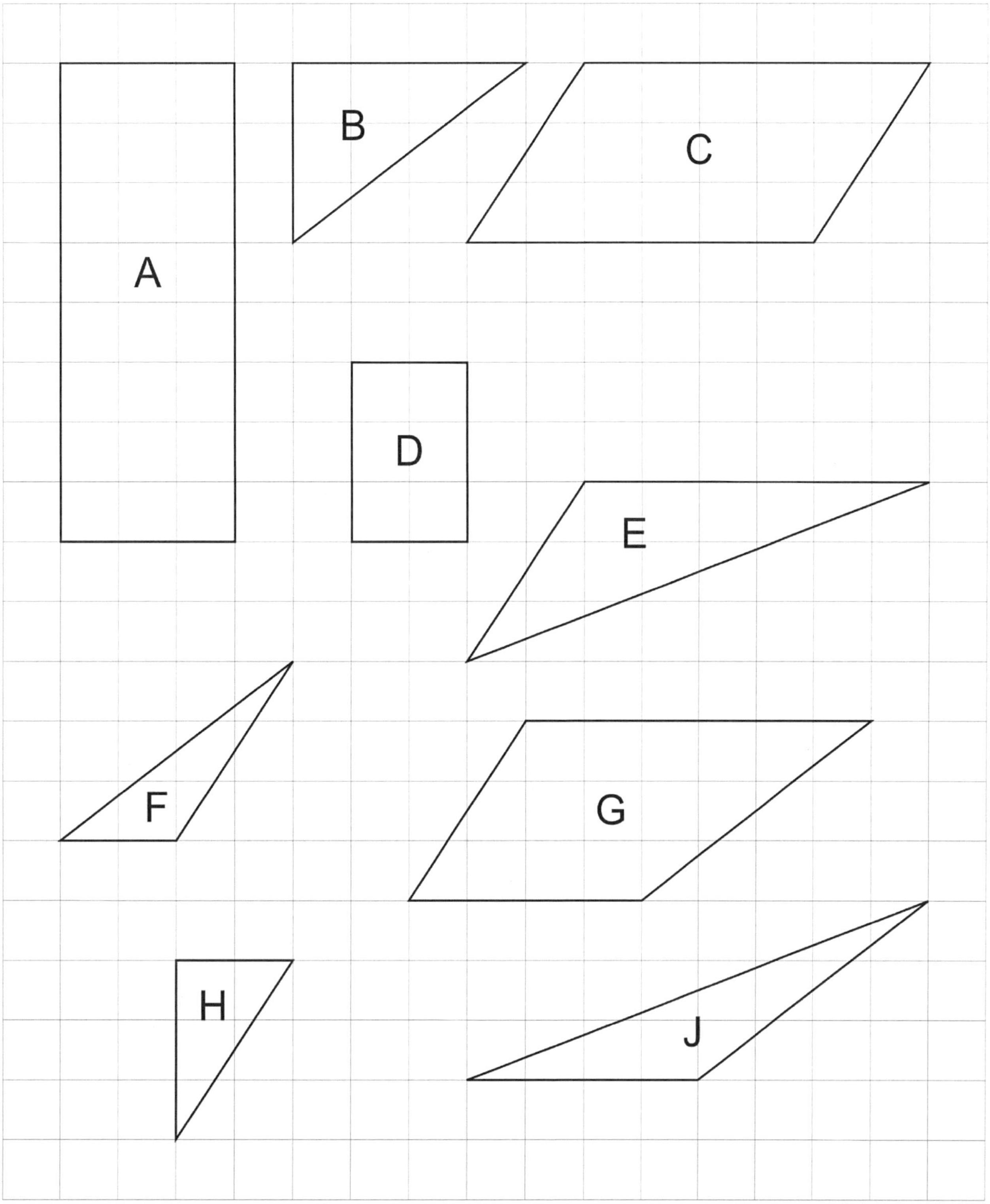

Name ____________________ Date ________________

Master 6.14

Patio Grid for Unit Problem

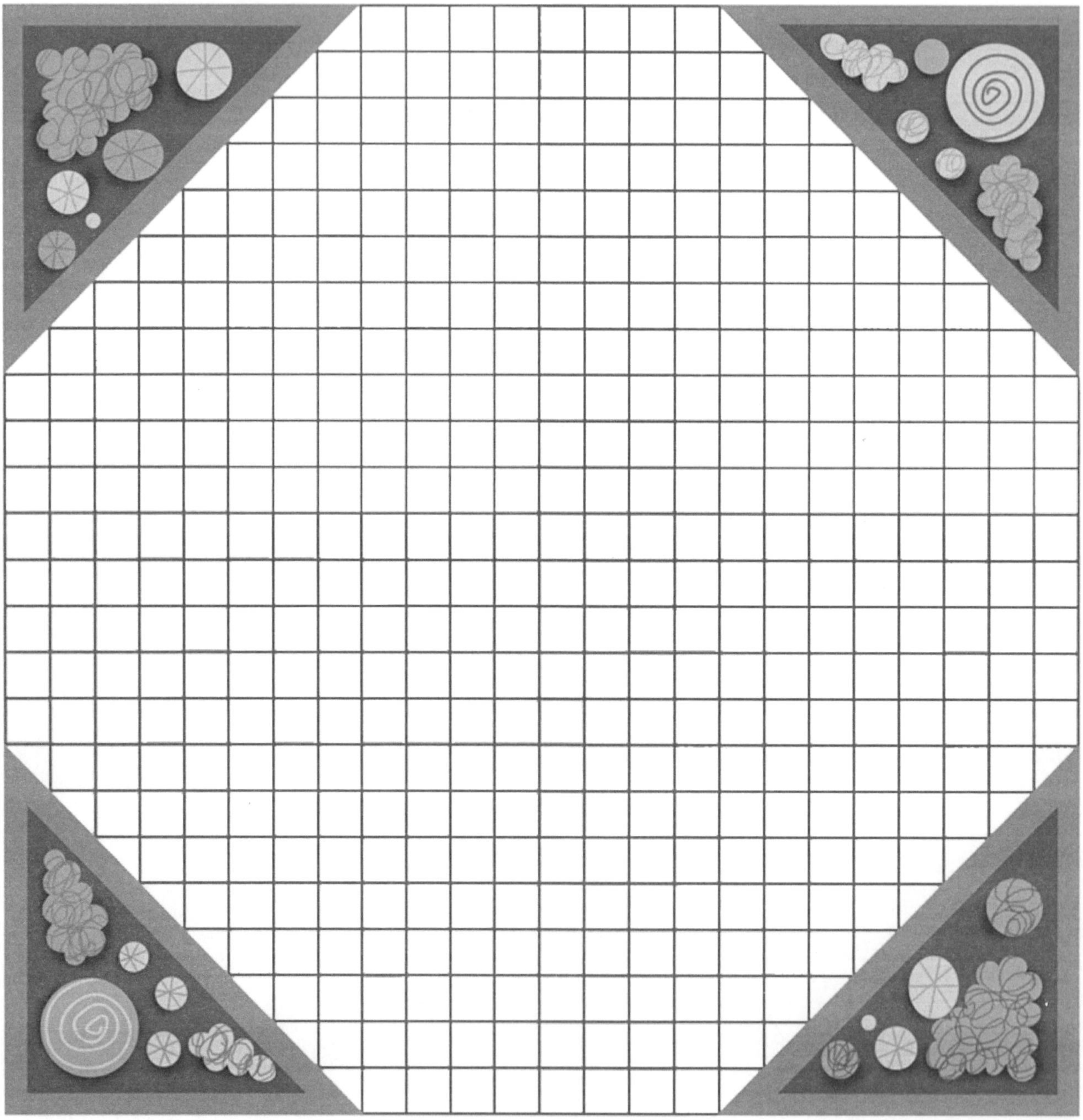

Name ____________________ Date ______________

Master 6.15a

Unit Test: Unit 6 Measuring Perimeter and Area

1. Use 1-cm grid paper.

a) Draw a triangle with area 12 cm^2.

b) Draw a parallelogram with area 18 cm^2.

c) Draw a trapezoid with area 20 cm^2.

2. Find the area and perimeter of each figure.
Explain your strategies.

a)

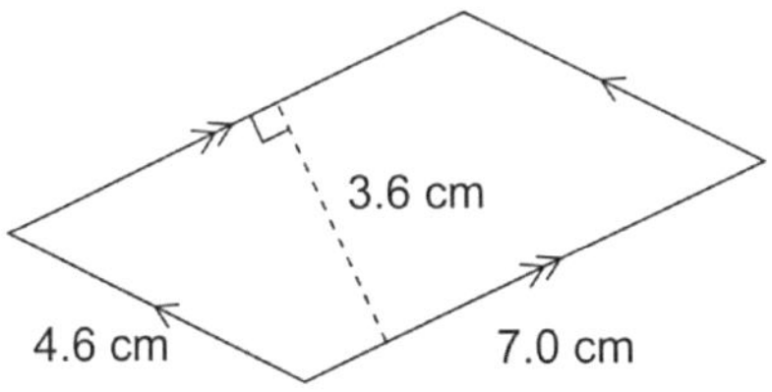

b)

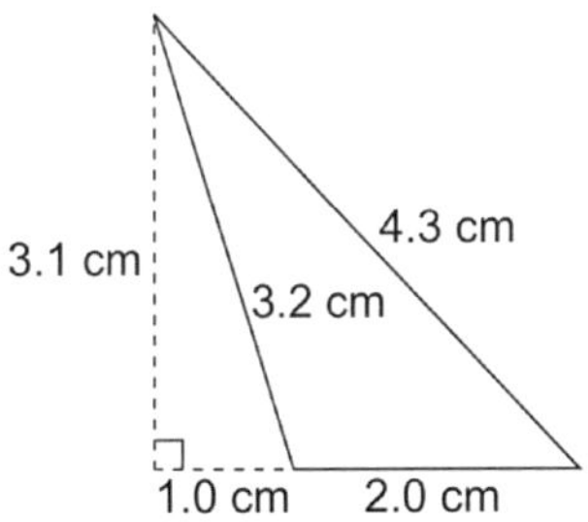

c)

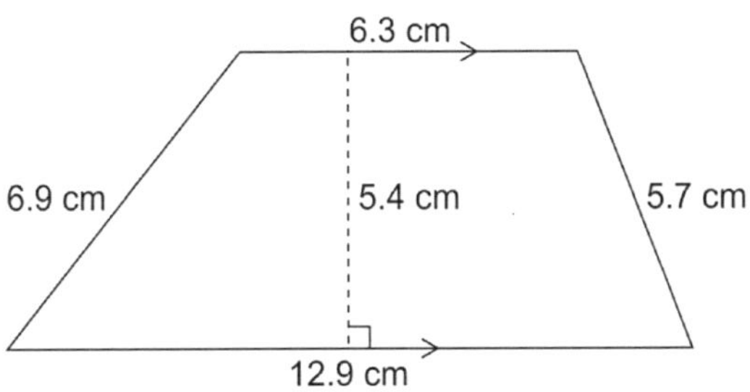

d)

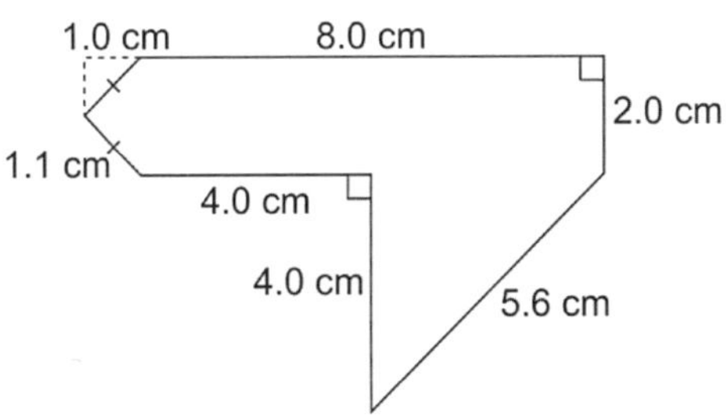

Master 6.15b **Unit Test continued**

3. The dimensions of 4 figures are given.

a) Which figure has the greatest area?

i) a rectangle with base 7 m and height 4 m

ii) a parallelogram with base 6 m and height 5 m

iii) a triangle with base 9 m and height 7 m

iv) a trapezoid with parallel sides 3.0 m and 6.0 m, and height 2.5 m

b) Which figure has the least area?

4. The Rosano family decided to put a patio in their backyard, with a flower garden beside it.

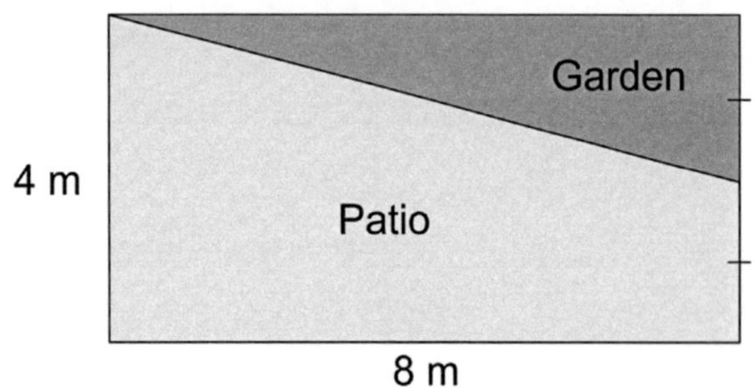

a) What is the area of the flower garden?

Name ____________________ Date ______________

Master 6.15c **Unit Test continued**

b) What is the area of the patio?

c) Each patio stone is square with side length 30 cm.
One stone costs $1.95.

i) How many stones are needed for the patio?
What assumptions do you make?

ii) How much will the stone for the patio cost?

5. A trapezoid has height 3 cm. The length of one parallel side is 4 cm.
The area of the trapezoid is 15 cm^2.
Find the length of the other parallel side. Draw a diagram.
Show your work.

Name ____________________ Date ______________

Master 6.16

Sample Answers

Unit Test – Master 6.15

1. **a)**

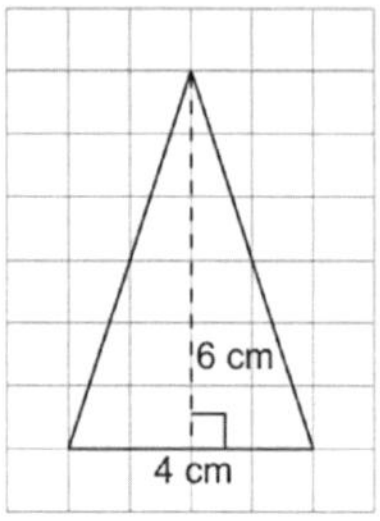

b)

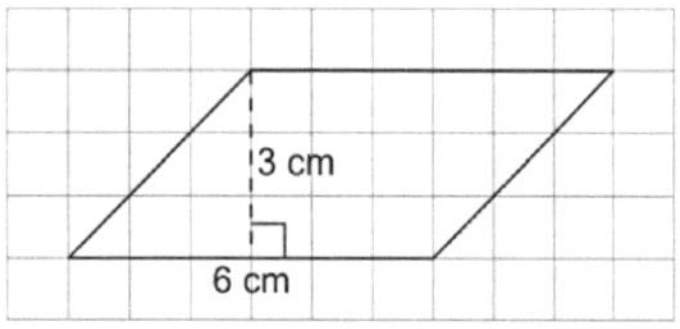

c)

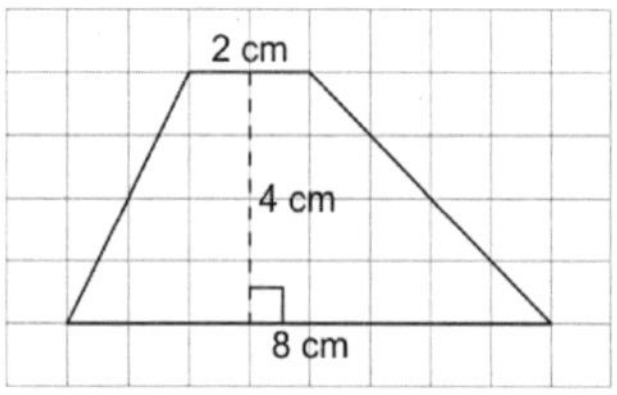

2. **a)** $A = 25.2\text{ cm}^2$, $P = 23.2\text{ cm}$
b) $A = 3.1\text{ cm}^2$, $P = 9.5\text{ cm}$
c) $A = 51.84\text{ cm}^2$, $P = 31.8\text{ cm}$
d) $A = 25\text{ cm}^2$, $P = 25.8\text{ cm}$

3. **a)** The triangle has the greatest area: 31.5 m^2.
b) The trapezoid has the least area: 11.25 m^2.

4. **a)** The area of the flower garden is 8 m^2.
b) The area of the patio is 24 m^2.
c) **i)** About 270 stones; this assumes that stones can be cut and parts of stones can be used.
ii) About $526.50

5. Area of the parallelogram is twice the area of the trapezoid: $2 \times 15\text{ cm}^2 = 30\text{ cm}^2$. The formula for the area of a parallelogram is $A = bh$.
The height is 3, so the base is $30 \div 3 = 10$. For the trapezoid, one parallel side is 4 cm, so the other parallel side is 10 cm – 4 cm = 6 cm.

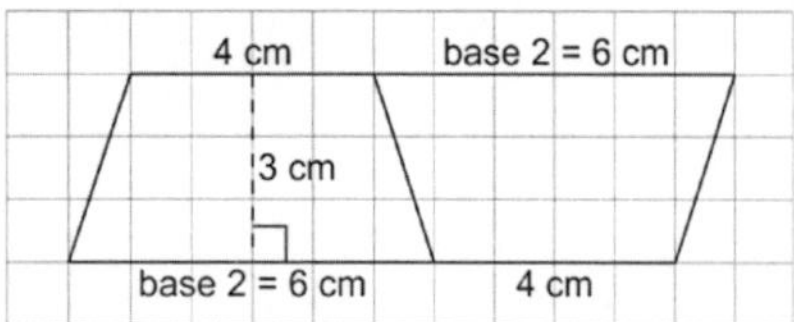

Extra Practice Masters 6.17–6.21

Go to the CD-ROM to access editable versions of these Extra Practice Masters

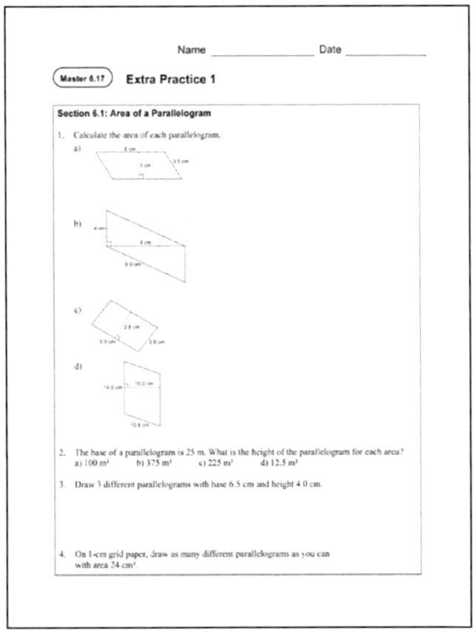
Name ______________ Date __________

Master 6.17 Extra Practice 1

Section 6.1: Area of a Parallelogram

1. Calculate the area of each parallelogram.

2. The base of a parallelogram is 25 m. What is the height of the parallelogram for each area?
a) 100 m² b) 375 m² c) 225 m² d) 12.5 m²

3. Draw 3 different parallelograms with base 6.5 cm and height 4.0 cm.

4. On 1-cm grid paper, draw as many different parallelograms as you can with area 24 cm².

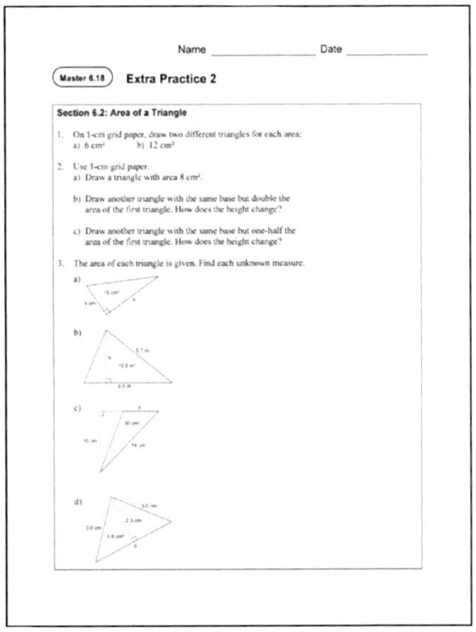
Name ______________ Date __________

Master 6.18 Extra Practice 2

Section 6.2: Area of a Triangle

1. On 1-cm grid paper, draw two different triangles for each area:
a) 6 cm² b) 12 cm²

2. Use 1-cm grid paper.
a) Draw a triangle with area 8 cm².
b) Draw another triangle with the same base but double the area of the first triangle. How does the height change?
c) Draw another triangle with the same base but one-half the area of the first triangle. How does the height change?

3. The area of each triangle is given. Find each unknown measure.

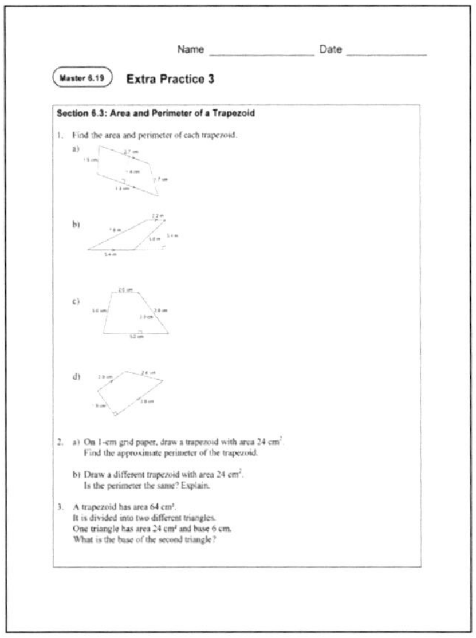
Name ______________ Date __________

Master 6.19 Extra Practice 3

Section 6.3: Area and Perimeter of a Trapezoid

1. Find the area and perimeter of each trapezoid.

2. a) On 1-cm grid paper, draw a trapezoid with area 24 cm². Find the approximate perimeter of the trapezoid.
b) Draw a different trapezoid with area 24 cm². Is the perimeter the same? Explain.

3. A trapezoid has area 64 cm². It is divided into two different triangles. One triangle has area 24 cm² and base 6 cm. What is the base of the second triangle?

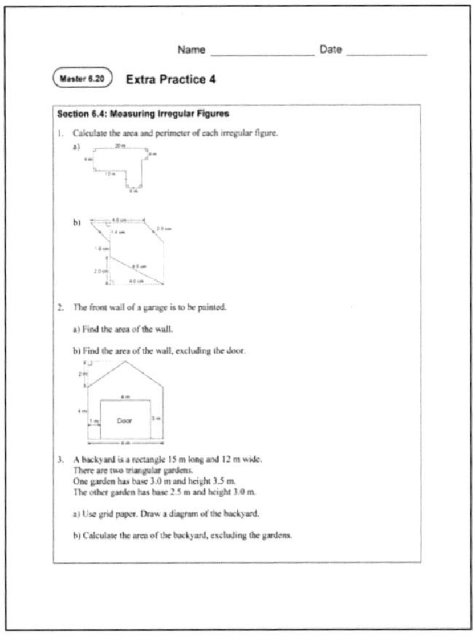
Name ______________ Date __________

Master 6.20 Extra Practice 4

Section 6.4: Measuring Irregular Figures

1. Calculate the area and perimeter of each irregular figure.

2. The front wall of a garage is to be painted.
a) Find the area of the wall.
b) Find the area of the wall, excluding the door.

3. A backyard is a rectangle 15 m long and 12 m wide. There are two triangular gardens. One garden has base 3.0 m and height 3.5 m. The other garden has base 2.5 m and height 3.0 m.
a) Use grid paper. Draw a diagram of the backyard.
b) Calculate the area of the backyard, excluding the gardens.

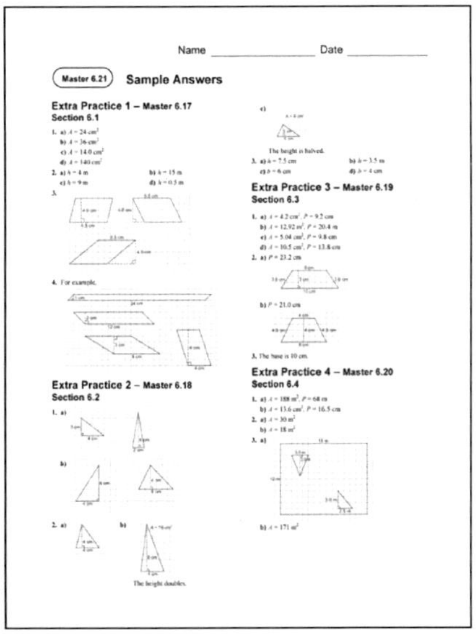
Name ______________ Date __________

Master 6.21 Sample Answers

Extra Practice 1 – Master 6.17
Section 6.1

Extra Practice 2 – Master 6.18
Section 6.2

Extra Practice 3 – Master 6.19
Section 6.3

Extra Practice 4 – Master 6.20
Section 6.4

Addison Wesley
Mathematics Makes Sense

Program Authors

Jason Johnston
Bryn Keyes
Mary Doucette
Antonietta Lenjosek
Steve Thomas
Margaret Sinclair
Trevor Brown
Cathy Heideman
Don Jones
Michael Davis
Jennifer Paziuk
Ken Harper
Sharon Jeroski
Ray Appel
Laura Weatherhead
Betty Milne
Jim Mennie
Lynn Strangway

Printed and bound in Canada

10 17

PEARSON
Education Canada

ADDISON WESLEY

Ontario

Math Makes Sense 7

Ontario Teacher Guide

Unit 7: Geometry

PEARSON

Addison Wesley

UNIT 7

Geometry

"The goal of work with two-dimensional figures is that students will learn the names of different figures; be able to identify their properties; and express relationships within and among figures."

Pothier and Vance Cathcart, *Learning Mathematics in Elementary and Middle School*, 4th Edition

FOCUS STRAND
Geometry and Spatial Sense

SUPPORTING STRANDS
Measurement
Patterning and Algebra

TIPS
Students come to class with significant but varying prior knowledge. Such prior knowledge should be valued and used during instruction.

Mathematics Background

What Are the Big Ideas?

- Figures can be classified according to their geometric properties.
- Congruent figures have the same size and shape.
- A figure and its image under a translation, reflection, and rotation are congruent.
- A figure tiles the plane if congruent copies of the figure cover a surface and leave no gaps.
- A figure may be transformed repeatedly to create a pattern.

How Will the Concepts Develop?

Students use measurement to classify figures in different ways. They use line symmetry and rotational symmetry to explore polygons.

Students construct triangles using given measurements and identify the conditions for congruent triangles and congruent quadrilaterals.

Students explore translations, reflections, and rotations on a coordinate grid and establish that, under these transformations, a figure and its image are congruent.

Students use different figures and their tracings to investigate which congruent figures will tile a plane. Students make designs to cover a page, then explain their designs in terms of transformation images. They use a computer to transform figures, and to create, then analyse, their designs.

Why Are These Concepts Important?

A good understanding of spatial concepts is important if students are to understand and appreciate our geometric world. Geometry is used daily by scientists, architects, and engineers. Geometric attributes, such as congruence and symmetry, enable students to see the world around them in a different way. A strong understanding of transformations helps students better understand the patterns and designs they see outside the classroom.

Students who develop a strong spatial sense and who comprehend the concepts and language of geometry will be better prepared for the higher mathematical concepts they will encounter in later grades.

Curriculum Overview

Cluster 1: Exploring Figures

Overall Expectations
- Identify, describe, compare, and classify geometric figures. (7m47)
- Identify congruent . . . figures. (7m49)
- Use mathematical language effectively to describe geometric concepts, reasoning, and investigations. (7m52)

Specific Expectations
- Identify two-dimensional shapes that meet certain criteria. (7m57)
- Explain why two shapes are congruent. (7m58)
- Identify through investigation the conditions that make two shapes congruent. (7m59)
- Create and solve problems involving the congruence of shapes. (7m60)

Launch

Section 7.1: Classifying Figures

Section 7.2: Congruent Figures

Mid-Unit Review

Cluster 2: Transformational Geometry

Overall Expectations
- Explore transformations of geometric figures. (7m50)
- Understand, apply, and analyse key concepts in transformational geometry using concrete materials and drawings. (7m51)
- Use mathematical language effectively to describe geometric concepts, reasoning, and investigations. (7m52)

Specific Expectations
- Recognize the image of a two-dimensional shape under a translation, a reflection, and a rotation in a variety of contexts. (7m61)
- Create and analyse designs that include translated, rotated, and reflected two-dimensional images using concrete materials and drawings, and using appropriate computer applications. (7m62)
- Identify whether a figure will tile a plane. (7m63)
- Construct and analyse tiling patterns with congruent tiles. (7m64)
- Describe designs in terms of images that are congruent, translated, rotated, and reflected. (7m65)

Section 7.3: Transformations

Section 7.4: Tiling Patterns

Section 7.5: Using Transformations to Make Designs

Technology: Using a Computer to Transform Figures

Unit Review
Practice Test

Unit Problem
Tessellations

Curriculum across the Grades

Grade 6	Grade 7	Grade 8
Students sort regular polygons according to the number of lines of symmetry and the order of rotational symmetry. They classify figures according to angle and side properties, and demonstrate an understanding of similar and congruent figures. Students construct figures with more than one line of symmetry. They construct a variety of figures given specific measures of angles and sides. Students estimate the size of angles. Students use a computer to explore and extend geometric concepts. They use mathematical language to describe geometric ideas. Students visualize and describe the effect of translations, reflections, and rotations, and apply and analyse these transformations in a variety of geometric contexts. They construct tiling patterns to cover a plane.	Students identify figures that meet certain criteria. They identify through investigation the conditions that make two figures congruent. Students create and solve problems involving the congruence of figures. Students recognize the image of a figure under a translation, a reflection, and a rotation in a variety of contexts. They create and analyse designs that include translated, rotated, and reflected images of figures, using concrete materials and drawings, and using appropriate computer applications. Students identify whether a figure will tile a plane. They construct and analyse tiling patterns with congruent tiles. Students describe designs in terms of images that are congruent, translated, rotated, and reflected.	Students explore the relationship of the internal angles in a triangle. Students create and solve angle measurement problems for triangles. Students explain why the sum of the angles of a triangle is 180°. Students investigate the Pythagorean relationship using area models and diagrams. They apply the Pythagorean relationship to numerical problems involving area and right triangles. Students explain the Pythagorean relationship. Students identify the angle properties of intersecting, parallel, and perpendicular lines. They describe the relationships between pairs of angles within parallel lines and transversals, and solve angle measurement problems.

Materials for the Unit

Students may find the following web site useful when working with transformations. The address is correct at time of printing: http://www.nga.gov/kids/kidscredits.html.

Additional Activities

Know Your Triangles

For Extra Practice (Appropriate for use after Skills You'll Need)
Materials: *Know Your Triangles* (Master 7.5a), *Know Your Triangles Game Cards* (Master 7.5b)

Playing this game reinforces the skills of recognizing and describing triangles.

The work students do: Students work in pairs. Students place the game cards face down in a pile, then turn over the top card. Each student writes a description of the triangle, giving as much information as she can.

Students score one point for each correct description, and an additional two points for any correct information not given by her partner.

The player with the higher score after four rounds wins.

Take It Further: Students design their own game cards using different triangles.

Spatial/Social/Logical
Partner Activity

Skillful Drawing

For Extension (Appropriate for use after Skills You'll Need)
Materials: *Skillful Drawing* (Master 7.6), rulers, protractors, compasses

This activity reinforces the skills of constructing and describing triangles.

The work students do: Students work on their own. They follow instructions to construct several triangles with common sides. Students describe the final triangle they constructed.

Take It Further: Students describe the figure that comprises the four triangles they constructed.

Spatial/Kinesthetic
Individual Activity

Straw Triangles

For Extra Practice (Appropriate for use after Skills You'll Need)
Materials: *Straw Triangles* (Master 7.7), straws cut to lengths 3 cm, 5 cm, and 9 cm, twist ties, rulers, and scissors

This activity reinforces the skills of recognizing and naming triangles.

The work students do: Students play with a partner. One student chooses 3 straws and gives them to his partner. His partner decides whether the straws can be used to make a triangle. The partner either describes the triangle or explains why a triangle cannot be made.

Students score one point for a correct description or explanation. Students switch roles and play again using different combinations of straws. The player with more points after 5 rounds wins.

Take It Further: Students cut straws as necessary to make different types of triangles, as named by their partners.

Spatial/Kinesthetic/Social
Partner Activity

Point the Triangles

For Extra Practice (Appropriate for use after Skills You'll Need)
Materials: *Point the Triangles* (Master 7.8a), *Point the Triangles Grid* (Master 7.8b)

This activity reinforces students' knowledge of different types of triangles and plotting points on a coordinate grid.

The work students do: Students play with a partner. Students take turns to name the coordinates of a point, C, that will make $\triangle ABC$ an isosceles triangle. Students score one point for each correct coordinate.

Students repeat for other triangles, such as obtuse, scalene, and right isosceles.

Take It Further: Students name the coordinates of points C and D that make ABCD different types of quadrilaterals.

Social/Kinesthetic/Spatial
Partner Activity

Planning for Unit 7

Planning for Instruction

Suggested Unit time: About 3 weeks

Section	Time	Materials	Program Support
Launch, page 2	15–20 min	books and photographs of quilts	
Skills You'll Need, page 4	65–80 min	rulers protractors compasses square dot paper 1-cm grid paper isometric dot paper	PM 20: 1-cm Grid Paper PM 22: Square Dot Paper PM 23: Isometric Dot Paper
7.1: Classifying Figures, page 8 Identify, describe, and classify geometric figures.	80–100 min	rulers protractors tracing paper square dot paper isometric dot paper Figures for *Explore*	PM 22: Square Dot Paper PM 23: Isometric Dot Paper Master 7.14: Figures for 7.1 *Explore* Master 7.9: Step-by-Step 1 Master 7.20: Extra Practice 1
7.2: Congruent Figures, page 13 Identify the conditions for congruence.	80–100 min	rulers protractors compasses square dot paper isometric dot paper tracing paper (optional)	PM 22: Square Dot Paper PM 23: Isometric Dot Paper Master 7.10: Step-by-Step 2 Master 7.21: Extra Practice 2
Mid-Unit Review, page 18		rulers protractors compasses square dot paper isometric dot paper	PM 22: Square Dot Paper PM 23: Isometric Dot Paper
7.3: Transformations, page 19 Recognize transformation images.	80–100 min	tracing paper Miras rulers 1-cm grid paper Figures for *Explore* Grids for *Practice* Questions 4 and 5	Master 7.15: Figures for 7.3 *Explore* Master 7.16: Grids for *Practice* Questions 4 and 5 PM 20: 1-cm Grid Paper Master 7.11: Step-by-Step 3 Master 7.22: Extra Practice 3
7.4: Tiling Patterns, page 24 Construct and analyse tiling patterns.	80–100 min	index cards rulers scissors square dot paper 1-cm grid paper isometric dot paper tracing paper	PM 20: 1-cm Grid Paper PM 22: Square Dot Paper PM 23: Isometric Dot Paper Master 7.12: Step-by-Step 4 Master 7.23: Extra Practice 4
7.5: Using Transformations to Make Designs, page 28 Create and analyse designs using transformations.	80–100 min	Pattern Blocks square dot paper 1-cm grid paper isometric dot paper rulers Flooring Pattern coloured pencils or markers	PM 20: 1-cm Grid Paper PM 22: Square Dot Paper PM 23: Isometric Dot Paper Master 7.17: Flooring Pattern Master 7.13: Step-by-Step 5 Master 7.24: Extra Practice 5
Technology: Using a Computer to Transform Figures, page 32 Use technology to create and analyse designs.	40–50 min	computers with *The Geometer's Sketchpad*	

Section	Time	Materials	Program Support
Reading and Writing in Math: Choosing a Strategy, page 36		tangrams linking cubes rulers 1-cm grid paper calendar page (optional)	PM 20: 1-cm Grid Paper
Unit Review, page 39		square dot paper 1-cm grid paper isometric dot paper rulers, protractors tracing paper coloured pencils or markers	PM 20: 1-cm Grid Paper PM 22: Square Dot Paper PM 23: Isometric Dot Paper Extra Practice: Student Book page 444
Practice Test, page 41		protractors rulers tracing paper isometric dot paper	PM 23: Isometric Dot Paper
Unit Problem: Tessellations, page 42	40–50 min	cardboard square dot paper 1-cm grid paper rulers, scissors tracing paper, Miras coloured pencils or markers	PM 20: 1-cm Grid Paper PM 22: Square Dot Paper

etext online tutorial

This web-based tutorial uses voice, animation, and an optional quiz to present each core lesson, so that students can review content with a new approach.

Planning for Assessment

Purpose	Tools and Process	Recording and Reporting
Diagnostic	*Unit Launch* Question; conference; scaffold problems throughout the unit	PM 8: Conference Prompts
Formative	*Explore* – Ongoing Assessment: Observe and Listen	Master 7.2: Ongoing Observations: Geometry PM 1: Inquiry Process Check List PM 6: Observation Record 1 PM 7: Observation Record 2 PM 8: Conference Prompts PM 2: Self-Assessment PM 3: Self-Assessment: Problem Solving PM 9: Work Sample Records
Summative	Unit Review *Unit Problem* – Performance Assessment Unit Test Review assessment records; add unit results to ongoing records	Master 7.1: Unit Rubric: Geometry Master 7.3: Performance Assessment Rubric: Tessellations Master 7.4: Unit Summary: Geometry PM 10: Summary Class Records: Strands PM 11: Summary Class Records: Achievement Categories PM 12: Summary Record: Individual
Learning Skills/ Mathematical Disposition	Observe and record throughout the unit	PM 4: Learning Skills Check List PM 5: Mathematical Dispositions and Learning Skills

Program Masters (PM) are in the *Grade 7 Planning and Program Masters* module.
Extra Practice Masters are on the CD-ROM and are printed in reduced format on page 69 of this module.

SECTION ORGANIZER

15–20 min

Curriculum Focus: Activate prior learning about geometry.

Teacher Materials

- books and photographs of quilts, or a few quilts

ASSUMED PRIOR KNOWLEDGE

☑ Students can identify and classify geometric figures.

☑ Students can use mathematical language to describe figures.

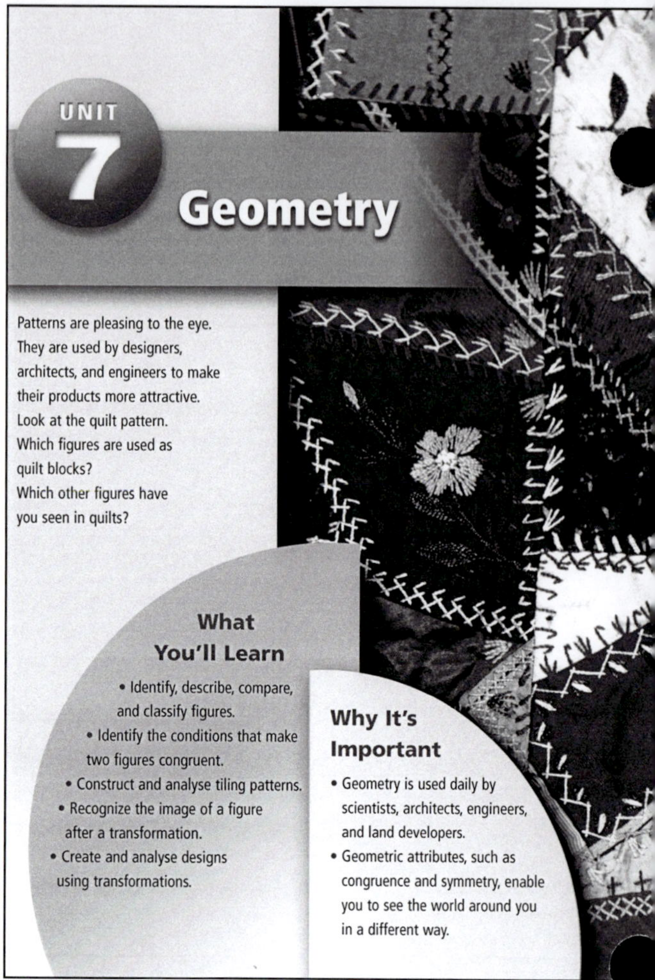

UNIT 7

Geometry

Patterns are pleasing to the eye. They are used by designers, architects, and engineers to make their products more attractive. Look at the quilt pattern. Which figures are used as quilt blocks? Which other figures have you seen in quilts?

What You'll Learn

- Identify, describe, compare, and classify figures.
- Identify the conditions that make two figures congruent.
- Construct and analyse tiling patterns.
- Recognize the image of a figure after a transformation.
- Create and analyse designs using transformations.

Why It's Important

- Geometry is used daily by scientists, architects, engineers, and land developers.
- Geometric attributes, such as congruence and symmetry, enable you to see the world around you in a different way.

ACTIVATE PRIOR LEARNING

Show students the books of quilts or the real thing. Have students look at the quilt pattern on pages 244 and 245 of the Student Book.

Ask questions, such as:

- What is a quilt block?
  (*A quilt block is the basic design unit of the quilt.*)
- What figures are used as quilt blocks in this pattern?
  (*Trapezoids, pentagons, quadrilaterals, heptagons, and triangles*)
- Which other figures have you seen in quilts?
  (*I have seen parallelograms, circles, squares, and rectangles.*)

Tell students that quilts are often made of square blocks that contain smaller figures, such as parallelograms, triangles, and squares. These smaller figures are often arranged to make a design, using different colours of materials.

Once the block has been designed, the same block is made many times, then sewn together to make a quilt. Some block patterns, such as the log cabin and the double pinwheel, are famous, and have been used for many years. Encourage students to find these and other quilt blocks on the Internet or in the library, then name the figures found in each block.

Tell students that, in this unit, they will investigate geometry. They will identify, describe, compare, and classify figures, and identify the conditions that make two figures congruent. Students will explore transformations, construct and analyse tiling patterns, and use transformations to create, then analyse, designs. They will also use a computer to transform figures and to create designs. At the end of the unit, students will use their understanding of geometry to create two designs using transformations.

Key Words

- convex polygon
- concave polygon
- tiling the plane
- tessellations

FROM THE LIBRARY

Geometry and Measurement: Grades 6-8: Inventive Exercises to Sharpen Skills and Raise Achievement (Basic, Not Boring 6 to 8) by Imogene Forte, Marjorie Frank, and Terri Breeden. Incentive Publications, 1997
ISBN: 0865303673
In this book, students develop and apply geometry and measurement skills to everyday situations. This book supplies practical information that should benefit every student.

REACHING ALL LEARNERS

Some students may benefit from using the virtual manipulatives on the e-Tools CD-ROM.
The e-Tools appropriate for this unit are *Geometry Shapes* and *Geometry Drawing.*

DIAGNOSTIC ASSESSMENT

What to Look For	What to Do
✔ Students can identify and classify geometric figures. ✔ Students can use mathematical language to describe figures.	***Extra Support:*** Students who have difficulty identifying and classifying geometric figures may benefit from listing the numbers of sides (and vertices) for a triangle, quadrilateral, pentagon, hexagon, heptagon, octagon, and so on. For more specific identification; for example, identifying the type of quadrilateral, students should sketch each type of figure and list its attributes. Students can refer to these notes as they identify and classify figures. *Work on this skill during Section 7.1.* Students who have difficulty using mathematical language to describe a figure may benefit from reviewing terms, such as parallel sides, acute angle, right angle, obtuse angle, vertex, side, regular polygon, and irregular polygon. Encourage students to use some of these terms when describing a figure. *Work on this skill during Sections 7.1 and 7.2.*

SECTION ORGANIZER

65–80 min

Skills in Review
- Classifying triangles
- Constructing a triangle
- Plotting points on a coordinate grid

Teacher Materials
- triangles from a geometry set
- ruler

Student Materials
- square dot paper (PM 22)
- isometric dot paper (PM 23)
- rulers
- protractors
- compasses
- 1-cm grid paper (PM 20)

Vocabulary: equilateral triangle, isosceles triangle, scalene triangle, acute triangle, right triangle, obtuse triangle, coordinates

Sample Answers

1. △ABC is an obtuse isosceles triangle because it has two sides equal and one angle greater than 90°.

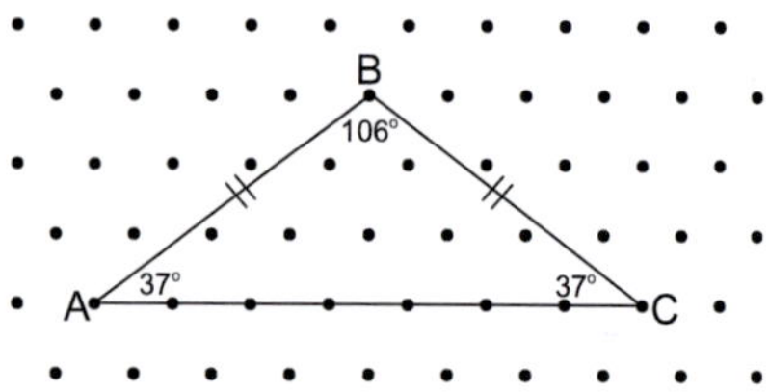

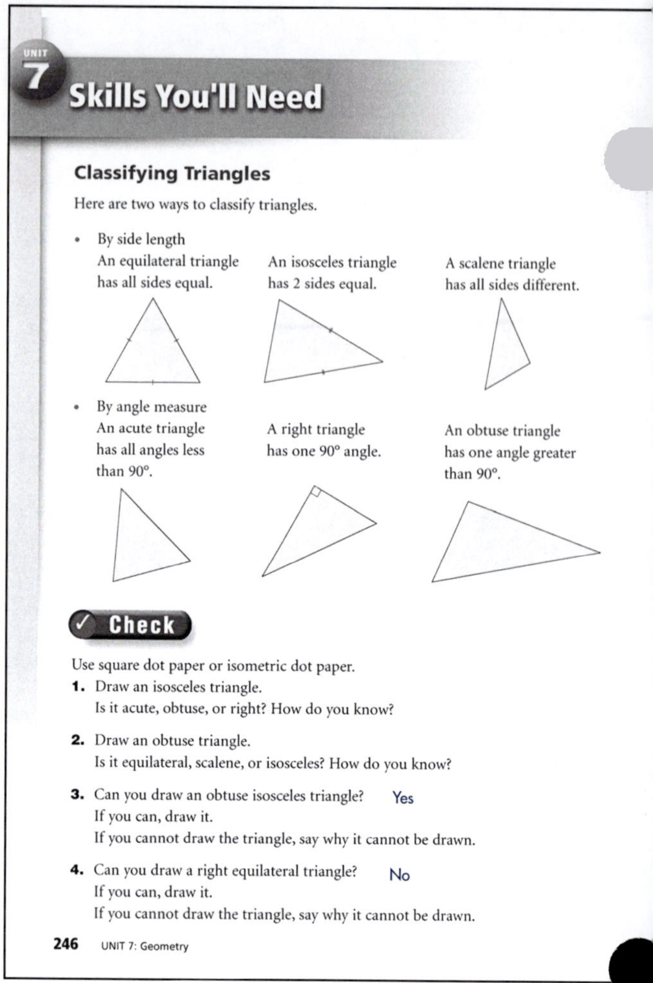

UNIT 7

Skills You'll Need

Classifying Triangles

Here are two ways to classify triangles.

- By side length
  An equilateral triangle has all sides equal. | An isosceles triangle has 2 sides equal. | A scalene triangle has all sides different.
- By angle measure
  An acute triangle has all angles less than 90°. | A right triangle has one 90° angle. | An obtuse triangle has one angle greater than 90°.

✓ Check

Use square dot paper or isometric dot paper.

1. Draw an isosceles triangle.
   Is it acute, obtuse, or right? How do you know?
2. Draw an obtuse triangle.
   Is it equilateral, scalene, or isosceles? How do you know?
3. Can you draw an obtuse isosceles triangle? Yes
   If you can, draw it.
   If you cannot draw the triangle, say why it cannot be drawn.
4. Can you draw a right equilateral triangle? No
   If you can, draw it.
   If you cannot draw the triangle, say why it cannot be drawn.

246 UNIT 7: Geometry

Classifying Triangles

Write the terms *right angle, acute angle,* and *obtuse angle* on the board. Have volunteers sketch each angle on the board. Then draw a line segment to form a triangle with each angle. Encourage students to investigate triangles that have two forms of classification, such as right isosceles and obtuse scalene.

After students have completed the *Check,* have them discuss the different types of triangles that are possible. Students should discover that they can draw an acute, an obtuse, and a right isosceles triangle; a scalene and an isosceles obtuse triangle; and an acute equilateral triangle.

Common Misconceptions

➤ Students do not recognize that a triangle can be classified by side length and by angle measure.

How to Help: Have students sketch each type of triangle that can be classified by side length. Then have them identify, by measuring or inspection, the types of angles in each triangle, and use these angles to name the triangle a second way.

For extra practice, have students play *Know Your Triangles* (Masters 7.5a and 7.5b).

Constructing a Triangle

Tell students that we can only use these triangles to construct triangles that have angles of 30°, 45°, 60°, or 90°. Ask students what other angles they could draw using combinations of these angles (*105°, 120°, 135°, 150°*).

For triangles that contain other angles, use a protractor. For triangles in which only side lengths are given, use a compass. Use the *Examples* to review these other methods of constructing triangles. Have students relate this

Constructing a Triangle

Here are two ways to construct a triangle, using a ruler, compass, and protractor.

ample 1

onstruct △ABC with AB = 4 cm, BC = 6 cm, and CA = 7 cm.

Solution

You will need a ruler and compass.

Step 1 Sketch the triangle.

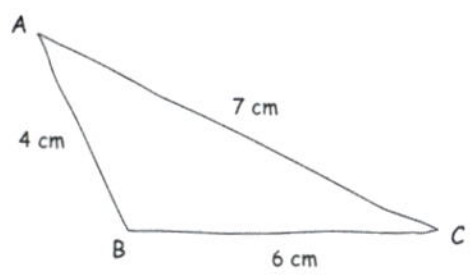

Step 2 Construct the triangle:
Use a ruler to draw side BC = 6 cm.
With the compass point and pencil 7 cm apart, put the compass point on C and draw an arc.
All points on this arc are 7 cm from C.
With the compass point and pencil 4 cm apart, put the compass point on B and draw an arc.
All points on this arc are 4 cm from B.
Make sure the arc intersects the first arc you drew.
Mark a point where the arcs intersect.
This point is 7 cm from C and 4 cm from B.
Label the point A. Join AB and AC. Label each side with its length.

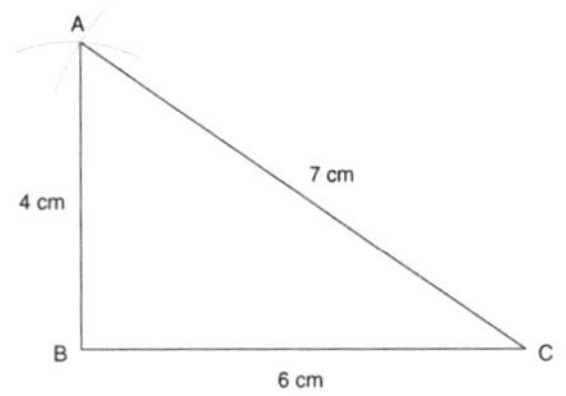

Skills You'll Need 247

Optional Example

Draw a square, ABCD. Draw a rectangle, PQRS.
Draw diagonals AC and PR.
Describe △ABC and △PQR.

Solution

Both △ABC and △PQR are right triangles because each has one 90° angle.
△ABC is a right isosceles triangle because it also has two sides equal.
△PQR is a right scalene triangle because it has all sides different.

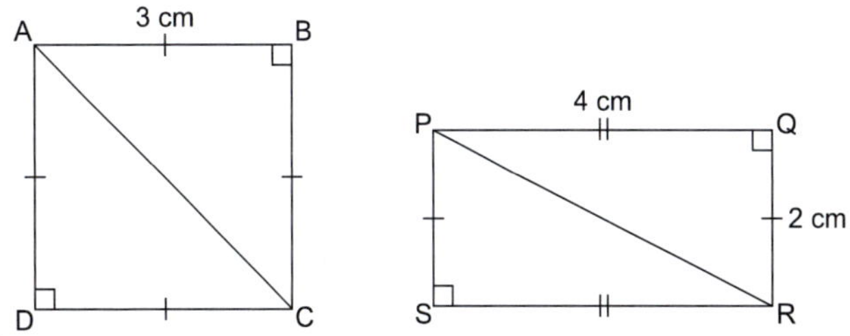

2. △DEF is an obtuse scalene triangle because it has all sides different and one angle greater than 90°.

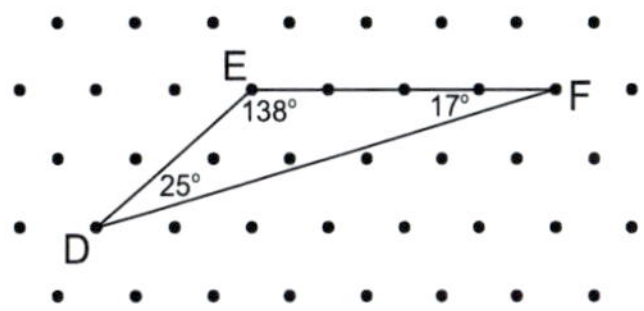

work to the preceding work, and describe each triangle by side length and angle measure.

For extra practice, have students do the additional activities *Skillful Drawing* (Master 7.6) and *Straw Triangles* (Master 7.7).

Common Misconceptions

➤ Students do not know how to start their drawing.

How to Help: Encourage students to sketch any triangle first, then label the known sides and/or angles. This sketch is not accurate but it shows each given measure. By looking at the sketch, a student should be able to see where to start.

➤ Students use the wrong scale on a protractor when marking or measuring an angle.

How to Help: Model how to measure an angle using a protractor. Place the base line of the protractor along one arm of the angle, with the centre of the baseline at the vertex of the angle. Read the angle measure from the scale that has 0 on the arm of the angle.

Plotting Points on a Coordinate Grid

Remind students that an ordered pair, such as (4, 2), tells the position of a point on a grid. In an ordered pair, the first number is the horizontal distance from the origin, O. The second number is the vertical distance from the origin. We use a letter to label the point. The numbers in an ordered pair are also called the coordinates of a point.

If time permits, have students draw line segments on a grid to represent their names or initials. They then identify the minimum number of points they would need to plot (and their coordinates) to draw these letters.

For extra practice, have students do the Additional Activity *Point the Triangles* (Masters 7.8a and 7.8b).

Alternative Example 1

Construct △PQR with PQ = 3 cm, QR = 8 cm, and ∠PQR = 60°

Solution

Step 1 Sketch the triangle.

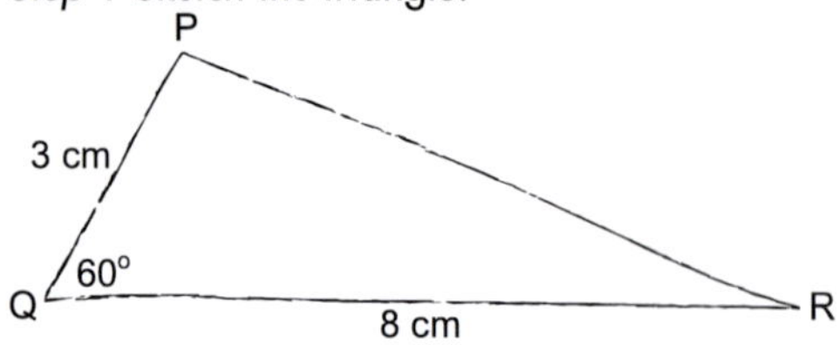

Step 2 Construct the triangle.
Use a ruler to draw side QR = 8 cm.
Use a protractor to make an angle of 60° at Q.
Use a ruler to draw QP = 3 cm.
Join PR.
Label the known sides and angle with their measures.

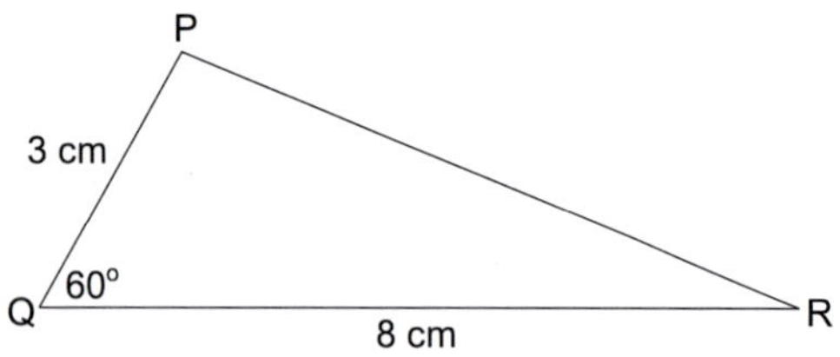

3. See △ABC in question 1.
4. An equilateral triangle has all sides equal and all angles equal. Each angle in an equilateral triangle is 60°. A right triangle has one 90° angle. So, it is impossible to draw a right equilateral triangle.

Example 2

Construct △BCD with BC = 6 cm, ∠B = 110°, and ∠C = 30°.

Solution

You will need a ruler and protractor.
Step 1 Sketch the triangle.

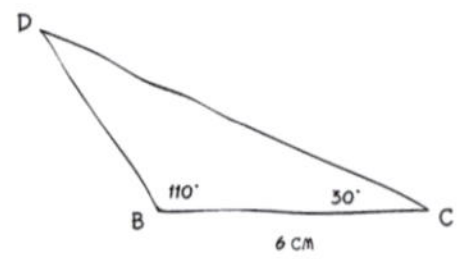

Step 2 Construct the triangle:
Use a ruler to draw side BC = 6 cm.
Use a protractor to make an angle of 110° at B.
Use a protractor to make an angle of 30° at C.
Label point D where the arms of the angles intersect.
Label the known side and angles.

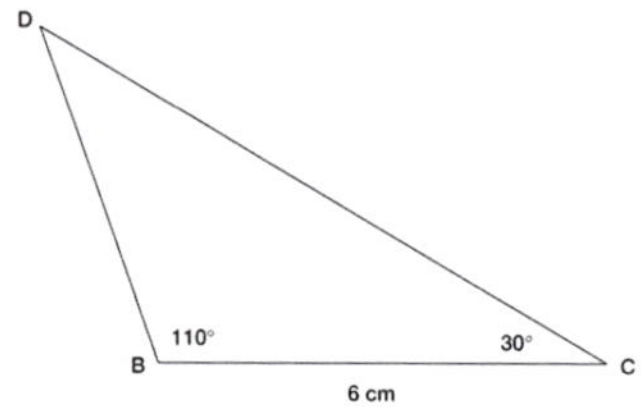

Check

5. Construct each triangle.
   a) △CDE with CD = 4 cm, DE = 7 cm, CE = 9 cm
   b) △DEF with DE = 7 cm, ∠D = 80°, ∠E = 30°

248 UNIT 7: Geometry

Common Misconceptions

➤ Students think, for example, that (6, 2) and (2, 6) represent the same point.

How to Help: Model how to plot these points on a grid. Show students that to plot the point (6, 2), we start at 6 on the horizontal axis, then move up 2. To plot the point (2, 6), we start at 2 on the horizontal axis, then move up 6. Students see that the two points are different.

➤ Students think the first number in the coordinates of a point represents the vertical distance moved on a grid.

How to Help: Remind students that the first number is the horizontal distance and the second number is the vertical distance. Since *horizontal* comes before *vertical* alphabetically, we always move the first number, the horizontal distance, first. Ask students where else in mathematics order is important (the order of operations used to evaluate a numerical expression).

Optional Example

On grid paper, draw a coordinate grid.
Plot each point on the grid.
A(1, 5), B(4, 5), C(3, 4), D(4, 3), E(1, 3)
Join the points in order to form figure ABCDE.
Describe the figure.

Solution

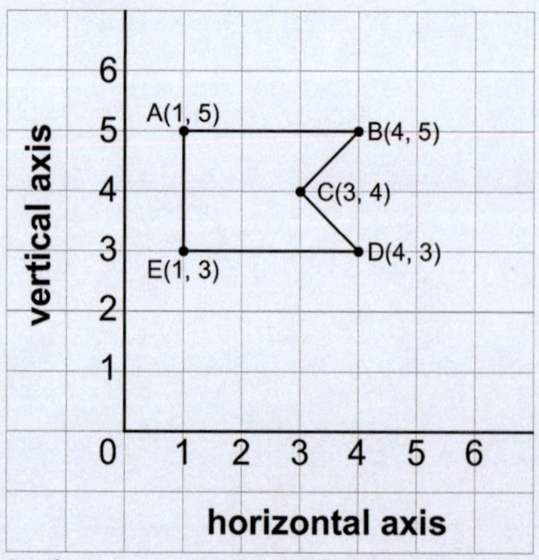

The figure is a pentagon with one line of symmetry. It resembles a flag.

Plotting Points on a Coordinate Grid

When we draw a horizontal axis and a vertical axis on grid paper,
have a coordinate grid.
axes intersect at the origin, O.

/e label each axis with numbers, beginning with 0 at the origin.

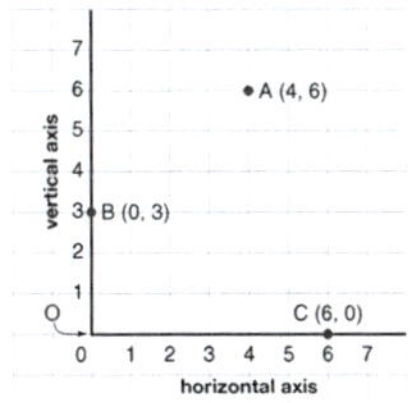

A point on a grid is described by its coordinates.

Point A has coordinates (4, 6).
To plot point A, start at 4 on the horizontal axis, then move up 6 spaces.
Mark a point. This is point A.

Point B has coordinates (0, 3).
To plot point B, start at 0, then move up 3 spaces. Point B is on the vertical axis.

Point C has coordinates (6, 0).
To plot point C, mark a point at 6 on the horizontal axis.

✓ Check

6. On grid paper, draw a coordinate grid.
Plot each point on the grid.
A(5, 7), B(3, 8), C(10, 4), D(9, 1), E(0, 8), F(5, 0)

7. a) Where are all the points with horizontal coordinate 0? On the vertical axis
b) Where are all the points with vertical coordinate 0? On the horizontal axis

Alternative Example 2

Remind students of the work they did in an earlier grade, using the triangles in a geometry set to construct angles. Show students these triangles and point out that one triangle contains angles of 30°, 60°, and 90°, while the other triangle has two 45° angles and one 90° angle. Use these triangles and a ruler on an overhead transparency to model how to construct △DEF, where ∠D is 30°, ∠E is 45°, and the length of DE is 6 cm.

Solution

Use a ruler to draw side DE = 6 cm.
Place the 30° angle of the right triangle on vertex D, with the base of the triangle on DE.
Draw a long line from D along the opposite edge of the triangle.
Place the 45° angle of the isosceles triangle on vertex E, with the base of the triangle on DE.
Draw a long line from E along the opposite edge of the triangle.
Mark a point where the two lines intersect.
Label the point F.
Label the triangle with its measures.

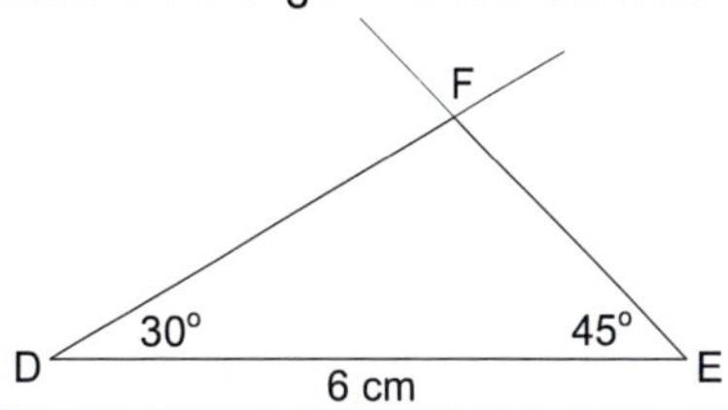

Sample Answers

5. a)

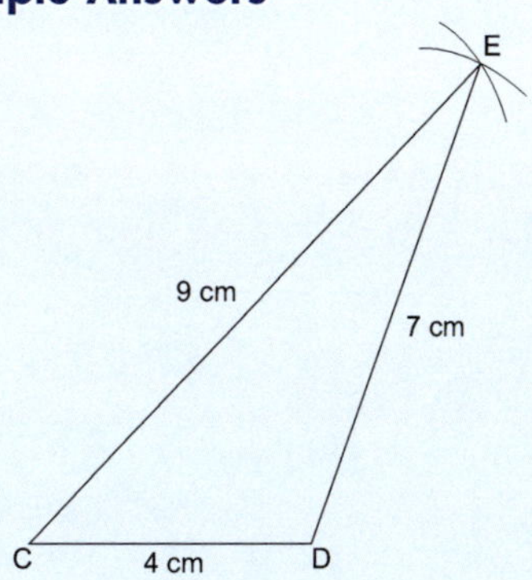

b)

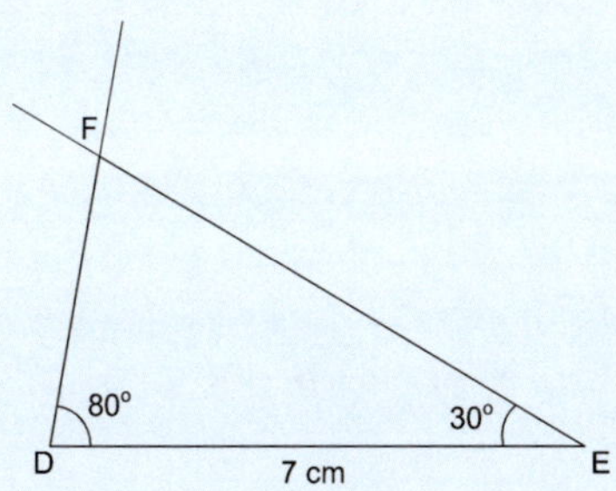

6.

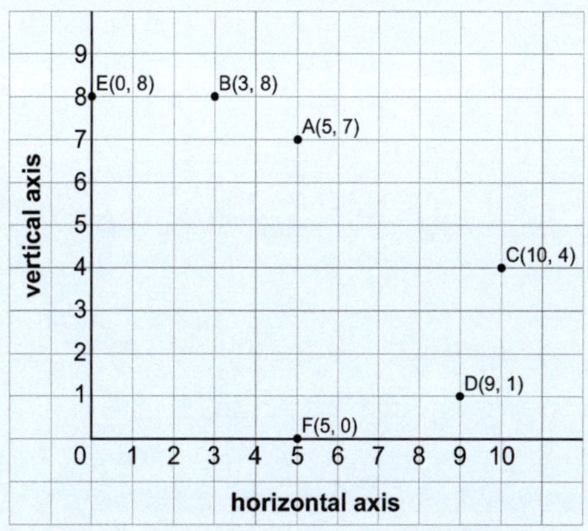

7. a) All the points with horizontal coordinate 0 are on the vertical axis.
b) All the points with vertical coordinate 0 are on the horizontal axis.

Classifying Figures

SECTION ORGANIZER (80–100 min)

Curriculum Focus: Identify, describe, and classify geometric figures. (7m57)

Student Materials
- Figures for 7.1 *Explore* (Master 7.14)
- rulers
- protractors
- tracing paper
- square dot paper (PM 22)
- isometric dot paper (PM 23)

Optional
- Step-by-Step 1 (Master 7.9)
- Extra Practice 1 (Master 7.20)

Vocabulary: convex polygon, concave polygon, reflex angle

Assessment: Master 7.2 Ongoing Observations: Geometry

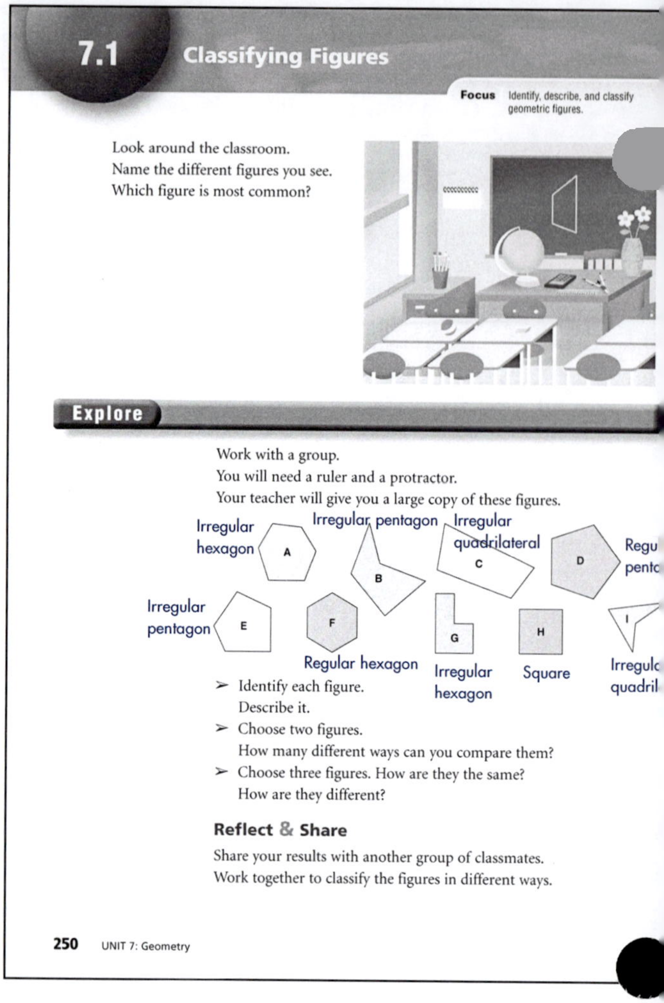
7.1 Classifying Figures

Focus Identify, describe, and classify geometric figures.

Look around the classroom.
Name the different figures you see.
Which figure is most common?

Explore

Work with a group.
You will need a ruler and a protractor.
Your teacher will give you a large copy of these figures.

➢ Identify each figure.
Describe it.
➢ Choose two figures.
How many different ways can you compare them?
➢ Choose three figures. How are they the same?
How are they different?

Reflect & Share

Share your results with another group of classmates.
Work together to classify the figures in different ways.

250 UNIT 7: Geometry

Key Math Learnings

1. A regular polygon has all sides equal, all angles equal, line symmetry, and rotational symmetry.
2. A convex polygon has all angles less than 180°. A concave polygon has at least one angle greater than 180°.

BEFORE — Get Started

Discuss the different figures students see in the classroom. Ask questions, such as:

- Which figures do you see around you?
  (*The blackboard is rectangular; the computer disc is circular; the calendar is square; and the Pattern Block is triangular.*)
- Which figure is most common?
  (*The rectangle; the blackboard, the bulletin board, the desks, the windows, and most books are rectangular.*)
- What do we mean when we say a figure is a regular figure?
  (*It has all sides equal and all angles equal.*)
- What is an example of a regular figure?
  (*A square and an equilateral triangle*)

Remind students that figures can be classified by: the number of sides, the side lengths, the number of angles, and the angle measures.

Present *Explore*. Distribute copies of *Figures for 7.1 Explore* (Master 7.14) to groups of students. Each student needs a ruler and a protractor. Ensure students understand they are to measure the angles and side lengths of each figure.

DURING — Explore

Ongoing Assessment: Observe and Listen

As students work, ask questions, such as:

- What figures did you identify?
  (*Figure A is an irregular hexagon; Figure B is an irregular pentagon; Figure C is an irregular quadrilateral; Figure D is a regular pentagon; Figure E is an irregular pentagon; Figure F is a regular hexagon; Figure G is an irregular hexagon; Figure H is a square; and Figure I is an irregular quadrilateral.*)
- How can you describe Figure H?
  (*It has 4 equal sides. Each angle is a right angle. It has two pairs of parallel sides.*)

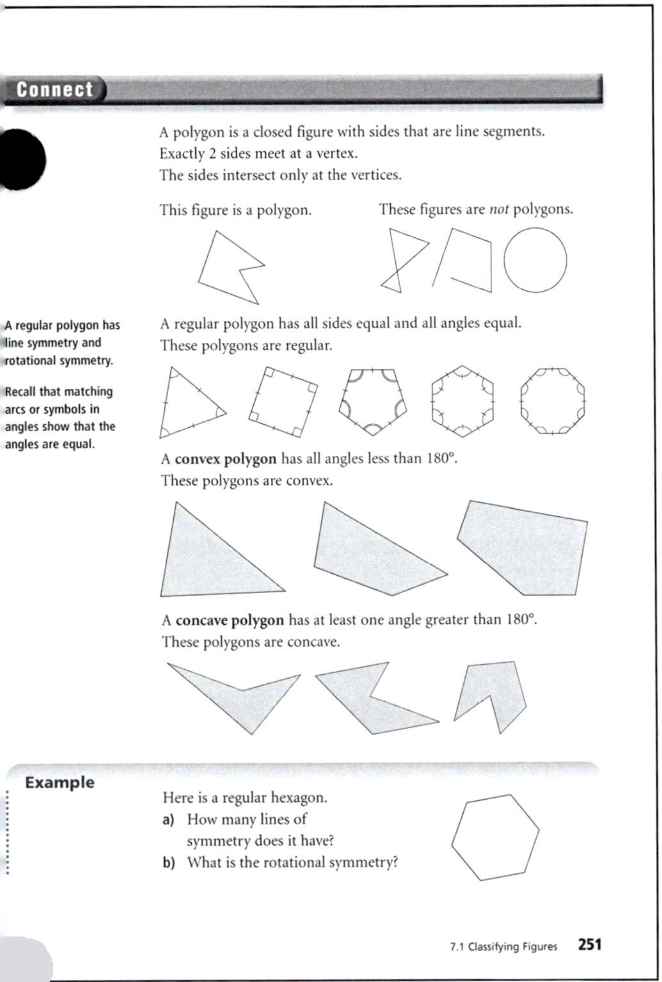

Connect

A polygon is a closed figure with sides that are line segments.
Exactly 2 sides meet at a vertex.
The sides intersect only at the vertices.

This figure is a polygon. These figures are *not* polygons.

A regular polygon has line symmetry and rotational symmetry.

Recall that matching arcs or symbols in angles show that the angles are equal.

A regular polygon has all sides equal and all angles equal.
These polygons are regular.

A **convex polygon** has all angles less than 180°.
These polygons are convex.

A **concave polygon** has at least one angle greater than 180°.
These polygons are concave.

Example

Here is a regular hexagon.
a) How many lines of symmetry does it have?
b) What is the rotational symmetry?

7.1 Classifying Figures 251

REACHING ALL LEARNERS

Alternative Explore

Materials: a collection of geometric figures found in the classroom, including Pattern Blocks and tangrams

Students work in pairs to name and describe each figure. Students choose two figures, then list the similarities and differences between them. Students choose three figures, then describe how they are the same and how they are different.

Early Finishers

Students use an atlas or the Internet to find other flags that contain interesting geometric figures. Students identify and describe each figure they find.

Common Misconceptions

➤ Students do not recognize that some figures may be described using different names.

How to Help: Illustrate this concept by using a student in the class; for example, a student is a member of the chess club and the stamp club. In the same way, a square belongs to three "clubs": a rectangle, a parallelogram, and a trapezoid.

ESL Strategies

Students for whom English is a second language may benefit from writing the prefixes "tri," "quad," "penta," "hexa," "hepta," "octa," and "deca" on an index card, then writing the corresponding number beside each prefix: 3, 4, 5, 6, 7, 8, and 10. Students can refer to this card as they identify and classify figures.

- How can you describe Figure D? (*It has 5 equal sides and each angle is 108°.*)
- How can you describe Figure A? (*It has 6 sides. It has no parallel sides. It does not have all sides equal and it does not have all angles equal.*)
- Which two figures did you choose to compare? (*Figures A and F*) What did you find? (*Both figures have 6 sides. Both figures have all obtuse angles. Figure A has no parallel sides. Figure F has 3 pairs of parallel sides. Figure A does not have all sides equal and all angles equal. Figure F has all sides equal and all angles equal.*)
- Which three figures did you choose to compare? (*Figures C, H, and I*) How are they the same? (*All figures have 4 sides.*) How are they different? (*Figures C and I have no parallel sides while Figure H has 2 pairs of parallel sides. Figure C has 2 obtuse angles and 2 acute angles, Figure H has all right angles, and Figure I has 3 acute angles and 1 reflex angle. Figure H has all sides equal. Figures C and I do not have all sides equal.*)

AFTER Connect

Invite students to share their results. Discuss how we sort figures according to the different attributes. Elicit from students that there are many ways to sort figures.

Ask:

- How did you classify the figures? (*We classified the figures by the number of sides, and whether all sides of each figure are equal.*)
- What other way can you classify the figures? (*We can classify the figures according to the number of parallel sides.*)
- What other way can you classify the figures? (*We can classify the figures according to the number of right angles, acute angles, obtuse angles, or equal angles. We can also classify the figures according to the number of lines of symmetry.*)

Math Link

Some road signs students could find are: pentagon: school zone, school crossing, one way; octagon: stop sign; square: do not enter, no passing, no parking, no u-turn, no stopping; circle: stop lights, do not enter; rectangle: speed limits, no passing, no standing, informational signs (distances to cities); triangle: yield

Number Strategies

In the first pattern, the rule is: Start at 23. Add 5 to get the next term. Subtract 2 to get the next term. Continue to alternate adding and subtracting. For the second pattern, the rule is: Start at 6. Add 3. Multiply the number added by 2 each time. For the third pattern, the rule is: Start at 1. Multiply by 3 each time.

Assignment Guidelines

If your students do not have time to complete all the *Practice* questions on pages 252, 253, and 254, these questions provide minimum curriculum coverage:
1, 2, 4, 5, 6, 7, 9, *Reflect*
To assess the 4 Achievement Chart categories listed in the curriculum document, have students complete these *Practice* questions: Understanding Concepts: 5; Application: 6; Problem Solving: 9; Communication: *Reflect*

Solution

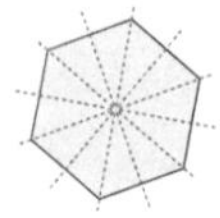

a) Trace the hexagon.
Fold the tracing paper so that one part of the hexagon coincides with the other.
The fold line is a line of symmetry.
Repeat the folding as many times as possible.

A regular hexagon has 6 lines of symmetry: 3 lines join opposite vertices, and 3 lines join the midpoints of opposite sides.

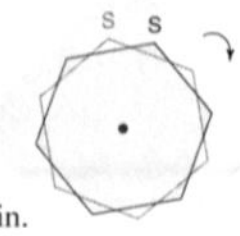

b) Trace the hexagon. Place the tracing to coincide with the hexagon.
Rotate the tracing about its centre until the tracing coincides with the hexagon again.
Count how many times you can do this.

Label two corresponding vertices. Then you know when the tracing is back at the starting position.

The tracing coincides with the hexagon 6 times.
So, a regular hexagon has rotational symmetry of order 6.

Practice

1. Explain why each figure is not a polygon.
a) b)

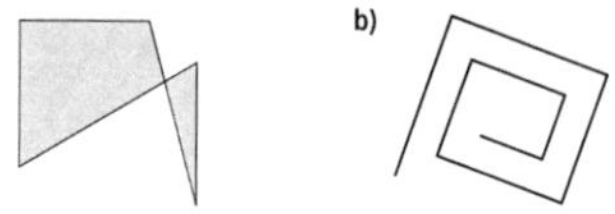

2. a) Is each polygon regular? How do you know?
i) ii) iii)

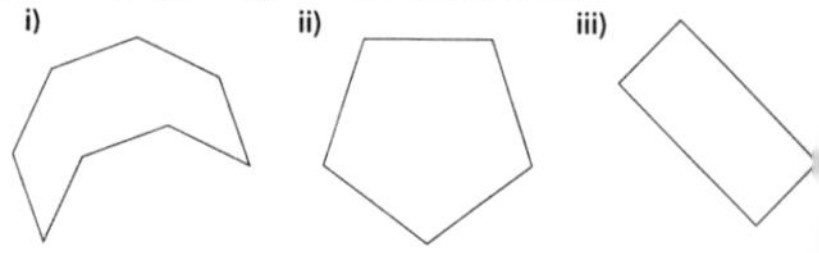

b) Which polygons in part a have:
i) line symmetry? ii) rotational symmetry?
How do you know?

252 UNIT 7: Geometry

Use *Connect* to introduce the terms **convex polygon** and **concave polygon.** Remind students that an angle that is greater than 180° is a **reflex angle.**

Use the *Example* to illustrate how a regular polygon has line symmetry and rotational symmetry.

Practice

Have square dot paper (PM 22) and isometric dot paper (PM 23) available for questions 6, 8, and 9. Have tracing paper available for question 2. Students may require rulers and protractors for questions 3, 5, 6, 7, 8, 9, 10, and *Reflect*. For question 8, students should change one vertex or side each time. By changing one vertex or side, more than one attribute, such as side length and angle measure, may change.

Assessment Focus: Question 9

Students investigate different positions for the fourth vertex to make the first 3 polygons. To make a pentagon, students should realize they need 2 more vertices. Some students may find as many other figures as they can by adding one or two more vertices. Stronger math students may add many vertices to create polygons with many sides, such as octagons and decagons. Many students may overlook the triangle, which can be formed using the 3 given vertices. Ensure students include a description of each figure sketched and named.

Students who need extra support to complete Assessment Focus questions may benefit from the Step-by-Step masters (Masters 7.9–7.13).

3. Identify the figures in each flag.
Describe each figure as many ways as you can.
a) Congo b) Bosnia-Herzegovina c) Guyana d) Seychelles

4. Describe each figure. How are the figures the same? Different?

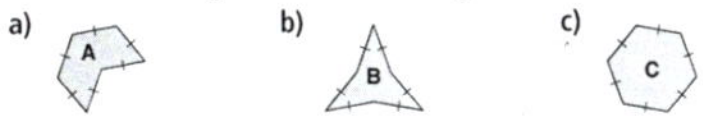

5. Match each polygon with its description below.

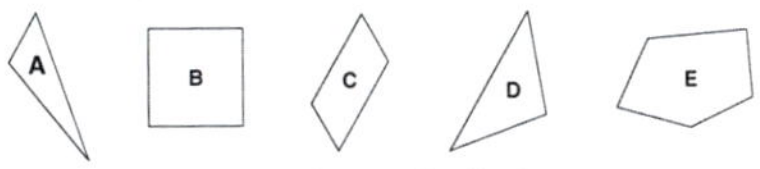

a) an isosceles triangle with an angle of 40° Figure D
b) a rhombus with a right angle Figure B
c) a pentagon with an angle of 120° Figure E
d) a parallelogram with an angle of 60° Figure C
e) an obtuse triangle with an angle of 110° Figure A

6. Use square dot paper or isometric dot paper.
Draw each polygon.
a) an isosceles triangle with a height of 4 units
b) a parallelogram with an angle of 45°
c) a trapezoid with a 90° angle and a 45° angle
d) a kite with exactly one right angle
e) a parallelogram with a 90° angle
f) a scalene obtuse triangle
g) an isosceles right triangle
h) a hexagon with exactly 3 right angles

7. Identify each polygon.
Describe it as many ways as you can.

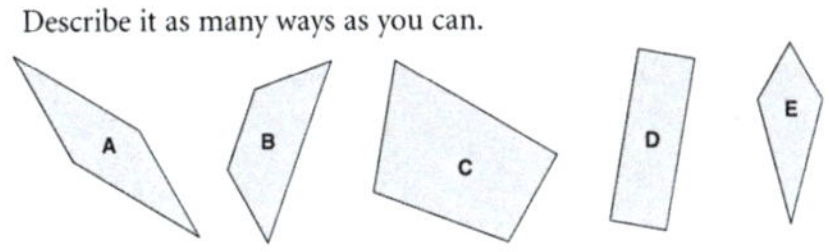

Sample Answers

1. a) More than 2 sides meet at a vertex.
   b) The figure is not closed.
2. a) i) No, because all angles are not equal
   ii) Yes, because all sides are equal and all angles are equal
   iii) No, because all sides are not equal
   b) i) All polygons in part a have line symmetry. I know this because when I trace each figure, I can find at least one fold line so that one part of the polygon coincides with the other.
   ii) Polygons ii and iii have rotational symmetry. I know this because I can rotate a tracing of each of these polygons about its centre so that the tracing coincides with the polygon at least once.
3. a) There are 2 right isosceles triangles and 1 parallelogram.
   b) There are 1 right triangle, 1 rectangle, 1 trapezoid, and 7 irregular decagons.
   c) There are 2 right triangles, 1 equilateral triangle, and 1 kite.
   d) There are 2 right triangles, 2 obtuse scalene triangles, and 1 quadrilateral.
4. a) Concave hexagon
   b) Concave hexagon
   c) Regular hexagon
   All figures are hexagons with 6 equal sides. Each figure has at least one line of symmetry. The figures are different in that only Figure C has equal angles, and only Figures B and C have rotational symmetry.
7. Polygon A: parallelogram; Polygon B: trapezoid;
   Polygon C: quadrilateral; Polygon D: rectangle; Polygon E: kite

(*Answers continue below.*)

(*Sample Answers, continued*)

8. a)

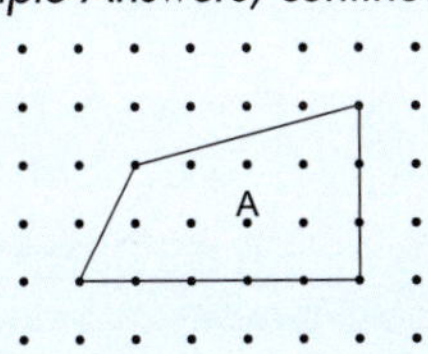

b)

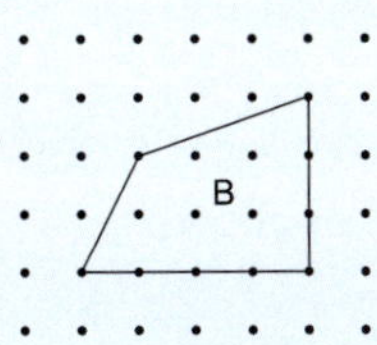

c)

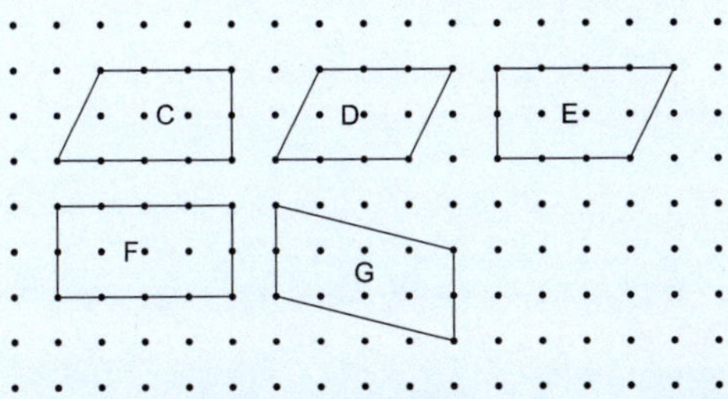

Squares, rhombuses, parallelograms, rectangles, trapezoids, and kites are possible. Many different shapes and sizes are possible.

9. a) i)

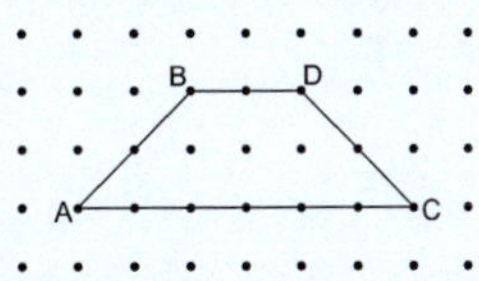

ii)

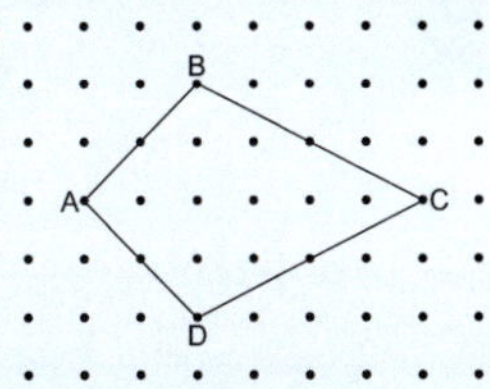

iii)

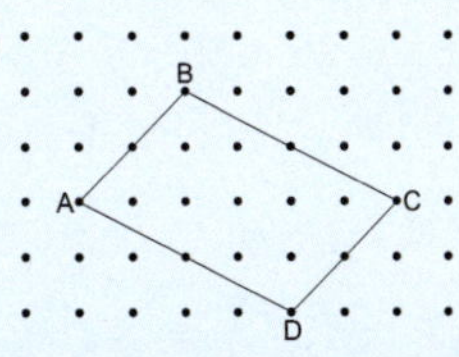

iv)

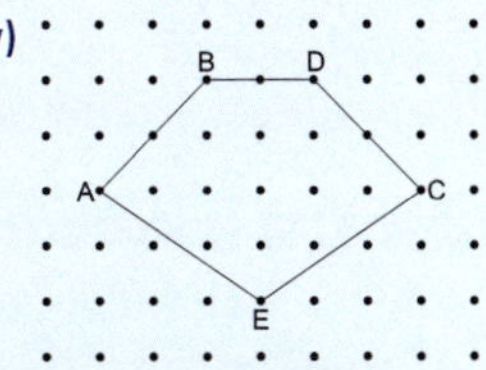

b) Many different figures can be made: a triangle, trapezoids, parallelograms, rectangles, kites, pentagons, hexagons, octagons, and so on. Students should include a description of each figure they make.

10. a) Students could draw a trapezoid, a kite, a rectangle, a parallelogram, and an irregular quadrilateral.
b) A rectangle is possible because opposite sides are equal and all angles are right angles. A kite is possible because there would be 2 pairs of equal adjacent sides, 1 right angle, and 1 pair of equal angles. A trapezoid and a parallelogram are also possible, both drawn as rectangles.

REFLECT: I chose a triangle, a kite, and a pentagon. All the triangles have 3 sides, but the types of angles in the triangles vary. All the kites have 4 sides, 2 pairs of equal adjacent sides, and 1 pair of equal opposite angles. All the pentagons have 5 sides but the side lengths and angle measures vary. Students should describe each polygon they draw.

A quadrilateral is a polygon with 4 sides.

8. Use dot paper.
a) Draw a quadrilateral. Label it A.
b) Draw another quadrilateral that differs from quadrilateral A in only one way. Label it B.
c) Continue to draw quadrilaterals that differ in only one way. Label each one you draw.
How many different quadrilaterals can you draw?

Number Strategies

Find the next 3 numbers in each pattern.
What is each pattern rule?
- 23, 28, 26, 31, 29,... 34, 32, 37
- 6, 9, 15, 27, 51,... 99, 195, 387
- 1, 3, 9, 27,... 81, 243, 729

9. Assessment Focus
The 3 points A, B, C are vertices of a polygon.
Copy the points on dot paper.
a) Find other vertices and sketch each figure.
i) a trapezoid with line symmetry
ii) a kite
iii) a parallelogram
iv) a pentagon
b) How many other figures can you make that have these points as 3 vertices?
Identify each figure. Describe it as many ways as you can.

10. The lengths of three sides of a quadrilateral are 5 cm, 5 cm, and 8 cm.
a) Sketch and name the different quadrilaterals possible.
b) Suppose one angle is 90°. Which quadrilaterals are possible now? Justify your answer.

Math Link

Your World
The Department of Highways uses different figures for road signs. Which road signs use each of these figures: pentagon, octagon, square, circle, rectangle, triangle?

Reflect

Choose 3 different polygons. Sketch each polygon as many different ways as you can. Describe each polygon.

254 UNIT 7: Geometry

ASSESSMENT FOR LEARNING

What to Look For	What to Do
Understanding concepts ✔ Students understand that a convex polygon has all angles less than 180°, and a concave polygon has at least one angle greater than 180°. ***Applying procedures*** ✔ Students can identify, describe, and classify geometric figures. ✔ Students can compare two or more different figures. ***Communicating*** ✔ Students can describe a geometric figure using mathematical terminology.	***Extra Support:*** Students who have difficulty classifying figures may benefit from selecting one attribute, such as number of sides, and classifying all figures using this attribute. As students become more comfortable, they can select other attributes. Students can use Step-by-Step 1 (Master 7.9) to complete question 9. ***Extra Practice:*** Have students cut out, then classify, figures they find in old magazines. Students can complete Extra Practice 1 (Master 7.20). ***Extension:*** Have students find examples of irregular polygons that have line and/or rotational symmetry (for example, isosceles triangle, kite, rectangle).

Recording and Reporting
Master 7.2 Ongoing Observations: Geometry

7.2 Congruent Figures

Focus Identify the conditions for congruence.

Explore

Work on your own.
You will need a ruler, protractor, and compass.
For each set of measurements given, how many different triangles can you draw?

- Construct a triangle with sides of length 5 cm, 7 cm, and 9 cm.
- Construct a triangle with two sides of length 9 cm and 5 cm, and one angle of 30°.
- Construct a triangle with one side of length 5 cm and two angles of 40° and 60°.

Reflect & Share

Compare your triangles with those of several classmates.

- How many different triangles can you draw in each case?
  - when you know 3 sides
  - when you know 2 sides and 1 angle
  - when you know 1 side and 2 angles
- What measurements do you need to know to be able to draw exactly one triangle?

Connect

- When 3 sides of a triangle are given, only one triangle can be drawn. So, if we know that two triangles have the same 3 sides, those triangles must be congruent.

Congruent figures have the same size and shape. These triangles are drawn to scale.

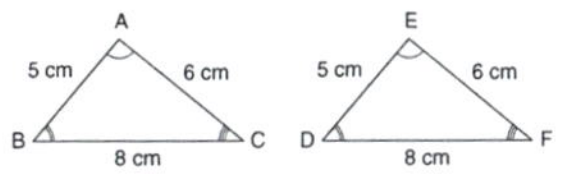

We say: Triangle ABC is congruent to triangle EDF.
We write: △ABC ≅ △EDF

7.2 Congruent Figures 255

Congruent Figures

SECTION ORGANIZER (80–100 min)

Curriculum Focus: Identify the conditions for congruence. (7m58, 7m59, 7m60)

Teacher Materials
- plastic triangle

Student Materials
- rulers
- protractors
- compasses
- square dot paper (PM 22)
- isometric dot paper (PM 23)

Optional
- tracing paper
- Step-by-Step 2 (Master 7.10)
- Extra Practice 2 (Master 7.21)

Vocabulary: congruent

Assessment: Master 7.2 Ongoing Observations: Geometry

Key Math Learnings

1. Two triangles are congruent if they have the same 3 sides; if 2 sides and the angle between the two sides are the same; or if 2 angles and the side between them are the same.
2. Two polygons are congruent if all corresponding sides are equal and all corresponding angles are equal.

BEFORE Get Started

Trace a plastic triangle on an overhead transparency. Rotate the plastic triangle, then trace again. Flip the plastic triangle, then trace again. Show students the three tracings. Ask:

- How many different triangles do you see? (3)
- Does anyone disagree with this answer? (*Yes*) Explain. (*The 3 triangles are the same because they have the same size and shape.*)
- How could we find out if the triangles are the same? (*We could cut out one of the triangles, then rotate it or flip it to see if it coincides with the other triangles. If the triangle coincides with another triangle, the two triangles are the same, or congruent.*)

Present *Explore*. Remind students to find as many different triangles as they can, and that a different orientation does not make a triangle different.

DURING Explore

Ongoing Assessment: Observe and Listen

As students work, ask questions, such as:

- How many different triangles can you draw with sides of length 5 cm, 7 cm, and 9 cm? (*I can only draw one triangle. No matter which side I draw first, I always get the same triangle, but oriented differently.*)
- How many different triangles can you draw with two sides of length 9 cm and 5 cm, and one angle of 30°? (*I can only draw one triangle if the angle of 30° is between the two given sides. If the angle is not between the two given sides, then I can draw 2 different triangles: one obtuse triangle and one acute triangle.*)
- How many different triangles can you draw with one side of length 5 cm and two angles of 40° and 60°?

REACHING ALL LEARNERS

Early Finishers

Challenge students to draw two congruent irregular pentagons, then explain how they know the pentagons are congruent.

Common Misconceptions

➤ Students do not recognize congruent figures that are oriented differently.

How to Help: Remind students that a figure may need to be rotated or flipped to show that it is congruent to another figure.

➤ Students think that two triangles with corresponding angles equal are congruent.

How to Help: Draw a triangle with angles 40°, 60°, and 80° on the board. Start with a base of length 10 cm. Draw another triangle with the same angles, but this time start with a base of 20 cm. Students will see that the two triangles have corresponding angles equal, but corresponding sides are not equal. The two triangles have the same shape but not the same size. So, the two triangles are similar and not congruent.

ESL Strategies

Have students draw and label 3 pairs of congruent triangles on index cards. Each pair of triangles should represent one of the 3 conditions of congruence: 3 equal sides, 2 equal sides with the angles between them equal, and 2 equal angles with the sides between them equal. Students can refer to these cards as they check for congruence.

△ABC and △EDF have:

We list the corresponding vertices of the triangles in the same order.

corresponding sides equal	and	corresponding angles equal
AB = ED		∠A = ∠E
BC = DF		∠B = ∠D
AC = EF		∠C = ∠F

➤ When 2 sides and 1 angle of a triangle are given, there are two cases to consider.

- The given angle is between the 2 sides.
  Only one triangle can be drawn.

You may have to flip or rotate one triangle so both triangles face the same way.

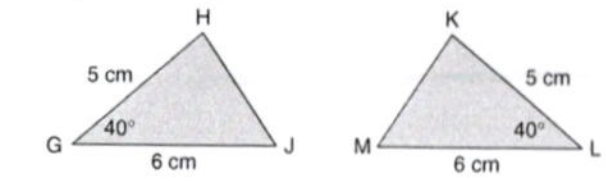

So, triangle GHJ is congruent to triangle LKM or △GHJ ≅ △LKM

- The given angle is *not* between the 2 sides.
  Sometimes more than one triangle can be drawn.

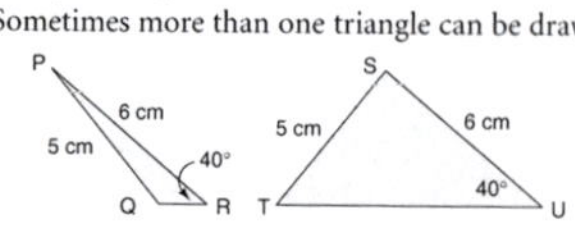

△PQR and △STU are *not* congruent.

➤ When 2 angles and 1 side are given, only one triangle can be drawn.

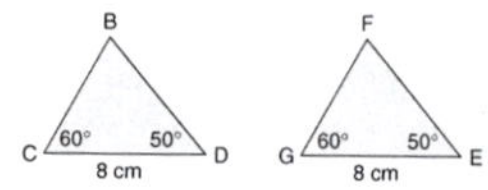

△BCD ≅ △FGE

Example

Are the figures in each pair congruent? How do you know?

a)

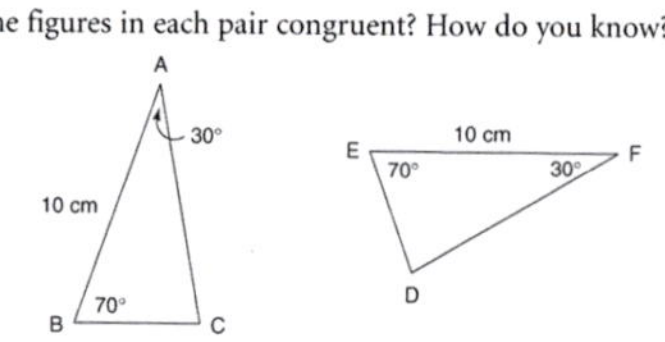

(*I can draw three triangles: one with the 5-cm side between the two angles; one with the 60° angle opposite the 5-cm side, and one with the 40° angle opposite the 5-cm side.*)

Encourage students who have difficulty seeing that some of their triangles are the same to use tracing paper. Students could trace a triangle, cut it out, then rotate or flip the tracing to check to see if it coincides with another triangle. Remind students that if the triangles coincide, they are congruent triangles.

AFTER Connect

Invite volunteers to share and compare their triangles.

Ask questions, such as:

- How many different triangles can you draw when you know 3 sides? (*1*) When you know 2 sides and 1 angle? (*1 triangle if the angle is between the 2 sides, and 2 triangles if the angle is not between the two sides.*) When you know 1 side and 2 angles? (*1 triangle if the side is between the two angles, and 2 triangles if the side is not between the 2 angles.*)
- What measurements do you need to know to be able to draw exactly one triangle?
  (*I need to know 3 sides, 2 sides and the angle between them, or 2 angles and the side between them.*)

Some students may think that two triangles with all corresponding angles equal are congruent. Suggest students try to draw as many different triangles as they can with angles of 30°, 70°, and 80°. Students should discover that many different triangles are possible. Remind students that these triangles are **similar**.

When you review the different triangles for 2 angles and 1 side given, show students the two possible triangles for the side *not* between the two angles.

b)

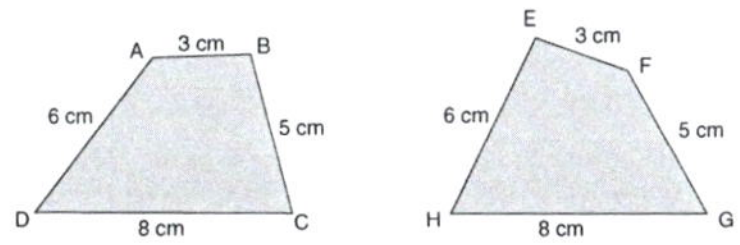

Solution

a) △ABC and △FED have 2 pairs of corresponding angles equal and 1 pair of corresponding sides equal:
∠A = ∠F = 30°
∠B = ∠E = 70°
AB = FE = 10 cm
So, △ABC and △FED are congruent: △ABC ≅ △FED

b) Quadrilateral ABCD and quadrilateral EFGH have 4 pairs of corresponding sides equal. But the quadrilaterals have different shapes. So, the quadrilaterals are not congruent.

Part b of the *Example* shows that for two quadrilaterals to be congruent, it is not sufficient that 4 pairs of corresponding sides are equal. We need to know that the corresponding angles are equal, too.

Practice

1. Look at the triangles below.
Find pairs of congruent triangles.
Explain why they are congruent.

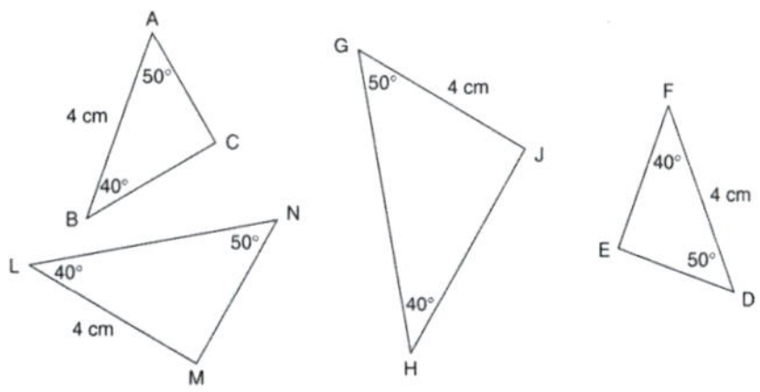

Sample Answers

1. △ABC and △DFE are congruent because ∠A = ∠D = 50°, ∠B = ∠F = 40°, AB = DF = 4 cm.
2. The quadrilaterals have 4 pairs of corresponding sides equal and 4 pairs of corresponding angles equal.
3. a) △ABC and △ADC are congruent because all corresponding sides are equal. The triangles are also congruent because 2 pairs of corresponding sides and the angles between them are equal.
   b) By the definition of a parallelogram, opposite sides are equal and opposite angles are equal. △PSR and △RQP are congruent because all pairs of corresponding sides are equal. The triangles are also congruent because 2 pairs of corresponding sides and the angles between them are equal.
   c) By the definition of a rhombus, all sides are equal and opposite angles are equal. △EFH and △GHF are congruent because all pairs of corresponding sides are equal. The triangles are also congruent because 2 pairs of corresponding sides and the angle between them are equal.
   d) By the definition of a rectangle, opposite sides are equal and all angles are right angles. △JKL and △LMJ are congruent because all pairs of corresponding sides are equal. The triangles are also congruent because 2 pairs of corresponding sides and the angle between them are equal.
4. i) b) The lengths of 2 non-equal sides and the angle between them.

This is also illustrated in the triangles in *Practice* question 1.

Work through the *Example* in *Connect*. Ensure students understand that two quadrilaterals with 4 pairs of corresponding angles equal are similar and not congruent. Draw a square with side length 8 cm on the board. Draw a rectangle with side lengths 6 cm and 10 cm. Point out that both figures have all right angles, but corresponding side lengths are not equal. So, the two quadrilaterals are not congruent.

Practice

Questions 4, 5, 6, and 9 require rulers, protractors, and possibly compasses. Question 6 requires square dot paper (PM 22) or isometric dot paper (PM 23). Check that students name pairs of congruent figures with corresponding vertices in the same order.

Assessment Focus: Question 6

Students understand that two quadrilaterals are congruent if the 4 pairs of corresponding sides are equal and the 4 pairs of corresponding angles are equal. In part b, some students may draw the same quadrilateral twice, while stronger math students may change the orientation of the second quadrilateral. All quadrilaterals should be labelled, and explanations should contain mathematical language.

c) Since opposite sides and opposite angles of a parallelogram are equal, two parallelograms are congruent if all corresponding sides and all corresponding angles are equal.

ii) b) The lengths of two non-equal sides are needed.

c) By definition, a rectangle has all right angles. So, two rectangles are congruent if corresponding sides are equal.

iii) b) The length of one side is needed.

c) By definition, a square has all sides equal and all right angles. So, two squares are congruent if they have the same side length.

5. b) I need to know the length of the third side of each triangle, or I need to know the measures of ∠B and ∠E.

6. a)

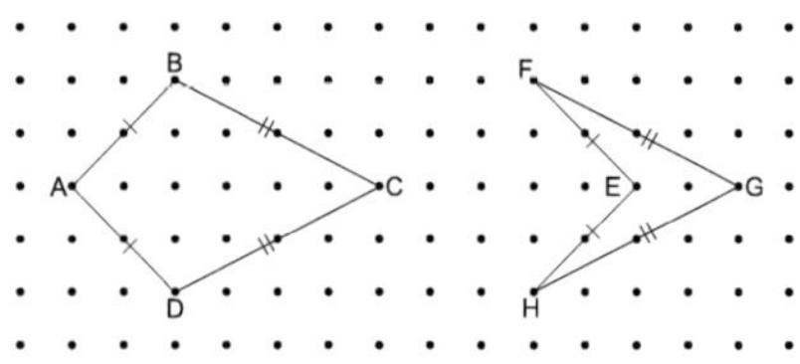

The quadrilaterals are not congruent because corresponding angles are not equal.

b)

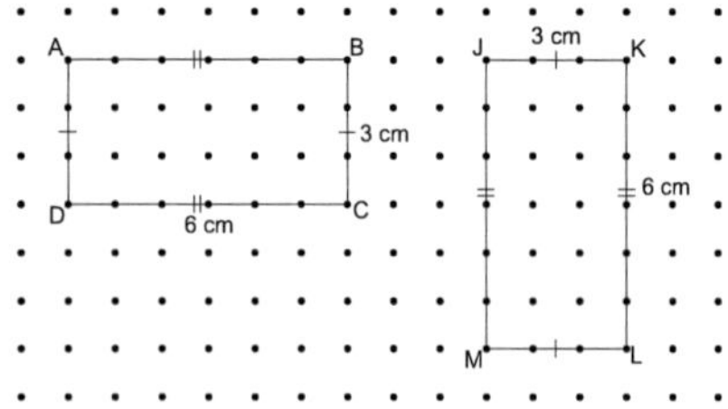

The quadrilaterals are congruent because all corresponding sides are equal and all corresponding angles are equal.

2. Are quadrilaterals ABCD and KLMN congruent? Yes
How do you know?

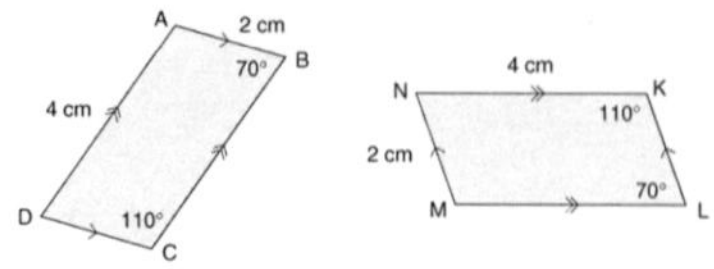

When you name congruent triangles, remember to list corresponding vertices in the same order.

3. In each figure below, name pairs of congruent triangles. Explain how you know they are congruent. Try to find more than one way to show the triangles are congruent.
a) ABCD is a kite.
b) PQRS is a parallelogram.

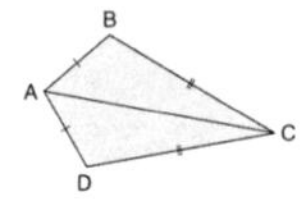

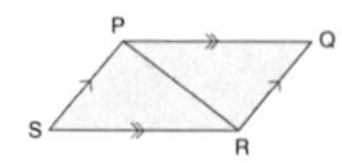

c) EFGH is a rhombus.
d) JKLM is a rectangle.

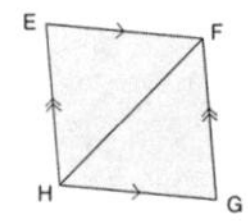

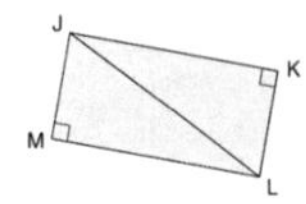

4. For each figure below:
a) Sketch the figure.
b) What are the fewest measurements you need to know to draw the figure?
c) How does your answer to part b help you identify congruent figures of this type?
i) parallelogram ii) rectangle iii) square

5. △ABC and △DEF have AB = DE = 6 cm and BC = EF = 7 cm.
a) Sketch the triangles.
b) What else do you need to know to tell if the triangles are congruent?

(Answers continue below.)
(Sample Answers, continued)

c) The quadrilaterals in part a do not have corresponding angles equal. The quadrilaterals in part b have corresponding angles equal.

7. The 4 measures represent the side lengths of a quadrilateral but the salesperson does not know its shape.

8. a) All isosceles triangles with two 50° angles are not congruent because they could have different side lengths; for example, the greater the length of the base of the triangle, the greater the length of the two equal sides.

b) When 2 angles and the side between them are given, only one triangle can be drawn. Since there is only one 10 cm side, it must be between the two angles, because the sides not between the two equal angles are equal. So, all isosceles triangles with two 50° angles and exactly one side of length 10 cm are congruent.

9. c) I drew one side, the base, of length 5 cm. I then drew a long line to represent the other short side, at right angles to the base. When I drew the hypotenuse of length 8 cm from the base to the other side, I found there was only one possible length for the other side, about 6.2 cm. Because the triangle is a right triangle, when 2 sides and 1 angle are given, only one triangle can be drawn.

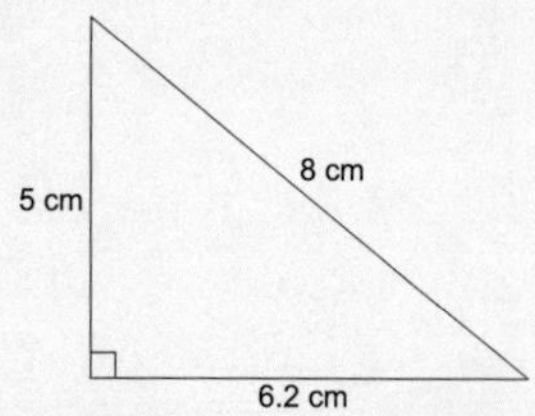

REFLECT: Two triangles are congruent when all 3 corresponding pairs of sides are equal; when 2 pairs of corresponding sides and the angles between them are equal; and when 2 pairs of corresponding angles and the sides between them are equal.

Mental Math

Which three factors of 24 have a sum of 20?

2, 6, and 12

6. **Assessment Focus** Use dot paper.

a) Draw two quadrilaterals with equal sides, but the quadrilaterals are not congruent.
Explain why the quadrilaterals are not congruent.

b) Use the 4 side lengths in part a. Draw two congruent quadrilaterals with these side lengths.
Explain how you know the quadrilaterals are congruent.

c) Explain how the quadrilaterals in parts a and b are different.

7. Alex called a carpet store. He wanted a piece of carpet to repair a damaged rug.
Alex asked for a piece measuring 3 m by 4 m by 5 m by 6 m.
Explain why the salesperson could not help Alex.

8. a) Are all isosceles triangles with two 50° angles congruent? No
Explain.

b) Are all isosceles triangles with two 50° angles and exactly one side of length 10 cm congruent? Explain. Yes

Take It Further

9. Construct a right triangle with one side 5 cm and the longest side 8 cm.

a) Can you draw two different triangles with those measurements? No

b) If your answer to part a is yes, draw the triangles.

c) If your answer to part a is no, explain how you know that only one triangle can be drawn with these measurements.

Reflect

Describe the different ways you can tell if two triangles are congruent.

7.2 Congruent Figures **259**

Mental Math

Students should recall that a factor is a number that divides exactly into another number. Students list the factors of 24, then find three factors that add to 20. The factors of 24 are: 1, 2, 3, 4, 6, 8, 12, and 24.

Assignment Guidelines

If your students do not have time to complete all the *Practice* questions on pages 257, 258, and 259, these questions provide minimum curriculum coverage: 1, 2, 3, 5, 6, 8, *Reflect*
To assess the 4 Achievement Chart categories listed in the curriculum document, have students complete these *Practice* questions:
Understanding Concepts: 3
Application: 6
Problem Solving: 8
Communication: *Reflect*

ASSESSMENT FOR LEARNING

What to Look For

Understanding concepts

✔ Students understand the conditions for the congruence of triangles and quadrilaterals.

Applying procedures

✔ Students can identify and draw pairs of congruent triangles and quadrilaterals, and explain how they know they are congruent.

Communicating

✔ Students can use mathematical language to describe the different ways to tell if two triangles are congruent.

What to Do

Extra Support: Students who have difficulty recognizing congruent figures may benefit from tracing one figure, cutting it out, then rotating or flipping the figure to see if it coincides with the other figure.
Students can use Step-by-Step 2 (Master 7.10) to complete question 6.

Extra Practice: Have students look through newspapers and magazines for example of congruent figures. Students display the pictures for others to see.
Students can complete Extra Practice 2 (Master 7.21).

Extension: Have students investigate whether all triangles with the same perimeter are congruent. (*No*) Students investigate whether two congruent triangles have the same perimeter (*Yes*) and area (*Yes*).

Recording and Reporting

Master 7.2 Ongoing Observations: Geometry

SECTION ORGANIZER

Student Materials
- square dot paper (PM 22)
- isometric dot paper (PM 23)
- rulers
- protractors
- compasses

Assessment: Masters 7.1 Unit Rubric: Geometry, 7.4 Unit Summary: Geometry

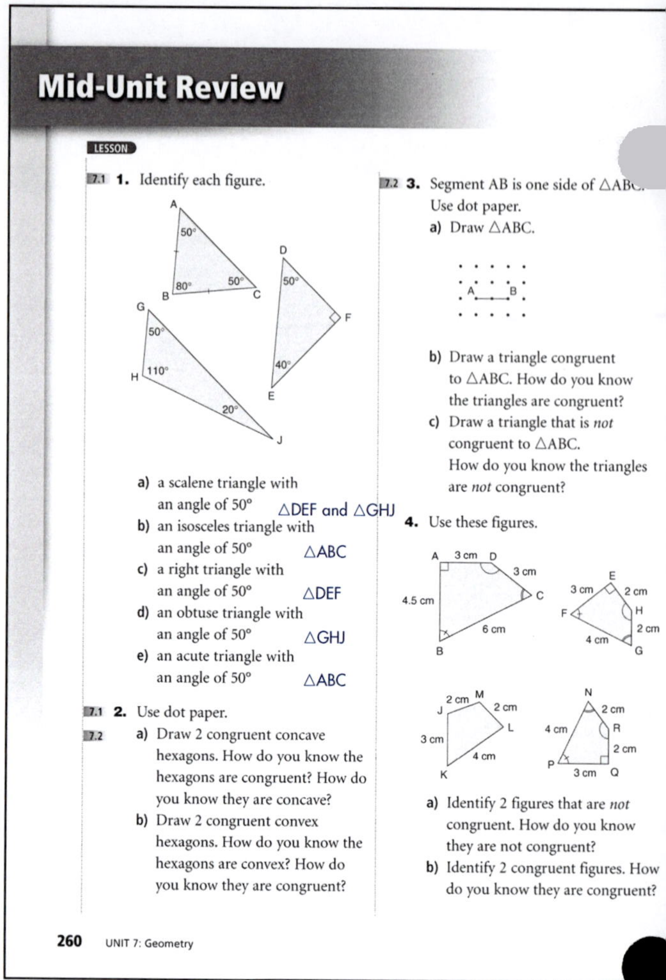

Mid-Unit Review

LESSON

7.1 **1.** Identify each figure.

a) a scalene triangle with an angle of 50° △DEF and △GHJ
b) an isosceles triangle with an angle of 50° △ABC
c) a right triangle with an angle of 50° △DEF
d) an obtuse triangle with an angle of 50° △GHJ
e) an acute triangle with an angle of 50° △ABC

7.1 7.2 **2.** Use dot paper.
a) Draw 2 congruent concave hexagons. How do you know the hexagons are congruent? How do you know they are concave?
b) Draw 2 congruent convex hexagons. How do you know the hexagons are convex? How do you know they are congruent?

7.2 **3.** Segment AB is one side of △ABC. Use dot paper.
a) Draw △ABC.
b) Draw a triangle congruent to △ABC. How do you know the triangles are congruent?
c) Draw a triangle that is *not* congruent to △ABC. How do you know the triangles are *not* congruent?

4. Use these figures.

a) Identify 2 figures that are *not* congruent. How do you know they are not congruent?
b) Identify 2 congruent figures. How do you know they are congruent?

260 UNIT 7: Geometry

Sample Solutions

2. a)

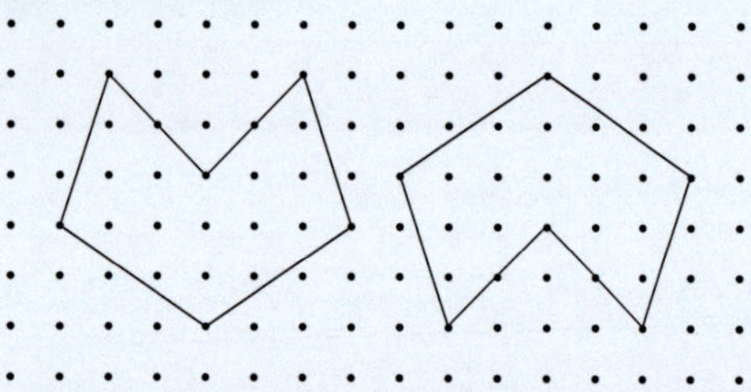

The hexagons are congruent because corresponding sides are equal and corresponding angles are equal. The hexagons are concave because each has one angle greater than 180°.

b)

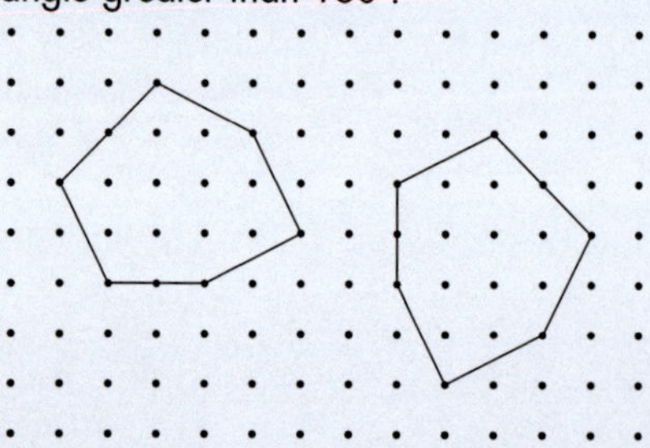

The hexagons are convex because they have all angles less than 180°. The hexagons are congruent because corresponding sides are equal and corresponding angles are equal.

3. a)

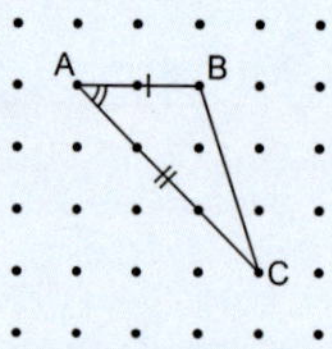

b)

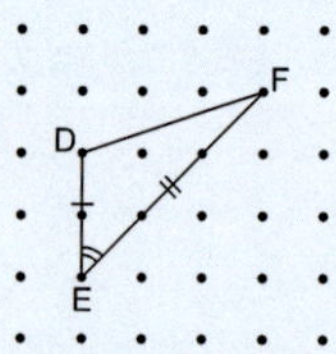

The triangles are congruent because 2 corresponding sides and the corresponding angles between them are equal.

c)

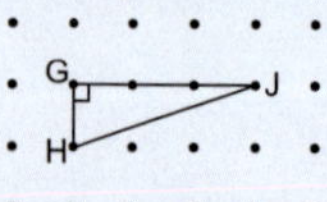

The triangles are not congruent because corresponding angles are not equal and corresponding sides are not equal.

4. a) Figure ABCD and Figure JKLM are not congruent because corresponding sides are not equal.
The figures are not the same size.
Figure ABCD and Figure EFGH are not congruent because corresponding sides are not equal.
The figures are not the same size.
Figure ABCD and Figure QPNR are not congruent because corresponding sides are not equal.
The figures are not the same size.

b) Figure EFGH and Figure QPNR are congruent because all corresponding sides are equal and all corresponding angles are equal.

7.3 Transformations

Focus Recognize transformation images.

Explore

Work with a partner.
Your teacher will give you a large copy of these figures.

Use tracing paper and a Mira if they help.

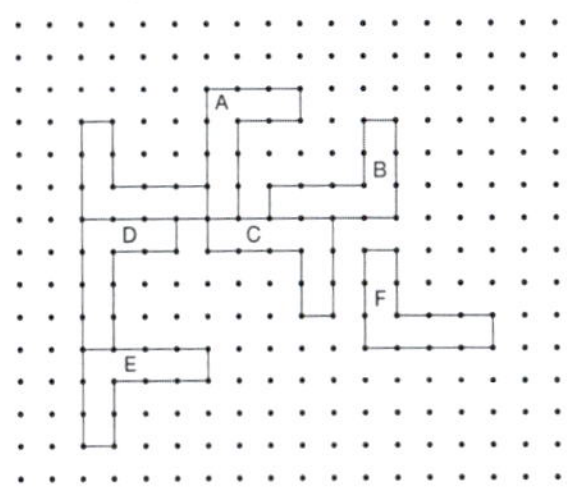

The shaded figure has been translated, rotated, and reflected.
Each labelled figure is the image after a transformation.
Identify the transformation that produced each image.
Explain how you know.

Reflect & Share

Discuss your strategies for identifying each transformation.
What is special about a reflection image? A translation image?
A rotation image?

7.3 Transformations 261

Transformations

SECTION ORGANIZER (80–100 min)

Curriculum Focus: Recognize transformation images. (7m61, 7m62, 7m65)

Student Materials
- Figures for 7.3 *Explore* (Master 7.15)
- tracing paper
- Miras
- 1-cm grid paper (PM 20)
- rulers
- Grids for *Practice* Questions 4 and 5 (Master 7.16)

Optional
- Step-by-Step 3 (Master 7.11)
- 0.5-cm grid paper (PM 14)

Vocabulary: transformation, translation, reflection, rotation

Assessment: Master 7.2 Ongoing Observations: Geometry

Key Math Learnings

1. A figure can be transformed using a translation, a reflection, and a rotation.
2. A figure and its image under a transformation are congruent.

BEFORE Get Started

Review the different types of transformations.

Ask questions, such as:
- What are the 3 types of transformations? (*Translations, reflections, and rotations*)
- What is a translation? (*A translation moves a figure along a straight line.*)
- What is a reflection? (*A reflection is a flip. The figure and its image face opposite ways and are the same distance from the mirror line.*)
- What is a rotation? (*A rotation is a turn. The figure and its image may face different ways.*)

If you have not completed *Plotting Points on a Coordinate Grid* in the *Skills You'll Need* section, on page 249 of the Student Book, this would be a good time to do so.

Present *Explore*. Distribute copies of *Figures for 7.3 Explore* (Master 7.15) to pairs of students. Have Miras and tracing paper available.

DURING Explore

Ongoing Assessment: Observe and Listen

As students work, ask questions, such as:
- Which transformation produced Image A? (*The figure was rotated 90° or a $\frac{1}{4}$ turn clockwise, or 270° or a $\frac{3}{4}$ turn counterclockwise about its lower-right vertex.*) How do you know? (*I rotated a tracing of the figure and it coincided with the image.*)
- Which transformation produced Image B? (*The figure was reflected in a vertical line midway between the figure and its image.*) How do you know? (*I placed the Mira on the mirror line. The figure and its image coincided.*) Image C? (*The figure was rotated 180° about its lower-right vertex.*) Image D? (*The figure was rotated 90° clockwise about its lower-left vertex.*) Image E? (*The figure was reflected in a horizontal line midway between the figure and its image.*) Image F? (*The figure was translated 9 units right, then 4 units down.*)

REACHING ALL LEARNERS

Early Finishers

Have students identify the transformations that take various images in *Explore* to other images; for example, Image E to Image F, or find a combination of transformations that moves any figure to any other figure.

Common Misconceptions

➤ Students do not flip a figure when they reflect it.
How to Help: Have students use a Mira to draw the reflection image.
➤ Students have difficulty identifying a rotation.
How to Help: Suggest students use tracing paper. Students should trace the figure, and rotate it as many ways as they can to see if the image can be made to coincide with the figure. Remind students to try different turn centres.

Number Strategies

Students write each pair of fractions with a common denominator before adding or subtracting.

$\frac{5}{8} + \frac{7}{6} = \frac{15}{24} + \frac{28}{24} = \frac{43}{24} = 1\frac{19}{24}$

$\frac{17}{10} - \frac{3}{4} = \frac{34}{20} - \frac{15}{20} = \frac{19}{20}$

$\frac{11}{12} - \frac{2}{3} = \frac{11}{12} - \frac{8}{12} = \frac{3}{12} = \frac{1}{4}$

$\frac{4}{5} + \frac{5}{6} = \frac{24}{30} + \frac{25}{30} = \frac{49}{30} = 1\frac{19}{30}$

Connect

We can show transformations on a grid.

Translation

The translation image and the shaded figure are congruent.

The shaded figure is translated 5 units right and 3 units up. Its translation image is figure A. The translation arrow shows the movement in a straight line.

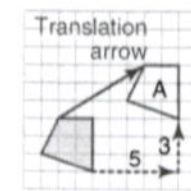

Reflection

The reflection image and the shaded figure are congruent.

The shaded figure is reflected in a horizontal line 1 unit below the figure. Its reflection image is figure B.

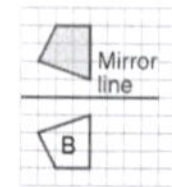

The figures have different orientations. That is, you flip one figure to make it coincide with the other figure.

Rotation

The rotation image and the shaded figure are congruent.

The shaded figure is rotated a $\frac{1}{4}$ turn clockwise. The turn centre is the vertex indicated. The rotation image is figure C.

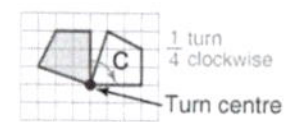

We get the same image if the shaded figure is rotated a $\frac{3}{4}$ turn counterclockwise about the turn centre.

Here are the three images and the shaded figure on the same grid.

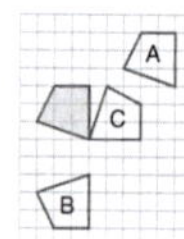

262 UNIT 7: Geometry

How do you know?
(I checked that the figures are congruent, then I counted how many squares horizontally and vertically to move a vertex on the figure to its corresponding vertex on the image.)

AFTER Connect

Have students share their strategies for identifying each transformation with the class.

Ask:

- How can you identify a translation?
(The figure and its image face the same direction, and the slide can be described with a vertical and/or horizontal motion.)
- How can you identify a reflection?
(When I see that the figure and its image face opposite ways, I know the figure was reflected. I use a Mira to find the mirror line.)
- How can you identify a rotation?
(When I see the figure and its image face different ways, but not opposite ways, I think rotation. I rotate a tracing of the figure about different turn centres until the figure and its image coincide.)
- What do all 3 transformations have in common?
(The figure and its image are always congruent.)

Review *Connect.*

Ensure students understand that a figure can be:

- Translated: horizontally
vertically
diagonally
- Reflected: in the side of a figure
in a line through a figure
in a line outside a figure
- Rotated: about a vertex
about a point on the side of a figure
about a point inside or outside a figure

We can show transformations on a coordinate grid.

Example Look at these rectangles.

Is one rectangle a transformation image of the other? Explain.

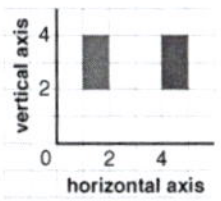

Solution Let the blue rectangle be the original figure. And let the red rectangle be the image.

Solution 1 The red rectangle is the image after a translation of 3 units right. The translation arrow shows the movement.

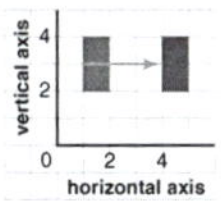

Solution 2 The red rectangle is the image after a reflection in a vertical line through (3, 0) on the horizontal axis.

Use a Mira to verify the image.

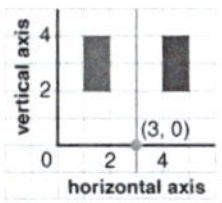

Solution 3 The red rectangle is the image after a rotation of a $\frac{1}{2}$ turn about the point with coordinates (3, 3).

Use tracing paper to verify the image.

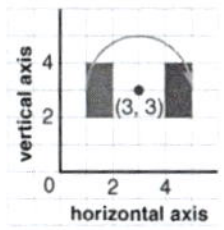

The *Example* shows that an image may be the result of any one of the 3 transformations.
It also shows a rotation about a turn centre that is not on the figure.

Sample Answers

1. a) Figure A is translated 3 units right and 3 units up.
   b) Figure A is rotated a $\frac{1}{2}$ turn about the common vertex.
   c) Figure B is reflected in a vertical line one unit to the right of the figure.
   d) Figure D is translated 4 units left and 2 units up.
   e) Figure D is rotated a $\frac{1}{2}$ turn about the common vertex.
2. a) Figure B is rotated a $\frac{1}{4}$ turn counterclockwise, or a $\frac{3}{4}$ turn clockwise, about the common vertex.
   b) Figure C is translated 2 units up.
   c) Figure D is rotated a $\frac{1}{4}$ turn counterclockwise, or a $\frac{3}{4}$ turn clockwise, about the common vertex.
   d) Figure A is rotated a $\frac{1}{2}$ turn about the turn centre, the midpoint of the common side.
3. a) to d) e) and f)

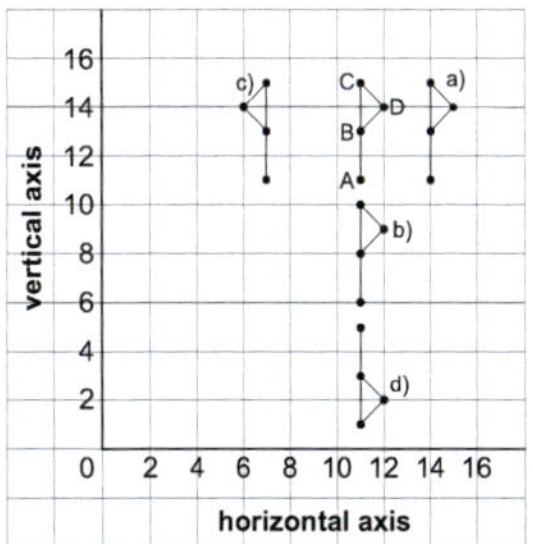

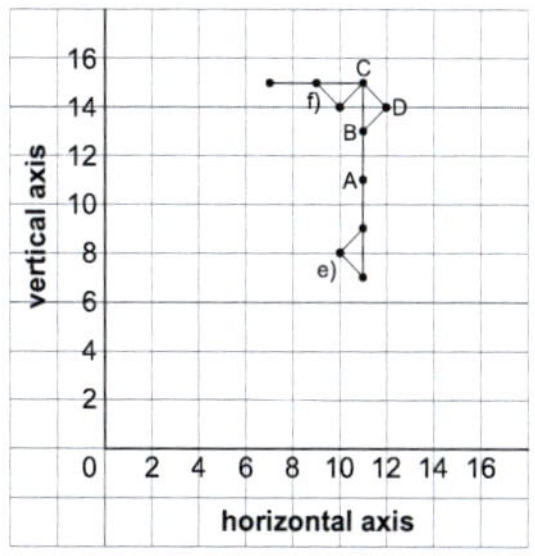

4. Each figure can be described as a transformation of another figure in 3 different ways. For example, Figure A is rotated a $\frac{1}{4}$ turn clockwise about the turn centre (4.5, 5.5) to get Figure B. Figure A is rotated a $\frac{1}{2}$ turn about the turn centre (5, 5.5) to get Figure C. Figure A is rotated a $\frac{1}{4}$ turn counterclockwise about

Review the *Example*. Ensure students understand that translation arrows, mirror lines, and turn centres should be labelled when identifying transformations.

Ensure students are comfortable drawing transformation images. Encourage students who are having difficulty to transform each vertex of a figure, then join the points to create the image.

Show students that a rotation of 180°, or a $\frac{1}{2}$ turn, can also be described as a reflection. To find the mirror line, fold a tracing of the figure and its image until the two figures coincide. Make a crease along this fold. The crease represents the mirror line.

Remind students that they do not need to give a direction when the rotation is a $\frac{1}{2}$ turn. A $\frac{1}{2}$ turn counterclockwise and a $\frac{1}{2}$ turn clockwise represent the same rotation.

To find a turn centre that is not on a figure, students may have to use tracing paper, along with the guess and check strategy.

Practice

Have Miras and tracing paper available for all questions. Questions 3 and 6 require 1-cm grid paper (PM 20). In questions 1 and 2, have students identify and describe each transformation. Questions 4 and 5 require *Grids for Practice Questions 4 and 5* (Master 7.16).

the turn centre (5, 6) to get Figure D. Figure B is rotated a $\frac{1}{4}$ turn clockwise about the turn centre (5, 5) to get Figure C. Figure B is reflected in the vertical line through (5, 5) to get Figure D. Figure C is rotated a $\frac{1}{4}$ turn clockwise about the turn centre (5, 5.5) to get Figure D.

5. a) Figures A and B are not related by a translation because they have different orientations. Try a rotation; Figures A and B are not related by a rotation because there is no turn centre for which A coincides with B after a rotation. Figures E and F are not related by a translation because they have different orientations. It takes 2 transformations to move Figure E to Figure F (a reflection and a translation).
   b) Figure C is rotated a $\frac{1}{4}$ turn clockwise about the turn centre (7, 2) to get Figure D.
   Figure E is reflected in the vertical line through (16, 0), then translated 1 unit up to get Figure F.

6. a)

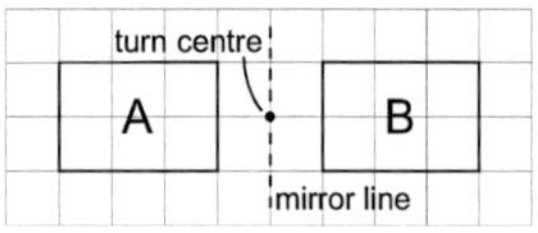

The figure is a rectangle with 2 lines of symmetry.
Figure A is reflected in a vertical line 1 unit to the right.
Figure A is translated 5 units right.
Figure A is rotated a $\frac{1}{2}$ turn about the turn centre marked.

   b)

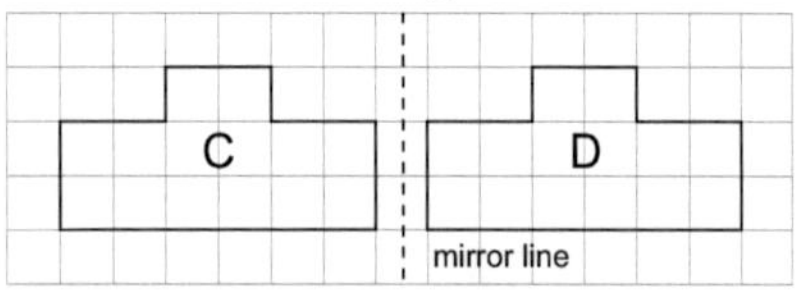

The figure is an irregular octagon with 1 line of symmetry.
Figure C is reflected in a vertical line $\frac{1}{2}$ unit to the right.
Figure C is translated 7 units right.

Practice

1. Use the figures below.

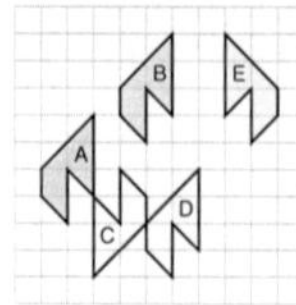

Identify the transformation for which:
a) Figure B is the image of Figure A.
b) Figure C is the image of Figure A.
c) Figure E is the image of Figure B.
d) Figure A is the image of Figure D.
e) Figure C is the image of Figure D.

Number Strategies

Add or subtract, as indicated.
- $\frac{5}{8} + \frac{7}{6} = 1\frac{19}{24}$
- $\frac{17}{10} - \frac{3}{4} = \frac{19}{20}$
- $\frac{11}{12} - \frac{2}{3} = \frac{1}{4}$
- $\frac{4}{5} + \frac{5}{6} = 1\frac{19}{30}$

2. Identify each transformation.

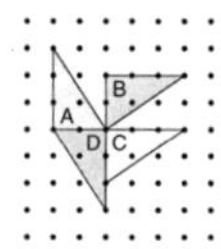

a) Figure A is the image of Figure B.
b) Figure B is the image of Figure C.
c) Figure C is the image of Figure D.
d) Figure D is the image of Figure A.

3. Draw this flag on a coordinate grid. The coordinates are A(11, 11), B(11, 13), C(11, 15), and D(12, 14).

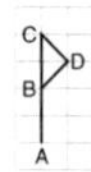

Draw the image of the flag after each transformation.
a) a translation 3 units right
b) a translation 5 units down
c) a reflection in a vertical line through (9, 0)
d) a reflection in a horizontal line through (0, 8)
e) a rotation of a $\frac{1}{2}$ turn about point A
f) a rotation of a $\frac{1}{4}$ turn clockwise about point C

264 UNIT 7: Geometry

Assessment Focus: Question 6

Students may draw figures on grid paper for which they know names, such as a square or a parallelogram. Other students may draw more general figures, such as irregular quadrilaterals. Some students may realize that a figure for part a will have 2 or more lines of symmetry and rotational symmetry, a figure for part b will have 1 line of symmetry and rotational symmetry, and a figure for part c will have no lines of symmetry and no rotational symmetry. Ensure students understand that the image drawn must always be a translation image.

REFLECT: For a translation, the figure and its image face the same way. The figure is moved along a straight line.

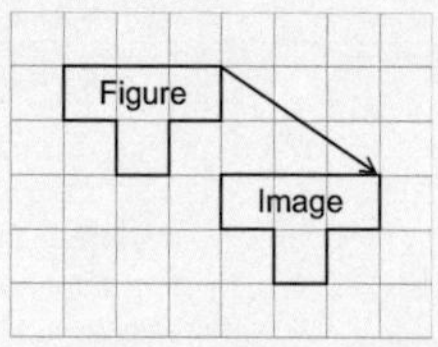

For a reflection, the figure and its image face opposite ways. The figure has been flipped.

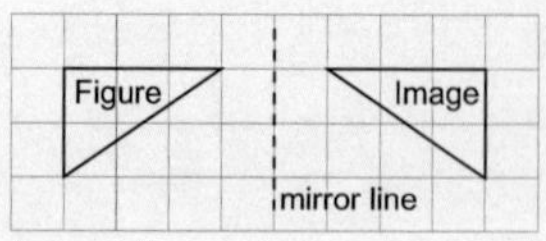

For a rotation, the figure and its image may face different ways. The figure has been turned.

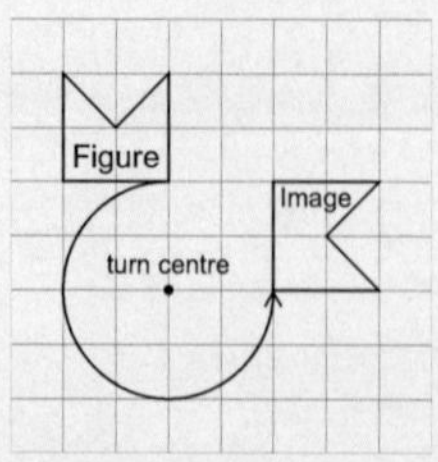

In all transformations, the figure and its image are congruent.

4. How many different ways can each figure be described as a transformation of another figure? Explain.

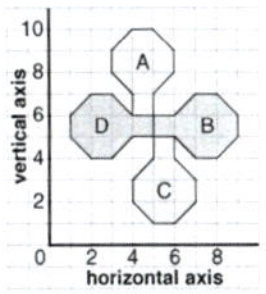

5. a) Which pairs of congruent figures do *not* represent a figure and its transformation image? How do you know?

Figures A and B,
Figures E and F

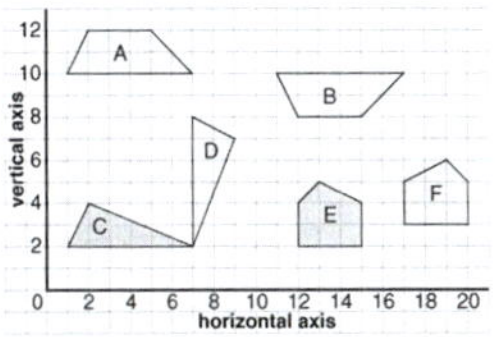

b) For each pair of congruent figures that do show a transformation, identify the transformation.

6. **Assessment Focus** Use grid paper.
In each case, describe the figure you drew.
a) Draw a figure for which a translation image is also a reflection image and a rotation image. Draw the translation image.
b) Draw a figure for which a translation image is also a reflection image, but *not* a rotation image. Draw the translation image.
c) Draw a figure for which a translation image is *not* a reflection image *nor* a rotation image. Draw the translation image.

Take It Further

7. Describe Figure A as a transformation image of Figure B as many different ways as possible.

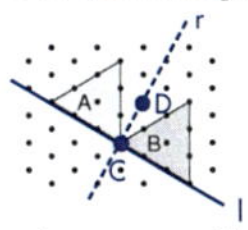

Reflect

When you see a figure and its transformation image on a grid, how do you identify the transformation?
Use diagrams in your explanation.

7.3 Transformations 265

c)

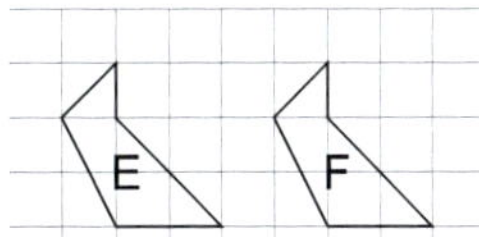

The figure is an irregular pentagon with no line of symmetry.
Figure E is translated 4 units right.

7. Figure B is translated diagonally 3 units along line *l* to get Figure A. Figure B is rotated 120° counterclockwise about the common vertex (Point C) to get Figure A. Figure B is reflected in a diagonal line through the common vertex (Line *r*) to get Figure A. Figure B is rotated 240° clockwise or 120° counterclockwise about Point D to get Figure A.

Assignment Guidelines

If your students do not have time to complete all the *Practice* questions on pages 264 and 265, these questions provide minimum curriculum coverage: 1, 3, 4, 6, *Reflect*
To assess the 4 Achievement Chart categories listed in the curriculum document, have students complete these *Practice* questions:
Understanding Concepts: 1
Application: 3
Problem Solving: 6
Communication: *Reflect*

ASSESSMENT FOR LEARNING

What to Look For

Understanding concepts

✔ Students understand that a figure and its image under a transformation are congruent.

Applying procedures

✔ Students can identify and describe different transformations.
✔ Students can draw the image of a figure under a transformation.

Communicating

✔ Students can use mathematical language to describe a transformation.

What to Do

Extra Support: Students who have difficulty with transformations may benefit from working with one transformation at a time. For example, have students draw a figure on dot paper. Students trace the figure, then rotate the tracing by a $\frac{1}{4}$ turn, a $\frac{1}{2}$ turn, and a $\frac{3}{4}$ turn, clockwise and counterclockwise, about different vertices.
When students become comfortable with rotations, they can work with translations, then reflections.
Students can use Step-by-Step 3 (Master 7.11) to complete question 6.

Extra Practice: One student draws a figure on grid paper, then gives his partner a transformation. He challenges his partner to draw the transformation image. Students switch roles.
Students can complete Extra Practice 3 (Master 7.22).

Recording and Reporting
Master 7.2 Ongoing Observations: Geometry

Tiling Patterns

SECTION ORGANIZER — 80–100 min

Curriculum Focus: Construct and analyse tiling patterns. (7m63, 7m64)

Student Materials
- index cards
- rulers
- scissors
- tracing paper
- square dot paper (PM 22)
- isometric dot paper (PM 23)
- 1-cm grid paper (PM 20)

Optional
- Step-by-Step 4 (Master 7.12)
- Extra Practice 4 (Master 7.23)

Vocabulary: tiling the plane

Assessment: Master 7.2 Ongoing Observations: Geometry

Key Math Learnings

1. A figure tiles the plane if congruent copies of the figure cover a page and leave no gaps.
2. A triangle and a quadrilateral always tile the plane.

7.4 Tiling Patterns

Focus Construct and analyse tiling patterns.

Explore

Work on your own.
You will need index cards, a ruler, and scissors.

> Draw a triangle on a card. Cut it out.
Use tracings of the triangle to cover a piece of paper.

> Draw a quadrilateral on a card. Cut it out.
Use tracings of the quadrilateral to cover a piece of paper.

> Draw a pentagon on a card. Cut it out.
Use tracings of the pentagon to cover a piece of paper.

You can rotate or flip the figure to try to make it fit.

Reflect & Share

Share your results with the class.
- Will congruent triangles cover a page and leave no gaps? Explain. Yes
- Will congruent quadrilaterals cover a page and leave no gaps? Explain. Yes
- Will congruent pentagons cover a page and leave no gaps? Explain. Not always

How can you tell if congruent figures will cover a page and leave no gaps?

Connect

When congruent copies of a figure cover a page and leave no gaps, we say the figure **tiles the plane.**

> A triangle always tiles the plane.

At any point where vertices meet, the angles add to 360°.

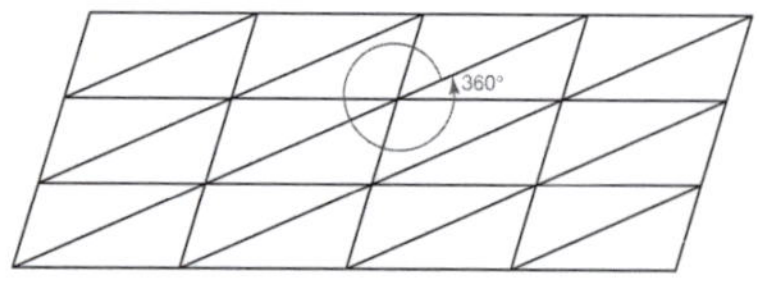

266 UNIT 7: Geometry

BEFORE — Get Started

Discuss where students have seen tiling in their environment.

Ask questions, such as:
- Where have you seen tiling patterns? (*On brick walls, floors, counters, checkerboards, and on interlocking driveways*)
- Which figures do you know that tile a surface? (*A square and a rectangle*)
- What do we mean when we say that a figure tiles a surface? (*We mean that the figure covers a surface with no gaps or overlaps.*)

Present *Explore*. Encourage students to use non-symmetrical triangles, quadrilaterals, and pentagons. Distribute index cards and tracing paper.

DURING — Explore

Ongoing Assessment: Observe and Listen

As students work, ask questions, such as:
- Did congruent copies of your triangle cover a page and leave no gaps? (*Yes*) Explain. (*I was able to flip, translate, and rotate my triangle so that it covered the page with no gaps.*) Describe your triangle. (*My triangle is an obtuse scalene triangle, with no angles equal.*)
- Did anyone find a triangle that did not tile the page? (*No*)
- Did congruent copies of your quadrilateral cover a page and leave no gaps? (*Yes*) Explain. (*I was able to reflect, translate, and rotate my quadrilateral so that it covered the page and left no gaps.*) Describe your quadrilateral. (*My quadrilateral has 2 sides equal, 2 right angles, 1 obtuse angle, and 1 acute angle.*)
- Did anyone find a quadrilateral that did not tile the page? (*No*)

➢ A quadrilateral always tiles the plane.

y point where
ices meet, the
angles add to 360°.

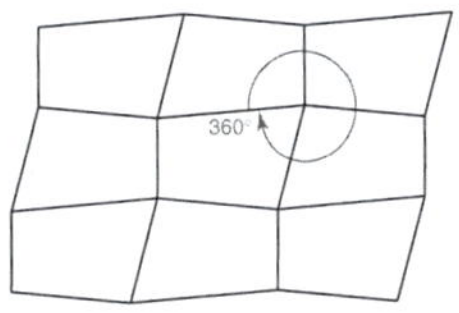

Example Will a pentagon always tile the plane? Explain.

Solution If we can find a pentagon that does *not* tile the plane, we can say that a pentagon does not always tile the plane.
Draw a regular pentagon.
Use tracing paper to repeat the pentagon to try to cover the page.

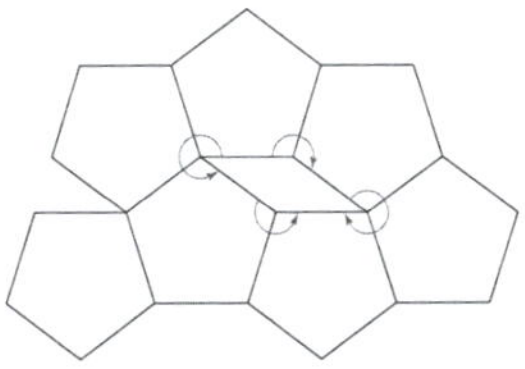

This pentagon does not cover the page.
It leaves gaps that are rhombuses.
Five vertices do not meet.
There are points where 3 vertices meet and the sum of the angles is less than 360°.
There are points where 2 vertices meet and the sum of the angles is less than 360°.
So, a pentagon does not always tile the plane.

In the *Practice* questions, you will investigate to find which other figures *do* tile the plane.

7.4 Tiling Patterns 267

REACHING ALL LEARNERS

Alternative Explore

Students may find it easier to use plastic figures, such as Paver Polygons, instead of figures on card.

Early Finishers

Have students identify the figures that "fill in the gaps" between congruent copies of a figure that does not tile the plane.

Common Misconceptions

➤ Students think that a regular pentagon tiles the plane because all the gaps can be filled with congruent rhombuses.

How to Help: Remind students that a figure tiles a plane only if congruent copies of that figure can cover a page and leave no gaps. Ensure students understand they are to work with one figure at a time, and they cannot add other figures to make the tiling work.

Calculator Skills

Students should realize that the TI-15 calculator follows the order of operations: brackets first, then division and multiplication, then addition and subtraction.
For 23.56 + 27.39 × 4.35, the calculator performs the multiplication first, then the addition.
For (23.56 + 27.39) × 4.35, the calculator performs the addition inside the brackets first, then the multiplication.

- Did congruent copies of your pentagon cover a page and leave no gaps? (*Yes*) Explain. (*I was able to reflect, translate, and rotate my pentagon so that it covered the page and left no gaps.*) Describe your pentagon. (*My pentagon is an irregular pentagon, with 3 sides equal and another pair of equal sides, 2 right angles, and 3 angles of 120°.*)
- Did anyone find a pentagon that did not tile the page? (*Yes*) Describe your pentagon. (*My pentagon is a regular pentagon, with all sides equal and all angles equal.*)
- What can we say about all triangles and quadrilaterals? (*All triangles and quadrilaterals tile a surface.*)
- What can we say about pentagons? (*Not all pentagons tile a surface.*)

AFTER Connect

Have volunteers use the overhead projector to show how their triangles, quadrilaterals, and pentagons were used to cover the page. Invite volunteers to show how their pentagons could not tile the page.

Use *Connect* to introduce **tiling the plane.** Use the *Example* to show how we can use the sum of the angles at a vertex to explain why pentagons do not always tile the plane.

Sample Answers

1. Yes, the convex hexagon does tile the plane. It covers a page and leaves no gaps. Where any three vertices meet, the sum of the angles is 360°.

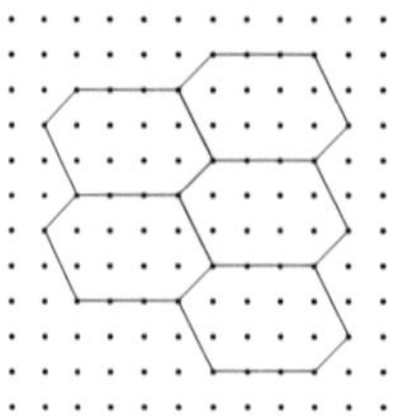

2. Yes, the concave hexagon does tile the plane. It covers a page and leaves no gaps. Where any four vertices meet, the sum of the angles is 360°.

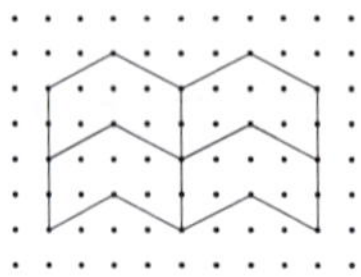

3. A regular octagon does not tile the plane. It leaves gaps that are squares. Where 2 vertices meet, the sum of the angles is less than 360°; the sum is 270°.

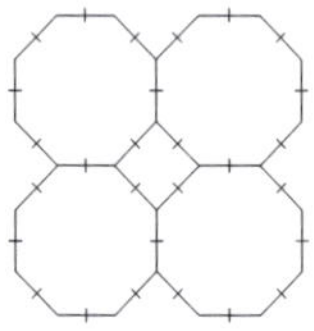

4. Escher started with a regular hexagon. Three vertices meet at each point and the sum of the angles is 360°. The hexagon covers the plane and there are no gaps. The reptiles are drawn symmetrically and each reptile covers parts of several hexagons. There are 3 types of reptiles: heads point down and to the left; heads point up and to the left; and heads point right. Each group of 3 heads has a common vertex and the angle on each head at the vertex is 120°.

(Answers continue below.)

Practice

1. Use dot paper.
   Draw a convex hexagon that is not regular.
   Try to cover the dot paper with copies of this hexagon.
   Does the hexagon tile the plane? Explain.
2. Use dot paper.
   Draw a concave hexagon.
   Try to cover the dot paper with copies of this hexagon.
   Does the hexagon tile the plane? Explain.
3. Here is a regular octagon.

   Trace this octagon.
   Try to tile the plane.
   What do you notice?
4. Look at the picture called *Reptiles*, drawn by M.C. Escher.

   Which figure do you think Escher started with?
   Explain how Escher's reptiles tile the plane.

268 UNIT 7: Geometry

Practice

Have square dot paper (PM 22) and isometric dot paper (PM 23) available for questions 1, 2, 3, and 5. Have 1-cm grid paper available for questions 7 and 8. Have tracing paper available for questions 1, 2, 3, 5, 7, and 8. For questions 1 and 2, some students may draw a hexagon that tiles the plane while other students may not. Discuss the different hexagons drawn and explain why some hexagons tiled the plane and others did not.

Assessment Focus: Question 7

Students draw different pentagons until they find a pentagon that tiles the plane. Students should recall that for a pentagon to tile the plane, the sum of the angles where vertices meet must be 360°. Students answer should include drawings as well as explanations as to why each pentagon did or did not tile the plane.

(Sample Answers, continued)

5. The floor can be tiled with the regular hexagon without any gaps. However, a full tile will not cover parts of the edges of the floor. Tiles will have to be cut to fit. The part tiles are isosceles trapezoids, or isosceles triangles.

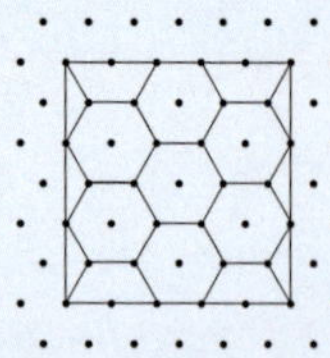

6. Squares and rectangles are used in most tiling patterns in floors and patios because they can be arranged in many different ways without creating gaps, and they will tile to fit a square or rectangular surface without being cut. Where rectangles and squares meet, there are 4 vertices, and each angle is 90°. So, the sum of the angles is always $4 \times 90° = 360°$.

(Answers continue on page 27.)

Calculator Skills

... + 27.39 × 4.35 = 142.7065
- (23.56 + 27.39) × 4.35 = 221.6325

Why are the answers different?

5. A floor tile is a regular hexagon.
What happens when you try to tile a rectangular floor with a regular hexagon?
Use isometric dot paper to find out.

6. Why do most tiling patterns in floors and patios use squares or rectangles?

7. Assessment Focus
Not all pentagons tile the plane. Use grid paper.
a) Find a pentagon that will tile the plane.
Describe the pentagon.
Explain how it tiles the plane.
b) How many different pentagons can you find that will tile the plane? Draw each pentagon and show how it tiles the plane.
c) Explain why some pentagons tile the plane, while others do not.

8. In question 3, you discovered that a regular octagon will not tile the plane.
Use grid paper. Find an octagon that will tile the plane.
Explain how it tiles the plane.

Take It Further

9. Think about "tiling" in nature. Which figures are used?

Reflect

How can you tell if a polygon will tile the plane?
Use examples in your explanation.

(Sample Answers, continued)

7. a) This pentagon tiles the plane. The pentagons are placed beside each other to form a row, then the row is reflected in a horizontal line through the lowest vertex. The reflected row is then translated 1 square right and 1 square up.

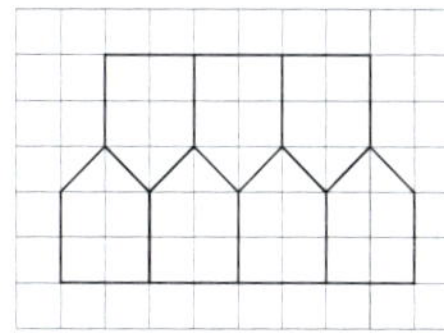

b) There are many different pentagons that will tile the plane; for example,

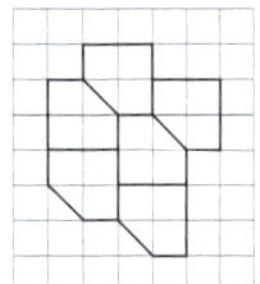

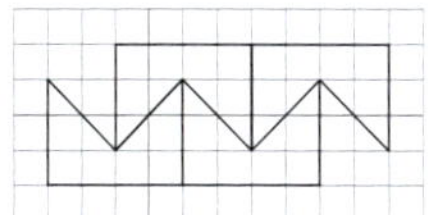

c) Pentagons that tile the plane have vertices that meet at points where the sum of the angles is 360°. A regular pentagon has 5 equal angles and each angle is 108°. Since 108 does not divide exactly into 360, I know that a regular pentagon will not tile the plane. There will be gaps.

(Answers continue on page 34.)

Assignment Guidelines

If your students do not have time to complete all the *Practice* questions on pages 268 and 269, these questions provide minimum curriculum coverage: 1, 3, 5, 7, 8, *Reflect*
To assess the 4 Achievement Chart categories listed, have students complete these *Practice* questions:
Understanding Concepts: 1; Application: 5;
Problem Solving: 7; Communication: *Reflect*

ASSESSMENT FOR LEARNING

What to Look For	What to Do
Understanding concepts ✔ Students understand that a figure tiles the plane if congruent copies of the figure cover a page and leave no gaps. ✔ Students understand that a triangle and a quadrilateral always tile the plane. ***Applying procedures*** ✔ Students can draw different polygons that tile the plane, and explain how each polygon tiles the plane. ***Communicating*** ✔ Students can describe how to tell if a polygon will tile the plane.	***Extra Support:*** Students may have difficulty tiling a plane with a triangle. Show them how to reflect or flip the triangle (that is, turn it over) and/or rotate it. Students can use Step-by-Step 4 (Master 7.12) to complete question 7. ***Extra Practice:*** Students draw tessellations using other figures, such as trapezoids, right scalene triangles, or kites. Students can complete Extra Practice 4 (Master 7.23). ***Extension:*** Students investigate tiling the plane with concave figures, such as quadrilaterals and pentagons, or with heptagons (7-sided figures) or nonagons (9-sided figures) drawn on grid paper.

Recording and Reporting
Master 7.2 Ongoing Observations: Geometry

Using Transformations to Make Designs

SECTION ORGANIZER

80–100 min

Curriculum Focus: Create and analyse designs using transformations. (7m62, 7m65)

Student Materials
- isometric dot paper (PM 23)
- Pattern Blocks (PM 25)
- rulers
- 1-cm grid paper (PM 20)
- square dot paper (PM 22)
- Flooring Pattern (Master 7.17)
- coloured pencils or markers

Optional
- Step-by-Step 5 (Master 7.13)
- Extra Practice 5 (Master 7.24)

Assessment: Master 7.2 Ongoing Observations: Geometry

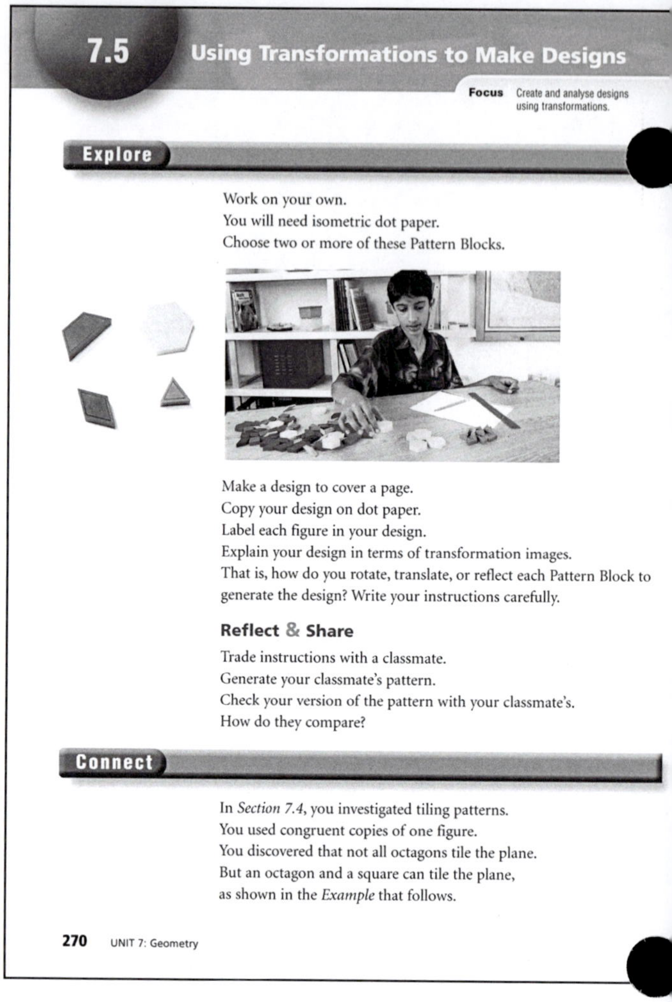

7.5 Using Transformations to Make Designs

Focus Create and analyse designs using transformations.

Explore

Work on your own.
You will need isometric dot paper.
Choose two or more of these Pattern Blocks.

Make a design to cover a page.
Copy your design on dot paper.
Label each figure in your design.
Explain your design in terms of transformation images.
That is, how do you rotate, translate, or reflect each Pattern Block to generate the design? Write your instructions carefully.

Reflect & Share

Trade instructions with a classmate.
Generate your classmate's pattern.
Check your version of the pattern with your classmate's.
How do they compare?

Connect

In *Section 7.4*, you investigated tiling patterns.
You used congruent copies of one figure.
You discovered that not all octagons tile the plane.
But an octagon and a square can tile the plane, as shown in the *Example* that follows.

270 UNIT 7: Geometry

Key Math Learning

Transformations can be used to create and describe tiling patterns.

BEFORE Get Started

Students may not have used Pattern Blocks for some time. Review the Pattern Blocks with students. Ask questions, such as:

- Which Pattern Block has 6 lines of symmetry and rotational symmetry of order 6? (*The yellow hexagon*)
- Which Pattern Blocks have 2 lines of symmetry and rotational symmetry of order 2? (*The blue rhombus and the tan rhombus*)
- Which Pattern Blocks have a translation image that is also a reflection image and a rotation image? (*The yellow hexagon, the orange square, the green triangle, the blue rhombus, and the tan rhombus*) Why? (*All of them have 2 or more lines of symmetry and rotational symmetry.*)
- Which Pattern Block has a translation image that is also a reflection image, but not a rotation image? (*The red trapezoid*) Why? (*It has only 1 line of symmetry and no rotational symmetry.*)

Present *Explore*. Distribute isometric dot paper (PM 23) and Pattern Blocks. It is possible that students could make a design that covers the plane but does not repeat. Ensure students understand that the pattern should be a repeating pattern. Students who have difficulty may benefit from taping their two or more blocks together to make a single tile, then using the tile to tile the plane. Encourage students to use tiles that form an irregular figure.

Example

Use transformations to describe how to construct this design.

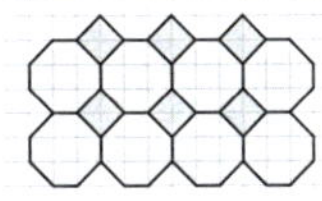

Solution

Label the figures in the design, as shown.

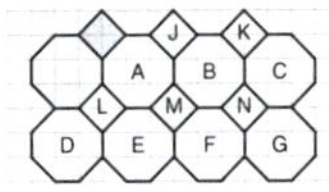

Start with the shaded octagon.

Step 1 To get octagon A, rotate the shaded octagon a $\frac{1}{2}$ turn about a turn centre that is at the midpoint of the right side.

Repeat a similar rotation to get figure B from figure A.

Step 2 To get octagon D, rotate the shaded octagon a $\frac{1}{2}$ turn about a turn centre that is at the midpoint of the bottom side.

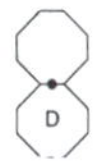

Repeat a similar rotation to get octagon E from octagon A.

Look at the shaded square.

Step 3 To get square J, rotate the shaded square a $\frac{1}{2}$ turn about the midpoint of the top side of octagon A.

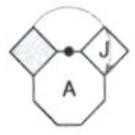

Repeat a similar rotation to get square K from square J.

REACHING ALL LEARNERS

Early Finishers

Students look for designs created by transformations, such as designs on wallpaper, then describe the transformations used to create the designs.

Common Misconceptions

➤ Students have difficulty visualizing or drawing the rotation or reflection image of a figure.

How to Help: Encourage students to use tracing paper and Miras, with manipulatives, so they can physically rotate or reflect the figure.

➤ Students create a design that does not have a repeating pattern.

How to Help: Remind students that tiling patterns must repeat. Show students examples of tilings, such as quilting patterns or Escher designs, and point out how each tiling pattern repeats.

Number Strategies

Students should recall that sum indicates addition and product indicates multiplication. Students list all the factors of 30, then find their sum: 1 + 2 + 3 + 5 + 6 + 10 + 15 + 30 = 72. Students list all the factors of 46, then find their sum: 1 + 2 + 23 + 46 = 72. Students list all the factors of 67, then find their product: 1 × 67 = 67. Students find the least number.

DURING Explore

Ongoing Assessment: Observe and Listen

Ask questions, such as:

- Which Pattern Blocks did you choose?
  (I chose the green triangle and the red trapezoid.)
- How did you label each figure in your design?
  (I labelled each figure with a different letter, and coloured the original figures their corresponding colours.)
- How can you explain your design in terms of transformation images?
  (To get trapezoid A, reflect the red trapezoid in a vertical line through its upper-right vertex. To get triangle F, translate the green triangle 5 units right. To get triangle G, translate the green triangle 10 units right. Reflect the first row in a horizontal line through the bottom side of each figure to get the second row. Continue to reflect each resulting row in the same way.)

AFTER Connect

Invite students to share their design with the class. Students could use overhead Pattern Blocks to model their design, then explain their design in terms of transformation images.

What you might see:

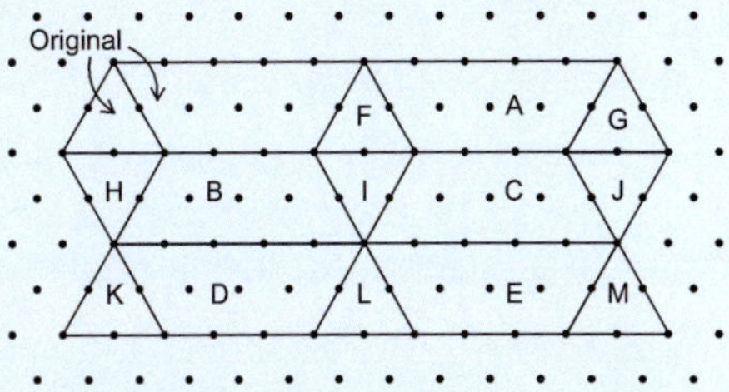

Ask:

- How did your classmate's version of your pattern compare with your own pattern?
  (They were the same.)
- If the patterns were not the same, what might have happened?
  (Either I did not write the instructions correctly, or my classmate made an error when following my instructions.)

Sample Answers

1. a) The letters are those used in the Solution on page 271. Translate the original octagon 3 units right to get octagon A, and 3 units down to get octagon D. Translate octagon A 3 units right to get octagon B, and 3 units down to get octagon E. Translate octagon B 3 units right to get octagon C, and 3 units down to get octagon F. Translate octagon C 3 units down to get octagon G. Translate the original square 3 units right to get square J, and 3 units down to get square L. Translate square J 3 units right to get square K, and 3 units down to get square M. Translate square K 3 units down to get square N.

   b) Reflect the original octagon in the vertical line through the side common to this octagon and octagon A to get octagon A. Repeat with octagon A to get octagon B, and with octagon B to get octagon C. Reflect the original octagon in the horizontal line through the side common to this octagon and octagon D to get octagon D. Repeat with octagon A to get octagon E, octagon B to get octagon F, and octagon C to get octagon G. Reflect the original square in a vertical line through the midpoint of the top side of octagon A to get square J. Repeat with square J to get square K. Reflect the original square in a horizontal line through the midpoint of the left side of octagon A to get square L. Repeat with square J to get square M, and with square K to get square N.

2. Rotate the figure a $\frac{1}{4}$ turn clockwise about point A to get Figure B. Rotate Figure B a $\frac{1}{4}$ turn clockwise about point A to get figure C. Rotate Figure C a $\frac{1}{4}$ turn clockwise about point A to get figure D.

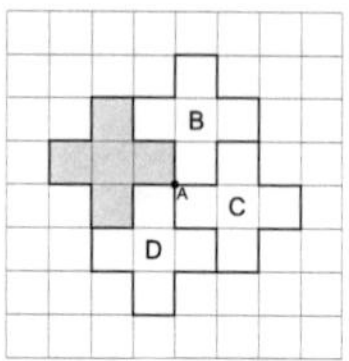

Step 4 To get square L, rotate the shaded square a $\frac{1}{2}$ turn about the midpoint of the left side of octagon A.

Repeat a similar rotation to get square M from square J.

Practice

1. Here is the design from the *Example*.

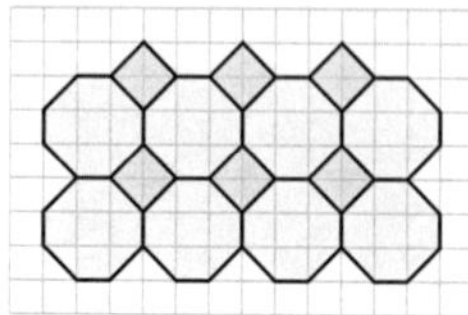

a) Use translations to describe how to construct this design.
b) Use reflections to describe how to construct this design.

2. Use this figure and transformations to create a design on grid paper.

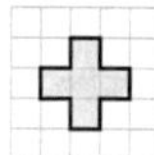

Describe the design in terms of transformations.

3. Use isometric paper. Use a parallelogram and an equilateral triangle to make a design. Use transformations to describe the design.

4. Draw a figure. Use transformations of the figure to make a border design for a photo frame. Draw the design. Describe how you made it.

Number Strategies

Which number is the least?
- the sum of all the factors of 30 = 72
- the sum of all the factors of 46 = 72
- the product of all the factors of 67 = 67

The least number is 67.

- Could some of the instructions have been written differently?
  (*Yes, the triangle could have been reflected in a vertical line, the line of symmetry of the red trapezoid, instead of being translated 5 units right. The trapezoid could have been rotated a $\frac{1}{2}$ turn about the midpoint of its lowest side. The image would be the same.*)

Review the *Example* in *Connect*. Have volunteers describe how to get from one figure in the given design to another; for example, have a volunteer explain how to get from square N to square L using a reflection.

Ensure students understand that a pattern may often be described using more than one set of repeated transformations.

Ensure students understand the importance of labelling the figures in a design to make it easier to explain how transformations were used to create the pattern.

Practice

Students require: 1-cm grid paper (PM 20) for questions 2 and 6; isometric dot paper for question 3; square dot paper (PM 22) for questions 5 and 6; coloured pencils or markers for question 6; and *Flooring Pattern* (Master 7.17) for question 7.

Assessment Focus: Question 6

Some students will use regular figures to create simple designs. Stronger math students may use 2 or more irregular figures to create more complex designs. The design should contain a repeating pattern and there should be no gaps. Some students may benefit from using Pattern Blocks, or tracing paper and cardboard figures. A level 4 response will include more than one description of the same design.

5. The Alhambra is a walled city and fortress in Granada, Spain. It was built in the 14th century. Here is part of one of its many tiling patterns.

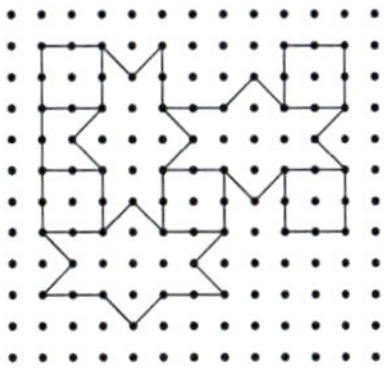

Copy this pattern on dot paper.
Continue the pattern to cover the page.
Use transformations to describe the pattern.

6. **Assessment Focus**
Use dot paper or grid paper.
Create a design that uses 2 or more figures that together tile the plane.
Colour your design.
Use transformations to describe your design.
Try to describe your design as many ways as you can.

7. Here is a flooring pattern.

Use a copy of this pattern.
Use transformations to describe the patterns in one square.

Reflect

When you use transformations to describe a design, how do you decide which transformation to use?
Include a design in your explanation.

3. To get parallelogram B, reflect parallelogram A in a vertical line through its top right vertex. To get triangle F, rotate triangle B a $\frac{1}{2}$ turn about turn centre *t*. To get the second row, reflect the first row in a horizontal line through the bottom sides of parallelograms A and B.

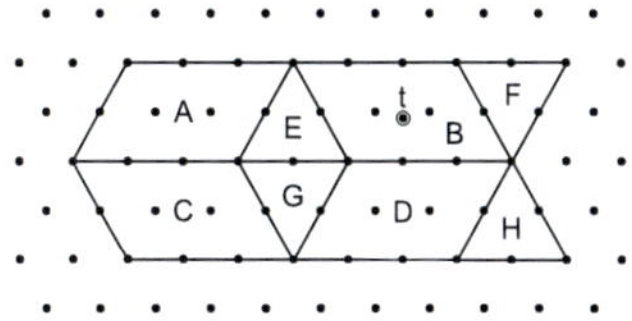

(*Answers continue on page 35.*)

Assignment Guidelines

If your students do not have time to complete all the *Practice* questions on pages 272 and 273, these questions provide minimum curriculum coverage: 1, 3, 5, 6, *Reflect*

To assess the 4 Achievement Chart categories listed in the curriculum document, have students complete these *Practice* questions:
Understanding Concepts: 1
Application: 5
Problem Solving: 6
Communication: *Reflect*

ASSESSMENT FOR LEARNING

What to Look For	What to Do
Understanding concepts ✔ Students understand that transformations can be used to create tiling patterns that involve two or more figures.	***Extra Support:*** Students who have difficulty describing how a design was constructed may benefit from using simple designs that use only one kind of transformation, for example, a tile ceiling or a checkerboard created by translation. Have students describe how the design was created. Students can use Step-by-Step 5 (Master 7.13) to complete question 6.
Applying procedures ✔ Students can apply transformations to two or more figures to create a design that tiles the plane.	***Extra Practice:*** Have students repeat *Explore* using a different combination of Pattern Blocks. Students can complete Extra Practice 5 (Master 7.24).
Communicating ✔ Students can use mathematical language to describe transformations used to create a design.	***Extension:*** Have students create a design using 3 different figures that uses at least one translation, one reflection, and one rotation. Students describe the transformations used.

Recording and Reporting
Master 7.2 Ongoing Observations: Geometry

Using a Computer to Transform Figures

SECTION ORGANIZER 40–50 min

Curriculum Focus: Use technology to create and analyse designs. (7m62, 7m65)

Student Materials

- computers with *The Geometer's Sketchpad*

Using a Computer to Transform Figures

Focus Use technology to create and analyse designs.

Software, such as *The Geometer's Sketchpad*, can be used to transform figures.
Follow these steps:

1. Open *The Geometer's Sketchpad*.
   From the File menu, choose **New Sketch**.

To make a "grid paper" screen:

2. From the **Edit** menu, click on **Preferences**.
   Select the **Units** tab.
   Check that the Distance Units are cm.
   Click **OK**.
3. From the **Graph** menu, choose **Define Coordinate System**.
   The screen has grid lines and two numbered axes.
4. Click on each axis and the two red dots.
   The axes and the dots are highlighted.
   From the **Display** menu, choose **Hide Objects**.
   The axes and dots disappear.
   The screen appears like a piece of grid paper.
5. From the **Graph** menu, choose **Snap Points**.

Translating a Figure

6. To create a quadrilateral:
   From the **Toolbox**, choose ⁄.
   Click and drag to construct a quadrilateral.
7. To translate the quadrilateral:
   From the **Toolbox**, choose ↖.
   Click each side of the quadrilateral to select it.
   The quadrilateral is highlighted.

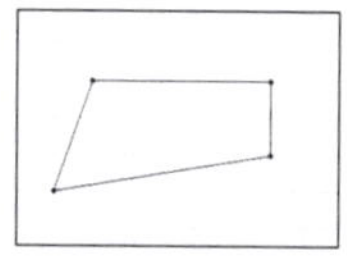

274 UNIT 7: Geometry

Key Math Learning

Computers can be used to transform figures and create designs.

Explain to students that they will be using a computer with *The Geometer's Sketchpad* to make designs by transforming figures. Remind students of the three transformations they have worked with: translation, reflection, and rotation.

Instructions for performing transformations using *Microsoft Word*:

1. Open a new document in *Microsoft Word*.
2. Set the measurement units to centimetres.
   Click **Tools**. Click **Options**.
   Click the tab labelled **General**.
   Look for **Measurement units**. Click ▼.
   Click **Centimeters**.
   Click **OK**.
3. Display the Drawing toolbar.
   Click **Tools**. Click **Customize**.
   Click **Toolbars**.
   The box next to 'Drawing' should have a check mark in it.
   If not, click on the box.
   Click **Close**.
   You should see this bar at the edge of your screen:

4. Select grid settings.
   Click **Draw**. Click **Grid**.
   The box next to **Snap objects to grid** should have a check mark in it.
   If not, click on the box.

   Grid settings should be:
   ➢ **Horizontal spacing:** 1 cm
   ➢ **Vertical spacing:** 1 cm
   If they are not, click in each box and enter 1 cm.

   The box next to **Display gridlines on screen** should have a check mark in it.
   If not, click on the box.
   Click **OK**.

8. From the **Transform** menu, choose **Translate**.
Under **Translation Vector:**, choose **Rectangular**.
Under **Horizontal:**, choose **Fixed Distance**.
Enter 2.0 cm for the Horizontal distance.
Under **Vertical:**, choose **Fixed Distance**.
Enter 2.0 cm for the Vertical distance (below left).
Click **Translate** to get the quadrilateral and its image after a translation 2 right, 2 up (below right).

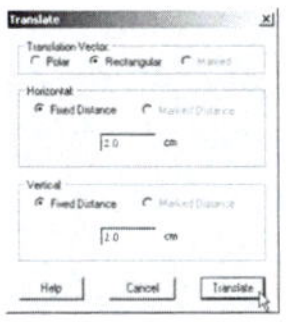
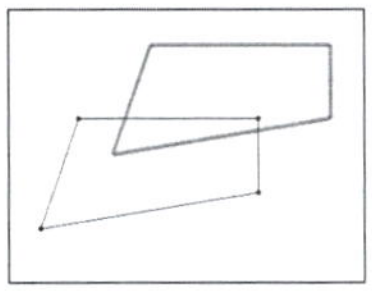

9. Drag any vertex or side of the original figure.
See what happens to the translation image.

10. From the **Edit** menu, choose **Undo Translate Point**.
The screen shows the original quadrilateral and translation image.
To print the quadrilateral and its translation image, from the **File** menu, choose **Print**.

11. Repeat *Steps 7* to *10* using different horizontal and vertical distances.

Rotating a Figure

12. From the **File** menu, choose **New Sketch**.
Follow *Steps 2* to *5* to make a "grid paper" screen.

13. To create a triangle:
From the **Toolbox**, choose .
Click and drag to construct a triangle.

14. To rotate the triangle:
From the **Toolbox**, choose .
Click to place a point near the triangle.

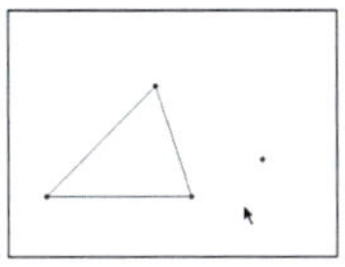

REACHING ALL LEARNERS

Early Finishers

Have students create a design that has exactly 2 lines of symmetry.

Common Misconceptions

➤ Students draw new figures rather than copy and transform existing figures.

How to Help: Remind students that they should make 2 or more different figures, then copy and paste the figures, and use the mouse to transform the pasted figures.

5. Use these tools to draw:
   ➢ Click **AutoShapes** on the Drawing toolbar.
   ➢ Click **Lines** or **Basic Shapes.**
   ➢ Click on a figure or line that you would like to draw.

   The cursor will look like +.

6. Draw your figure.
   ➢ Click and hold down the mouse button.
   Drag the cursor until the figure is the size and shape you want.
   Release the mouse button.
   ➢ If you are making a square, a circle, or a regular polygon, hold down the Shift key while you click and drag.

7. To copy a figure
   ➢ Click: **Edit** ➢ Click: **Copy Crtl+C**
   ➢ Click: **Edit** ➢ Click: **Paste Crtl+V**

   The copy shows on top of the figure.
   Click and drag the copy to where you want it.

8. To **translate a figure**, put the cursor inside the figure.
   Click and hold down the mouse button.
   Drag the figure to where you want it.
   Release the mouse button.

9. To **rotate a figure**, select the figure.
   Click **Draw.** Click **Rotate or Flip.**
   Click **Free Rotate.**
   The vertices of your figure will have green dots.
   Click on a green dot. Hold down the mouse button.
   Move the mouse to rotate the figure.
   Alternatively, click **Rotate Left** or **Rotate Right** to rotate by a $\frac{1}{4}$ turn.

10. To **reflect a figure**, select the figure.
    Click **Draw.** Click **Rotate or Flip.**
    Click **Flip Horizontal** or **Flip Vertical.**

(Sample Answers for Section 7.4, page 269, continued)

8. These octagons tile the plane because they can be used to cover the page without leaving any gaps. At any point where vertices meet, the angles add to 360°.

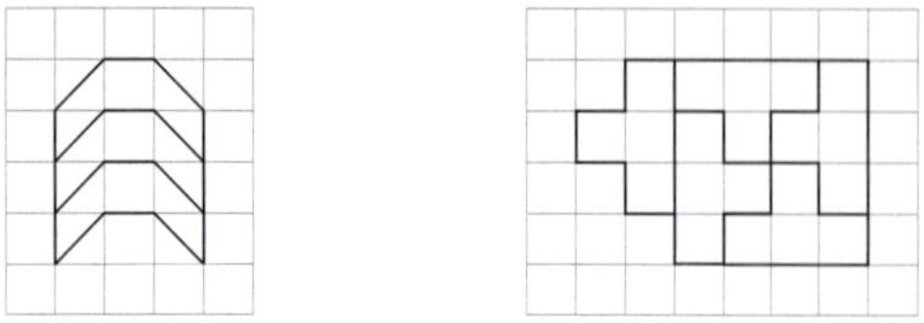

9. The cross-section of a honeycomb is a tiling of regular hexagons. Graphite is formed from carbon atoms arranged in a honeycomb pattern.

REFLECT: Polygons will tile a plane if, at any point where vertices meet, the angles add to 360°. For example, a parallelogram with angles of 130° and 50° will tile a plane because 4 of these parallelograms can be put together so that the sum of the angles is 360°. A regular octagon has 8 equal angles, with each angle measuring 135°. Since 135 does not divide exactly into 360, a regular octagon will not tile the plane. There will be gaps. Polygons with right angles and lines of symmetry are more likely to tile the plane.

15. Click to select the point.
From the **Transform** menu, choose **Mark Center**.
This is the turn centre for your rotation.

16. From the **Toolbox**, choose the selection arrow tool.
Click to select each side of the triangle.
The triangle is highlighted.

17. From the **Transform** menu, choose **Rotate**.
Under **Rotate By:**, choose **Fixed Angle**.
Enter 90 degrees. Click **Rotate** to show the triangle and its image after a rotation of 90° counterclockwise.

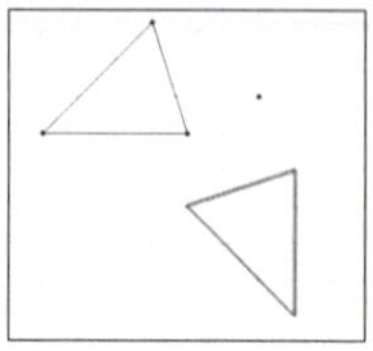

18. Drag any vertex or side of the original figure.
See what happens to the rotation image.

19. From the **Edit** menu, choose **Undo Translate Point**.
The screen shows the original triangle and rotation image.

20. Repeat *Steps 16* to *19* using a different number of degrees of rotation. Print the figure and its rotation image.

Reflecting a Figure

21. Repeat *Step 12*.

22. To create a polygon:
From the **Toolbox**, choose the straightedge tool.
Click and drag to construct a polygon.

23. To reflect the polygon:
With the Straightedge Tool still selected, draw a vertical line near your polygon. The line is highlighted.

11. To colour a figure, click twice on the square to select it.
Click on the tab labelled **Colours and Lines.**
Click ▼ next to **Fill.**
Click on a colour.
Click **OK.**

12. Use *Steps 6* to *11* to create a design using transformations.

13. Save your design.
➢ Click: **File**
➢ Click: **Save As. . . Shift+Crtl+S**
Name your file. Then click **Save.**

14. Print your design.
➢ Click: **File** ➢ Click: **Print Crtl+P**
➢ Click **OK.**

Invite students to share their designs. Have students explain the transformations they used.

(Sample Solutions for Unit Review, page 282, continued)

5. For example,

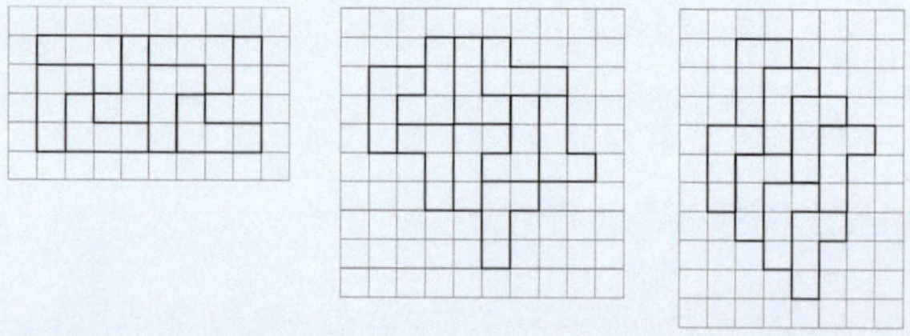

6. Translate the shaded octagon 3 units right to get octagon A. Reflect the shaded octagon in a horizontal line through its bottom side to get octagon B. Translate octagon B 3 units right to get octagon C. Translate the shaded square 3 units right to get square D, and 3 units left to get square E. Reflect the shaded square in a horizontal line through the bottom side of octagon B to get square F. Continue using these transformations to cover the page.

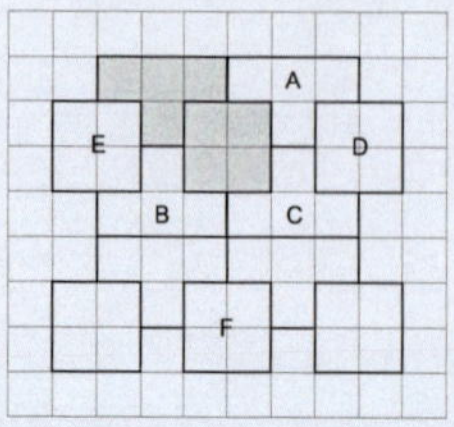

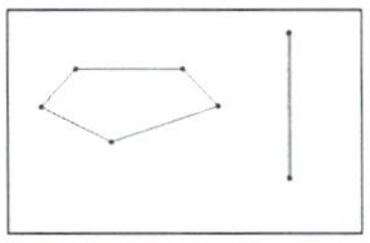

24. From the **Transform** menu, choose **Mark Mirror.**
The line is a mirror line.

25. From the **Toolbox,** choose.
Click to select each side of the polygon.
The polygon is highlighted.

26. From the **Transform** menu, choose **Reflect.**
The polygon and its reflection image are shown.

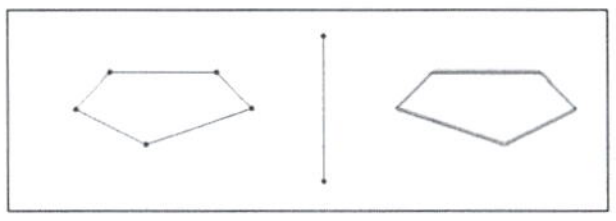

27. Drag any vertex or side of the original figure.
See what happens to the reflection image.

28. Drag either end point from the mirror line.
See what happens.

29. From the **Edit** menu, choose **Undo Translate Point.**
Do this two times. The screen shows the original polygon and its reflection image.

30. Repeat *Steps 23* to *28* using a horizontal mirror line.
Print the figure and its reflection image.

✓ Check

Use any or all of the transformations above to make a design that covers the screen.
Print your design.

(*Sample Answers for Section 7.5, page 273, continued*)

4. To get trapezoid A, rotate the shaded trapezoid a $\frac{1}{2}$ turn about turn centre *l*. To get trapezoid B, rotate trapezoid A a $\frac{1}{2}$ turn about turn centre *m*. To get trapezoid C, reflect trapezoid B in a mirror line through the right side of trapezoid B. To get trapezoid D, rotate trapezoid C a $\frac{1}{2}$ turn about turn centre *n*. To get trapezoid E, rotate trapezoid D a $\frac{1}{2}$ turn about turn centre *o*. To get trapezoid F, reflect trapezoid E in a mirror line through the bottom side of trapezoid E. To get trapezoid G, rotate trapezoid F a $\frac{1}{2}$ turn about turn centre *p*. To get trapezoid H, rotate trapezoid G a $\frac{1}{2}$ turn about turn centre *q*. To get trapezoid I, reflect trapezoid H in a mirror line through the left side of trapezoid H. To get trapezoid J, rotate trapezoid I a $\frac{1}{2}$ turn about turn centre *r*. To get trapezoid K, rotate trapezoid J a $\frac{1}{2}$ turn about turn centre *s*.

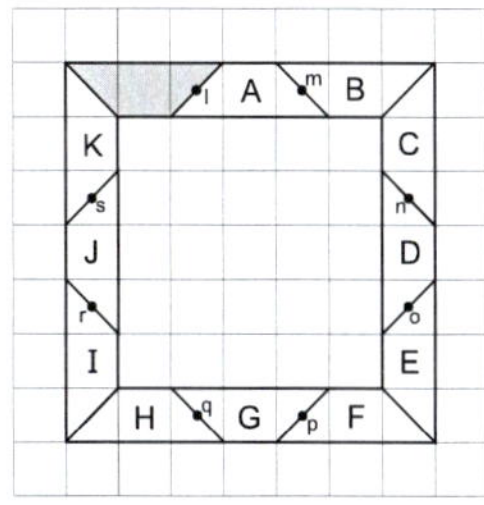

5. Figure A is rotated a $\frac{1}{4}$ turn clockwise about turn centre *j* to get Figure B. Figure B is rotated a $\frac{1}{4}$ turn clockwise about turn centre *k* to get Figure C. Figure C is rotated a $\frac{1}{4}$ turn clockwise about turn centre *l* to get Figure D. Square E is translated 4 units right to get square F. Square F is translated 4 units right to get square G. Square G is translated 4 units right to get square H. Each section of the design, as described above,

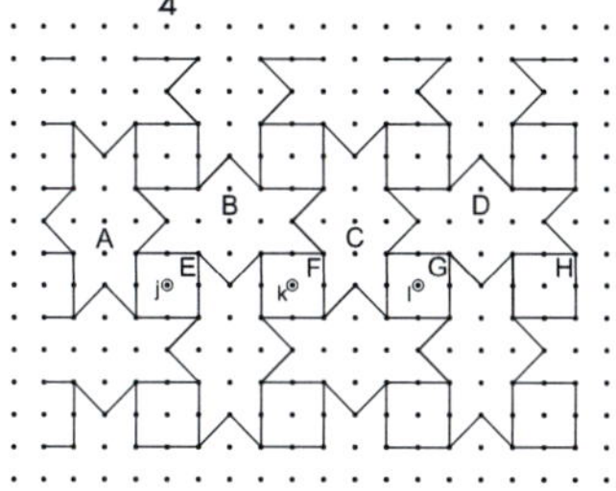

(*Sample Answers continue below.*)

(*Sample Answers, continued*)

is then translated 4 units down and 4 units right, or 4 units down and 4 units left to fill the page.

6. Figure A is translated 2 units right to get Figure B. Figure B is translated 4 units right to get Figure C. Figure C is translated 2 units right to get Figure D. Figure E is translated 6 units right to get Figure F. Figure E is reflected in a horizontal line through its bottom vertex to get Figure G. Figure F is reflected in a horizontal line through its bottom vertex to get Figure H. The section is then translated down to continue the design.
Instead of using translations to describe some of the transformations, I could use rotations. For example, Figure A is rotated a $\frac{1}{2}$ turn about turn centre *j* to get Figure B. I could also describe more of the transformations using reflections. For example, reflect Figure B in mirror line *l* to get Figure C.

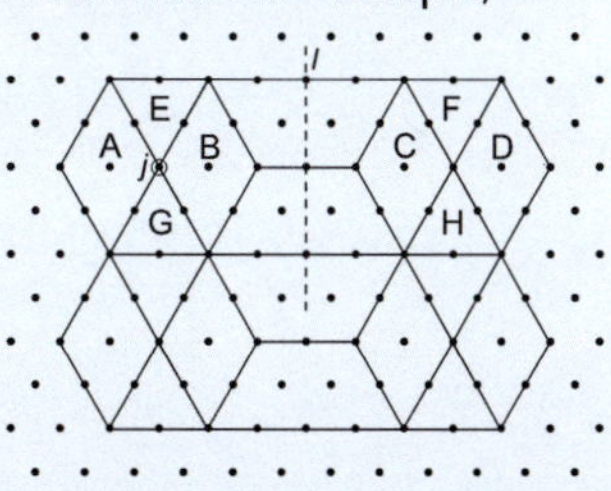

7. There are many ways to describe this pattern. Here is one way. The flooring pattern is a large square that contains 4 squares, with each square further divided into 4 smaller squares. Each smaller square is rotated a $\frac{1}{4}$ turn clockwise, about the vertex all 4 small squares share, to get the next square.

REFLECT: If a figure and its image have the same orientation, I look for a translation. If a figure and its image face opposite ways, I look for a reflection. If a figure and its image face different ways, but not opposite ways, I look for a rotation. Student answer should include a design that uses all 3 transformations.

Choosing a Strategy

SECTION ORGANIZER

Student Materials
- 1-cm grid paper (PM 20)
- tangrams
- rulers
- calendar page (optional)
- linking cubes

Assessment: Master 7.2 Ongoing Observations: Geometry

Choosing a Strategy

1. A train is travelling at a rate of 1 km every 45 s. At this rate, how far will the train travel in 1 h? 80 km

Remember to count squares of different sizes.

2. How many squares are in this rectangle? 50 squares

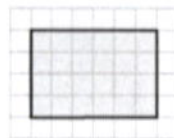

3. Use grid paper. Try to draw a quadrilateral with each number of lines of symmetry.
   a) 0 b) 1 c) 2
   d) 3 e) 4 f) 5
   Which quadrilaterals could you not draw? Explain.

Strategies
- Make a table.
- Use a model.
- Draw a diagram.
- Solve a simpler problem.
- Work backward.
- Guess and check.
- Make an organized list.
- Use a pattern.
- Draw a graph.
- Use logical reasoning.

4. Use grid paper. Draw this figure:
   It has at least 1 line of symmetry.
   It has perimeter 24 units.
   It has area 23 square units.

5. Copy the diagram below.
   Write these numbers in the boxes: $\frac{1}{6}, \frac{1}{3}, \frac{1}{2}, \frac{2}{3}, \frac{5}{6}$, 1;
   so the sum of the fractions along each side is :
   a) $1\frac{1}{2}$ b) 2

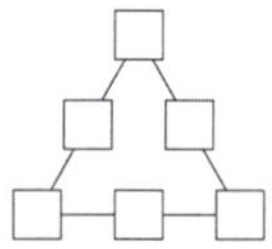

6. What fraction of the area of a tangram is triangles? $\frac{3}{4}$

7. Write the next five terms in each pattern.
   Describe each pattern rule.
   a) A E F / B C D — G H I J K
   b) 1, 5, 10, 25, … 100, 200, 500, 1000, 2000
   c) O, T, T, F, F, S, S, … E, N, T, E, T

278 UNIT 7: Geometry

Sample Solutions

1. 1 h = 60 min
   1 min = 60 s
   So, 1 h = 60 × 60 s = 3600 s
   The train travels 1 km every 45 s. So, the distance in kilometres is 3600 ÷ 45 = 80. The train travels 80 km in 1 h.

2.

Side length of square (units)	Number of squares
1	24
2	15
3	8
4	3

There are 24 + 15 + 8 + 3 = 50 squares in the rectangle.

3. a)

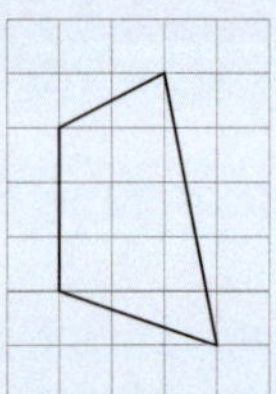

b)

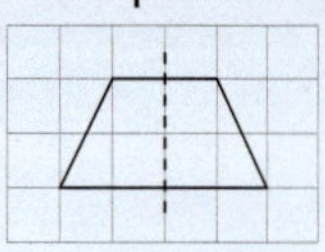

c)

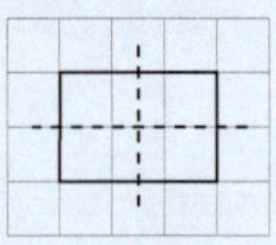

d) I cannot draw a quadrilateral with 3 lines of symmetry.

e)

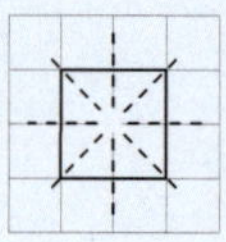

f) A quadrilateral has 4 sides so a quadrilateral can have no more than 4 lines of symmetry.

4.

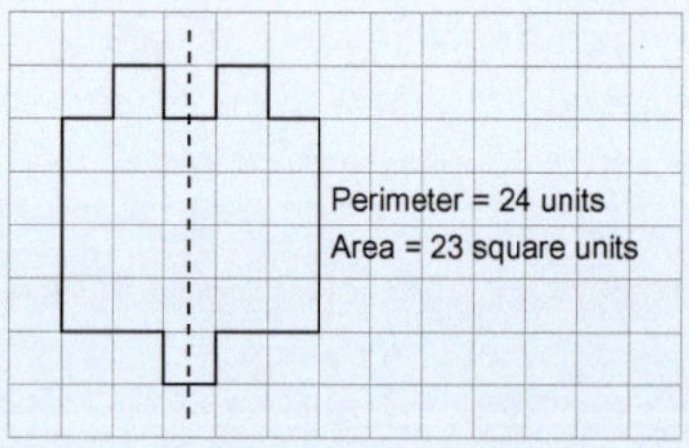

5. a)

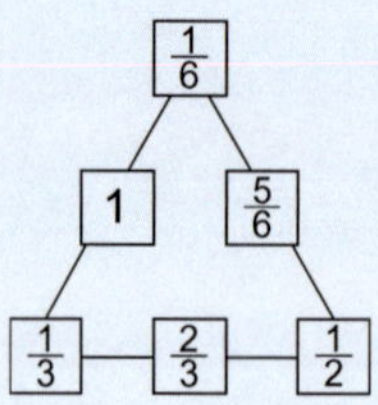

b)

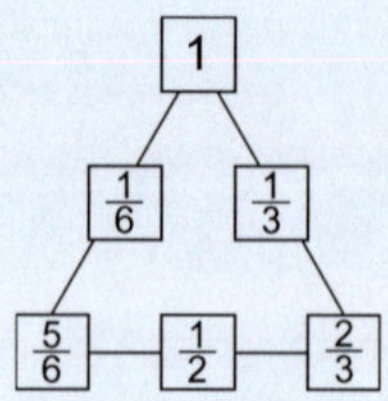

Reading and Writing in Math

8. This rectangular prism is made with 12 different coloured cubes. The colours are black, white, red, orange, light green, dark green, light blue, dark blue, brown, yellow, pink, and purple.

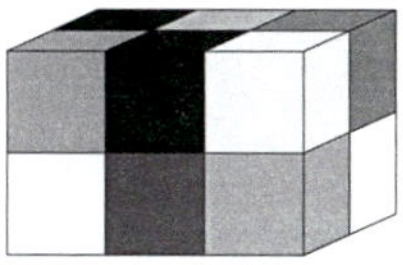

Using linking cubes to build the prism.

a) The colours on the left face are light green, orange, brown, and red.
Draw and colour the back face of the prism.
Another congruent prism is made from the coloured cubes. The colours on the front face are: red, orange, dark green, light blue, black, and white.
The colours on the top face are: red, black, white, pink, purple, and yellow.
The colours on the right face side are: light blue, white, yellow, and brown.
The colours on the left face side are: red, dark green, pink, and dark blue.
b) Build the prism. Sketch the prism.
c) What colours are on the bottom face of the prism? How do you know?

9. In her fitness program Jessie runs on Mondays, Wednesdays, and Saturdays, and swims on Tuesdays and Fridays. Malcolm runs every third day and swims on the day after each run.
Jessie and Malcolm run together on Saturday July 6.
On what days and dates in July will they:
a) run together again? Monday July 15, Wednesday July 24, Saturday July 27
b) swim together? Tuesday July 16, Friday July 19

Reading and Writing in Math: Choosing a Strategy **279**

Question Number	Possible Strategy
1	Use logical reasoning
2	Draw a diagram; make a table
3	Draw a diagram
4	Draw a diagram; guess and check
5	Guess and check; work backward
6	Draw a diagram; use logical reasoning
7	Use a pattern; use logical reasoning
8	Use a model; draw a diagram
9	Draw a diagram; use a pattern

6. Students could draw the tangram on grid paper, then count grid squares. The triangles cover 4 + 4 + 8 + 16 + 16 = 48 grid squares. The tangram covers 64 grid squares. So, the triangles cover $\frac{48}{64}$ or $\frac{3}{4}$ of the tangram.

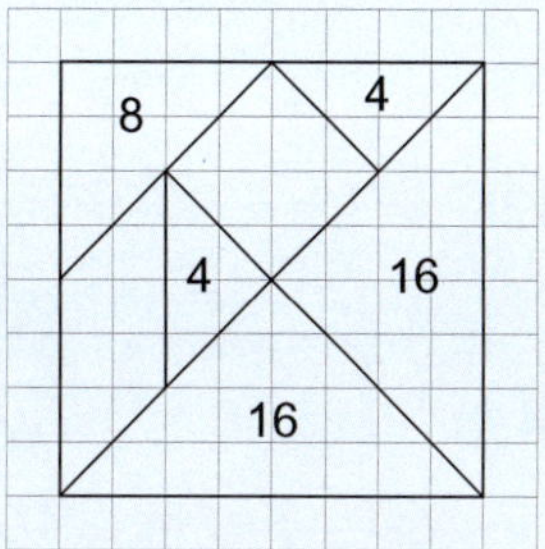

7. a) The letters that are made with straight line segments are on top. The letters that have curves are on the bottom.
b) This pattern represents the number of cents in each of the Canadian coins and bills, starting with the penny and increasing in value each time.
c) The letters represent the first letter of each of the counting numbers, starting with one.

8 a)

Green	Light Blue	Brown
White	Dark Blue	Red

b)

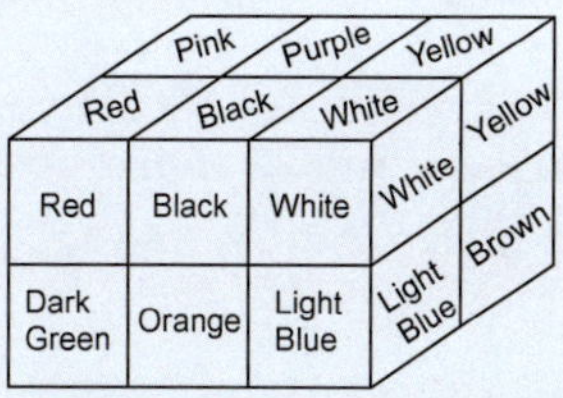

c) The colours on the bottom row of the front and side faces will be on the bottom face, along with the colour in the middle of the bottom row of the back face. This is the only colour not mentioned when describing the other faces, light green.

Dark Blue	Light Green	Brown
Dark Green	Orange	Light Blue

9.

July

S	M	T	W	T	F	S
	1 JR	2 JS	3 JR	4	5 JS	6 JR MR
7 MS	8 JR	9 JS MR	10 JR MS	11	12 JS MR	13 JR MS
14	15 JR MR	16 JS MS	17 JR	18 MR	19 JS MS	20 JR
21 MR	22 JR MS	23 JS	24 JR MR	25 MS	26 JS	27 JR MR
28 MS	29 JR	30 JS MR	31 JR MS			

Office Space Planner

Office Space Planner

An office space planner plans the best use of the office space. He ensures that employees have a workplace that is functional a attractive. Systems furniture is a series of connected partitions, w surfaces, and cabinets. It is frequently used in offices. The planner uses a computer to design multiple 'standard' work areas. Each work area is designed to meet the needs of a group of employees with similar jobs. The work areas are also designed to 'fit' with other work areas of the same size and shape, and with work areas that have different sizes and shapes. It's all a bit of a puzzle! The space planner must solve the puzzle using geometry and an understanding of how people work and interact (ergonomics).

A workplace, where every work area or 'cubicle' is identical, is often seen as 'cell-like' or dehumanizing. Suppose you are an office planner. What might you do to make groups of work areas more appealing, and still make the best use of the available floor area?

280 UNIT 7: Geometry

Sample Solution:

I would try to make each person's work area as private as possible. I would ensure that there is enough shelving and storage space so the workspace is not cluttered. I would give as many cubicles as possible a window or natural lighting.
I would also make sure that every cubicle has a good computer system. I would also try to ensure that the walkways between cubicles are wide enough for 2 people to pass easily, and free of clutter so that nobody trips and falls.

Making the best use of available space, whether in offices, factories, homes, vehicles, parks or gardens, offers interesting challenges to designers. A knowledge of geometrical figures and objects and how they fit together, combined with a knowledge of transformations can be useful.

Have groups of students brainstorm a list of design jobs in which a knowledge of geometry and transformations would be useful.

Have groups share their results and discuss the mathematics required.

Jobs and discussions may include:

- Schools: Could schools and classrooms be designed differently? How? Why?
- Motor Homes: What has to be included? What is the best layout?
- Cruise ship cabins: Why do they use a modular construction? Why are they usually designed in mirror-image pairs?
- Space vehicles: What are the challenges in designing a space vehicle?

Office Designs: When a number of employees perform similar tasks, they are often located in rectangular or square cubicles with partitions, rather than walled offices.

For someone designing these workspaces, a knowledge of the properties of geometric figures, combined with a knowledge of polygons that tile the plane, can be useful. Instead of offices being rectangular, could they be trapezoidal, polygonal, or T-shaped?

Would this be more attractive to employees? Could different figures be used?

Other factors to consider include the positioning of desks, chairs, computers, cabinets, and personal space. Colours of walls, floors, and furniture are important, as are the locations of meeting rooms and lunchrooms.

Unit Review

Review any lesson with etext online tutorial

What Do I Need to Know?

✓ **Conditions for Congruent Triangles**

Two triangles are congruent if:

- three pairs of corresponding sides are equal

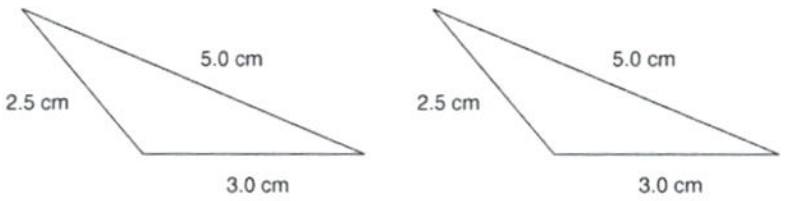

- two pairs of corresponding sides are equal and the corresponding angles between these sides are equal

- two pairs of corresponding angles are equal and one pair of corresponding sides are equal

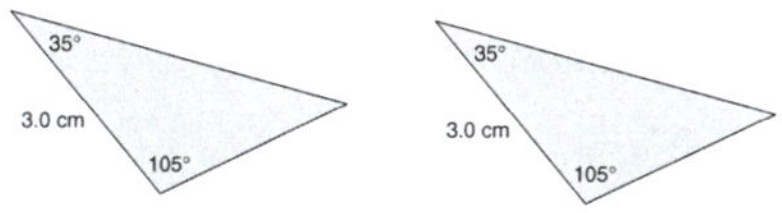

✓ **Conditions for Congruent Figures**

For figures that are not triangles, two figures are congruent if corresponding sides are equal *and* corresponding angles are equal.

Unit Review **281**

SECTION ORGANIZER

Student Materials

- 1-cm grid paper (PM 20)
- square dot paper (PM 22)
- isometric dot paper (PM 23)
- rulers
- protractors
- coloured pencils or markers
- tracing paper

Assessment: Masters 7.1 Unit Rubric: Geometry, 7.4 Unit Summary: Geometry

Correlation of Extra Practice questions on page 444:

Section	Questions
7.1	1, 6, 7
7.2	2
7.3	3, 8
7.4	4
7.5	5

Sample Solutions

1. a)

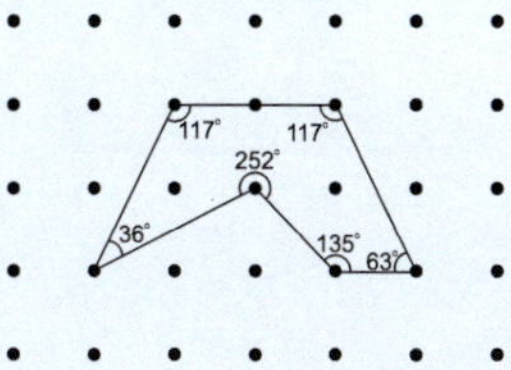

b)

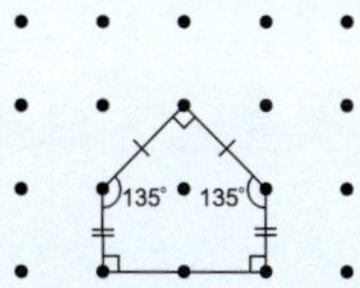

c)

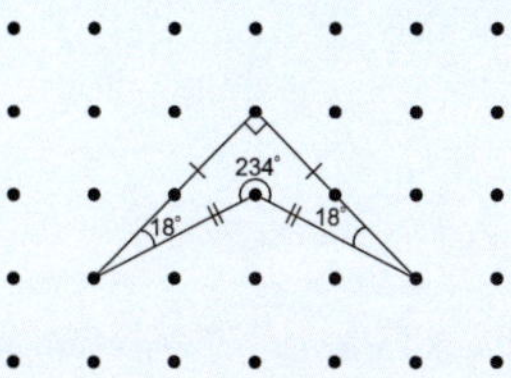

d)

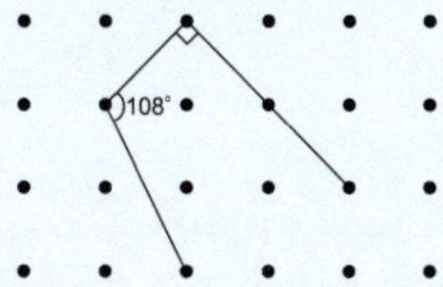

e)

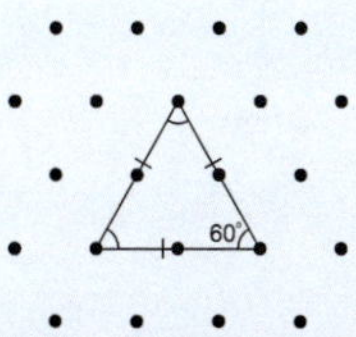

2. a) The hexagon has 6 sides, with 4 sides equal and the other pair of sides equal. There are 4 equal angles and another pair of equal angles. Two angles are acute and 4 angles are obtuse.

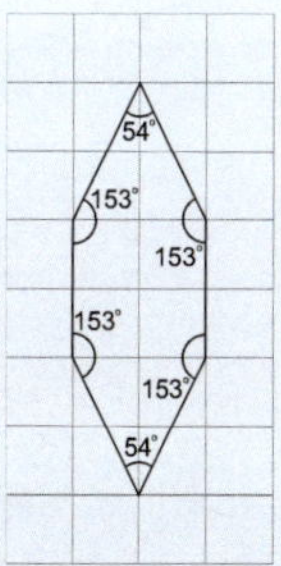

b) The triangle is an equilateral triangle with all sides equal and all angles equal. Each angle is 60°.

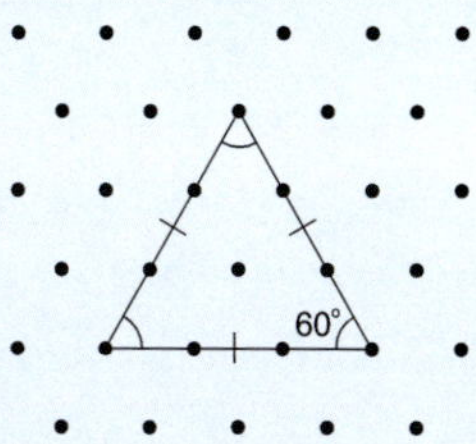

c) The pentagon has 5 sides with no sides equal and no angles equal. It is a concave pentagon as one angle is greater than 180°.

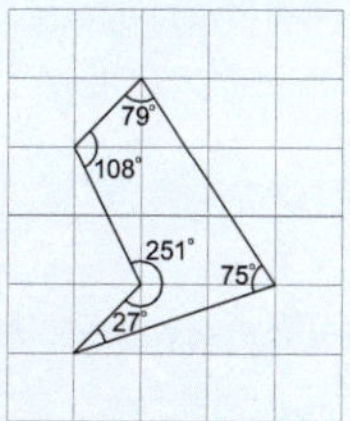

d) The pentagon has 5 sides, with 2 pairs of equal sides. There are 2 pairs of equal angles. Three angles are obtuse and 2 angles are acute.

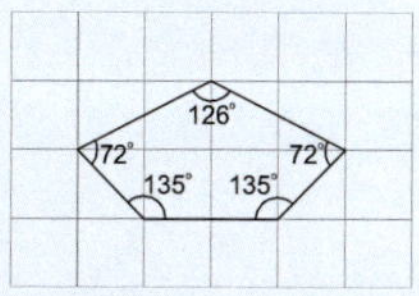

3. a) No, all pairs of corresponding sides are not equal: AE ≠ FJ and DE ≠ IJ; and not all pairs of corresponding angles are equal: ∠A ≠ ∠F, ∠E ≠ ∠J, and ∠D ≠ ∠I.
   b) Yes, all pairs of corresponding sides are equal: AB = DE, BC = EF, and CA = FD.

4. a) The quadrilateral is rotated a $\frac{1}{4}$ turn clockwise about point C to get Image A.
   b) The quadrilateral is reflected in the horizontal line going through the point (7, 11) to get Image B.
   c) The quadrilateral is translated 2 units right and 5 units down to get Image C.

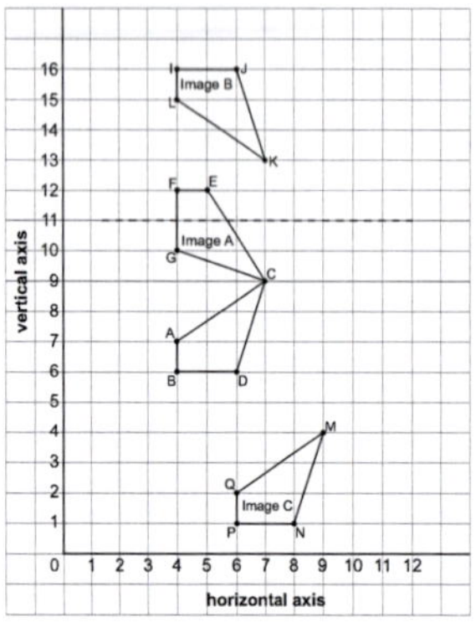

(*Solutions continue on page 34.*)

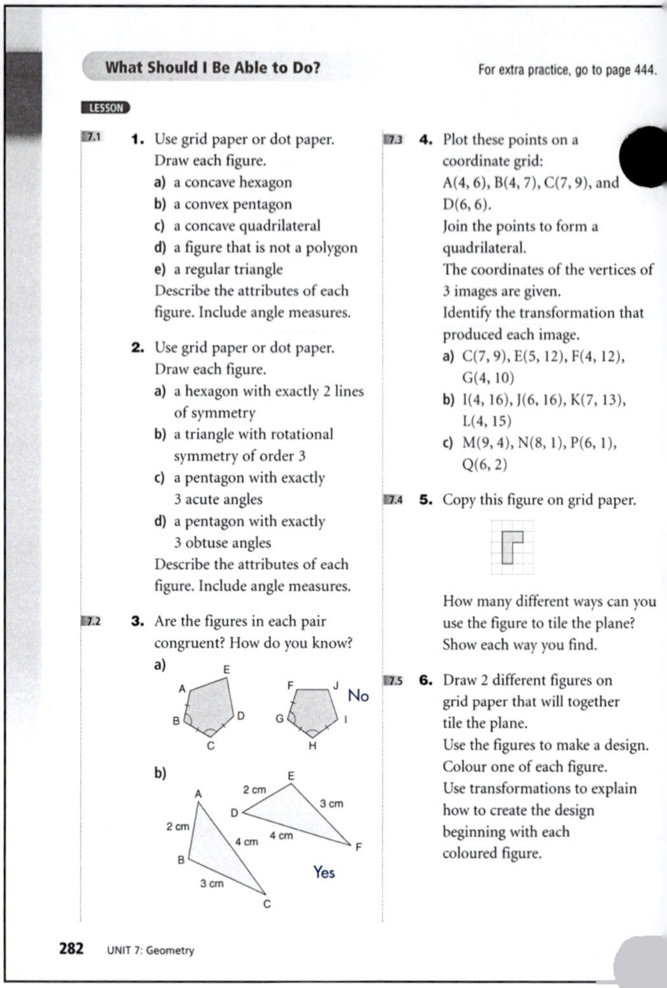

What Should I Be Able to Do?

For extra practice, go to page 444.

LESSON

7.1 **1.** Use grid paper or dot paper. Draw each figure.
a) a concave hexagon
b) a convex pentagon
c) a concave quadrilateral
d) a figure that is not a polygon
e) a regular triangle
Describe the attributes of each figure. Include angle measures.

2. Use grid paper or dot paper. Draw each figure.
a) a hexagon with exactly 2 lines of symmetry
b) a triangle with rotational symmetry of order 3
c) a pentagon with exactly 3 acute angles
d) a pentagon with exactly 3 obtuse angles
Describe the attributes of each figure. Include angle measures.

7.2 **3.** Are the figures in each pair congruent? How do you know?
a) No
b) 2 cm, 2 cm, 3 cm, 3 cm, 4 cm, 4 cm — Yes

7.3 **4.** Plot these points on a coordinate grid: A(4, 6), B(4, 7), C(7, 9), and D(6, 6).
Join the points to form a quadrilateral.
The coordinates of the vertices of 3 images are given.
Identify the transformation that produced each image.
a) C(7, 9), E(5, 12), F(4, 12), G(4, 10)
b) I(4, 16), J(6, 16), K(7, 13), L(4, 15)
c) M(9, 4), N(8, 1), P(6, 1), Q(6, 2)

7.4 **5.** Copy this figure on grid paper.
How many different ways can you use the figure to tile the plane? Show each way you find.

7.5 **6.** Draw 2 different figures on grid paper that will together tile the plane.
Use the figures to make a design.
Colour one of each figure.
Use transformations to explain how to create the design beginning with each coloured figure.

282 UNIT 7: Geometry

ASSESSMENT FOR LEARNING

What to Look For

Understanding of concepts

✔ **Question 1:** Student understands that a convex polygon has all angles less than 180°, and a concave polygon has at least one angle greater than 180°.

✔ **Question 5:** Student understands that a figure tiles the plane if congruent copies of the figure cover a page and leave no gaps.

Application of mathematical procedures

✔ **Question 2:** Student can describe the attributes of a geometric figure.

✔ **Question 4:** Student can identify and describe different transformations.

✔ **Question 6:** Student can apply transformations to two or more figures to create a design that tiles the plane.

Communicating

✔ **Question 3:** Student can use mathematical language to describe how they know whether two figures are congruent.

Recording and Reporting
Master 7.1 Unit Rubric: Geometry
Master 7.4 Unit Summary: Geometry

Practice Test

1. Use the figures below.

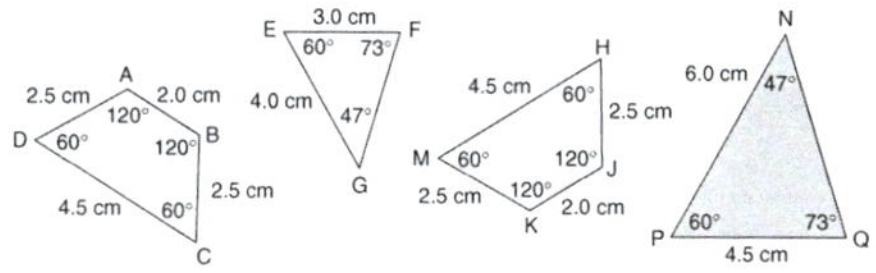

Identify:

a) two congruent figures, and explain how you know they are congruent   Figure ABCD and Figure JKMH

b) two figures that are *not* congruent, and explain how you know they are not congruent   △EFG and △PQN

c) a scalene triangle with a 60° angle   △EFG and △PQN

d) a quadrilateral with a 60° angle   Figure ABCD and Figure JKMH

2. Two triangles are congruent if they have 3 matching sides. Suppose two triangles have 3 matching angles. Are the triangles congruent?   No
Justify your answer.

3. Three students looked at a figure and its transformation image.
Igal said the picture showed a translation.
Shaian said the picture showed a rotation.
Cherie said the picture showed a reflection.
All three students were correct. What might the picture be?
Draw a diagram to show your thinking.

4. Julie will use both of these tiles to cover her floor.

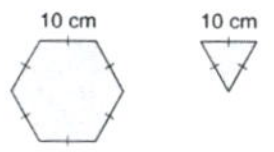

Use isometric paper.
Draw 2 different designs Julie could use.
For each design, use transformations to explain how to create the design.

SECTION ORGANIZER

Student Materials

- isometric dot paper (PM 23)
- rulers
- tracing paper
- protractors

Assessment: Masters 7.1 Unit Rubric: Geometry,
7.4 Unit Summary: Geometry

Assignment Guidelines

To assess the 4 Achievement Chart categories listed in the curriculum document, use these test questions:
Understanding Concepts: 1
Communication: 2
Problem Solving: 3
Application: 4

Sample Solutions

1. a) Figure ABCD is congruent to Figure JKMH because 4 pairs of corresponding sides are equal and 4 pairs of corresponding angles are equal: AB = JK, BC = KM, CD = MH, AD = JH, ∠A = ∠J, ∠B = ∠K, ∠C = ∠M, and ∠D = ∠H.

b) △EFG and △PQN are not congruent because corresponding pairs of sides are not equal.

c) Both △EFG and △PQN are scalene triangles with a 60° angle, because all sides are different.

d) Both Figure ABCD and Figure JKMH have a 60° angle and 4 sides.

2. Two triangles with 3 matching angles are congruent only if corresponding sides are equal. Otherwise, the triangles are similar.

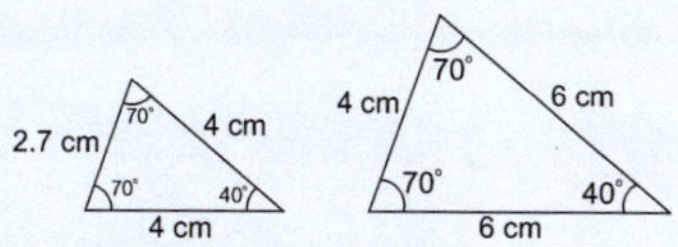

3. The picture could be any figure that has 2 or more lines of symmetry, and rotational symmetry.

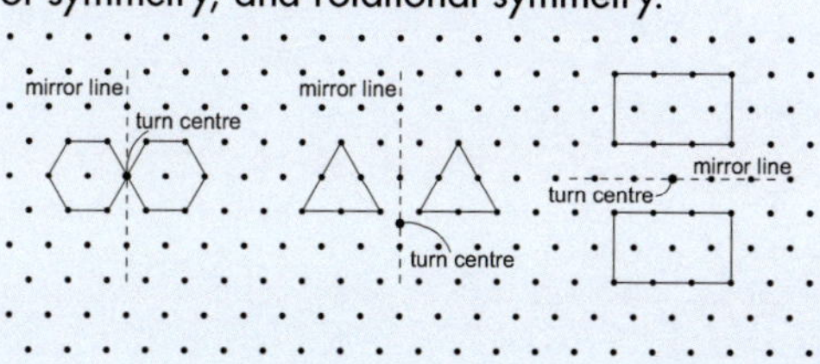

4. Design 1: Translate the shaded hexagon 2 units right to get hexagon A. Translate the shaded triangle 2 units right to get triangle E. Reflect the shaded triangle in a horizontal line through its bottom vertex to get triangle D. Translate triangle D 2 units right to get triangle F. Translate the section down each time to cover the page.

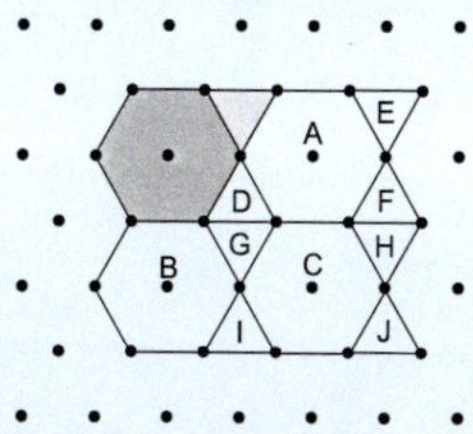

Design 2: Translate the shaded hexagon 3 units right to get hexagon A. Reflect the shaded triangle in its right side to get triangle D. Translate the shaded triangle 1 unit right to get triangle E. Reflect the shaded triangle in a horizontal line through its bottom vertex to get triangle F. Reflect triangle F in its right side to get triangle G. Translate triangle F 1 unit right to get triangle H. Translate the section down and right or left to cover the page.

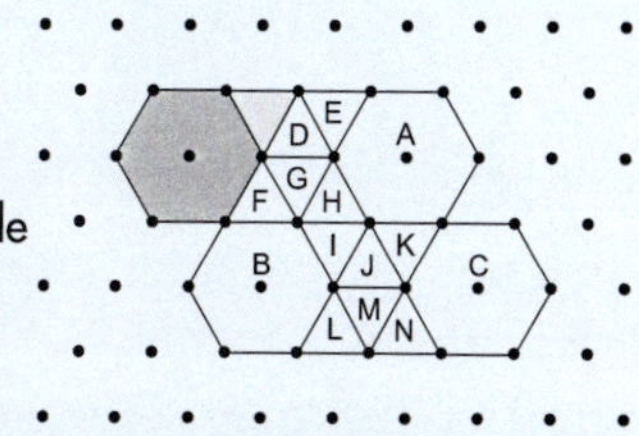

Tessellations

SECTION ORGANIZER

40–50 min

Student Grouping: Individual
Student Materials
- square dot paper (PM22)
- 1-cm grid paper (PM 20)
- rulers
- tracing paper
- scissors
- cardboard
- Miras
- coloured pencils or markers

Assessment: Masters 7.3 Performance Assessment Rubric: Tessellations, 7.4 Unit Summary: Geometry

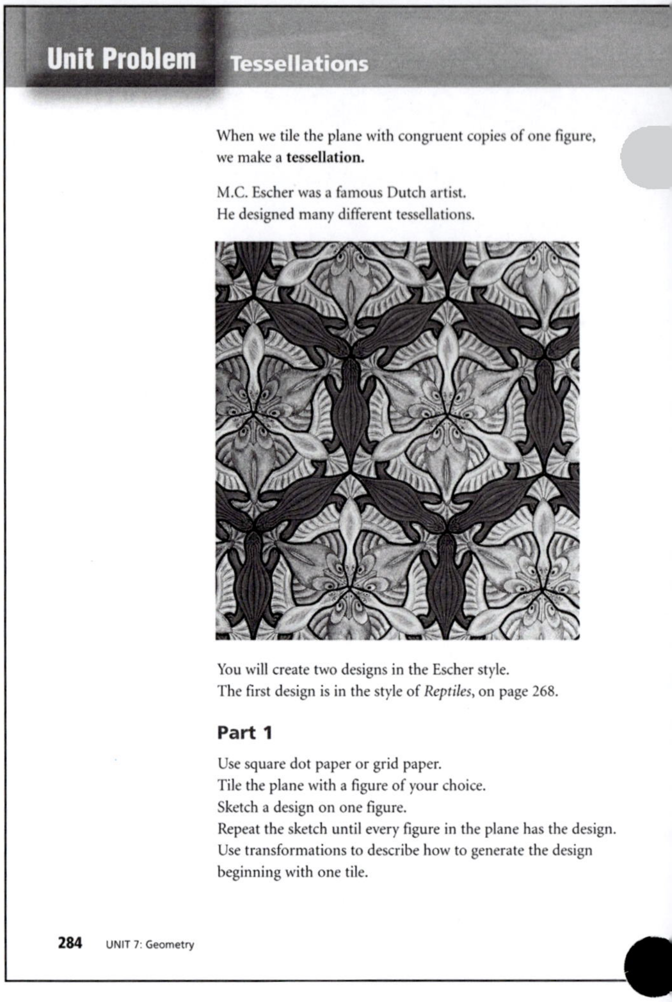
Unit Problem Tessellations

When we tile the plane with congruent copies of one figure, we make a **tessellation.**

M.C. Escher was a famous Dutch artist.
He designed many different tessellations.

You will create two designs in the Escher style.
The first design is in the style of *Reptiles*, on page 268.

Part 1

Use square dot paper or grid paper.
Tile the plane with a figure of your choice.
Sketch a design on one figure.
Repeat the sketch until every figure in the plane has the design.
Use transformations to describe how to generate the design beginning with one tile.

284 UNIT 7: Geometry

Present the *Unit Problem.* Introduce the term **tessellation.** Ensure students understand what they are expected to do.

Remind students that they should use the Check List to assess their work before handing it in. You may also wish to provide students with copies of Master 7.3 Performance Assessment Rubric: Tessellations so they will know how their work will be assessed.

Remind students that their designs should cover the plane with no gaps. Encourage students to use tracing paper and Miras to check that the designs on the images have been transformed correctly. Encourage students to use colour to make their designs attractive and eye catching, like the Escher designs in the Student Book.

Sample Solution

Part 1

I translated the original triangle 6 units right to get triangle A. I translated triangle A 6 units right to get triangle B. I rotated the original triangle a $\frac{1}{2}$ turn about the midpoint of its right side to get triangle C. I translated triangle C 6 units right to get triangle D. I translated triangle D 6 units right to get triangle E. I reflected the section in a horizontal line through the bottom side of the

(*Solution continues below right.*)

(*Sample Solution, continued*)

original triangle to get the next section. I continued reflecting to cover the page.

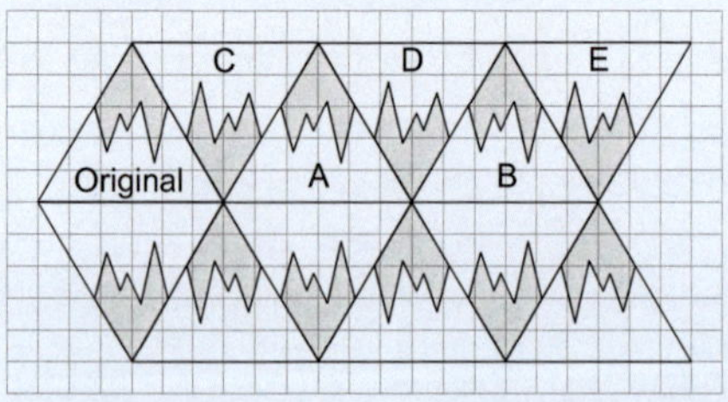

Part 2

I translated the original figure 8 units right to get Image A. I translated Image A 6 units right to get Image B. I translated the first row down 6 units to get the second row. I continued to translate rows to cover the page.

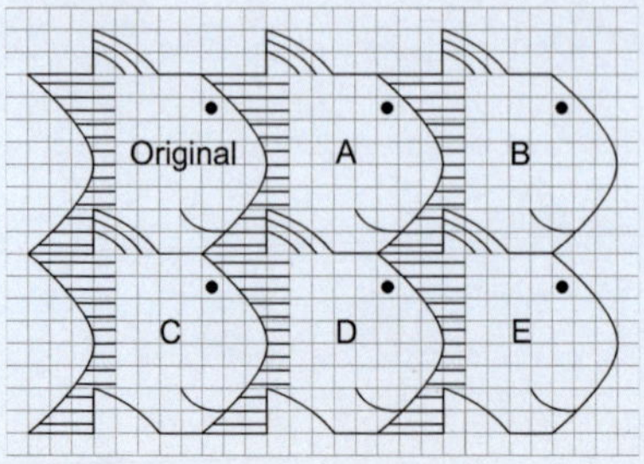

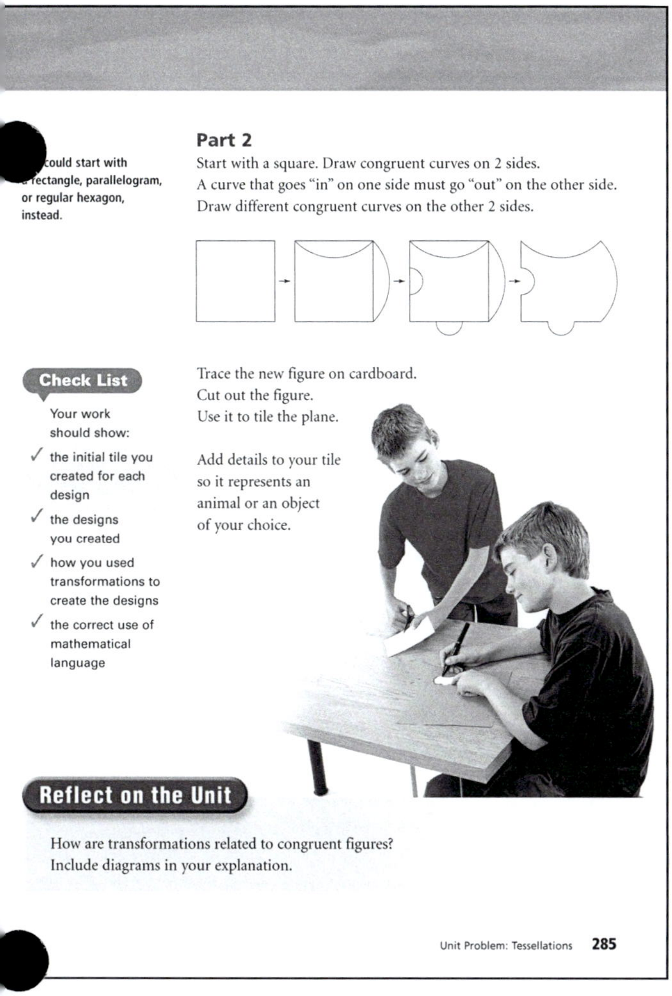

could start with rectangle, parallelogram, or regular hexagon, instead.

Part 2

Start with a square. Draw congruent curves on 2 sides.
A curve that goes "in" on one side must go "out" on the other side.
Draw different congruent curves on the other 2 sides.

Trace the new figure on cardboard.
Cut out the figure.
Use it to tile the plane.

Add details to your tile so it represents an animal or an object of your choice.

Check List

Your work should show:

- ✓ the initial tile you created for each design
- ✓ the designs you created
- ✓ how you used transformations to create the designs
- ✓ the correct use of mathematical language

Reflect on the Unit

How are transformations related to congruent figures?
Include diagrams in your explanation.

Unit Problem: Tessellations 285

REFLECT ON THE UNIT: A figure and its transformation image are congruent. The transformation could be a translation, a rotation, or a reflection. In all cases, the figure and its image have the same size and shape, but they are in different positions. Sometimes the figure and its image face the same way (translation). Sometimes they face opposite ways (reflection). Sometimes they face different ways, but not opposite ways (rotation). In all 3 examples, Figure 1 and Figure 2 (the image of Figure 1) are congruent.

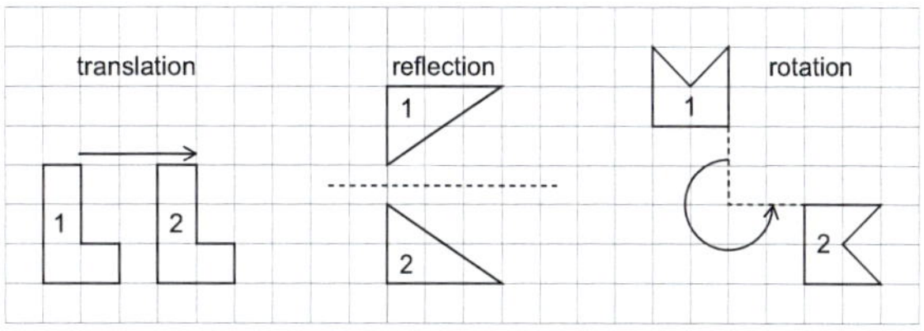

Teaching notes for the Cross Strand Investigation *Pick's Theorem* are in the *Additional Assessment Support* module.

ASSESSMENT FOR LEARNING

What to Look For

Understanding concepts

✔ Students understand how to apply transformations to a figure to create a design that will tile the plane.

Applying procedures

✔ Students can create tiling patterns that use translations, reflections, and rotations.

Communicating

✔ Students describe designs clearly, using appropriate mathematical terminology.

✔ Students present work, including designs and diagrams, clearly.

What to Do

Extra Support: Make the problem accessible.

For Part 1, some students may benefit from being given a figure that tiles the plane, then being told which transformations they could use to create a design.

For Part 2, students having difficulty could start with a cardboard square. Have students "take a bite" out of the left side of the square, then slide it across and tape it to the right side. Have students "take a bite" out of the bottom side of the square, then slide it up and tape it to the top side. This figure will tile the plane using translations.

Recording and Reporting

Master 7.3 Performance Assessment Rubric: Tessellations
Master 7.4 Unit Summary: Geometry

Evaluating Student Learning: Preparing to Report: Unit 7 Geometry

This unit provides an opportunity to report on the **Geometry and Spatial Sense** strand. *Master 7.4: Unit Summary: Geometry* provides a comprehensive format for recording and summarizing evidence collected.

Here is an example of a completed summary chart for this Unit:

Strand: *Geometry and Spatial Sense*	**Problem Solving**	**Understanding of Concepts**	**Application of mathematical procedures**	**Communication**	***Overall***
Ongoing Observations	4	3	4	4	4
Work samples or portfolios; conferences	4	3	4	3	3/4
Unit Review	4	4	4	3	4
Practice Test	3	3	4	3	3
Unit Problem Tessellations	3	4	3	4	3/4
Achievement Level for reporting					3/4

Recording	How to Report
Ongoing Observations	Use *Master 7.2 Ongoing Observations: Geometry* to determine the most consistent level achieved in each category. Enter it in the chart. Choose to summarize by achievement category, or simply to enter an overall level. Observations from late in the unit should be most heavily weighted.
Portfolios or collections of work samples; conferences, or interviews	Use *Master 7.1 Unit Rubric: Geometry* to guide evaluation of collections of work and information gathered in conferences. Teachers may choose to focus particular attention on the Assessment Focus questions. Work from late in the unit should be most heavily weighted.
Unit Review	*Master 7.1 Unit Rubric: Geometry* may be helpful in determining levels of achievement. #1 and 5 provide evidence of Understanding of concepts; #2, 4, and 6 provide evidence of Application of mathematical procedures; #5 provides evidence of Problem solving; #3 provides evidence of Communication.
Practice Test	*Master 7.1 Unit Rubric: Geometry* may be helpful in determining levels of achievement. #1 provides evidence of Understanding of concepts; #4 provides evidence of Application of mathematical procedures; #3 provides evidence of Problem solving; #2 provides evidence of Communication.
Unit Problem	Use *Master 7.3 Performance Assessment Rubric: Tessellations.* The *Unit Problem* offers a snapshot of students' achievement. In particular, it shows their ability to synthesize and apply what they have learned.
Student Self-Assessment	Note students' perceptions of their own progress. This may take the form of an oral or written comment, or a self-rating.
Comments	Analyse the pattern of achievement to identify strengths and needs. In some cases, specific actions may need to be planned to support the learner.

Learning Skills	Ongoing Records
PM 4: Learning Skills Check List Use to record and report throughout a reporting period, rather than for each unit and/or strand.	*PM 10: Summary Class Records: Strands* *PM 11: Summary Class Records: Achievement Categories* *PM 12: Summary Record: Individual* Use to record and report evaluations of student achievement over several clusters, a reporting period, or a school year. These can also be used in place of the Unit Summary.

Name ____________________ Date ______________

Master 7.1

Unit Rubric: Geometry

	Level 1	Level 2	Level 3	Level 4
Problem solving • chooses and carries out a range of strategies (for example, drawing, creating a diagram, using a computer, creating a pattern) to solve problems involving congruence and transformations (designs and tiling patterns)	with assistance, chooses and carries out a limited range of appropriate strategies for problems involving congruence and transformations, rarely resulting in an accurate solution	with limited assistance, chooses and carries out appropriate strategies for problems involving congruence and transformations, that frequently result in an accurate solution	chooses and carries out appropriate strategies for problems involving congruence and transformations that usually result in an accurate solution	chooses and carries out appropriate strategies for problems involving congruence and transformations, may offer an innovative approach; results in an accurate solution
Understanding of concepts • shows understanding by demonstrating and explaining: – congruence – transformations in a variety of contexts – tiling patterns and designs	shows little understanding; may be unable to demonstrate, analyse, or explain: – congruence – transformations in a variety of contexts – tiling patterns and designs	shows some understanding; partially able to demonstrate, analyse, or explain: – congruence – transformations in a variety of contexts – tiling patterns and designs	shows understanding; able to clearly and appropriately demonstrate, analyse, or explain: – congruence – transformations in a variety of contexts – tiling patterns and designs	shows thorough understanding; able to accurately and effectively demonstrate, analyse, or explain: – congruence – transformations in a variety of contexts – tiling patterns and designs
Application of mathematical procedures • accurately: – classifies figures – identifies congruent figures – identifies images that are translated, rotated, reflected – determines whether a figure will tile a plane	limited accuracy; major errors or omissions in: – classifying figures – identifying congruent figures – identifying images that are translated, rotated, reflected – determining whether a figure will tile a plane	somewhat accurate; several minor errors or omissions in: – classifying figures – identifying congruent figures – identifying images that are translated, rotated, reflected – determining whether a figure will tile a plane	generally accurate; few minor errors or omissions in: – classifying figures – identifying congruent figures – identifying images that are translated, rotated, reflected – determining whether a figure will tile a plane	accurate and precise; no errors in: – classifying figures – identifying congruent figures – identifying images that are translated, rotated, reflected – determining whether a figure will tile a plane
Communication • explains concepts, reasoning, and procedures clearly, using appropriate mathematical language	unable to explain reasoning and procedures clearly	partially explains reasoning and procedures	explains reasoning and procedures clearly	explains reasoning and procedures clearly, precisely, and confidently
• presents work clearly, including appropriate diagrams, labels, and symbols	presents work with little clarity; rarely uses appropriate diagrams, labels, and symbols	presents work with some clarity; uses some appropriate diagrams, labels, and symbols	presents work clearly and precisely; uses appropriate diagrams, labels, and symbols	presents work clearly and precisely; uses a range of appropriate diagrams, labels, and symbols

Name ____________________ Date ________________

Master 7.2

Ongoing Observations: Geometry

The behaviours described under each heading are examples; they are not intended to be an exhaustive list of all that might be observed. More detailed descriptions are provided in each lesson under *Assessment for Learning.*

STUDENT ACHIEVEMENT: Geometry				
Student	**Problem solving** ▪ Chooses and carries out appropriate strategies to solve problems involving congruence and transformations	**Understanding of concepts** ▪ Explains and demonstrates: – congruence – transformations, including tiling patterns and designs	**Application of mathematical procedures** ▪ Identifies congruent figures ▪ Identifies images that are translated, rotated, reflected ▪ Determines when a figure will tile a plane	**Communication** ▪ Explains concepts, reasoning, and procedures clearly ▪ Presents work clearly

Level 1 – very limited; Level 2 – somewhat or limited; Level 3 – satisfactory; Level 4 – thorough

Name ____________________ Date ______________

Master 7.3

Performance Assessment Rubric: Tessellations

	Level 1	Level 2	Level 3	Level 4
Problem solving • chooses appropriate strategies to create two designs by tiling a plane (tessellating) according to specifications given	uses few simple strategies to create designs by tessellating; limited success (does not meet several specifications; may not completely cover the plane)	uses some appropriate strategies to create designs by tessellating; some success (meets most specifications)	uses appropriate strategies to create designs by tessellating; successful (meets specifications)	uses innovative and appropriate strategies to create designs by tessellating; successful and effective (may be relatively complex)
Understanding of concepts • shows understanding of transformations and tiling patterns in descriptions and explanations of the designs and how they were created	shows very limited understanding; may be unable to give appropriate descriptions and explanations of the designs and how they were created; uses few relevant concepts	shows limited understanding by giving some appropriate but incomplete descriptions and explanations of the designs and how they were created; uses some relevant concepts	shows understanding by giving appropriate descriptions and explanations of the designs and how they were created; uses most relevant concepts	shows thorough understanding by giving appropriate and complete descriptions and explanations of the designs and how they were created; uses all relevant concepts
Application of mathematical procedures • repeats the chosen figure to tile the plane • provides accurate diagrams for each design	limited accuracy; major errors or omissions in designs and diagrams	somewhat accurate; several minor errors or omissions in designs and diagrams	generally accurate; few minor errors or omissions in designs and diagrams	accurate and precise; no errors in designs and diagrams
Communication • describes designs clearly, using appropriate mathematical terminology	describes designs unclearly and imprecisely, using few mathematical terms	describes designs with some clarity, using some appropriate mathematical terms	describes designs clearly and precisely, using appropriate mathematical terms	describes designs clearly, precisely, and confidently, using a range of appropriate mathematical terminology
• presents work, including sketches, designs, and diagrams, clearly	presents work with little clarity	presents work with some clarity	presents work clearly	presents work clearly and precisely

Name ____________________ Date ______________

Master 7.4

Unit Summary: Geometry

Review assessment records to determine the most consistent achievement levels for the assessments conducted. Some cells may be blank. *Overall* achievement levels may be recorded in each row, rather than identifying levels for each achievement category.

	Most Consistent Level of Achievement*				
Strand: *Geometry and Spatial Sense*	**Problem solving**	**Understanding of concepts**	**Application of mathematical procedures**	**Communication**	***Overall***
Ongoing Observations					
Work samples or portfolios; conferences					
Unit Review					
Practice Test					
Unit Problem: Tessellations					
Achievement Level for reporting					

* Use Ontario Achievement Levels 1, 2, 3, 4.

Self-Assessment:

Comments: (Strengths; Needs, Next Steps)

Name ____________________ Date ______________

Master 7.5a

Additional Activity 1: Know Your Triangles

Play with a partner.

You will need *Know Your Triangles* game cards and scissors.

How to Play:

1. Cut out the game cards.
Place them face down in a pile.
Turn over the top card.

2. Each player writes a description of the triangle.
Include as much information as you can.

3. Compare descriptions.
Score one point for a correct description.
Score two points for any correct information that is not listed by your partner.

4. Repeat with the next game card.
The player with the most points after 4 rounds wins.

Take It Further: Make your own game cards using different triangles.
Play the game again with the new game cards.

Name ____________________ Date ________________

Master 7.5b

Know Your Triangles Game Cards

Cut out these cards for use with the Additional Activity *Know Your Triangles*.

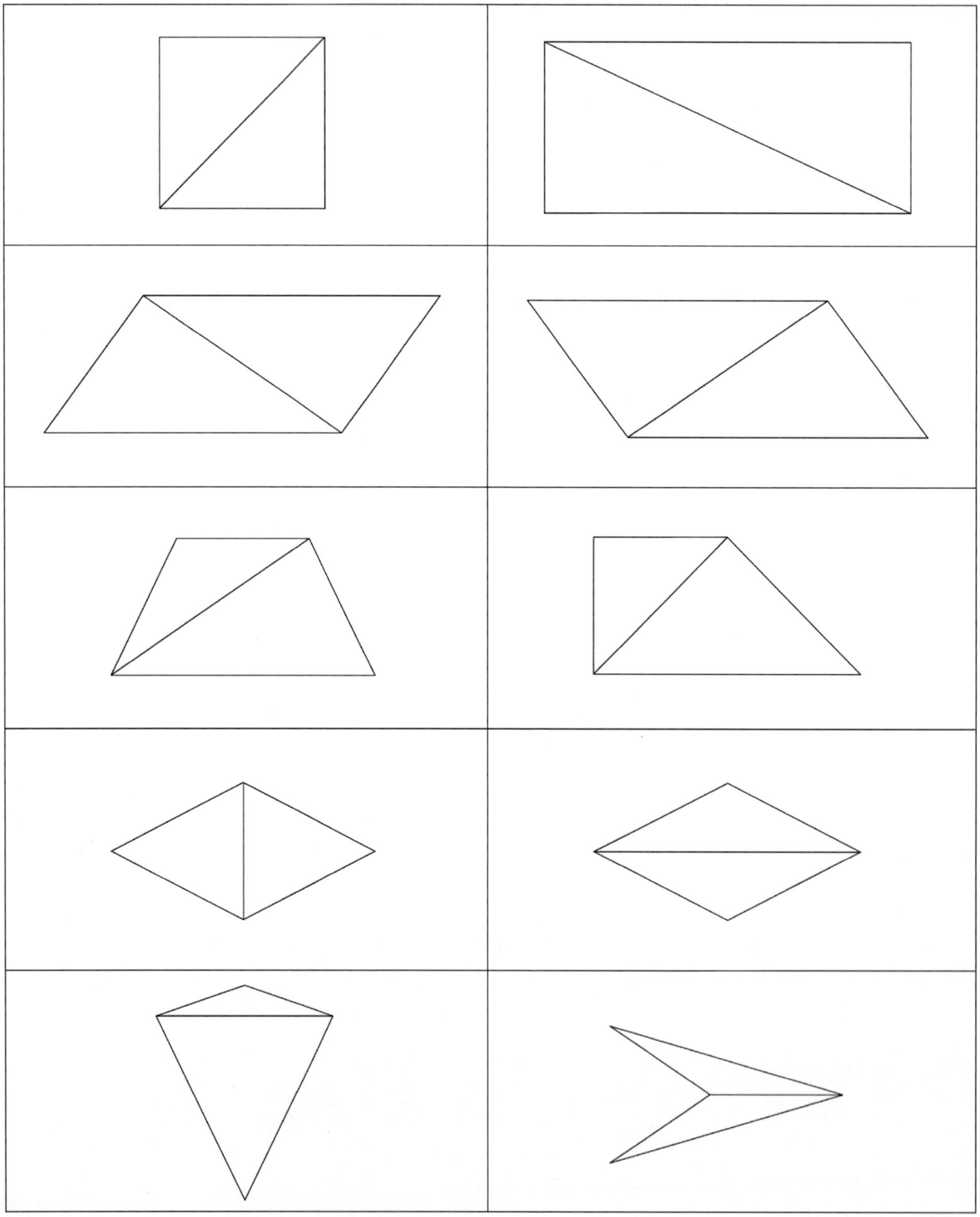

Name ____________________ Date ______________

Master 7.6

Additional Activity 2: Skillful Drawing

Work on your own.

You will need a ruler, a protractor, and a compass.

Follow these instructions to construct several triangles with common sides.
Sketch the triangles before you draw them.

1. Construct ΔABC with BC = 6 cm, angle ABC = 45°, and angle ACB = 35°.

2. Construct equilateral triangle ABD.

3. Construct ΔEAC with AE = 3.5 cm, and angle CAE = 110°.

4. Join DE.

5. Describe ΔADE.

Take It Further: Describe figure BCED.
Measure and label each side and angle that has not yet been measured.

Name ____________________ Date ________________

Master 7.7

Additional Activity 3: Straw Triangles

Play with a partner.

You will need straws, twist ties, a ruler, and scissors.
Cut the straws to lengths of 3 cm, 5 cm, and 9 cm.
You will need 3 straws of each length.

How to Play:

1. Place the straws between you on the table.
   Player A chooses 3 straws.
   List the 3 straws used, so you do not choose that combination again.

2. Player B finds out if the straws can make a triangle.
   Player B describes the triangle, or explains why a triangle cannot be made.

3. One point is scored for a correct description or explanation.

4. Switch roles. Use a different combination of straws.

5. The player with the greater number of points after 5 rounds wins.
   Combinations of straws cannot be repeated.

Take It Further: One player names a type of triangle.
The other player cuts straws to make the triangle.

Name ____________________ Date _______________

Master 7.8a

Additional Activity 4: Point the Triangles

Play with a partner.

You will need several copies of *Point the Triangles* grid.

How to Play:

1. Take turns to name the coordinates of a point C that will make ΔABC isosceles. Score one point for each correct answer.

2. Repeat to make ΔABC a right triangle.

3. Repeat to make ΔABC an obtuse triangle.

4. Repeat to make ΔABC an acute triangle.

5. Choose a different triangle, such as obtuse scalene. Repeat to make ΔABC this type of triangle.

6. The player with more points at the end of the game wins.

Take It Further: Students name the coordinates of points C and D that make figure ABCD a rectangle, a square, a parallelogram, a trapezoid, a rhombus, or a kite.

Name ____________________ Date ________________

Master 7.8b ***Point the Triangles* Grid**

For use with the Additional Activity *Point the Triangles.*

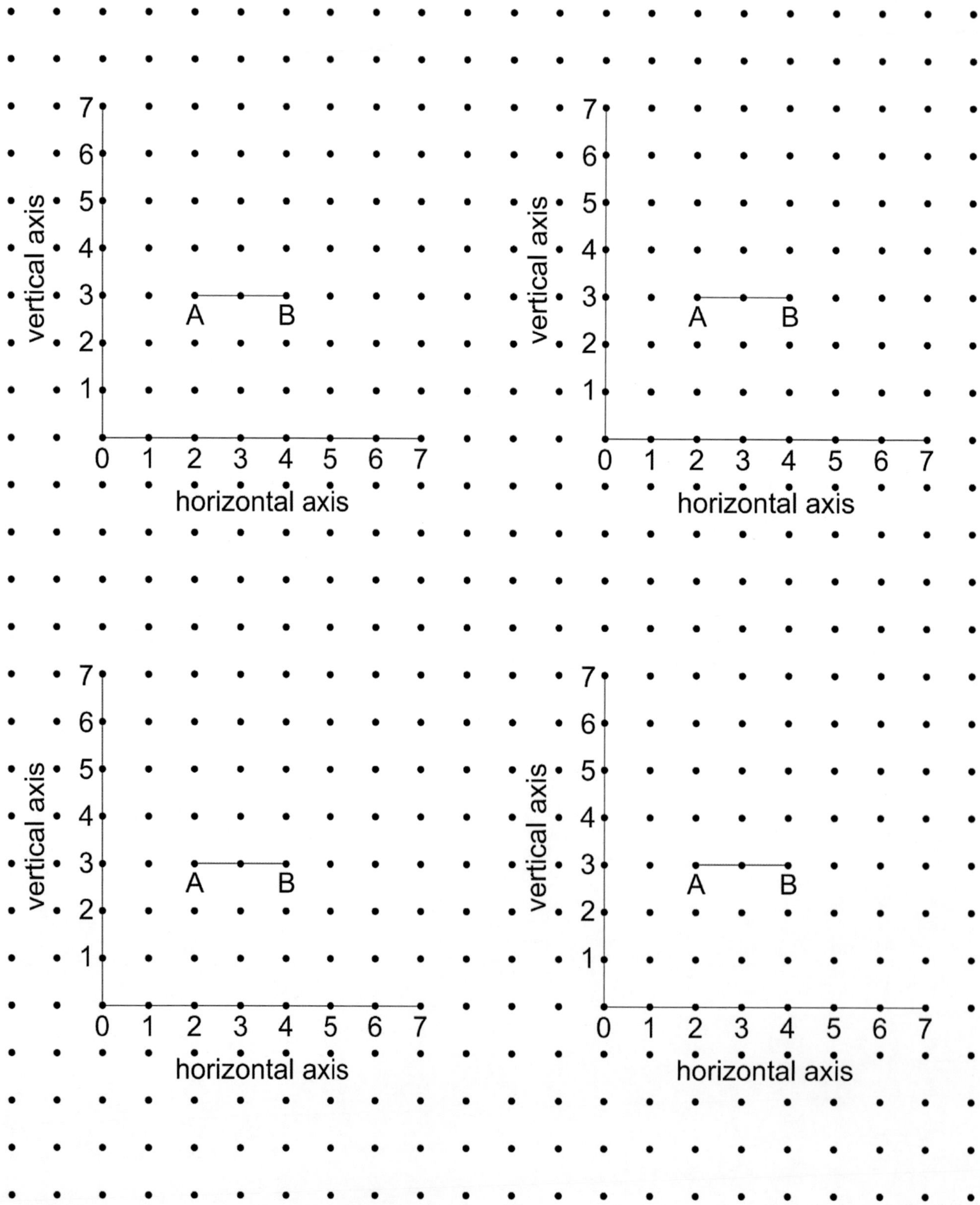

Name ____________________ Date _______________

Master 7.9

Step-by-Step 1

Section 7.1, Question 9

You will need square dot paper.

Step 1 Mark a point D so that ABCD is a trapezoid.
Draw the trapezoid.
Does it have line symmetry? _____
If your answer is no, move point D so the trapezoid does have line symmetry.

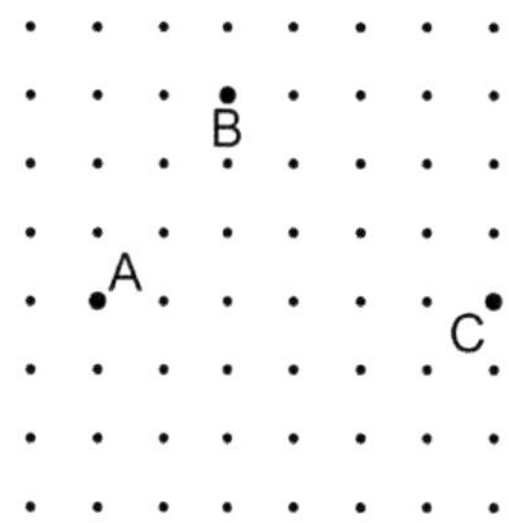

Step 2 Mark a point E below B so that ABCD is a kite.

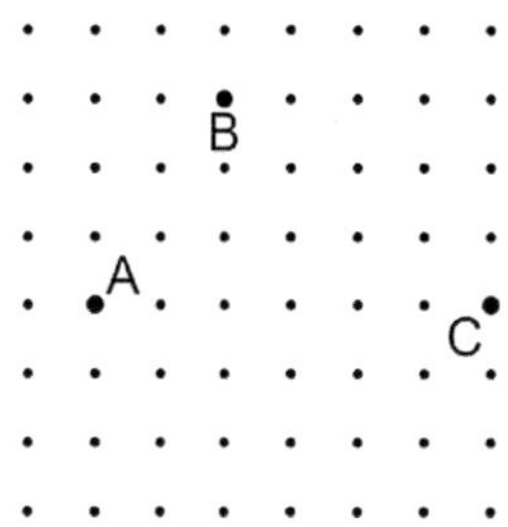

Step 3 Mark a point F on the same horizontal line as B, so that ABFC is a parallelogram.

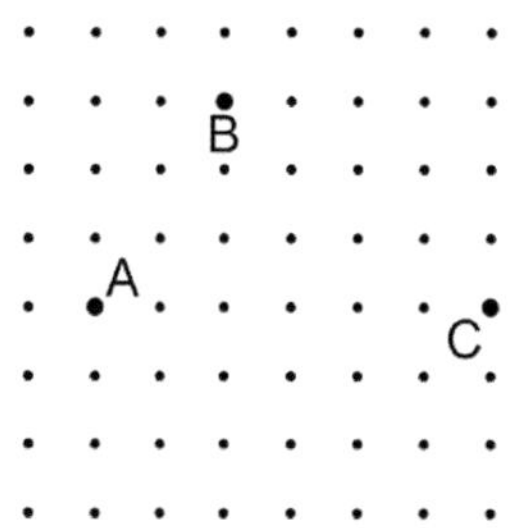

Step 4 Mark two points G and H so ABCGH is a pentagon.

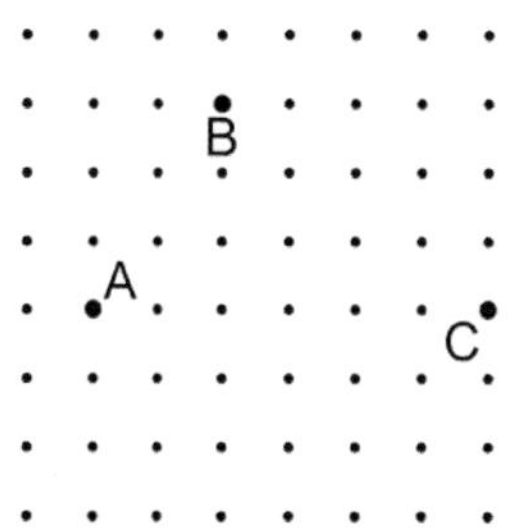

Step 5 Copy the diagram of dots A, B, C on dot paper.
Make other figures with A, B, and C as vertices.
Write about each figure you make.

Name ____________________ Date ______________

Master 7.10

Step-by-Step 2

Section 7.2, Question 9

You will need dot paper.

Step 1 Draw this figure on isometric dot paper.

Label it Figure A.

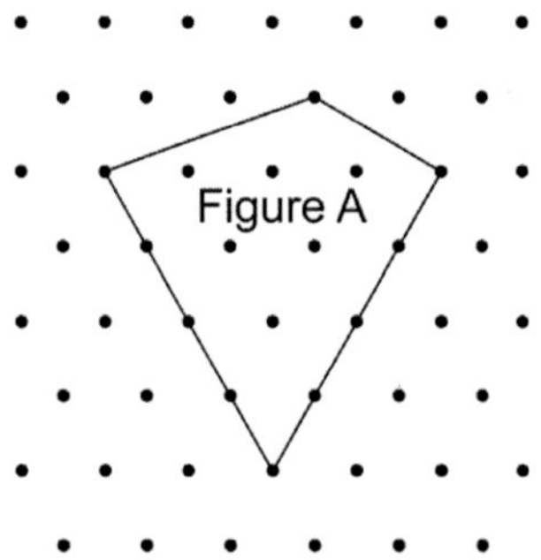

Step 2 Draw a different figure with sides the same length.

Try to draw a concave figure. Label it Figure B.

Mark the sides that are equal in both figures.

How do you know Figure A and Figure B are *not* congruent?

____

____

Step 3 Draw a figure that is congruent to Figure B. Label it Figure C.

How do you know Figure B and Figure C are congruent?

____

____

Step 4 How is Figure A different from Figure C?

____

____

Name ____________________ Date ________________

Master 7.11

Step-by-Step 3

Section 7.3, Question 6

You will need grid paper and tracing paper.

Step 1 Draw a square on grid paper.

Label it Figure A.

Translate the square to the right.

Label the translation image Figure B.

Draw the mirror line for which Figure B is the reflection image of Figure A.

Use tracing paper. Find the turn centre for which Figure B is the rotation image of Figure A.

Step 2 Draw an isosceles triangle on grid paper.

Label it Figure C.

Translate the triangle to the right.

Label the translation image Figure D.

Draw the mirror line for which Figure D is the reflection image of Figure C.

How do you know that Figure D is *not* a rotation image of Figure C?

____

Step 3 Draw a figure that has no symmetry.

Label it Figure E.

Translate the figure to the right.

Label the translation image Figure F.

How do you know that Figure F is *not* a reflection image of Figure E?

____

How do you know that Figure F is *not* a rotation image of Figure E?

____

Name ____________________ Date ________________

Master 7.12 **Step-by-Step 4**

Section 7.4, Question 7

You will need grid paper.

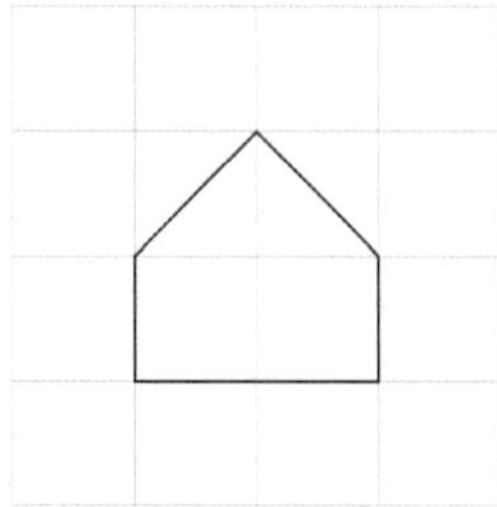

Step 1 Copy this pentagon on grid paper.

Will it tile the plane? _____

If your answer is yes, show how it tiles the grid paper.

If your answer is no, explain why it does not tile the plane.

____

____

Step 2 Repeat *Step 1* for this pentagon.

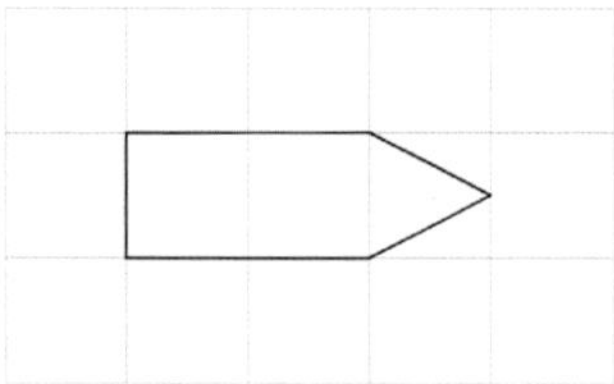

____

____

Step 3 Draw another pentagon that tiles the plane.

Show how it tiles the plane.

Step 4 Why do some pentagons tile the plane and some do not?

____

____

Name ____________________ Date ______________

Master 7.13

Step-by-Step 5

Section 7.5, Question 6

You will need grid paper.

Step 1 On grid paper, draw a square attached to an isosceles triangle.

Draw the figures so they combine to tile the plane.

Tile the plane.

Colour your design.

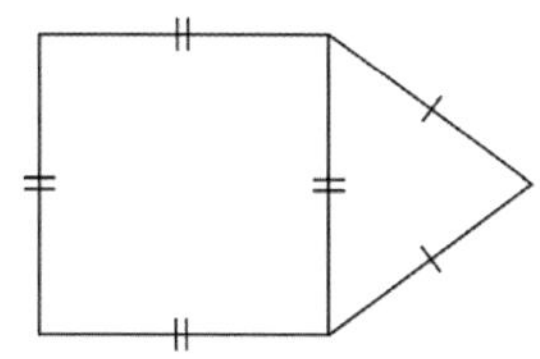

Step 2 Choose 2 adjacent figures in your design.

Label them Figure A and Figure B.

Is Figure B a translation image of Figure A? _______

If your answer is yes, describe the translation.

____

Step 3 Is Figure B a reflection image of Figure A? _______

If your answer is yes, describe the reflection.

____

Step 4 Is Figure B a rotation image of Figure A? _______

If your answer is yes, describe the rotation.

____

Step 5 If your answer to each of *Steps 2* to *4* was no, choose and label 2 figures in your design that are related by a transformation.

Describe the transformation.

____

____

Name ______________________ Date ________________

Master 7.14

Figures for 7.1 *Explore*

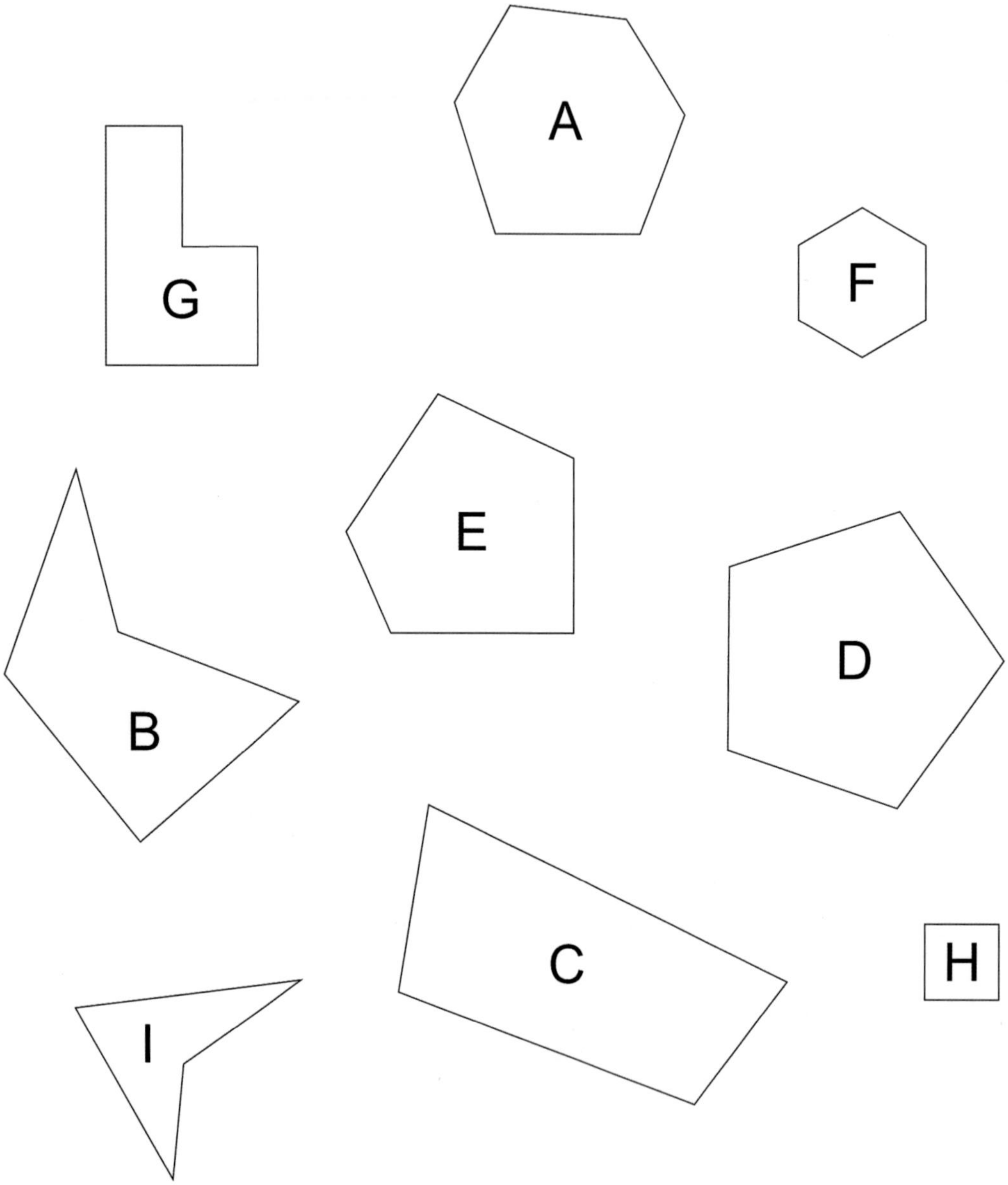

Name ____________________ Date ______________

Master 7.15

Figures for 7.3 *Explore*

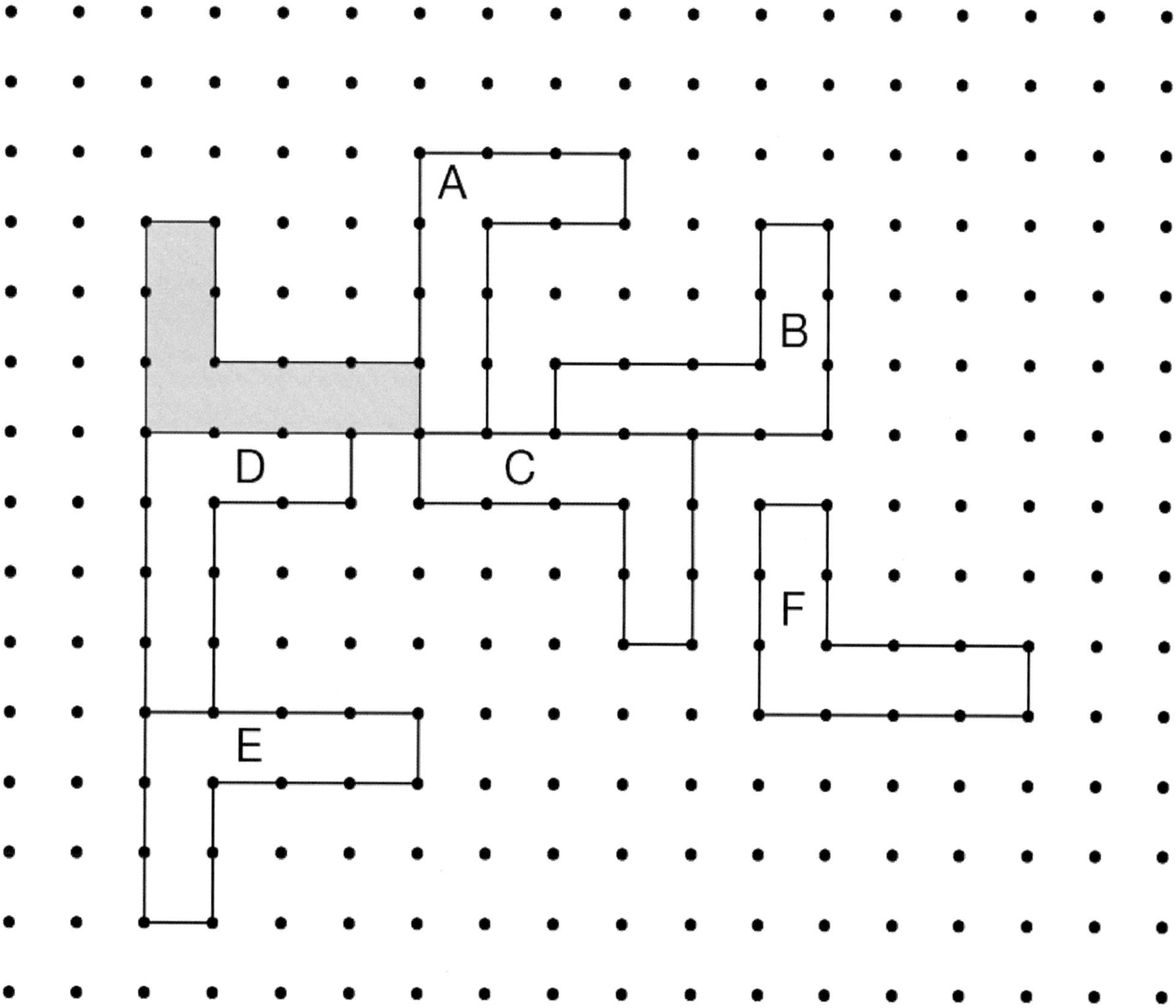

Name ____________________ Date ________________

Master 7.16

Grids for *Practice* Questions 4 and 5

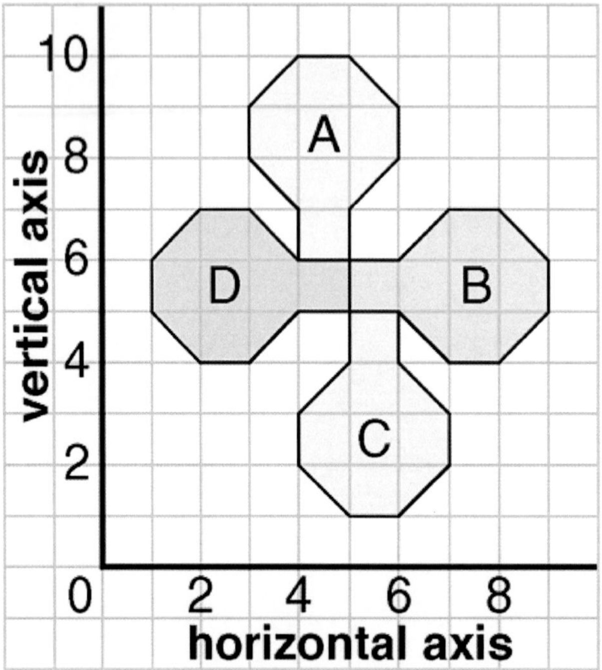

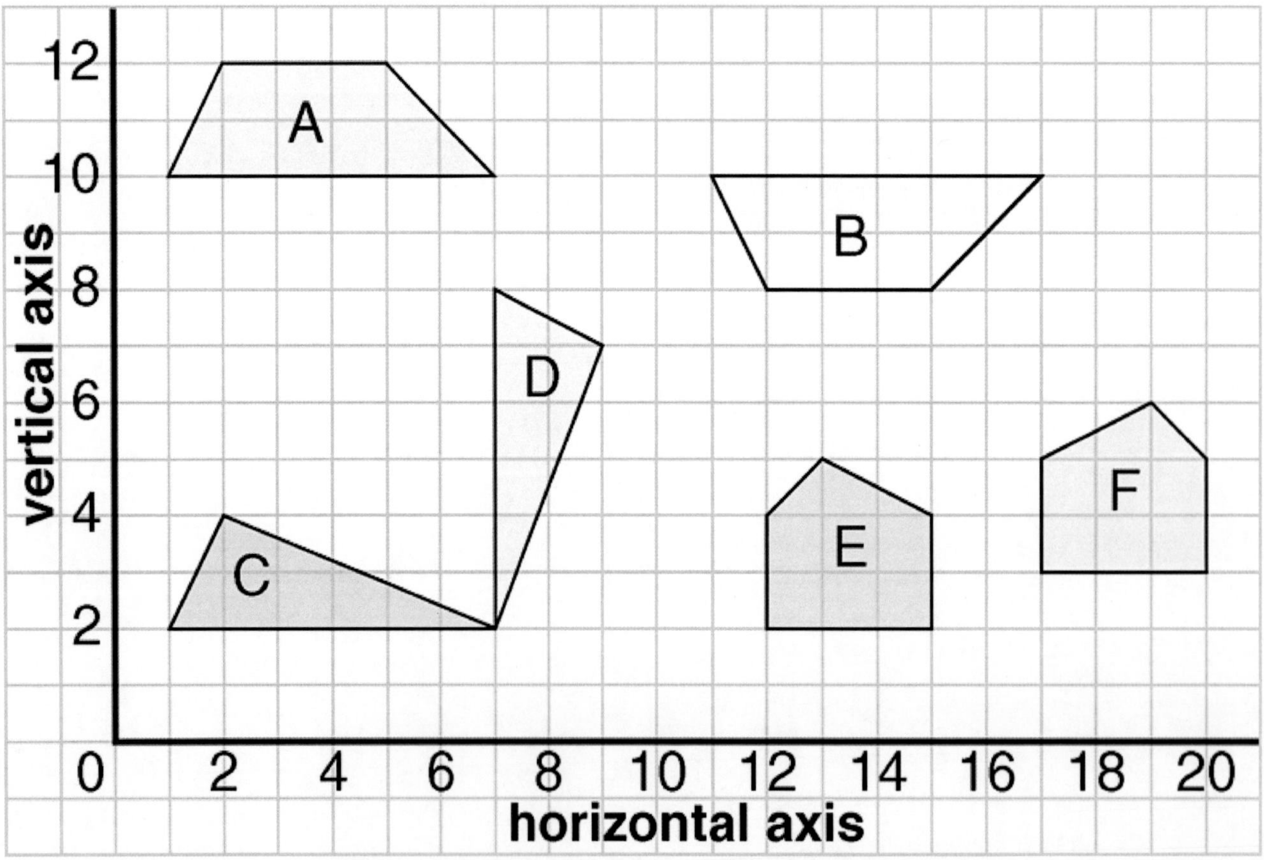

Name ____________________ Date ______________

Master 7.17

Flooring Pattern

Name ____________________ Date ______________

Master 7.18a

Unit Test: Unit 7 Geometry

1. **a)** Describe each figure below.
   b) Choose pairs of figures. Say how they are alike and how they are different.
   c) Identify:
      i) an isosceles triangle with angle 50°
      ii) a parallelogram with side lengths 3 cm and 5 cm
      iii) a quadrilateral that is *not* regular

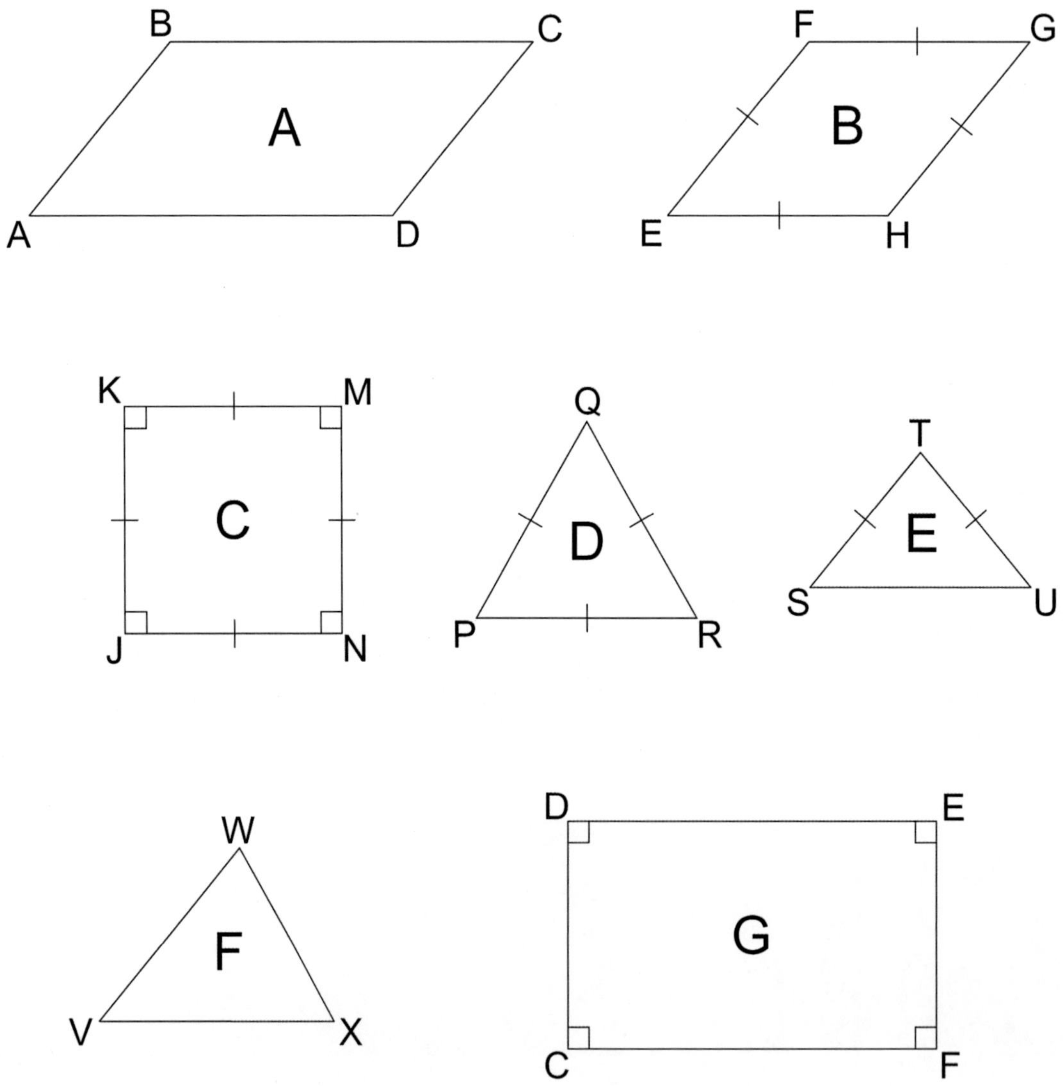

Name ____________________ Date ______________

Master 7.18b

Unit Test continued

2. Triangle PQR and ΔJKM have ∠Q = ∠K = 45° and PQ = JK = 5 cm.
   a) Which of the following measurements would ensure the triangles are congruent?
   b) For each condition for congruent triangles, sketch the triangles and explain how you know they are congruent.
      i) QR = KM = 8 cm
      ii) PR = JM = 4 cm
      iii) ∠P = ∠J = 50°

3. Use grid paper or dot paper.
   a) Draw two octagons that have matching side lengths but different angles. Are the octagons congruent? Explain.
   b) Draw two octagons that have matching angles but different side lengths. Are the octagons congruent? Explain.
   c) Draw two congruent octagons with different orientations. Explain how you know they are congruent.

4. Describe the transformation for which each of the figures A, B, and C are the images of the shaded figure.

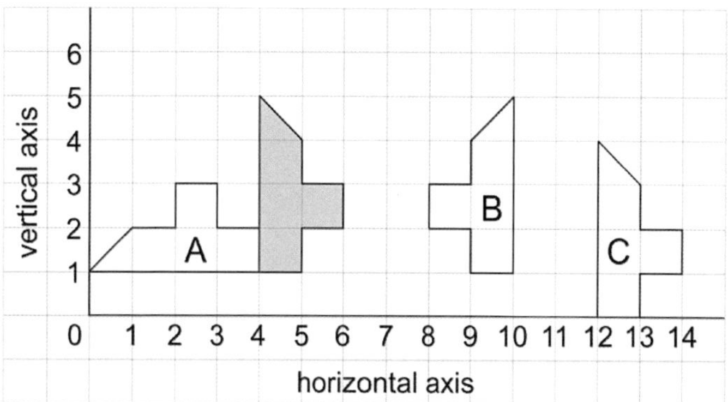

Name ____________________ Date ________________

Master 7.18c

Unit Test continued

5. Which of the following polygons can be used to tile the plane? Explain.

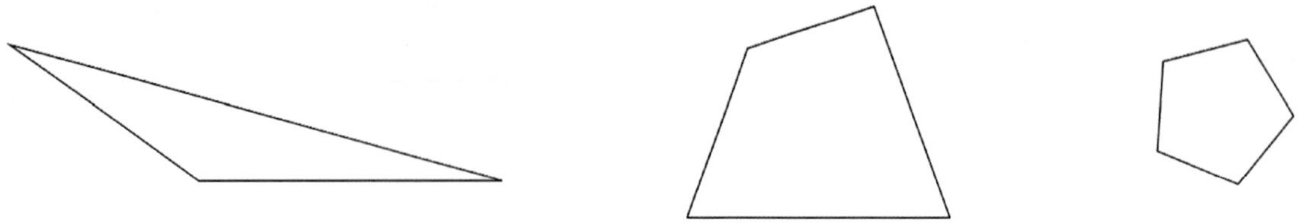

6. a) Show how the trapezoid and the right triangle can be used to tile the plane. Show two different solutions.

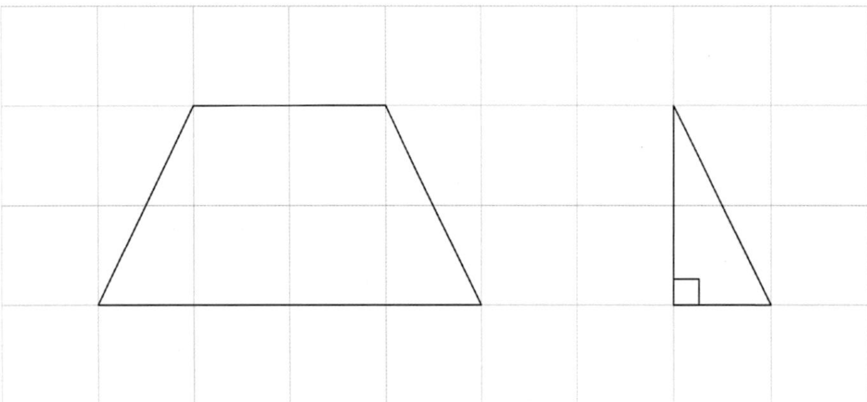

b) Explain how you can use transformations to describe each tiling.

Name ____________________ Date ______________

Master 7.19 Sample Answers

Unit Test – Master 7.18

1. a) Figure A is a parallelogram with 4 sides, 2 pairs of parallel sides, opposite sides equal, opposite angles equal, 2 obtuse angles, and 2 acute angles.
Figure B is a rhombus with 4 sides, all sides equal, opposite angles equal, and 2 pairs of parallel sides. Two angles are acute and 2 angles are obtuse.
Figure C is a square with 4 sides, 2 pairs of parallel sides, all sides equal, and all right angles.
Figure D is an equilateral triangle with 3 equal sides and 3 equal acute angles. It is an acute triangle with each angle measuring 60°.
Figure E is an isosceles triangle with 3 sides, 2 equal sides, 2 equal angles, and 3 acute angles.
Figure F is a scalene triangle with 3 sides, no equal sides, and no equal angles. Each angle is an acute angle.
Figure G is a rectangle with 4 sides, 2 pairs of parallel sides, opposite sides equal, and all right angles.
   b) Figure B and Figure C both have 4 sides, with each side 3 cm. Figure B has 2 acute angles and 2 obtuse angles. Figure C has all right angles.
Figure A and Figure G both have 4 sides, with 2 pairs of parallel sides and opposite sides equal. Figure A has 2 acute angles and 2 obtuse angles. Figure G has all right angles.
Figure E and Figure F both have 3 sides, one angle of 50°, and all acute angles. Figure E has 2 equal sides and 2 equal angles. Figure F has no equal sides and no equal angles.
   c) i) Figure E
   ii) Figure A
   iii) Figures A, B, and G
2. a) i) iii)
   b) i)

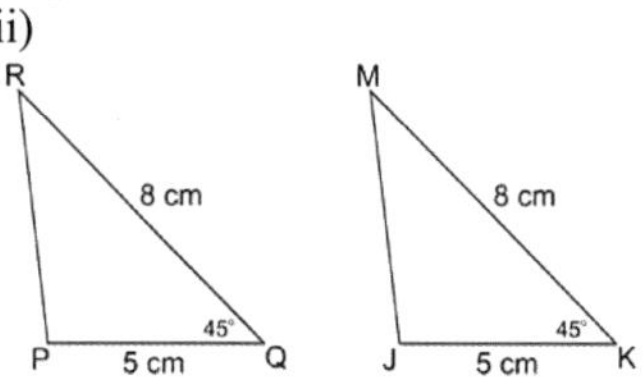

The triangles are congruent because 2 pairs of corresponding sides and the angle between them are equal: PQ = JK, QR = KM, ∠Q = ∠K.

   iii)

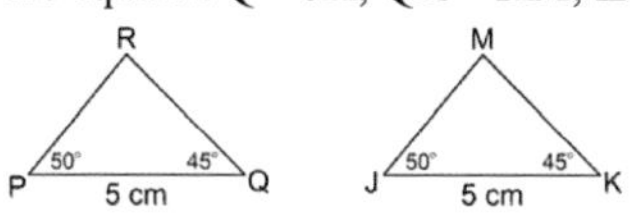

The triangles are congruent because 2 pairs of corresponding angles and the side between them are equal: PQ = JK, ∠P = ∠J, ∠Q = ∠K.

3. a)

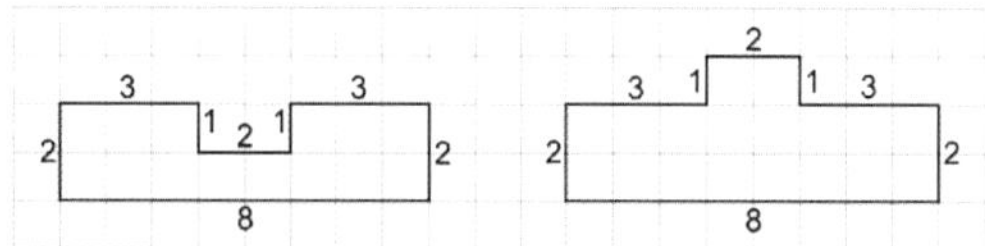

The octagons are not congruent because corresponding angles are not equal.

   b)

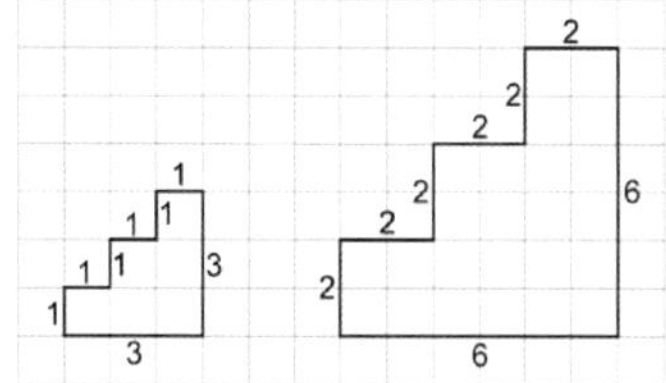

The octagons are not congruent because corresponding sides are not equal.

   c)

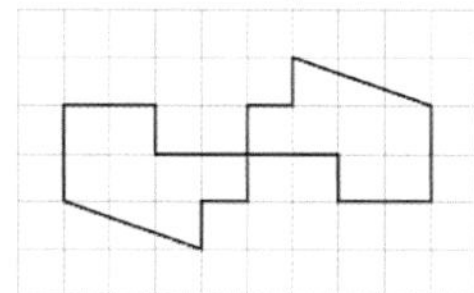

The octagons are congruent because corresponding sides are equal and corresponding angles are equal.

4. Rotate the shaded figure a $\frac{1}{4}$ turn counterclockwise about its bottom left vertex to get Figure A.
Reflect the shaded figure in the vertical line through the point (7, 0) to get Figure B.
Translate the shaded figure 9 units right and 1 unit down to get Figure C.
5. The obtuse triangle can be used to tile the plane because all triangles tile the plane. The triangles can be arranged without gaps, and at any point where vertices meet, the angles add to 360º.
The quadrilateral can be used to tile the plane because all quadrilaterals tile the plane. The quadrilaterals can be arranged without gaps, and at any point where vertices meet, the angles add to 360º. The regular pentagon cannot be used to tile the plane. A regular pentagon has 5 equal angles and each angle is 108º. Since 108 does not divide exactly into 360, I know that a regular pentagon will not tile the plane. There will be gaps.

6. a)

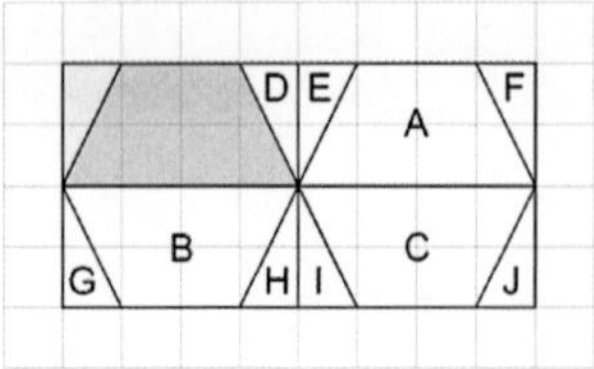

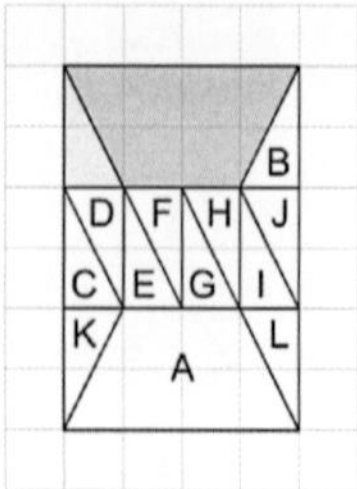

b) Design 1: Translate the shaded trapezoid 4 units right to get trapezoid A. Reflect the shaded triangle in a vertical line through the midpoint of the bottom side of the shaded trapezoid to get triangle D. Reflect triangle D in its right side to get triangle E. Reflect triangle E in a vertical line through the midpoint of the bottom side of trapezoid A to get triangle F. Reflect the section in a horizontal line through the bottom side of trapezoid A to get the next row. Continue reflecting to cover the page.

Design 2: Reflect the shaded trapezoid in a horizontal line 1 unit down from its bottom side to get trapezoid A. Reflect the shaded triangle in a vertical line through the midpoint of the bottom side of the shaded trapezoid to get triangle B. Translate the shaded triangle down 2 units to get triangle C. Rotate triangle C a $\frac{1}{2}$ turn about the midpoint of its hypotenuse to get triangle D. Translate triangles C and D 1 unit right to get triangles E and F. Translate triangles E and F 1 unit right to get triangles G and H. Translate triangles G and H 1 unit right to get triangles I and J. Reflect triangle C in its bottom side to get triangle K. Translate triangle J down 2 units to get triangle L. Translate the section down 6 units to get the next row. Continue translating to cover the page.

Extra Practice Masters 7.20–7.25

Go to the CD-ROM to access editable versions of these Extra Practice Masters.

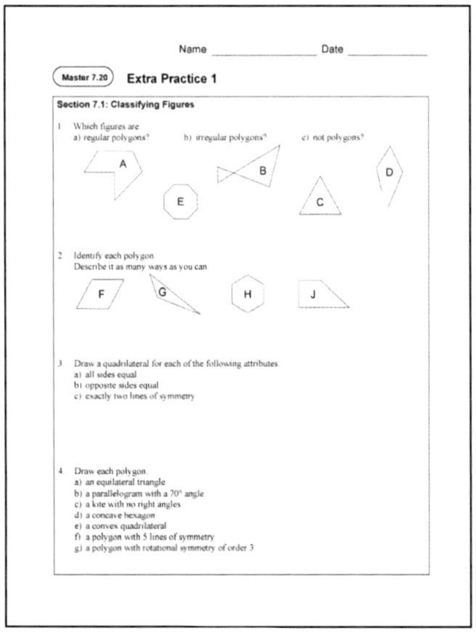

Name ____________ Date ____________

Master 7.20 **Extra Practice 1**

Section 7.1: Classifying Figures

1. Which figures are
a) regular polygons? b) irregular polygons? c) not polygons?

2. Identify each polygon.
Describe it as many ways as you can.

3. Draw a quadrilateral for each of the following attributes.
a) all sides equal
b) opposite sides equal
c) exactly two lines of symmetry

4. Draw each polygon.
a) an equilateral triangle
b) a parallelogram with a 70° angle
c) a kite with no right angles
d) a concave hexagon
e) a convex quadrilateral
f) a polygon with 5 lines of symmetry
g) a polygon with rotational symmetry of order 3

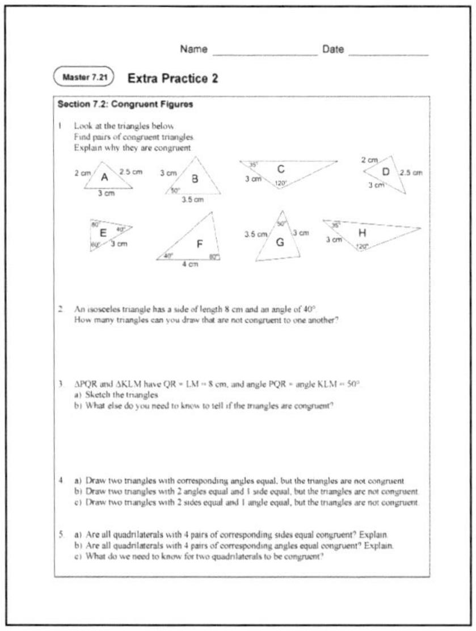

Name ____________ Date ____________

Master 7.21 **Extra Practice 2**

Section 7.2: Congruent Figures

1. Look at the triangles below.
Find pairs of congruent triangles.
Explain why they are congruent.

2. An isosceles triangle has a side of length 8 cm and an angle of 40°.
How many triangles can you draw that are not congruent to one another?

3. △PQR and △KLM have QR = LM = 8 cm, and angle PQR = angle KLM = 50°.
a) Sketch the triangles.
b) What else do you need to know to tell if the triangles are congruent?

4. a) Draw two triangles with corresponding angles equal, but the triangles are not congruent.
b) Draw two triangles with 2 angles equal and 1 side equal, but the triangles are not congruent.
c) Draw two triangles with 2 sides equal and 1 angle equal, but the triangles are not congruent.

5. a) Are all quadrilaterals with 4 pairs of corresponding sides equal congruent? Explain.
b) Are all quadrilaterals with 4 pairs of corresponding angles equal congruent? Explain.
c) What do we need to know for two quadrilaterals to be congruent?

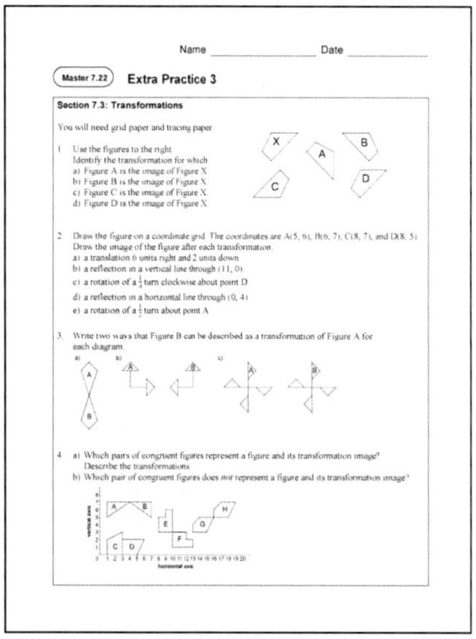

Name ____________ Date ____________

Master 7.22 **Extra Practice 3**

Section 7.3: Transformations

You will need grid paper and tracing paper.

1. Use the figures to the right.
Identify the transformation for which
a) Figure A is the image of Figure X.
b) Figure B is the image of Figure X.
c) Figure C is the image of Figure X.
d) Figure D is the image of Figure X.

2. Draw the figure on a coordinate grid. The coordinates are A(5, 6), B(6, 7), C(8, 7), and D(8, 5).
Draw the image of the figure after each transformation.
a) a translation 6 units right and 2 units down
b) a reflection in a vertical line through (11, 0)
c) a rotation of a $\frac{1}{4}$ turn clockwise about point D
d) a reflection in a horizontal line through (0, 4)
e) a rotation of a $\frac{1}{2}$ turn about point A

3. Write two ways that Figure B can be described as a transformation of Figure A for each diagram.

4. a) Which pairs of congruent figures represent a figure and its transformation image?
Describe the transformations.
b) Which pair of congruent figures does *not* represent a figure and its transformation image?

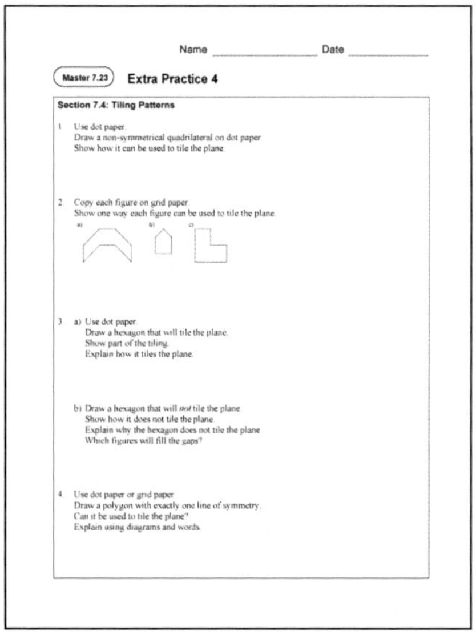

Name ____________ Date ____________

Master 7.23 **Extra Practice 4**

Section 7.4: Tiling Patterns

1. Use dot paper.
Draw a non-symmetrical quadrilateral on dot paper.
Show how it can be used to tile the plane.

2. Copy each figure on grid paper.
Show one way each figure can be used to tile the plane.

3. a) Use dot paper.
Draw a hexagon that will tile the plane.
Show part of the tiling.
Explain how it tiles the plane.

b) Draw a hexagon that will *not* tile the plane.
Show how it does not tile the plane.
Explain why the hexagon does not tile the plane.
Which figures will fill the gaps?

4. Use dot paper or grid paper.
Draw a polygon with exactly one line of symmetry.
Can it be used to tile the plane?
Explain using diagrams and words.

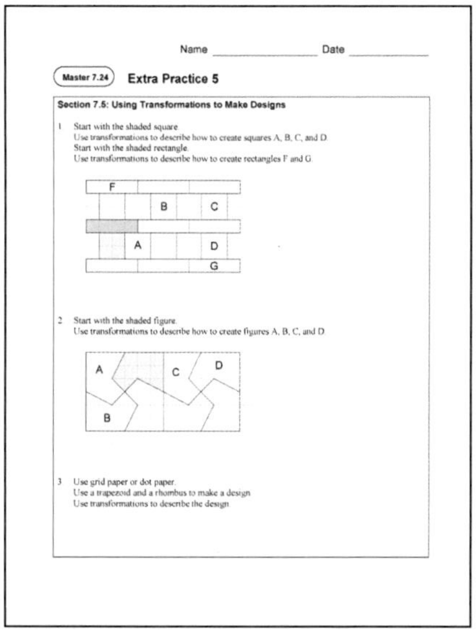

Name ____________ Date ____________

Master 7.24 **Extra Practice 5**

Section 7.5: Using Transformations to Make Designs

1. Start with the shaded square.
Use transformations to describe how to create squares A, B, C, and D.
Start with the shaded rectangle.
Use transformations to describe how to create rectangles F and G.

2. Start with the shaded figure.
Use transformations to describe how to create figures A, B, C, and D.

3. Use grid paper or dot paper.
Use a trapezoid and a rhombus to make a design.
Use transformations to describe the design.

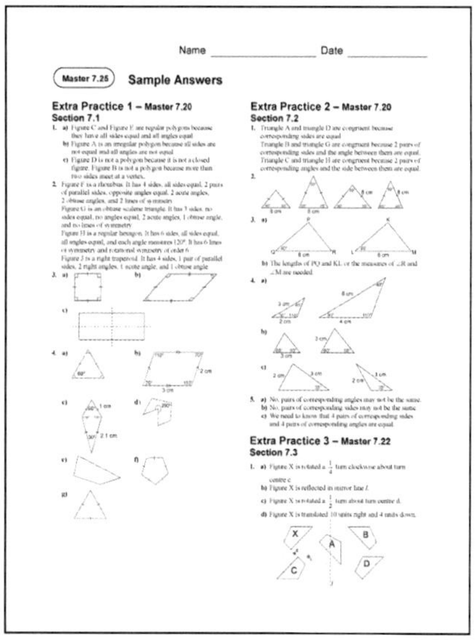

Name ____________ Date ____________

Master 7.25 **Sample Answers**

Extra Practice 1 – Master 7.20
Section 7.1

Extra Practice 2 – Master 7.20
Section 7.2

Extra Practice 3 – Master 7.22
Section 7.3

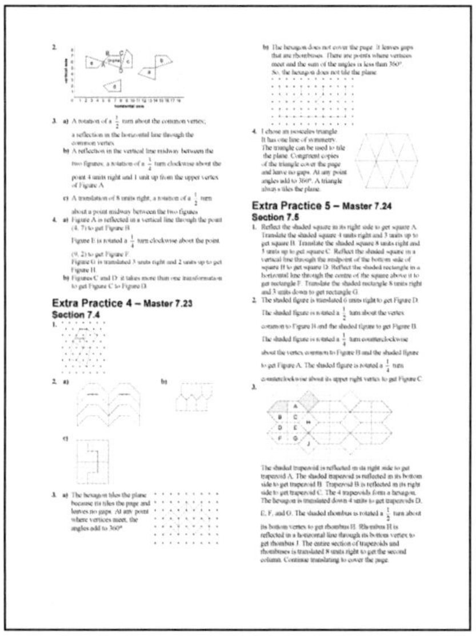

Extra Practice 4 – Master 7.23
Section 7.4

Extra Practice 5 – Master 7.24
Section 7.5

Addison Wesley
Mathematics
Makes Sense

Program Authors

Jason Johnston
Bryn Keyes
Mary Doucette
Antonietta Leujosek
Steve Thomas
Margaret Sinclair
Trevor Brown
Cathy Heideman
Don Jones
Michael Davis
Jennifer Paziuk
Ken Harper
Sharon Jeroski
Ray Appel
Laura Weatherhead
Betty Milne
Jim Mennie
Lynn Strangway

Printed and bound in Canada

10 17

PEARSON
Education
Canada

ADDISON WESLEY

Ontario

Math Makes Sense 7

Ontario Teacher Guide

Unit 8: Working with Percents

PEARSON
Addison Wesley

UNIT 8

Working with Percents

"The connection of percents to fraction and decimal concepts is so strong that it makes sense to discuss percents as students begin to have a good grasp of the fraction-decimal relationships."

John A. Van de Walle

FOCUS STRANDS
Number Sense and Numeration
Data Management and Probability

SUPPORTING STRAND
Measurement

TIPS
Consider prior knowledge, achievement on particular tasks, social skills, learning skills, gender, and exceptionalities when determining a grouping for a particular task.

Mathematics Background

What Are the Big Ideas?

- Decimals are another way to write fractions. It is important to understand the relationships between them.
- Percents and hundredths are the same. Percent is another way to write fractions and decimals.
- Multiplying (or dividing) two numbers will result in the same digits, regardless of the positions of the decimal point. To multiply (or divide) two decimals, multiply (or divide) as whole numbers, then estimate to place the decimal point in the answer.

How Will the Concepts Develop?

Students investigate the relationships among fractions, decimals, and percents. They convert among fractions, decimals, and percents, and draw number lines to illustrate the relationships. Students use mental math strategies to estimate and to calculate percents.

Students use their knowledge of the multiplication of decimals with tenths to multiply decimals with hundredths to find percents. They use their understanding of the relationship among fractions, decimals, and percents to investigate how data can be represented using circle graphs. They analyse circle graphs and use mathematical language to describe their findings.

Students divide decimals with hundredths to find percents. They communicate their understanding as they solve problems that involve working with percents.

Why Are These Concepts Important?

Decimals and fractions are two different ways of representing the same part-to-whole relationship. Percents are hundredths and represent a third way to write fractions and decimals.

We see uses of percent everywhere. Percents appear in newspapers, on television, and in stores. For example, interest is paid on money invested in banks. The interest rate is given as a percent. Items in stores are often advertised at a sale price that is a certain percent off the regular price. It is useful to be able to calculate the cost of these items. Tax is applied to most items purchased. It is good to be able to calculate the sales tax to know if you have enough money to buy the item.

Curriculum Overview

Overall Expectations
- Compare, order, and represent decimals, … . (7m1)
- Use estimation to justify or assess the reasonableness of calculations. (7m5)
- Solve and explain multi-step problems involving simple fractions, decimals, and percents. (7m6)
- Explain, in writing, the process of problem solving using appropriate mathematical language. (7m7)
- Use a calculator to solve number questions that are beyond the proficiency expectations for operations using pencil and paper. (7m8)
- Systematically …, organize, and analyse data. (7m81)
- Interpret displays of data and present the information using mathematical terms. (7m86)

Specific Expectations
- Compare and order decimals. (7m9)
- Perform three-step problem solving that involves whole numbers and decimals related to real-life experiences, using calculators. (7m14)
- Ask "what if" questions; pose problems involving simple fractions, decimals, and percents; and investigate solutions. (7m23)
- Explain the process used and any conclusions reached in problem solving and investigations. (7m24)
- Solve problems that involve converting between fractions, decimals, and percents. (7m27)
- Use conventional …, titles, and labels when displaying data. (7m98)
- Read and report information about data presented on … circle graphs, and use the information to solve problems. (7m100)
- Display data on … circle graphs, …, without the help of technology. (7m102)

Launch

Section 8.1: Relating Fractions, Decimals, and Percents

Section 8.2: Estimating and Calculating Percents

Section 8.3: Multiplying to Find Percents

Mid-Unit Review

Section 8.4: Drawing Circle Graphs

Section 8.5: Dividing to Find Percents

Unit Review
Practice Test

Unit Problem
At the Shopping Mall

Curriculum across the Grades

Grade 6	Grade 7	Grade 8
Students relate fractions to decimals and percents, using concrete materials, drawings, and symbols. Students explore the relationships among fractions, decimals, and simple percents using a calculator, concrete materials, and drawings. They estimate and calculate percent. Students select operations and solve multi-step problems involving whole numbers and decimals with and without a calculator. They pose problems involving decimals, and percents, and solve them. Students explain their thinking when solving problems involving fractions, decimals, and percents. Students recognize that different types of graphs can present the same data differently.	Students compare and order decimals. They perform three-step problem solving that involves whole numbers and decimals related to real-life experiences, using calculators. Students ask "what if" questions; pose problems involving simple fractions, decimals, and percents; and investigate solutions. They solve problems involving fractions and decimals. Students solve problems that involve converting between fractions, decimals, and percents. Students read and write information about data presented on circle graphs, and use the information to solve problems. They display data on circle graphs, with and without the help of technology.	Students perform multi-step calculations involving whole numbers and decimals in real-life situations, involving calculators. Students ask "what if" questions; pose problems involving simple fractions, decimals, and percents; and investigate solutions. They solve problems that involve converting among fractions, decimals, and percents. Students apply percents in solving problems involving discounts, sales tax, commission, and simple interest. Students read and report information about data presented on circle graphs, and use the information to solve problems. They construct circle graphs, with and without the help of technology, and use the information to solve problems.

Materials for This Unit

Students require labels from canned food, cereal boxes, or other food in Section 8.4. You may want to copy, cut out, then laminate the cards for the Additional Activities and the *Showdown* game.

Additional Activities

Squeeze Play

For Extra Practice (Appropriate for use after Section 8.1)
Materials: *Squeeze Play* (Master 8.5a), *Squeeze Play* Game Cards (Master 8.5b)

Playing this game reinforces the skills of comparing and ordering fractions, decimals, and percents, and converting among them.

The work students do: Students play with a partner. Player A tries to find a card that will "squeeze" between the target cards. If Player A has a "squeeze" card, she places it face up, on top of one of the target cards. If Player A does not have a "squeeze" card, she places another card from her hand face up, on top of one of the target cards, then draws another card. Player B takes a turn. The first player to have no cards left wins.

Take It Further: Students must state a decimal, fraction, or percent equivalent to the "squeeze" card.

Kinesthetic/Social/Logical
Partner Activity

Concentration

For Extra Support (Appropriate for use after Section 8.1.)
Materials: *Concentration* (Master 8.6), *Squeeze Play* Game Cards (Master 8.5b)

Playing this game reinforces the skills of comparing and ordering fractions, decimals, and percents, and converting among them.

The work students do: Students take turns to turn over 3 cards. A match is made when all 3 cards represent the same number. A student keeps the cards when a match is made. If a match is not made, the cards are turned face down again. The student with the most matches wins.

Take It Further: Students play with the 100% card. Students turn over one card, then find a second card of greater value. If students are successful, they keep the paired cards. The player with the most pairs at the end of the game wins.

Logical/Mathematical/Social
Partner Activity

Link 5

For Extra Practice (Appropriate for use after Section 8.3)
Materials: *Link 5* (Master 8.7a), *Link 5* Game Board (Master 8.7b), *Link 5* Game Cards (Master 8.7c), red and yellow counters, calculators

Playing this game reinforces the skill of calculating a percent of a number.

The work students do: The goal of the game is to link 5 squares diagonally, vertically, or horizontally. Each player chooses a counter colour. Red turns over a card in Row 1, then draws a number card. He uses the percent card to find that percent of the number. If Red is correct, a red counter is placed on the square. If Red is incorrect, the percent card is turned face down and Yellow takes a turn. The first player to make a link of 5 squares wins.

Take It Further: Students draw 2 number cards at a time, and use a percent card to find that percent of each number. Both answers must be correct to place a counter on the square.

Logical/Mathematical/Social
Partner Activity

Planning for Unit 8

Planning for Instruction

Suggested Unit time: About 3 weeks

Section	Time	Materials	Program Support
Launch, page 2	15–20 min		
Skills You'll Need, page 4	65–80 min	blank hundred charts calculators	PM 16: Blank 10 × 10 Chart
8.1: Relating Fractions, Decimals, and Percents, page 6 Relate percent to fractions and decimals.	80–100 min	puzzle for *Explore* calculators rulers isometric grid paper 2-cm grid paper coloured pencils hundred charts	Master 8.13: Puzzle for *Explore* PM 24: Isometric Grid Paper PM 21: 2-cm Grid Paper PM 13: Hundred Chart Master 8.8: Step-by-Step 1 Master 8.18: Extra Practice 1
Game: Showdown, page 10		2 sets of *Showdown* playing cards scissors calculators	Masters 8.14a and 8.14b: *Showdown* Playing Cards
8.2: Estimating and Calculating Percents, page 11 Use mental math and estimation.	80–100 min	old newspapers masking tape measuring tape or metre stick rulers calculators	Master 8.9: Step-by-Step 2 Master 8.19: Extra Practice 2
8.3: Multiplying to Find Percents, page 16 Multiply decimals with hundredths.	80–100 min	calculators Pattern Blocks	PM 25: Pattern Blocks Master 8.10: Step-by-Step 3 Master 8.20: Extra Practice 3
Mid-Unit Review, page 19		calculators rulers 2-cm grid paper	PM 21: 2-cm Grid Paper
8.4: Drawing Circle Graphs, page 20 Use circle graphs to display data and solve problems.	80–100 min	percent circles 4-column charts protractors rulers labels from canned food, cereal boxes, or other food compasses	Master 8.15: Percent Circle PM 19: 4-Column Charts Master 8.11: Step-by-Step 4 Master 8.21: Extra Practice 4
8.5: Dividing to Find Percents, page 25 Divide decimals with hundredths.	80–100 min	calculators counters (optional) play money (optional)	Master 8.12: Step-by-Step 5 Master 8.22: Extra Practice 5
Reading and Writing in Math: Choosing a Strategy, page 28		calculators square dot paper 1-cm grid paper linking cubes	PM 20: 1-cm Grid Paper PM 22: Square Dot Paper
Unit Review, page 31		1-cm grid paper percent circles calculators, compasses protractors, rulers	PM 20: 1-cm Grid Paper Master 8.15: Percent Circle Extra Practice: Student Book page 445
Practice Test, page 33		rulers, calculators compasses, protractors	
Unit Problem: At the Shopping Mall, page 34	40–50 min	calculators	

etext online tutorial

This web-based tutorial uses voice, animation, and an optional quiz to present each core lesson, so that students can review content with a new approach.

Planning for Assessment

Purpose	Tools and Process	Recording and Reporting
Diagnostic	*Unit Launch* Question; conference; scaffold problems throughout the unit	PM 8: Conference Prompts
Formative	*Explore* – Ongoing Assessment: Observe and Listen	Master 8.2 Ongoing Observations: Working with Percents PM 1: Inquiry Process Check List PM 6: Observation Record 1 PM 7: Observation Record 2 PM 8: Conference Prompts PM 2: Self-Assessment PM 3: Self-Assessment: Problem Solving PM 9: Work Sample Records
Summative	*Unit Review* *Unit Problem* – Performance Assessment Unit Test Review assessment records; add unit results to ongoing records	Master 8.1 Unit Rubric: Working with Percents Master 8.3 Performance Assessment Rubric: At the Shopping Mall Master 8.4 Unit Summary: Working with Percents PM 10: Summary Class Records: Strands PM 11: Summary Class Records: Achievement Categories PM 12: Summary Record: Individual
Learning Skills/Mathematical Disposition	Observe and record throughout the unit	PM 4: Learning Skills Check List PM 5: Mathematical Dispositions and Learning Skills

Program Masters (PM) are in the *Grade 7 Planning and Program Masters* module.
Extra Practice Masters are on the CD-ROM and are printed in reduced format on page 62 of this module.

SECTION ORGANIZER

15–20 min

Curriculum Focus: Activate prior learning about decimals and percents.

ASSUMED PRIOR KNOWLEDGE

- ☑ Students can calculate simple percents.
- ☑ Students can recognize the relationships among fractions, decimals, and simple percents.

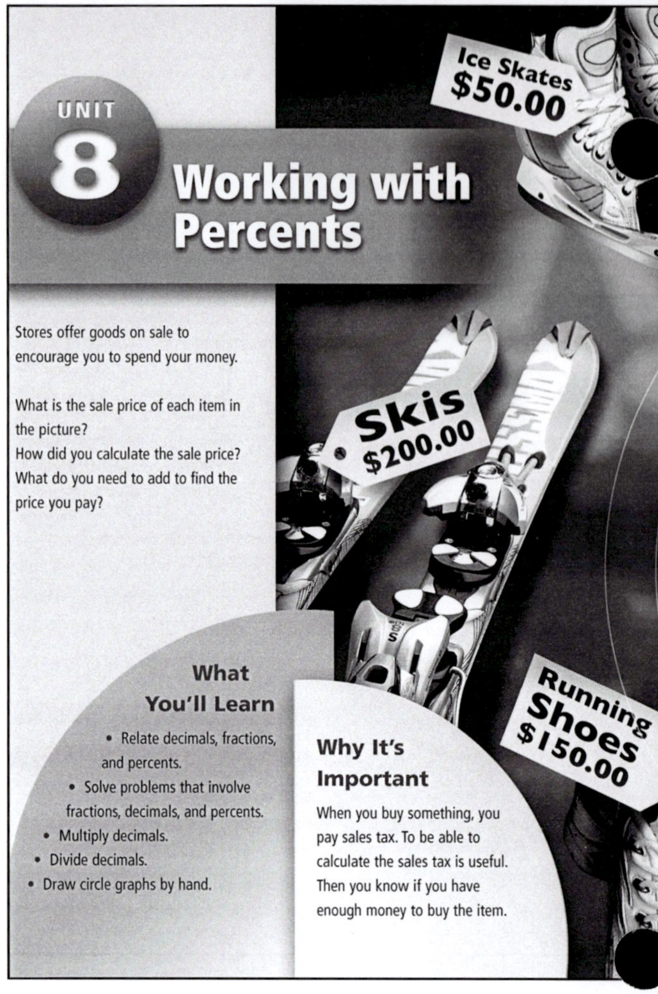
UNIT 8

Working with Percents

Ice Skates $50.00

Skis $200.00

Running Shoes $150.00

Stores offer goods on sale to encourage you to spend your money.

What is the sale price of each item in the picture?
How did you calculate the sale price?
What do you need to add to find the price you pay?

What You'll Learn

- Relate decimals, fractions, and percents.
- Solve problems that involve fractions, decimals, and percents.
- Multiply decimals.
- Divide decimals.
- Draw circle graphs by hand.

Why It's Important

When you buy something, you pay sales tax. To be able to calculate the sales tax is useful. Then you know if you have enough money to buy the item.

ACTIVATE PRIOR LEARNING

Have students look at the pictures of sports items and their price tags on pages 288 and 289 of the Student Book. Ask questions, such as:

- Why do stores offer a "percent off?"
  (*To lure more people into the store; to encourage people to buy*)
- Is it better for the consumer to get a greater or a lesser percent off the price of an item?
  (*Greater*) Why? (*The store will take more off the price and the consumer will pay less for the item.*)
- What is the sale price of the ice skates?
  (*$25.00*)
- How did you calculate the sale price?
  (*I found 50% or one-half of $50.00; one-half of $50.00 is $25.00.*)
- What is the sale price of the skis? (*$100.00*)
  The running shoes? (*$75.00*)
  The hockey sweater? (*$40.00*)
- What do you need to add to find the price you pay?
  (*I need to add the provincial sales tax and the GST.*)

Tell students that provincial sales taxes differ from province to province. The GST is a 7% tax added to most goods and services. These taxes are collected by the provincial and federal governments to help pay for various services.

Tell students that, in this unit, they will investigate percents. They will examine the relationships among fractions, decimals, and percents and they will learn why calculating percent is a useful mathematical tool. At the end of the unit, students will use their understanding of percents to spend $500.00 at the shopping mall.

Key Words

- percent
- percent circle

FROM THE LIBRARY

Decimals: A Place Value Approach by Linda Patriarca, Marilyn Scheffel, and Sheila Hedeman. Dale Seymour Publications, 1998
ISBN: 0866519580
This book presents a logical, step-by-step sequence for teaching decimal concepts as an extension of the place-value system.
It introduces the concepts of tenths, hundredths, and thousandths, followed by comparing and ordering quantities.

Masterminds Skills Boosters for the Reluctant Math Student by B. Opie and D. McAvinn. Incentive Publications Inc., 2000
ISBN: 0865304483
This book brings excitement and impact to otherwise routine math lessons and practice sessions. Students solve riddles while covering important skills, including work with fractions, decimals, and percents.

REACHING ALL LEARNERS

Some students may benefit from using the virtual manipulatives on the e-Tools CD-ROM.
The e-Tool appropriate for this unit is *Fractions.*

DIAGNOSTIC ASSESSMENT

What to Look For	What to Do
✔ Students can calculate simple percents. ✔ Students can recognize the relationships among fractions, decimals, and simple percents.	***Extra Support:*** Students who have difficulty calculating a simple percent of a number could write the percent as a fraction and use division. For example, 50% is $\frac{1}{2}$, so divide the number by 2 to find 50%; 25% is $\frac{1}{4}$, so divide the number by 4 to find 25%. *Work on this skill during Sections 8.1 and 8.2.* On the bulletin board, place a table of conversions among decimals, percents, and fractions that students can refer to. *Work on this skill during Sections 8.1 and 8.2.*

SECTION ORGANIZER

65–80 min

Skills in Review

- Writing a fraction as a decimal
- Representing percents on a hundred chart

Teacher Materials

- calculators
- blank 10 × 10 charts (PM 16)

Vocabulary: percent

Alternative Example 1

Convert each fraction to a decimal.

a) $\frac{3}{20}$ **b)** $\frac{11}{12}$

Solution

a) $\frac{3}{20}$

Write an equivalent fraction.

$\frac{3}{20} \overset{\times 5}{=} \frac{15}{100}$

$\frac{15}{100} = 0.15$

So, $\frac{3}{20} = 0.15$

b) $\frac{11}{12}$

We can not write an equivalent fraction with denominator 100.

Use a calculator.

$\frac{11}{12}$ means 11 ÷ 12

Key in: 11 [÷] 12 [=] to display 0.9166666667

$\frac{11}{12} = 0.91\overline{6}$

UNIT 8

Skills You'll Need

Writing a Fraction As a Decimal

To write a fraction as a decimal, try to write an equivalent fraction with denominator 100.

When we cannot write an equivalent fraction, we use a calculator to divide.

Example 1

Convert each fraction to a decimal.

a) $\frac{3}{5}$ b) $\frac{7}{8}$

Solution

a) $\frac{3}{5}$

Write an equivalent fraction.

$\frac{3}{5} \overset{\times 20}{=} \frac{60}{100}$

$\frac{60}{100} = 0.60$

So, $\frac{3}{5} = 0.60$

b) $\frac{7}{8}$

We cannot write an equivalent fraction with denominator 100.

Use a calculator.

$\frac{7}{8}$ means 7 ÷ 8.

Key in: 7 [÷] 8 [=] to display 0.875

$\frac{7}{8} = 0.875$

Some conversions from fractions to decimals are worth remembering.

Try to remember these:

$\frac{1}{2} = 0.5$ $\frac{1}{4} = 0.25$ $\frac{1}{5} = 0.2$ $\frac{1}{8} = 0.125$ $\frac{1}{10} = 0.1$ $\frac{1}{100} = 0.01$

You can use these conversions to write other fractions as decimals.

For example, since $\frac{1}{10} = 0.1$, then $\frac{2}{10} = 0.2$, $\frac{3}{10} = 0.3$, and so on.

✓ Check

1. Write each fraction as a decimal. Use mental math.

a) $\frac{3}{4}$ 0.75 b) $\frac{2}{5}$ 0.4 c) $\frac{6}{10}$ 0.6 d) $\frac{68}{100}$ 0.68

2. Write each fraction as a decimal.

a) $\frac{5}{8}$ 0.625 b) $\frac{3}{16}$ 0.1875 c) $\frac{3}{8}$ 0.375 d) $\frac{7}{16}$ 0.4375

290 UNIT 8: Working with Percents

Writing a Fraction As a Decimal

Use a hundred chart to review fractions with denominators 10 and 100. Shade in 30 squares to illustrate $\frac{3}{10}$ and $\frac{30}{100}$. Remind students of the decimal form of each fraction: $\frac{3}{10} = 0.3$; $\frac{30}{100} = 0.30$, and the fact that the fractions are equivalent and the decimals are equivalent because they represent the same amount, or number.

Use the *Example* to illustrate how to convert from a fraction to a decimal when the numerator is not 10 or 100. If necessary, use part b of the *Alternative Example* above to show how some fractions convert to repeating decimals.

Suggest students make a table of conversions of the benchmark fractions to which they can refer when necessary.

Common Misconceptions

➤ Students erroneously write a fraction with denominator 100 as a decimal with tenths; for example, $\frac{3}{100}$ as 0.3.

How to Help: Use a hundred chart and a place-value chart to illustrate $\frac{3}{100}$ and $\frac{3}{10}$; and the fact that $\frac{3}{10} = \frac{30}{100}$. Encourage students to use hundred charts, or mental images of them, when they convert fractions to decimals.

Percent

Percent means per hundred. One whole, or 1, is 100%.
So, 70% means $\frac{70}{100}$, 4% means $\frac{4}{100}$, and 100% means $\frac{100}{100}$, or 1.

Example 2

What percent of this hundred chart is shaded each colour?
a) Red **b)** Blue **c)** Yellow

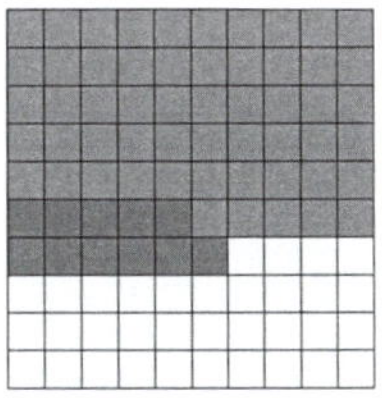

Solution

a) There are 11 red squares out of 100 squares.
That is: $\frac{11}{100} = 11\%$
b) There are 55 blue squares out of 100 squares.
That is: $\frac{55}{100} = 55\%$
c) There are 34 yellow squares out of 100 squares.
That is: $\frac{34}{100} = 34\%$

✓ Check

Use a hundred chart.

3. Shade:
a) 15% red 15 squares red **b)** 26% yellow 26 squares yellow **c)** 43% green 43 squares green **d)** 10% blue 10 squares blue

4. What percent of the hundred chart in question 3 is not shaded? 6%

Skills You'll Need 291

Alternative Example 2

Use a hundred chart to show each percent.
a) 12% blue **b)** 38% orange **c)** 100% yellow

Solution

a) $12\% = \frac{12}{100}$; Shade 12 of the 100 squares blue.
b) $38\% = \frac{38}{100}$; Shade 38 of the 100 squares orange.
c) $100\% = \frac{100}{100}$; Shade all 100 squares yellow.

Percent

Use a hundred chart to review 1 square on the chart is $\frac{1}{100}$ of the chart, and 1% of the chart. One row or column of squares is $\frac{10}{100}$ or $\frac{1}{10}$ of the chart, and 10% of the chart.

Ensure students understand that any 10 squares on the chart constitute 10%. The squares do not have to be in a row or column.

Ask:

- Two rows of a hundred chart are shaded. What percent is this? (*20%*) How do you know?
  (*Each row is 10%; two rows are 10% × 2 = 20%.*)
- A hundred chart has 44 squares shaded. What fraction of the chart is shaded? ($\frac{44}{100}$) What percent of the chart is shaded? (*44%*)

Students could also shade a fraction circle with hundredths to model percents and fractions in hundredths.

Common Misconceptions

➤ Students erroneously think 100% means 0.100.

How to Help: Write the number 0.100 on a place-value chart. Review the fact that the 1 is in the tenths place, so 0.100 is the same as: 0.1 or $\frac{1}{10}$; 0.10 or $\frac{10}{100}$; and 0.100 or $\frac{100}{1000}$. All these fractions are equivalent to $\frac{1}{10}$ in simplest form. Have students shade $\frac{1}{10}$ of a hundred chart, then write the fraction as 10%.

Relating Fractions, Decimals, and Percents

SECTION ORGANIZER — 80–100 min

Curriculum Focus: Relate percent to fractions and decimals. (7m9, 7m27)

Student Materials
- Puzzle for *Explore* (Master 8.13)
- calculators
- rulers
- isometric grid paper (PM 24)
- 2-cm grid paper (PM 21)
- coloured pencils
- hundred charts (PM 13)

Optional
- Step-by-Step 1 (Master 8.8)
- Extra Practice 1 (Master 8.18)

Assessment: Master 8.2 Ongoing Observations: Working with Percents

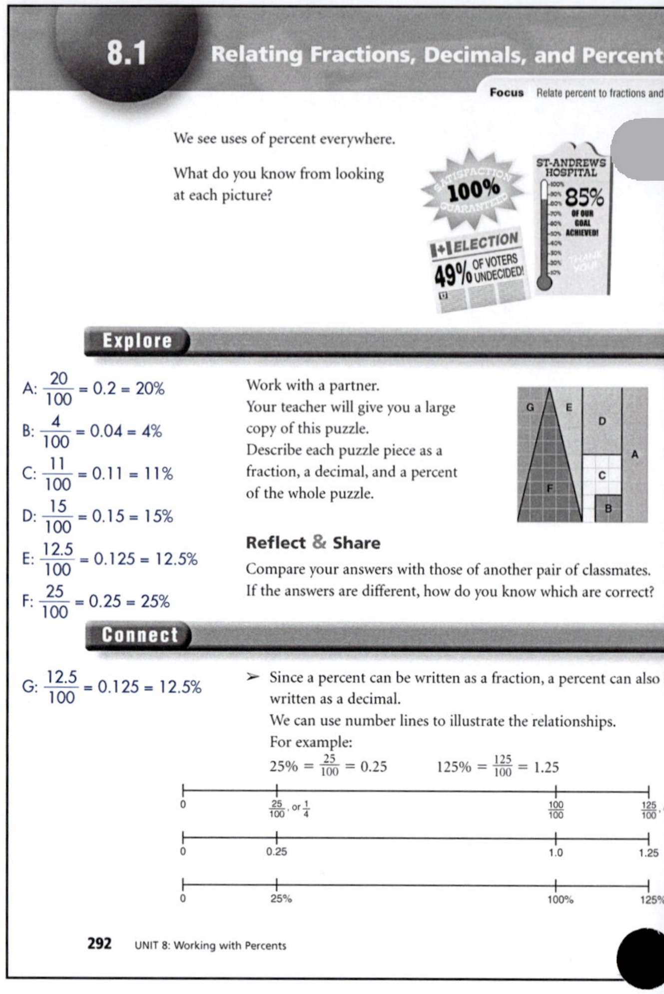
8.1 Relating Fractions, Decimals, and Percents

Focus Relate percent to fractions and

We see uses of percent everywhere.

What do you know from looking at each picture?

Explore

A: $\frac{20}{100} = 0.2 = 20\%$

B: $\frac{4}{100} = 0.04 = 4\%$

C: $\frac{11}{100} = 0.11 = 11\%$

D: $\frac{15}{100} = 0.15 = 15\%$

E: $\frac{12.5}{100} = 0.125 = 12.5\%$

F: $\frac{25}{100} = 0.25 = 25\%$

Work with a partner.
Your teacher will give you a large copy of this puzzle.
Describe each puzzle piece as a fraction, a decimal, and a percent of the whole puzzle.

Reflect & Share

Compare your answers with those of another pair of classmates. If the answers are different, how do you know which are correct?

Connect

G: $\frac{12.5}{100} = 0.125 = 12.5\%$

➢ Since a percent can be written as a fraction, a percent can also written as a decimal.
We can use number lines to illustrate the relationships.
For example:
$25\% = \frac{25}{100} = 0.25$ $\quad$ $125\% = \frac{125}{100} = 1.25$

292 UNIT 8: Working with Percents

Key Math Learnings

1. Any fraction or decimal can be written as a percent, and vice versa.
2. Percent is another name for hundredths.
3. Number lines can be used to show how fractions, decimals, and percents are related.

BEFORE — Get Started

Invite students to examine the pictures on page 292 of the Student Book.

Ask:

- Where have you seen percents?
  (On my test scores, in the bank, on advertisements and billboards)
- What do you know from looking at the picture that says, "Satisfaction Guaranteed 100%?"
  (The company guarantees its product 100%; it is sure that the customer will be completely satisfied.)
- What do you know from looking at the election picture?
  ($50\% = \frac{1}{2}$; 49% is slightly less than 50%. So, just under one-half of all voters are undecided.)
- What do you know from looking at the picture for St-Andrews Hospital?
  (The hospital is close to reaching 100% of its goal; it only needs to raise 15% more.)

Present *Explore*. Distribute copies of the *Puzzle for Explore* (Master 8.13) to pairs of students. Encourage students to refer to the pieces by letter name rather than by colour, as the copies they work with have no colour.

DURING — Explore

Ongoing Assessment: Observe and Listen

As students work, model good mathematical language. In particular, use the term 1 whole and 100% interchangeably.

Ask questions, such as:

- How can you describe puzzle piece A as a fraction, a decimal, and a percent?
  (The puzzle covers 100 grid squares. Puzzle piece A covers 20 grid squares. This represents $\frac{20}{100}$ = 0.2 = 20%.)

➢ Conversely, a decimal can be written as a percent:

$0.15 = \frac{15}{100} = 15\%$ $\quad$ $1.15 = \frac{115}{100} = 115\%$

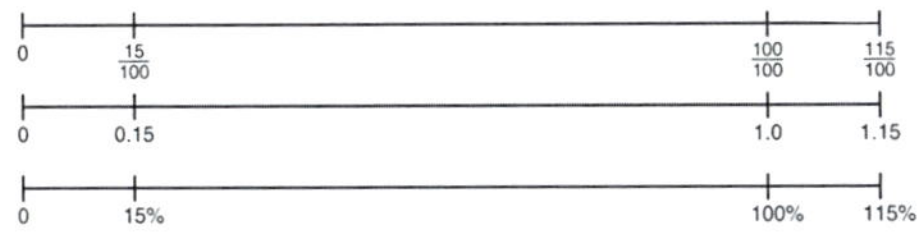

➢ To write a fraction as a percent, first write the fraction with denominator 100.

For example:

$\frac{1}{2} = \frac{50}{100} = 50\%$ (× 50) and $\frac{3}{2} = \frac{150}{100} = 150\%$ (× 50)

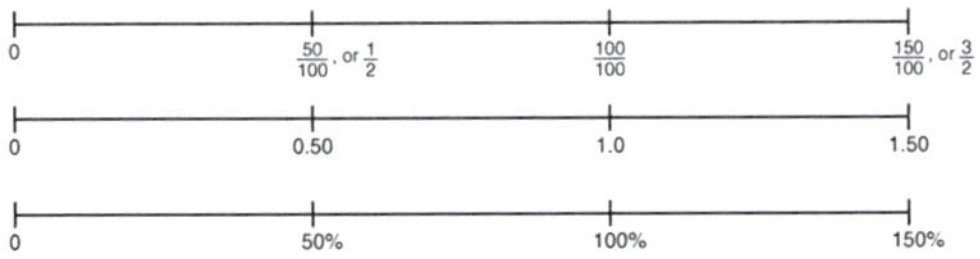

When a decimal has 3 digits after the decimal point, we can write it as a fraction with denominator 1000.

➢ Some fractions cannot be written with denominator 100. Use a calculator to divide.

$\frac{5}{8} = 0.625$

$= \frac{625}{1000}$ Divide numerator and denominator by 10.

$= \frac{62.5}{100}$

$= 62.5\%$

Example

a) Write each percent as a fraction and as a decimal.
i) 75% ii) 9% iii) 130%

b) Write each fraction as a percent and as a decimal.
i) $\frac{2}{5}$ ii) $\frac{5}{2}$

Draw number lines to show how the numbers are related.

8.1 Relating Fractions, Decimals, and Percents **293**

REACHING ALL LEARNERS

Alternative Explore

Materials: 1-cm grid paper (PM 20), coloured pencils, ruler

Students use a ruler to draw a figure, such as a triangle, a square, a rectangle, or a pentagon, on grid paper. The figure should have an area of 100 cm^2. Students use a ruler to subdivide the figure into smaller figures, then label each smaller figure. Students describe each smaller figure as a fraction, a decimal, and a percent of the larger figure.

Early Finishers

Have students use rulers to draw accurate number lines for those they sketched in question 2, or to sketch number lines for the numbers in question 3.

Common Misconceptions

➤ Students have difficulty converting a fraction greater than 1 to a percent.

How to Help: Tell students to first write the fraction as a mixed number. For example, $\frac{7}{2}$ can be written as $3\frac{1}{2}$. Students write $\frac{1}{2}$ as a percent: $\frac{1}{2} = 50\%$. The 3 in $3\frac{1}{2}$ represents 3 wholes or 300%. So, $3\frac{1}{2} = 300\% + 50\% = 350\%$. Alternatively, $\frac{7}{2}$ is $7 \times \frac{1}{2}$, is $7 \times 50\% = 350\%$.

Number Strategies

Students understand that 1 m = 100 cm. They use this relationship to find 1 m^2 = (100 × 100) cm^2, and 1 m^3 = (100 × 100 × 100) m^3. Students' pictures should be a line, a square, and a cube.

- How can you describe puzzle piece D? (*Puzzle piece D covers 15 grid squares. This represents $\frac{15}{100} = 0.15 = 15\%$.)*
  Puzzle piece C? (*Puzzle piece C covers 11 grid squares. This represents $\frac{11}{100} = 0.11 = 11\%$.)*
  Puzzle piece B? (*Puzzle piece B covers 4 grid squares. This represents $\frac{4}{100} = 0.04 = 4\%$.)*
  Puzzle piece E? (*Puzzle piece E covers $12\frac{1}{2}$ grid squares. This represents $\frac{12.5}{100} = 0.125 = 12.5\%$.)*
  Puzzle piece G? (*Puzzle piece G is congruent to puzzle piece E. It also covers $12\frac{1}{2}$ grid squares. This represents $\frac{12.5}{100} = 0.125 = 12.5\%$.)*
  Puzzle piece F? (*Puzzle piece F covers about 25 grid squares. This represents $\frac{25}{100} = 0.25 = 25\%$.)*
- How did you find the number of squares in puzzle piece E?
  (*I used the formula for the area of a triangle: $A = \frac{1}{2}bh$. The base is 2.5 units. The height is 10 units. So, $b \times h = 2.5 \times 10 = 25$. Divide by 2: $25 \div 2 = 12.5$.)*

AFTER Connect

Invite students to share their answers with the class.

Ask questions, such as:

- How do you know your answers are correct?
  (*When I add the percents covered by the puzzle pieces, I get 100%. When I add the fractions or the decimals covered by the pieces, I get 1. The whole puzzle represents 100% or 1.*)
- How would you know if your classmate's answer was not correct?
  (*The percents would not add to 100%.*)

Use the examples in *Connect* to reinforce the relationships among fractions, decimals, and percents.

Number lines provide a visual representation of the relative sizes of percents. Some students have difficulty understanding percents greater

Sample Answers

2.

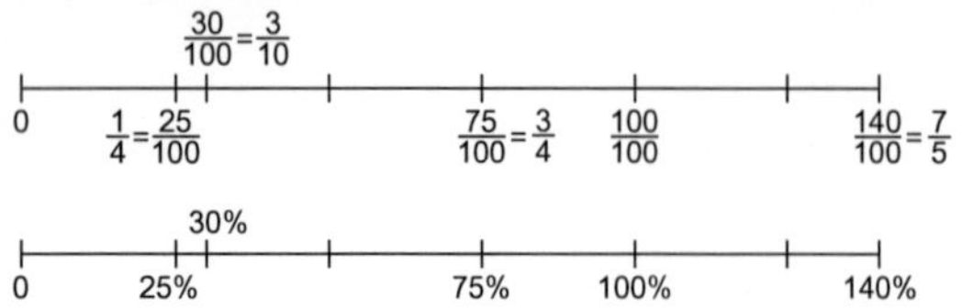

4. Fred scored 8 out of 10. That is $\frac{8}{10} = \frac{80}{100} = 80\%$; 80 < 82

5. 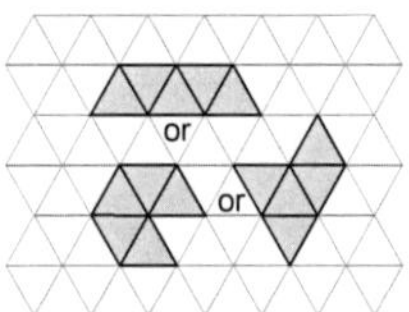

For example, the larger figure is made of 5 equilateral triangles. There is more than one answer depending on how the triangles are arranged.

6. The relative positions of the squares may vary.

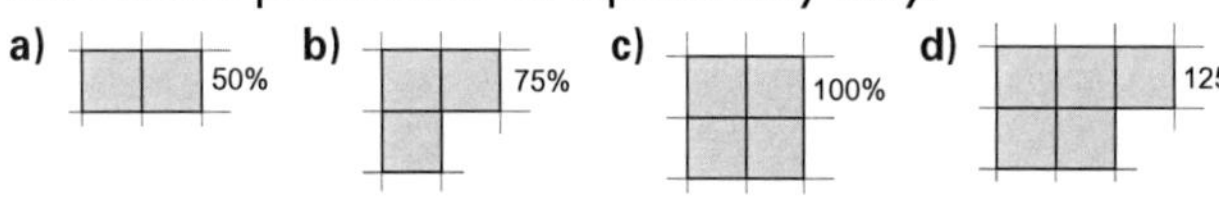

7. I converted $\frac{1}{2}$ to 50%. I know the whole paper represents 1 whole or 100%. I used a ruler to divide the page into 10 congruent rectangles: 5 rows of 2 rectangles in each row. Each rectangle is 10% of the page. $\frac{1}{2}$ is 50%, so I coloured 5 rectangles blue. I coloured 1 rectangle red. 25% is $\frac{25}{100}$ or $\frac{2.5}{10}$, so I coloured $2\frac{1}{2}$ rectangles yellow. That left $1\frac{1}{2}$ rectangles green. $1\frac{1}{2}$ out of 10 is $\frac{1.5}{10} = \frac{15}{100}$, so 15% of the page is green.
8. "She gave it 110%" means that she gave more than her whole effort. We sometimes say that a person gave 110% if he or she went beyond the effort that was expected.

Solution

a) i) $75\% = \frac{75}{100} = 0.75$

ii) $9\% = \frac{9}{100} = 0.09$

iii) $130\% = \frac{130}{100} = 1.30$

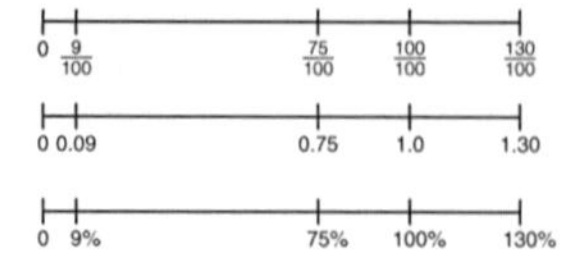

b) i) $\frac{2}{5} = \frac{40}{100} = 40\%$ (× 20 top and bottom) ii) $\frac{5}{2} = \frac{250}{100} = 250\%$ (× 50 top and bottom)

$\frac{40}{100} = 0.40$ $\frac{250}{100} = 2.50$

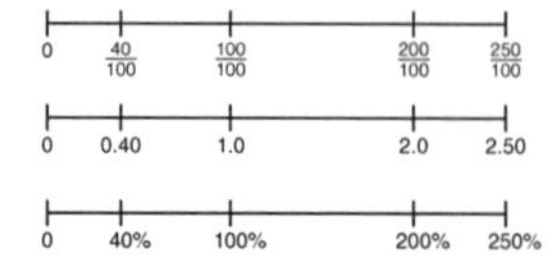

Practice

1. What percent of each hundred chart is shaded?
Write each percent as a fraction and a decimal.

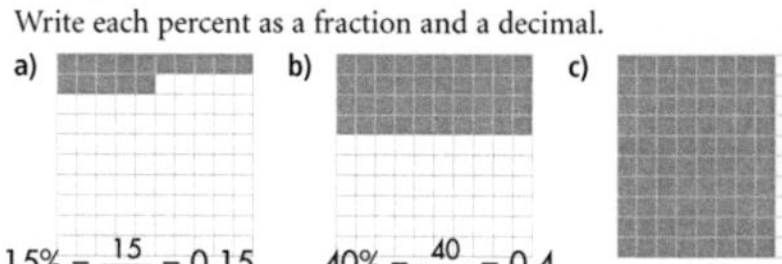

a) $15\% = \frac{15}{100} = 0.15$ b) $40\% = \frac{40}{100} = 0.4$ c) $80\% = \frac{80}{100} = 0.8$

2. Write each fraction as a percent.
Sketch number lines to show how the numbers are related.
a) $\frac{1}{4}$ 25% b) $\frac{3}{10}$ 30% c) $\frac{7}{5}$ 140% d) $\frac{3}{4}$ 75%

3. Write each fraction as a decimal and a percent.
a) $\frac{2}{10}$ b) $\frac{3}{50}$ c) $\frac{4}{25}$ d) $\frac{23}{20}$ e) $\frac{14}{10}$
0.2; 20% 0.06; 6% 0.16; 16% 1.15; 115% 1.4; 140%

294 UNIT 8: Working with Percents

than 100%. A number line can facilitate this understanding. By aligning number lines vertically, the equivalent forms of a fraction, decimal, and percent are illustrated.

Practice

Question 5 requires isometric grid paper (PM 24). Question 6 requires 2-cm grid paper (PM 21). Question 7 requires coloured pencils. Question 9 requires hundred charts (PM 13).

Assessment Focus: Question 7

Students apply their knowledge of fractions, decimals, and percents to solve an area problem. Students could use grid paper, or use a ruler to measure on plain paper. Students may convert the fraction and percents to decimals, or the percents to a fraction, or the fraction to a percent.

Students who need extra support to complete Assessment Focus questions may benefit from the Step-by-Step masters (Masters 8.8-8.12).

4. Fred had 8 out of 10 on a test. Janet had 82% on the test. Who did better? How do you know? Janet

5. This equilateral triangle is 20% of a larger figure. Use triangular grid paper. Draw a figure that shows 100%. Is there more than one answer? Explain. Yes

6. This orange square represents 25% of a larger figure. Use 2-cm grid paper.
   a) Draw 50% of the larger figure.
   b) Draw 75% of the larger figure.
   c) Draw the larger figure.
   d) Draw 125% of the larger figure.

Number Strategies

How many:
- centimetres in 1 m? 100 cm
- square centimetres in 1 m^2? 10 000 cm^2
- cubic centimetres in 1 m^3? 1 000 000 cm^3

Sketch a picture to show each relationship.

7. **Assessment Focus** You will need a sheet of paper and coloured pencils. Divide the paper into these 4 sections.
   - 1 blue section that is $\frac{1}{2}$ the page
   - 1 red section that is 10% of the page
   - 1 yellow section that is 25% of the page
   - 1 green section to fill the remaining space

   Explain how you did this. What percent of the page is the green section? 15% How do you know?

8. What does it mean when someone states, "She gave it 110%"? How can this comment be explained using math?

Take It Further

9. Suppose each pattern is continued on a hundred chart. The numbers in each pattern are coloured red. For each pattern, what percent of the numbers on the chart are red? Explain your strategy for each pattern.
   a) 4, 8, 12, 16, 20, … 25% b) 1, 3, 5, 7, … 50%
   c) 2, 4, 8, 16, … 6% d) 1, 3, 7, 13, … 10%

Reflect

Suppose you know your mark out of 20 for an English test. How could you write the mark as a percent?

8.1 Relating Fractions, Decimals, and Percents 295

9. a) In the first 20 numbers, 5 numbers are red. There are 5 groups of 20 in 100. So, in 100 numbers, $5 \times 5 = 25$ numbers are red.

b) Every odd number is red. Every other number is an odd number. So, in 100 numbers, one-half will be even and one-half will be odd. Fifty of the 100 numbers will be red.

c) I continued the pattern using the pattern rule: Start at 2. Multiply by 2 to get the next term. The numbers coloured red are 2, 4, 8, 16, 32, and 64; $64 \times 2 = 128$ is too large to appear on the chart. Six of the 100 squares are red.

d) The pattern rule is: Start at 1. Add 2. Increase the number added by 2 each time. I continued the pattern: 1, 3, 7, 13, 21, 31, 43, 57, 73, 91 (111 is too large to appear on the chart). Ten of the 100 squares are red.

REFLECT: I would write my mark as a fraction, with 20 as the denominator. I would then write the fraction with denominator 100, by multiplying both the numerator and denominator of the original fraction by 5. The numerator of the new fraction represents my mark as a percent. For example, if my mark was 15 out of 20, I would write $\frac{15}{20} = \frac{75}{100} = 75\%$. My mark would be 75%.

Assignment Guidelines

If your students do not have time to complete all the *Practice* questions on pages 294 and 295, these questions provide minimum curriculum coverage: 2, 3, 4, 6, 7, *Reflect*

To assess the 4 Achievement Chart categories listed in the curriculum document, have students complete these *Practice* questions:

Understanding Concepts: 2	Application: 4
Problem Solving: 6	Communication: 7

ASSESSMENT FOR LEARNING

What to Look For

Understanding concepts

✔ Students understand relationships among fractions, decimals, and percents.

Applying procedures

✔ Students can write a fraction as a decimal and a percent, a decimal as a fraction and a percent, and a percent as a fraction and a decimal.

✔ Students can sketch number lines to show how fractions, decimals, and percents are related.

What to Do

Extra Support: Students can play the Additional Activity *Concentration* (Master 8.6).
Students can use Step-by-Step 1 (Master 8.8) to complete question 7.

Extra Practice: Students can play the Additional Activity *Squeeze Play* (Master 8.5a).
Students can complete Extra Practice 1 (Master 8.18).

Extension: Have students use the method of question 9 to create a number pattern of their own, continue the pattern on a hundred chart by colouring the numbers blue, then find the percent of the numbers on the chart that are blue.

Recording and Reporting

Master 8.2 Ongoing Observations: Working with Percents

Showdown

SECTION ORGANIZER

Student Materials

- *Showdown* playing cards (Masters 8.14a and 8.14b)
- scissors
- calculator

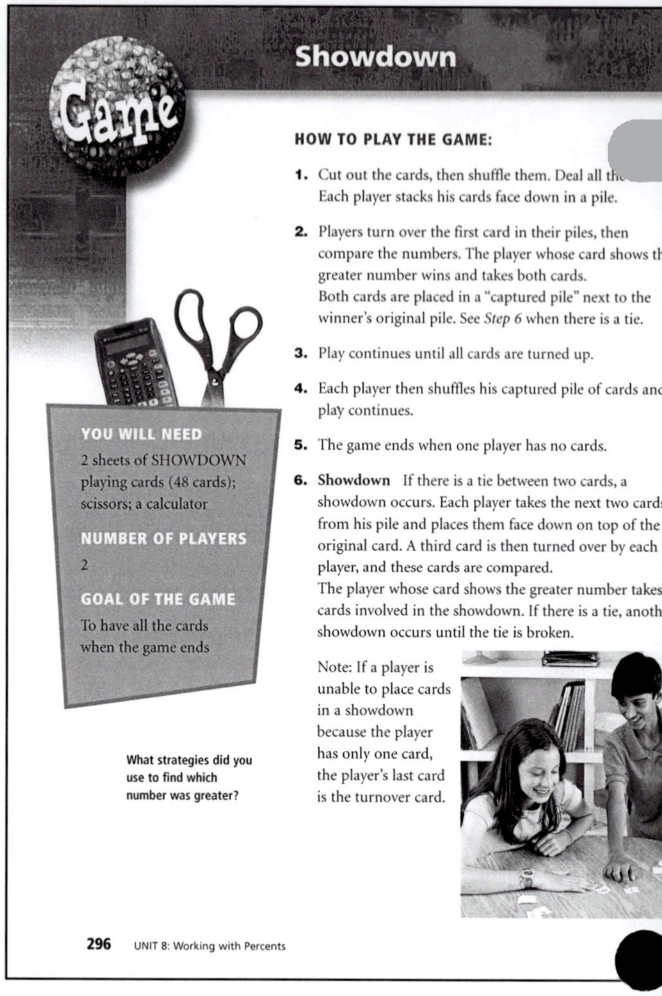

Showdown

HOW TO PLAY THE GAME:

1. Cut out the cards, then shuffle them. Deal all th… Each player stacks his cards face down in a pile.
2. Players turn over the first card in their piles, then compare the numbers. The player whose card shows th… greater number wins and takes both cards. Both cards are placed in a "captured pile" next to the winner's original pile. See *Step 6* when there is a tie.
3. Play continues until all cards are turned up.
4. Each player then shuffles his captured pile of cards and play continues.
5. The game ends when one player has no cards.
6. **Showdown** If there is a tie between two cards, a showdown occurs. Each player takes the next two cards from his pile and places them face down on top of the original card. A third card is then turned over by each player, and these cards are compared. The player whose card shows the greater number takes cards involved in the showdown. If there is a tie, anoth… showdown occurs until the tie is broken.

Note: If a player is unable to place cards in a showdown because the player has only one card, the player's last card is the turnover card.

YOU WILL NEED
2 sheets of SHOWDOWN playing cards (48 cards); scissors; a calculator

NUMBER OF PLAYERS
2

GOAL OF THE GAME
To have all the cards when the game ends

What strategies did you use to find which number was greater?

296 UNIT 8: Working with Percents

Take It Further

Each player can turn over 2 cards at a time, then compare the 4 numbers to find the greatest number.

Invite a volunteer to read the game rules. Model how to play the game to ensure students understand the rules. Be sure to model a showdown so students know the procedure when there is a tie between two cards.

Suggest students use a calculator to convert fractions to decimals only when necessary.

As students play, ask questions such as:

- What is the greatest number you have found on the cards? (*1.00 and 1*)
- What is the least number you have found on the cards? (*0.10 and 10%*)

Ensure students model the correct language. For example, students should read 0.12 aloud as twelve hundredths rather than "zero decimal one two."

After all students have played at least one game, ask questions, such as:

- What strategy did you use to find which number was greater?
  (*I converted fractions and decimals to percents, then compared the two percents. I find percents easier to work with.*)
- When did you use a calculator?
  (*I used a calculator to convert a fraction whose denominator is not a factor of 100; for example, $\frac{7}{8}$.*)
- Why are some fractions easier to convert than others?
  (*Fractions like $\frac{4}{5}$ and $\frac{3}{10}$ have denominators that are factors of 100. These fractions are easy to convert to both decimals and percents.*)
- When did you have a tie?
  (*When the cards were $\frac{1}{4}$ and 25%*)

8.2 Estimating and Calculating Percents

Focus Use mental math and estimation.

Explore

Work with a partner.
Look at the surface of your desk.

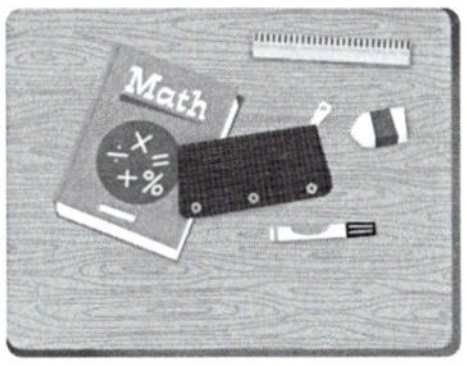

There is probably a textbook on it, and maybe a pencil case, an eraser, or a ruler.

How much of the surface is covered?
How much of the surface is not covered?

Use a calculator and a ruler.
Estimate the percent of your desk's surface that is covered and the percent that is not. Show your work.

Reflect & Share

Compare your results with those of another pair of classmates.
Discuss the strategies you used to find the percent of surface not covered.

Connect

Here is a sketch of a yard.

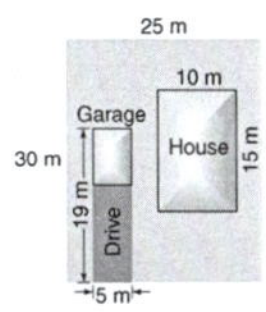

➢ To find the percent of the yard that is covered by the house, garage, and drive, calculate the area covered by
- the house: 15 m × 10 m = 150 m^2
- the garage and the drive: 19 m × 5 m = 95 m^2

Total area covered is: 150 m^2 + 95 m^2 = 245 m^2
The area of the yard is: 30 m × 25 m = 750 m^2
The fraction of the yard that is covered is: $\frac{245}{750}$
For an estimate of the fraction, round 245 to 250.
The fraction of the yard that is covered is about $\frac{250}{750} = \frac{1}{3}$.
$\frac{1}{3}$ is about 30%.
So, about 30% of the yard is covered by the house, garage, and drive.

Round 245 to 250 to get a "friendly" number. Both 250 and 750 have 250 as a common factor.

Estimating and Calculating Percents

SECTION ORGANIZER 80–100 min

Curriculum Focus: Use mental math and estimation. (7m5, 7m27)

Teacher Materials
- old newspapers
- masking tape
- measuring tape or metre stick

Student Materials
- rulers
- calculators

Optional
- Step-by-Step 2 (Master 8.9)
- Extra Practice 2 (Master 8.19)

Assessment: Master 8.2 Ongoing Observations: Working with Percents

Key Math Learnings

1. One strategy to estimate percent is to approximate a fraction to a "friendly" fraction that can easily be converted to a percent.
2. A quick way to find 10% of a number is to move the decimal point 1 place to the left. This number can then be doubled to find 20%, halved to find 5%, and so on.

BEFORE Get Started

Have students look at a rectangular bulletin board in the classroom and a piece of paper on the board. Ask:

- About what percent of the bulletin board does this piece of paper cover? (*15%*)
  How did you estimate?
  (*I could cover the board with 8 pieces of paper, so one piece of paper covers $\frac{1}{8}$, which I know is $12\frac{1}{2}$%, so I rounded it to 15%.*)
- How could we find a closer estimate?
  (*We could compare the area of the paper with the area of the board.*)

Present *Explore*. Ensure students understand they are to estimate their answers. Exact answers are not required.

DURING Explore

Ongoing Assessment: Observe and Listen

As students are measuring the area of their desks and the area of the items on their desks, ask questions, such as:

- How did you find the area of your desk?
  (*I multiplied the length of the desk by its width; 45 cm × 60 cm = 2700 cm^2.*)
- What items are on your desk?
  (*My math book, a ruler, a notebook, and a pencil*)
- What area is covered by your math book?
  (*About 600 cm^2: 22 cm × 28 cm ≐ 20 cm × 30 cm = 600 cm^2*) By your notebook? (*About 600 cm^2, the same area as my math book*) By your ruler? (*About 90 cm^2: 30 cm × 3 cm = 90 cm^2*) By your pencil? (*About 8 cm^2: 16 cm × 0.5 cm = 8 cm^2, which I rounded to 10 cm^2*)

REACHING ALL LEARNERS

Early Finishers

Have students estimate the percent of a newspaper page that is covered with typeface, ads, or photographs.

Common Misconceptions

➤Students have difficulty finding "friendly" fractions.

How to Help: Have students write a list of the denominators that round easily to each "friendly" denominator – such as 5: 3, 4, 6, 7; 10: 8, 9, 11, 12, 13, 14, 15; 20: 16, 17, 18, 19, 21, 22; and so on.

Mental Math

Students count the number of squares with side length 1 unit (64), then the number of squares with side length 2 units (49), 3 units (36), 4 units (25), 5 units (16), 6 units (9), 7 units (4), and 8 units (1). Students then add to find the total number of squares. Students may notice that the sum is that of the first 8 square numbers.

➤ To find the percent of the yard made up of garden and grass:
The yard is 100%.
Subtract: 100% − 30% = 70%
So, about 70% of the yard is made up of garden and gr
We can show these percents on a number line.

We can use mental math to estimate and calculate percent.

Example 1

There are 27 students in the Grade 7 class.
Five students are left-handed.

a) What is the fraction of students who are left-handed?
b) Estimate the percent of students who are left-handed.

Solution

a) The fraction of students who are left-handed is $\frac{5}{27}$.
b) *Method 1*
One whole or 100% is 27 students.
50% of 27 students is about 14 students.
25% of 27 students is about 7 students.
So, the percent of students who are left-handed is less than 25%

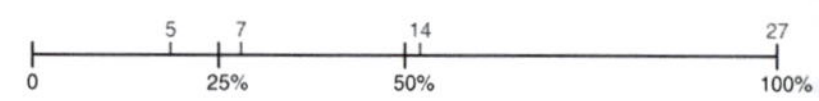

Method 2
Approximate $\frac{5}{27}$ to a "friendly" fraction: $\frac{5}{27} \doteq \frac{5}{25}$

$\frac{5}{25} = \frac{20}{100} = 20\%$ (× 4)

Approximately 20% of the students are left-handed.

A "friendly" fraction has a denominator such as 5, 10, 20, 25, 50. A fraction with one of these denominators can be more easily converted to a percent.

298 UNIT 8: Working with Percents

- How did you estimate the percent of your desk's surface that is covered?
(I added the areas covered by the items on my desk: 600 cm² + 600 cm² + 90 cm² + 10 cm² = 1300 cm². I know that 50% of 2700 cm² is one-half of 2700 cm², which is 1350 cm²; 1300 is just less than 1350. So, I estimated that almost 50% of my desk was covered.)
- How did you estimate the percent that is not covered?
(The area of my desk is 100%. Since just less than 50% is covered, then just more than 50% of my desk is not covered.)

AFTER Connect

Invite volunteers to share their results and strategies with the class.

Ask questions, such as:

- What strategy did you use to find the percent of surface covered?
(I found the percent covered by each item on my desk, then added the percents. I borrowed math books from my classmates to cover my desk, and found that about 5 books would cover it, so one book covers $\frac{1}{5}$, or 20%. I could fit 2 rulers along one side of my desk, and 15 rulers across my desk, so that's 30 rulers in all. So, one ruler covers $\frac{1}{30}$, which is about 3%.)

Use the examples in *Connect* to introduce some strategies for estimating percents.

To help students complete *Practice* question 7, use the following example to illustrate how to round a given percent to a "friendly" number, to estimate a percent.

Example 2

A pair of pants costs $39.99.
The sales tax is 15%.
Estimate the cost of the pants.

Solution

Round $39.99 to $40.
To find 15%, find 10% and 5%.
10% of $40 = 0.1 × $40 = $4
5% is $\frac{1}{2}$ of 10%.
So, 5% of $40 = $\frac{1}{2}$ of $4 = $2
So, the sales tax is $4 + $2 = $6.
The cost of the pants is about $40 + $6 = $46.
We can show these percents on a number line.

Mental math strategy: A quick way to find 10% is to move the decimal point 1 place to the left: 10% of 40. = 4.0

Practice

1. Estimate the percent of each figure that is shaded.

a) 
About 25%

b) 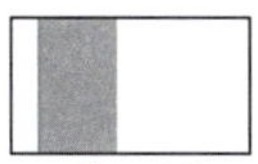
About 30%

c) 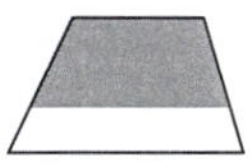
About 60%

d) 
About 90%

2. Find 10% of each number.

a) 50 5 b) 40 4 c) 90 9 d) 300 30
e) 75 7.5 f) 33 3.3 g) 45 4.5 h) 18 1.8

3. Use your answers to question 2.
Find 5% of each number in question 2.
a) 2.5; b) 2; c) 4.5; d) 15; e) 3.75; f) 1.65; g) 2.25; h) 0.9

8.2 Estimating and Calculating Percents 299

Sample Answers

5.

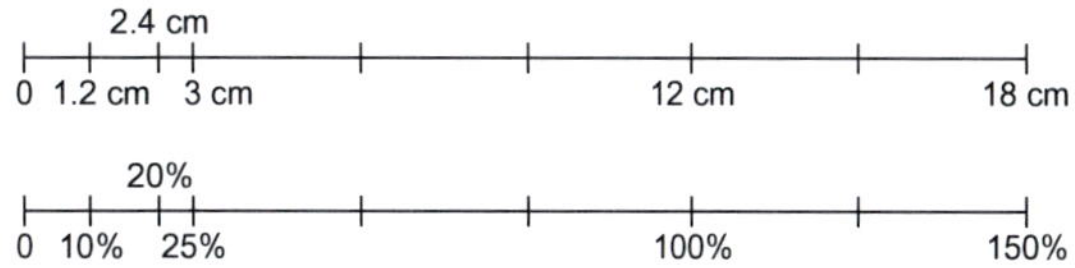

6. To find 15% of $65:
Find 10% and 5%.
10% of $65 is 0.1 × $65 = $6.50 5% is $\frac{1}{2}$ of 10%.
So, 5% of $65 = $\frac{1}{2}$ of $6.50 = $3.25
So, 15% of $65 is $6.50 + $3.25 = $9.75.
The shoes cost: $65 + $9.75 = $74.75
Another method is to say that the total cost is 115% of $65.
100% of $65 = $65
10% of $65 = $6.50
1% of $65 = $0.65, so 5% of $65 = $0.65 × 5
= $3.25
So the total cost is $65 + $6.50 + $3.25 = $74.75.

8. No, 10% of 160 is 16. So, 20% of 160 is 16 × 2 = 32.
Since 22% > 20%, the estimate should be greater than 32.

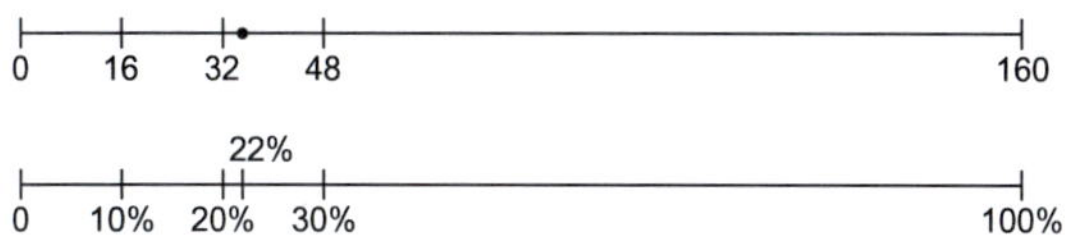

Example 1

The 26 000-seat arena was 52% full. About how many people were at the game?

Solution

Since 52% is close to 50%, and 50% is a "friendly" number, use 50% in place of 52%.
50% is $\frac{1}{2}$ of 26 000 or 13 000. About 13 000 people were at the game.
Students could also round the given number to make calculating the percent easier.

Example 2

6073 people completed the survey. Twenty-five percent answered no. About how many people answered no?

Solution

25% = $\frac{1}{4}$
I know 4 is a factor of 6000. 6000 is close to 6073.
Use 6000 in place of 6073.
To find 25% of 6000 divide: 6000 ÷ 4 = 1500
About 1500 people answered no.

11. I measured the dimensions of the front cover and multiplied them to get its area:
$22 \text{ cm} \times 28 \text{ cm} \doteq 20 \text{ cm} \times 30 \text{ cm} = 600 \text{ cm}^2$
The area of the back cover is also 600 cm^2.
The area of the spine is $28 \text{ cm} \times 3 \text{ cm} \doteq 30 \text{ cm} \times 3 \text{ cm} = 90 \text{ cm}^2$, which is about 100 cm^2.
The total area of the book cover is about
$600 \text{ cm}^2 + 600 \text{ cm}^2 + 100 \text{ cm}^2 = 1300 \text{ cm}^2$.
I measured the dimensions of the photograph of the cougar.
It is a square of side length about 20 cm.
The area of the square is $20 \text{ cm} \times 20 \text{ cm} = 400 \text{ cm}^2$
The fraction of the book cover that is illustrated
$= \frac{400}{1300} \doteq \frac{400}{1200} = \frac{1}{3}$.s
The percent of the book cover that is illustrated is about 30%.

4. Use your answers to questions 2 and 3.
Find 15% of each number in question 2.
a) 7.5, b) 6, c) 13.5, d) 45, e) 11.25, f) 4.95, g) 6.75
5. This strip is 12 cm long.

Find the length of:
a) 25% of the strip 3 cm b) 10% of the strip 1.2 cm
c) 20% of the strip 2.4 cm d) 150% of the strip 18 cm
Sketch number lines to illustrate your answers.

Mental Math

How many squares are there on an 8 by 8 checkerboard?
Remember to count squares of all sizes.
64 + 49 + 36 + 25 + 16 + 9 + 4 + 1 = 204

6. A pair of shoes costs $65. The sales tax is 15%. Explain how to find the cost of the shoes using two different methods.

7. Estimate.
a) 49% of 150 About 75 b) 31% of 40 About 12
c) 149% of 60 About 90 d) 98% of 54 About 53
e) 90% of 44 About 40 f) 61% of 88 About 54
g) 2% of 200 About 4 h) 5% of 81 About 4

8. Scott estimated that 22% of 160 is approximately 30.
Do you agree with his estimate? Explain.
Sketch number lines to support your answer.

9. There were 341 pine trees and spruce trees in a woodlot.
One hundred twenty-two trees were pine.
a) What fraction of the trees were spruce? $\frac{219}{341}$
b) Estimate the percent of spruce trees. About 60%

10. In a parking lot, there are 45 North American cars and 21 foreign cars.
a) What fraction of the cars are foreign? $\frac{21}{66}$
b) Estimate the percent of cars that are foreign. About 30%
c) Estimate the percent of cars that are not foreign. About 70

11. Assessment Focus Look at the front and back cover of this textbook, including the spine. Explain how you might estimate the percent of the book cover that is illustrated.
Show all your steps. Provide numbers to support your answer.

300 UNIT 8: Working with Percents

Practice

Students should be discouraged from using a calculator. The questions in this section are to be estimated only.

Assessment Focus: Question 11

Students add these numbers to find the total area of the cover of the textbook. Students may consider the only illustration to be that of the cougar. Any other illustrations that students may consider, such as the logo on the spine, are insignificant. Students measure the area of the rectangular picture, and the total area of the cover, then write the smaller area as a percent of the larger. Other students may simply estimate the area of the picture as a percent of the area of the cover, then halve the percent to get an estimate of the answer.

Making Connections

Health Link: Students could use the given percents on a box of cereal to find the mass of each nutrient in 1 serving. Some cereal boxes give the mass of each nutrient instead. For these boxes, students could calculate the percent of each nutrient. Students report their findings, then discuss ways in which their eating habits could be improved.

12. About 8% of Canada is covered by fresh water.
The area of Canada is approximately 9 970 000 km².

a) Estimate the area of Canada covered by fresh water. About 1 million km^2

b) About how much of Canada is not covered by fresh water? About 9 million km^2

13. About 23% of Canada is covered by tundra.
Use the data in question 12.
Estimate the area of tundra in Canada. About 2 500 000 km^2

14. Raji's bedroom floor has an area of 12 m^2. She estimates that her bed, desk, and bookshelf cover approximately 7.5 m^2 of floor space.

a) What fraction of the floor space is not covered? $\frac{4.5}{12}$

b) What percent of the floor space is not covered?
Sketch number lines to illustrate your answers.

Take It Further

15. Edward estimates he has travelled approximately 80 km.
The total length of Edward's trip is 430 km.
About what percent does Edward still have left to go?

Reflect

Which percents can you find by using mental math or estimation?
Give an example of how to find each percent you name.

Math Link

Your World

Percents are printed on the side of a cereal box to indicate the nutritional value of the contents. The percents relate to every 30-g serving (about 1 cup). Suppose there is a 10% sugar content. Then, in a 30-g serving, there are 3 g of sugar per cup of cereal. Next time you look for a box of your favourite cereal, check out the percents of sugar and fat. Compare them to another brand of cereal. Would your family doctor or dentist approve of your choice? Explain.

14. b) I made a "friendly" fraction. $\frac{4.5}{12} \doteq \frac{4}{10} = 40\%$
About 40% of the floor space is not covered.

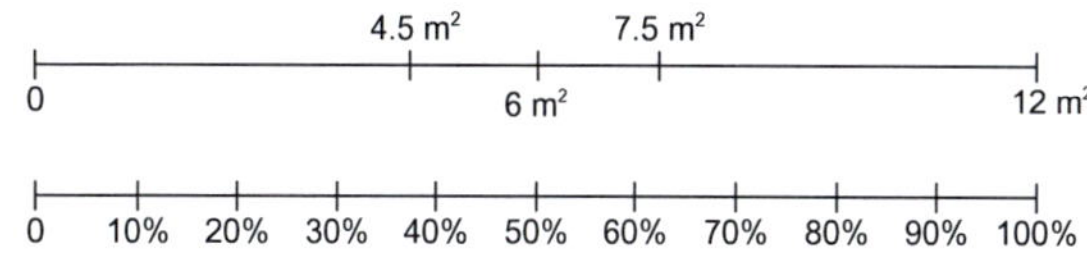

15. $\frac{80}{430} \doteq \frac{80}{400} = \frac{1}{5}$; I know that $\frac{1}{5} = 0.2$. Edward has travelled about 20% of the distance.
So, Edward still has about 100% − 20% = 80% left to travel.

REFLECT: I can use mental math to find percents that are multiples of 5 or 10. For example, to find 25% of 60, find $\frac{1}{4}$ of 60, which is $60 \div 4 = 15$.
I can use estimation when the percent required is close to a "friendly" percent.
For example, 51% of 120 $\doteq$ 50% of 120 = $\frac{1}{2}$ of 120 = 60
I can use estimation when the fraction given is close to a "friendly" fraction. For example, $\frac{26}{55} \doteq \frac{25}{50} = \frac{1}{2}$ and $\frac{1}{2} = 50\%$

Assignment Guidelines

If your students do not have time to complete all the *Practice* questions on pages 299, 300, and 301, these questions provide minimum curriculum coverage:
1, 2, 3, 5, 7, 10, 11, 12, *Reflect*
To assess the 4 Achievement Chart categories listed in the curriculum document, have students complete these *Practice* questions:

Application: 5 — Understanding Concepts: 7
Communication: 8 — Problem Solving: 11

ASSESSMENT FOR LEARNING

What to Look For	What to Do
Understanding concepts ✔ Students understand that mental math can be used to estimate and calculate percent. ***Applying procedures*** ✔ Students can apply mental math and estimation strategies to find percents. ***Problem solving*** ✔ Students can use appropriate estimation strategies to solve problems involving percent.	***Extra Support:*** Students who have difficulty estimating percents could begin with estimating percents that are close to 50%, such as 48%, 49%, 51%, 52%, and calculate the percent by dividing by 2. Students can use Step-by-Step 2 (Master 8.9) to complete question 11. ***Extra Practice:*** Have students use number lines to illustrate 5%, 10%, and 15% of each number in *Practice* question 2 (see *Practice* questions 3 and 4). Students can complete Extra Practice 2 (Master 8.19). ***Extension:*** Have students use a ruler to measure dimensions, to calculate the percent of each figure shaded in question 1.

Recording and Reporting
Master 8.2 Ongoing Observations: Working with Percents

Multiplying to Find Percents

SECTION ORGANIZER (80–100 min)

Curriculum Focus: Multiply decimals with hundredths. (7m5, 7m24)

Student Materials
- calculators
- Pattern Blocks (PM 25)

Optional
- Step-by-Step 3 (Master 8.10)
- Extra Practice 3 (Master 8.20)

Assessment: Master 8.2 Ongoing Observations: Working with Percents

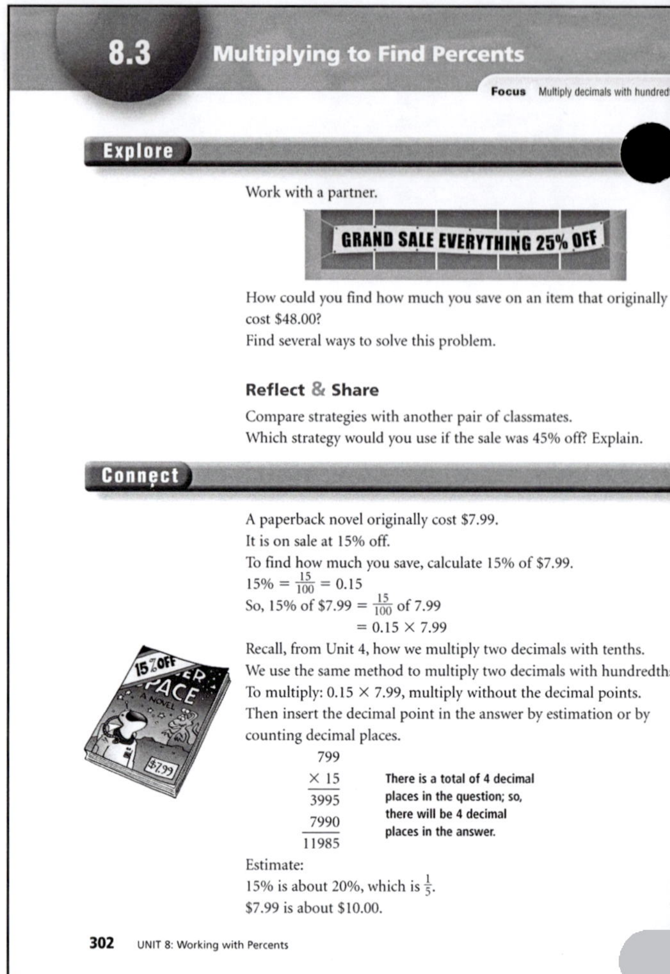

8.3 Multiplying to Find Percents

Focus Multiply decimals with hundredths

Explore

Work with a partner.

GRAND SALE EVERYTHING 25% OFF

How could you find how much you save on an item that originally cost $48.00?
Find several ways to solve this problem.

Reflect & Share

Compare strategies with another pair of classmates.
Which strategy would you use if the sale was 45% off? Explain.

Connect

A paperback novel originally cost $7.99.
It is on sale at 15% off.
To find how much you save, calculate 15% of $7.99.

$15\% = \frac{15}{100} = 0.15$

So, 15% of $\$7.99 = \frac{15}{100}$ of 7.99
$= 0.15 \times 7.99$

Recall, from Unit 4, how we multiply two decimals with tenths.
We use the same method to multiply two decimals with hundredths.
To multiply: 0.15×7.99, multiply without the decimal points.
Then insert the decimal point in the answer by estimation or by counting decimal places.

$$\begin{array}{r} 799 \\ \times\ 15 \\ \hline 3995 \\ 7990 \\ \hline 11985 \end{array}$$

There is a total of 4 decimal places in the question; so, there will be 4 decimal places in the answer.

Estimate:
15% is about 20%, which is $\frac{1}{5}$.
$7.99 is about $10.00.

302 UNIT 8: Working with Percents

Key Math Learnings

1. The percent of a number can be found by writing the percent as a decimal, then multiplying.
2. The number of decimal places in the product should be the same as the total number of decimal places in the question.
3. When multiplying decimals, estimate the product to place the decimal point in the answer.

Number Strategies

If the red block represents 1 whole, the green block represents $\frac{1}{3}$; the blue block represents twice the green block or $2 \times \frac{1}{3} = \frac{2}{3}$; and the yellow block represents $2 \times 1 = 2$.

BEFORE Get Started

Initiate a discussion about the last time students went shopping with their friends.

Ask questions, such as:
- What items were you hoping to buy? (*A pair of jeans and a DVD*)
- How did you decide which store to buy from? (*I chose the store that offered the items at the lowest price; for example, at one store, everything was 40% off.*)
- How could you estimate the cost of a $60 pair of jeans, before tax, if they were 40% off? (*If the jeans were 50% off, then the discount would be $\frac{1}{2}$ of $60 = $30. Since 40% < 50%, this discount would be less than $30, so I'd pay more than $30.*)
- How can you estimate if you have enough money to pay for an item, including taxes? (*I can find 10% of the cost of the item, then multiply this value by 2 to get 20%. I add this amount to the original cost to get the total cost, including taxes. If I have this amount of money, I will have enough to buy the item because taxes are usually 15%.*)

Present *Explore*. Students should recall some of the strategies they used in the previous sections of the unit, then use these strategies to find an exact answer.

DURING Explore

Ongoing Assessment: Observe and Listen

As students work, ask questions, such as:
- What is 10% of $48? (*$4.80*)
  How do you know?(*I moved the decimal point one place to the left.*)
- What is 5% of $48? (*$2.40*)
  How do you know? (*5% is $\frac{1}{2}$ of 10%. So, 5% of $48 = $\frac{1}{2}$ of $4.80 = $2.40*)
- What is 25% of $48? (*$12*)
  How do you know? (*25% = 10% + 10% + 5% = $4.80 + $4.80 + $2.40 = $12.00*)

So, 0.15×7.99 is about $\frac{1}{5}$ of 10, which is 2.
So, $0.15 \times 7.99 = 1.1985$
Round to 2 decimal places.
1.1985 is 1.20, to 2 decimal places.
You save \$1.20 by buying the book on sale.
We can show this on a number line.

Example

A park has an area of 52.6 km^2.
Sixty-five percent of the park is forest.
The rest of the park is lakes.
What is the area of the lakes?

Solution

65% of the park is forest.
So, 100% − 65%, or 35% of the park is lakes.
The area of the lakes is: 35% of 52.6
$35\% = \frac{35}{100} = 0.35$
So, 35% of 52.6 = 0.35×52.6
Multiply: 526×35

$$\begin{array}{r} 526 \\ \times\ 35 \\ \hline 2630 \\ 15780 \\ \hline 18410 \end{array}$$

Since the area of the park is given to 1 decimal place, we round the answer to 1 decimal place.

Estimate:
35% of 52.60 is about 50% of 50, which is 25.
So, $0.35 \times 52.6 = 18.41$
35% of 52.6 km^2 is 18.41 km^2.
The area of the lakes is about 18.4 km^2.

8.3 Multiplying to Find Percents 303

REACHING ALL LEARNERS

Early Finishers

Have students draw number lines to illustrate their solutions to questions 4 and 5.

Common Misconceptions

➤ Students do not know that to calculate the cost of an item with tax, directly, they multiply the price by 1.15.

How to Help: Show students the two methods to calculate the cost, including tax. Method 1: Calculate 15% of the cost, then add it to the cost. Method 2: Calculate 115% of the cost; that is, multiply by 1.15. Students will see that the two methods produce the same result.

Assignment Guidelines

If your students do not have time to complete all the *Practice* questions on page 304, these questions provide minimum curriculum coverage:
1, 2, 4, 5, 6, 8, *Reflect*
To assess the 4 Achievement Chart categories listed in the curriculum document, have students complete these *Practice* questions:
Understanding Concepts: 2
Application: 5
Communication: 7
Problem Solving: 8

- How much would you save on an item that originally cost \$48? (*I would save \$12.*) What would the sale price be? (*\$36; \$48 – \$12 = \$36*)
- Did anyone find a different way? Explain. (*I know that 25% = $\frac{1}{4}$; to find $\frac{1}{4}$, I divided \$48 by 4: 48 ÷ 4 = 12. So, $\frac{1}{4}$ of \$48 is \$12.*)

AFTER — Connect

Have students share their strategies with the class.

Ask:

- Which strategy would you use if the sale was 45% off?
(*I would find the amount saved at 50% off, then subtract 5% of the original cost from this amount because 45% is 5% less than 50%. 50% of \$48 = $\frac{1}{2}$ of \$48 = \$24; 5% is $\frac{1}{10}$ of 50%, so 5% of \$48 = $\frac{1}{10}$ of \$24 = \$2.40. I would save \$24 – \$2.40 = \$21.60.*)

Review the examples in *Connect* and the two ways to place the decimal point in the product of two decimals. Ensure students understand that the word "of" in a statement involving fractions, decimals, or percents represents a multiplication sign. Students can replace "of" with "×."

Practice

When students draw number lines for question 7, make sure the lines are drawn to scale. The \$15 line could be 6 cm long, so 25% of it is 1.5 cm long. The \$25 line could be drawn 10 cm long, so 15% of it is 1.5 cm long. The amounts must align vertically to see how the percents are related.

Assessment Focus: Question 6

Students should realize that multiplying 52.3 by 0.02, by 0.2, and by 2 results in the same digits. The products are differentiated only by the positions of the decimal point. A level 4 response would begin with 52.3×2, since this is the easiest product to find.

Sample Answers

6. b) I chose 126.4 and found 6%, 60%, and 600%.

   i) 6% of 126.4 = 0.06 × 126.4
   Find 6 × 1264 = 7584
   There are 3 decimal places in the question.
   So, 0.06 × 126.4 = 7.584

   ii) 60% of 126.4 = 0.6 × 126.4
   There are 2 decimal places in the question.
   So, 0.6 × 126.4 = 75.84

   iii) 600% of 126.4 = 6 × 126.4
   There is 1 decimal place in the question.
   So, 6 × 126.4 = 758.4

7. 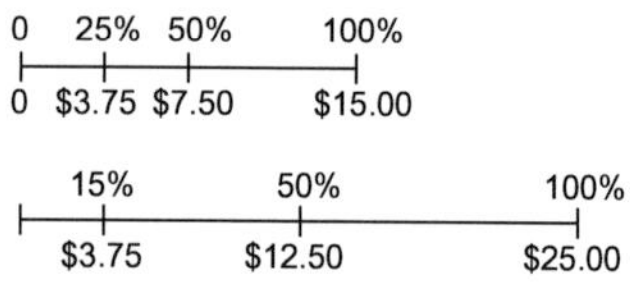

To calculate 25% of $15.00, I multiply 0.25 × 15.00. When I multiply without the decimal points, it becomes 25 × 1500. To calculate 15% of $25.00, I multiply 0.15 × 25.00. When I multiply without the decimal points, it becomes 15 × 2500. Both these sentences can be written as 25 × 15 × 100. The order does not matter when multiplying. In both cases, the answer is $3.75. The calculations are different because in one sentence the 2 zeros are with the 15 and in the other sentence, the 2 zeros are with the 25.

REFLECT: I chose 27% and $88.25. 27% = 0.27
So, 27% of $88.25 = 0.27 × $88.25
Estimate: 27% is about 25%, which is $\frac{1}{4}$. $88.25 is about $100.00. So, 0.27 × 88.25 is about $\frac{1}{4}$ of 100, which is 25. So, 0.27 × $88.25 = $23.8275 Since the number is an amount of money, I rounded to 2 decimal places: $23.83.

Practice

1. Calculate.
   a) 10% of 27.3 2.73 b) 20% of 48.4 9.68 c) 1% of 30.6 0.306 d) 120% of 97.44
2. Find.
   a) 18% of 36 6.48 b) 24% of 67 16.08 c) 98% of 28 27.44 d) 67% of 112 75.04
3. Find each percent of $59.99.
   a) 25% $15 b) 75% $45 c) 30% $18 d) 70% $41.99 e) 80% $47.99 f) 90% $53.99
4. The regular price of a radio is $60.00. Find the sale price when the radio is on sale for:
   a) 25% off $45 b) 30% off $42 c) 40% off $36
5. Find the cost of each item on sale.
   Each item has a 15% sales tax added to the sale price.
   a) coat: 55% off $90 $46.58 b) shoes: 45% off $40 $25.30
6. **Assessment Focus**
   a) Calculate each percent of 52.3.
   How can you do this by completing only one multiplication?
   i) 2% 1.046 ii) 20% 10.46 iii) 200% 104.6
   b) Make up a similar example. Choose a number and 3 related percents. Show how you only need to multiply once to find all the percents of the number.

Number Strategies

Use Pattern Blocks.
Suppose the red block represents 1 whole.
What does each block represent?
- the blue block $\frac{2}{3}$
- the green block $\frac{1}{3}$
- the yellow block 2

7. How is calculating 25% of $15.00 the same as calculating 15% of $25.00? How are the calculations different? Sketch number lines to illustrate your answer.
8. A garage floor is rectangular.
   Its length is 9.0 m and its width is 5.1 m.
   The length and width of a Toyota Corolla are 4.5 m and 1.7 m.
   What percent of the garage floor is occupied by the car?
   About 17%

Reflect

Choose a percent. Choose an amount of money.
Calculate the percent of the money. Show your work.

304 UNIT 8: Working with Percents

ASSESSMENT FOR LEARNING

What to Look For	What to Do
Understanding concepts ✔ Students understand that the percent of a number can be found by writing the percent as a decimal, then multiplying. ***Applying procedures*** ✔ Students can estimate the answer to help position the decimal point when multiplying decimals. ✔ Students can multiply decimals to find percents.	***Extra Support:*** Students who have difficulty with long multiplication may find it easier to break the problem into parts; for example, 799 × 15 = 799 × 10 + 799 × 5 = 7990 + 3995 = 11 985. Students can use Step-by-Step 3 (Master 8.10) to complete question 6. ***Extra Practice:*** Students can play the Additional Activity *Link 5* (Master 8.7a). Students can complete Extra Practice 3 (Master 8.20). ***Extension:*** Have students make up, then solve problems similar to question 5. They could use flyers to find authentic prices and discounts.

Recording and Reporting
Master 8.2 Ongoing Observations: Working with Percents

Mid-Unit Review

LESSON

8.1 **1.** Write each fraction as a decimal and as a percent. Sketch number lines to illustrate.
a) $\frac{4}{5}$ b) $\frac{3}{25}$ c) $\frac{118}{50}$ d) $\frac{7}{20}$

2. Write each fraction as a decimal and as a percent. Sketch number lines to illustrate.
a) $\frac{27}{20}$ b) $\frac{14}{25}$ c) $\frac{15}{8}$ d) $\frac{7}{16}$

3. This right isosceles triangle is 20% of a larger figure.

Draw a figure that represents 100%.

8.2 **4.** Estimate the percent of each figure that is shaded.

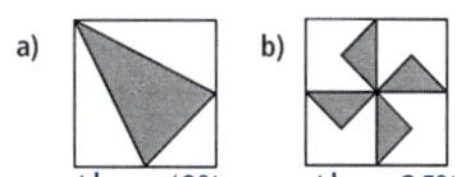

5. In a piggy bank, there were 21 pennies, 32 nickels, and 13 dimes.
a) What fraction of the coins were nickels? $\frac{32}{66}$ or $\frac{16}{33}$
b) Estimate the percent of coins that were nickels.
c) How much money was in the piggy bank? $3.11
d) Estimate the percent of money that was in dimes.

6. Find 10% of each number.
a) 28 b) 66 c) 35 d) 180
2.8 6.6 3.5 18

7. Use the results of question 6. Find 60% of each number in question 6. 16.8, 39.6, 21, 108

8. Use estimation. Find an approximate percent for each fraction.
a) $\frac{14}{17}$ b) $\frac{21}{30}$ c) $\frac{118}{60}$ d) $\frac{172}{80}$ e) $\frac{2}{21}$
a) About 80% b) About 70% c) About 200% d) About 210% e) About 10%

9. Estimate.
a) 14% of 98 About 14 b) 61% of 52 About 30
c) 76% of 202 About 150 d) 98% of 134 About 133

8.3 **10.** a) Find:
i) 5% of $1.00 $0.05
ii) 30% of $1.00 $0.30
iii) 130% of $1.00 $1.30
iv) 20% of $1.00 $0.20
b) Sketch a number line to illustrate your answers to part a.

11. Toni wants to buy a shirt. The original price is $85.00, but it is on sale for 30% off. Toni will pay 15% sales tax. How much will the shirt cost? 11. $68.43

12. How is calculating 85% of $40.00 the same as calculating 40% of $85.00? How are the calculations different? Sketch number lines to illustrate your answers.

Mid-Unit Review 305

SECTION ORGANIZER

Student Materials
- calculators
- rulers
- 2-cm grid paper (PM 21)

Assessment: Masters 8.1 Unit Rubric: Working with Percents, 8.4 Unit Summary: Working with Percents

Sample Solutions

1. a) 0.8, 80% b) 0.12, 12%
c) 2.36, 236% d) 0.35, 35%

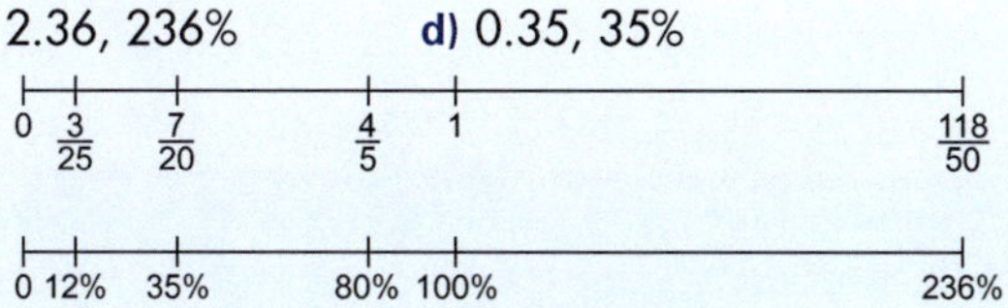

2. a) 1.35, 135% b) 0.56, 56%
c) 1.875, 187.5% d) 0.4375, 43.75%

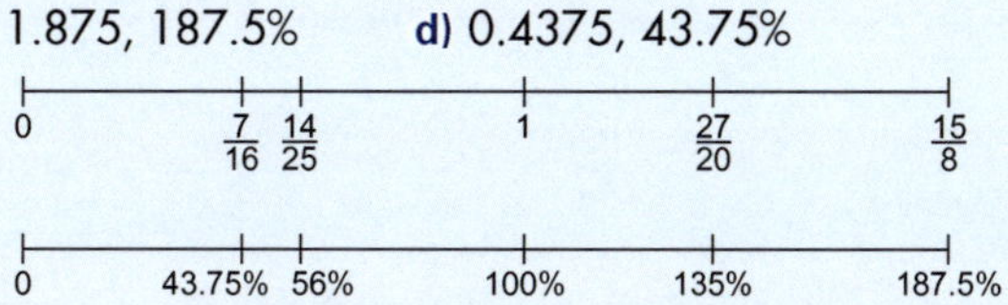

3. 20% is $\frac{1}{5}$ of 100%. To draw the larger figure, I join 5 of the isosceles triangles. I used 2-cm paper. To get 2 isosceles right triangles I drew a diagonal in a square.

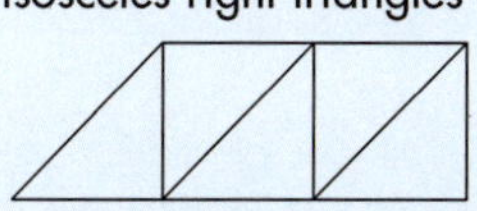

5. b) $\frac{32}{66} \doteq \frac{32}{64} = \frac{1}{2} = 50\%$
About 50% were nickels.
d) There were 13 dimes; 13 × $0.10 = $1.30.
The fraction of money that was in dimes is $\frac{1.30}{3.11}$.
This is about $\frac{1.20}{3.00} = \frac{120}{300} = \frac{12}{30} = \frac{2}{5} = 40\%$.
About 40% of the money was in dimes.

10. b)

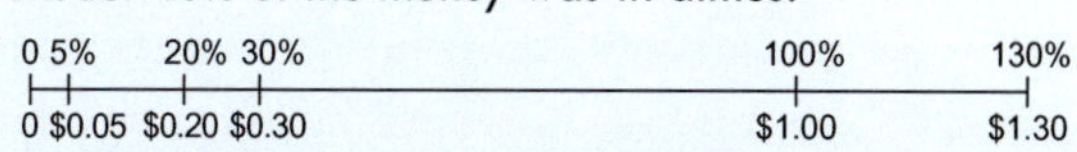

12. To calculate 85% of $40.00, I multiply 0.85 × 40.00. When I multiply without the decimal points, it becomes 85 × 4000. To calculate 40% of $85.00, I multiply 0.40 × 85.00. When I multiply without the decimal points, it becomes 40 × 8500. Both these sentences can be written as 85 × 40 × 100. The order does not matter when multiplying. In both cases, the answer is $34.00. The calculations are different because in one sentence the 2 zeros are with the 40 and in the other sentence, the 2 zeros are with the 85.

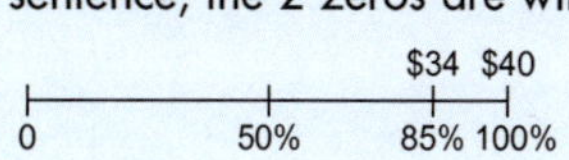

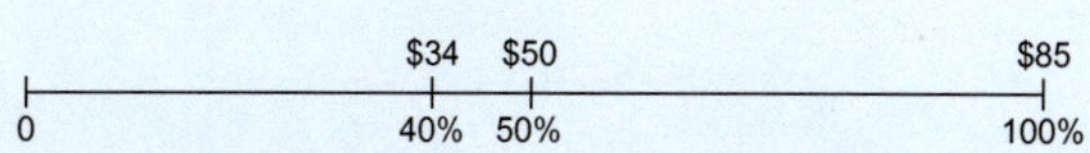

The $40 line could be 4 cm long, so 85% = 3.40 cm
The $85 line could be 8.5 cm long, so 40% = 3.40 cm

Drawing Circle Graphs

SECTION ORGANIZER (80–100 min)

Curriculum Focus: Use circle graphs to display data and solve problems. (7m98, 7m100, 7m102)

Student Materials
- percent circles (Master 8.15)
- 4-column charts (PM 19)
- protractors
- rulers
- labels from canned food, cereal boxes, or other food
- compasses

Optional
- Step-by-Step 4 (Master 8.11)
- Extra Practice 4 (Master 8.21)

Vocabulary: percent circle

Assessment: Master 8.2 Ongoing Observations: Working with Percents

8.4 Drawing Circle Graphs

Focus Use circle graphs to display data and solve problems.

You have drawn a circle graph using a computer.
Now that you can calculate percents,
you can draw a circle graph by hand.
This is a **percent circle**.
The circle is divided into
100 congruent sectors.
Each sector is 1% of
the whole circle.
You can draw a circle graph
on a percent circle.

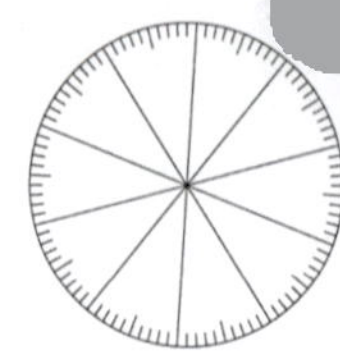

Explore

Work with a partner.
Your teacher will give you a percent circle.
Everyone in the class writes on the board the number of siblings he or she has.
Copy this table.
Record the data.

0 Siblings	1 Sibling	2 Siblings	More than 2 Siblings

Use the percent circle.
Draw a circle graph to display the data.
Write 2 questions you can answer by looking at the graph.

Reflect & Share

Trade questions with another pair of classmates.
Use your graph to answer your classmates' questions.
Compare graphs. If they are different, try to find out why.
How did you use fractions and percents to draw a circle graph?

Connect

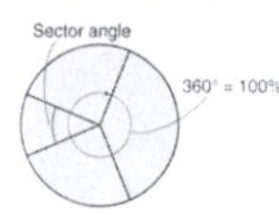

Recall that a circle graph shows how parts of a set of data compare with the whole set.
Each sector of a circle graph represents a percent of the whole circle.
The whole circle represents 100% and has a central angle of 360°.

Key Math Learnings

1. Each sector of a circle graph represents a percent of the whole circle. The whole circle represents 100% and has a central angle of 360°.
2. A percent circle is a circle divided into 100 congruent sectors. Each sector is 1% of the whole circle.

BEFORE Get Started

Remind students of the hundred charts they shaded in *Skills You'll Need* to show percents. Tell students that a **percent circle** is similar to a hundred chart in that they are both divided into 100 congruent parts. In both cases, each part represents 1% of the whole. In the percent circle, we call each part a sector. Every sector is marked with a short line segment, with the 5th, 15th, 25th, and so on, sectors having slightly longer segments, and every 10th sector has a line segment with one line end point at the centre of the circle. This makes it easier to read percents displayed on the circle.

Ask:
- How would you shade a percent circle to represent 10%? (*I would shade the sector between 2 segments that meet at the centre.*)
- How would you shade a percent circle to represent 3%? (*I would shade 3 small sectors.*) To represent 100%? (*I would shade the whole circle.*) To represent 50%? (*I would shade one-half of the circle.*)

Present *Explore*. Distribute copies of 4-column charts (PM 19) for students to record the data, and copies of *Percent Circles* (Master 8.15).

DURING Explore

Ongoing Observations: Observe and Listen

As students work, ask questions, such as:
- How did you find the total or whole? (*I added the numbers in the columns of the table: 5 + 10 + 7 + 3 = 25.*)
- What fraction of the class has 0 siblings? ($\frac{5}{25}$) How do you know? (*There are 5 students with no siblings and there are 25 students in the class.*)

This table shows the 2003 top 10 Ladies' Professional Golf Association (LPGA) money winners' place of birth.

Asia	Australia	Europe	North America
Kung	Teske	Sorenstam	Daniel
Pak			Inkster
Park			Jones
Han			Ochoa

To draw a circle graph to show what percent of the top 10 were born in each place, follow these steps.

Step 1
Write the number of players born in each place as a fraction of 10, then as a percent.

Asia: $\frac{4}{10} = 0.4 = \frac{40}{100} = 40\%$ Australia: $\frac{1}{10} = 0.1 = \frac{10}{100} = 10\%$

Europe: $\frac{1}{10} = 0.1 = \frac{10}{100} = 10\%$ North America: $\frac{4}{10} = 0.4 = \frac{40}{100} = 40\%$

The area of the circle represents all the golfers.
All the sector angles add to 360°.

Step 2
To find the sector angle for each place of birth, multiply each decimal by 360°.
Round to the nearest degree, when necessary.
Asia 40%: 0.40 × 360° = 144°
Australia 10%: 0.10 × 360° = 36°
Europe 10%: same as Australia, so 36°
North America 40%: same as Asia, so 144°

To check, add the angles.
The sum should be 360°.

$$\begin{array}{r} 144° \\ 36° \\ 36° \\ +\ 144° \\ \hline 360° \end{array}$$

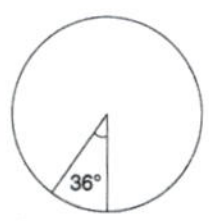

Step 3
Construct a circle.
Use a protractor to construct each sector angle.
Start with the smallest angle. Draw a radius.
Measure 36°.

Start the next sector where the previous sector finished.
Label each sector with its name and percent.
Write a title for the graph.

Top 10 LPGA Winners' Place of Birth

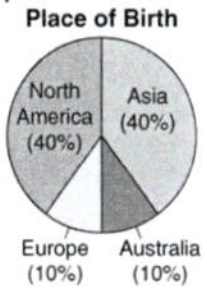

8.4 Drawing Circle Graphs **307**

REACHING ALL LEARNERS

Alternative Explore

Materials: percent circles (Master 8.15)
Five hundred people were asked the question, "What is your favourite colour of car?"
The results are recorded in the table below.

Colour	Number of People
Black	200
Silver	175
Red	80
Blue	25
Other	20

Use a percent circle. Draw a circle graph to display the data.
Write 2 questions you can answer by looking at the graph.

Early Finishers

Have students record the hair colour of each classmate in a table. Students use a circle graph to display the data.

Common Misconceptions

➤ Students think that every 1° angle in a circle graph represents 1%.

How to Help: Show students 2 large congruent circles. One is divided into 360°. The other is divided into 100%. Students will see that a sector for 1% is greater than a sector for 1°. If necessary, post these circles on the bulletin board for students to refer to.

- What percent of the class has 0 siblings? (*20%*) How do you know? (*I found an equivalent fraction with denominator 100:* $\frac{5}{25} = \frac{20}{100} = 20\%$.)
- What fraction of the class has 1 sibling? ($\frac{10}{25}$) How do you know? (*There are 10 students with 1 sibling and there are 25 students in the class.*)
- What percent of the class has 1 sibling? (*40%*) How do you know? (*I found an equivalent fraction with denominator 100:* $\frac{10}{25} = \frac{40}{100} = 40\%$.)
- What fraction of the class has 2 siblings? ($\frac{7}{25}$) What percent is that? (*28%*)
- What fraction of the class has more than 2 siblings? ($\frac{3}{25}$) What percent is that? (*12%*)
- How do you know your fractions are correct? (*They add to 1 whole:* $\frac{5}{25} + \frac{10}{25} + \frac{7}{25} + \frac{3}{25} = \frac{25}{25} = 1$.)
- How do you know your percents are correct? (*They add to 100%: 20% + 40% + 28% + 12% = 100%.*)
- How did you represent these percents on a percent circle? (*I shaded 20 sectors to represent 0 siblings, 40 sectors to represent 1 sibling, 28 sectors to represent 2 siblings, and 12 sectors to represent more than 2 siblings. I used a different colour to shade each percent. I added labels and a title to my graph.*)
- What question can you answer by looking at the graph? (*What percent of the class has 2 or more siblings?*)
- How can you answer that question using the graph? (*I know that 28% have 2 siblings and 12% have more than 2 siblings. I add to find the percent with 2 or more siblings: 28% + 12% = 40%.*)
- What other question can you answer by looking at the graph? (*How many siblings does most of the class have?*)

Sample Answers

2. a) The data in table i can be displayed in a circle graph because the sum of the percents is 100%. The data in table ii cannot be displayed in a circle graph because the percents do not add to 100%. The data do not represent 1 whole.
   b) I would use a bar graph, with each bar representing one type of appliance.

3. b) **The Number of Students with Each Eye Colour At Northern Public School**

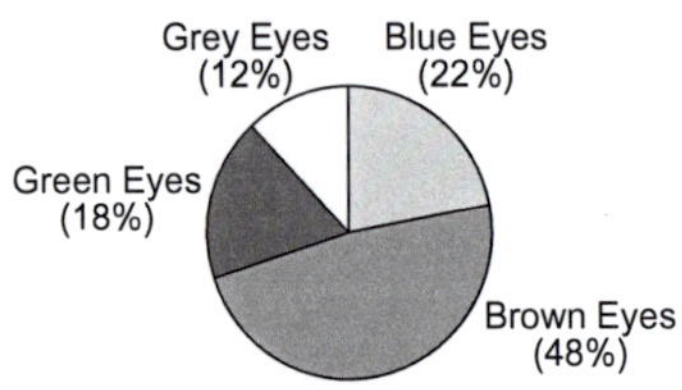

4. c) **Favourite Radio Station**

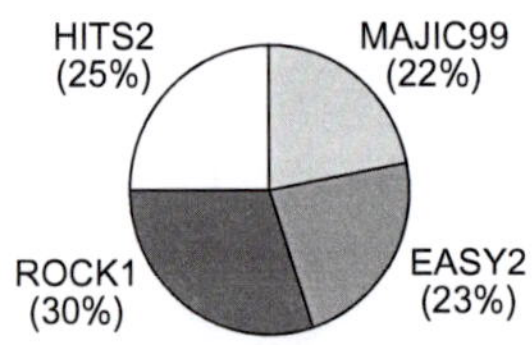

5. a) Soda Crackers (20 g serving):
   Energy: 88 cal/370 kJ; Protein: 2.1 g; Fat: 2.6 g;
   Carbohydrates: 14 g; Other: 1.3 g; Total mass is 20 g.
   b) Protein: $\frac{2.1}{20} = \frac{10.5}{100} = 10.5\%$; Fat: $\frac{2.6}{20} = \frac{13.0}{100} = 13\%$;
   Carbohydrates: $\frac{14}{20} = \frac{70}{100} = 70\%$; Other: $\frac{1.3}{20} = \frac{6.5}{100} = 6.5\%$

Example 1

This circle graph shows the world's gold production.

World's Gold Production

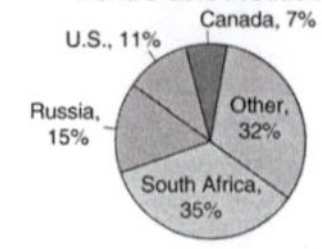

In 2002, the world's gold production was approximately 2300 t. About how much gold would have been produced in each country?
a) Canada   b) South Africa

Solution

a) 7% is produced in Canada.
Mass of gold = 7% × 2300
= 0.07 × 2300
= 161
About 161 t would have been produced in Canada.

b) 35% is produced in South Africa.
Mass of gold = 35% × 2300
= 0.35 × 2300
= 805
About 805 t would have been produced in South Africa.

Example 2

These four oceans have an area of approximately 337 million km².
a) Draw a circle graph to represent the data in the table.
b) Find the area of the largest ocean.

Ocean	Percent of Total Area
Atlantic	25
Arctic	3
Indian	22
Pacific	50

Solution

a) Each area is written as a percent of the total area of the oceans.
The area of the circle represents the total area of the oceans.
To find the sector angle for each ocean, multiply each percent by 360°.
Atlantic: 25% of 360° = 0.25 × 360°
= 90°
Arctic: 3% of 360° = 0.03 × 360°
= 10.8°
≐ 11°

Round each angle to the nearest degree, when necessary.

308 UNIT 8: Working with Percents

- How can you answer that question using the graph?
  (The largest sector of the circle represents students who have 1 sibling.)

Ensure students understand that a circle graph must have labels and a title.

AFTER Connect

Have volunteers share their graphs and questions with the class.
What you might see:

0 Siblings	1 Sibling	2 Siblings	More than 2 Siblings
5	10	7	3

Number of Siblings the Students in a Grade 7 Class Have

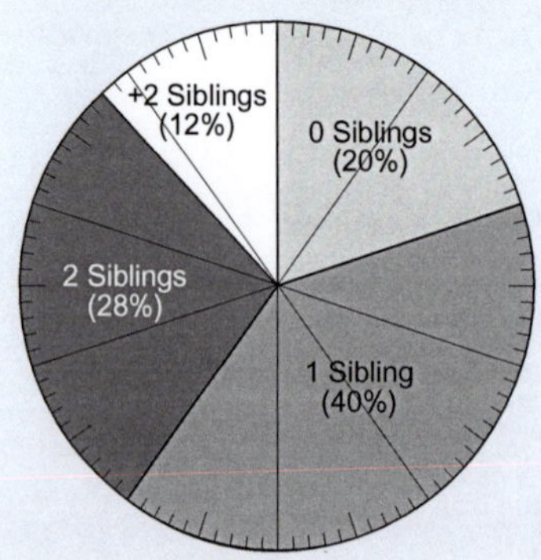

Ask:
- How could you use fractions to draw a circle graph?
  (I could write each fraction as an equivalent fraction, with denominator 100. Each sector of the percent circle represents $\frac{1}{100}$. I would shade to represent each fraction.)

Tell students that we can extend our knowledge of using percent circles to drawing circle graphs, where 1% is represented by an

Indian: 22% of 360° $= 0.22 \times 360°$
$= 79.2°$
$\doteq 79°$
Pacific: 50% of 360° $= 0.50 \times 360°$
$= 180°$

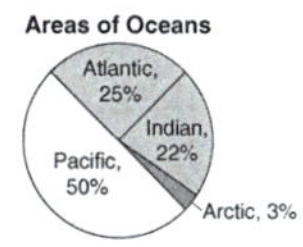

Construct a circle.
Use a protractor to construct each sector angle.
Label each sector with its name and percent.
Write a title for the graph.

b) The largest ocean is the Pacific Ocean.
Its area is:
50% of 337 000 000 km² $= 0.50 \times 337\,000\,000$ km²
$= 168\,500\,000$ km²
The largest ocean has an area about 168 500 000 km².

Practice

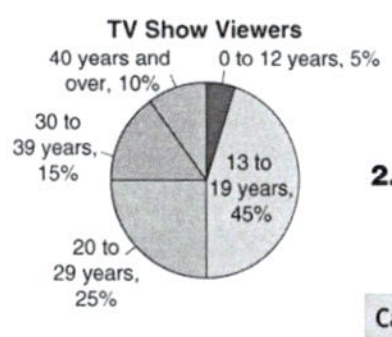

1. This circle graph shows the ages of viewers of a TV show.
One week, approximately 250 000 viewers tuned in.
How many viewers were in each age group?
a) 13 to 19 b) 20 to 29 c) 40 and over
112 500 62 500 25 000

2. a) Can the data in each table below be displayed in a circle graph? Explain.
i) Yes ii) No

Canadians, Educational Attainment, 2001	
0 to 8 years of elementary school	10%
Some secondary school	17%
Graduated from high school	20%
Some post secondary education	9%
Post-secondary certificate or diploma	28%
University degree	16%

Canadian Households with These Appliances, 2000	
Automobiles	64%
Cell phone	42%
Dishwasher	51%
Internet	42%

b) For the data that could not be displayed in a circle graph, state what type of graph you would use to display it.

8.4 Drawing Circle Graphs 309

c) Protein: 10.5% of 50 g $= 0.105 \times 50$ g $= 5.25$ g
Fat: 13% of 50 g $= 0.13 \times 50$ g $= 6.5$ g
Carbohydrates: 70% of 50 g $= 0.70 \times 50$ g $= 35$ g
Other: 6.5% of 50 g $= 0.065 \times 50$ g $= 3.25$ g

d)

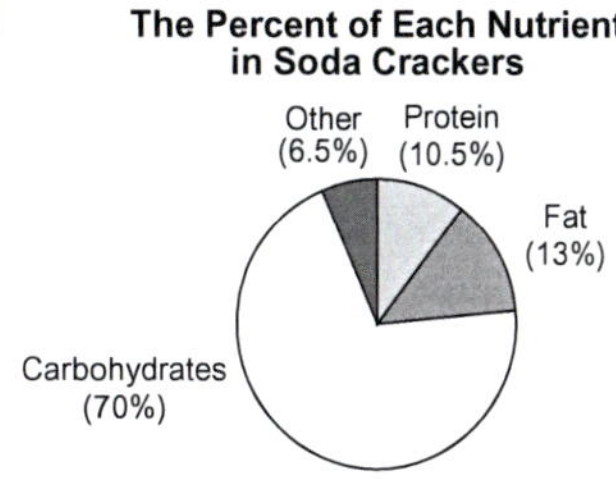

6. The approximate area of South America is 147 million km². Similarly, the areas of the other continents are approximately:
Antarctica: 98 million km²; Europe: 85 million km²;
Australia: 61 million km²; Asia: 366 million km²
Africa: 244 million km²

REFLECT: I need to know that each sector of a circle graph represents a percent of the whole circle. The whole circle represents 100% and has a central angle of 360°. I must write each fraction as a percent and the sum of the percents must be 100%. If the sum of the percents is not 100%, the data cannot be displayed on a circle graph.

angle of 3.6° and the whole circle represents 100%. Remind students that a circle graph displays ratios rather than quantities; a circle graph shows parts of a whole and the circle represents one whole.

Work through the examples in *Connect*. Ensure students understand that a quick way to check their graphs is to make sure that the sum of the angles is 360° and the sum of the percents is 100%.

Practice

Questions 3, 4, and 5 require students to draw circle graphs. Students will need compasses and protractors if they draw circle graphs without using percent circles. The graphs in the answers that follow are drawn on percent circles. You decide, or allow your students to decide, how each graph is to be drawn.

Students require labels from canned food, cereal boxes, or other foods for question 5. Students may require calculators for questions 5 and 6.

Assessment Focus: Question 5

Students should add the masses of the nutrients. The sum should be the same as the serving size listed. If not, students should include the category "Other" to represent the mass not accounted for. Students should recall that a circle graph can only be drawn if the sum of the percents is 100%. Students find the mass of each nutrient as a percent, convert the percent to a decimal, then multiply the decimal by 50 g. The circle graphs students draw should include labels and a title. For students who are not comfortable drawing circle graphs, allow them to use percent circles, and omit part c.

For example, there are 30 students in my class. Twelve students have black hair, 9 have brown hair, 6 have blond hair, and 3 have red hair. I find the fraction, then the percent, of the class with each hair colour.

Black: $\frac{12}{30} = \frac{4}{10} = \frac{40}{100} = 40\%$; Brown: $\frac{9}{30} = \frac{3}{10} = \frac{30}{100} = 30\%$

Blond: $\frac{6}{30} = \frac{2}{10} = \frac{20}{100} = 20\%$; Red: $\frac{3}{30} = \frac{1}{10} = \frac{10}{100} = 10\%$

I add the percents to check: 40% + 30% + 20% + 10% = 100%.
I can represent the data on a circle graph.
Students' responses should include the graph.

Calculator Skills

Students enter [2] [×] [2] [=] [=] [=] ... on a 4-function calculator, until the product gets too great for the calculator display. This occurs when [=] is pressed for the 23rd time. The greatest product is 2^{23}. On the TI-15, the greatest product is 2^{33}.

Assignment Guidelines

If your students do not have time to complete all the *Practice* questions on pages 309 and 310, these questions provide minimum curriculum coverage: 1, 2, 4, 5, *Reflect*

To assess the 4 Achievement Chart categories listed in the curriculum document, have students complete these *Practice* questions:

Understanding Concepts: 1
Problem Solving: 4
Application: 5
Communication: *Reflect.*

---

3. The table shows the number of Grade 7 students with each eye colour at Northern Public School.

Eye Colour	Number of Students
Blue	11 22%
Brown	24 48%
Green	9 18%
Grey	6 12%

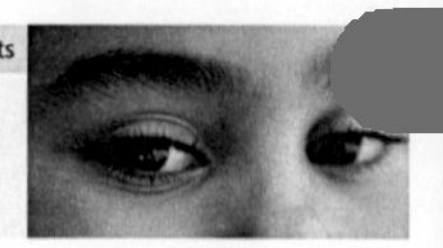

a) Calculate the percent of students with each eye colour.
b) Draw a circle graph to represent the data.

4. In a telephone survey, 400 people voted for their favourite radio station.

Radio Station	Votes
MAJIC99	88 22
EASY2	? 23
ROCK1	120 30
HITS2	100 25

a) How many people chose EASY2? 92
b) Write the number of people people who voted for each station as a percent of the total number surveyed.
c) Draw a circle graph to display the results of the survey.

Calculator Skills

How many times can you multiply 2 by itself until the product gets too big for your calculator display? Write the greatest product as a power of 2. 2^{23}

5. Assessment Focus Choose some labels from canned food, cereal boxes, or other foods.
a) List the nutritional information on each label.
b) Calculate the mass of each nutrient as a percent of the total mass.
c) Find the mass of each nutrient in 50 g of the food.
d) Draw a circle graph to display the percent of each nutrient. Show your work.

Take It Further

6. This circle graph shows the percent of Earth's land occupied by each continent. The area of North America is approximately 220 million km^2. Use the percents in the circle graph. Find the approximate area of each of the other continents.

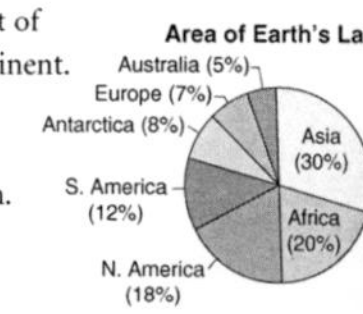

Reflect

What do you need to know about percents to be able to draw a circle graph? Include an example in your answer.

ASSESSMENT FOR LEARNING

What to Look For	What to Do
Understanding concepts ✔ Students understand that each sector of a circle graph represents a percent of the whole circle and the whole circle represents 100% or 1 whole.	***Extra Support:*** Students who have difficulty constructing a circle graph by hand may benefit from using a percent circle and shading the appropriate number of sectors to represent each percent. Students can use Step-by-Step 4 (Master 8.11) to complete question 5.
Applying procedures ✔ Students can interpret data displayed on a circle graph and use it to solve problems. ✔ Students can create a circle graph, including labels and a title, and use it to display data clearly and accurately.	***Extra Practice:*** Have students display each set of data in *Practice* question 2 on the appropriate type of graph. Students can complete Extra Practice 4 (Master 8.21). ***Extension:*** Have students write a survey question with 5 possible answers. Students survey their classmates, record the data in a table, then display the data on a circle graph.

Recording and Reporting
Master 8.2 Ongoing Observations: Working with Percents

8.5 Dividing to Find Percents

Focus Divide decimals with hundredths.

Explore

Work with a partner.

Suppose you pay $15.00 for a shirt. How could you find out what the original price was?
Draw a diagram to model this problem.
Show several strategies for solving the problem.

Reflect & Share

Compare your strategies with those of another pair of classmates.
Which strategies can you use to find the original price if you paid 35% of the original price? Explain.

Connect

Jenny wanted to know her brother Alan's mass.
Alan told Jenny that 15% of his mass is 6.75 kg.

Jenny knows what 15% is.
She wants to find 100%.

15% is 6.75.
So, 1% is: $\frac{6.75}{15}$
Use long division: 6.75 ÷ 15
1% is 0.45.
So, 100% is: 0.45 × 100 = 45
Alan's mass is 45 kg.

$$\begin{array}{r} 0.45 \\ 15\overline{)6.75} \\ \underline{6\,0} \\ 75 \\ \underline{75} \\ 0 \end{array}$$

8.5 Dividing to Find Percents 311

Dividing to Find Percents

SECTION ORGANIZER (80–100 min)

Curriculum Focus: Divide decimals with hundredths. (7m6, 7m14, 7m23, 7m27)

Student Materials
- calculators

Optional
- counters
- play money
- Step-by-Step 5 (Master 8.12)
- Extra Practice 5 (Master 8.22)

Assessment: Master 8.2 Ongoing Observations: Working with Percents

Key Math Learning

When given a percent of a whole, we can divide to find 100%.

Number Strategies

Students rewrite each pair of fraction with a common denominator before adding or subtracting.

$\frac{3}{5} + \frac{3}{6} = \frac{18}{30} + \frac{15}{30} = \frac{33}{30} = \frac{11}{10}$

$\frac{4}{5} - \frac{1}{2} = \frac{8}{10} - \frac{5}{10} = \frac{3}{10}$

$\frac{3}{4} + \frac{4}{3} = \frac{9}{12} + \frac{16}{12} = \frac{25}{12}$

$\frac{5}{6} - \frac{1}{4} = \frac{10}{12} - \frac{3}{12} = \frac{7}{12}$

BEFORE — Get Started

Present *Explore*. Suggest students could use counters, play money, or a number line to model and solve the problem.

DURING — Explore

Ongoing Observations: Observe and Listen

Ask questions, such as:

- What strategy did you use to solve the problem?
  (I know $15 represents 75%. I know 75% = $\frac{3}{4}$ and 100% = $\frac{4}{4}$. I modelled the problem with counters. I divided 15 counters into 3 equal groups. There were 5 counters in each group. Each group represents $\frac{1}{4}$. So, $\frac{4}{4}$ = 5 × 4 = 20. The original price was $20.)
- You know that 75% of the original price is $15.00. How could you find out what 1% is?
  (I could divide $15 by 75. I use a calculator to find that 1% is 20¢.)
- Now you know what 1% is. How could you find what 100% is?
  (I multiply 20¢ by 100 to get $20.)
- How did you use play money to solve the problem?
  (I divided $15 into 75 groups. Each group is 1%. Each group is 20¢. So, 1% is 20¢. Then I multiplied by 100 to find that 100% is $20. The shirt originally cost $20.)

AFTER — Connect

Invite students to share their strategies and diagrams with the class.
What you might see:

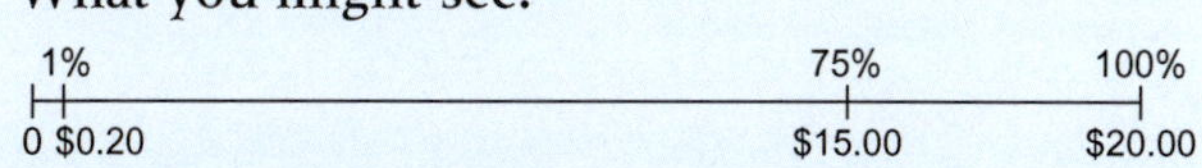

Use *Connect* to introduce the strategy of dividing decimals with hundredths.

When we know a percent of the whole, there is a 2-step process to find the whole:

REACHING ALL LEARNERS

Early Finishers

Have students look through store flyers. Students calculate the original price of various items, given the sale price and the percent off.

Common Misconceptions

➤ Students divide by the wrong percent when finding 1%. For example, Buffy paid $25 for a T-shirt. It was 30% off. What was the original price? There was no tax.

How to Help: Remind students that the original price had been reduced by 30%. Buffy paid 100% – 30% = 70% of the original price. To find the value of 1%, we must divide $25 by 70.

ESL Strategies

Encourage students for whom English is a second language to use number lines and diagrams to help them explain their answers to *Practice* question 9. It may be difficult for them to explain their thinking in words.

Sample Answers

1.
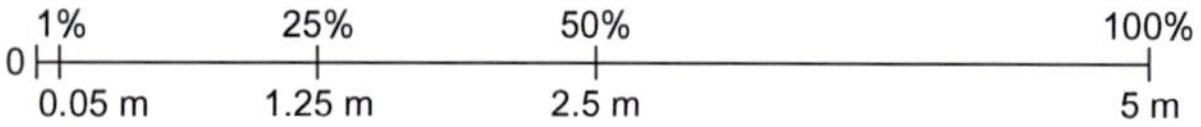

2.

3.
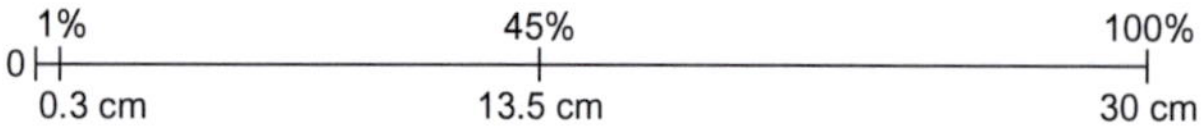

(*Answers continue below right.*)

Example

This sign appeared in a shop window.

Eric pays $58.50 for a jacket. What is the list price of the jacket?

Solution

Use a calculator or long division to find $\frac{\$58.50}{65}$.

65% of the list price is $58.50.
So, 1% of the list price is: $\frac{\$58.50}{65} = \$0.90$

And, 100% is: $\$0.90 \times 100 = \$90.00$
The list price of the jacket is $90.00.

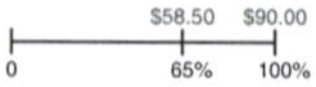

Practice

1. 25% is 1.25 m.
   a) What is 50%? 2.5 m b) What is 100%? 5 m
   Sketch a number line to show your answer.

2. 35% is 4.2 kg.
   a) What is 1%? 0.12 kg b) What is 100%? 12 kg
   Sketch a number line to show your answer.

3. 45% is 13.5 cm.
   a) What is 1%? 0.3 cm b) What is 100%? 30 cm
   Sketch a number line to show your answer.

4. The principal reported that 75% of the total number of families attended the school's Fun Fair. Three hundred sixty families wen to the fair. How many families have children at the school? 480 families

5. A hockey team played 30 games. It won 60% of the games. How many games did the team lose? 12 games

6. Grace has read 30% of a book. She has read 72 pages. How many pages are in the book? 240 pages

Step 1: Divide the given amount by the given percent, to find out what 1% of the whole is.

Step 2: Multiply the amount that represents 1% by 100, to get the whole.

For many students, it is not intuitive that if they know, for example, what 40% is, then to find out what 1% is, they divide by 40.

Practice

Have calculators available for all questions.

Assessment Focus: Question 9

Students could use their knowledge that the order in which numbers are multiplied does not affect the product to discover that the cost is the same in both situations. Some students may use the fact that 30% off means you pay 70% of the original price. That is, they will not find 30% then subtract; they simply find 70%.

(*Sample Answers, continued*)

9. a) The blouse will be reduced by 30%: $\$75 \times 0.30 = \$22.50$. The blouse will cost $\$75.00 - \$22.50 = \$52.50$, plus tax. The tax is 15%: $\$52.50 \times 0.15 = \$7.88$. The blouse will cost $\$52.50 + \$7.88 = \$60.38$.

b) i) The blouse will cost $60.38 as shown in part a.

ii) $\$75 \times 0.15 = \$11.25$. The blouse, with tax added, is $\$75 + \$11.25 = \$86.25$.

To take 30% off of this amount, I multiply $\$86.25 \times 0.30 = \$25.87$. The blouse will cost $\$86.25 - \$25.87 = \$60.38$. The blouse will cost the same in each situation because order does not matter when multiplying.

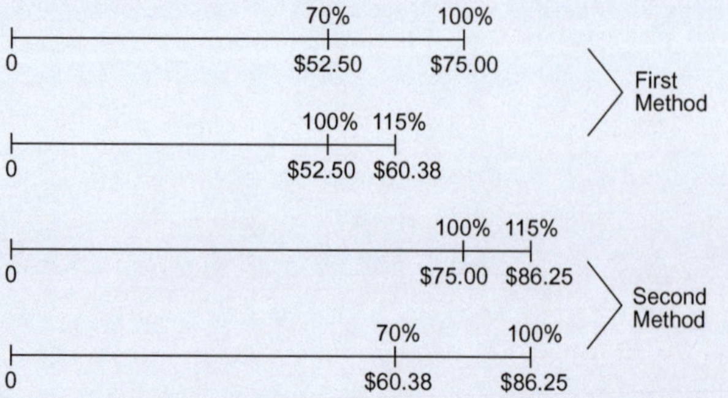

Number Strategies

dd or subtract.

- $\frac{3}{5} + \frac{3}{6} = \frac{11}{10}$
- $\frac{4}{5} - \frac{1}{2} = \frac{3}{10}$
- $\frac{3}{4} + \frac{4}{3} = \frac{25}{12}$
- $\frac{5}{6} - \frac{1}{4} = \frac{7}{12}$

7. Paco ate 25% of a 16-slice pizza and placed the rest in the fridge. Santos ate 25% of the leftovers.
a) How many pieces were left? 9 pieces
b) What percent of the original pizza remained? 56.25%

8. This year, 40 more children joined the local soccer club than last year. This is a 10% increase. How many students played in the club last year? 400 students

9. **Assessment Focus** Anika wants to buy a blouse.
The original price is \$75.00. It is on sale for 30% off.
Anika will pay 15% sales tax.
a) How much will the blouse cost? \$60.38
b) Does it make any difference to the cost in each situation? No
i) The 30% is taken off before the 15% tax is added.
ii) The 15% tax is added before the 30% is taken off.
Explain. Draw number lines to show your thinking.

10. Write your own problem that involves working with percents. Solve your problem. Show your work.

Take It Further

11. A pair of shoes in a clearance store went through a series of reductions.
The regular price was \$125. The shoes were reduced by 20%.
Three weeks later, the shoes were reduced by a further 20%.
Later in the year, the shoes were advertised for sale at $\frac{3}{4}$ off the ticket price.
Sean wants to buy the shoes. He has to pay 15% sales tax.
a) Sean has \$40.00. Can Sean buy the shoes? Explain. Yes
b) If your answer to part a is yes, how much change does Sean get? \$17
Sketch number lines to illustrate your work.

12. A box was $\frac{3}{4}$ full. The box fell on the floor.
Thirty marbles fell out. This was 20% of the marbles that were in the box. How many marbles were in a full box? 200 marbles

Reflect

How does a good understanding of percents help you outside the classroom? Give an example.

11. a) Yes. Regular price: \$125
20% reduction means the new price is 80% of \$125 $= 0.80 \times \$125 = \$100$.
A further 20% reduction means the new price is 80% of \$100 = \$80. A "$\frac{3}{4}$ off" reduction means that the new price is $\frac{1}{4}$ of \$80 = \$20. The price Sean pays, including tax, is 115% of \$20 $= 1.15 \times \$20 = \$23$.
Sean has enough money.

REFLECT: If I understand percent, I can find how much money I can save when shopping. For example, a DVD costs \$24.99. It is on sale for 30% off. I have to pay 15% sales tax. How much does the DVD cost?
Solution: 30% off means I pay 70% of \$24.99 $= 0.70 \times \$24.99 = \$17.49$ rounded to the nearest cent. 15% sales tax means I pay 115% of \$17.49 $= 1.15 \times \$17.49 = \$20.11$.

Assignment Guidelines

If your students do not have time to complete all the *Practice* questions on pages 312 and 313, these questions provide minimum curriculum coverage: 1, 2, 5, 6, 7, 9, 10, *Reflect*
To assess the 4 Achievement Chart categories listed in the curriculum document, have students complete these *Practice* questions:
Understanding Concepts: 2
Application: 6
Problem Solving: 7
Communication: 9

ASSESSMENT FOR LEARNING

What to Look For	What to Do
Understanding concepts ✔ Students understand the two-step process to find the whole when given a percent of it. ***Applying procedures*** ✔ Students can divide decimals with hundredths to find percents. ***Problem solving*** ✔ Students can solve problems that involve working with percents.	***Extra Support:*** Students who have difficulty with long division could use grid paper to align the digits and decimal points. Students could divide the numbers without decimal points, then use estimation to place the decimal point. Students can use Step-by-Step 5 (Master 8.12) to complete question 9. ***Extra Practice:*** Have students write problems similar to *Practice* questions 5 and 6. Students trade problems with a classmate and solve each other's problems. Students can complete Extra Practice 5 (Master 8.22). ***Extension:*** Have students find the original price of a jacket that was purchased for \$51.92, including 15% tax. The item was on sale for 50% off, and then the cashier reduced the sale price by a further 30%. (*Answer: \$129*)

Recording and Reporting
Master 8.2 Ongoing Observations: Working with Percents

Choosing a Strategy

SECTION ORGANIZER

Student Materials
- calculators
- square dot paper (PM 22)
- 1-cm grid paper (PM 20)
- linking cubes

Assessment: Master 8.2 Ongoing Observations: Working with Percents

Choosing a Strategy

Strategies
- Make a table.
- Use a model.
- Draw a diagram.
- Solve a simpler problem.
- Work backward.
- Guess and check.
- Make an organized list.
- Use a pattern.
- Draw a graph.
- Use logical reasoning.

Use a calculator when you need to.

1. Write 720 as the product of consecutive whole numbers. Find all the possible ways.

2. A digital clock shows this time. Seven minutes past 7 is a palindromic time.

a) List all the palindromic times between noon and midnight.
b) What is the shortest time between two palindromic times? 2 min

3. I am a perfect square less than 400. The sum of my digits is also a perfect square. Which number could I be? Find all possible numbers.

4. The trail around Lake Pender is 20 km long. How long do you think it would take you to walk around the lake? Explain.

5. Jack's heart rate is 72 beats/min. How long will it take for Jack's heart to beat one million times? 231.5

6. A 4-cm cube is painted red on the top and bottom faces, blue on the front and back faces, and green on the side faces. The cube is cut into 1-cm cubes.

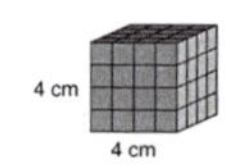

How many of the small cubes will have:
a) 3 colours of paint? 8 cubes
b) 2 colours? 24 cubes
c) 1 colour? 24 cubes
d) no paint? 8 cubes

7. Use dot paper. Draw a quadrilateral with at least two sides equal. How many different quadrilaterals can you draw?

314 UNIT 8: Working with Percents

Sample Solutions

1. $1 \times 2 \times 3 \times 4 \times 5 \times 6$; $2 \times 3 \times 4 \times 5 \times 6$; $8 \times 9 \times 10$
2. a) 12:21, 1:01, 1:11, 1:21, 1:31, 1:41, 1:51, 2:02, 2:12, 2:22, 2:32, 2:42, 2:52, 3:03, 3:13, 3:23, 3:33, 3:43, 3:53, 4:04, 4:14, 4:24, 4:34, 4:44, 4:54, 5:05, 5:15, 5:25, 5:35, 5:45, 5:55, 6:06, 6:16, 6:26, 6:36, 6:46, 6:56, 7:07, 7:17, 7:27, 7:37, 7:47, 7:57, 8:08, 8:18, 8:28, 8:38, 8:48, 8:58, 9:09, 9:19, 9:29, 9:39, 9:49, 9:59, 10:01, 11:11
   b) 2 minutes (between 9:59 and 10:01)
3. I found all the perfect squares less than 400:
   1, 4, 9, 16, 25, 36, 49, 64, 81, 100, 121, 144, 169, 196, 225, 256, 289, 324, 361.
   I then found those numbers whose digits add to a number that is also a perfect square: 36, 81, 100, 121, 144, 169, 196, 225, 324
4. I can walk about 4 km/h. If I walk at the same rate and I make no stops, it would take me about $20 \div 4 = 5$ h.
5. Jack's heart beats 72 times in 1 min.
   It will take $1\,000\,000 \div 72 \doteq 13\,889$ min to beat 1 million times.
   There are 60 min in 1 h. $13\,889 \div 60 \doteq 231.5$
   It will take about 231.5 h to beat one million times.
6. Use linking cubes to make the large cube. There will be $4 \times 4 \times 4 = 64$ 1-cm cubes.
7. Many answers are possible. For example:

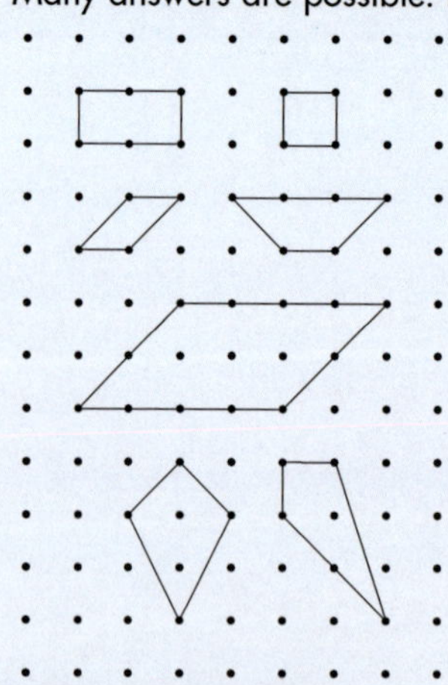

8. $0.1 + 0.9 + 1.0 = 2$
   $0.2 + 0.8 + 1.0 = 2$
   $0.3 + 0.7 + 1.0 = 2$
   $0.3 + 0.8 + 0.9 = 2$
   $0.4 + 0.6 + 1.0 = 2$
   $0.4 + 0.7 + 0.9 = 2$
   $0.5 + 0.6 + 0.9 = 2$
   $0.5 + 0.7 + 0.8 = 2$

Reading and Writing in Math

8. The decimals 0.1, 0.2, 0.3, up to 1.0, are written on ten cards.
How many sets of three cards have a sum of 2? 8 sets

9. Use 1-cm grid paper.
Draw a 6 cm by 4 cm rectangle.
Shade $\frac{1}{4}$ red.
Shade $\frac{1}{3}$ of the remainder blue.
Shade $\frac{1}{2}$ of the unshaded area green.
What fraction is unshaded? $\frac{1}{4}$ is unshaded.

10. A small company consists of the owner and 3 employees.
The owner earns $10 000 a month. The employees earn $4000, $4000, and $6000 per month.
a) The employees ask the owner for a pay raise.
Should they use the mean, median or mode salary when they present their case? Explain.
b) Should the owner use the mean, median or mode when she explains she cannot give the employees a raise? Explain.

11. The area of a rectangular field is 3496 m^2.
Its perimeter is 260 m.
What are the dimensions of the field? 38 m by 92 m

12. This figure comprises a square and two halves of a congruent square.

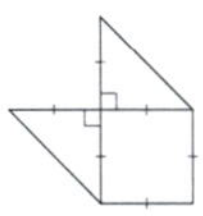

Arrange the parts of the figure to produce each new figure.
a) a rectangle b) a parallelogram c) a trapezoid d) a triangle
Sketch your answers.

Question Number	Possible Strategy
1	Make an organized list.
2	Make an organized list.
3	Make an organized list; use logical reasoning.
4	Use logical reasoning.
5	Use logical reasoning.
6	Use a model.
7	Draw a diagram.
8	Make an organized list.
9	Draw a diagram; use logical reasoning.
10	Use logical reasoning.
11	Work backward; guess and check; use logical reasoning.
12	Guess and check; use a model.

9.

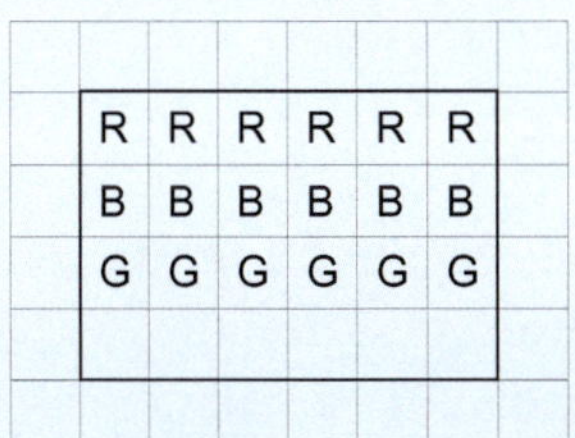

$\frac{1}{4} = \frac{6}{24}$ of the squares are unshaded

10. The mean = ($10 000 + $4000 + $4000 + $6000) ÷ 4 = $24 000 ÷ 4 = $6000
The mode is the value that occurs most often: $4000.
The median is the mean of the 2 middle numbers:
($4000 + $6000) ÷ 2 = $10 000 ÷ 2 = $5000
a) The employees should use the mean because two of the three employees earn less than the mean and the third employee earns the mean.
b) The owner should use the mode because 2 employees earn the mode and 1 employee earns more than the mode.

11. Use guess and check to find two numbers whose product is 3496 and whose sum is one-half the perimeter; that is, $\frac{1}{2}$ of 260 = 130.
The perimeter = 38 m + 38 m + 92 m + 92 m = 260 m
The area = 38 m × 92 m = 3496 m^2

12.

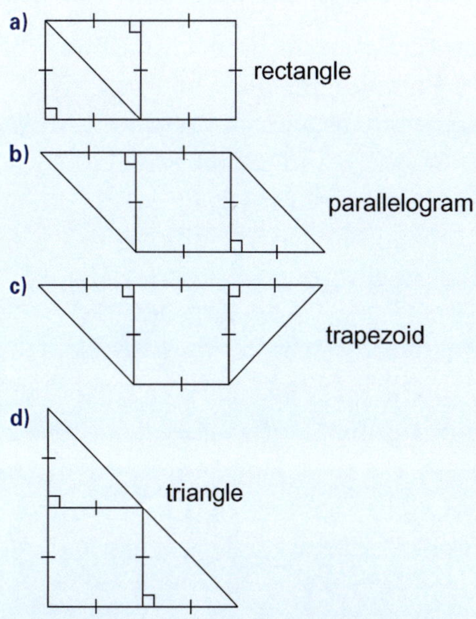

Sports Trainer

Sample Solution

The ratio of magnesium to calcium is 1:2. So, there is twice as much calcium in a scoop of the sports drink as there is magnesium. If there are 100 mg of calcium in 1 scoop, there are $\frac{1}{2} \times 100$ mg = 50 mg of magnesium.

You could ask students to calculate how much of 50 g of magnesium would be absorbed (87% of 50 g = 0.87×50 g = 43.5 g) and how much of 100 g of calcium would be absorbed (44% of 100 g = 44 g) to find out that the body absorbs about the same mass of each ingredient.

Sports Trainer

Sports trainers use scientific research and scientific techniques to maximize an athlete's performance. An athlete may be measured for percent body fat, or percent of either fast- or slow-twitch muscle fibre.

A trainer may recommend the athlete eat pre-event meals that contain a certain percent of carbohydrate, or choose a "sports drink" that contains a high percent of certain minerals. The trainer creates and monitors exercise routines. These enable the athlete to attain a certain percent of maximum heart rate, speed, or power.

Most sports drinks contain minerals. Research shows that the most effective sports drink has a magnesium to calcium ratio of 1:2. The body absorbs about 87% of magnesium in a drink, and about 44% of calcium in a drink. One sports drink lists 100 mg of calcium per scoop. About how much magnesium is there in 1 scoop?

316 UNIT 8: Working with Percents

Here are some careers that involve working with percent.

Camera and platemaking occupations: These occupations include people who operate graphic arts cameras and scanners, assemble film and negatives, and prepare and etch printing plates for printing presses. People who work in this field are often employed by commercial printing companies, newspapers, magazines, and companies with in-house printing departments. These people must be able to read and write percents, calculate what percent one number is of another, and calculate a percent of a number; for example, calculating the percent a photograph needs to shrink or expand to fill a space.

Business managers: A business manager is responsible for running a company. Depending on the size of a company, a business manager may oversee some or all of the following: coordinating human resources, inventory control, distribution of products, finances, logistics of production, marketing, and sales. Business managers use percents to compare productivity from one year to another, to prepare budgets, to manage payroll, and to calculate taxes.

Unit Review

Review any lesson with eText online tutorial

What Do I Need to Know?

✓ Here are some fractions, decimals, and percents you should know.

$1 = 1.0 = 100\%$ | $\frac{1}{5} = 0.2 = 20\%$
$\frac{1}{2} = 0.5 = 50\%$ | $\frac{1}{10} = 0.1 = 10\%$
$\frac{1}{4} = 0.25 = 25\%$ | $\frac{1}{100} = 0.01 = 1\%$

What Should I Be Able to Do?

For extra practice, go to page 445.

LESSON

8.1 **1.** Write each fraction as a decimal and as a percent.
a) $\frac{8}{20}$ 0.4, 40% b) $\frac{14}{5}$ 2.8, 280% c) $\frac{14}{25}$ 0.56, 56%
d) $\frac{7}{10}$ 0.7, 70% e) $\frac{9}{8}$ 1.125, 112.5% f) $\frac{17}{10}$ 1.7, 170%

2. Write each number two other ways.
a) 0.18 18%, $\frac{9}{50}$ b) 0.3 30%, $\frac{3}{10}$
c) 80% 0.8, $\frac{4}{5}$ d) $\frac{3}{8}$ 0.375, 37.5%

3. This rectangle is 40% of a larger figure.

Use grid paper.
a) Draw a figure that shows 100%.
b) Draw a figure that shows 120%.

8.2 **4.** Estimate.
a) 39% of 250 b) 41% of 89
c) 19% of 60 d) 91% of 46
e) 97% of 64 f) 59% of 98
g) 3% of 300 h) 4% of 92

5. A DVD costs $29.99.
The sales tax is 15%.
Estimate the cost of the DVD.
About $34.50

8.3 **6.** There are 35 students in a Grade 7 class. On one day, 20% of the students were at a sports meet.
How many students were in class?
28 students

7. The regular price of a DVD player is $120.00. What is the sale price in each case?
a) 25% off $90 b) 30% off $84
c) 40% off $72 d) 50% off $60
e) 60% off $48 f) 45% off $66

8. The regular price for a mountain bike is $640.00.
It is on sale for 30% off.
The sales tax is 15%.
a) Jamie bought the bike at the regular price.
What did it cost her? $736.00
b) Sam bought the bike on sale.
How much did Sam save?
$220.80

Unit Review **317**

SECTION ORGANIZER

Student Materials
- 1-cm grid paper (PM 20)
- percent circles (Master 8.15)
- calculators
- compasses
- protractors
- rulers

Assessment: Masters 8.1 Unit Rubric: Working with Percents, 8.4 Unit Summary: Working with Percents

Sample Solutions

3. a) Figures may vary, but areas should equal those shown.

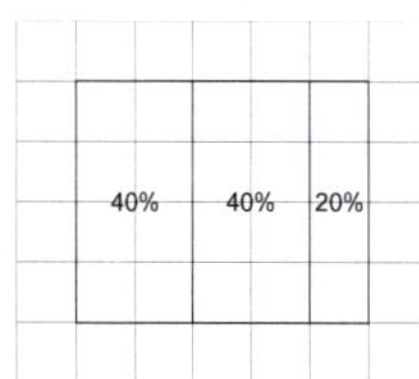

b)

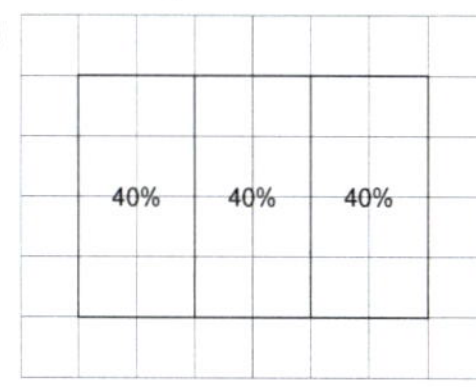

4. For example:

a) 39% of 250 ≐ 40% of 250
10% of 250 = 25; 40% = 4 × 10% = 4 × 25 = 100

b) 41% of 89 ≐ 40% of 90
10% of 90 = 9; 40% = 4 × 10% = 4 × 9 = 36

c) 19% of 60 ≐ 20% of 60
10% of 60 = 6; 20% = 2 × 10% = 2 × 6 = 12

d) 91% of 46 ≐ 90% of 45
10% of 45 = 4.5; 90% = 9 × 10% = 9 × 4.5 = 40.5 ≐ 41

(Solutions continue below.)

(Sample Solutions, continued.)

e) 97% of 64 is almost 100% of 64. 97% of 64 is about 63.

f) 59% of 98 ≐ 60% of 100
10% of 100 = 10; 60% = 6 × 10% = 6 × 10 = 60

g) 3% of 300 ≐ 5% of 300
10% of 300 = 30; 5% = $\frac{1}{2}$ × 10% = $\frac{1}{2}$ × 30 = 15

h) 4% of 92 ≐ 5% of 90
10% of 90 = 9; 5% = $\frac{1}{2}$ × 10% = $\frac{1}{2}$ × 9 = 4.5 ≐ 5

8. a) Jamie paid 115% of $640.00 = 1.15 × $640.00 = $736.00.

b) The sale price of the bike is 70% of $640.00 = 0.7 × $640.00 = $448.00. Sam paid 15% tax.
He paid 115% of $448.00 = 1.15 × $448.00 = $515.20.
The regular price of the bike, with tax, is $736.00.
Sam saved $736.00 – $515.20 = $220.80.

9. a) $\frac{1}{4}$ = 25%; 24% is close to 25%, so Lake Huron is the lake with a surface area about $\frac{1}{4}$ of the total area.

b) Lake Superior has the greatest surface area of all the Great Lakes.

c) 11% of 244 000 = 0.11 × 244 000 = 26 840

10. a)

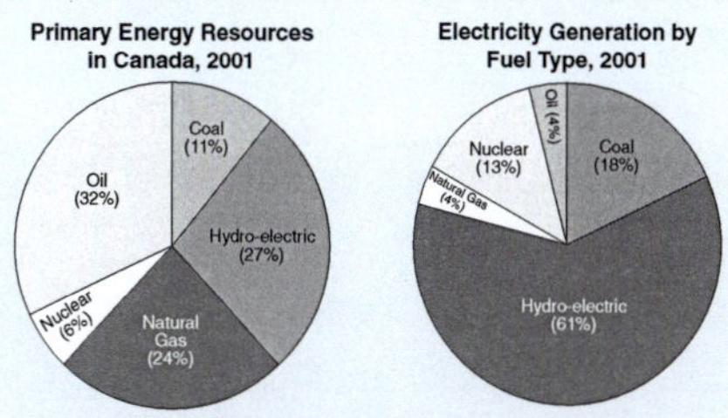

b) I know that the greatest primary energy resource in Canada in 2001 was oil, and the least was nuclear.
I know that hydro-electricity generated the most electricity, and oil and natural gas generated the least.

11. a)

b) The U.S. sector would decrease in size to 12% of the circle, and the USSR sector would increase in size to 12% of the circle.

12.

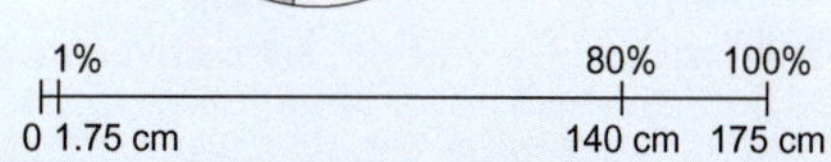

13.

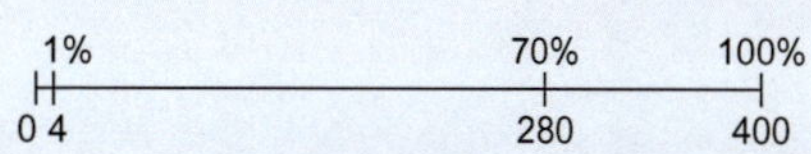

Correlation of Extra Practice questions on page 445:

Section	Questions
8.1	2
8.2	1, 3, 4
8.3	5, 6
8.4	9
8.5	7, 8

YOUR NOTES

LESSON

8.4 **9.** This circle graph shows the surface area of the Great Lakes.

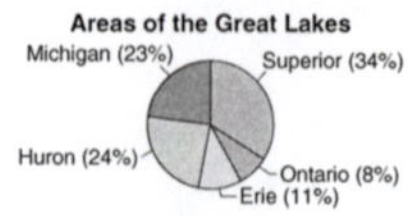

a) Which lake has a surface area about $\frac{1}{4}$ of the total area? Lake Huron

b) Explain why Lake Superior has that name.

c) The total area of the Great Lakes is about 244 000 km². Find the surface area of Lake Erie.
About 26 840 km²

10. These tables show energy resources and electricity generation in Canada.

Primary Energy Resources in Canada, 2001	
Coal	11%
Hydro-electric	27%
Natural gas	24%
Nuclear	6%
Oil	32%

Electricity Generation by Fuel Type, 2001	
Coal	18%
Hydro-electric	61%
Natural gas	4%
Nuclear	13%
Oil	4%

a) Draw a circle graph to display the data in each table.

b) What do you know from looking at the two graphs?

11. Here are 25 players on the Toronto Maple Leafs roster for the 2003/2004 season.
The table shows each pla
place of birth.

USSR	Canada	Europe	U.S.
Antropov	Belak	Berg	Fitzgerald
Mogilny	Belfour	Kaberle	Johnson
	Berehowsky	Nolan	Kidd
	Domi	Pilar	Klee
	Marchment	Ponikarovsky	
	McCabe	Reichel	
	Nieuwendyk	Renberg	
	Perrott	Sundin	
	Roberts		
	Stajan		
	Tucker		

a) Draw a circle graph to show what percent of the team was born in each place.

b) What if a U.S.-born player was traded for a USSR-born player? How would the graph change?

8.5 **12.** Eighty percent of Areyana's height is 140 cm. How tall is Areyana? Draw a number line to illustrate your answer. 17

13. At Lakehead Elementary School, 280 students participate in a walk for charity.
That is 70% of the students in the school. How many students attend the school? 400 students

318 UNIT 8: Working with Percents

ASSESSMENT FOR LEARNING

What to Look For

Understanding of concepts

✔ **Questions 1 and 2:** Students can write a fraction as a decimal and a percent, a decimal as a fraction and a percent, and a percent as a fraction and a decimal.

✔ **Question 4:** Student understands how to apply estimation strategies to find percents.

✔ **Question 5:** Student can calculate the sales tax on an item and determine its cost.

Application of mathematical procedures

✔ **Questions 6 and 7:** Student can multiply decimals to find percents.

✔ **Questions 10 and 11:** Student can create a circle graph to display data.

✔ **Question 12:** Student can divide decimals to find percents.

Communicating

✔ **Question 10:** Student can interpret a circle graph.

Problem solving

✔ **Questions 8 and 13:** Student can solve problems that involve working with percents.

Recording and Reporting

Master 8.1 Unit Rubric: Working with Percents

Master 8.4 Unit Summary: Working with Percents

Practice Test

1. How can 25% of one item be different from 25% of another? Explain.
2. The strip below is 25% of a longer strip.
   a) What is the length of a strip that is 80% of the longer strip? 16 cm
   b) Draw the longer strip.
3. Find.
   a) 600% of 40 240
   b) 60% of 40 24
   c) 6% of 40 2.4
   What patterns do you see in the answers?
4. The regular price of a pair of shoes is $75.00.
   The shoes are on sale for 25% off.
   The sales tax is 15%.
   a) What is the sale price of the pair of shoes? $56.25
   b) What do the shoes cost, with sales tax? $64.69

Type of Land Cover in Canada

Type	Percent of Total Area
Forest and taiga	45
Tundra	23
Wetlands	12
Fresh water	8
Cropland and rangeland	8
Ice and snow	3
Human use	1

5. The table shows the type of land cover in Canada, as a percent of the total area.
   a) Draw a circle graph to display these data.
   b) Did you need to know the area of Canada to draw the circle graph? Explain. No
6. This spring, 26 dogs were adopted from the local animal shelter.
   This is 130% of the number of dogs that were adopted last spring.
   How many dogs were adopted last spring? 20 dogs
   Draw a number line to illustrate your answer.

Practice Test 319

SECTION ORGANIZER

Student Materials

- rulers
- calculators
- compasses
- protractors

Assessment: Masters 8.1 Unit Rubric: Working with Percents, 8.4 Unit Summary: Working with Percents

Assignment Guidelines

To assess the 4 Achievement Chart categories listed in the curriculum document, use these test questions:
Communication: 1
Understanding Concepts: 2
Application: 4
Problem Solving: 6

Sample Solutions

1. When I calculate 25%, I find $\frac{25}{100}$ or $\frac{1}{4}$ of an item. If Item A is greater than Item B, then $\frac{1}{4}$ of Item A is greater than $\frac{1}{4}$ of Item B. For example, 25% of \$100 = 0.25 × \$100 = \$25 while 25% of \$80 = 0.25 × \$80 = \$20
   For example, 25% of 12 cm = 0.25 × 12 cm = 3 cm while 25% of 28 cm = 0.25 × 28 cm = 7 cm
2. a) The strip shown is 5 cm long.
   25% = 5 cm
   50% = 2 × 25% = 2 × 5 cm = 10 cm
   100% = 2 × 50% = 2 × 10 cm = 20 cm
   The longer strip is 20 cm long.
   80% of 20 cm = 0.80 × 20 cm = 16 cm
   b) Students should draw a 20-cm strip.
3. 600% of 40 = 6 × 40 = 240
   60% of 40 = 0.6 × 40 = 24
   6% of 40 = 0.06 × 40 = 2.4
   The decimal point in the answer moves 1 place to the left each time.
   Each answer is the previous answer divided by 10 because each percent is $\frac{1}{10}$ of the preceding percent.
4. a) The shoes are reduced by 25%.
   The sale price is 75% of \$75.00
   = 0.75 × \$75.00
   = \$56.25.
   b) With 15% tax, the shoes cost 115% of \$56.25 = 1.15 × \$56.25 ≐ \$64.69
   The cost, with sales tax, is \$64.69.
5. a)

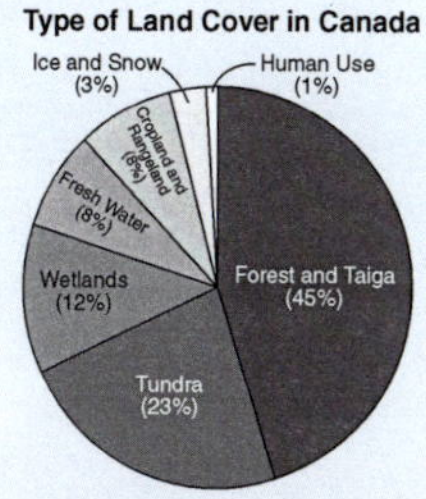

   b) No, I can draw a circle graph given only percents as long as the sum of the percents is 100%. A circle graph does not show quantities. A circle graph shows parts of one whole.
6. 26 dogs represents 130%.
   $1\% = \frac{26}{130} = 0.2$
   100% = 100 × 0.2 = 20
   20 dogs were adopted last spring.

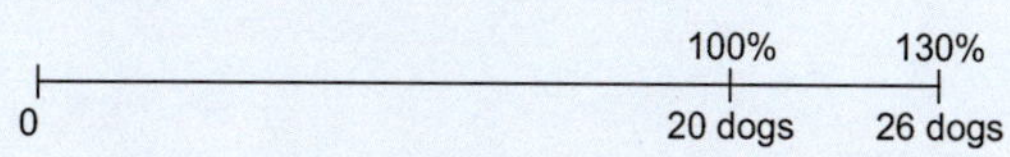

At the Shopping Mall

SECTION ORGANIZER

40–50 min

Student Grouping: Individual
Student Materials
- calculators

Assessment: Masters 8.3 Performance Assessment Rubric: At the Shopping Mall, 8.4 Unit Summary: Working with Percents

Sample Solution

I chose 4 items that I really wanted, then estimated their prices, including tax.
Bicycle: The bicycle is about $250. It is reduced by 20%.
So, I pay 80% of $250 = 0.8 × $250 = $200. The tax is 15%.
So, I pay 115% of $200 = 1.15 × $200 = $230.
The bicycle, including taxes, will cost about $230.

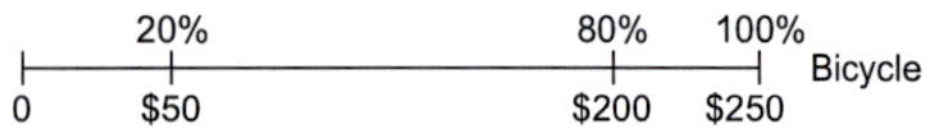

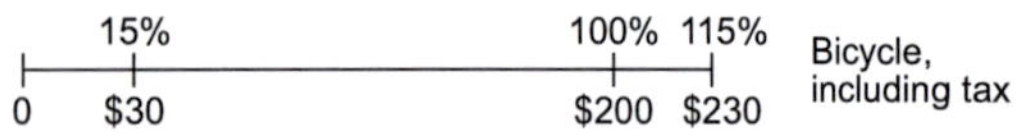

Bike helmet: The bike helmet is about $40. It is reduced by 25%.
So, I pay 75% of $40 = 0.75 × $40 = $30. The tax is 15%.
So, I pay 115% of $30 = 1.15 × $30 = $34.50.
The bike helmet, including taxes, will cost about $34.50.

(*Solution continues below right.*)

Have students turn to pages 288 and 289 of the Student Book.

Tell students they are to communicate their thinking in as much detail as possible. Ensure students understand that their assessment will also include how well they communicate their strategies and understanding to others.

Before students begin, remind students that a quick way to find 10% of a number is to move the decimal point 1 place to the left. Once 10% of a number is know, it is easy to mentally find 5%, 20%, 30%, and so on, of the number. Ensure students know they are to use a number line to illustrate each calculation.

(*Sample Solution, continued.*)

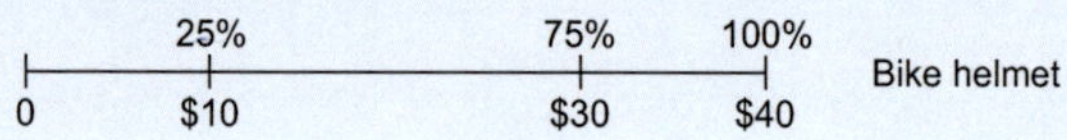

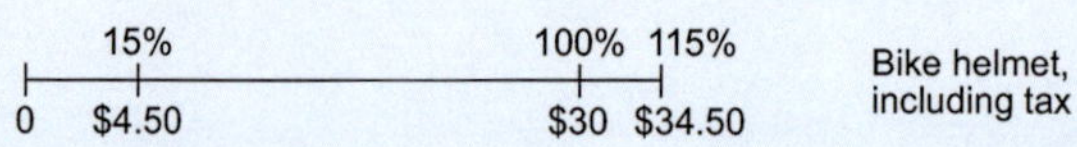

DVD player: The DVD player is about $130. It is reduced by 30%. So, I pay 70% of $130 = 0.7 × $130 = $91. I will round this to $90.
The tax is 15%. So, I pay 115% of $90 = 1.15 × $90 = $103.50.
The DVD player, including taxes, will cost about $103.50.

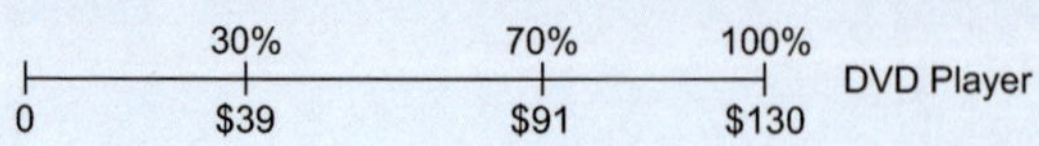

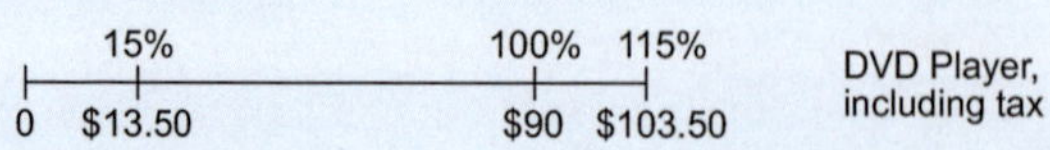

Portable CD player: The portable CD player is about $140. It is reduced by 35%.
So, I pay 65% of $140 = 0.65 × $140 = $91. I round this to $90.
The tax is 15%. So, I pay the same as I paid for the DVD player, which is about $103.50.

Check List

Your work should show:

- ✓ a list of the items you bought and what you paid for each one
- ✓ a number line to illustrate each calculation
- ✓ how much you saved by buying the items on sale
- ✓ how you calculated the sales tax

Reflect on the Unit

What have you learned about percents and how they are used?

Unit Problem: At the Shopping Mall 321

Portable CD Player

Portable CD Player, including tax

These items will cost about $230 + $34.50 + $103.50 + $103.50 = $471.50.

I still have about $500 – $471.50 = $28.50 left to spend. I have enough money to buy 3 paperback books. I am going to estimate the cost of the books as 3 × $9 = $27.

I assumed that the discount of 15% and the tax of 15% will be about the same. I will spend a total of approximately $498.50.

If I bought these items at regular price, they would cost ($249.99 + $39.99 + $129.99 + $139.99 + $8.99 + $8.99 + $8.99) × 1.15 = $586.93 × 1.15 = $674.97.

I save about $674.97 – $498.50 = $176.47 by buying the items on sale.

REFLECT ON THE UNIT: I have learned:

- a percent is the same as a fraction with denominator 100, which is the same as a decimal.
- a percent is a part of a whole and percents are used to calculate sales tax, to find discounts, and to help compare amounts.
- how to use mental math to estimate and calculate percent; for example, to find 1% of a number by dividing by 100 or by moving the decimal point 2 places to the left; to find 10% of a number by moving the decimal point 1 place to the left; and 5% is one-half of 10%.
- how to use circle graphs to display data and solve problems.

ASSESSMENT FOR LEARNING

What to Look For

Understanding concepts

✔ Students understand how percent is used to find the sale price of an item and its sales taxes.

Applying procedures

✔ Students can accurately calculate discounts, sales tax, total cost, and total savings.

✔ Students can draw a number line to illustrate each calculation.

Problem solving

✔ Students can choose an appropriate strategy to choose items totalling less than $500, including tax, and calculate money saved.

What to Do

Extra Support: Make the problem accessible.

Suggest that students round each price to the nearest dollar before finding the sale price. Remind them of the quicker way to find the sale price; for example, if the reduction is 20% off, then the sale price is 80% of the regular price.

Encourage students to estimate the cost of each item, including tax, as they compile their lists. They could keep a "running total" to make sure they do not exceed $500.

Recording and Reporting

Master 8.3 Performance Assessment Rubric: At the Shopping Mall
Master 8.4 Unit Summary: Working with Percents

Cumulative Review

SECTION ORGANIZER

Student Materials
- 0.5-cm grid paper (PM 14)
- calculators
- square dot paper (PM 22)
- 1-cm grid paper (PM 20)
- rulers
- protractors

Assessment: PM 9 Work Sample Record

Sample Solutions

1. The square root of each number is the side length of a square with area equal to the given number.

a) 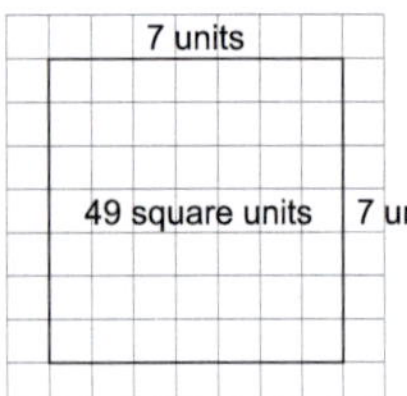

b) 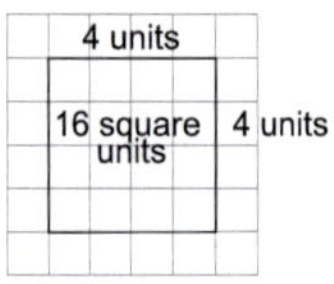

(*Solutions continue below right.*)

Units 1–8 Cumulative Review

UNIT

1 **1.** Use grid paper.
Draw a picture that shows a square root of each number.
a) 49 7 b) 16 4 c) 144 12

2 **2.** To make a pot of tea for 4 people, you need 3 tea bags.
a) How many tea bags are needed for each number of people?
i) 8 6 ii) 12 9 iii) 16 12 iv) 20 15
b) How many tea bags are needed for 6 people? Explain.

3 **3.** Students in a Grade 7 class are filling shoe boxes with toys for children in other countries. A shoe box measures 30 cm by 18 cm by 16 cm.
a) Find the volume of a shoe box. $8640\ cm^3$
The students fill 24 shoe boxes. Eight shoe boxes are packed into a larger box.
b) What could the dimensions of this larger box be?
c) What are the most likely dimensions of the larger box? Justify your choice.

4 **4.** a) Multiply: 3.6×2.4 8.64
b) Which other pair of factors has the same product as the product in part a?
How many different pairs of factors can you find?
Explain your work.

5 **5.** To celebrate his birthday, Justi[n and] his friends played miniature go[lf].
Here are their scores: 29, 33, 37, 24, 41, 38, 48, 26, 36, 33, 40, 29, 36, 22, 31, 38, 42, 35, 33
a) Draw a stem-and-leaf plot.
It was a par 36 course. This means that a good golfer takes 36 strokes to complete the course.
b) How many scores were under par? 10 At par? 2 Over par? 7
c) What was the range of the scores? 2
d) Calculate the mean, median, and mode scores. 34.3 35 33

6. Some Grade 7 students were surveyed about the average number of hours they spend reading each week, and their overall English mark out of 100. Here are the data:

Time (h)	Mark	Time (h)	Mark
0	55	0	60
0.5	65	0.5	62
1	70	1	84
1	68	1.5	75
1.5	78	2	83
2	85	2	77
2	88	2	81
2.5	91	2.5	79
2.5	80	3	90

a) Draw a scatter plot. What trends do you see?
b) Do you think a student will get a better English mark if he reads more? Explain.

322 Units 1–8

Students can use this review to evaluate their progress in the mathematical content of Units 1 through 8.

Remind students that the unit containing the content required to answer each question is shown in red beside the question.

Encourage students to refer to the *Connect* sections of the relevant units.

Encourage students to draw on each other's skills as they work through the review.

Students who have identified areas in which they are strong may wish to act as volunteer tutors for students who require assistance.

(*Sample Solutions, continued.*)

c) 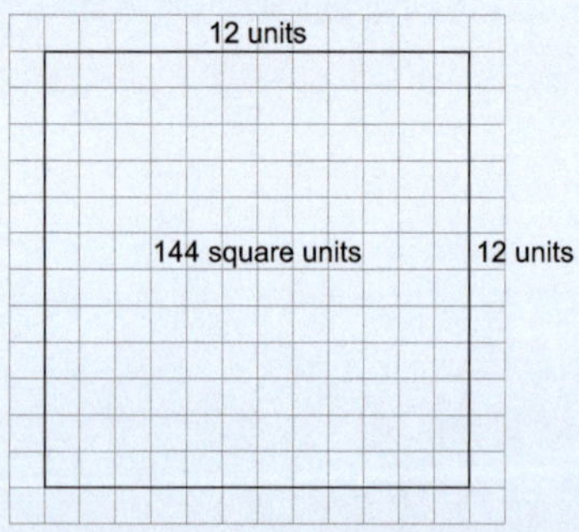

2. b) For example, 5 tea bags; you need $4\frac{1}{2}$ tea bags but you cannot break a tea bag in half. So, you would probably use 5 tea bags.

3. a) Volume = $l \times w \times h = 30 \times 18 \times 16 = 8640$

b) There are many possible dimensions: For example, I assume the boxes were placed with the largest face horizontal.
If there are 2 boxes per layer, and 4 layers:
30 cm by 36 cm by 64 cm; or
18 cm by 60 cm by 64 cm
If there are 4 boxes per layer, and 2 layers:
30 cm by 72 cm by 32 cm; or
120 cm by 18 cm by 32 cm; or
60 cm by 36 cm by 32 cm

UNIT

7. A parallelogram has base 2.4 cm and height 3.9 cm.
   a) What is the area of the parallelogram? 9.36 cm²
   b) What is the area of a triangle with the same base and height as the parallelogram? 4.68 cm²

8. Find the area and perimeter of this trapezoid. $A = 30.72$ cm², $P = 24$ cm

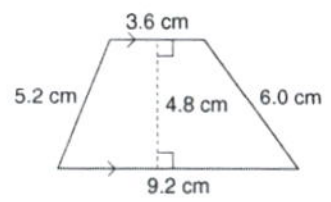

9. Find the area and perimeter of this figure. $A = 33$ cm², $P = 28$ cm

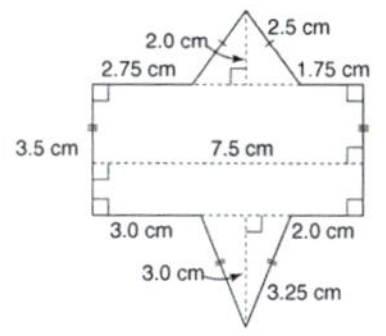

10. Use dot paper.
    Draw two congruent figures.
    Trade figures with a classmate.
    Explain how you know your classmate's figures are congruent.

11. These quadrilaterals are congruent.

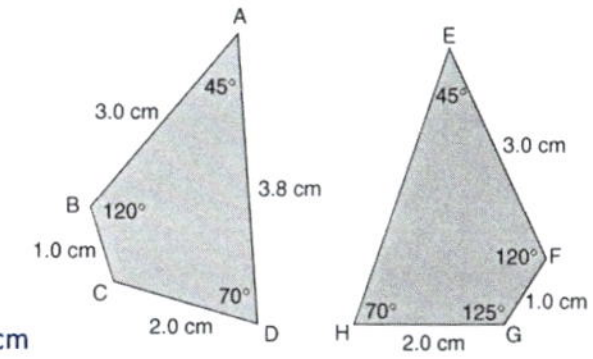

   a) What is the length of EH? 3.8 cm
   b) What is the measure of ∠BCD? Justify your answers. 125°

12. Use grid paper.
    a) Choose a figure that tiles the plane. Create a design with your figure.
    b) Choose one figure as Figure A. Describe the position of another figure as a transformation image of Figure A. Do this for 5 different figures.

13. The regular price of a scooter is \$89.99. The scooter is on sale for 20% off.
    a) What is the sale price of the scooter? \$71.99
    b) There is 15% sales tax. What would a person pay for the scooter? \$82.79

14. How is calculating 30% of \$70 the same as calculating 70% of \$30? Sketch number lines to illustrate your answer.

If there is 1 layer of 8 boxes:
30 cm by 144 cm by 16 cm; or
60 cm by 72 cm by 16 cm; or
240 cm by 18 cm by 16 cm
If the boxes were laid with a different face horizontal, there are many other possible dimensions.

c) A larger box with dimensions 36 cm by 60 cm by 32 cm is most likely as this box has the least surface area.

4. b) For example, 36×0.24; 0.36×24; 0.18×48; 18×0.48
There are many different pairs of factors.

5. a)

Miniature Golf Scores	
Stem	**Leaf**
2	2 4 6 9 9
3	1 3 3 3 5 6 6 7 8 8
4	0 1 2 8

6. a) **Average Number of Hours Spent Reading and Overall English Mark of Grade 7 Students**

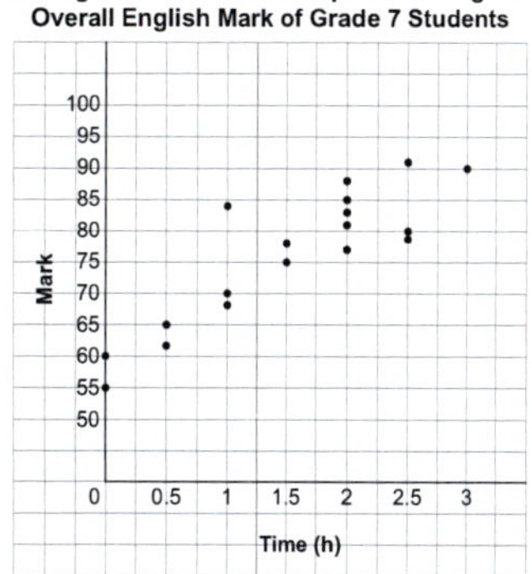

There is an upward trend from left to right. Generally, the graph shows that the more a student reads each week, the

(*Solutions continue below.*)

(*Sample Solutions, continued.*)

better English mark he or she gets.

b) Yes. The graph shows that students who read 1.5 h or more per week tend to do better than students who read less than 1.5 h per week. The graph shows that no student who reads 1.5 h or more per week scored less than 75 out of 100. There will be exceptions, but the more a student reads, the more likely he or she will succeed in English.

7. b) The area of the triangle is one-half the area of the parallelogram in part a: $\frac{1}{2}$ of $9.36 = 4.68$

9. A = area of top triangle + area of rectangle + area of bottom triangle $= \frac{1}{2}(3 \times 2) + (3.5 \times 7.5) + \frac{1}{2}(2.5 \times 3)$
$= 3 + 26.25 + 3.75 = 33$
$P = 3.0 + 3.25 + 3.25 + 2.0 + 3.5 + 1.75 + 2.5 + 2.5 + 2.75 + 3.5 = 28$

10. For example,

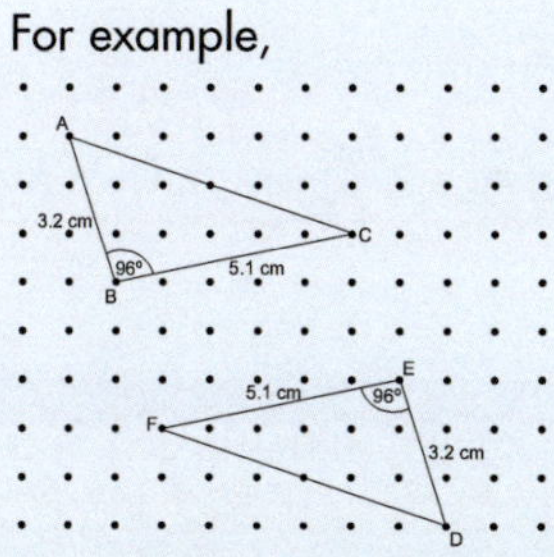

The two triangles are congruent because 2 pairs of corresponding angles and 1 pair of corresponding sides are equal.

12. a) For example,

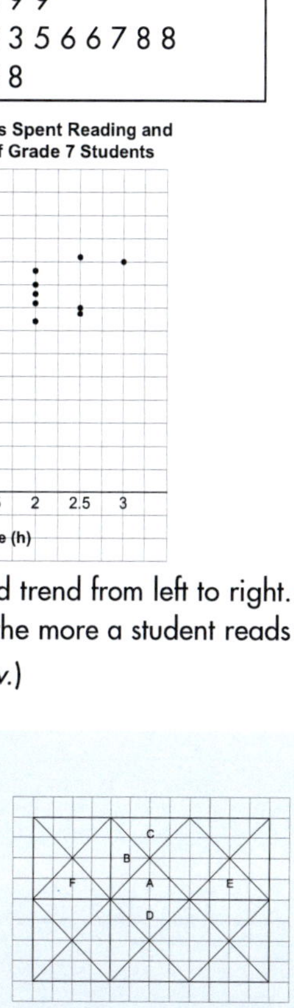

b) Figure A is rotated $\frac{1}{4}$ turn clockwise about the turn centre to get Figure B.
Figure A is rotated $\frac{1}{2}$ turn about the turn centre to get Figure C.
Figure A is reflected in a horizontal line through its base to get Figure D.
Figure A is translated 4 units right to get Figure E.
Figure A is translated 4 units left to get Figure F.

14. To calculate 30% of \$70.00, I multiply 0.30×70.00. When I multiply without the decimal points, it becomes 30×7000. To calculate 70% of \$30.00, I multiply 0.70×30.00. When I multiply without the decimal points, it becomes 70×3000. Both of these sentences can be written as $30 \times 70 \times 100$. The order does not matter when multiplying. In both cases, the answer is \$21.00.

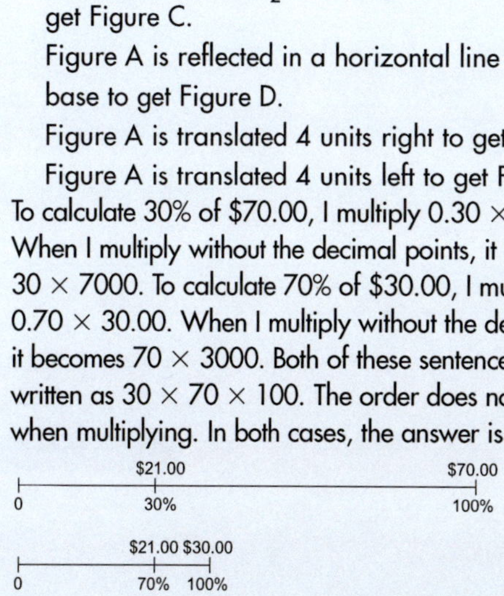

Evaluating Student Learning: Preparing to Report: Unit 8 Working with Percents

This unit provides an opportunity to report on the **Number Sense and Numeration** and **Data Management and Probability** strands.
Master 8.4: Unit Summary: Working with Percents provides a comprehensive format for recording and summarizing evidence collected.

Here is an example of a completed summary chart for this Unit:

Strand: *Number Sense and Numeration/Data Management and Probability*	**Problem Solving**	**Understanding of Concepts**	**Application of mathematical procedures**	**Communication**	***Overall***
Ongoing Observations	4	4	4	3	4
Work samples or portfolios; conferences	3	4	4	4	4
Unit Review	4	4	4	4	4
Practice Test	4	4	4	3	4
Unit Problem At the Shopping Mall	3	4	4	4	4
Achievement Level for reporting					4

Recording	**How to Report**
Ongoing Observations	Use *Master 8.2 Ongoing Observations: Working with Percents* to determine the most consistent level achieved in each category. Enter it in the chart. Choose to summarize by achievement category, or simply to enter an overall level. Observations from late in the unit should be most heavily weighted.
Portfolios or collections of work samples; conferences, or interviews	Use *Master 8.1 Unit Rubric: Working with Percents* to guide evaluation of collections of work and information gathered in conferences. Teachers may choose to focus particular attention on the Assessment Focus questions. Work from late in the unit should be most heavily weighted.
Unit Review	*Master 8.1 Unit Rubric: Working with Percents* may be helpful in determining levels of achievement. #1, 2, 4, and 5 provide evidence of Understanding of concepts; #6, 7, 10, 11, and 12 provide evidence of Application of mathematical procedures; #8 and 13 provide evidence of Problem solving; #10 provides evidence of Communication.
Practice Test	*Master 8.1 Unit Rubric: Working with Percents* may be helpful in determining levels of achievement. #3 provides evidence of Understanding of concepts; #4 provides evidence of Application of mathematical procedures; #6 provides evidence of Problem solving; #1 provides evidence of Communication.
Unit Problem	Use *Master 8.3 Performance Assessment Rubric: At the Shopping Mall.* The *Unit Problem* offers a snapshot of students' achievement. In particular, it shows their ability to synthesize and apply what they have learned.
Student Self-Assessment	Note students' perceptions of their own progress. This may take the form of an oral or written comment, or a self-rating.
Comments	Analyse the pattern of achievement to identify strengths and needs. In some cases, specific actions may need to be planned to support the learner.

Learning Skills	**Ongoing Records**
PM 4: Learning Skills Check List Use to record and report throughout a reporting period, rather than for each unit and/or strand.	*PM 10: Summary Class Records: Strands* *PM 11: Summary Class Records: Achievement Categories* *PM 12: Summary Record: Individual* Use to record and report evaluations of student achievement over several clusters, a reporting period, or a school year. These can also be used in place of the Unit Summary.

Name ____________________ Date ______________

Master 8.1

Unit Rubric: Working with Percents

	Level 1	Level 2	Level 3	Level 4
Problem solving • chooses and carries out a range of strategies (e.g., tables) to create and solve multi-step problems related to real life involving fractions, decimals, and percents	with assistance, chooses and carries out a limited range of appropriate strategies to create and solve multi-step problems involving fractions, decimals, and percents, rarely resulting in an accurate solution	with limited assistance, chooses and carries out appropriate strategies to create and solve multi-step problems involving fractions, decimals, and percents, frequently resulting in accurate solutions	chooses and carries out appropriate strategies to create and solve multi-step problems involving fractions, decimals, and percents; usually resulting in accurate solutions	chooses and carries out the most appropriate strategies (may be innovative) to create and solve multi-step problems involving fractions, decimals, and percents; results in accurate solutions
Understanding of concepts • shows understanding of concepts by explaining and demonstrating: – relationship of fractions, decimals, and percent – multiplication and division of decimals – construction of circle graphs	shows little understanding; may be unable to explain or demonstrate processes and conclusions related to fractions, decimals, and percents, and their application in real-life situations	shows some understanding; partially able to explain and demonstrate processes and conclusions related to fractions, decimals, and percents, and their application in real-life situations	shows understanding; able to clearly and appropriately explain and demonstrate processes and conclusions related to fractions, decimals and percents, and their application in real-life situations	shows thorough understanding; able to accurately and effectively explain and demonstrate processes and conclusions related to fractions, decimals, and percents, and their application in real-life situations
Application of mathematical procedures • accurately: – converts among fractions, decimals, and percents – calculates percents – multiplies and divides decimals – draws circle graphs	limited accuracy; major errors or omissions in: – converting among fractions, decimals, and percents – calculating percents – multiplying and dividing decimals – drawing circle graphs	somewhat accurate; several minor errors or omissions in: – converting among fractions, decimals, and percents – calculating percents – multiplying and dividing decimals – drawing circle graphs	generally accurate; few minor errors or omissions in: – converting among fractions, decimals, and percents – calculating percents – multiplying and dividing decimals – drawing circle graphs	accurate and precise; no errors in: – converting among fractions, decimals, and percents – calculating percents – multiplying and dividing decimals – drawing circle graphs
Communication • explains reasoning and procedures clearly, including appropriate terminology	unable to explain reasoning and procedures clearly	partially explains reasoning and procedures	explains reasoning and procedures clearly	explains reasoning and procedures clearly, precisely, and confidently
• presents work clearly, including appropriate symbols	presents work with little clarity; rarely uses appropriate symbols	presents work with some clarity; uses some appropriate symbols	presents work clearly and precisely; uses appropriate symbols	presents work clearly and precisely; uses a range of appropriate symbols

Name ____________________ Date ________________

Master 8.2

Ongoing Observations: Working with Percents

The behaviours described under each heading are examples; they are not intended to be an exhaustive list of all that might be observed. More detailed descriptions are provided in each lesson under *Assessment for Learning.*

STUDENT ACHIEVEMENT: Working with Percents

Student	**Problem solving** ▪ Chooses and carries out appropriate strategies to solve multi-step problems involving fractions, decimals, and percents	**Understanding of concepts** ▪ Explains and demonstrates relationships of fractions, decimals, and percents	**Application of mathematical procedures** ▪ Converts among fractions, decimals, and percents ▪ Calculates percents ▪ Divides and multiplies decimals	**Communication** ▪ Explains reasoning clearly ▪ Presents work clearly

Level 1 – very limited; Level 2 – somewhat or limited; Level 3 – satisfactory; Level 4 – thorough

Name ____________________ Date ________________

Master 8.3

Performance Assessment Rubric: At the Shopping Mall

	Level 1	Level 2	Level 3	Level 4
Problem solving • chooses appropriate strategies (for example, estimating; using tables, number lines, patterns) to choose items totalling less than $500, including tax, and calculate money saved	uses few simple strategies to solve the problem; limited success	uses some appropriate strategies to solve the problem; some success	uses appropriate strategies to solve the problem; successful	uses appropriate and often innovative strategies to solve the problem; successful and effective (efficient)
Understanding of concepts • shows understanding of concepts related to percents and decimals in explaining how sales tax was calculated (operations with decimals; two-steps — sales tax applied after discount)	shows very limited understanding by using few relevant mathematical concepts in explanations	shows limited understanding by using some relevant concepts in appropriate but incomplete explanations	shows understanding by using relevant concepts in appropriate and complete explanations	shows thorough understanding by using all relevant concepts in appropriate, complete, and insightful explanations
Application of mathematical procedures • accurately calculates discounts, sales tax, total cost, and total saving	limited accuracy; major errors or omissions in calculating: – discounts – sales tax – total cost – total saving	somewhat accurate; several minor errors or omissions in calculating: – discounts – sales tax – total cost – total saving	generally accurate; few minor errors or omissions in calculating: – discounts – sales tax – total cost – total saving	accurate and precise; no errors in calculating: – discounts – sales tax – total cost – total saving
Communication • explains reasoning clearly, using appropriate mathematical terminology	explains reasoning unclearly and imprecisely, using few mathematical terms	explains reasoning with some clarity, using some appropriate mathematical terms	explains reasoning clearly and precisely, using appropriate mathematical terms	explains reasoning clearly, precisely, and confidently, using a range of appropriate mathematical terminology
• presents work clearly	presents work with little clarity	presents work with some clarity	presents work clearly	presents work clearly and precisely

Name ____________________ Date ________________

Master 8.4

Unit Summary: Working with Percents

Review assessment records to determine the most consistent achievement levels for the assessments conducted. Some cells may be blank. *Overall* achievement levels may be recorded in each row, rather than identifying levels for each achievement category.

	Most Consistent Level of Achievement*				
Strand: *Number Sense and Numeration/Data Management and Probability*	**Problem solving**	**Understanding of concepts**	**Application of mathematical procedures**	**Communication**	***Overall***
Ongoing Observations					
Work samples or portfolios; conferences					
Unit Review					
Practice Test					
Unit Problem: At the Shopping Mall					
Achievement Level for reporting					

* Use Ontario Achievement Levels 1, 2, 3, 4.

Self-Assessment:

Comments: (Strengths; Needs, Next Steps)

Name ____________________ Date ________________

Master 8.5a

Additional Activity 1: Squeeze Play

Play with a partner.

You will need a set of *Squeeze Play* game cards.

How to Play:

1. Decide who will be the dealer.
Shuffle the cards. Deal 5 cards to each player.
From the remaining cards, turn two cards face up, side by side, on the table.
The cards must have different values.
These are the target cards.
Place the remaining cards face down in a pile.

2. Player A finds a card that has a value between the 2 target cards.
This is called the "squeeze" card.
If Player A has a "squeeze" card, she places it face up on top of one of the target cards.
If Player A does not have a "squeeze" card, she places another card from her hand on top of one of the target cards, then draws another card from the pile.

3. Player B takes his turn following the rules above.

4. Play continues until one player has no cards left.
That player is the winner.

Take It Further:
Play the game again. This time, before a player can make a "squeeze," he must state a decimal, fraction, or percent equivalent to the "squeeze" card. If a player is incorrect, the card cannot be played and his turn is lost.

Name ____________________ Date ________________

Master 8.5b

Squeeze Play Game Cards

$\frac{1}{4}$	$\frac{3}{10}$	$\frac{1}{2}$	$\frac{1}{5}$	$\frac{7}{10}$
$\frac{3}{4}$	$\frac{2}{5}$	$\frac{3}{5}$	$\frac{4}{5}$	$\frac{1}{8}$
$\frac{3}{8}$	30%	25%	50%	20%
$\frac{5}{8}$	75%	0.7	0.4	12.5%
0.375	0.50	0.25	0.3	0.625
0.6	40%	0.20	70%	0.8
80%	0.75	0.125	37.5%	60%
0.9	62.5%	90%	100%	$\frac{9}{10}$

Name ____________________ Date ______________

Master 8.6

Additional Activity 2: Concentration

Play with a partner.

You will need a set of *Squeeze Play* game cards.

How to Play:

1. Remove the 100% card from the deck.
Lay out all the cards face down on the table.

2. Player A turns over 3 cards to make a match.
A match is made when all 3 cards represent the same number.

3. If a match is made, keep the cards.
If a match is not made, turn the cards face down again.

4. Player B takes a turn.

5. Players continue to take turns until there are no cards left.
The player with the most matches at the end of the game wins.

Take It Further:
Put the 100% card back in the deck.
This time, turn over one card, then find a card of greater value.
If the first card turned over is the 100% card, your turn is lost.
If a player finds a second card of greater value, she keeps the paired cards.
Play continues until all possible pairs have been found.
The player with the most pairs at the end of the game wins.

Name ____________________ Date ______________

Master 8.7a

Additional Activity 3: Link 5

Play with a partner.

You will need a *Link 5* game board, a set of *Link 5* game cards, red and yellow counters, and a calculator.

The object of the game is to be the first player to link 5 squares diagonally, vertically, or horizontally. Blocking your opponent is allowed as long as you follow the rules.

How to Play:

1. Shuffle the percent cards.
Place 1 card face down on each square of the game board.
Shuffle the number cards and place them face down on the table in a pile.
Each player chooses a counter colour.

2. Red goes first. Turn over a card in Row 1.
Draw a number card from the pile and place it face up on the table.
Use the percent card to find the percent of the number.
Yellow checks the answer with a calculator.
If Red is correct, place a red counter on the square of the game board.
If Red is incorrect, turn the card face down.
Yellow takes a turn.

3. A player must have a counter in Row 1 before he can proceed to Row 2, and so on.
After each turn, discard your number card and draw a new one.

4. The first player to make a link of 5 squares wins.

Take It Further:
Play again. Draw 2 number cards at a time. Use the percent card to find the percent of each number. Both answers must be correct to place a counter on the square.

Name ____________________ Date ______________

Master 8.7b

Link 5 Game Board

Row 5					
Row 4					
Row 3					
Row 2					
Row 1					

Name ____________________ Date ______________

Master 8.7c

Link 5 Game Cards

Percent Cards

30%	20%	25%	50%	75%
10%	15%	40%	60%	90%
70%	80%	45%	150%	200%
95%	1%	10%	100%	25%
35%	55%	65%	85%	5%

Number Cards

25	50	75	20	80	125
200	500	225	40	150	60

Name ____________________ Date ______________

Master 8.8

Step-by-Step 1

Section 8.1, Question 7

Step 1 Fold a sheet of paper in half lengthwise.

Fold it in half again widthwise.

Unfold the paper. There are 4 congruent sections.

How many sections will you shade blue to represent $\frac{1}{2}$? ____

Shade the sections.

Step 2 Write 25% as a fraction in simplest form. _____

How many sections will you shade yellow? _____

Shade the section(s).

Step 3 What fraction of the page is not shaded? __________

What percent is this? _________

Divide the section into 5 equal rows.

What percent does each row represent? ______

How many rows will you shade to show 10%? ______

Shade the rows red.

Step 4 Shade the remaining rows green. How many rows are green? ____

What percent of the page is the green section? ______

How do you know?

____

____

Name ____________________ Date ________________

Master 8.9

Step-by-Step 2

Section 8.2, Question 11

Step 1 What is the length of the front cover? _____

What is its width? _____

Multiply to find the area of the front cover. _____ cm^2

What is the area of the back cover? _____ cm^2

What is the length of the spine? ____

What is its width? ____

Multiply to find the area of the spine. _____ cm^2

Add to find the total area of the cover.

____

Step 2 Look at the rectangular photograph of the cougar.

What is the length and width of the rectangle? _______________

Multiply to find the area of the rectangle. ___________________

Assume this is the only illustration on the cover.

Step 3 Write the area of the photo as a fraction of the area of the cover.

The area of the photo is the numerator.

The area of the cover is the denominator. ______________

Approximate the fraction to a friendly fraction. ____________

What percent does this fraction represent? ________

About what percent of the book cover is illustrated? ___________

Name ____________________ Date _______________

Master 8.10

Step-by-Step 3

Section 8.3, Question 6

Step 1 To find 2% of 52.3, we multiply 0.02×52.3.

Find 2×523, then count decimal places to place the decimal point in the product. _______

Step 2 To find 20% of 52.3, we multiply 0.2×52.3.
How can you use the result of *Step 1* to find this product? ________________________

____

Step 3 To find 200% of 52.3, we multiply 2×52.3.

How can you use the result of *Step 1* to find this product? ________________________

____

Step 4 Choose a number. ________

Choose 3 percents that are related. ____________________

Repeat *Steps 1* to *3* for your number and 3 related percents.

Name ____________________ Date ______________

Master 8.11

Step-by-Step 4

Section 8.4, Question 5

Step 1 Choose a food label that shows the mass of each nutrient.

Choose 4 nutrients. Write each nutrient and its mass in grams.

____

____

____

____

Add these masses. ___________

Subtract this total mass from the mass of one serving. ___________

Label this difference as "Other." ______________

Step 2 Write the mass of each nutrient and "Other" as a fraction of the mass of one serving.

____

____

____

____

____

Write each fraction as a percent.

____

____

____

____

____

Step 3 Use the percents from *Step 2.* Use a percent circle.

Draw a circle graph. Label each sector.

Give the graph a title.

Name ____________________ Date _______________

Master 8.12

Step-by-Step 5

Section 8.5, Question 9

Step 1 The original price of a blouse is $75.00.

The price is reduced by 30%.

So, the reduced cost is 100% – 30% = 70%.

Find 70% of $75.00. ____________

Step 2 Sales tax is 15%.

To find the cost with sales tax, find 115% of the reduced cost in *Step 1*. ___________

Step 3 Draw a number line.

Step 4 The original price of a blouse is $75.00.

Add the sales tax first.

Find 115% of $75.00. ______________

Step 5 The price is reduced by 30%.

So, the reduced cost, with tax, is 70% of the cost with tax from *Step 4*.

Find 70% of the cost with tax in *Step 4*. _______________

Step 6 Draw a number line.

Step 7 Look at your answers in *Steps 2* and *5*.

Does it matter when the tax is added? __________

Explain. ____

____

Name ____________________ Date ________________

Master 8.13

Puzzle for *Explore*

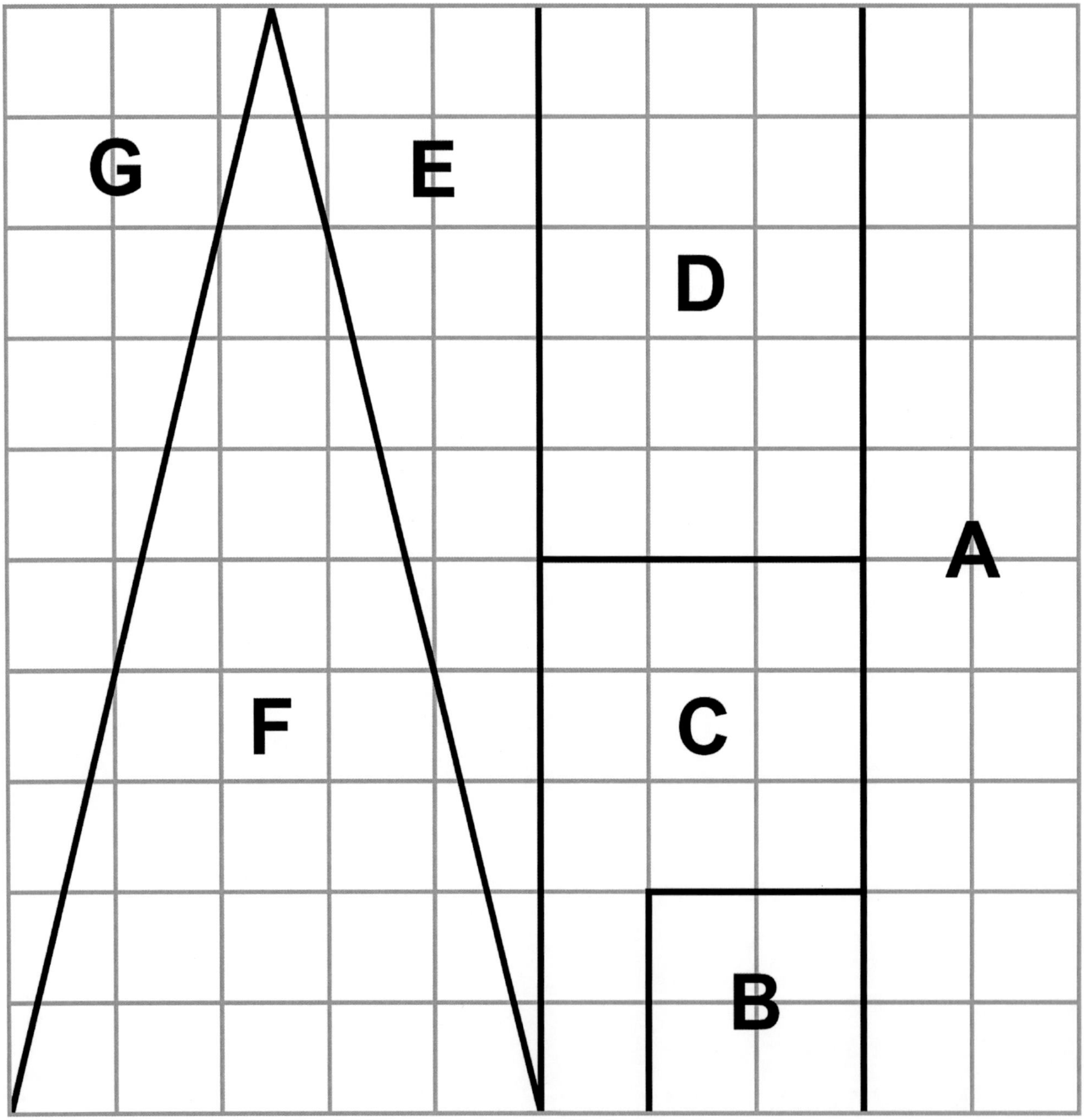

Name ____________________ Date ________________

Master 8.14a

Showdown Playing Cards 1

$\frac{1}{4}$	$\frac{1}{10}$	$\frac{2}{5}$	$\frac{3}{5}$
$\frac{4}{5}$	$\frac{9}{10}$	$\frac{3}{4}$	$\frac{1}{5}$
$\frac{1}{2}$	$\frac{1}{8}$	$\frac{2}{8}$	$\frac{3}{8}$
$\frac{5}{8}$	$\frac{7}{8}$	$\frac{7}{10}$	$\frac{3}{10}$
10%	12%	15%	20%
25%	30%	35%	40%

Name ____________________ Date ______________

Master 8.14b

Showdown Playing Cards 2

50%	55%	60%	68%
75%	80%	89%	95%
0.10	0.14	0.20	0.25
0.30	0.36	0.40	0.50
0.60	0.70	0.75	0.80
0.89	0.95	1.00	1

Name ____________________ Date ________________

Master 8.15

Percent Circles

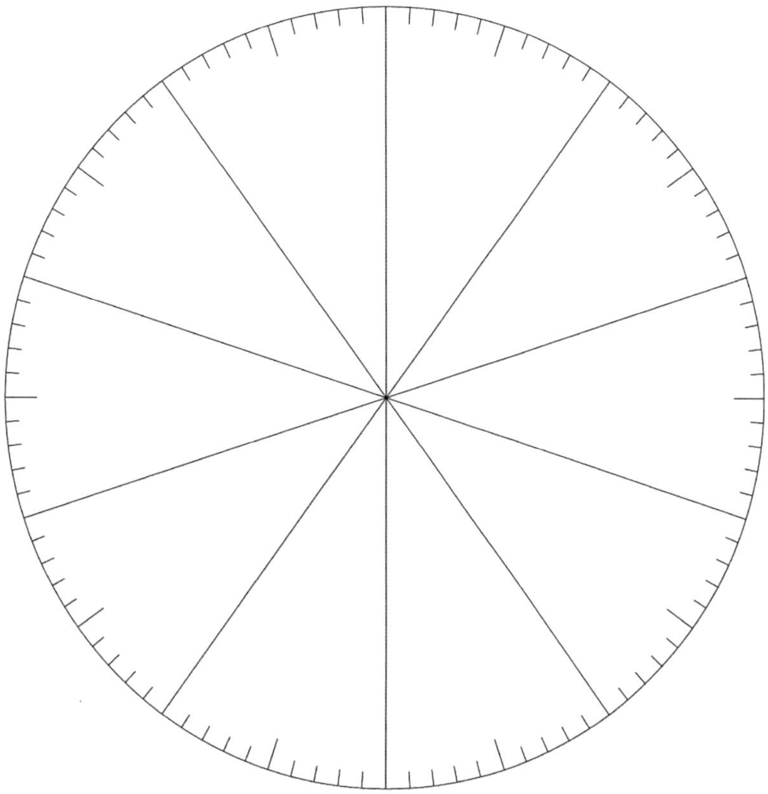

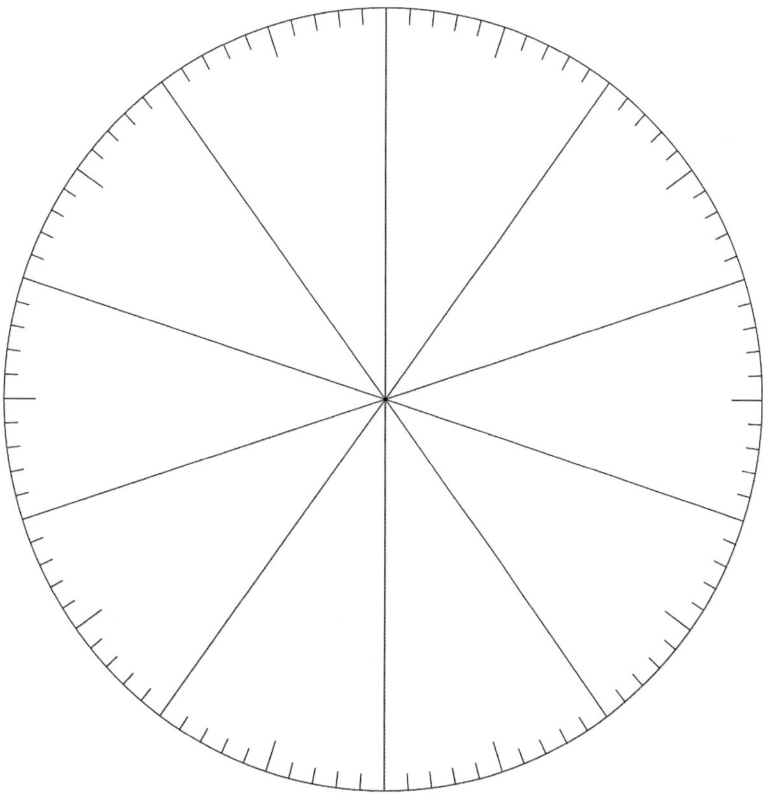

Name ____________________ Date ________________

Master 8.16a

Unit Test: Unit 8 Working with Percents

1. Write each fraction as a decimal and a percent. Sketch a number line to illustrate.

a) $\frac{3}{4}$ **b)** $\frac{3}{10}$

c) $\frac{6}{25}$ **d)** $\frac{27}{20}$

2. Estimate.

a) 48% of 220 **b)** 39% of 25 **c)** 3% of 69 **d)** 5% of 341

3. **a)** Find 15% and 20% of each number.

i) 60 **ii)** 140 **iii)** 340

b) What patterns do you see in the answers in part a?

4. A square with side length 4 cm represents 20% of a larger figure. What is the area of the larger figure? Use grid paper. Draw the larger figure.

Name ____________________ Date ________________

Master 8.16b

Unit Test continued

5. Twenty thousand fans were in attendance at a hockey game. The table shows the results of a survey that asked fans to state their favourite hockey team.

Favourite Team	**Number of Fans**
Montreal	2000
Toronto	5300
Vancouver	7500
Edmonton	1500
Calgary	1100
Detroit	1200
Other	?

a) How many fans cheer for "Other" teams?

b) Write the number of fans for each team as a percent of the total number of fans.

c) Draw a circle graph to display the data.

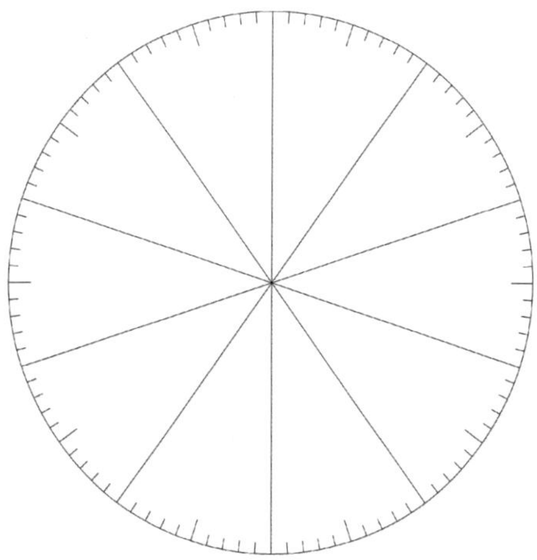

d) Write 2 questions you can answer by looking at the table or the graph. Answer your questions.

Name ____________________ Date ______________

Master 8.16c **Unit Test continued**

6. Ivan has completed 45% of his walk.
He has already walked 9 km. How much farther does he have left to walk?

7. In 1 h, Ioana painted 35 m^2 of wall space.
This represents 20% of the total area.

   a) What is the total area of the walls to be painted? Show all work.

   b) How many more hours will it take Ioana to paint one-half of the total area?
   What assumptions do you make?

8. a) You have saved $130 for a new pair of skis. They have a regular price of $189. They have been reduced by 30%. There is 15% tax.
Do you have enough money to buy the skis? Show your work.

   b) Next week, the skis will be reduced by a further 10%. Your parents have offered to give you an amount equal to 7% of your savings. Will you have enough money to buy the skis next week?
   If your answer is yes, how much change will you get?
   If your answer is no, by how much money are you short?

Master 8.17 Sample Answers

Unit Test – Master 8.16

1. **a)** 0.75, 75% **b)** 0.3, 30%
   c) 0.24, 24% **d)** 1.35, 135%

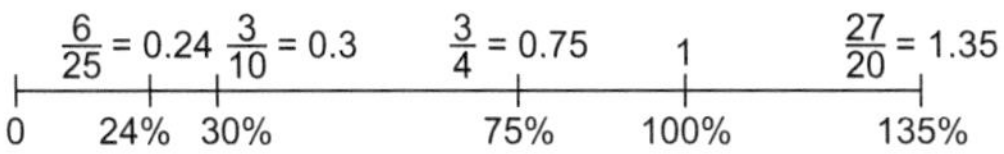

2. For example:
   a) About 110 **b)** About 10
   c) About 2 **d)** About 17

3. **a) i)** 9, 12 **ii)** 21, 28 **iii)** 51, 68
   b) The numbers in each pair are consecutive multiples; that is, $3 \times 3 = 9$, $4 \times 3 = 12$; $3 \times 7 = 21$, $4 \times 7 = 28$; $3 \times 17 = 51$, $4 \times 17 = 68$. In each case, we have found (15%) $\frac{3}{20}$ of a number and (20%) $\frac{4}{20}$ of a number.

4. 80 cm^2
   Shapes of figures may vary. All figures should have area 80 cm^2.

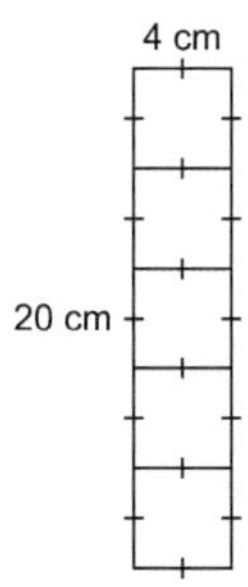

5. **a)** 1400
   b) Montreal: 10%
   Toronto: 26.5%
   Vancouver: 37.5%
   Edmonton: 7.5%
   Calgary: 5.5%
   Detroit: 6%
   Other: 7%
   c) Favourite Hockey Teams

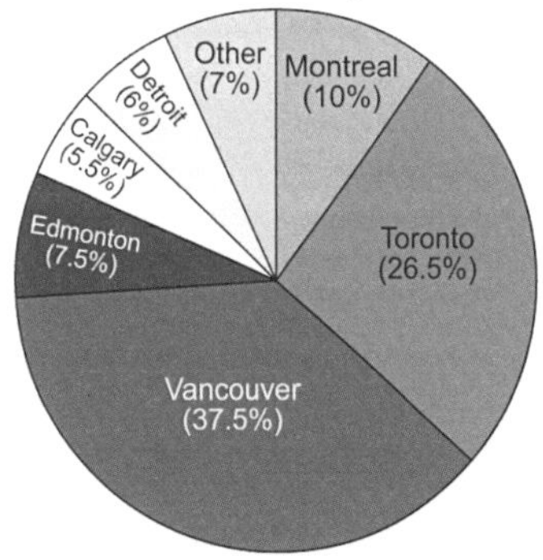

   d) Which team has about one-quarter of the fan support? (*Toronto*)
   Which is the least popular team among the fans in attendance? (*Calgary*)

6. 11 km
   45% is 9 km
   1% is $\frac{9}{45}$ km = 0.2 km
   So, 100% = 100×0.2 km = 20 km
   20 km – 9 km = 11 km

7. **a)** 20% = 35 m^2
   100% = $5 \times 20\%$
   = 5×35 m^2
   = 175 m^2
   The total area of the walls to be painted is 175 m^2.
   b) 20% = 1 h
   10% = 0.5 h
   So, 50% = 5×0.5 h
   = 2.5 h
   She has already painted for 1 h.
   2.5 h – 1 h = 1.5 h
   I assume she continues to paint at the same rate.

8. **a)** The skis, including tax, will cost $152.15.
   I have $130. I do not have enough money to buy the skis.
   b) Next week the skis, including tax, will cost $136.93. My parents will give me $9.10. I will have $130 + $9.10 = $139.10. I will have enough money to buy the skis. I will get $139.10 – $136.93 = $2.17 in change.

Extra Practice Masters 8.18–8.23

Go to the CD-ROM to access editable versions of these Extra Practice Masters.

Name ________ Date ________

Master 8.18 **Extra Practice 1**

Section 8.1: Relating Fractions, Decimals, and Percents

1. Write each fraction as a decimal and a percent.
a) $\frac{21}{35}$ b) $\frac{14}{20}$ c) $\frac{28}{56}$ d) $\frac{12}{16}$ e) $\frac{8}{5}$
f) $\frac{19}{20}$ g) $\frac{16}{25}$ h) $\frac{32}{40}$ i) $\frac{9}{30}$ j) $\frac{120}{75}$

2. Ruth's test scores were: $\frac{17}{20}$, $\frac{21}{28}$, and $\frac{40}{50}$
Convert each test score to a percent.
Order the test scores from greatest to least.

3. An equilateral triangle with side length 2 cm is 25% of a larger figure.
Use triangular grid paper.
a) Draw 50% of the larger figure.
b) Draw 75% of the larger figure.
c) Draw the larger figure.
d) Draw 150% of the larger figure.

4. In 5 min, Benjamin completed 27 of 30 multiple-choice questions.
Madison completed 83% of the questions.
Who completed more questions? How do you know?

Name ________ Date ________

Master 8.19 **Extra Practice 2**

Section 8.2: Estimating and Calculating Percents

1. Find 15% of each number.
a) 30 b) 60 c) 120 d) 200
e) 140 f) 90 g) 20 h) 300

2. Estimate.
a) 81% of 51 b) 49% of 119 c) 98% of 202
d) 2% of 253 e) 75% of 397 f) 39% of 849

3. There are 52 cards in a regular deck of cards.
Estimate or calculate each number of cards as a percent of the deck:
a) the clubs
b) the aces
c) the cards with odd numbers
d) the cards with even numbers
e) the red jacks

4. Ms. Leitch has 27 students in her class.
About 30% of the students in Ms. Leitch's class enjoy playing soccer.
a) About how many students enjoy soccer?
b) The school has a total of 539 students.
About what percent of the school's population is in Ms. Leitch's class?

Name ________ Date ________

Master 8.20 **Extra Practice 3**

Section 8.3: Multiplying to Find Percents

1. Calculate.
a) 10% of 7.85 b) 1% of 87.2 c) 20% of 66.5
d) 90% of 120 e) 120% of 85 f) 200% of 76.6

2. Find each percent of $79.99.
a) 20% b) 75% c) 24% d) 82% e) 95% f) 42%

3. The regular price of a skateboard is $74.99.
Find the sale price when the skateboard is on sale for:
a) 30% off b) 25% off c) 60% off d) 50% off
Find the final cost of the skateboard with 15% sales tax added to each sale price.

4. A sofa is 2.2 m long and 0.9 m wide. It sits in a room that is 5 m long and 4 m wide.
About what percent of the floor is covered by the sofa?

Name ________ Date ________

Master 8.21 **Extra Practice 4**

Section 8.4: Drawing Circle Graphs

1. The table shows the shoe size of students in Grade 7 at High Park School.

Shoe Size	Number of Students
5 or under	3
6	9
7	12
8	27
9	6
10 or over	3

a) Calculate the percent of students with each shoe size.
b) Draw a circle graph to represent the data.

2. The circle graph shows Samson's household budget for a month.

Samson's Household Budget for One Month

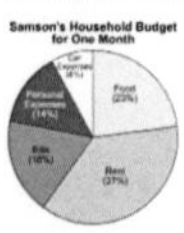

a) Samson takes home $2500 per month. How much does he budget for each item?
b) Samson gets a raise of $500 per month. How will this affect his food budget?

Name ________ Date ________

Master 8.22 **Extra Practice 5**

Section 8.5: Dividing to Find Percents

1. 25% is 150 cm.
a) What is 5%? b) What is 50%? c) What is 100%?
Sketch a number line to show your answer.

2. Lee has read 45% of his book. He has read 135 pages.
How many pages are in the book?

3. This year, Ferdinand spent $480 to send his daughter to hockey camp.
This is a 15% increase over last year.
How much did Ferdinand pay last year?

4. A box of paper clips was 62% full.
Remi used 20 of the paper clips for her history project.
The box originally contained 500 paper clips. How many remain?

Name ________ Date ________

Master 8.23 **Sample Answers**

Extra Practice 1 – Master 8.18

Section 8.1

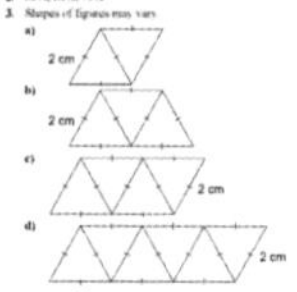

Extra Practice 2 – Master 8.19

Section 8.2

Extra Practice 3 – Master 8.20

Section 8.3

Extra Practice 4 – Master 8.21

Section 8.4

Shoe Size of Grade 7 Students at High Park School

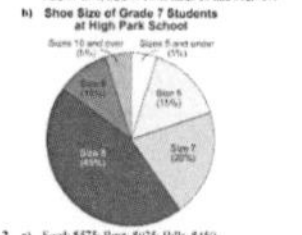

Extra Practice 5 – Master 8.22

Section 8.5

Addison Wesley
Mathematics
Makes Sense

Program Authors

Jason Johnston
Bryn Keyes
Mary Doucette
Antonietta Lenjosek
Steve Thomas
Margaret Sinclair
Trevor Brown
Cathy Heideman
Don Jones
Michael Davis
Jennifer Paziuk
Ken Harper
Sharon Jeroski
Ray Appel
Laura Weatherhead
Betty Milne
Jim Mennie
Lynn Strangway

Printed and bound in Canada

10 17

PEARSON
Education Canada

Addison Wesley

Ontario

Math Makes Sense 7

Ontario

Teacher Guide

Unit 9: Integers

PEARSON
Addison Wesley

UNIT 9 Integers

"By extending from whole numbers to integers, middle-grades students' intuitions about order and magnitude will be more reliable, and they have a glimpse into the way that systems of numbers work."

The Ontario Curriculum Grades 1–8 Mathematics

FOCUS STRAND
Number Sense and Numeration

TIPS
Adolescent learners understand a new concept by seeing models, hearing and giving explanations and doing activities which relate to it.

Mathematics Background

What Are the Big Ideas?

- Integers involve two concepts: size (magnitude) and sign (direction).
- A negative number and a positive number that have the same size are opposites.
- Integers are used to describe relative changes or values.

How Will the Concepts Develop?

Students activate their prior experience with positive and negative numbers by using integers to represent real-life situations. They compare and order integers on a number line to develop a sense of the relationships among integers and their relative sizes. Students use coloured tiles to represent integers. As they work with manipulatives and drawings, students' understanding that integers have both size and direction deepens. Students use coloured tiles and number lines to develop strategies for adding and subtracting integers and an understanding of *why* and *how* the strategies work.

Why Are These Concepts Important?

Developing a good understanding of integers permits students to model real-life situations that can be quantified and have direction. A thorough understanding of the representation of integers on a number line is key to graphing in all four quadrants. Students will use integer concepts to represent situations involving magnitude and direction, such as directed distances, temperature, and money concepts. Facility with integer operations is key to students successfully working with algebraic expressions in later grades. As students become more comfortable with integers, their understanding of the structure of numbers and the relationships among them will grow.

Curriculum Overview

Cluster 1: Representing and Ordering Integers

Overall Expectations
- Compare, order, and represent ..., integers, ... (7m1)

Specific Expectations
- Compare and order integers. (7m10)
- Explain numerical information in their own words and respond to numerical information in a variety of media. (7m12)
- Explain the process used and any conclusions reached in problem solving and investigations. (7m24)
- Reflect on learning experiences and describe their understanding using appropriate mathematical language. (7m25)

Cluster 2: Operations with Integers

Overall Expectations
- Compare, order, and represent ..., integers, ... (7m1)

Specific Expectations
- Represent the addition and subtraction of integers using concrete materials, drawings, and symbols. (7m21)
- Add integers, with and without the use of manipulatives. (7m22)
- Explain the process used and any conclusions reached in problem solving and investigations. (7m24)
- Reflect on learning experiences and describe their understanding using appropriate mathematical language. (7m25)

Launch

Section 9.1: What Is an Integer?

Section 9.2: Comparing and Ordering Integers

Section 9.3: Representing Integers

Section 9.4: Adding Integers with Tiles

Section 9.5: Adding Integers

Mid-Unit Review

Section 9.6: Subtracting Integers with Tiles

Section 9.7: Subtracting Integers

Unit Review
Practice Test

Unit Problem
What Time Is It?

Curriculum across the Grades

Grade 6	Grade 7	Grade 8
Students identify real-world applications of integers.	Students compare and order integers. Students represent the addition and subtraction of integers using concrete materials, drawings, and symbols. Students add integers with and without manipulatives.	Students compare and order integers. They discover the rules for the multiplication and division of integers through patterning and they multiply and divide integers. Students add and subtract integers, with and without manipulatives. They apply the order of operations with brackets for integers. Students solve and explain multi-step problems involving integers. They ask "what if" questions. Students pose problems involving integers and investigate solutions.

Materials for This Unit

If you do not have coloured tiles, you can use two colours of paper or cardstock cut into small congruent squares.

For several weeks, collect the financial sections of newspapers so students can see how stock prices change. Also use newspapers to collect the weather information for the temperatures of places in Canada or the world, when the temperatures are above and below 0°C.

Additional Activities

Greatest Sum

For Extra Practice (Appropriate for use after Skills You'll Need)
Materials: *Greatest Sum* (Master 9.5), 4 sets of number cards labelled 0 to 9, paper, and pens.

Playing this game reinforces the skills required for mental math.

The work students do: Students work in groups of 4. They draw number cards from a shuffled deck to make two 2-digit numbers with the goal of getting the greatest sum. The student with the greatest sum scores 1 point. If the student has the greatest sum possible from the 4 number cards, then she scores 2 points instead. The winner is the first player to get 10 points.

Take It Further: Students create pairs of 3-digit numbers. Students try to get the least difference.

Logical/Mathematical/Social
Group Activity

Magic Squares

For Extra Practice (Appropriate for use after Skills You'll Need)
Materials: *Magic Squares* (Master 9.6)

This game reinforces the skill of mental math. For more activities or information about magic squares go to: mathforum.org/alejandre/magic.square.html

The work students do: Students work alone. They look for patterns in 3 by 3 magic squares, extend these patterns, and complete a 4 by 4 magic square created by artist and mathematician, Albrecht Dürer.

Take It Further: Students make their own 3 by 3 magic square.

Mathematical/Logical
Individual Activity

Answers to Magic Squares:

22	15	20
17	19	21
18	23	16

37	30	35
32	24	36
33	38	31

100	93	98
96	97	98
96	101	94

Each magic square contains consecutive numbers.

The middle number is the middle consecutive number. The magic sum is three times the middle number. Add the same number to the middle number, or subtract the same number from the middle number to get the numbers in opposite corners.

28	21	26
23	25	27
24	29	22

74	67	72
69	71	73
70	75	68

240	233	238
235	237	239
236	241	234

16	3	2	13
5	10	11	8
9	6	7	12
4	15	14	1

The four corner numbers add to 34.

Middle opposite numbers add to 34.

(5 + 9 + 8 + 12 = 3 + 2 + 15 + 14 = 34)

Planning for Unit 9

Planning for Instruction

Suggested Unit time: About 3–4 weeks

Section	Time	Materials	Program Support
Launch, page 2	15–20 min	time zone map of Canada and of world on overhead transparency globe	
Skills You'll Need, page 4	20–35 min		
9.1: What is an Integer?, page 5 Use real-world applications of integers.	80–100 min	thermometer number lines calculators	Master 9.15: Number Lines Master 9.7: Step-by-Step 1 Master 9.18: Extra Practice 1
9.2: Comparing and Ordering Integers, page 8 Use a number line to order and compare integers.	80–100 min	atlases, Internet access, or elevation data number lines	Master 9.14: Elevation Data Master 9.15: Number Lines Master 9.8: Step-by-Step 2 Master 9.19: Extra Practice 2
9.3: Representing Integers, page 12 Use coloured tiles to represent integers.	80–100 min	yellow and red coloured tiles or counters paper bags or envelopes yellow and red markers or coloured pencils	Master 9.9: Step-by-Step 3 Master 9.20: Extra Practice 3
9.4: Adding Integers with Tiles, page 15 Use coloured tiles to add integers.	80–100 min	yellow and red coloured tiles	Master 9.10: Step-by-Step 4 Master 9.21: Extra Practice 4
9.5: Adding Integers, page 19 Add integers using number lines and patterns.	80–100 min	overhead transparency of number lines number lines coloured tiles (optional)	Master 9.15: Number Lines Master 9.11: Step-by-Step 5 Master 9.22: Extra Practice 5
Mid-Unit Review, page 23		coloured tiles number lines	Master 9.15: Number Lines
9.6: Subtracting Integers with Tiles, page 24 Use coloured tiles to subtract integers.	80–100 min	coloured tiles	Master 9.12: Step-by-Step 6 Master 9.23: Extra Practice 6
9.7: Subtracting Integers, page 29 Subtract integers using number lines and patterns.	80–100 min	overhead transparency of number lines number lines coloured tiles	Master 9.15: Number Lines Master 9.13: Step-by-Step 7 Master 9.24: Extra Practice 7
Reading and Writing in Math: Choosing a Strategy, page 34		1-cm grid paper calculators	PM 20: 1-cm Grid Paper
Unit Review, page 37		coloured tiles number lines	Master 9.15: Number Lines Extra Practice: Student Book page 446
Practice Test, page 39		coloured tiles number lines	Master 9.15: Number Lines
Unit Problem: What Time Is It? page 40	80–100 min	atlases coloured tiles coloured tiles (optional) number lines (optional)	Master 9.15: Number Lines

etext online tutorial

This web-based tutorial uses voice, animation, and an optional quiz to present each core lesson, so that students can review content with a new approach.

Planning for Assessment

Purpose	Tools and Process	Recording and Reporting
Diagnostic	*Unit Launch* Question; conference; scaffold problems throughout the unit	PM 8: Conference Prompts
Diagnostic	*Unit Launch* Question; conference; scaffold problems throughout the unit	PM 8: Conference Prompts
Formative	*Explore* – Ongoing Assessment: Observe and Listen	Master 9.2: Ongoing Observations: Integers PM 1: Inquiry Process Check List PM 6: Observation Record 1 PM 7: Observation Record 2 PM 8: Conference Prompts PM 2: Self-Assessment PM 3: Self-Assessment: Problem Solving PM 9: Work Sample Records
Summative	Unit Review *Unit Problem* – Performance Assessment Unit Test Review assessment records; add unit results to ongoing records	Master 9.1: Unit Rubric: Integers Master 9.3: Performance Assessment Rubric: What Time Is It? Master 9.4: Unit Summary: Integers PM 10: Summary Class Records: Strands PM 11: Summary Class Records: Achievement Categories PM 12: Summary Record: Individual
Learning Skills/ Mathematical Disposition	Observe and record throughout the unit	PM 4: Learning Skills Check List PM 5: Mathematical Dispositions and Learning Skills

Program Masters (PM) are in the *Grade 7 Planning and Program Masters* module.
Extra Practice Masters are on the CD-ROM and are printed in reduced format on page 61 of this module.

SECTION ORGANIZER

15–20 min

Curriculum Focus: Activate necessity to learn about integers.

Teacher Materials

- time zone map of Canada and of world on overhead transparency
- globe

Vocabulary: time zone

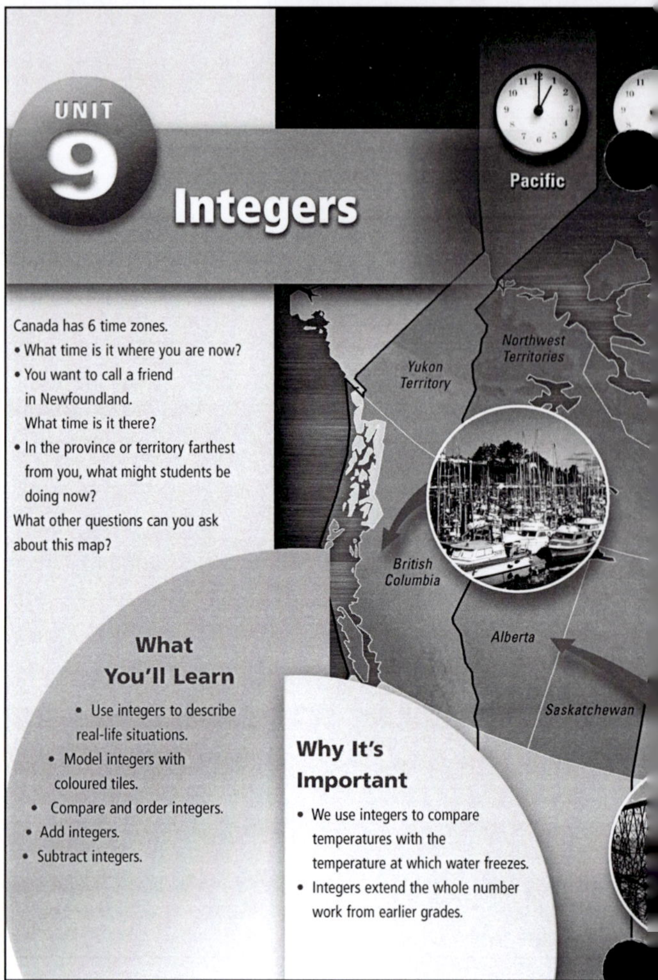
UNIT 9
Integers

Canada has 6 time zones.
- What time is it where you are now?
- You want to call a friend in Newfoundland. What time is it there?
- In the province or territory farthest from you, what might students be doing now?

What other questions can you ask about this map?

What You'll Learn
- Use integers to describe real-life situations.
- Model integers with coloured tiles.
- Compare and order integers.
- Add integers.
- Subtract integers.

Why It's Important
- We use integers to compare temperatures with the temperature at which water freezes.
- Integers extend the whole number work from earlier grades.

ASSUMED PRIOR KNOWLEDGE

- ☑ Students can compare and order whole numbers.
- ☑ Students can use counters to add and subtract whole numbers.
- ☑ Students can use number lines to add and subtract whole numbers.

ACTIVATE PRIOR LEARNING

Have students examine the map of time zones in Canada.

Discuss the questions in the Student Book and record students' responses on the board.

Sample Responses

It is 1:00 p.m. now.

In Newfoundland, it is one and a half hours ahead, so it will be 2:30 p.m.

British Columbia and Yukon Territory are farthest away from Ontario. They are 3 hours behind us, so it would be 10:00 a.m. The students will be in school.

Ask students how they can calculate the time in Newfoundland when they know the time in Ontario. (*Add $1\frac{1}{2}$ hours to the time in Ontario to get the time in Newfoundland.*)

Ask students how they can calculate the time in Yukon when they know the time in Ontario. (*Subtract 3 hours to the time in Ontario to get the time in Yukon.*)

Other questions about this map:

- Why are there different time zones in Canada? (*Canada is a very large country. Suppose we did not have time zones, and the whole country had the same time as Ontario. Then, when the sun rose at 6:00 a.m. in Ontario, in Newfoundland it would rise at 4:30 a.m. and in Yukon, it would rise at 9:00 a.m.*)
- Why are the time zone lines not vertical lines; for example, the Eastern time zone is wider than the others? (*The time zones follow lines of longitude, where possible, but each province has the same time zone, so the lines change to accommodate this. Ontario and Quebec are in the same time zone, so this zone is wider.*)
- What happens when we change to daylight saving time? Do all provinces do this? (*As of 2004, on the first Sunday in April, clocks are moved forward one hour. On the last Sunday in October, clocks are moved backward one hour. Some areas of Canada do not use Daylight Saving Time, including Fort St. John, Charlie Lake, Taylor and*

Key Words

- positive number
- negative number
- integer
- positive integer
- negative integer
- opposite integers
- zero pair

FROM THE LIBRARY

Pre-Algebra: Grades 6-8: Inventive Exercises to Sharpen Skills and Raise Achievement (Basic, Not Boring 6 to 8) by Imogene Forte and Marjorie Frank. Incentive Publications, 2000
ISBN: 0865304475
Students will participate in the exciting escapades of some adventuresome campers. While exploring, they will practise skills, including how to identify opposites for positive and negative integers.

REACHING ALL LEARNERS

e-tools Some students may benefit from using the virtual manipulatives on the e-Tools CD-ROM.
The e-Tools appropriate for this unit are *Counters.*

Dawson Creek in British Columbia, Creston in the East Kootenays, and most of Saskatchewan.)

Use a globe to show students lines of longitude.

Tell students that in this unit, they will compare, order, add, and subtract integers. At the end of this unit, they will use integers to find and compare times in locations throughout the world.

DIAGNOSTIC ASSESSMENT

What to Look For	What to Do
✔ Students can compare and order whole numbers.	***Extra Support:*** Have students use number lines to order whole numbers. Remind them that we read from left to right for an order that is least to greatest number. *Work on this skill during Section 9.2.*
✔ Students can use counters to add and subtract whole numbers. ✔ Students can use number lines to add and subtract whole numbers.	Have students use number lines to add and subtract whole numbers. For adding, begin at the first number, then count on (to the right) a number of spaces equal to the second number. For subtracting, begin at the first number, then count back (to the left) a number of spaces equal to the second number. *Work on this skill during Sections 9.5 and 9.7.*

SECTION ORGANIZER — 25–30 min

Skills in Review
- Using mental math strategies for addition and subtraction

Alternative Example

Add or subtract. Use mental math.
a) 29 + 85 b) 143 − 97

Solution

a) 29 + 85
Make a friendly number.
Add 1 to 29. Subtract 1 from 85.
30 + 84
Add the ones. Add the tens.
30 + 84 = 114

b) 143 − 97
Add 3 to 97 to make 100. Add 3 to 143 to make 146.
146 − 100 = 46

Sample Answers

1. One strategy is make friendly numbers. Other strategies may be used instead.
2. Find the magic number by adding up a row, column, or diagonal where all three entries are known. Fill in blanks by adding two known entries and subtracting from the magic number to get the third.

UNIT 9

Skills You'll Need

Mental Math Strategies for Addition and Subtractio

Example

Add or subtract.
Use mental math.
a) 38 + 17 b) 111 − 64

Solution

a) 38 + 17
Make a friendly number. Subtract from one number and add to the other.
So, 38 + 17 = 38 + 2 + 17 − 2 — Subtract 2 from 17. Add 2 to 38.
= 40 + 15
= 55

b) 111 − 64
Subtract the ones, then subtract the tens.
Subtract 4: 111 − 4 = 107 — Count back by 1s to subtract 4.
Then subtract 60: 107 − 60 = 47
So, 111 − 64 = 47

✓ Check

Use mental math.

1. Add or subtract. What strategy did you use?
a) 22 + 88 = 110 b) 69 − 29 = 40 c) 93 + 38 = 131 d) 132 − 85 = 47

2. In a magic square every row, column, and diagonal has the same sum. Copy and complete each magic square. Explain how you did it.

a)

8	1	6
3	5	7
4	9	2

b)

17	10	15
12	14	16
13	18	11

326 UNIT 9: Integers

Mental Math Strategies for Addition and Subtraction

The student text illustrated the strategy of make friendly numbers for addition. Here is another strategy to review:
Use the strategy of adding on.
38 + 17
Start with the greater number, 38.
Add on by 10: 38 → 48
Then add 7: 48 → 55

The student text illustrated the strategy of subtracting ones, then subtracting tens for subtraction.
Here is another strategy to review:
Use the strategy of counting on.
111 − 64
Count on from 64. Count on by 10s, then by a single-digit number.
Count: 64 → 74 → 84 → 94 → 104 → 111
+10 +10 +10 +10 +7 = 47

For extra practice, have students play *Greatest Sum* (Master 9.5) and *Magic Squares* (Master 9.6).

Common Misconceptions

➤ Students confuse "mental math" with "estimation."

How to Help: Have students estimate each sum (38 + 17 → 40 + 20 = 60) and difference (111 − 64 → 110 − 60 = 50) to illustrate that estimation may not give the correct answer.

➤ Students do not know how to subtract when the digit for the number being subtracted is greater than the digit for the greater number.

How to Help: Have students use Base Ten Blocks; for example, for 111 − 64: show a hundred flat, a ten rod, and a unit cube. Trade the ten rod for 10 unit cubes, then remove 4 unit cubes. Trade the hundred flat for 10 rods, then remove 6 rods. There are 4 rods and 7 unit cubes left.

9.1 What Is an Integer?

Focus Use real-world applications of integers.

We measure temperature in degrees Celsius.
The highest temperature in Prince George, BC, on April 27, 2004, was 12°C.
12 is a **positive number**.
12°C is the difference between the temperature of the air and the temperature at which water freezes, 0°C.

We may not be able to use a positive number to express a difference.
For example, the temperature inside a freezer is 4°C less than the freezing point of water. We represent this difference as −4°C.

−4 is a **negative number**.
We say "negative 4."

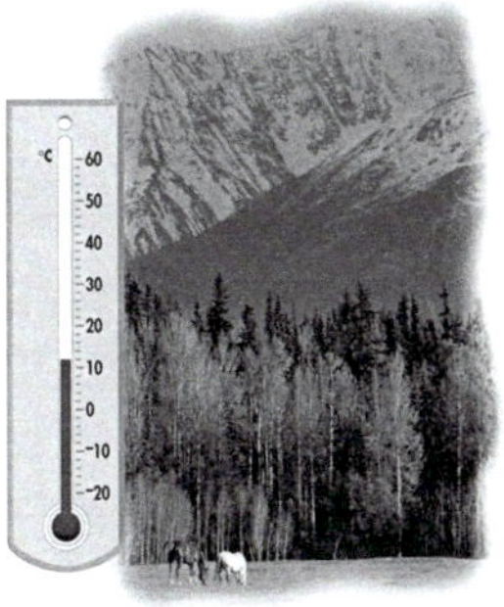

When we talk about temperatures below zero, we say "minus 4," rather than "negative 4."

Explore

Work with a partner.
Use a positive or a negative number to represent each situation.

- eight degrees above zero +8
- ten degrees below zero −10
- parking three levels below ground level −3
- two points ahead in a soccer game +2
- a loss of sixteen dollars −16
- taking four steps backward −4

Reflect & Share

Compare your answers with those of another pair of classmates.
For each situation, how did you decide whether to use a positive number or a negative number?

9.1 What Is an Integer? 327

What Is an Integer?

SECTION ORGANIZER (80–100 min)

Curriculum Focus: Use real-world applications of integers. (7m10, 7m25)

Teacher Materials
- thermometer

Student Materials
- number lines (Master 9.15)
- calculators

Optional
- Step-by-Step 1 (Master 9.7)
- Extra Practice 1 (Master 9.18)

Vocabulary: positive number, negative number, integer, positive integer, negative integer, number line, opposite integers

Assessment: Master 9.2 Ongoing Observations: Integers

Key Math Learnings

1. Numbers greater than zero are positive integers.
2. Numbers less than zero are negative integers.
3. Opposite integers are equal distances from zero, on opposite sides of zero.

Mental Math

Encourage students to find expressions using addition and multiplication. Provide time for students to share their results.
Some expressions are:

$2 \times 5 \times 10 = 100$ $10^2 = 100$

If each number is used more than once:

$(10 + 10) \times 5 = 100$ $(5 \times 10) + (5 \times 10) = 100$

$(10 \times 2) + (10 \times 2) + (10 \times 2) + (10 \times 2) + (10 \times 2) = 100$

BEFORE Get Started

Show students a thermometer. Ask:

What is the temperature in the classroom?
(*The temperature will likely be about 22°C.*)

What would the outside temperature be on a hot (cold) day in the summer (winter)?
(*About 30°C (−10°C)*)

Have students find these temperatures on the thermometer. Note that a thermometer does not show the negative sign to indicate negative temperatures. We use the term "negative" rather than "minus" when describing negative numbers, to avoid confusing the sign of the integer with the operation of subtracting. Temperature is the exception. Present *Explore.*

DURING Explore

Ongoing Assessment: Observe and Listen

As students work, ask questions, such as:

- What kind of numbers do we use to represent temperatures above (below) zero?
(*Positive numbers* (*Negative numbers*))
- What words indicate a situation that can be represented by positive numbers?
(*Increase, up, above, gain, ahead, higher, forward*)
- What words indicate a situation can be represented by negative numbers?
(*Decrease, down, below, loss, lower, backward)*
- How did you decide to use a positive number for the fourth statement?
(*Two points "ahead" meant this team had more points than the other, and "more" suggests "positive."*)
- How did you decide to use a negative number for the third statement?
(*Three levels "below" meant the parking was below ground, and "below" suggests negative, as below zero is a negative temperature.*)

REACHING ALL LEARNERS

Early Finishers

Have students write about other situations where positive or negative numbers are used. If they need help, suggest they consider sports, money, and distance above or below sea level.

Common Misconceptions

➤ Students do not know whether real-life examples represent positive or negative integers.

How to Help: Work with students to make separate lists of words that represent positive and negative integers. Some of these words are listed in *During Explore*, page 5.

ESL Strategies

Have students make a two-column list with words and phrases that indicate positive and negative integers.

Sample Answers

1.
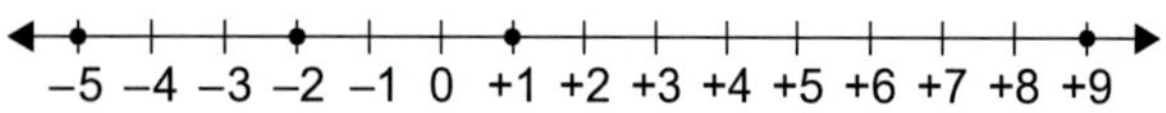

4. a) I saved $4.
   b) I am 5 cm shorter than my sister.
   c) One candidate in the local election had 120 more votes than another candidate.
   d) Eight thousand five hundred fewer shares were sold.

Connect

Mental Math

Use any math operation. Use the numbers around the circle. Write as many ways as you can to make the number in the circle.

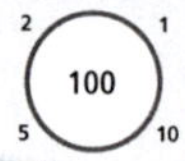

Positive and negative whole numbers are called **integers**.
We put + in front of a number to indicate it is a **positive integer**.

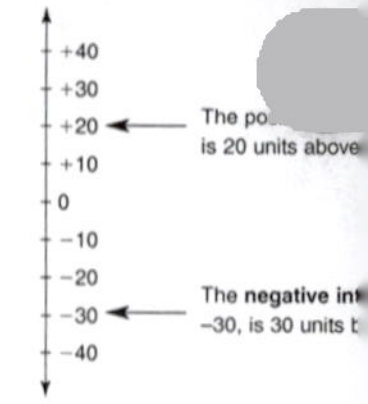

We can show integers on a number line.
The number line may be vertical, like a thermometer.

A number line may be horizontal.

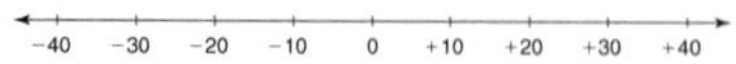

Opposite integers are the same distance from 0 but are on opposite sides of 0.
For example, +2 and −2 are opposite integers.
They are the same distance from 0 and are on opposite sides of

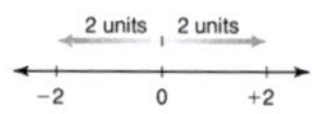

+4 and −4 are also opposite integers, as are +21 and −21.

Practice

1. Mark each integer on a number line.
   a) +1 b) −5 c) −2 d) +9

2. Write the opposite of each integer.
   a) +3 –3 b) −1 +1 c) −8000 +8000 d) +10 –

3. Use a positive or negative integer to represent each situation
   a) thirty-five degrees Celsius below zero in Yellowknife –3
   b) a weather balloon 28 000 m above Earth's surface +28
   c) diving 35 m below the ocean's surface –35 m
   d) earning $500 +$500

Use question 3 as a model.

4. Use each integer below to describe a situation.
   a) +4 b) −5 c) +120 d) −8500

AFTER Connect

Invite students to share their ideas of other situations that can be represented by integers. To prompt ideas, suggest areas from sports, money or geography.
(*Golf scores, hockey +/– statistics, having money, owing money, distances above or below sea level*)

Students should recognize that the counting numbers (1, 2, 3, ...) are positive integers. Negative integers are the opposites of the counting numbers.

Practice

Have blank Number Lines (Master 9.15) available for all questions. Have calculators available for question 6.

Assessment Focus: Question 6

Students should understand that births and immigration are positive data, while deaths and emigration are negative data. The choice of integers for parts c and d will depend on the order in which the numbers are subtracted.

Students who need extra support to complete Assessment Focus questions may benefit from the Step-by-Step masters (Masters 9.7–9.13).

Assignment Guidelines

If your students do not have time to complete all the *Practice* questions on pages 328 and 329, these questions provide minimum curriculum coverage: 1, 2, 4, 6, *Reflect*
To assess the 4 Achievement Chart categories listed in the curriculum document, have students complete these *Practice* questions: Understanding Concepts: 2; Application: 3; Problem Solving: 6; Communication: 4

5. Describe two situations in which you might use negative and positive integers. Write integers for your situations.

6. **Assessment Focus** Statistics Canada reported these data about Canada's population.

Years	Births	Deaths	Immigration	Emigration
1961-66	2 249 000	731 000	539 000	280 000
1996-2001	1 704 000	1 095 000	1 051 000	270 000

a) Which numbers can be represented by positive integers? Births/immigration
Negative integers? Explain. Deaths/emigration

b) For each column of data in the table, find the difference in the numbers. Write the difference as a positive or negative integer. Explain your choice of integer.
−545 000; +364 000; +512 000; −10 000

c) Choose one time period. Use a number line and integers to explain the relationship between births and deaths.

d) Choose one time period. Use integers to explain the relationships between immigration and emigration.

Take It Further

7. Changes in stock prices on the Stock Exchange are written as positive or negative integers.

a) Express each change as an integer.
   i) The value of Apple Computers increased $2. +$2
   ii) Palm Tech dropped from $25 to $22. −$3
   iii) MDS started the day at $13 and ended the day at $12. −$1
   iv) Steve bought Global stock at $10 and sold it for $15. +$5

b) Look at the two stock prices in part a, ii.
How are the prices related? The second is $3 less than the first.

c) Look at the two stock prices in part a, iv.
How are the prices related? The second is $5 more than the first.

d) How can an integer be used to show the relationship between two prices of a stock? Explain.

Find the price of a stock in the financial section of a newspaper. Follow the price every day for one month. How are integers used to show how the stock price changes?

Reflect

Suppose you read a situation that can be described with integers. What clues do you look for to help you decide whether to use a positive or negative integer? Use examples in your explanation.

9.1 What Is an Integer? 329

5. The yearbook committee sold $500 of advertising space: +500
The yearbook committee spent $35 on telephone calls: −35

6. a) Numbers that show how the population increases are positive integers. Numbers that show how the population decreases are negative integers.

b) The differences are overprinted. The difference in births is negative, because births decreased from 1961-66 to 1996-2001. The difference in deaths is positive, because the deaths increased. The difference in immigration is positive, because the immigration increased. The difference in emigration is negative, because the emigration decreased.

c) I chose 1961-66. The number of deaths is a negative integer, so that is to the left of 0. The number of births is a positive integer, so that is to the right of 0.

d) I chose 1961-66. The number of immigrants is a positive integer, so that is to the right of 0. The number of emigrants is a negative integer, so that is to the left of 0.

7. d) If the stock price increases, the change is shown as a positive integer. If the stock price decreases, the change is shown as a negative integer.

REFLECT: The words or pictures indicate if a positive or negative integer should be used. Positive words would be: higher, increase, above, up, gain, ahead, forward.
Negative words would be: lower, decrease, below, down, loss, behind, backward. A loss of $10 would be −10. A gain of $20 would be +20.

ASSESSMENT FOR LEARNING

What to Look For

Understanding concepts

✔ Students recognize negative and positive integers used in real-life problems.

Applying procedures

✔ Students can place integers on a number line.

Communicating

✔ Students use correct terminology when describing situations with positive and negative integers.

What to Do

Extra Support: Have students use a number line to find the opposites of integers.
Students can use Step-by-Step 1 (Master 9.7) to complete question 6.

Extra Practice: Have students describe a situation that can be represented by each integer: −7, +12, −22
Students can complete Extra Practice 1 (Master 9.18).

Extension: Have students find the population of your school in the years 1971 and 2001.
Students express the change in population from 1971 to 2001 as an integer.

Recording and Reporting
Master 9.2 Ongoing Observations: Integers

Comparing and Ordering Integers

SECTION ORGANIZER (80–100 min)

Curriculum Focus: Use a number line to order and compare integers. (7m10, 7m25)

Student Materials
- atlases, Internet access, or elevation data (Master 9.14)
- number lines (Master 9.15)

Optional
- Step-by-Step 2 (Master 9.8)
- Extra Practice 2 (Master 9.19)

Vocabulary: elevation, sea level

Assessment: Master 9.2 Ongoing Observations: Integers

Key Math Learning

Greater integers are to the right of lesser integers on a number line.

9.2 Comparing and Ordering Integers

Focus Use a number line to order and compare integers.

Elevation is the height above or below sea level. Elevation influences climate and how people live. For example, crops will not grow at elevations above 5300 m.

Explore

Work with a partner.
You will need an atlas or Internet access.
Here are some examples of extreme elevations around the world:

Vinson Massif, Antarctica	4897 m above sea level
Dead Sea, Israel/Jordan	411 m below sea level
Bottom of Great Slave Lake	458 m below sea level
Mt. Nowshak, Afghanistan	7485 m above sea level
Challenger Deep, Pacific Ocean	10 924 m below sea level

Research to find at least 4 more extreme elevations in Canada.
Two should be above sea level, and two should be below sea level.
Order *all* the elevations from least to greatest.

Reflect & Share

What strategies did you use to order the elevations?
What other ways could you display these data to show the different elevations?

Connect

We use the symbols > and < to show order.
The symbol points to the lesser number.

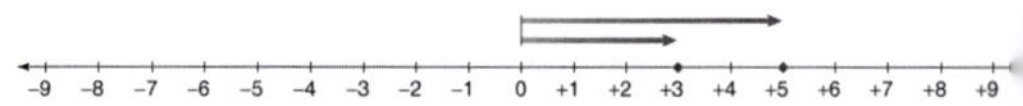

+5 is to the right of +3 on a number line.
+5 is greater than +3, so we write: +5 > +3
+3 is less than +5, so we write: +3 < +5

330 UNIT 9: Integers

BEFORE — Get Started

Ask students:
- What does "sea level" mean?
  (*Surface of a calm sea*)
- How would you order the numbers 885, 342, 889, and 311 from least to greatest?
  (*Compare the hundreds digits, then the tens digits, then the ones digits: 311, 342, 885, and 889.*)
- When you compare two numbers on a number line, how are their positions related?
  (*The lesser number is to the left and the greater number is to the right.*)

Present *Explore.* Ensure students can use atlases or the Internet (search using "elevation") correctly to find data. If you do not have atlases or Internet access, provide students with copies of Master 9.14: *Elevation Data.*

DURING — Explore

Ongoing Assessment: Observe and Listen

As students work, ask questions, such as:
- What extreme elevations did you choose?
  (*We chose the Puerto Rico Trench, 8648 m below sea level; Mount Kilimanjaro, 5895 m above sea level; Mount Everest, 8850 m above sea level; and Bentley Subglacial Trench, 2540 m below sea level.*)
- How could integers be used to write each elevation?
  (*Above sea level are positive integers, below sea level are negative integers.*)
- How did you order the elevations from least to greatest?
  (*The least elevations are the farthest below sea level and the greatest elevations are the highest above sea level. The elevations from least to greatest are: –10 924, –8648, –2540, –458, –411, +4897, +5895, +7485, +8850*)

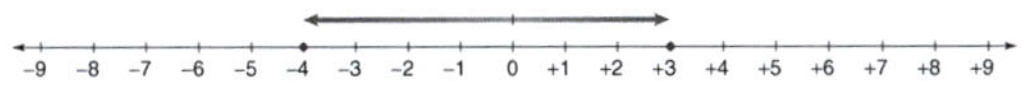

+3 is to the right of −4 on a number line.
+3 is greater than −4, so we write: +3 > −4
−4 is less than +3, so we write: −4 < +3

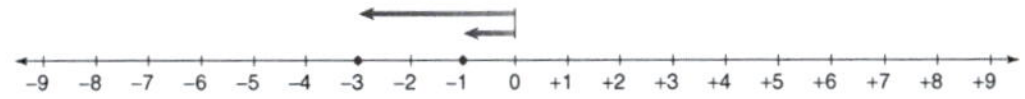

−3 is to the left of −1 on a number line.
−3 is less than −1, so we write: −3 < −1
−1 is greater than −3, so we write: −1 > −3

Example

For the integers 0, +1, −2, +3, −5:

a) Use a number line to order the integers from least to greatest.
b) Write the opposite of each integer.
Show the opposites on a number line.
c) Order the opposites from least to greatest.

Solution

a) Mark each integer on a number line.

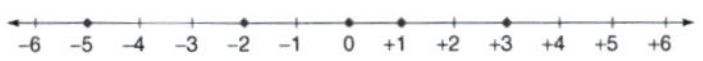

The integers increase from left to right.
So, the integers from least to greatest: −5, −2, 0, +1, +3

b) The opposite of an integer is its mirror image reflected in a vertical line drawn through 0 on a number line.
The opposite of −5 is +5. The opposite of −2 is +2.
Since 0 is the reference point, 0 is its own opposite.
The opposite of +1 is −1. The opposite of +3 is −3.

c) So, the opposite integers from least to greatest: −3, −1, 0, +2, +5

REACHING ALL LEARNERS

Early Finishers

Have students research then order other extreme elevations. They can investigate categories such as cities, mountains, and lakes. Have students compare their findings with those of others.

Common Misconceptions

➤Students confuse the symbols for *less than* and *greater than*.
How to Help: Have students examine the < symbol. Ask which side of the symbol is larger. Tell students that this side of the symbol goes with the greater number. The pointed side of the symbol points to the lesser number.

➤Students order negative integers in reverse order.
How to Help: Students' understanding of negative integers will increase if they relate them to real-life situations. Have students answer questions, such as:
Which temperature is higher: −20° C or −15° C? (*−15° C*)
So, which integer is greater:
−20 or −15? (*−15*)
Who is higher: Diver A at 13 m below sea level (−13) or Diver B at 25 m below sea level (−25)? (*The diver at −13 m is higher.*)
So, which integer is greater: −13 or −25? (*−13*)

ESL Strategies

For students from other countries, suggest they research elevations in the countries where they were born.

AFTER Connect

Invite students to share the strategies they used to order the elevations.

Students may use vertical number lines, organize all positive integers then all negative integers, or pick two to place in order, then order the rest one by one in correct relative position to these.

The data could be displayed as a bar graph above and below a horizontal line.

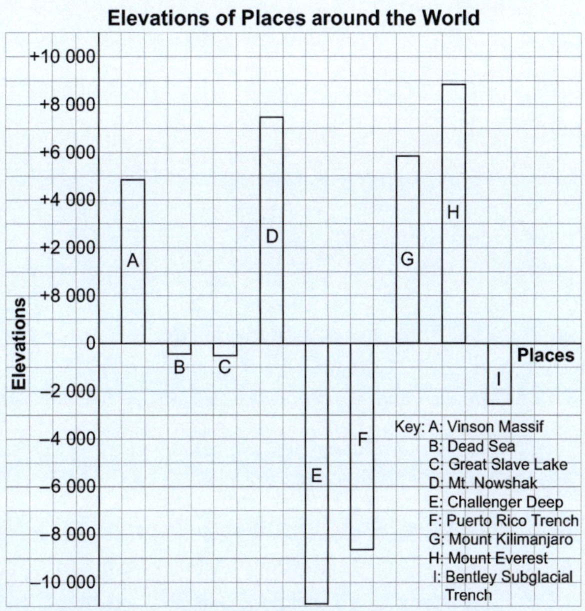

Math Link: Have students discuss how elevation above or below sea level affects life in specific countries.

Sample Answers

6. b) The least temperature is the lowest number on the thermometer going up to the greatest temperature which is the highest number on the thermometer.
8. b) Which integers are opposites? +8 and −8
   Which is the greatest integer? +9
   Which is the least integer? −8
   Which integer is closest to 0? +4
9. The warmest temperature is the one closest to 0°C on a thermometer and the coldest is the one farthest from 0°C on a thermometer when all temperatures are below 0°C.
10. b) The number that is halfway between −5 and +1 is −2.
   The number that is halfway between −5 and −1 is −3.
   The halfway numbers are different because the numbers +1 and −1 are on opposite sides of 0. So, the distance between −5 and +1 is 6 spaces and the distance between −5 and −1 is 4 spaces.
   c) There are many answers here.
   Some pairs of integers are shown below: −4, −2; −5, −1; 0, −6; ... This pattern continues.

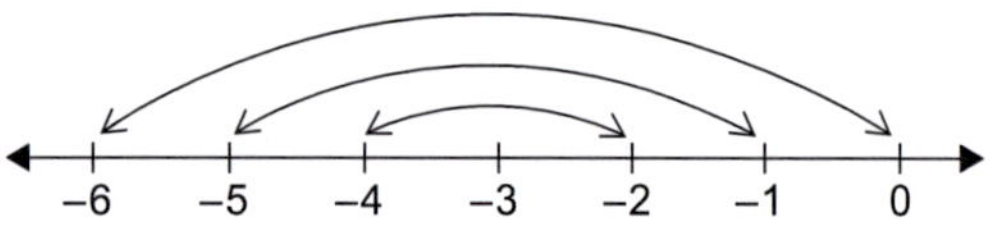

Practice

1. Copy each number line. Fill in the missing integers.
   a) −4, −3, −2, −1, 0, +1, +2, +3, +4
   b) −8, −7, −6, −5, −4, −3, −2, −1, 0, +1
2. Order the integers in each set from least to greatest.
   a) +5, +13, +1 — +1, +5, +13
   b) −3, −5, −4 — −5, −4, −3
   c) +4, −2, +3 — −2, +3, +4
3. Order the integers in each set from greatest to least.
   a) +4, +1, +8 — +8, +4, +1
   b) −7, −5, −3 — −3, −5, −7
   c) 0, +4, −4 — +4, 0, −4
4. Order the integers in each set from least to greatest.
   a) −5, −2, +2, +4, +5
   b) −12, −10, −8, 0, +10
   c) +41, −39, −41, −15, −25 — −41, −39, −25, −15, +41
   d) +1, −1, +2, −2, +3 — −2, −1, +1, +2, +3
5. Order the integers in each set from greatest to least.
   a) +14, −25, −30, +3, −10 — +14, +3, −10, −25, −30
   b) 0, +1, +2, −1, −2 — +2, +1, 0, −1, −2
   c) −29, +27, −11, −4, +6 — +27, +6, −4, −11, −29
   d) −7, +8, −9, +10, −11 — +10, +8, −7, −9, −11
6. This table shows the coldest temperatures ever recorded in 6 provinces and territories.
   a) Draw a thermometer like the one shown.
   Mark each temperature on it.

A real thermometer does not show negative signs. We include them for better understanding.

Province or Territory	Coldest Temperature °C
Alberta	− 61
Manitoba	− 53
Nova Scotia	− 47
Nunavut	− 64
Ontario	− 58
Quebec	− 54

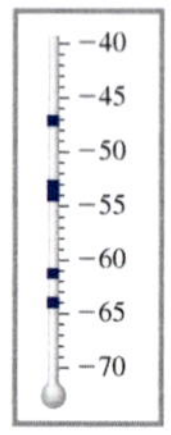

   b) Order the temperatures in part a from least to greatest.
   How can you use your thermometer to do this?
   −64, −61, −58, −54, −53, −47
7. Copy and complete by placing < or > between the integers.
   Use a number line if it helps.
   a) +5 < +10 b) −5 > −10 c) −6 < 0
   d) −5 < −4 e) +100 > −101 f) −80 < −40

332 UNIT 9: Integers

Reinforce that the integers increase as we move from left to right on the number line. The lesser numbers are to the left and greater numbers are to the right.

Review the *Examples* in *Connect*.

Math Note

On a number line, a positive integer is a measured distance to the right of 0. A negative integer is a measured distance to the left of 0. An integer is a directed distance, and *not* a point on a line. To emphasize this, use an arrow to represent an integer.

As an extension, challenge students to create other patterns similar to those in *Practice* question 12. Have students work in pairs to find their partner's pattern. Ensure students explain the pattern rules after a solution is attempted.

Practice

Provide students with copies of *Number Lines* (Master 9.15).

Assessment Focus: Question 8

Students will likely use a number line to answer these questions. Although students have not yet learned to add and subtract integers, the questions they make up may involve concepts of "more than" and "less than."

Assignment Guidelines

If your students do not have time to complete all the *Practice* questions on pages 332 and 333, these questions provide minimum curriculum coverage: 4, 5, 6, 7, 8, *Reflect*
To assess the 4 Achievement Chart categories listed in the curriculum document, have students complete these *Practice* questions: Understanding Concepts: 4; Application: 6; Problem Solving: 8; Communication: *Reflect*

Calculator Skills

Tina bought 6 packages kers for her Each package 4.95. The cashier charged 15% tax. Tina left the store with $13.42. How much money did Tina start with?

$47.58

8. **Assessment Focus**

   Look at the integers in the box.

	+4	
−8		−5
	+9	
0		+8

   a) Which integers are:
      i) greater than 0? +4, +8, +9
      ii) between −3 and +3? 0
      iii) greater than −10 and less than −5? −8
      iv) less than +1? 0, −5, −8

   b) What other questions can you ask about these integers? Write down your questions and answer them.

9. On January 18, 2002, the temperature in Charlottetown, Prince Edward Island, was −21°C; in Sydney, Nova Scotia, it was −23°C; in Point Lepreau, New Brunswick, it was −22°C. Which place was the warmest? Coldest? How do you know? Charlottetown, P.E.I.; Sydney, Nova Scotia

Take It Further

10. a) Draw a number line from −6 to +6. Find the integer that is:
       i) halfway between −6 and +6 0
       ii) halfway between −5 and +1 −2
       iii) halfway between −5 and −1 −3
       iv) 1 less than +3 +2
       v) 3 more than −4 −1
       vi) 4 less than −1 −5

    b) Explain why the answer for part a, ii is different from the answer for part a, iii.

    c) −3 is halfway between two integers on a number line. Draw a number line and mark the two integers on it.

11. One day, the temperature in Wabash Lake, Newfoundland, was −41°C; in Pelly Bay, Nunavut, it was −51°C. The temperature in Churchill, Manitoba, was halfway between these temperatures. What was the temperature in Churchill? −46°C

12. Copy each pattern. Extend the pattern for 3 more terms. Describe each pattern in words.
    a) −5, −3, −1, +1, ... +3, +5, +7
    b) +7, +4, +1, −2, ... −5, −8, −11
    c) −20, −18, −16, −14, ... −12, −10, −8
    d) −5, −10, −15, −20, ... −25, −30, −35

Reflect

When two integers have different signs, how can you tell which is greater? When two integers have the same sign, how can you tell which is greater?

12. a) Start at −5. Move 2 spaces right on a number line each time.
    b) Start at +7. Move 3 spaces left on a number line each time.
    c) Start at −20. Move 2 spaces right on a number line each time.
    d) Start at −5. Move 5 spaces left on a number line each time.

REFLECT: When two integers have different signs, the positive integer is always greater: +4 > −2.
When two integers have the same sign, there are two cases.
If both integers are positive, the one with the larger size (number part) is greater: +5 > +3.
If both integers are negative, the one with the smaller size (number part) is greater: −5 > −8.
Compare the numbers on a number line. A number to the right is always greater than a number to the left.

Calculator Skills

Before-tax cost of 6 markers: 6 × 4.95 = $29.70
Tax: 29.70 × 0.15 = $4.46
Total: $29.70 + $4.46 = $34.16
Or: Total = $29.70 × 1.15 = $34.16
Amount Tina started with is $13.42 + $34.16 = $47.58.

ASSESSMENT FOR LEARNING

What to Look For	What to Do
Understanding concepts ✔ Students recognize that greater numbers are to the right of lesser numbers on a number line. ***Applying procedures*** ✔ Students can mark positive and negative integers on a number line. ✔ Students can order integers. ***Problem solving*** ✔ Students can choose appropriate strategies to solve ordering integer problems.	***Extra Support:*** Have students turn a piece of paper sideways and sketch a number line that includes more numbers than those on *Number Lines* (Master 9.15). These sketches do not have to be accurate—they are models. Students can use Step-by-Step 2 (Master 9.8) to complete question 8. ***Extra Practice:*** Have students use weather reports from newspapers to order the temperatures from greatest to least for places in Canada, or around the world, where the temperatures are above and below zero. Students can complete Extra Practice 2 (Master 9.19).

Recording and Reporting
Master 9.2 Ongoing Observations: Integers

Representing Integers

SECTION ORGANIZER — 80–100 min

Curriculum Focus: Use coloured tiles to represent integers. (7m12, 7m24, 7m25)

Teacher Materials
- yellow and red tiles for the overhead projector

Student Materials
- yellow and red coloured tiles or counters
- paper bags or envelopes

Optional
- yellow and red markers or coloured pencils
- Step-by-Step 3 (Master 9.9)
- Extra Practice 3 (Master 9.20)

Vocabulary: zero pair

Assessment: Master 9.2 Ongoing Observations: Integers

Key Math Learnings

1. Coloured tiles can be used to represent integers.
2. A zero pair is one tile representing +1 and one tile representing −1.

Mental Math

Add 3 h to 7:00 a.m. to get 10:00 a.m. Add 41 min to 45 min to get 86 min or 1 h and 26 min. Add 10:00 a.m. to 1 h 26 min to get 11:26 a.m.

Math Link

Have a student who plays golf discuss the scoring in golf and demonstrate how it is done for several holes.

9.3 Representing Integers

Focus Use coloured tiles to represent

We can use coloured tiles to represent integers.

One yellow tile can represent +1.

One red tile can represent −1.

A red tile and a yellow tile combine to model 0: −1, +1 — We call this a **zero pair.**

Explore

Work with a partner.
You will need coloured tiles.
How many different ways can you use coloured tiles to model each number?

➢ 0, +1, +2, +3, +4
➢ −1, −3, −5, −6

Draw a picture to show the tiles you used for each way you foun

Reflect & Share

Compare your models with those of another pair of classmates.
Look at all the models that represent one integer.
How do you know that all the models represent that integer?

Connect

We can model any integer in many ways.

Each set of tiles below models +5.

Each pair of 1 yellow tile and 1 red tile makes a zero pair. The pair models 0.

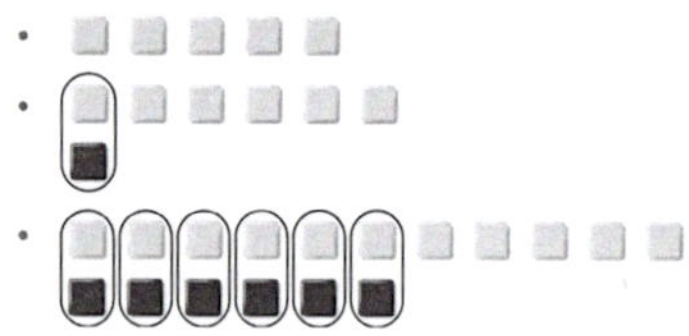

334 UNIT 9: Integers

BEFORE — Get Started

Ask students:

- How can tiles be used to represent whole numbers?
  (Each tile represents 1 so three tiles would be the number 3.)

Show students how two colours of tiles can model positive and negative integers. Place three yellow tiles on the overhead projector.

- What integer does this represent? (*+3*)

Place three red tiles on the overhead projector.

- What integer does this represent? (*–3*)

Place two red tiles above the three yellow tiles so two zero pairs are formed. Review **zero pair.**

- What integer does this represent? (*+1*) How do you know?
  (Two red tiles and two yellow tiles form a zero pair, so 1 yellow tile is left.)

Present *Explore.* If you do not have coloured tiles or counters, make squares from coloured paper or cardstock.

DURING — Explore

Ongoing Assessment: Observe and Listen

As students work, ask questions, such as:

- Is there only one way to model each integer? (*No*) Why?
  (Any integer can be modelled with the correct number and colour of tiles for the integer, plus any number of zero pairs.)
- How can you tell if the model represents a positive or a negative integer?
  (If there are more yellow tiles than red tiles, the integer is positive. If there are more red tiles than yellow tiles, the integer is negative.)

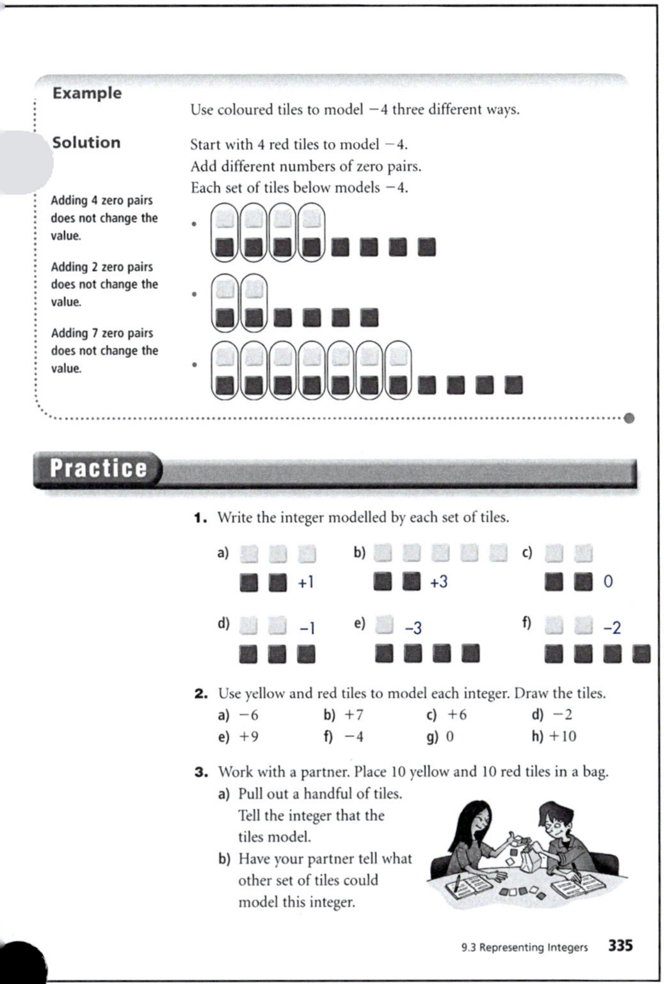
Example

Use coloured tiles to model -4 three different ways.

Solution

Start with 4 red tiles to model -4.
Add different numbers of zero pairs.
Each set of tiles below models -4.

Adding 4 zero pairs does not change the value.

Adding 2 zero pairs does not change the value.

Adding 7 zero pairs does not change the value.

Practice

1. Write the integer modelled by each set of tiles.
   a) +1 b) +3 c) 0
   d) −1 e) −3 f) −2

2. Use yellow and red tiles to model each integer. Draw the tiles.
   a) −6 b) +7 c) +6 d) −2
   e) +9 f) −4 g) 0 h) +10

3. Work with a partner. Place 10 yellow and 10 red tiles in a bag.
   a) Pull out a handful of tiles. Tell the integer that the tiles model.
   b) Have your partner tell what other set of tiles could model this integer.

9.3 Representing Integers 335

REACHING ALL LEARNERS

Alternative Explore

Materials: 1-cm grid paper, yellow and red markers or pencil crayons

Students colour in squares on grid paper to represent different ways to model the integers in *Explore*.

Early Finishers

Have students model an integer for their partner. The partner identifies the integer, then makes another model of it. Students then reverse roles.

Common Misconceptions

➤Students are confused by the many ways to model an integer.

How to Help: Have students begin by using tiles of only one colour to model each integer, then add one pair of red and yellow tiles each time to show other models for the same integer.

Sample Answers

2. a) Y
RRRRRRR

b) YYYYYYYYY
RR

c) YYYYYYYYY
RRR

d) Y
RRR

e) YYYYYYYYYYY
RR

f) YYYY
RRRRRRRR

g) YYY
RRR

h) YYYYYYYYYYYY
RR

3. a) If 5 yellow tiles and 2 red tiles are pulled from the bag, this represents +3.

b) Adding a zero pair of yellow and red tiles to have a total of 6 yellow tiles and 3 red tiles would be another model.

AFTER Connect

Invite students to report on their conclusions. Record their results on the board.

The examples in *Connect* show more than one way to represent 2 different integers. Ensure students recognize that adding or taking away a pair of red and yellow tiles does not change the integer value that is represented.

Practice

Questions 2, 3, and 4 require coloured tiles. To enhance students' understanding of integers, encourage students to model each integer in question 2 two ways: using one colour of tile and using two colours of tiles.

Students can use coloured pencils to record their work for questions 2 and 4.

Assessment Focus: Question 4

For part a, students should choose any positive or negative integer, rather than 0. Students should recognize there are many ways to model an integer using coloured tiles. They should see patterns in the numbers and types of coloured tiles used to model an integer in different ways. Students should then apply the pattern to model larger and smaller numbers.

Assignment Guidelines

If your students do not have time to complete all the *Practice* questions on pages 335 and 336, these questions provide minimum curriculum coverage: 1, 2, 4, *Reflect*

To assess the 4 Achievement Chart categories listed in the curriculum document, have students complete these *Practice* questions: Understanding Concepts: 1; Application: 3; Problem Solving: 4; Communication: *Reflect*

4. a) I chose −4, so I need 4 red tiles to model it.
b) I add a zero pair of tiles each time. I can do this as many times as I like. So, there is no end to the models that can be made for +4.

Number of yellow tiles	Number of red tiles	Integer modelled
0	4	−4
1	5	−4
2	6	−4
3	7	−4
4	8	−4

c) As the number of yellow tiles increases, the number of red tiles increases by the same amount once the minimum number of coloured tiles is used.
d) For an integer between −90 and +60, find the minimum number of coloured tiles needed to model this integer (no zero pairs), then add zero pairs of coloured tiles to create more models of the integer.

5. a) 8 red tiles are needed to make 8 zero pairs, leaving 2 yellow tiles to model +2.
b) 98 red tiles are needed to make 98 zero pairs, leaving 2 yellow tiles to model +2.

REFLECT: There are many ways to model a given integer. If the integer is positive, select that number of yellow tiles. To make different models, add pairs of red and yellow tiles. If the integer is negative, select that number of red tiles. To make different models, add pairs of red and yellow tiles.

Mental Math

Sarah ran a marathon in 3 h and 41 min. The race started at 7:45 a.m. At what time did Sarah finish?
11:26 a.m.

4. **Assessment Focus**
a) Choose an integer between −9 and +6. Use coloured tiles to model the integer.
b) How many more ways can you find to model the i Create a table to order your work.
c) What patterns can you find in your table?
d) Explain how the patterns in your table can help you model an integer between −90 and +60.

5. a) Suppose you have 10 yellow tiles. How many red tiles would you need to model +2? 8 How do you know?
b) Suppose you have 100 yellow tiles. How many red tiles would you need to model +2? 98 How do you know?

Math Link

Sports
In golf, a hole is given a value called **par**.
Par is the number of strokes a good golfer takes to reach the hole.
A score of +2 means a golfer took 2 strokes more than par, or 2 strokes over par.
A score of −1 means a golfer took 1 stroke fewer than par, or 1 stroke under par.
Some scores have special names.
A score of +1 is a bogey.
A score of −1 is a birdie.
A score of −2 is an eagle.
In a golf tournament, the golfer with the fewest strokes wins the game.

Reflect

Explain how it is possible to use different sets of red and yellow ti to model the same integer.

336 UNIT 9: Integers

ASSESSMENT FOR LEARNING

What to Look For	What to Do
Understanding concepts ✔ Students understand that the combination of a yellow tile and a red tile is 0. ✔ Students understand there are many ways to model a given integer. ***Applying procedures*** ✔ Students can model a given integer one or more ways. ***Communicating*** ✔ Students can explain why a given set of tiles models a particular integer.	***Extra Support:*** Give students a set of tiles and ask them to write the integer that is modelled. Have students add pairs of red and yellow tiles to the set and write the integer that is represented. Students can use Step-by-Step 3 (Master 9.9) to complete question 4. ***Extra Practice:*** Give students 5 yellow and 5 red tiles. Have students use 1 or more tiles each time to find all the possible integers that can be modelled by these tiles. Students can complete Extra Practice 3 (Master 9.20). ***Extension:*** For question 3, ask students which integer is modelled by the tiles still in the bag. Ask what relationship exists between the tiles in the bag, and the tiles pulled out.

Recording and Reporting
Master 9.2 Ongoing Observations: Integers

9.4 Adding Integers with Tiles

Focus Use coloured tiles to add integers.

Recall that when you add two numbers, such as 5 + 3, you combine 5 counters with 3 counters to obtain 8 counters.

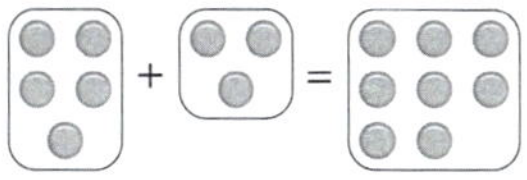

You can add two integers in a similar way.
You know that +1 and −1 combine to make a zero pair.
We can combine coloured tiles to add integers.

Explore

Work with a partner.
You will need coloured tiles.

- Choose two different positive integers.
  Add the integers.
  Draw a picture of the tiles you used.
  Write the addition equation.
- Repeat the activity for a positive integer and a negative integer.
- Repeat the activity for two different negative integers.

Reflect & Share

Share your equations with another pair of classmates.
How did you use the tiles to find a sum of integers?
How can you predict the sign of the sum?

Connect

- To add two positive integers: (+5) + (+4)
  Model each integer with tiles.

+5:
+4:

9.4 Adding Integers with Tiles 337

Adding Integers with Tiles

SECTION ORGANIZER (80–100 min)

Curriculum Focus: Use coloured tiles to add integers. (7m21, 7m22, 7m25)

Teacher Materials

- yellow and red tiles for the overhead projector

Student Materials

- red and yellow coloured tiles

Optional

- Step-by-Step 4 (Master 9.10)
- Extra Practice 4 (Master 9.21)

Assessment: Master 9.2 Ongoing Observations: Integers

Key Math Learnings

1. Coloured tiles can be used to add integers.
2. The concept of zero pairs is used to add integers.

BEFORE Get Started

Place 5 yellow tiles and 2 red tiles on the overhead projector.

Ask:

- What integer is modelled by the yellow tiles? (+5)
- What integer is modelled by the red tiles? (–2)
- What integer is modelled by the red and yellow tiles? (+3)

Present *Explore*.

DURING Explore

Ongoing Assessment: Observe and Listen

As students work, ask questions, such as:

- Which two positive integers did you choose?
  (*+4 and +5*)
- How did you add them?
  (*I put 4 yellow tiles and 5 yellow tiles together, then added the tiles to get 9 yellow tiles, which is +9.*)
- What addition equation did you write?
  (*I wrote +4 plus +5 = +9.*)
- Which positive and negative integer did you choose?
  (*+6 and –9*)
- How did you add them?
  (*I put 6 yellow tiles and 9 red tiles together. I removed 6 zero pairs by counting 6 yellow tiles and 6 red tiles. That left 3 red tiles, which is –3.*)

REACHING ALL LEARNERS

Early Finishers

Have students use question 6 as a model to describe situations that the sums in questions 4 and 5 represent; such as temperature changes, earning and spending money, and so on.

Common Misconceptions

➤ Students do not group all possible pairs of tiles that form zero pairs.

How to Help: Help students understand that after all zero pairs are combined, tiles of only 1 colour should remain. If both red and yellow tiles are left, more zero pairs can be made.

➤ Students add integers incorrectly when coloured tiles are not used.

How to Help: Encourage students to use tiles for all questions until the concepts have been reinforced.

Making Connections

A *Math Link* in Section 9.3 described scoring in golf. The total score is the sum of the scores on all holes. Have students who are golfers share a set of scores for the class to add.

Combine the tiles. There are 9 yellow tiles.
They model +9.
So, (+5) + (+4) = +9

This is an addition equation.

➢ To add a negative integer and a positive integer: (−6)
Model each integer with tiles. Circle zero pairs.

There are 6 zero pairs.
There are 3 yellow tiles left.
They model +3.
So, (−6) + (+9) = +3

➢ To add two negative integers: (−3) + (−7)
Model each integer with tiles.

Combine the tiles. There are 10 red tiles.
They model −10.
So, (−3) + (−7) = −10

Example

Add. (+6) + (−5) + (−4)

Solution

(+6) + (−5) + (−4)
Model each integer with tiles.
Circle zero pairs.

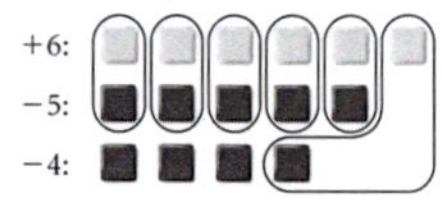

There are 3 red tiles left.
They model −3.
So, (+6) + (−5) + (−4) = −3

338 UNIT 9: Integers

- What addition equation did you write?
  (*I wrote +6 plus −9 = −3.*)
- What was your addition equation for the two negative integers?
  (*−7 plus −4 = −11*)
- How could you tell if the sum would be a positive or a negative integer each time?
  (*When I add two positive integers, the sum is always positive. When I add two negative integers, the sum is always negative. When I add two integers with different signs, the sign of the sum is the sign that matches the greater number of tiles.*)

AFTER Connect

Invite students to share the strategies they used to add integers. Ask students which strategies work best and why. Have students formulate a general rule for predicting the sign of a sum.

Use the examples in *Connect* to show students how to write an integer in brackets when it is part of an addition statement or equation. Have students say an equation, such as (−6) + (+9) = +3, as "negative 6 plus positive 9 equals positive 3," so they differentiate between the + that means *positive* and the + that means *add*.

Practice

Use coloured tiles.

1. What sum does each set of tiles model?
Write the addition equation.
a) (+4) + (−2) = +2 b) (+2) + (−3) = −1
c) (−4) + (−2) = −6 d) (+6) + (−3) = +3
e) (+1) + (−4) = −3 f) (+3) + (+2) = +5

2. What sum does each set of tiles model?
How do you know you are correct?
a) 3 yellow tiles and 2 red tiles +1
b) 3 yellow tiles and 4 red tiles −1
c) 2 red tiles and 2 yellow tiles 0

3. Use coloured tiles to represent each sum. Find each sum.
Sketch the tiles you used.
a) (+2) + (−2) = 0 b) (−4) + (+4) = 0 c) (+5) + (−5) = 0

4. Add. Sketch coloured tiles to show how you did it.
a) (+2) + (+3) = +5 b) (−3) + (+4) = +1 c) (−4) + (−1) = −5
d) (+1) + (−1) = 0 e) (−3) + (−4) = −7 f) (+5) + (−2) = +3

5. Add.
a) (+4) + (+3) = +7 b) (−7) + (+5) = −2 c) (−4) + (−5) = −9
d) (+8) + (−1) = +7 e) (−10) + (−6) = −16 f) (+4) + (−13) = −9

6. Represent each sentence with integers, then find each sum.
a) The temperature is −3°C and rises 4 degrees Celsius. (−3) + (+4) = +1
b) Ravinder earned $5 and spent $3. (+5) + (−3) = +2

7. Write 3 integer addition problems.
Trade problems with a classmate.
Solve your classmate's problems with coloured tiles.

9.4 Adding Integers with Tiles 339

Number Strategies

Students could copy each diagram onto a 4 by 4 square grid.
$\frac{1}{16}$ of the first and second squares are shaded.
About $\frac{1}{8}$ of the third square is shaded.

Assignment Guidelines

If your students do not have time to complete all the *Practice* questions on pages 339 and 340, these questions provide minimum curriculum coverage: 1, 4, 6, 10, 11, *Reflect*
To assess the 4 Achievement Chart categories listed in the curriculum document, have students complete these *Practice* questions: Understanding Concepts: 4; Application: 6; Communication: 10; Problem Solving: 11

Sample Answers

2. a) Two yellow tiles and two red tiles form zero pairs. One yellow tile is left, so the sum is +1.
b) Three yellow tiles and three red tiles form zero pairs. One red tile is left, so the sum is −1.
c) Two yellow tiles and two red tiles form zero pairs. No tiles are left, so the sum is 0.

3. a) Y Y / R R b) Y Y Y Y / R R R R c) Y Y Y Y Y / R R R R R

4. a) Y Y / Y Y Y b) R R R / Y Y Y Y c) R R R R / R
d) Y / R e) R R R / R R R R f) Y Y Y Y Y / R R

(Answers continue below.)

Practice

Have coloured tiles available for all questions. For question 6, remind students that earnings are represented by positive integers and expenditures are represented by negative integers.

Assessment Focus: Question 10

Students should notice that the order in which integers are added does not affect the sum. When the integers in a sum are changed to their opposites, the second sum is the opposite of the first sum.

(Sample Answers, continued)

8. a) Y YY YYY b) YY YYY / R
c) RRR R R d) YYYY Y / RRR
e) RRRR RR / Y f) RRRRR RRR RR

10. a) Three yellow tiles and 7 red tiles make 3 zero pairs, with 4 red tiles left.
So, (+3) + (−7) = −4
Y Y Y / R R R R R R R
b) The order in which the integers are added does not change the number of zero pairs, so the sum is the same.
R R R R R R R / Y Y Y
c) (−3) + (+7) = +4; each integer has been replaced by its opposite, so the sum is also replaced by its opposite.
R R R / Y Y Y Y Y Y Y

11. Calculate the sum of the integers in the diagonal to get the magic sum, then fill in rows, columns, or diagonals, where two integers are known, and find the third number needed to get the magic sum.

13. I used guess and check. I put −1, −2, and −3 at the vertices. Then I put −6 (the least integer) between the 2 greatest integers (−1, −2), then I put −4 (the greatest integer) between the two lesser integers (−2, −3), and −5 went in the remaining space.

REFLECT: Model each integer with yellow tiles if they are positive integers (and red tiles if they are negative integers). Add how many tiles altogether. That is the sum.
Model the positive integer with yellow tiles and the negative integer with red tiles. Combine red and yellow tiles to get zero pairs. The tiles that are left represent the sum. If the tiles are red, the sum is negative. If the tiles are yellow, the sum is positive.

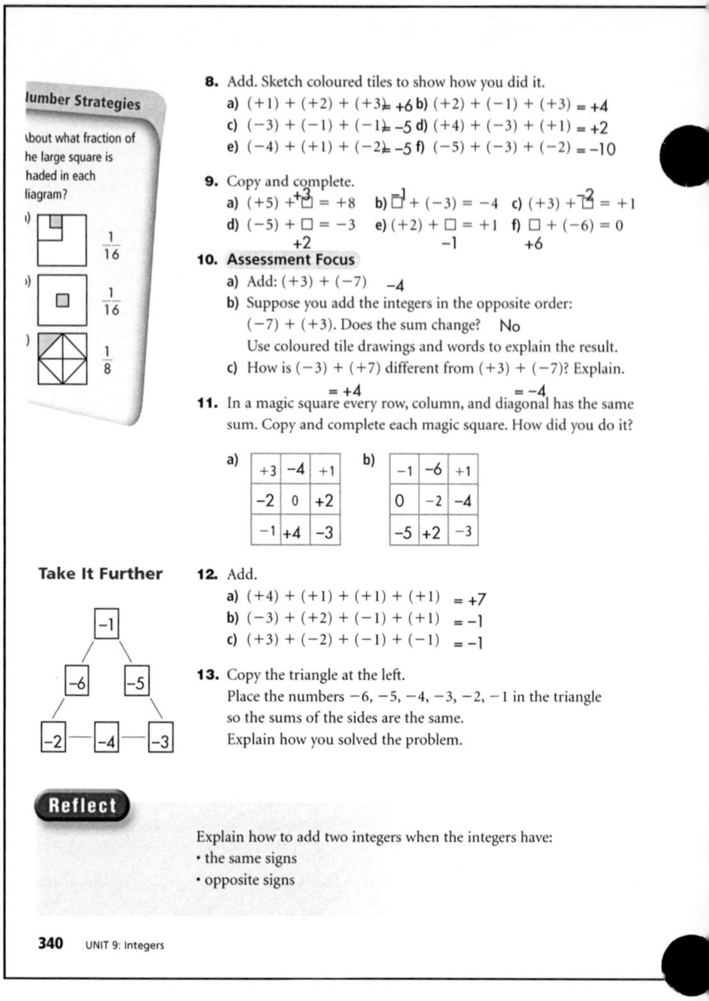

Number Strategies

About what fraction of the large square is shaded in each diagram?

a) $\frac{1}{16}$

b) $\frac{1}{16}$

c) $\frac{1}{8}$

8. Add. Sketch coloured tiles to show how you did it.
a) $(+1) + (+2) + (+3) = +6$
b) $(+2) + (-1) + (+3) = +4$
c) $(-3) + (-1) + (-1) = -5$
d) $(+4) + (-3) + (+1) = +2$
e) $(-4) + (+1) + (-2) = -5$
f) $(-5) + (-3) + (-2) = -10$

9. Copy and complete.
a) $(+5) + \square = +8$ (+3)
b) $\square + (-3) = -4$ (−1)
c) $(+3) + \square = +1$ (−2)
d) $(-5) + \square = -3$ (+2)
e) $(+2) + \square = +1$ (−1)
f) $\square + (-6) = 0$ (+6)

10. **Assessment Focus**
a) Add: $(+3) + (-7)$ −4
b) Suppose you add the integers in the opposite order: $(-7) + (+3)$. Does the sum change? No
Use coloured tile drawings and words to explain the result.
c) How is $(-3) + (+7)$ different from $(+3) + (-7)$? Explain.
= +4 = −4

11. In a magic square every row, column, and diagonal has the same sum. Copy and complete each magic square. How did you do it?

a)

+3	−4	+1
−2	0	+2
−1	+4	−3

b)

−1	−6	+1
0	−2	−4
−5	+2	−3

Take It Further

12. Add.
a) $(+4) + (+1) + (+1) + (+1)$ = +7
b) $(-3) + (+2) + (-1) + (+1)$ = −1
c) $(+3) + (-2) + (-1) + (-1)$ = −1

13. Copy the triangle at the left.
Place the numbers −6, −5, −4, −3, −2, −1 in the triangle so the sums of the sides are the same.
Explain how you solved the problem.

Reflect

Explain how to add two integers when the integers have:
• the same signs
• opposite signs

340 UNIT 9: Integers

ASSESSMENT FOR LEARNING

What to Look For	What to Do
Understanding concepts ✔ Students understand that integers can be added by combining two colours of tiles.	***Extra Support:*** Have students use coloured tiles to complete all questions. Students can use Step-by-Step 4 (Master 9.10) to complete question 10.
Applying procedures ✔ Students can add integers with coloured tiles.	***Extra Practice:*** Have students find different pairs of integers whose sum is a given integer. Students can complete Extra Practice 4 (Master 9.21).
Communicating ✔ Students can write an addition equation to represent the sum of integers.	***Extension:*** Have students create their own magic squares or triangles like those in questions 11 and 13.

Recording and Reporting
Master 9.2 Ongoing Observations: Integers

Adding Integers

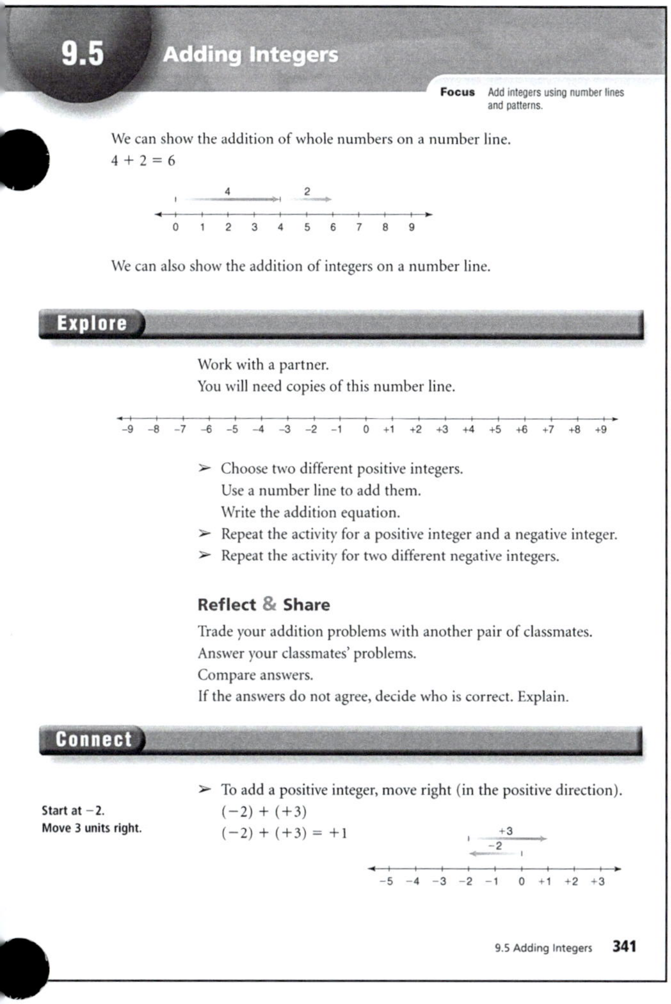

9.5 Adding Integers

Focus Add integers using number lines and patterns.

We can show the addition of whole numbers on a number line.
4 + 2 = 6

We can also show the addition of integers on a number line.

Explore

Work with a partner.
You will need copies of this number line.

➢ Choose two different positive integers.
Use a number line to add them.
Write the addition equation.
➢ Repeat the activity for a positive integer and a negative integer.
➢ Repeat the activity for two different negative integers.

Reflect & Share

Trade your addition problems with another pair of classmates.
Answer your classmates' problems.
Compare answers.
If the answers do not agree, decide who is correct. Explain.

Connect

➢ To add a positive integer, move right (in the positive direction).
(−2) + (+3)
(−2) + (+3) = +1

Start at −2.
Move 3 units right.

9.5 Adding Integers 341

SECTION ORGANIZER (80–100 min)

Curriculum Focus: Add integers using number lines and patterns. (7m21, 7m22, 7m25)

Teacher Materials
- horizontal and vertical number lines on an overhead transparency or board
- coloured tiles

Student Materials
- number lines (Master 9.15)

Optional
- coloured tiles
- Step-by-Step 5 (Master 9.11)
- Extra Practice 5 (Master 9.22)

Assessment: Master 9.2 Ongoing Observations: Integers

Key Math Learnings

1. A number line can be used to add integers.
2. An arrow to the right represents a positive integer. An arrow to the left represents a negative integer.
3. The sum of opposite integers is zero.

BEFORE Get Started

Have students look at the number line at the top of page 341.

Ask:
- How do you know where to put the arrows when adding whole numbers on a number line?
(*Always start at 0. Draw an arrow from 0 to 4 then draw an arrow 2 units long from 4 to 6.*)

Present *Explore*. Provide students with copies of *Number Lines* (Master 9.15).

DURING Explore

Ongoing Assessment: Observe and Listen

As students work, ask questions, such as:
- How can you show −3 on a number line?
(*Draw an arrow to the left from 0 to −3.*)
- How can you use a number line to find (+5) + (−3)?
(*Draw an arrow from 0 to the right 5 units, then draw an arrow from 5 to the left 3 units. The result is +2.*)
- Does the result match what you know using coloured tiles?
(*Yes, 5 yellow tiles plus 3 red tiles gives 3 zero pairs with 2 yellow tiles remaining, which represent +2.*)
- How can you use a number line to find (−2) + (−3)? (*Draw an arrow to the left from 0 to −2, then draw an arrow from −2 to the left 3 units. The result is −5.*)

REACHING ALL LEARNERS

Early Finishers

Have students create addition statements using three integers. They should try different combinations of positive and negative integers.

Common Misconceptions

➤Students incorrectly illustrate addition on a number line.

How to Help: Make sure students draw an arrow on a number line with a head and a tail, so that the tail of the second integer is placed at the head of the first integer and points in the direction of its sign.

Math Note

Commutative Property: The addition of integers is commutative; that is, the order of the integers in the addition statement can change, and the sum is the same; for example, (+5) + (−3) = (−3) + (+5) = +2. The subtraction of integers is *not* commutative.

Start at −2.
Move 3 units left.

➢ To add a negative integer, move left (in the negative direction).

(−2) + (−3)

(−2) + (−3) = −5

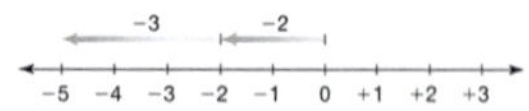

We can use patterning to add integers.

Example 1

Add. (+5) + (−2)

Solution

(+5) + (−2)
Think of a pattern. Start with facts you know.
Continue the pattern until you reach the fact you want.
(+5) + (+2) = +7
(+5) + (+1) = +6
(+5) + (0) = +5
(+5) + (−1) = +4
(+5) + (−2) = +3

Example 2

Sandra and Joe buy and sell CDs at a flea market.
In August, they bought 14 CDs for $5 each.
They sold 6 CDs for $9 each.

a) Did Sandra and Joe make money or lose money in August?
b) How much money did they make or lose?

Solution

Expenses: 14 × $5 = $70 Income: 6 × $9 = $54

a) Since the expenses are greater than the income, Sandra and Joe lost money in August.
b) Draw a number line.

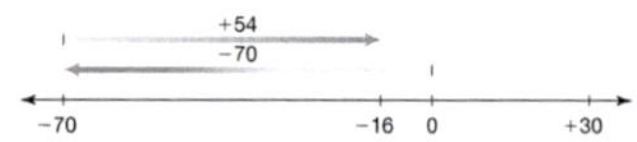

(−70) + (+54) = −16

In August, Sandra and Joe lost $16.

342 UNIT 9: Integers

- Does the result match what you know using coloured tiles?
  (*Yes, 2 red tiles plus 3 red tiles is 5 red tiles, which represent −5.*)

AFTER Connect

Invite students to share their examples and observations about adding integers on a number line. Students should understand that integers with the same sign have arrows that continue in the same direction and integers with opposite signs have arrows that go in opposite directions. Review the examples in *Connect*.

Example 1 shows a pattern strategy for adding integers with opposite signs. To use this strategy, show how to begin with the sum of two integers with the same sign, then add +1 or −1 each time. An alternative starting equation could be (−5) + (−2) = −7, but there are 10 further equations before reaching (+5) + (−2) = +3.

For *Example 2*, remind students that expenses are represented by a negative integer and income is represented by a positive integer. Ask students how this number line is different from other lines in this section. This line has been drawn to scale, but there is no room to show every number. Students need to know that the difference between 70 and 54 is 16.

It may help some students if you draw a number line with arrows representing an addition expression, and ask students to write the expression, then the sum.

As a further exercise, have students represent the letters in the alphabet on a number line, with A = −13, B = −12, and so on. Z is +12. Make up words so that the sum of the letters is 0. Alternatively, have students find the integer total of the letters of their names.

Practice

Use a number line when it helps.

1. Add.

a) (+1) + (+3) = +4 b) (−1) + (+3) = +2
c) (−3) + (+1) = −2 d) (−1) + (−3) = −4

2. Find each sum. Use a pattern when you can.

a) (+4) + (+2) = +6 b) (+5) + (−3) = +2
c) (−4) + (−2) = −6 d) (−8) + (+2) = −6

3. a) Reverse the order of the integers in question 2, then add. +6, +2, −6, −6
b) Compare your answers to the answers in question 2.
What do you notice? The answers are the same.
c) Make a general statement about your observations.
The order of addition of integers does not matter.

4. Look at these thermometers. Find each temperature after:

a) it falls 4°C b) it falls 7°C c) it rises 6°C

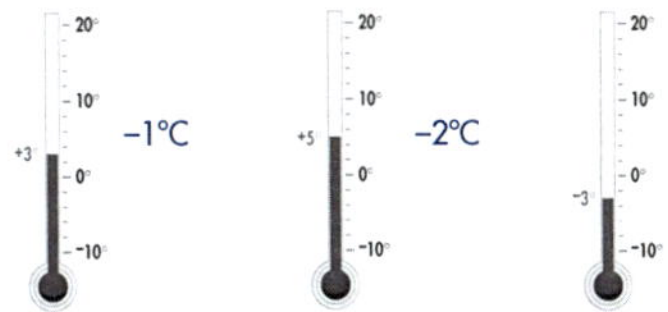

5. a) The temperature rises 7°C, then drops 2°C.
What is the overall change in temperature? +5°C
b) Adrian loses $4, then earns $8.
Did Adrian gain or lose overall? Gain
c) The value of a stock went up $3, then down $2.
What was the final change in the value of the stock? +$1

6. Add.

a) (+12) + (+3) = +15 b) (+13) + (−7) = +6
c) (−5) + (−10) = −15 d) (−5) + (+8) = +3
e) (−8) + (−7) = −15 f) (+4) + (−10) = −6

Mental Math

Students may use these strategies:

12 × 4 × 50 = 12 × 200 = 12 × 2 × 100 = 2400
25 × 10 × 10 = 25 × 100 = 2500
24 × 100 = 2400
99 × 20 + 420 = 100 × 20 − 1 × 20 + 420
= 2000 − 20 + 420 = 2400
90 × 30 − 300 = 2700 − 300 = 2400

All the answers are 2400 except 25 × 10 × 10 = 2500, so it does not belong.

Assignment Guidelines

If your students do not have time to complete all the *Practice* questions on pages 343 and 344, these questions provide minimum curriculum coverage:
1, 2, 6, 8, 10, *Reflect*
To assess the 4 Achievement Chart categories listed in the curriculum document, have students complete these *Practice* questions:
Understanding Concepts: 6;
Problem Solving: 8;
Application: 10;
Communication: *Reflect*

Practice

Provide students with copies of *Number Lines* (Master 9.15).

Assessment Focus: Question 8

Students should refer to the length and the direction of the arrows on a number line that represent the integers in their explanations.

Sample Answers

2. d) Known fact: (−8) + (−2) = −10
(−8) + (−1) = −9
(−8) + 0 = −8
(−8) + (+1) = −7
(−8) + (+2) = −6
Keep increasing the second integer and sum until you reach the original question and its sum.

8. a) Opposite integers are arrows with the same length, but opposite direction. So, if we begin at 0 and add opposite integers, we shall always end up at zero.
(−4) + (+4) = 0

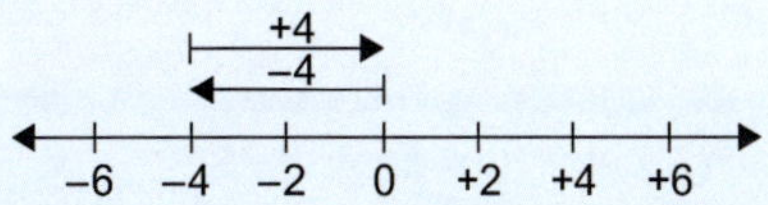

b) Positive integers are arrows to the right. So, if we begin at 0, we shall always end up with a positive integer.
(+4) + (+3) = +7

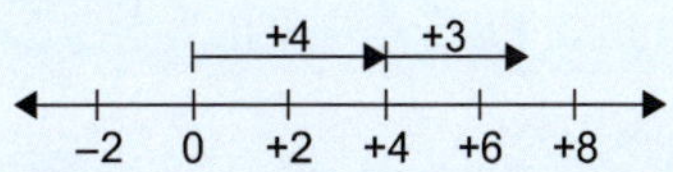

c) Negative integers are arrows to the left. So, if we begin at 0, we shall always end up with a negative integer.
(−3) + (−5) = −8

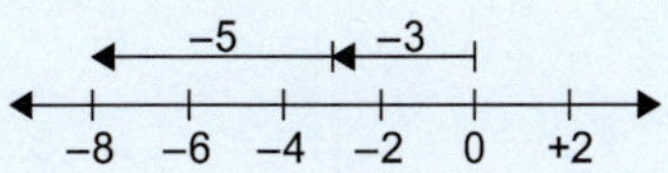

d) The sum of a positive integer and a negative integer is: positive, when the positive integer has a longer arrow than the negative integer; and negative when the negative integer has a longer arrow than the positive integer.

(+3) + (−5) = −2

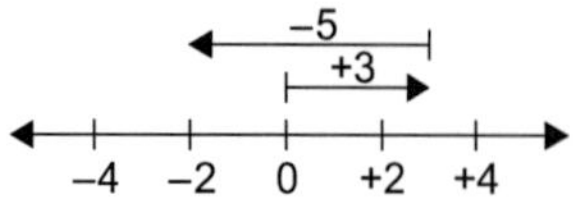

(−3) + (+5) = +2

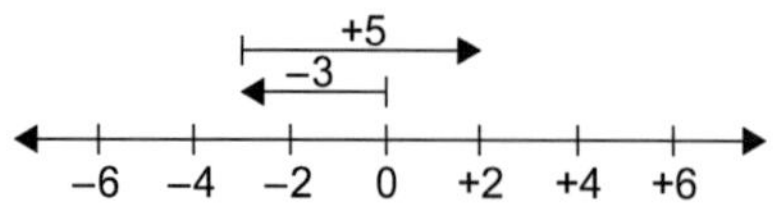

10. (+23) + (−7) + (+12) = +28: I added the original temperature to the temperature change to get +28°C. I used a vertical number line.

REFLECT: I prefer to use coloured tiles to add integers. It is easy to pair tiles that model 0, then count the remaining tiles to find the sum, remembering that if red tiles remain, the sum is a negative integer, and if yellow tiles remain, the sum is a positive integer.

Mental Math

Which expression does not belong? Why?

12 × 4 × 50
25 × 10 × 10
24 × 100
99 × 20 + 420
80 × 30
90 × 30 − 300

7. Add.

a) (+30) + (+10) = +40 b) (+20) + (−10) = +10
c) (−35) + (−5) = −40 d) (−15) + (+18) = +3
e) (−82) + (+79) = −3 f) (−58) + (−22) = −80

8. **Assessment Focus** Use an example to explain why each statement is true.
Use a number line to support your explanations.

a) The sum of two opposite integers is 0.
b) The sum of two positive integers is always positive.
c) The sum of two negative integers is always negative.
d) The sum of a negative integer and a positive integer is sometimes negative and sometimes positive.

9. Add.

a) (+4) + (+3) + (−6) = +1 b) (−2) + (−4) + (+1) = −5
c) (−5) + (+3) + (−4) = −6 d) (+6) + (−8) + (+2) = 0
e) (+12) + (−3) + (−2) = +7 f) (−5) + (−8) + (−10) = −23

10. The temperature in North Bay is 23°C.
The temperature falls 7°C, then rises 12°C.
What is the final temperature? +28°C
How did you find out?
Which model did you use?

11. Susanna earned $24, spent $7, earned $12 more, and spent $10 more. Express her earnings and spendings using integers.
How much money does Susanna have left over from her earnings and spendings? $19

Take It Further

12. Copy and complete.

a) (+10) + □ = +25 (+15) b) (−10) + □ = −25 (−15)
c) (+20) + □ = +15 (−5) d) (−20) + □ = −15 (+5)
e) (+35) + □ = +17 (−18) f) (−35) + □ = −17 (+18)

Reflect

You have used three models to add integers.
Which model do you prefer? Why?

344 UNIT 9: Integers

ASSESSMENT FOR LEARNING

What to Look For

Understanding concepts

✔ Students understand that, on a number line, a positive integer is represented by an arrow to the right, and a negative integer by an arrow to the left.

✔ Students understand that 2 or more arrows, shown head-to-tail on a number line, represent integer addition.

Applying procedures

✔ Students can use a number line to add integers.

Problem solving

✔ Students choose an appropriate strategy or model to solve an integer addition problem.

What to Do

Extra Support: Have students use coloured tiles to check the additions done with a number line.
Students can use Step-by-Step 5 (Master 9.11) to complete question 8.

Extra Practice: Pairs of students can use positive and negative integer cards to play an addition game. Deal the shuffled cards between the players. They simultaneously turn over their top cards and the first person to state the correct sum wins both cards. The game ends when one person has all the cards. If using a deck of playing cards, black colours are positive and red are negative. Assign values to the face cards.
Students can complete Extra Practice 5 (Master 9.22)

Recording and Reporting

Master 9.2 Ongoing Observations: Integers

SECTION ORGANIZER

Student Materials
- coloured tiles
- number lines (Master 9.15)

Assessment: Masters 9.1 Unit Rubric: Integers, 9.4 Unit Summary: Integers

Mid-Unit Review

LESSON

9.1 **1.** Draw a number line. Show each integer on the number line: +3, −2, −5, 0

2. Use an integer to represent each situation.
a) 12°C below zero −12
b) a golf score of 3 strokes above par +3
c) 10 m above sea level +10
d) a drop of $2 in the price of a stock −2
e) $25 earned +25
f) a mountain elevation of 1500 m +1500

9.2 **3.** Order these integers from least to greatest.
a) +4, −3, −2, +1, −4   −4, −3, −2, +1, +4
b) +18, +50, 0, −50, −17   −50, −17, 0, +18, +50

9.3 **4.** Use red and yellow tiles to model each integer two different ways. Draw the tiles.
a) −5   b) 0
c) +8   d) −1
e) +3   f) −7

9.4 **5.** Use coloured tiles to add. Draw pictures of the tiles you used.
a) (+4) + (−1) = +3
b) (−3) + (−2) = −5
c) (−5) + (+1) = −4
d) (+6) + (+3) = +9
e) (−4) + (−8) = −12
f) (+4) + (+8) = +12

9.5 **6.** Use a number line to add.
a) (+3) + (+2) = +5   b) (−5) + (−1) = −6
c) (−10) + (+8) = −2   d) (+6) + (−5) = +1
e) (−8) + (+8) = 0   f) (−5) + (+12) = +7

7. Use patterns to add.
a) (+6) + (−3) = +3   b) (−2) + (+8) = +6
c) (+5) + (−9) = −4   d) (−4) + (+9) = +5

8. Add.
a) (+4) + (+1) + (−2) = +3
b) (−3) + (−1) + (−4) = −8
c) (−5) + (+1) + (+3) = −1
d) (+6) + (−5) + (−8) = −7

9. a) Puja earned $50, was given $10, and spent $20. How much did Puja then have? $40

b) The temperature starts at +5°C, goes up 2°C, then drops 10°C. What is the final temperature? −3°C
c) The population of a city was 124 000, then it dropped by 4000 people. What was the population then? 120 000

10. a) Add. (+4) + (−5) = −1
b) Find another pair of integers that has the same sum as part a. Do this 3 times. (−4) + (+3), (+2) + (−3), (−7) + (+8)

Mid-Unit Review 345

Sample Solutions

1.

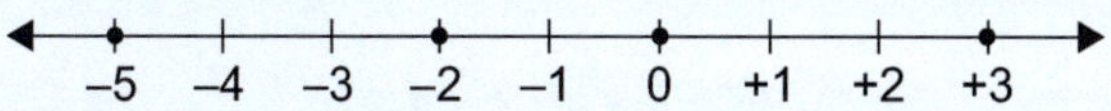

4. a) R R R R R or Y / R R R R R R

b) Y / R or Y Y / R R

c) Y Y Y Y Y Y Y Y or Y Y Y Y Y Y Y Y Y / R

d) R or Y Y / R R R

e) Y Y Y or Y Y Y Y Y / R R

f) R R R R R R R or Y / R R R R R R R R

5. a) Y Y Y Y / R

b) R R R   R R

c) R R R R R / Y

d) Y Y Y Y Y Y   Y Y Y

e) R R R R   R R R R R R R R

f) Y Y Y Y   Y Y Y Y Y Y Y Y

7. a) (+6) + (+2) = +8
(+6) + (+1) = +7
(+6) + 0 = +6
(+6) + (−1) = +5
(+6) + (−2) = +4
(+6) + (−3) = +3

b) (+2) + (+8) = +10
(+1) + (+8) = +9
0 + (+8) = +8
(−1) + (+8) = +7
(−2) + (+8) = +6

c) (−1) + (−9) = −10
0 + (−9) = −9
(+1) + (−9) = −8
(+2) + (−9) = −7
(+3) + (−9) = −6
(+4) + (−9) = −5
(+5) + (−9) = −4

d) (+1) + (+9) = +10
0 + (+9) = +9
(−1) + (+9) = +8
(−2) + (+9) = +7
(−3) + (+9) = +6
(−4) + (+9) = +5

Subtracting Integers with Tiles

SECTION ORGANIZER (80–100 min)

Curriculum Focus: Use coloured tiles to subtract integers. (7m21, 7m25)

Teacher Materials

- yellow and red coloured tiles for the overhead projector

Student Materials

- coloured tiles

Optional

- Step-by-Step 6 (Master 9.12)
- Extra Practice 6 (Master 9.23)

Assessment: Master 9.2 Ongoing Observations: Integers

Key Math Learnings

1. Coloured tiles can be used to subtract integers.
2. Zero pairs may be used to subtract opposite integers.

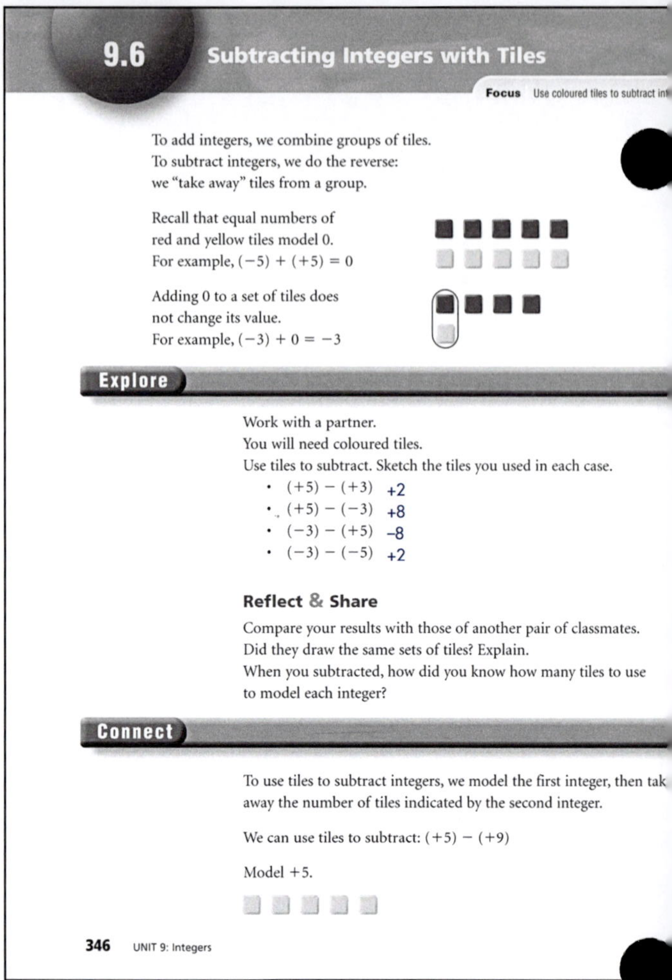

9.6 Subtracting Integers with Tiles

Focus Use coloured tiles to subtract int

To add integers, we combine groups of tiles.
To subtract integers, we do the reverse:
we "take away" tiles from a group.

Recall that equal numbers of red and yellow tiles model 0.
For example, $(-5) + (+5) = 0$

Adding 0 to a set of tiles does not change its value.
For example, $(-3) + 0 = -3$

Explore

Work with a partner.
You will need coloured tiles.
Use tiles to subtract. Sketch the tiles you used in each case.

- $(+5) - (+3)$ +2
- $(+5) - (-3)$ +8
- $(-3) - (+5)$ –8
- $(-3) - (-5)$ +2

Reflect & Share

Compare your results with those of another pair of classmates.
Did they draw the same sets of tiles? Explain.
When you subtracted, how did you know how many tiles to use to model each integer?

Connect

To use tiles to subtract integers, we model the first integer, then tak away the number of tiles indicated by the second integer.

We can use tiles to subtract: $(+5) - (+9)$

Model +5.

346 UNIT 9: Integers

BEFORE Get Started

Use counters to model how to subtract the whole numbers: 7 – 2. Remind students that any integer can be presented many different ways using coloured tiles. Have students suggest different ways to model the integer +5 with coloured tiles. Record these ways on the board or overhead projector. Review the work with zero pairs at the top of page 346.

Present *Explore*. Ensure students understand what they are required to do with coloured tiles.

DURING Explore

Ongoing Assessment: Observe and Listen

As students work, ask questions, such as:

- How can you change the model for the first integer if you don't have enough of one coloured tile to take away the second integer? (*Create a different model that has enough zero pairs to include all the colours needed for the second integer.*)
- How did you subtract: (+5) – (+3)? (*I placed 5 yellow tiles on the desk, then took away 3 of them. That left 2 yellow tiles, so that is +2. So, (+5) – (+3) = +2*)
- Did you subtract –3 the same way? (*No, I started the same way with 5 yellow tiles for +5, but then I needed 3 red tiles to be able to take away –3, so I added 3 zero pairs to +5. Then I had 8 yellow tiles and 3 red tiles. Then I took away the 3 red tiles, so that left 8 yellow tiles, or +8. So, (+5) – (–3) = +8*)

There are not enough tiles to take away +9.
To take away +9, we need 4 more yellow tiles.

We add zero pairs without changing the value.
Add 4 yellow tiles and 4 red tiles. They represent 0.

By adding 0, the integer the tiles represent has not changed.
Now take away the 9 yellow tiles.

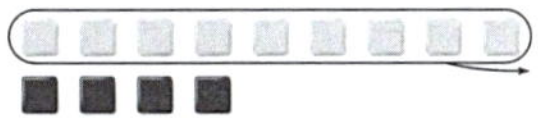

Since 4 red tiles remain, we write: (+5) − (+9) = −4

Example

Use tiles to subtract.
a) (−2) − (−6) b) (−6) − (+2) c) (+2) − (−6)

Solution

a) (−2) − (−6)
Model −2.

There are not enough tiles to take away −6.
To take away −6, we need 4 more red tiles.

We add zero pairs without changing the value.
Add 4 red tiles and 4 yellow tiles.

Now take away 6 red tiles.

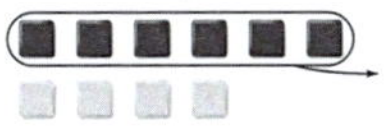

Since 4 yellow tiles remain, we write: (−2) − (−6) = +4

9.6 Subtracting Integers with Tiles **347**

REACHING ALL LEARNERS

Early Finishers

Have students create as many different types of subtraction problems that have a result of −6. Repeat for +8.

Common Misconceptions

➤ Students are unable to determine the number of tiles necessary to solve a subtraction problem.
How to Help: Have students make a list of possible ways to represent the first number in the subtraction problem. Have them decide which model has enough tiles of the correct colour for the subtraction.

➤ Students think that if they subtract opposite integers, the difference is zero.
How to Help: Have students model a problem, such as (+5) − (−5) with coloured tiles, to see that to be able to take away −5, they need 10 yellow tiles and 5 red tiles, so the difference is +10.

➤ In question 10b, students read "Subtract −1," and think it means "Subtract 1."
How to Help: Have students model each number in the magic square before they subtract, and realize that, to be able to subtract −1, they need to take away 1 red tile.

- What did you do to take +5 away from −3?
  (I started with 3 red tiles. I added 5 zero pairs, which meant I had 8 red tiles and 5 yellow tiles. Then I took away the 5 yellow tiles, which left 8 red tiles, which is −8. So, (−3) − (+5) = −8)
- How did you subtract: (−3) − (−5)?
  (At first, I didn't think that I could take away 5 red tiles when I only had 3 red tiles, but then I added 2 zero pairs, which gave me a total of 5 red tiles and 2 yellow tiles. I took away the 5 red tiles, and I had 2 yellow tiles left, which is +2. So, (−3) − (−5) = +2)
- For which subtraction question did you not have to use zero pairs? *((+5) − (+3))*

AFTER Connect

Invite students to share the strategies they used to subtract integers.

This is what you might see:

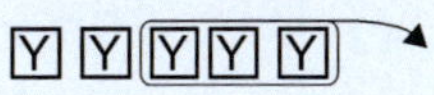

(+5) − (+3) = +2

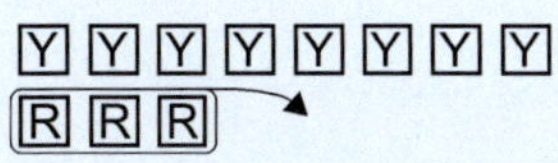

(+5) − (−3) = +8

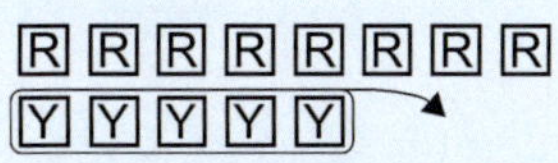

(−3) − (+5) = −8

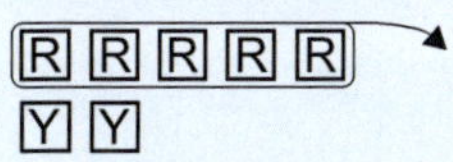

(−3) − (−5) = +2

To summarize ask:

- Think about the integers you used in *Explore*. For what other subtraction problems would we not need to use zero pairs?
  ((−5) − (−3), (+5) − (+5), (−5) − (−5), (−3) − (−3))

Sample Answers

1. a) 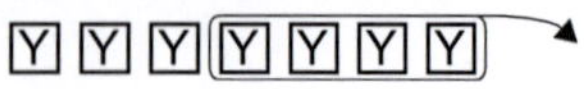

b) 

c) 

d) 

e) 

f) 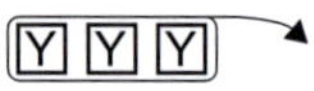

7. **b)** In each case, I use the same integers but take them away in a different order.
   The answers are opposites.
8. I used the results of question 7. When I change the order to subtract integers, the answer is the opposite. So, since (+5) – (–2) = +7, I expect (–2) – (+5) to be –7.
9. I decided to use patterns. I found a problem for each difference, then used a pattern to get the next few problems. I could have continued the pattern forever. So, I could have written as many problems as I wanted.
   a) (+7) – (+5), (+8) – (+6), (+9) – (+7), (+10) – (+8)
   b) (–1) – (+2), (–2) – (+1), (–3) – 0, (–4) – (–1)
   c) (–4) – (–9), (–3) – (–8), (–2) – (–7), (–1) – (–6)
   d) (+4) – (+10), (+3) – (+9), (+2) – (+8), (+1) – (+7)

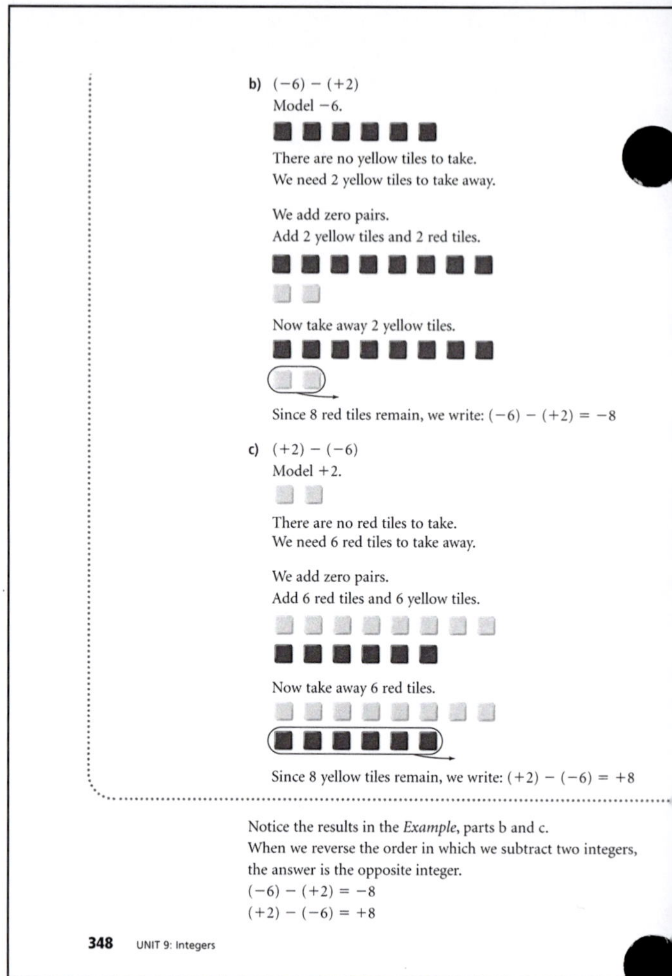
b) (−6) − (+2)
Model −6.

There are no yellow tiles to take.
We need 2 yellow tiles to take away.

We add zero pairs.
Add 2 yellow tiles and 2 red tiles.

Now take away 2 yellow tiles.

Since 8 red tiles remain, we write: (−6) − (+2) = −8

c) (+2) − (−6)
Model +2.

There are no red tiles to take.
We need 6 red tiles to take away.

We add zero pairs.
Add 6 red tiles and 6 yellow tiles.

Now take away 6 red tiles.

Since 8 yellow tiles remain, we write: (+2) − (−6) = +8

Notice the results in the *Example*, parts b and c.
When we reverse the order in which we subtract two integers, the answer is the opposite integer.
(−6) − (+2) = −8
(+2) − (−6) = +8

348 UNIT 9: Integers

- How do you know when you *don't* need to add zero pairs?
  (*When the integers have the same sign, and the integer I take away is represented with fewer tiles than the integer I'm taking it away from.*)
- How do you know when you *do* need to add zero pairs?
  (*When the integers have opposite signs, I always need to add zero pairs. I also have to add zero pairs when both integers are positive, and the integer I take away is greater than the integer I'm taking it from; and when both integers are negative and the integer I take away is less than the integer I'm taking it away from.*)

Have different students model each example in *Connect* on the overhead projector or board.

As an extension, challenge students to solve problems for which coloured tiles would be impractical. For example, solve:

(+98) – (+47) (+51)
(+104) – (–38) (+142)
(–245) – (–126) (–119)
(–894) – (+681) (–1575)

Practice

1. Use tiles to subtract. Draw pictures of the tiles you used.
   a) (+7) − (+4) = +3 b) (−2) − (−2) = 0 c) (−9) − (−6) = −3
   d) (+4) − (+2) = +2 e) (−8) − (−1) = −7 f) (+3) − (+3) = 0
2. Use tiles to subtract.
   a) (−1) − (−4) = +3 b) (+3) − (+8) = −5 c) (−4) − (−11) = +7
   d) (+7) − (+8) = −1 e) (−4) − (−6) = +2 f) (+1) − (+10) = −9
3. Subtract.
   a) (−4) − (−1) = −3 b) (+8) − (+3) = +5 c) (−11) − (−4) = −7
   d) (+8) − (+7) = +1 e) (−6) − (−4) = −2 f) (+10) − (+1) = +9
4. Subtract.
   a) (+4) − (−7) = +11 b) (−2) − (+8) = −10 c) (−9) − (+5) = −14
   d) (+6) − (−8) = +14 e) (−3) − (+6) = −9 f) (−5) − (+7) = −12
5. Subtract.
   a) (+4) − (+5) = −1 b) (−3) − (+5) = −8 c) (−4) − (+3) = −7
   d) (−1) − (−8) = +7 e) (+8) − (−2) = +10 f) (+4) − (−7) = +11
6. Write 3 integer subtraction problems. (+10) − (−13) = +23
   Trade problems with a classmate. (−13) − (−5) = −8
   Solve your classmate's problems. (−5) − (−5) = 0

7. a) Use coloured tiles to subtract each pair of integers.
   i) (+3) − (+1) and (+1) − (+3) +2, −2
   ii) (−3) − (−2) and (−2) − (−3) −1, +1
   b) What do you notice about each pair of problems in part a?
   Signs opposite, size the same.
8. (+5) − (−2) = +7
   Predict the value of (−2) − (+5). = −7
   Explain the reasoning for your choice.
9. **Assessment Focus** Use integers.
   Write a subtraction problem that would give each answer.
   How many problems can you write each time?
   a) +2 b) −3 c) +5 d) −6

9.6 Subtracting Integers with Tiles **349**

10. a)

−4	+1	−6
−5	−3	−1
0	−7	−2

The sum of each row, column, and diagonal is −9, which is 12 less than the original magic sum, so the square is still magic. Since each entry has been reduced by +4, the overall square remains magic.

b)

+1	+6	−1
0	+2	+4
+5	−2	+3

Since each entry has been reduced by −1, the overall square remains magic and the magic number is now +6.

c)

−7	−2	−9
−8	−6	−4
−3	−10	−5

Each entry of the original magic square has been reduced by 7 (subtract +7), so the magic number is now −18.

11. a) Students may use trial and error or patterns to get the solution of +2 and −3.
Try (+5) + (−6) = −1, but (+5) − (−6) = +11. The sum is correct but the difference is +6, which is too great.
Try (+4) + (−5) = −1, but (+4) − (−5) = +9. This is better but needs to have a lesser difference.
Try (+2) + (−3) = −1 and (+2) − (−3) = +5. This is correct.

b) Find two integers with a sum of +2 and a difference of −10.
Answer:
(+6) + (−4) = +2
(−4) − (+6) = −10

(Answers continue below.)

Practice

All questions require coloured tiles. Questions 2 and 3 are the same except the order of the integers has been switched. This demonstrates that subtraction is not commutative—switching the order gives the opposite answer.

Assessment Focus: Question 9

Students may use trial and error to solve the problem. To create a problem, students may work backward, starting with an integer and finding what needs to be subtracted to give the required result. A level 2 response would be integer questions where the integers have the same sign and no zero pairs are needed to subtract. A level 4 response would be where students develop a pattern for each set of problems.

(Sample Answers, continued)

14. a) The expression in part i is greater because it begins with +3, and, to take away −1, I have to add a zero pair, which will make the answer greater than +3. In part ii, the expression begins with −3, and, to take away +1, I have to add a zero pair, which will make the answer less than −3.

b) In part i, I take away a negative integer that is less than the integer I take it from, so the answer will be positive. In part ii, I take away a positive integer that is greater than the integer I take it from, so the answer will be negative. So, the expression in part i is greater.

REFLECT:
(−3) − (−2)
To solve, use 3 red tiles and take away 2 red tiles. The result is 1 red tile, or −1.
(−2) − (+3)
To solve, model −2 with 3 yellow tiles and 5 red tiles. Take away 3 yellow tiles. The result is 5 red tiles, or −5.
(+1) − (+3)
To solve, model +1 with 3 yellow tiles and 2 red tiles. Take away 3 yellow tiles. The result is 2 red tiles, or −2.
(+2) − (−5)
To solve, model +2 with 7 yellow tiles and 5 red tiles. Take away 5 red tiles. The result is 7 yellow tiles, or +7.

Calculator Skills

Students could use guess and check to multiply 24 by numbers to give a product of 888. $24 \times 30 = 720$ is too low and $24 \times 40 = 960$ is too high. The units digit must multiply with 4 to give an 8 so $24 \times 37 = 888$. Students could use repeated subtraction of 240 (ten 24s) and then repeated subtractions of 24.
So $888 - 240 - 240 - 240 = 168$ and
$168 - 24 - 24 - 24 - 24 - 24 - 24 - 24 = 0$.
A total of thirty-seven 24s are subtracted, so $888 \div 24 = 37$.

Assignment Guidelines

If your students do not have time to complete all the *Practice* questions on pages 349 and 350, these questions provide minimum curriculum coverage: 4, 5, 7, 8, 9, *Reflect*
To assess the 4 Achievement Chart categories listed in the curriculum document, have students complete these *Practice* questions:
Understanding Concepts: 5;
Application: 7;
Communication: 8;
Problem Solving: 9

Calculator Skills

Assume the [÷] key on your calculator does not work.
Find two ways to use your calculator to divide:
888 [÷] 24 = 37

10. Here is a magic square:

0	+5	−2
−1	+1	+3
+4	−3	+2

a) Subtract +4 from each entry.
Is it still a magic square? Why?
b) Subtract −1 from each entry.
Is it still a magic square? Why?
c) Make up your own magic square.

Take It Further

11. a) Find two integers with a sum of −1 and a difference of +5. +2 and −3
b) Create and solve a similar integer problem.

12. Evaluate.
a) $(+4) + (+1) - (+3)$ = +2
b) $(+1) - (+2) - (-1)$ = 0
c) $(-3) - (+1) + (+4)$ = 0
d) $(-2) - (-4) + (-1)$ = +
e) $(+2) - (+1) - (+4)$ = −3
f) $(+1) - (+2) + (+1)$ = 0

13. Copy and complete.
a) $(+4) - \square = +3$ +1
b) $(+3) - \square = -1$ +4
c) $\square - (+1) = +4$ +5

14. Which expression in each pair has the greater value?
Explain your reasoning.
a) i) $(+3) - (-1)$ = +4; greater ii) $(-3) - (+1)$ = −4
b) i) $(-4) - (-5)$ = +1; greater ii) $(+4) - (+5)$ = −1

Reflect

Here are 4 types of subtraction problems:
- (negative integer) – (negative integer)
- (negative integer) – (positive integer)
- (positive integer) – (positive integer)
- (positive integer) – (negative integer)

Write a problem for each type of subtraction.
Show how you use tiles to solve each problem.

350 UNIT 9: Integers

ASSESSMENT FOR LEARNING

What to Look For	What to Do
Understanding concepts ✔ Students understand that the first integer in a subtraction question must be modelled to allow the second integer to be taken away from it. ***Applying procedures*** ✔ Students can use tiles to subtract integers. ***Problem solving*** ✔ Students create and solve their own subtraction problems. ***Communicating*** ✔ Students demonstrate clearly the subtraction of integers with coloured tiles.	***Extra Support:*** For questions 1 to 5, have students complete all the same type of question, then summarize the results: positive subtract positive (#1a, d, f; #2b, d, f; #3b, d, f; #5a) then negative subtract negative (#1b, c, e; #2a, c, e; #3a, c, e) then positive subtract negative (#4a, d; #5e, f) then negative subtract positive (#4b, c, e, f; #5b, c, d). Students can use Step-by-Step 6 (Master 9.12) to complete question 9. ***Extra Practice:*** Have students use any 2 of positive and negative 3, 4, 5, 6 to make as many different subtraction problems as possible. Students can complete Extra Practice 6 (Master 9.23).

Recording and Reporting
Master 9.2 Ongoing Observations: Integers

9.7 Subtracting Integers

Focus Subtract integers using number lines and patterns.

Just as we can show addition of whole numbers on a number line, we can show subtraction of whole numbers on a number line.
7 − 5 = 2

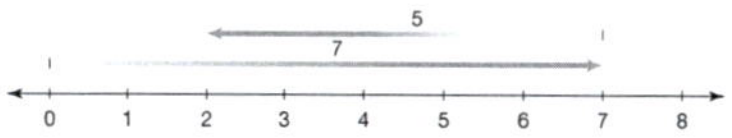

Explore

Work with a partner.
You will need copies of this number line.

➢ Use the number line to subtract.
(+6) − (−4) = +10 (−3) − (+5) = −8
(−5) − (−4) = −1 (+7) − (+10) = −3

Check your answers using coloured tiles.

Subtract.	Add.	
(+7) − (+2)	(+7) + (−2)	+5
(−7) − (−2)	(−7) + (+2)	−5
(+7) − (−2)	(+7) + (+2)	+9
(−7) − (+2)	(−7) + (−2)	−9

What do you notice about the answers in each row?
What patterns do you see in each subtraction and addition?
Check your pattern using other integers.

Reflect & Share

Compare your answers with those of another pair of classmates.
How can you use addition to subtract two integers?

Subtracting Integers

SECTION ORGANIZER (80–100 min)

Curriculum Focus: Subtract integers using number lines and patterns. (7m21, 7m24, 7m25)

Teacher Materials
- horizontal and vertical number lines on an overhead transparency or board
- coloured tiles

Student Materials
- number lines (Master 9.15)
- coloured tiles

Optional
- Step-by-Step 7 (Master 9.13)
- Extra Practice 7 (Master 9.24)

Assessment: Master 9.2 Ongoing Observations: Integers

Key Math Learnings

1. A number line can be used to subtract integers.
2. To subtract an integer, add its opposite.

BEFORE Get Started

Have students examine the number line at the top of page 351.

Ask:
- Why does the arrow that represents 5 point to the left?
  (5 is taken away from 7 so the result will be less than 7. On a number line, lesser numbers are to the left.)
- Where do you put the tail of the arrow that represents the number being subtracted?
  (The tail is always at the head of the arrow that represents the first number.)

Present *Explore*. Provide pairs of students with several copies of *Number Lines* (Master 9.15).

DURING Explore

Ongoing Assessment: Observe and Listen

Ask questions, such as:
- How did you show (+6) – (–4) on a number line?
  (I drew an arrow, to the right, from 0 to + 6. When I subtract a positive integer, the arrow points to the left, so when I subtract a negative integer, the arrow must point to the right. I drew an arrow, 4 units to the right, from +6 to +10. The difference is +10.)
- How did you check with coloured tiles?
  (I started with 6 yellow tiles. To be able to take away 4 red tiles, I added 4 zero pairs, then I had 10 yellow tiles and 4 red tiles. After I had taken the red tiles away, I had 10 yellow tiles, which is +10. So, my answer on the number line is correct.)

REACHING ALL LEARNERS

Early Finishers

Have students reverse the order of the integers in question 4, then subtract.

Common Misconceptions

➤ Students do not understand that the difference of two integers can be written two ways, as illustrated in the *Example*.

How to Help: Have students use a number line and coloured tiles to show that the order in which two integers are subtracted affects their difference.

Making Connections

Physical Education: Have students research +/− ratings of hockey players in the current season. Find reasons why this rating may not always indicate a player's value. Other students can research recent golf tournaments and compare the scores, relative to par, of players.

Connect

➢ To subtract two whole numbers, such as 5 − 2, we think, "What do we add to 2 to get 5?"
We add 3 to 2 to get 5; so, 5 − 2 = 3

We can do the same to subtract two integers.
For example, to subtract: (+5) − (−2)
Think: "What do we add to −2 to get +5?"

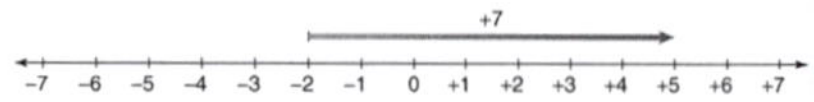

We add +7 to −2 to get +5; so, (+5) − (−2) = +7
We also know that (+5) + (+2) = +7.
We can look at other subtraction equations and related addition equations.

(+9) − (+4) = +5	(+9) + (−4) = +5
(−9) − (−4) = −5	(−9) + (+4) = −5
(−9) − (+4) = −13	(−9) + (−4) = −13
(+9) − (−4) = +13	(+9) + (+4) = +13

In each case, the result of subtracting an integer is the same as adding the opposite integer.
For example,
(−9) − (+4) = −13 (Subtract +4.) (−9) + (−4) = −13 (Add −4.)

➢ To subtract an integer, we add the opposite integer.
For example, to subtract: (+3) − (−6)
Add the opposite: (+3) + (+6)

The opposite of −6 is +6.

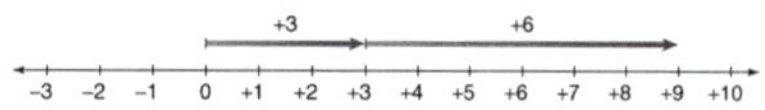

So, (+3) − (−6) = +9

352 UNIT 9: Integers

- How did you show (−3) − (+5) on a number line?
  (I drew an arrow from 0 to −3. To take away +5, I drew an arrow 5 units to the left of −3. The difference is −8.)
- What do you do to subtract a positive integer?
  (I draw an arrow to the left to represent the integer.)
- What do you do to subtract a negative integer?
  (I draw an arrow to the right to represent the integer.)
- What do you notice about the pairs of addition and subtraction problems?
  (In each case, the answers were the same.)
- What patterns do you see in these pairs of problems?
  (In each pair: the first numbers are the same; and the integer that is added is the opposite of the integer that is subtracted.)

AFTER Connect

Invite students to share their results and the patterns they noticed.

What you might see:

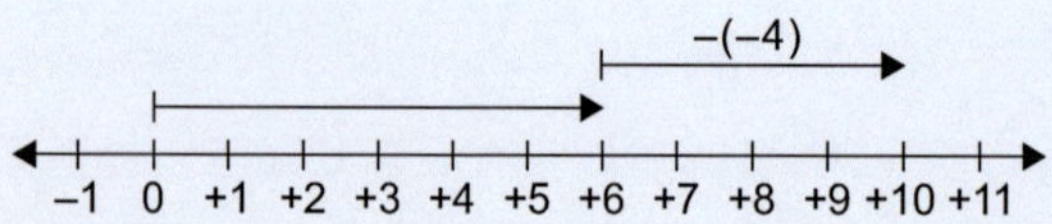

(+6) − (−4) = +10

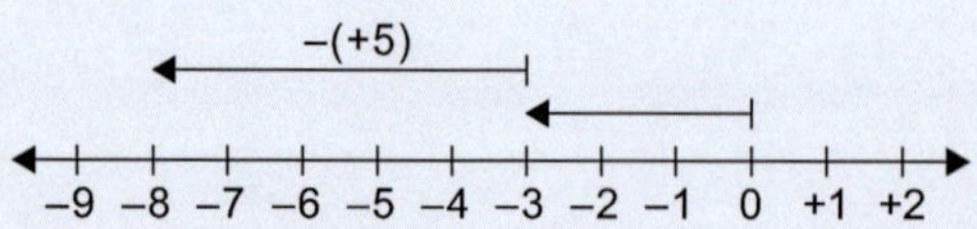

(−3) − (+5) = −8

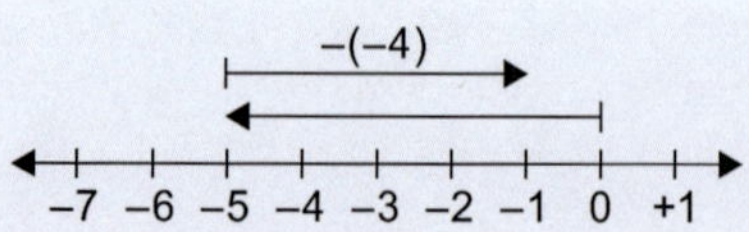

(−5) − (−4) = −1

Example 1

Use a number line to subtract.

a) $(+2) - (+9)$ b) $(+2) - (-9)$

Solution

a) To subtract: $(+2) - (+9)$
Add the opposite: $(+2) + (-9)$
Use a number line.
$(+2) + (-9) = -7$

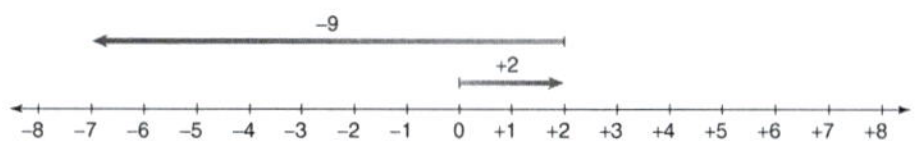

b) To subtract: $(+2) - (-9)$
Add the opposite: $(+2) + (+9)$
Use a number line.
$(+2) + (+9) = +11$

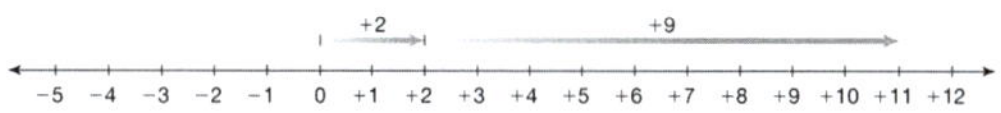

Example 2

On April 27, 2004, the highest temperature in Windsor was +5°C and the highest temperature in Yellowknife was −2°C.
What is the difference in temperature? Interpret the answer.

Solution

The difference between +5 and −2 can be written in two ways:

$(+5) - (-2)$	$(-2) - (+5)$
Add the opposite: $(+5) + (+2)$	Add the opposite: $(-2) + (-5)$
$(+5) + (+2) = +7$	$(-2) + (-5) = -7$
The difference in temperature is +7°C.	The difference in temperature is −7°C.
The temperature in Windsor is 7°C greater than the temperature in Yellowknife.	The temperature in Yellowknife is 7°C less than the temperature in Windsor.

9.7 Subtracting Integers 353

Calculator Skills

Students should remember to use the order of operations.

Assignment Guidelines

If your students do not have time to complete all the *Practice* questions on pages 354 and 355, these questions provide minimum curriculum coverage: 4, 5, 7, 8, 11, *Reflect*
To assess the 4 Achievement Chart categories listed in the curriculum document, have students complete these *Practice* questions: Understanding Concepts: 4; Application: 6; Problem Solving: 11; Communication: *Reflect*

Sample Answers

1. **a)** $(+6) + (-4)$ **b)** $(-5) + (-4)$ **c)** $(-2) + (+3)$
   d) $(+4) + (+2)$ **e)** $(+1) + (-1)$ **f)** $(+1) + (+1)$
3. **a)** $(+1) - (+2) = -1$ $(-3) - (+4) = -7$ $(-1) - (-4) = +3$
   $(+2) - (-5) = +7$ $(-6) - (-2) = -4$ $(-7) - (-3) = -4$
   b) The answers in part a are the opposites of those in question 2. When you change two integers to their opposites, their difference also changes to its opposite.
5. The answers may be positive or negative depending on which way the differences have been set up.
6. **a)** $(+13) - (-4) = +17$ or $(-4) - (+13) = -17$
   b) $(-10) - (-22) = +12$ or $(-22) - (-10) = -12$
   c) $(+12) - (-3) = +15$ or $(-3) - (+12) = -15$
   d) $(+13) - (+7) = +6$ or $(+7) - (+13) = -6$

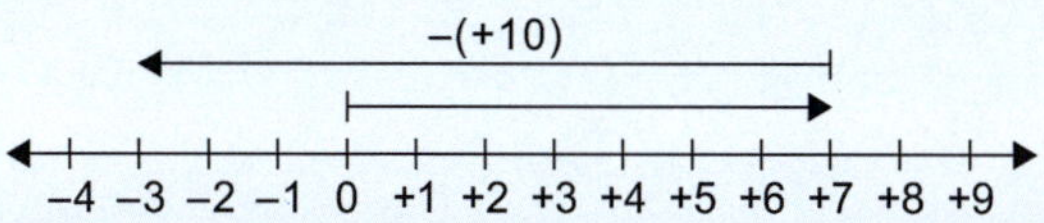

$(+7) - (+10) = -3$

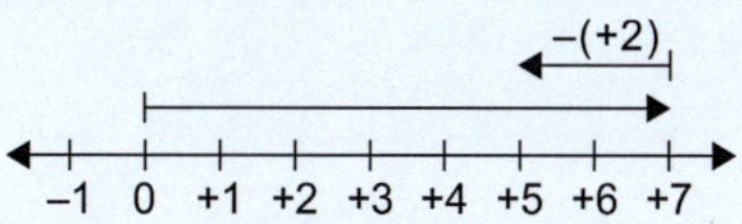

$(+7) - (+2) = +5$

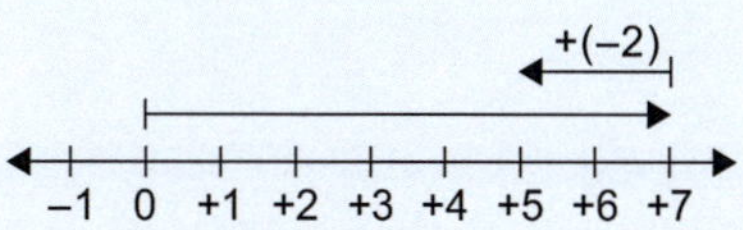

$(+7) + (-2) = +5$

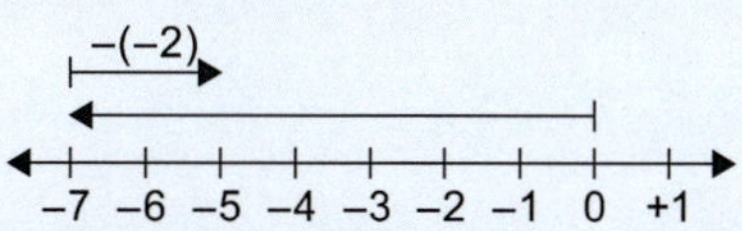

$(-7) - (-2) = -5$

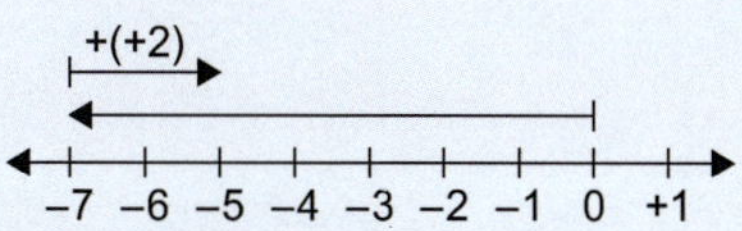

$(-7) + (+2) = -5$

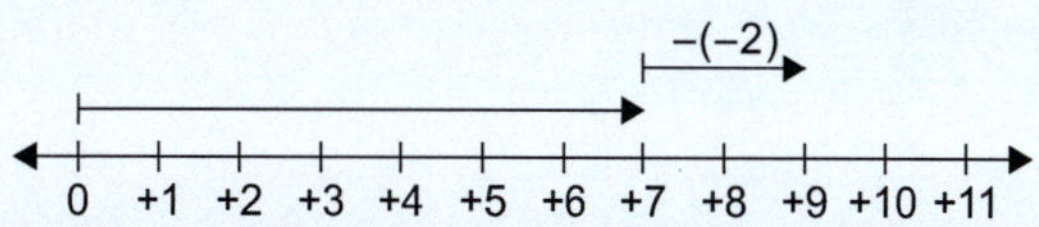

$(+7) - (-2) = +9$

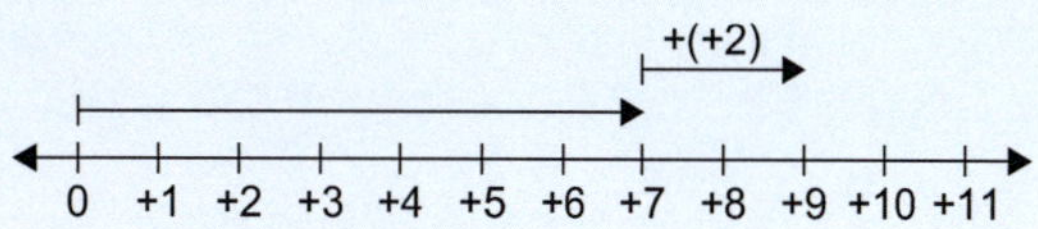

$(+7) + (+2) = +9$

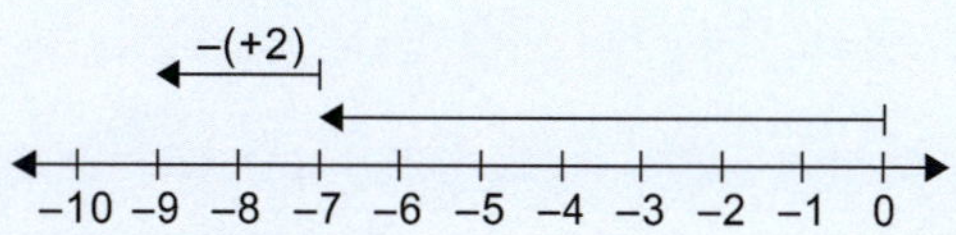

$(-7) - (+2) = -9$

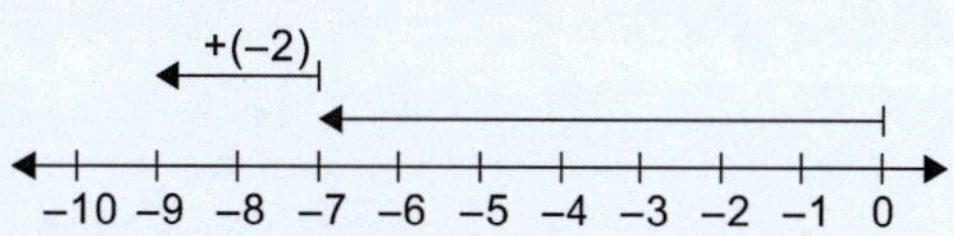

$(-7) + (-2) = -9$

7. a) $(+6) - (+5) = +1$
$(+5) - (+5) = 0$
$(+4) - (+5) = -1$
$(+3) - (+5) = -2$
$(+2) - (+5) = -3$

b) $(+7) - (+4) = +3$
$(+7) - (+3) = +4$
$(+7) - (+2) = +5$
$(+7) - (+1) = +6$
$(+7) - 0 = +7$
$(+7) - (-1) = +8$
$(+7) - (-2) = +9$
$(+7) - (-3) = +10$

c) $(+8) - (+7) = +1$
$(+7) - (+7) = 0$
$(+6) - (+7) = -1$
$(+5) - (+7) = -2$
$(+4) - (+7) = -3$
$(+3) - (+7) = -4$
$(+2) - (+7) = -5$
$(+1) - (+7) = -6$
$0 - (+7) = -7$
$(-1) - (+7) = -8$
$(-2) - (+7) = -9$
$(-3) - (+7) = -10$

Practice

1. Rewrite using addition.
   a) $(+6) - (+4)$ b) $(-5) - (+4)$ c) $(-2) - (-3)$
   d) $(+4) - (-2)$ e) $(+1) - (+1)$ f) $(+1) - (-1)$

2. Use a number line to subtract.
   Use coloured tiles to check your answers.
   a) $(+2) - (+1) = +1$ b) $(+4) - (-3) = +7$ c) $(-4) - (-1) = -3$
   d) $(-5) - (+2) = -7$ e) $(-2) - (-6) = +4$ f) $(-3) - (-7) = +4$

3. a) Reverse the order of the integers in question 2, then subtract.
   b) How are the answers different from those in question 2? Explain.

4. Use a number line to subtract.
   a) $(+10) - (+5) = +5$ b) $(+7) - (-3) = +10$ c) $(-8) - (+6) = -14$
   d) $(-10) - (+5) = -15$ e) $(-4) - (+4) = -8$ f) $(-4) - (-4) = 0$

5. Find the difference between:
   a) a temperature of +3°C and −5°C +8°C or −8°C
   b) a temperature of −15°C and −10°C −5°C or +5°C
   c) an elevation of 5 m above sea level and one of 2 m below sea level +7 m or −7 m
   d) a golf score of 1 below par and one of 3 below par +2 or −2

6. The table shows the average afternoon temperatures in January and April for four Canadian cities.
   Find the difference between the temperatures in April and January for each city. Show your work.

	City	January Temperature	April Temperature
a)	Calgary	−4°C	+13°C +17°C; −17°C
b)	Iqaluit	−22°C	−10°C +12°C; −12°C
c)	Toronto	−3°C	+12°C +15°C; −15°C
d)	Victoria	+7°C	+13°C +6°C; −6°C

354 UNIT 9: Integers

Ask students:

- How can you use addition to subtract integers?
  (*To subtract an integer, I can add its opposite; for example, (+3) – (–9) = (+3) + (+9).*)

Review *Connect.* The "add the opposite integer" concept will take time to solidify.

Ensure all students can find the opposites of both positive and negative integers. Make sure students know that to subtract integers using a number line, first write the subtraction statement as an addition statement, by adding the opposite integer.

Practice

Provide students with copies of *Number Lines* (Master 9.15). In question 9, if students need to be reminded of the meanings of median, range, and mode, direct them to the Glossary. Encourage students to use the Glossary to review any term whose meaning they have forgotten.

Assessment Focus: Question 8

Students should understand that switching the order of the terms in a subtraction problem gives the opposite answer. They should be able to demonstrate this on a number line or with patterning. And, replacing each term in a subtraction problem with its opposite also gives the opposite answer.

Calculator Skills

…nd each answer.

- 15 × (32 + 41) 1095
- 198 − 104 ÷ 13 190
- 14 × 15 − 16 × 9 66

7. Use patterns to subtract.

a) Subtract: (+2) − (+5)
Start the pattern with (+6) − (+5) = +1.

b) Subtract: (+7) − (−3)
Start the pattern with (+7) − (+4) = +3.

c) Subtract: (−3) − (+7)
Start the pattern with (+8) − (+7) = +1.

8. Assessment Focus

a) Subtract: (−6) − (+11) = −17

b) Suppose we subtract the integers in the opposite order:
(+11) − (−6) = +17
How does the answer compare with the answer in part a?
Use number lines or patterns to explain.

c) How is (+6) − (−11) different from (−6) − (+11)?
Explain.

9. This table shows the mean daily maximum temperatures in degrees Celsius for Rankin Inlet for each month.

Jan.	Feb.	Mar.	Apr.	May	June	July	Aug.	Sept.	Oct.	Nov.	Dec.
−28	−28	−23	−12	−2	+8	+16	+14	+6	−3	−16	−24

a) What is the median? −7.5 °C

b) What is the range? −44 °C

c) What is the mode? −28 °C

10. Evaluate.

a) (+4) − (+2) − (+1) = +1
b) (−2) − (+1) − (−4) = +1
c) (−1) + (−2) − (+1) = −4
d) (+5) − (+1) + (−2) = +2
e) (+10) − (+3) − (−5) = +12
f) (−7) − (+1) + (−3) = −11

11. Show three ways that +4 can be written as the difference of two integers.

Reflect

Choose two integers: one positive, one negative.
Add the integers. Subtract the integers.
Explain how the subtraction of two integers is related to addition.

9.7 Subtracting Integers 355

8. a) Write (−6) − (+11) as (−6) + (−11), by adding the opposite.
Use a number line to show that (−6) + (−11) = −17.

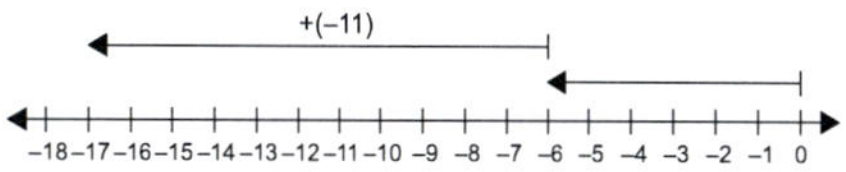

b) Write (+11) − (−6) as (+11) + (+6), then use a number line to show that the sum is +17.

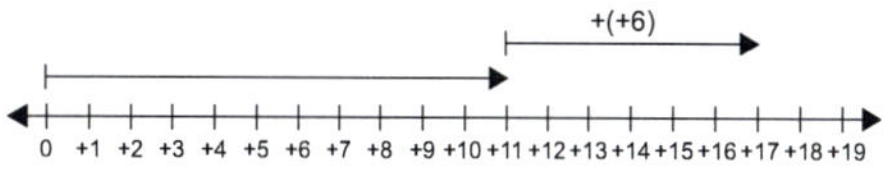

The answers are opposite integers because we changed the order of the integers we subtracted.

c) (+6) − (−11) = +17 and (−6) − (+11) = −17; this time, we subtract the opposites of the integers. We get the same answer as when we change the order of the integers. So, subtracting the opposites of given integers is the same as changing the order in which we subtract the given integers.

11. (+10) − (+6), (+2) − (−2), (−5) − (−9)

REFLECT: I chose +7 and −3.
Add the integers: (+7) + (−3) = +4
Subtract the integers: (+7) − (−3) = (+7) + (+3) = +10
We subtract by adding the opposite integer.

ASSESSMENT FOR LEARNING

What to Look For

Understanding concepts

✔ Students understand that subtracting an integer is the same as adding its opposite.

Problem solving

✔ Students use number lines, patterns, and other strategies to create and solve integer subtraction problems.

Communicating

✔ Students present subtraction correctly on a number line.

What to Do

Extra Support: Have students use coloured tiles as well as a number lines to subtract integers.
Students can use Step-by-Step 7 (Master 9.13) to complete question 8.

Extra Practice: Have students play a game with positive and negative integer cards from −10 to +10. Students deal the shuffled cards, then simultaneously turn cards over and state the difference. The first student with the correct answer takes the pair of cards. The winner is the person who gets all the cards.
Students can complete Extra Practice 7 (Master 9.24).

Extension: Have students make up their own addition and subtraction problems like those in question 10, then solve them.

Recording and Reporting
Master 9.2 Ongoing Observations: Integers

SECTION ORGANIZER

Student Materials
- 1-cm grid paper (PM 20)
- calculators

Assessment: Master 9.2 Ongoing Observations: Integers

Question Number	Possible Strategy
1	Guess and check; make an organized list
2	Work backward; use logical reasoning
3	Use logical reasoning
4	Draw a diagram
5	Use logical reasoning; draw a graph
6	Work backward; use logical reasoning; guess and check
7	Make an organized list; draw a diagram
8	Draw a diagram
9	Use logical reasoning
10	Make an organized list
11	Use logical reasoning
12	Make an organized list

Choosing a Strategy

Strategies
- Make a table.
- Use a model.
- Draw a diagram.
- Solve a simpler problem.
- Work backward.
- Guess and check.
- Make an organized list.
- Use a pattern.
- Draw a graph.
- Use logical reasoning.

1. A textbook is opened at random. The product of the page numbers is 23 256. What is the number on the left hand page? 152
2. Ms. Pantuso has a bag of candies that she wants to share equally among the students in her class.
   On Monday, all 20 students were present. If she had shared the candies, she would have had 7 candies left over.
   On Tuesday, two boys were absent. If she had shared the candies, she would again have had 7 left over.
   On Wednesday, the two boys were still absent and one girl was absent. Ms. Pantuso shared all the candies among the students with none left over.
   a) What was the least number of candies Ms. Pantuso could have had? 187
   b) How many candies did each student receive? 11
3. Briony wants to print copies of her new brochure.
   The local print shop charges 15¢ a copy for the first 25 copies, 12¢ a copy for the next 50 copies, and 8¢ a copy for any additional copies.
   How much would Briony pay for each number of copies?
   a) 60 copies $7.95 b) 240 copies $22.95
4. What is the greatest number of 5 cm by 3 cm rectangles that can be cut from a 20 cm by 10 cm sheet of cardboard? 12
5. Mr. Anders estimates it will take him 4 h to build a wall. His assistant would take 6 h to build the wall.
   a) What fraction of the wall could each person build in one hour? Mr. Anders: $\frac{1}{4}$ of the wall; his assistant: $\frac{1}{6}$ of the wall
   b) Suppose they worked together. What fraction could they build in one hour? $\frac{5}{12}$
   c) How long would it take them to build the wall? 2 h 24 min
6. The mean of five numbers is 13.
   The mode is 16.
   The median is 14.
   Write two sets of numbers that satisfy these conditions.
   7, 12, 14, 16, 16 or 8, 11, 14, 16, 16

356 UNIT 9: Integers

Sample Solutions

1. The two page numbers are consecutive numbers. Use a calculator to find two consecutive numbers with a product of 23 256.
   The lesser number is even and the greater number is odd (look at the numbers on these pages, the left hand page is even, the right hand page is odd).
   Guess: 144 × 145 = 20 880 — too low
   Try: 154 × 155 = 23 870 — too high, but close
   Try: 152 × 153 = 23 256 — correct
   The number on the left hand page is 152.
2. a) On Wednesday, there were 17 students in the class, so the number of candies must be a multiple of 17. On Tuesday there were 18 students. The number of candies is divisible by a number that is 7 more than a multiple of 18. On Monday, there were 20 students. The number of candies is divisible by a number that is 7 more than a multiple of 20. The prime factors of 20 are 2 × 2 × 5. The prime factors of 18 are 2 × 3 × 3. The lowest common multiple of 20 and 18 is 2 × 2 × 3 × 3 × 5 = 180.
   Try: 180 + 7 = 187; is this a multiple of 17?
   187 ÷ 17 = 11
   So, 187 is a multiple of 17.
   The least number of candies is 187.
   b) Each student received 11 candies.
3. a) Cost = 25 × $0.15 + (60 – 25) × $0.12 = $7.95
   b) Cost = 25 × $0.15 + 50 × $0.12 + (240 – 50 – 25) × $0.08 = $22.95
4. Draw a picture. The 5 cm side of the rectangles can be along the 20 cm side of the rectangle. Then, 4 rectangles fit in one row, and there are 3 rows, so 12 rectangles in all.

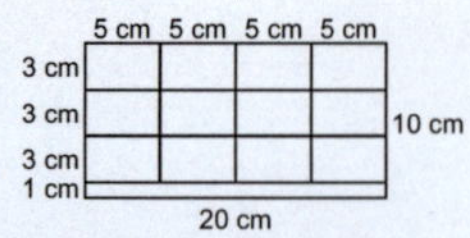

The 5 cm side can be along the 10 cm side of the rectangle. Then, 6 rectangles fit in one row, and there are 2 rows, so 12 rectangles in all.

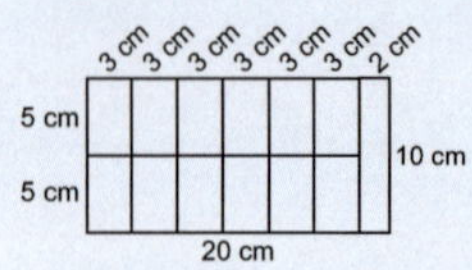

5. a) Mr. Anders will build $\frac{1}{4}$ of the wall in one hour and his assistant will build of the wall in one hour.
   b) Fraction of wall built in one hour = $\frac{1}{4} + \frac{1}{6} = \frac{5}{12}$
   c) $\frac{5}{12}$ can be built in 1 h, which is 60 min. So, $\frac{1}{12}$ can be built in $\frac{60 \text{ min}}{5}$ = 12 min. And, $\frac{12}{12}$ can be built in 12 × 12 min = 144 min. It takes the two people 2 h 24 min to build the wall.

Reading and Writing in Math

7. A rectangular prism has a square base, and a volume of 36 cm^3. What are the possible whole number dimensions of the prism? 1 cm by 1 cm by 36 cm, or 2 cm by 2 cm by 9 cm, or 3 cm by 3 cm by 4 cm, or 6 cm by 6 cm by 1 cm.

8. Copy this figure on grid paper. Add one square to make the figure symmetrical. How many solutions can you find? 4

9. Eight students wrote a math test. Their mean mark was 54%. Another student wrote the test and scored 99%. What is the mean mark for the nine students? 59%

10. Write 45 as the sum of consecutive integers. How many solutions can you find?

11. a) The product of two whole numbers is 1000. No number contains a zero. What are the numbers? 8 × 125 How many different answers can you find? 1 answer
    b) The product of three whole numbers is 1000. No number contains a zero. What are the numbers? How many different answers can you find? 3
    1 × 8 × 125; 8 × 5 × 25; 2 × 4 × 125

12. A book contains 124 pages numbered from 1 to 124. How many times does the digit 7 appear? 22 times

Reading and Writing in Math: Choosing a Strategy 357

6. If the mean is 13, then the sum of the numbers is $5 \times 13 = 65$.
   If the median is 14 and the mode is 16, then the numbers must be ____, ____, 14, 16, 16 and the two blanks must be different or there would be another mode.
   The three given numbers have a sum of 46, so the two remaining numbers must be less than 14 and have a sum of $65 - 46 = 19$
   The following sets of numbers satisfy these conditions: 7, 12, 14, 16, 16 or 8, 11, 14, 16, 16
7. Find all possible sets of 3 whole numbers that have a product of 36. Make an organized list. Start with the least possible numbers: $1 \times 1 \times 36$; $1 \times 1 \times 18$, $1 \times 3 \times 12$; $1 \times 4 \times 9$; $1 \times 6 \times 6$; $2 \times 2 \times 9$; $2 \times 3 \times 6$; $3 \times 3 \times 4$
   Choose the sets of numbers that have 2 factors the same, for the square base:
   1 cm by 1 cm by 36 cm, or 2 cm by 2 cm by 9 cm, or 3 cm by 3 cm by 4 cm, or 6 cm by 6 cm by 1 cm.
8. Line symmetry:

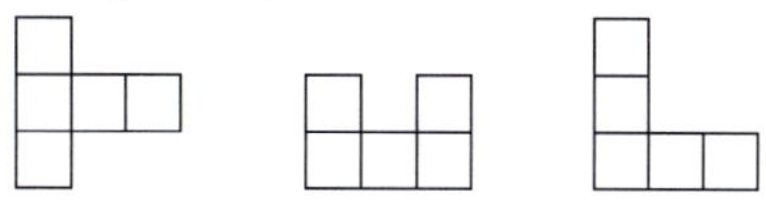

   Rotational symmetry:

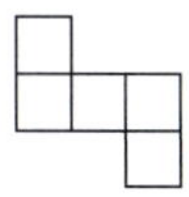

9. Total score for 8 students is $54\% \times 8 = 432\%$.
   Add the score for the 9th student: $432\% + 99\% = 531\%$
   Mean mark for 9 students: $\frac{531\%}{9} = 59\%$

(*Solutions continue below.*)

(*Sample Solutions, continued*)

10. Make an organized list. Begin with 2 numbers, then guess and check.
    $22 + 23 = 45$
    $14 + 15 + 16 = 45$
    $7 + 8 + 9 + 10 + 11 = 45$
    $5 + 6 + 7 + 8 + 9 + 10 = 45$
    $1 + 2 + 3 + 4 + 5 + 6 + 7 + 8 + 9 = 45$
    $0 + 1 + 2 + 3 + 4 + 5 + 6 + 7 + 8 + 9 = 45$
    $(-4) + (-3) + (-2) + (-1) + 0 + 1 + 2 + 3 + 4 + 5 + 6 + 7 + 8 + 9 + 10 = 45$
    $(-6) + (-5) + (-4) + (-3) + (-2) + (-1) + 0 + 1 + 2 + 3 + 4 + 5 + 6 + 7 + 8 + 9 + 10 + 11 = 45$
11. a) Make an organized list of all possible pairs of numbers with product 1000:
    1×1000, 2×500, 4×250, 8×125, 10×100, 20×50, 25×40. The only pair that does not have numbers with zero is 8×125.
    b) Use the list in part a. Try to write each factor as the product of 2 numbers that do not have a zero:
    $1 \times 8 \times 125$; $8 \times 5 \times 25$; $2 \times 4 \times 125$
12. Make an organized list.
    From 0 to 69, 7 occurs in 7, 17, 27, 37, 47, 57, 67 (7 times).
    From 70 to 79, 7 occurs in 70, 71, 72, 73, 74, 75, 76, 77, 78, 79 (11 times).
    From 80 to 124, 7 occurs in 87, 97, 107, 117 (4 times).
    So, between 1 and 124, the digit 7 appears 7 + 11 + 4, or 22 times.

Historian

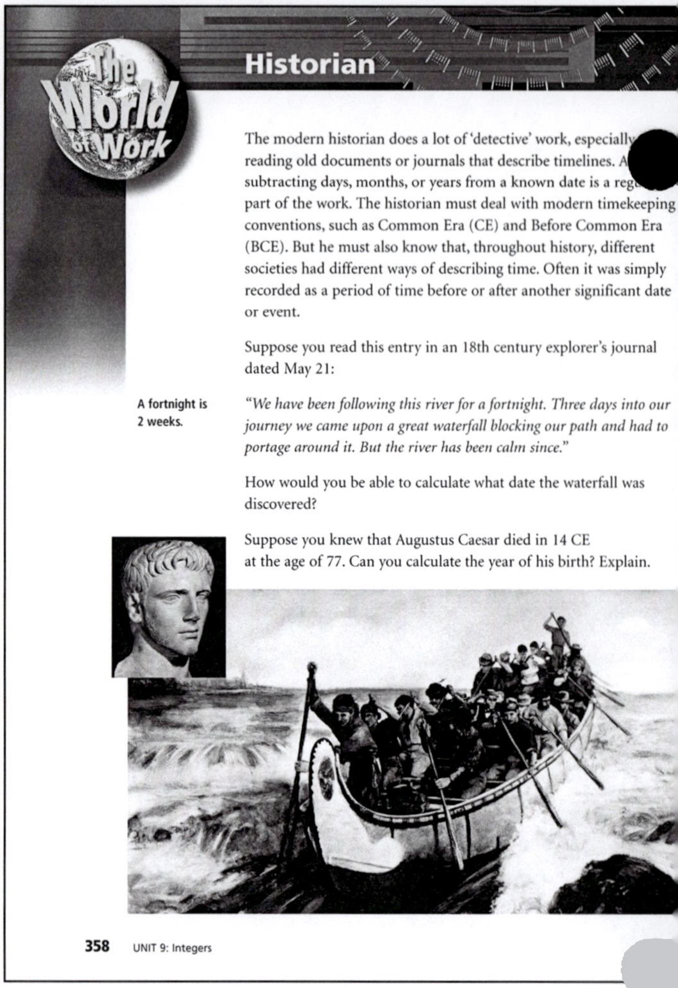

Historian

The modern historian does a lot of 'detective' work, especially reading old documents or journals that describe timelines. A subtracting days, months, or years from a known date is a reg part of the work. The historian must deal with modern timekeeping conventions, such as Common Era (CE) and Before Common Era (BCE). But he must also know that, throughout history, different societies had different ways of describing time. Often it was simply recorded as a period of time before or after another significant date or event.

Suppose you read this entry in an 18th century explorer's journal dated May 21:

A fortnight is 2 weeks.

"We have been following this river for a fortnight. Three days into our journey we came upon a great waterfall blocking our path and had to portage around it. But the river has been calm since."

How would you be able to calculate what date the waterfall was discovered?

Suppose you knew that Augustus Caesar died in 14 CE at the age of 77. Can you calculate the year of his birth? Explain.

358 UNIT 9: Integers

Sample Solution

May 21 subtract 14 days for a fortnight, then add 3 days
$(+21) - (+14) + (+3) = +10$
The waterfall was discovered May 10.

Consider dates after CE to be positive integers and dates BCE to be negative. The date of Augustus Caesar's death is +14.
$(+14) - (+77) = -63$ so Augustus Caesar was born 63 BCE.

The historian is just one example of how integers can be used in a career. For example, camera, platemaking and other pre-press occupations use negative integers when determining how much of a photo will be cropped off. Have students suggest other ways integers are used in careers or other areas of interest.
Suggestions: Banking, Stock Market Analyst, Sports, Weather
Have them suggest a question that might arise. Students may ask at home or other adults they know to give other suggestions of careers involving integers. Give time later to share the information gathered.

Unit Review

Review any lesson with etext online tutorial

What Do I Need to Know?

✓ **Integer Models**

- You can use a number line to show integers.

Negative numbers are to the left of 0. Positive numbers are to the right of 0.

- Coloured tiles model integers.

✓ **Adding Integers**

- You can use tiles to add integers.
(−7) + (+2) = −5

- You can use a number line to add integers.
(+6) + (−3) = +3

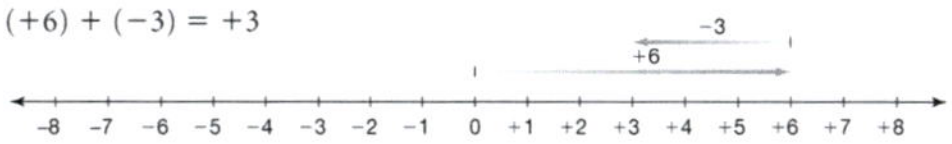

✓ **Subtracting Integers**

- You can use tiles to subtract integers: (+3) − (−7)
We need enough red tiles to take away 7 of them.
Model +3:

Since there are not enough tiles to take away −7, add 7 yellow tiles and 7 red tiles. Now take away 7 red tiles. There are 10 yellow tiles left.

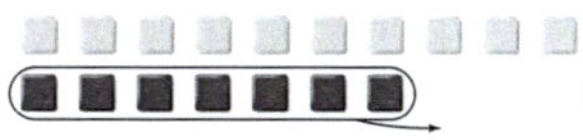

(+3) − (−7) = +10

- You can also subtract by adding the opposite:
(−5) − (−8) = −5 + (+8)
= +3

Unit Review 359

SECTION ORGANIZER

Student Materials

- coloured tiles
- number lines (Master 9.15)

Assessment: Masters 9.1 Unit Rubric: Integers, 9.4 Unit Summary: Integers

Sample Solutions

1.

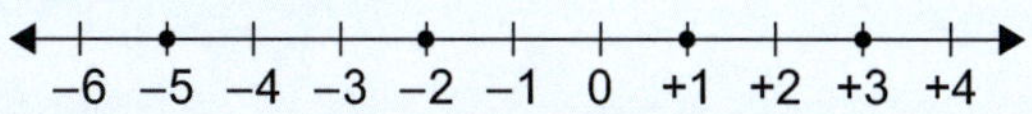

4. a) (−1) + (+3) = +2

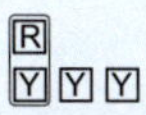

b) (+3) + (−4) = −1

c) (−2) − (+3) = −5

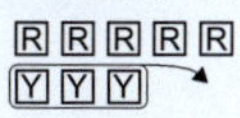

d) (−1) − (−3) = +2

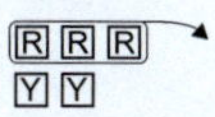

5. a) (−1) + (+3) = +2

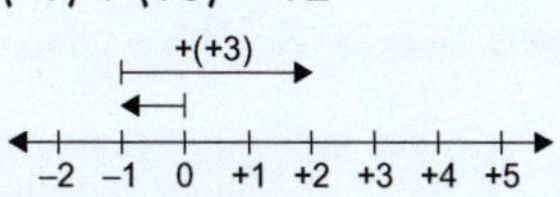

b) (+6) + (−4) = +2

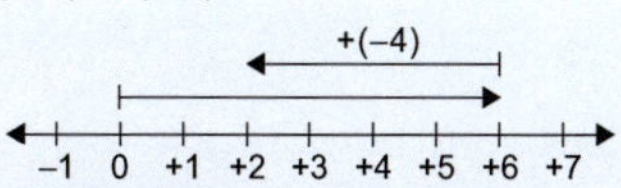

c) (−4) − (+6)
Rewrite as an addition statement.
(−4) + (−6) = −10

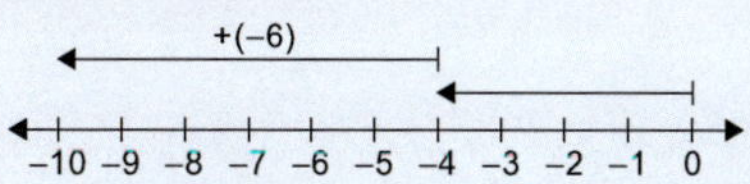

d) (−5) − (−3)
Rewrite as an addition statement.
(−5) + (+3) = −2

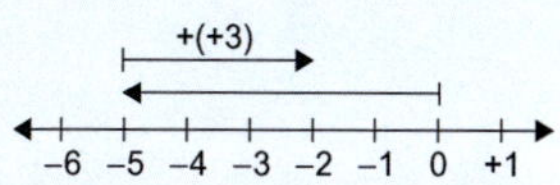

6. The difference of two positive integers is positive if the first integer is greater than the second integer. The difference of two positive integers is negative if the first integer is less than the second integer.

7. (−5) + (+12) + (−9) = −2
The final temperature was −2°C.

9. a) (+5) − (−7) = +12 or (−7) − (+5) = −12
The difference in temperature is +12°C or −12°C.
b) (−100) − (+50) = −150 or (+50) − (−100) = +150.
The difference in elevation is −150 m or +150 m.
c) (+1) − (−2) = +3 or (−2) − (+1) = −3
The difference in scores is +3 or −3.

10. a) (+3) − (+1) = (+3) + (−1) = +2
b) (−5) − (−2) = (−5) + (+2) = −3
c) (+100) − (+60) = (+100) + (−60) = +40
d) (−100) − (+60) = (−100) + (−60) = −160

11. Many pairs are possible.
a) (−1) + (−5), (−11) + (+5), (+7) + (−13), (+1) + (−7), (−2) + (−4)
b) (+5) − (+8), (−2) − (+1), (−6) − (−3), (+3) − (+6), (−4) − (−1)

Correlation of Extra Practice questions on page 446:

Section	Questions
9.1	1, 2
9.2	3, 4, 5, 6
9.4	7, 9, 12
9.5	7, 9, 12
9.6	8, 10, 11, 12
9.7	8, 10, 11, 12

What Should I Be Able to Do?

For extra practice, go to page 446.

LESSON

9.1 **1.** Draw a number line. Mark each integer on the number line: +3, −5, +1, −2

2. Use an integer to represent each situation.
a) a golf score of 2 strokes under par −2
b) 250 m below sea level −250 m
c) 32°C +32°C
d) a loss of $125 −$125
e) an increase of $3 in the monthly cost of cable television +$3

9.2 **3.** Order these integers from least to greatest:
+200, −55, +150, −3, −54
−55, −54, −3, +150, +200

9.4 9.6 **4.** Use tiles to add or subtract.
a) (−1) + (+3) = +2
b) (+3) + (−4) = −1
c) (−2) − (+3) = −5
d) (−1) − (−3) = +2

9.5 9.7 **5.** Use a number line to add or subtract.
a) (−1) + (+3) = +2
b) (+6) + (−4) = +2
c) (−4) − (+6) = −10
d) (−5) − (−3) = −2

6. When you add two positive integers, their sum is always a positive integer. When you subtract two positive integers, is their difference always a positive integer? Explain.

7. At midnight in North Bay, the temperature was −5°C. Duri the next 24 h, the temperatur rose 12°C, then dropped 9°C. What was the final temperature? Show your work. −2°C

9.6 9.7 **8.** Use tiles or a number line to subtract.
a) (+4) − (+1) = +3
b) (+5) − (−1) = +6
c) (+2) − (−2) = +4
d) (−4) − (+1) = −5
e) (−6) − (−2) = −4
f) (−10) − (−5) = −5
g) (−4) − (−2) = −2

9. Use tiles or a number line. Find the difference between:
a) a temperature of +5°C and −7°C +12°C or −12°C
b) an elevation of −100 m and +50 m −150 m or +150 m
c) a golf score of 1 over par and 2 under par +3 or −3

10. Subtract.
a) (+3) − (+1) = +2
b) (−5) − (−2) = −3
c) (+100) − (+60) = +40
d) (−100) − (+60) = −160

11. a) Find 5 pairs of integers with a sum of −6.
b) Find 5 pairs of integers with a difference of −3.

360 UNIT 9: Integers

ASSESSMENT FOR LEARNING

What to Look For

Understanding of concepts

✔ **Question 4:** Student understands that the combination of a yellow tile and a red tile is 0.

✔ **Question 5:** Student understands that, on a number line, a positive integer is represented by an arrow to the right, and a negative integer by an arrow to the left.

Application of mathematical procedures

✔ **Question 1:** Student can place integers on a number line.

✔ **Question 3:** Student can order integers.

✔ **Questions 8 and 9:** Student can use a number line to add and subtract integers.

Communicating

✔ **Question 6:** Student can explain how the subtraction of two integers is related to addition.

Problem solving

✔ **Questions 7 and 11:** Student can use number lines, patterns, and other strategies to solve integer problems.

Recording and Reporting

Master 9.1 Unit Rubric: Integers
Master 9.4 Unit Summary: Integers

Practice Test

1. We measure time in hours.
Suppose 12 noon is represented by the integer 0.
a) Which integer represents 1 p.m. the same day? +1
b) Which integer represents 10 a.m. the same day? −2
c) Which integer represents 12 midnight the same day? +12
d) Which integer represents 10 p.m. the previous day? −14

2. Order all the integers in question 1 from least to greatest.
−14, −2, +1, +12

3. Evaluate.
a) (+5) + (−8) = −3
b) (−3) − (+7) = −10
c) (−9) + (−1) = −10
d) (−4) + (+10) = +6
e) (−6) − (−2) = −4
f) (+12) − (−11) = +23

4. Without calculating the sum, how can you tell if the sum of two integers will be:
a) zero?
b) negative?
c) positive?
Include examples in your explanations.

5. Here is a different type of dartboard.

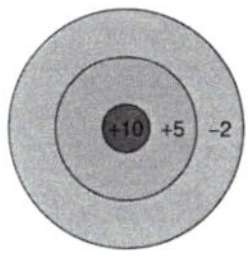

A player throws 3 darts at the board. His score is the sum of the integers in the areas his darts land.
Assume all 3 darts hit the board.
a) How many different scores are possible?
b) Find each score.

6. The lowest temperature possible is approximately −273°C.
The temperature at which water boils is 100°C.
What is the difference in these temperatures? +373°C or −373°C

SECTION ORGANIZER

Student Materials

- coloured tiles
- number lines (Master 9.15)

Assessment: Masters 9.1 Unit Rubric: Integers, 9.4 Unit Summary: Integers

Assignment Guidelines

To assess the 4 Achievement Chart categories listed in the curriculum document, use these test questions: Understanding Concepts: 3; Communication: 4; Problem Solving: 5; Application: 6

Sample Solutions

3. a) (+5) + (−8) = −3

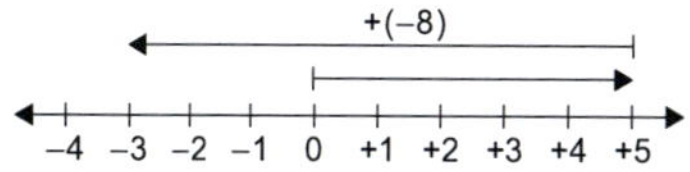

b) (−3) − (+7) = (−3) + (−7) = −10

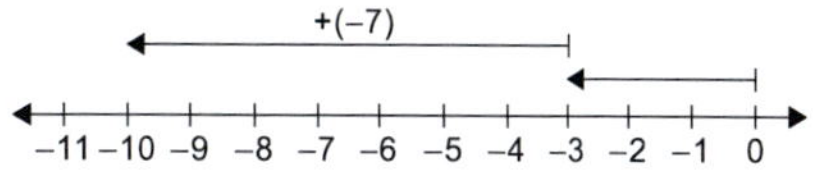

c) (−9) + (−1) = −10

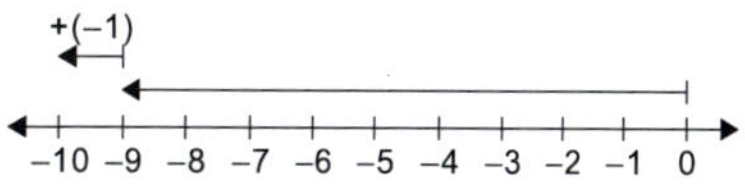

(Solutions continue below.)

(Sample Solutions, continued)

d) (−4) + (+10) = +6

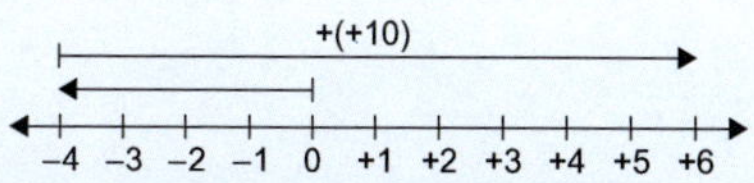

e) (−6) − (−2) = (−6) + (+2) = −4

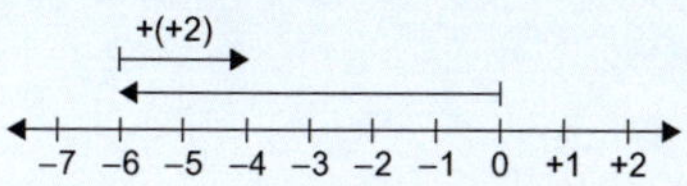

f) (+12) − (−11) = (+12) + (+11) = +23

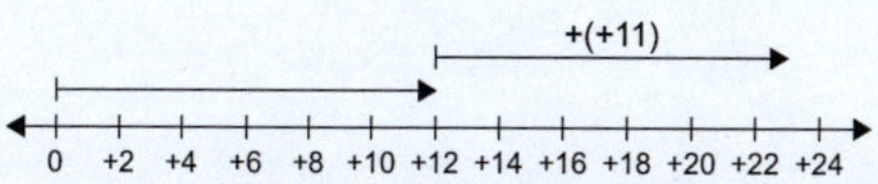

4. a) The sum of two integers is zero if the integers are opposites. For example, (+10) + (−10) = 0

b) The sum of two integers is negative if both integers are negative. For example, (−10) + (−10) = −20
And, the sum of two integers is negative if one integer is positive, and the other is negative, and the negative integer has the longer arrow on a number line.
For example, (−10) + (+5) = −5

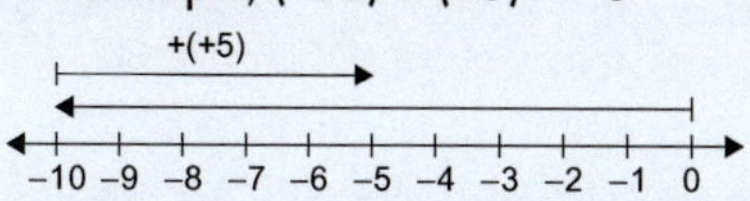

c) The sum of two integers is positive if both integers are positive. For example, (+10) + (+10) = +20
And, the sum of two integers is positive if one integer is positive and the other is negative, and the positive integer has the longer arrow on a number line.
For example, (+10) + (−5) = +5

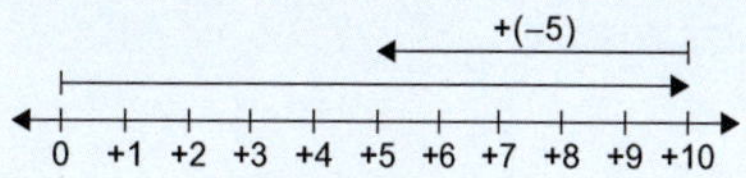

5. Make an organized list.
(+10) + (+10) + (+10) = +30
(+10) + (+10) + (+5) = +25
(+10) + (+10) + (−2) = +18
(+10) + (+5) + (−2) = +13
(+10) + (+5) + (+5) = +20
(+10) + (−2) + (−2) = +6
(+5) + (+5) + (+5) = +15
(+5) + (+5) + (−2) = +8
(+5) + (−2) + (−2) = +1
(−2) + (−2) + (−2) = −6
There are 10 possible scores.
The scores are the sums above.

6. −273 − (+100) = −373 or (+100) − (−273) = +373;
the difference in temperature is +373°C or −373°C.

What Time Is It?

SECTION ORGANIZER (80–100 min)

Teacher Materials
- Time Zones on an overhead transparency

Student Grouping: Individual

Student Materials
- atlases, Internet access

Optional
- number lines (Master 9.15)
- coloured tiles

Assessment: Masters 9.3 Performance Assessment Rubric: What Time Is It? 9.4 Unit Summary: Integers

Sample Solutions

1. Beijing, China is +8 h and Sudbury is –5 h from Greenwich, so Beijing is (+8) – (–5) = +13, or +13 h from Sudbury. Beijing is 13 h ahead of Sudbury. Convert each Beijing time to the 24-hour clock, then subtract (+13) from these times to find the local Sudbury time that the event is taking place.

Event	24-hour clock time	Conversion	Local Time
a) 200-m backstroke	2:00 p.m. is 14:00	(+14) – (+13) = +1	1:00 a.m.
b) 100-m dash	7:00 p.m. is 19:00	(+19) – (+13) = +6	6:00 a.m.
c) gymnastics	11:00 p.m. is 23:00	(+23) – (+13) = +10	10:00 a.m.
d) middleweight boxing	8:00 a.m. is 08:00	(+8) – (+13) = –5	7:00 p.m. the previous day

(*Solutions continue below right.*)

Unit Problem What Time Is It?

TIME ZONES

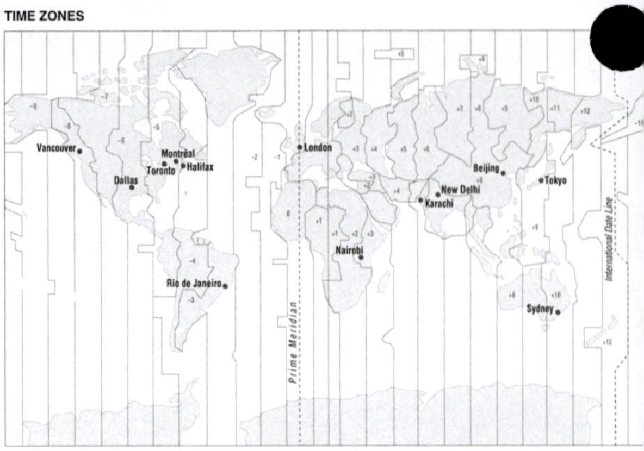

The map shows the world's time zones. Greenwich, in London, England, is the reference point, or the zero for the time zones. Its time is called UTC, or Coordinated Universal Time. London, England, is also in this time zone.
The positive and negative integers on the map show the changes in time from UTC.

The 2008 Summer Olympics will be held in Beijing, China.

1. The local start times of some Olympic events are given. If family members want to watch these events live, in Sudbury (the same time zone as Toronto), what time should they "tune in"?
   a) 200-m backstroke at 2:00 p.m. 1:00 a.m.
   b) 100-m dash at 7:00 p.m. 6:00 a.m.
   c) gymnastics at 11:00 p.m. 10:00 a.m.
   d) middleweight boxing at 8:00 a.m. 7:00 p.m.

362 UNIT 9: Integers

Present the *Unit Problem.* Invite volunteers to read the introduction and instructions for the problem aloud. Ensure students understand what they are expected to do.

Remind students that they should use the Check List to assess their work before handing it in. You may also wish to provide students with copies of Master 9.3 Performance Assessment Rubric: What Time Is It? so they will know how their work will be assessed.

Remind students there are 6 time zones in Canada. Ask students what time it is in other parts of Canada when it is 9:00 a.m. in Toronto. It is 10:00 a.m. in Halifax, 10:30 a.m. in Newfoundland, 8:00 a.m. in Winnipeg, 7:00 a.m. in Calgary, and 6:00 a.m. in Victoria.

It is important that students understand the 24-hour clock before finding times in different parts of the world using a map or globe.

(*Sample Solutions, continued*)

2. Montreal is in the same time zone as Sudbury, so Beijing is 13 h ahead of Montreal or Montreal is 13 h behind Beijing. The live event in Montreal at 9:00 p.m. is 21:00 on the
24-hour clock, so (+21) – (–13) = 34:00, which is one day and 10 h ahead, Beijing time. The event is happening on the next calendar day at 10:00 a.m. in Beijing.
3. Time Zones: Beijing: +8
   Arrival Time: 6:00 p.m. is 18:00 h.
   Tokyo: +9
   Sydney: +10
   Atsuko in Tokyo: (+9) – (+8) = +1, so she is 1 h ahead of Beijing time. The arrival time would be 19:00 h local time and she needs to account for 4 hours of travel time so Atsuko needs to fly out at 15:00 h local time or 3:00 p.m.
   Paula in Sydney: (+10) – (+8) = +2, so she is 2 h ahead of Beijing time. The arrival time would be 20:00 h local time, and she needs to account for 13 h of travel time so she needs to fly out at 7:00 h local time, which is 7 a.m.

2. An event is broadcast live in Montreal at 9:00 p.m.
What time is it taking place in Beijing? 10:00 a.m. the next day

3. Two pen pals plan to meet in Beijing for the Olympics.
Atsuko lives in Tokyo, Japan.
She can get a direct flight to Beijing that takes 4 h.
Paula lives in Sydney, Australia, and her direct flight takes 13 h.
What time does each girl leave her country to arrive in Beijing at 6 p.m., Beijing time?

Check List

Your work should show:

✓ how you used integers to solve each problem
✓ the strategies you used to add and subtract integers
✓ correct calculations
✓ a clear explanation of how integers relate to time zones

4. Olympic funding depends on money from North American television networks. What problems will the organizers of the Beijing Olympics encounter when they plan the times for events?

5. Make up your own problem about the time zone map.
Solve your problem.

Show your work. Show how you can use integers to solve each problem.

Reflect on the Unit

Choose a positive integer and a negative integer.
How many different ways can you add them? Subtract them?
Show your work.
If you used number lines, patterns, or coloured tiles, draw pictures to show how you used them.

Unit Problem: What Time Is It? 363

4. Use the time comparisons in question #1. Afternoon events will air live in North America while most people are asleep. Late evening events will air live in North America while many people are at work. Morning events (7:00 a.m. – 11:00 a.m.) will air live in North America from 6:00 p.m. to 10:00 p.m. the previous calendar day's evening. The organizers need to find times when the most popular events in North America can be televised during the North American evening time slot.

5. At 8:00 p.m., Monday, a grandchild in Ottawa wants to call his grandparents in Tokyo. What time will the grandparents receive the call?
Ottawa: −5 Tokyo: +9
(+9) − (−5) = +14, so Tokyo is 14 h ahead of Ottawa.
8:00 p.m. is 20:00 h, so (+20) + (+14) = +34, which is one day and 10 h ahead.
The grandparents will receive the call on Tuesday morning at 10:00 a.m.

REFLECT ON THE UNIT: I chose +5 and −7.
No matter which order they are added, the sum is −2. (+5) + (−7) = (−7) + (+5) = −2
When the order is switched in subtraction, the difference is the opposite integer.
(+5) − (−7) = (+5) + (+7) = +12 but (−7) − (+5) = (−7) + (−5) = −12
This can be shown using coloured tiles or number lines. Students' work should include number lines and/or coloured tiles.

ASSESSMENT FOR LEARNING

What to Look For	What to Do
Understanding concepts ✔ Students understand how integers can be used to compare and convert times in different time zones. ***Applying procedures*** ✔ Students can apply their knowledge of integers to time zone calculations. ***Problem solving*** ✔ Students choose appropriate strategies to convert times and make plans to meet in Beijing.	***Extra Support:*** Make the problem accessible. Some students may have difficulty converting times. Have them use a number line to compare times in different time zones. Relate the times to activities students would be performing and whether the activities would already be done. For example, if you are having breakfast in Toronto, what will people be doing in Halifax, in London, England, and in Beijing?

Recording and Reporting
Master 9.3 Performance Assessment Rubric: What Time Is It?
Master 9.4 Unit Summary: Integers

Evaluating Student Learning: Preparing to Report: Unit 9 Integers

This unit provides an opportunity to report on the **Number Sense and Numeration** strand.
Master 9.4: Unit Summary: Integers provides a comprehensive format for recording and summarizing evidence collected.

Here is an example of a completed summary chart for this Unit:

Strand: *Number Sense and Numeration*	**Problem solving**	**Understanding of concepts**	**Application of mathematical procedures**	**Communication**	***Overall***
Ongoing Observations	2	2	3	3	2/3
Work samples or portfolios; conferences	3	3	3	2	3
Unit Review	3	3	2	2	2/3
Unit Test	2	3	3	3	3
Unit Problem What Time Is It?	3	3	3	3	3
Achievement Level for reporting					3

Recording	How to Report
Ongoing Observations	Use *Master 9.2 Ongoing Observations: Integers* to determine the most consistent level achieved in each category. Enter it in the chart. Choose to summarize by achievement category, or simply to enter an overall level. Observations from late in the unit should be most heavily weighted.
Portfolios or collections of work samples; conferences or interviews	Use *Master 9.1 Unit Rubric: Integers* to guide evaluation of collections of work and information gathered in conferences. Teachers may choose to focus particular attention on the Assessment Focus questions. Work from late in the unit should be most heavily weighted.
Unit Review	*Master 9.1 Unit Rubric: Integers* may be helpful in determining levels of achievement. #4 and 5 provide evidence of Understanding of concepts; #1, 3, 8, and 9 provide evidence of Application of mathematical procedures; #7 and 11 provide evidence of Problem solving; #6 provides evidence of Communication.
Unit Test	*Master 9.1 Unit Rubric: Integers* may be helpful in determining levels of achievement. #3 provides evidence of Understanding of concepts; #6 provides evidence of Application of mathematical procedures; #5 provides evidence of Problem solving; #4 provides evidence of Communication.
Unit Problem	Use *Master 9.3 Performance Assessment Rubric: What Time Is It?* The *Unit Problem* offers a snapshot of students' achievement. In particular, it shows their ability to synthesize and apply what they have learned.
Student Self-Assessment	Note students' perceptions of their own progress. This may take the form of an oral or written comment, or a self-rating.
Comments	Analyse the pattern of achievement to identify strengths and needs. In some cases, specific actions may need to be planned to support the learner.

Learning Skills	Ongoing Records
PM 4: Learning Skills Check List Use to record and report throughout a reporting period, rather than for each unit and/or strand.	*PM 10: Summary Class Records: Strands;* *PM 11: Summary Class Records: Achievement Categories;* *PM 12: Summary Record: Individual* Use to record and report evaluations of student achievement over several clusters, a reporting period, or a school year. These can also be used in place of the Unit Summary.

Name ____________________ Date ______________

Master 9.1

Unit Rubric: Integers

	Level 1	Level 2	Level 3	Level 4
Problem solving • chooses and carries out a range of strategies (for example, concrete materials, drawings, number line, estimation) to create and solve problems involving integers and assess the reasonableness of the result	with assistance, chooses and carries out a limited range of appropriate strategies, rarely resulting in an accurate solution	with limited assistance, chooses and carries out appropriate strategies that frequently result in an accurate solution	chooses and carries out appropriate strategies that usually result in an accurate solution	chooses and carries out appropriate strategies; may offer an innovative approach; results in an accurate solution
Understanding of concepts • shows understanding by using concrete materials, drawings, and symbols to represent and explain: – positive and negative integers (symmetry of the number line around 0) – addition and subtraction of integers	shows little understanding; may be unable to represent and explain: – positive and negative integers (symmetry of the number line around 0) – addition and subtraction of integers	shows some understanding; partially able to represent and explain: – positive and negative integers (symmetry of the number line around 0) – addition and subtraction of integers	shows understanding; able to clearly and appropriately represent and explain: – positive and negative integers (symmetry of the number line around 0) – addition and subtraction of integers	shows thorough understanding; able to accurately and effectively represent and explain: – positive and negative integers (symmetry of the number line around 0) – addition and subtraction of integers
Application of mathematical procedures • compares and orders integers • uses concrete materials, drawings, and symbols to represent addition and subtraction • adds integers with and without manipulatives	limited accuracy; major errors or omissions in: – comparing and ordering integers – representing addition and subtraction – adding integers, with and without manipulatives	somewhat accurate; several minor errors or omissions in: – comparing and ordering integers – representing addition and subtraction – adding integers, with and without manipulatives	generally accurate; few minor errors in: – comparing and ordering integers – representing addition and subtraction – adding integers, with and without manipulatives	accurate and precise; no errors in: – comparing and ordering integers – representing addition and subtraction – adding integers, with and without manipulatives
Communication • explains reasoning and procedures clearly using appropriate terminology • presents representations and calculations clearly, including appropriate symbols	unable to explain reasoning and procedures clearly presents representations and calculations with little clarity; rarely uses appropriate symbols	partially explains reasoning and procedures presents representations and calculations with some clarity; uses some appropriate symbols	explains reasoning and procedures clearly presents representations and calculations clearly and precisely; uses appropriate symbols	explains reasoning and procedures clearly, precisely, and confidently presents representations and calculations clearly and precisely; uses a range of appropriate symbols

Name ____________________ Date _______________

Master 9.2

Ongoing Observations: Integers

The behaviours described under each heading are examples; they are not intended to be an exhaustive list of all that might be observed. More detailed descriptions are provided in each lesson under *Assessment for Learning*.

STUDENT ACHIEVEMENT: Integers				
Student	**Problem solving**	**Understanding of concepts**	**Application of mathematical procedures**	**Communication**
	▪ Chooses and carries out appropriate strategies to create and solve problems with integers; checks results (estimates)	▪ Explains and demonstrates positive and negative integers (number line)	▪ Compares and orders integers ▪ Represents addition and subtraction ▪ Adds integers	▪ Explains reasoning clearly ▪ Presents work clearly

Level 1 – very limited; Level 2 – somewhat or limited; Level 3 – satisfactory; Level 4 – thorough

Name ____________________ Date ______________

Master 9.3

Performance Assessment Rubric: What Time Is It?

	Level 1	Level 2	Level 3	Level 4
Problem solving • chooses appropriate strategies (for example, number line, coloured tiles, estimation, drawing, table, patterns) to create and solve problems based on interpreting a time zone map, and checks reasonableness of solutions	uses few simple strategies to create and solve time zone problems and check solutions; limited success	uses some appropriate strategies to create and solve time zone problems and check solutions; some success	uses appropriate strategies to create and solve time zone problems and check solutions; generally successful	uses innovative and appropriate strategies to solve time zone problems and check solutions; successful and effective
Understanding of concepts • shows understanding of integers by giving appropriate explanations and justifications of how integers were used to solve each problem	shows very limited understanding by giving few appropriate explanations or justifications	shows limited understanding by giving some appropriate but incomplete explanations and justifications	shows understanding by giving appropriate explanations and justifications	shows thorough understanding by giving appropriate and complete explanations and justifications
Application of mathematical procedures • accurately compares, orders, adds, and subtracts integers as required by the tasks	limited accuracy; major errors or omissions in: – comparing and ordering integers – adding integers – subtracting integers	somewhat accurate; several minor errors or omissions in: – comparing and ordering integers – adding integers – subtracting integers	generally accurate; few minor errors in: – comparing and ordering integers – adding integers – subtracting integers	accurate and precise; no errors in: – comparing and ordering integers – adding integers – subtracting integers
Communication • explains reasoning clearly using appropriate mathematical terminology	explains reasoning unclearly and imprecisely, using few mathematical terms	explains reasoning with some clarity, using some appropriate mathematical terms	explains reasoning clearly and precisely, using appropriate mathematical terms	explains reasoning clearly, precisely, and confidently, using a range of appropriate mathematical terminology
• presents work, including representations and symbols, clearly	presents work with little clarity	presents work with some clarity	presents work clearly	presents work clearly and precisely

Name ____________________ Date ______________

Master 9.4

Unit Summary: Integers

Review assessment records to determine the most consistent achievement levels for the assessments conducted. Some cells may be blank. *Overall* achievement levels may be recorded in each row, rather than identifying levels for each achievement category.

	Most Consistent Level of Achievement*				
Strand: *Number Sense and Numeration*	**Problem Solving**	**Understanding of concepts**	**Application of mathematical procedures**	**Communication**	***Overall***
Ongoing Observations					
Work samples or portfolios; conferences					
Unit Review					
Practice Test					
Unit Problem: What Time Is It?					
Achievement Level for reporting					

* Use Ontario Achievement Levels 1, 2, 3, 4

Self-Assessment:

Comments: (Strengths, Needs, Next Steps)

Name ____________________ Date ________________

Master 9.5

Additional Activity 1: Greatest Sum

Play with a partner.

You will need 4 sets of cards numbered 0 to 9 and a sheet of paper for a game card.

The goal is to get the greatest sum of two 2-digit numbers.

How to Play:

1. Write blanks on the game card, as shown below.
   ____ ____ + ____ ____ =

2. Take turns to draw a number card from the shuffled deck.
   After each draw, write a digit in one of the blanks.
   Do not let the other player see your choice.

3. When all the blanks have been filled, use mental math to add.

4. Compare sums. The player with the greater sum scores 1 point.

5. Use the 4 digits to find what the greatest possible sum is.
   If the winning player had that sum, the player scores another point.

6. The winner is the first person to get 10 points.

Take It Further:
Play the game again. This time, find the least difference of two numbers.
If the second number on the game card is greater than the first number, so you cannot subtract, you lose 1 point.

Name ____________________ Date ______________

Master 9.6

Additional Activity 2: Magic Squares

Work on your own.

Complete each magic square so every row, column, and diagonal has the same sum.

22		
	19	21
		16

32	34	36
	38	

100	93	98
96		

Look for patterns in the completed squares. Consider:
- the numbers used in each square
- the middle number compared to the other numbers
- the numbers in opposite corners

Use the patterns you found. Complete these magic squares.

	25	

	67	

240		

Take It Further:
Albrecht Dürer was a famous German painter in the 16th century. One of his paintings called *Melancholia,* contained a 4 by 4 magic square. Complete his magic square.

16			13
		11	
	6	7	
4	15	14	1

Name ____________________ Date ________________

Master 9.7

Step-by-Step 1

Section 9.1, Question 6

You will need a calculator.

Step 1 Circle the categories that increase Canada's population.

Births Deaths Immigration Emigration

Why can these numbers be represented by positive integers?

____

Which categories decrease Canada's population? ____________________
Why can these numbers be represented by negative integers?

____

Step 2 In each column, subtract the lesser number from the greater number.

____

Step 3 Write each answer in *Step 2* as a positive or a negative integer.
Each integer shows the increase or decrease from 1961-66 to 1996-2001.

Change in number of births:________________
Change in number of deaths:________________
Change in number of immigrants:________________
Change in number of emigrants:________________

Step 4 Write **B** on the number line for the approximate number of births in 1961-66.
Write **D** on the number line for the approximate number of deaths in 1961-66.

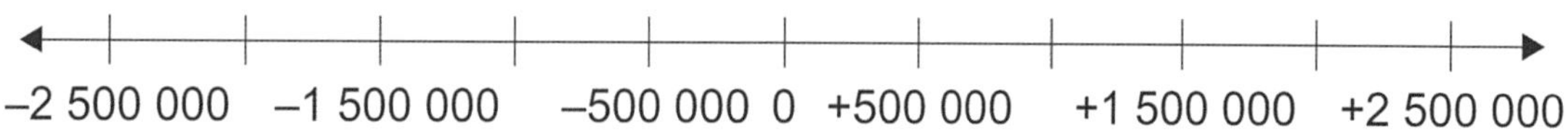

How are the numbers of births and deaths related?

____

Step 5 Write **I** on the number line for the approximate number of immigrants in 1961-66.
Write **E** on the number line for the approximate number of emigrants in 1961-66.

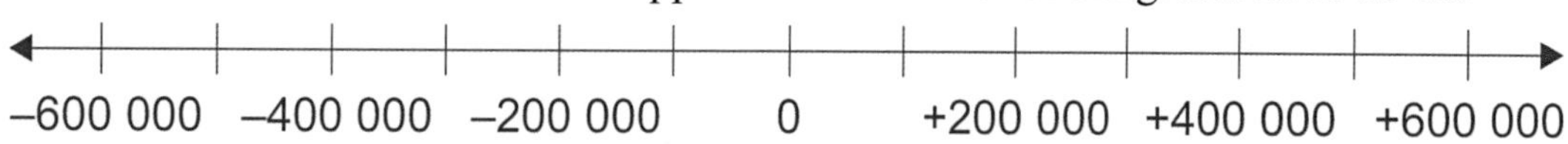

How are the numbers of immigrants and emigrants related?

____

Name ____________________ Date ________________

Master 9.8

Step-by-Step 2

Section 9.2, Question 8

Step 1 Mark each number in the box on the number line below.

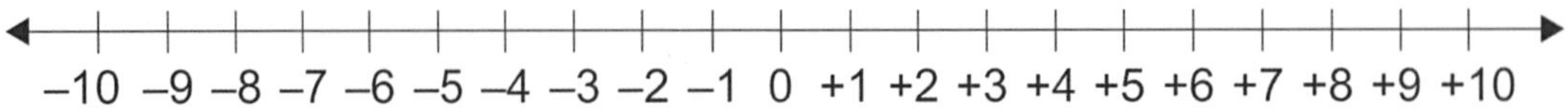

Use the integers you marked on this line in the steps that follow.

Step 2 Which integers are greater than 0? How do you know?

____

Step 3 Which integers are between –3 and +3? How do you know?

____

Step 4 Which integers are greater than –10 and less than –5? How do you know?

____

Step 5 Which integers are less than +1? How do you know?

____

Step 6 Record three other relationships between pairs of integers on the line. Use words, such as: greater than, less than, between, opposites.

Step 7 Make up a question for each relationship. Answer the question.

____

____

____

Name ____________________ Date _______________

Master 9.9

Step-by-Step 3

Section 9.3, Question 4

You will need red and yellow coloured pencils or markers.

Step 1 Choose an integer between –9 and +6. _______
Colour in the fewest tiles needed to model this integer.

Yellow									
Red									

Step 2 Draw another model of the same integer, using some zero pairs.

Yellow												
Red												

Step 3 Repeat *Step 2*, three more times, making a different model each time.

Yellow												
Red												

Yellow												
Red												

Yellow												
Red												

Step 4 How many more ways could you find? Explain.

____

Step 5 What patterns do you see in the tables above?

____

Step 6 Choose an integer between –90 and +60.
How do patterns help you model this integer?

____

____

Name ____________________ Date ________________

Master 9.10

Step-by-Step 4

Section 9.4, Question 10

You will need red and yellow coloured tiles and coloured pencils or markers.

Step 1 Use coloured tiles to model (+3) + (–7). Sketch the tiles you used.

What is (+3) + (–7)? __________

Step 2 Use coloured tiles to model (–7) + (+3). Sketch the tiles you used.

What is (–7) + (+3)? __________

Step 3 How are the sums in *Steps 1* and *2* related? Use your sketches to help you explain.

____

____

Step 4 Use coloured tiles to model (–3) + (+7). Sketch the tiles you used.

What is (–3) + (+7)? __________

Step 5 How are the statements and sums in *Steps 1* and *4* related? Explain.

____

____

Name ____________________ Date ______________

Master 9.11

Step-by-Step 5

Section 9.5, Question 8

You will need a copy of *Number Lines* (Master 9.15). Use the lines labelled –10 to +10.

Step 1 Mark two opposite integers on a number line.
Write an addition equation for these two integers. ________________________
Show this sum on the number line.
Why is the sum of two opposite integers zero?

____

Step 2 Choose two positive integers from a number line.____________

Write an addition equation for these two integers. ______________________
Show this sum on the number line.
Why is the sum of two positive integers always positive?

____

Step 3 Choose two negative integers from a number line.____________

Write an addition equation for these two integers. _______________________
Show this sum on the number line.
Why is the sum of two negative integers always negative?

____

Step 4 Choose two integers with different signs from a number line.

Do *not* choose opposite integers. ____________

Write an addition equation for these two integers. ________________________
Show this sum on the number line.
Explain why the sum has the sign it does.

____

Step 5 Write the opposites of the integers you added in *Step 4*.

Write an addition equation for these two integers. ________________
Show this sum on a number line.
Explain why the sum has the sign it does.

____

Name ____________________ Date ______________

Master 9.12

Step-by-Step 6

Section 9.6, Question 9

You will need coloured tiles.

Step 1 Subtract: (+3) – (+1) = ________

(+4) – (+2) = ________

(+5) – (+3) = ________

What patterns do you see in the subtraction statements?

____

Continue the patterns to write 3 more subtraction equations.

____

Step 2 Subtract: (–5) – (–2) = ________

(–6) – (–3) = ________

(–7) – (–4) = ________

What patterns do you see in the subtraction statements?

____

Continue the patterns to write 3 more subtraction equations.

____

Step 3 Subtract: (–2) – (–7) = ________

(–3) – (–8) = ________

(–4) – (–9) = ________

What patterns do you see in the subtraction statements?

____

Continue the patterns to write 3 more subtraction equations.

____

Step 4 Subtract: (–1) – (+5) = ________

(–2) – (+4) = ________

(–3) – (+3) = ________

What patterns do you see in the subtraction statements?

____

Continue the patterns to write 3 more subtraction equations.

____

Step 5 In *Steps 1* to *4*, how many more equations could you have written each time? Explain.

____

____

Name ________________ Date ____________

Master 9.13

Step-by-Step 7

Section 9.7, Question 8

Step 1 Use the number line below to subtract: (–6) – (+11) = ______

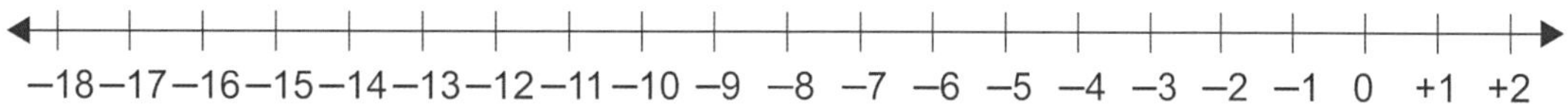

Step 2 Use the number line below to subtract: (+11) – (–6) = ______

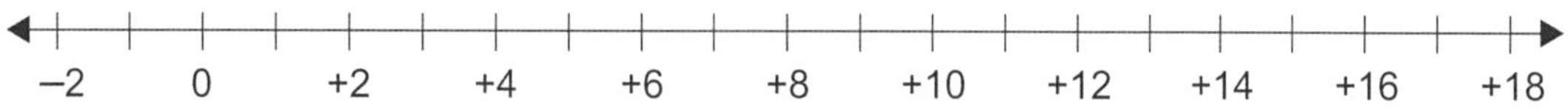

Step 3 Look at the subtraction statements in *Steps 1* and *2*.
How are the statements alike?

____

How are the statements different?

____

Look at the answers in *Steps 1* and *2*.
How are the answers alike? Explain.

____

How are the answers different? Explain.

____

Step 4 Use the number line below to subtract: (+6) – (–11) = ________

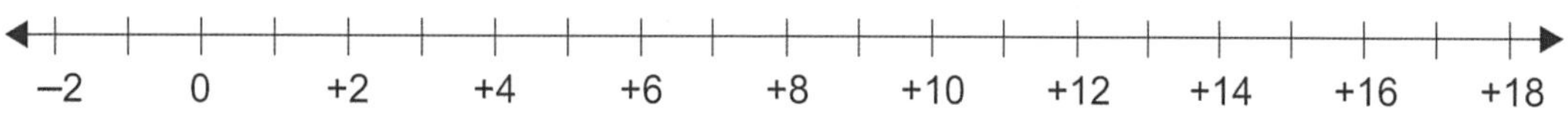

Step 5 Look at the subtraction statements in *Steps 1* and *4*.
How are the statements alike?

____

How are the statements different?

____

Look at the answers in *Steps 1* and *4*.
How are the answers alike? Explain.

____

How are the answers different? Explain.

____

Name ____________________ Date ________________

Master 9.14
Elevation Data

Location	Elevation
Aconcagua, Argentina	6960 m above sea level
Bahia Blanca, Argentina	42 m below sea level
Bentley Subglacial Trench	2540 m below sea level
Caspian Sea Shore	28 m below sea level
Death Valley, California	86 m below sea level
Elbrus, Russia	5642 m above sea level
Eurasia Basin, Arctic Ocean	5450 m below sea level
Everest, Nepal	8850 m above sea level
Java Trench, Indian Ocean	7125 m below sea level
Kilimanjaro, Tanzania	5895 m above sea level
Kosciusko, Australia	2228 m above sea level
Lake Assal, Djibouti	156 m below sea level
Lake Eyre	12 m below sea level
McKinley, Alaska	6194 m above sea level
Mont Blanc, France/Italy	4807 m above sea level
Puerto Rico Trench, Atlantic Ocean	8648 m below sea level
Puncak Jaya, New Guinea	5040 m above sea level
Whitney, California	4418 m above sea level

Name ____________________ Date _______________

Master 9.15

Number Lines

–10 –9 –8 –7 –6 –5 –4 –3 –2 –1 0 +1 +2 +3 +4 +5 +6 +7 +8 +9 +10

–10 –9 –8 –7 –6 –5 –4 –3 –2 –1 0 +1 +2 +3 +4 +5 +6 +7 +8 +9 +10

–10 –9 –8 –7 –6 –5 –4 –3 –2 –1 0 +1 +2 +3 +4 +5 +6 +7 +8 +9 +10

–10 –9 –8 –7 –6 –5 –4 –3 –2 –1 0 +1 +2 +3 +4 +5 +6 +7 +8 +9 +10

–10 –9 –8 –7 –6 –5 –4 –3 –2 –1 0 +1 +2 +3 +4 +5 +6 +7 +8 +9 +10

–10 –9 –8 –7 –6 –5 –4 –3 –2 –1 0 +1 +2 +3 +4 +5 +6 +7 +8 +9 +10

–10 –9 –8 –7 –6 –5 –4 –3 –2 –1 0 +1 +2 +3 +4 +5 +6 +7 +8 +9 +10

–100 –90 –80 –70 –60 –50 –40 –30 –20 –10 0 +10 +20 +30 +40 +50 +60 +70 +80 +90 +100

–100 –90 –80 –70 –60 –50 –40 –30 –20 –10 0 +10 +20 +30 +40 +50 +60 +70 +80 +90 +100

–50 –45 –40 –35 –30 –25 –20 –15 –10 –5 0 +5 +10 +15 +20 +25 +30 +35 +40 +45 +50

–20 –18 –16 –14 –12 –10 –8 –6 –4 –2 0 +2 +4 +6 +8 +10 +12 +14 +16 +18 +20

–200 –160 –100 –80 –40 0 +40 +80 +120 +160 +200

Name ____________________ Date ______________

Master 9.16a

Unit Test: Unit 9 Integers

1. Order these integers from least to greatest.
+15, +3, –18, –7, 0, –12, +7

2. Look at these integers.
+1, –8, +9, –2, +8, –4, –1, +3, –7, +6, 0
List the integers that are:
a) less than 0

b) between –5 and +5

3. Use tiles to add. Sketch the tiles you used.
a) (+5) + (–2) **b)** (–7) + (+4)

4. Use tiles to subtract. Sketch the tiles you used.
a) (+6) – (+5) **b)** (+2) – (–3)

Name ____________________ Date ______________

Master 9.16b

Unit Test continued

5. Use the number line to add or subtract.
a) (+6) + (–4) **b)** (–3) – (+4)

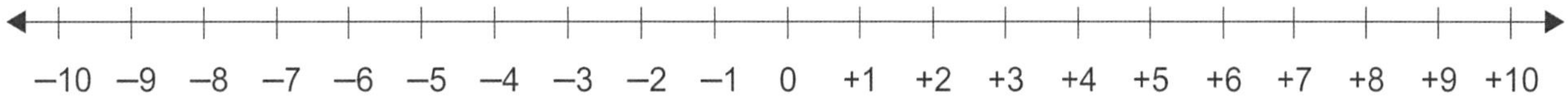

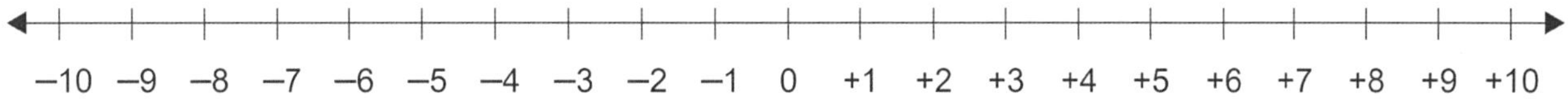

6. **a)** Suppose you are adding two negative integers. Will the sum be positive or negative? Use an example to explain how you know.

b) Suppose you are subtracting a positive integer from a negative integer. Will the difference be positive or negative? Use an example to explain how you know.

7. **a)** Show two ways that –2 can be written as the sum of two integers.

b) Show two ways that +2 can be written as the difference of two integers.

8. Puncak Jaya, New Guinea, is 5040 m above sea level. Lake Assal, Djibouti, is 156 m below sea level.
What is the difference in elevations of these two locations?

Name ____________________ Date ______________

Master 9.17

Sample Answers

Unit Test – Master 9.16

1. –18, –12, –7, 0, +3, +7, +15
2. **a)** –8, –2, –4, –1, –7
   b) +1, –2, –4, –1, +3, 0
3. **a)** +3

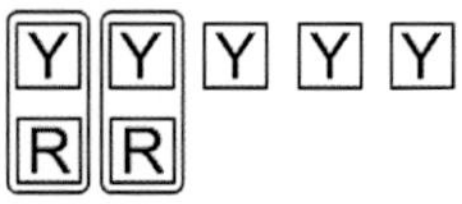

b) –3

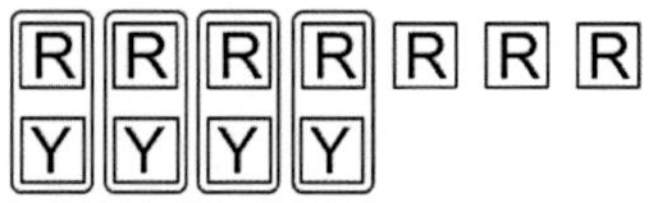

4. **a)** +1

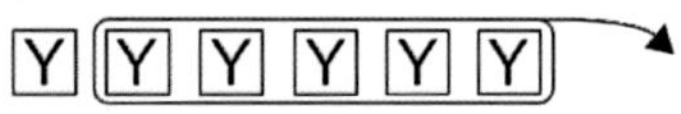

b) +5

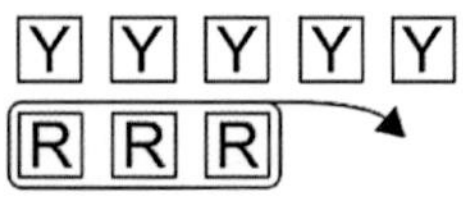

5. **a)** +2

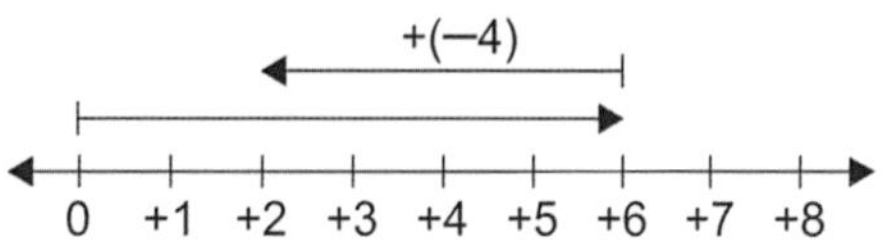

b) –7

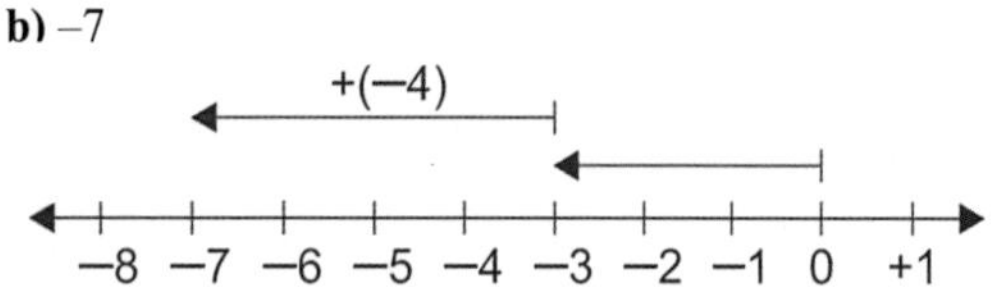

6. **a)** When I add two negative integers, their sum is always negative.
   For example, (–4) + (–3) = (–7); I used 4 red tiles and 3 red tiles to get 7 red tiles. I did not use yellow tiles, so the answer cannot be positive.
   b) When I subtract a positive integer from a negative integer, the answer is always negative. For example, (–4) – (+3) = –7; to take away +3, I need 3 yellow tiles, so I add 3 zero pairs to 4 red tiles, to have a total of 7 red tiles and 3 yellow tiles. Then I take away the 3 yellow tiles.
   Another example, (–1) – (+6) = –7; to take away +6, I need 6 yellow tiles, so I add 6 zero pairs to 1 red tile to have a total of 7 red tiles and 6 yellow tiles. Then I take away the 6 yellow tiles.
7. **a)** I chose two integers with opposite signs. The negative integer has an arrow that is 2 units longer than the positive integer. For example, (+8) + (–10) = –2; (–4) + (+2) = –2
   b) I start with two positive integers. One integer has an arrow that is 2 units longer than the other.
   For example, (+10) – (+8) = +2
   I start with two negative integers. The integer I take away has an arrow that is 2 units longer than the other integer.
   For example, (–4) – (–6) = +2
8. Either (+5040) – (–156) = +5196 or
   (–156) – (+5040) = –5196
   The difference is +5196; then Puncak Jaya is 5196 m higher than Lake Assal or, the difference is –5196; then Lake Assal is 5196 m lower than Puncak Jaya.

Extra Practice Masters 9.18–9.25

Go to the CD-ROM to access editable versions of these Extra Practice Masters.

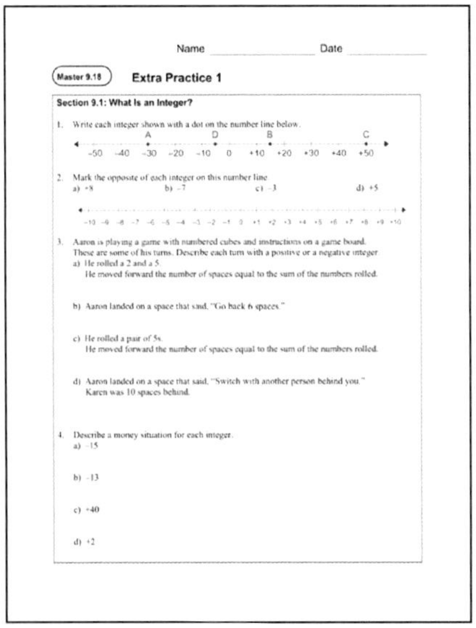
Name ______ Date ______

Master 9.18 Extra Practice 1

Section 9.1: What Is an Integer?

1. Write each integer shown with a dot on the number line below.
2. Mark the opposite of each integer on this number line.
a) +8 b) −7 c) −3 d) +5
3. Aaron is playing a game with numbered cubes and instructions on a game board. These are some of his turns. Describe each turn with a positive or a negative integer.
a) He rolled a 2 and a 5. He moved forward the number of spaces equal to the sum of the numbers rolled.
b) Aaron landed on a space that said, "Go back 6 spaces."
c) He rolled a pair of 5s. He moved forward the number of spaces equal to the sum of the numbers rolled.
d) Aaron landed on a space that said, "Switch with another person behind you." Karen was 10 spaces behind.
4. Describe a money situation for each integer.
a) −15 b) −13 c) +40 d) +2

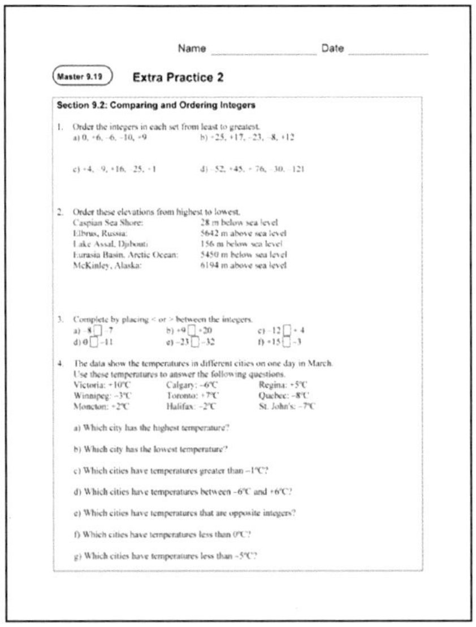
Name ______ Date ______

Master 9.19 Extra Practice 2

Section 9.2: Comparing and Ordering Integers

1. Order the integers in each set from least to greatest.
a) 0, +6, −6, −10, −9 b) −25, +17, −23, −8, +12
c) +4, −9, +16, −25, −1 d) −52, +45, −76, −30, −121
2. Order these elevations from highest to lowest.
Caspian Sea Shore: 28 m below sea level
Elbrus, Russia: 5642 m above sea level
Lake Assal, Djibouti: 156 m below sea level
Eurasia Basin, Arctic Ocean: 5450 m below sea level
McKinley, Alaska: 6194 m above sea level
3. Complete by placing < or > between the integers.
4. The data show the temperatures in different cities on one day in March. Use these temperatures to answer the following questions.
Victoria: +10°C Calgary: −6°C Regina: +5°C
Winnipeg: −3°C Toronto: +7°C Quebec: −8°C
Moncton: −2°C Halifax: −2°C St. John's: −7°C
a) Which city has the highest temperature?
b) Which city has the lowest temperature?
c) Which cities have temperatures greater than −1°C?
d) Which cities have temperatures between −6°C and +6°C?
e) Which cities have temperatures that are opposite integers?
f) Which cities have temperatures less than 0°C?
g) Which cities have temperatures less than −5°C?

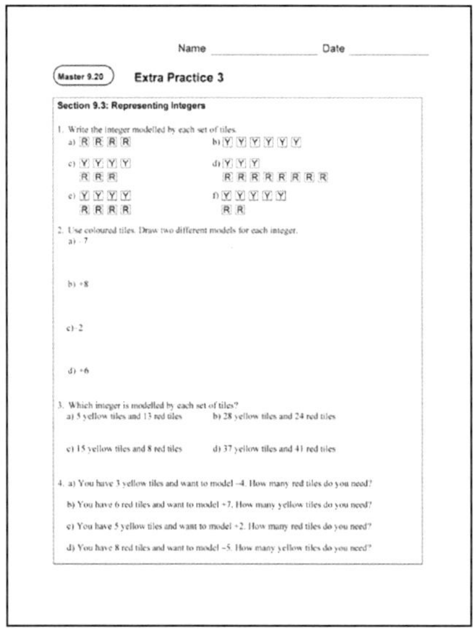
Name ______ Date ______

Master 9.20 Extra Practice 3

Section 9.3: Representing Integers

1. Write the integer modelled by each set of tiles.
2. Use coloured tiles. Draw two different models for each integer.
a) −7 b) +8 c) −2 d) +6
3. Which integer is modelled by each set of tiles?
a) 5 yellow tiles and 13 red tiles b) 28 yellow tiles and 24 red tiles
c) 15 yellow tiles and 8 red tiles d) 37 yellow tiles and 41 red tiles
4. a) You have 3 yellow tiles and want to model −4. How many red tiles do you need?
b) You have 6 red tiles and want to model +7. How many yellow tiles do you need?
c) You have 5 yellow tiles and want to model +2. How many red tiles do you need?
d) You have 8 red tiles and want to model −5. How many yellow tiles do you need?

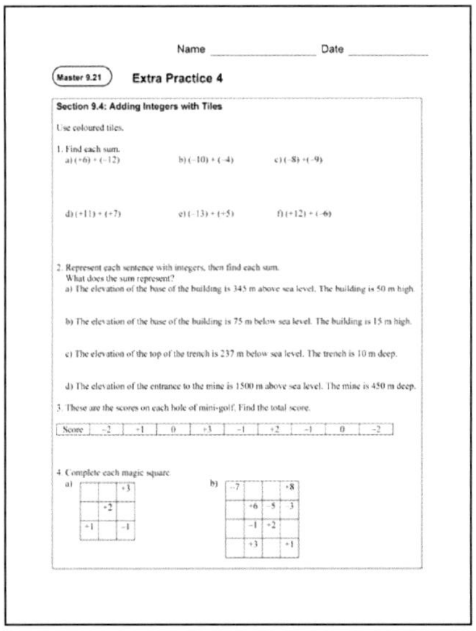
Name ______ Date ______

Master 9.21 Extra Practice 4

Section 9.4: Adding Integers with Tiles

Use coloured tiles.
1. Find each sum.
2. Represent each sentence with integers, then find each sum. What does the sum represent?
3. These are the scores on each hole of mini-golf. Find the total score.
4. Complete each magic square.

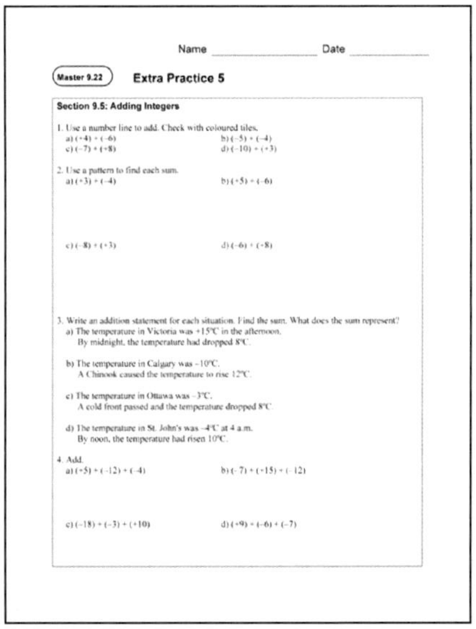
Name ______ Date ______

Master 9.22 Extra Practice 5

Section 9.5: Adding Integers

1. Use a number line to add. Check with coloured tiles.
2. Use a pattern to find each sum.
3. Write an addition statement for each situation. Find the sum. What does the sum represent?
4. Add.

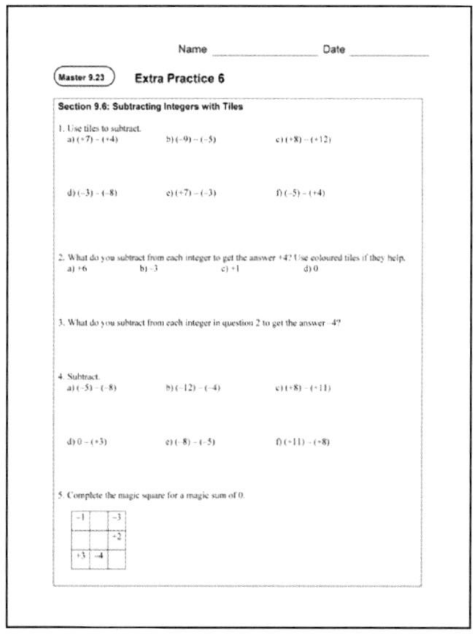
Name ______ Date ______

Master 9.23 Extra Practice 6

Section 9.6: Subtracting Integers with Tiles

1. Use tiles to subtract.
2. What do you subtract from each integer to get the answer +4? Use coloured tiles if they help.
3. What do you subtract from each integer in question 2 to get the answer −4?
4. Subtract.
5. Complete the magic square for a magic sum of 0.

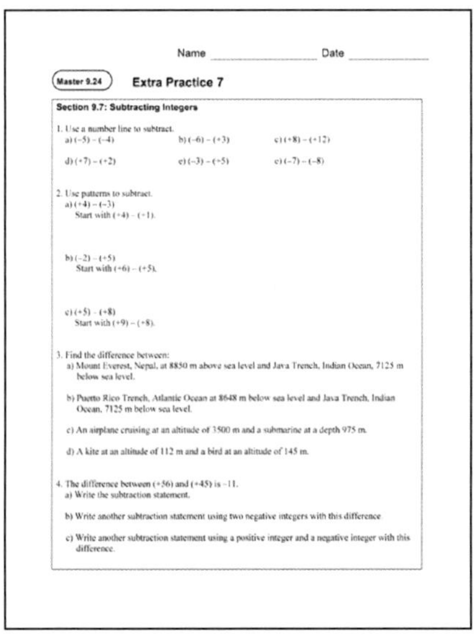
Name ______ Date ______

Master 9.24 Extra Practice 7

Section 9.7: Subtracting Integers

1. Use a number line to subtract.
2. Use patterns to subtract.
3. Find the difference between:
a) Mount Everest, Nepal, at 8850 m above sea level and Java Trench, Indian Ocean, 7125 m below sea level.
b) Puerto Rico Trench, Atlantic Ocean at 8648 m below sea level and Java Trench, Indian Ocean, 7125 m below sea level.
c) An airplane cruising at an altitude of 3500 m and a submarine at a depth 975 m.
d) A kite at an altitude of 112 m and a bird at an altitude of 145 m.
4. The difference between (+56) and (+45) is −11.
a) Write the subtraction statement.
b) Write another subtraction statement using two negative integers with this difference.
c) Write another subtraction statement using a positive integer and a negative integer with this difference.

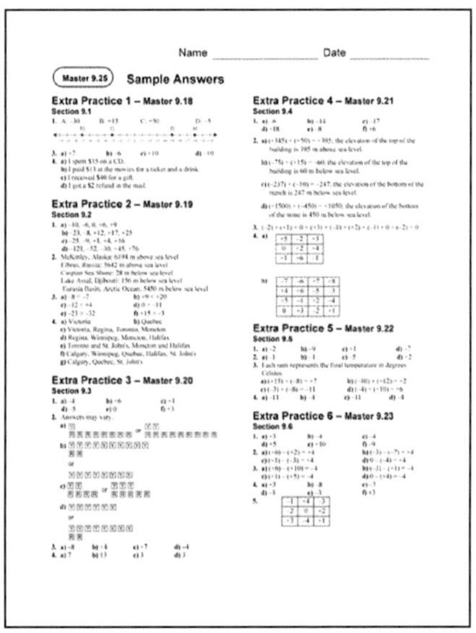
Name ______ Date ______

Master 9.25 Sample Answers

Extra Practice 1 – Master 9.18
Extra Practice 2 – Master 9.19
Extra Practice 3 – Master 9.20
Extra Practice 4 – Master 9.21
Extra Practice 5 – Master 9.22
Extra Practice 6 – Master 9.23

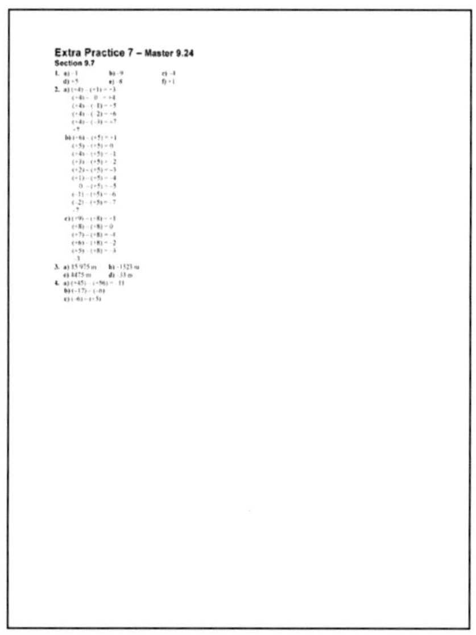
Extra Practice 7 – Master 9.24

Addison Wesley

Mathematics Makes Sense

Program Authors

Jason Johnston
Bryn Keyes
Mary Doucette
Antonietta Lenjosek
Steve Thomas
Margaret Sinclair
Trevor Brown
Cathy Heideman
Don Jones
Michael Davis
Jennifer Paziuk
Ken Harper
Sharon Jeroski
Ray Appel
Laura Weatherhead
Betty Milne
Jim Mennie
Lynn Strangway

Printed and bound in Canada

10 17

PEARSON
Education Canada

ADDISON WESLEY

Ontario

Math Makes Sense 7

Ontario

Teacher Guide

Unit 10: Patterning and Algebra

PEARSON
Addison Wesley

UNIT 10 Patterning and Algebra

"Variables constitute an extremely powerful method of expressing the regularities found in mathematics. Variables enable us to use mathematical symbolism as a tool to think and help better understand mathematical ideas in the same way physical objects and drawings are used."

John A. Van de Walle

FOCUS STRAND
Patterning and Algebra

SUPPORTING STRAND
Number Sense and Numeration

TIPS
Solving problems with algebra often helps students see patterns and relationships more readily.

Mathematics Background

What Are the Big Ideas?

- A pattern can be found in many different forms, and can be extended and used to make predictions.
- A variable is a symbol that represents a number or a set of numbers.
- An equation shows a relationship between two quantities.

How Will the Concepts Develop?

Students describe, extend, and explain number patterns, then use patterns to make predictions. They use a table and a graph to describe and illustrate a pattern.

Students use a variable to represent a set of numbers, then translate simple statements into algebraic expressions. Students evaluate a simple algebraic expression by substituting a number for a variable.

Students translate statements into equations and use a variable to represent a number. They learn that a solution to an equation makes the equation true. Students solve equations by inspection and by systematic trial.

Why Are These Concepts Important?

Algebraic reasoning involves identifying and extending patterns. Extending a pattern is a useful problem-solving strategy. As students develop algebraic reasoning, they also develop the ability to use variables and to solve equations. Using algebra is an efficient way to describe a pattern.

Algebra allows students to describe patterns and relationships they encounter in their study of math and other disciplines, as well as outside the classroom. The ability to analyse situations and to represent them using variables is essential.

Curriculum Overview

Cluster 1: Patterns

Overall Expectations
- Identify, extend, create, and discuss patterns using whole numbers and variables. (7m67)
- Apply and discuss patterning strategies in problem-solving situations. (7m69)

Specific Expectations
- Describe patterns in a variety of sequences using the appropriate language and supporting materials. (7m70)
- Extend a pattern, complete a table, and write words to explain the pattern. (7m71)
- Recognize patterns and use them to make predictions. (7m72)
- Present solutions to patterning problems and explain the thinking behind the solution process. (7m75)

Cluster 2: Algebraic Expressions and Equations

Overall Expectations
- Identify the relationships between whole numbers and variables. (7m66)
- Identify, create, and solve simple algebraic equations. (7m68)

Specific Expectations
- Interpret a variable as a symbol that may be replaced by a given set of numbers. (7m73)
- Write statements to interpret simple formulas. (7m74)
- Evaluate simple algebraic expressions by substituting natural numbers for the variables. (7m76)
- Translate simple statements into algebraic expressions or equations. (7m77)
- Solve equations of the form $ax = c$ and $ax + b = c$ by inspection and systematic trial, using whole numbers, with and without the use of a calculator. (7m78)
- Solve problems giving rise to first-degree equations with one variable by inspection or by systematic trial. (7m79)
- Establish that a solution to an equation makes the equation true. (7m80)

Launch

Section 10.1: Number Patterns

Section 10.2: Graphing Patterns

Section 10.3: Variables in Expressions

Mid-Unit Review

Section 10.4: Evaluating Algebraic Expressions

Section 10.5: Reading and Writing Equations

Section 10.6: Solving Equations

Unit Review
Practice Test

Unit Problem
Fund Raising

Curriculum across the Grades

Grade 6	Grade 7	Grade 8
Students recognize and discuss the mathematical relationships between and among patterns. They identify, extend, and create patterns in a variety of contexts. Students analyse number patterns and state the rule for any relationships. They discuss and defend the choice of a pattern rule. Students state a rule for the relationship between terms in a given data table of values and graph the relationship in the first quadrant. They apply patterning strategies to problem-solving situations. Students determine the value of a missing term or factor in simple formulas using guess-and-test methods, with and without the use of calculators.	Students identify, extend, create, and discuss patterns using whole numbers and variables. They use patterns to make predictions, and explain the thinking behind the solutions to patterning problems. Students identify the relationships between whole numbers and variables. They write statements to interpret simple formulas. Students identify, create, and solve simple algebraic equations. They establish that a solution to an equation makes the equation true. Students solve equations of the form $ax = c$ and $ax + b = c$. They solve problems giving rise to first-degree equations with one variable.	Students identify, create, and discuss patterns in algebraic terms. They apply and defend patterning strategies in problem-solving situations. Students use the concept of a variable to write equations and algebraic expressions. They write statements to interpret simple equations. Students evaluate simple algebraic expressions, with up to three terms, by substituting fractions and decimals for the variables. They solve and verify first-degree equations with one variable, involving whole numbers and decimals. Students create, then solve, problems giving rise to first-degree equations with one variable. They investigate inequalities and test whether they are true or false by substituting whole number values for the variables.

Additional Activities

Substitution Toss

For Extra Practice (*Appropriate for use after Section 10.4*)
Materials: *Substitution Toss* (Master 10.5a), *Substitution Expressions* (Master 10.5b), 2 number cubes labelled 1 to 6, scissors

Playing this game reinforces the skills of substitution, as well as order of operations and mental math strategies.

The work students do: Students work in pairs. Students use number cubes to determine the number to substitute into an algebraic expression. If the student evaluates correctly, she keeps the card. The winner is the student with more cards at the end of the game.

Take It Further: Students say each algebraic expression in words before rolling the number cubes.

Kinesthetic/Social/Logical
Partner Activity

Algebra Concentration

For Extra Practice (*Appropriate for use after Section 10.5*)
Materials: *Algebra Concentration* (Master 10.6), scissors

This activity reinforces the vocabulary of algebra.

The work students do: Students play with a partner. Students cut out the cards and lay them out face down on the table. Player A turns over a card, then tries to find the matching card. If Player A finds a matching pair, she keeps the cards. If the cards do not match, Player A turns both cards over. Player B takes a turn. Play continues until all matches have been made.

Take It Further: Students make cards for other words and their descriptions, then add the cards to the game. Students play the game again.

Logical/Social/Kinesthetic
Partner Activity

Algebra Game

For Extra Practice (*Appropriate for use after Section 10.6.*)
Materials: *Algebra Game* (Master 10.7a), *Algebra Game Board* (Master 10.7b), tiles to cover up the questions

This activity reinforces students' knowledge of the order of operations, expressions, and equations.

The work students do: Students play with a partner. Students take turns to answer a question. If the player is correct, he scores the points. If the answer is incorrect, the other player can answer the same question. If she is correct, she scores the points. Play continues until all questions have been revealed. The player with the greater number of points wins.

Take It Further: Students create their own Algebra Game Board, then exchange boards with another pair of students.

Spatial/Kinesthetic/Mathematical
Partner Activity

Algebra Word Search

For Extension (*Appropriate for use after Section 10.6*)
Materials: *Algebra Word Search* (Master 10.8)

This activity reinforces the key words of the unit and their meanings.

The work students do: Students work alone. Students find the key words, horizontally, vertically, or diagonally, in the grid. The words may be read forward or backward. Students circle the words as they find them.

Take It Further: Students write a meaning for each word they find.

Logical/Mathematical/Spatial
Individual Activity

Planning for Unit 10

Planning for Instruction

Suggested Unit time: About 3 weeks

Section	Time	Materials	Program Support
Launch, page 2	15–20 min	1-cm grid transparency overhead markers	PM 20: 1-cm Grid Paper
Skills You'll Need, page 4	65–80 min	1-cm grid and transparency overhead markers	PM 20: 1-cm Grid Paper
10.1: Number Patterns, page 6 Extend patterns and use them to make predictions.	80–100 min	counters Pattern Blocks square dot paper 0.5-cm grid paper (optional) geoboards and geobands (optional)	PM 25: Pattern Blocks PM 22: Square Dot Paper Master 10.9: Step-by-Step 1 Master 10.17: Extra Practice 1
10.2: Graphing Patterns, page 11 Use a table and a graph to describe a pattern.	80–100 min	rulers 0.5-cm grid paper calculators	PM 14: 0.5-cm Grid Paper Master 10.10: Step-by-Step 2 Master 10.18: Extra Practice 2
10.3: Variables in Expressions, page 16 Use a variable to represent a set of numbers.	80–100 min		Master 10.11: Step-by-Step 3 Master 10.19: Extra Practice 3
Mid-Unit Review, page 20		rulers 0.5-cm grid paper calculators	PM 14: 0.5-cm Grid Paper
10.4: Evaluating Algebraic Expressions, page 21 Substitute a number for a variable in an algebraic expression.	80–100 min		Master 10.12: Step-by-Step 4 Master 10.20: Extra Practice 4
10.5: Reading and Writing Equations, page 25 Translate statements into equations.	80–100 min		Master 10.13: Step-by-Step 5 Master 10.21: Extra Practice 5
10.6: Solving Equations, page 28 Solve equations by inspection and by systematic trial.	80–100 min		Master 10.14: Step-by-Step 6 Master 10.22: Extra Practice 6
Reading and Writing in Math: Choosing a Strategy, page 34		calculators red and blue tiles (optional) 0.5-cm grid paper (optional)	
Unit Review, page 36		0.5-cm grid paper calculators	PM 14: 0.5-cm Grid Paper Extra Practice: Student Book page 447
Practice Test, page 39		0.5-cm grid paper calculators	PM 14: 0.5-cm Grid Paper
Unit Problem: Fund Raising, page 40	40–50 min	rulers 0.5-cm grid paper calculators	PM 14: 0.5-cm Grid Paper

etext online tutorial This web-based tutorial uses voice, animation, and an optional quiz to present each core lesson, so that students can review content with a new approach.

Planning for Assessment

Purpose	Tools and Process	Recording and Reporting
Diagnostic	*Unit Launch* Question; conference; scaffold problems throughout the unit	PM 8: Conference Prompts
Formative	*Explore* – Ongoing Assessment: Observe and Listen	Master 10.2 Ongoing Observations: Patterning and Algebra PM 1: Inquiry Process Check List PM 6: Observation Record 1 PM 7: Observation Record 2 PM 8: Conference Prompts PM 2: Self-Assessment PM 3: Self-Assessment: Problem Solving PM 9: Work Sample Records
Summative	*Unit Review* *Unit Problem* – Performance Assessment Unit Test Review assessment records; add unit results to ongoing records	Master 10.1 Unit Rubric: Patterning and Algebra Master 10.3 Performance Assessment Rubric: Fund Raising Master 10.4 Unit Summary: Patterning and Algebra PM 10: Summary Class Records: Strands PM 11: Summary Class Records: Achievement Categories PM 12: Summary Record: Individual
Learning Skills/Mathematical Disposition	Observe and record throughout the unit	PM 4: Learning Skills Check List PM 5: Mathematical Dispositions and Learning Skills

Program Masters (PM) are in the *Grade 7 Planning and Program Masters* module.
Extra Practice Masters are on the CD-ROM and are printed in reduced format on page 63 of this module.

SECTION ORGANIZER

15–20 min

Curriculum Focus: Activate prior learning about patterning.

Teacher Materials

- 1-cm grid transparency (PM 20)
- overhead markers

ASSUMED PRIOR KNOWLEDGE

- ☑ Students can identify, extend, and create patterns.
- ☑ Students can recognize the patterns in a table of values.
- ☑ Students can draw a graph for a table of values.

UNIT 10

Patterning and Algebra

Students in a grade 7 class were raising money for charity. Some students had a "bowl-a-thon."

This table shows the money that one student raised for different bowling times.

Time (h)	Money Raised ($)
1	8
2	16
3	24
4	32
5	40
6	48

- What patterns do you see in the table?
- Suppose you drew a graph of the data. What might the graph look like?

What You'll Learn

- Describe, extend, and explain patterns.
- Use patterns to make predictions.
- Show patterns as graphs.
- Write and evaluate algebraic expressions.
- Read and write equations.
- Solve equations.

Why It's Important

- Extending a pattern is a useful problem-solving strategy.
- Using algebra is an efficient way to describe a pattern.

ACTIVATE PRIOR LEARNING

Have students look at the pictures on pages 364 and 365 of the Student Book and identify some of the ways students raised money for charity (*car wash, loose-change drive, selling coupons, head shaving*). Have students look at the table and identify any patterns they see.

Ask questions, such as:

- What is the pattern for time, in hours?
  (*The time starts at 1 and increases by 1 each time.*)
- What is the pattern for the money raised, in dollars?
  (*The money starts at 8 and increases by 8 each time.*)
- What is the pattern between the time and the money raised?
  (*The money raised in dollars is 8 times the time in hours.*)
- Suppose you drew a graph of the data. What might the graph look like?
  (*The graph would be a straight line going up to the right because the time in hours increases by the same amount each time and so does the money raised.*)

Use a 1-cm grid transparency on the overhead projector. Have a volunteer graph the data. Be sure that the axes are labelled and the graph has a title. Have students check their predictions.

Tell students that, in this unit, they will investigate patterning and algebra. They will describe, extend, and explain patterns, use patterns to make predictions, and show patterns on graphs. Students will learn how to use variables to translate simple statements into algebraic expressions (which they then evaluate) or equations (which they then solve). At the end of the unit, students will use their understanding of patterning and algebra to investigate the patterns in the money raised by two students in a bike-a-thon.

Key Words

- ordered pairs
- algebraic expressio
- evaluate
- equation
- solve an equation

FROM THE LIBRARY

A Gebra Named Al by Wendy Isdell. Free Spirit Publishing, 1993
ISBN: 091579358X
Julie hates algebra—until she meets a gebra named Al. Julie, frustrated with getting the wrong answer, gives up, rests her head on her book, and is awakened by an Imaginary Number who suddenly appears in her room. Julie follows the Number through a mysterious door, and enters the Land of Mathematics, where the Orders of Operations are real places. With Al and his friends, Julie travels to the Mathematician's Castle.

REACHING ALL LEARNERS

Some students may benefit from using the virtual manipulatives on the e-Tools CD-ROM.
The e-Tools appropriate for this unit are *Counters and Spreadsheet/Data/Grapher*.

DIAGNOSTIC ASSESSMENT

What to Look For

- ✔ Students can identify, extend, and create patterns.
- ✔ Students can recognize the relationship between terms in a given table of values.
- ✔ Students can draw a graph for a set of data.

What to Do

Extra Support:

Students who have difficulty identifying and extending a pattern may benefit from working with simple patterns, such as: Start with 1, add 2 each time.
Work on this skill during Sections 10.1 and 10.2.

Students who have difficulty recognizing the patterns in a table of values should try subtracting consecutive terms to find out if there is a constant number added; or dividing consecutive terms to find out if there is a constant number multiplied.
Work on this skill during Sections 10.1 and 10.2.

Students who have difficulty graphing a set of data may benefit from being given labelled axes on a grid, then writing the data as ordered pairs, and plotting the points.
Work on this skill during Section 10.2.

SECTION ORGANIZER — 65-80 min

Skills in Review
- Reviewing the order of operations
- Graphing on a coordinate grid

Teacher Materials
- 1-cm grid transparency (PM 20)
- overhead markers

Student Materials
- 1-cm grid paper (PM 20)

Vocabulary: ordered pairs

Alternative Example 1

Simplify.

a) $3 \times (4 + 2) - 8$ b) $8 \div 2 + 4 \times 3$ c) $(10 - 5) \times 4 \div 2$

Solution

a) $3 \times (4 + 2) - 8 = 3 \times 6 - 8$ Add in brackets first.
$= 18 - 8$ Then multiply.
$= 10$ Then subtract.

b) $8 \div 2 + 4 \times 3 = 4 + 4 \times 3$ Divide first.
$= 4 + 12$ Then multiply.
$= 16$ Then add.

c) $(10 - 5) \times 4 \div 2 = 5 \times 4 \div 2$ Subtract in brackets first.
$= 20 \div 2$ Then multiply.
$= 10$ Then divide.

UNIT 10

Skills You'll Need

Order of Operations

Recall this order of operations.

Brackets	Perform operations inside the brackets.
Divide and multiply	Do in order from left to right.
Add and subtract	Do in order from left to right.

Example

Simplify.

a) $6 + 3 \times 4$ b) $(5 + 3) \div 2$ c) $18 \div 3 \times 2$

Solution

a) $6 + 3 \times 4 = 6 + 12$ Multiply first.
$= 18$ Then add.

b) $(5 + 3) \div 2 = 8 \div 2$ Add in brackets first.
$= 4$ Then divide.

c) $18 \div 3 \times 2 = 6 \times 2$ Divide first.
$= 12$ Then multiply.

✓ Check

1. Simplify.
a) $5 \times 7 + 2$ 37 b) $5 \times (7 + 2)$ 45 c) $13 + 2 \times 8$ 29
d) $13 + 2 - 8$ 7 e) $13 + 8 \div 2$ 17 f) $13 - 8 \div 2$ 9
g) $12 \div 4 + 2$ 5 h) $12 \div (4 + 2)$ 2 i) $12 + 4 \div 2$ 14

2. a) Simplify.
i) $3 + 4 \times 2 + 5$ 16 ii) $3 \times 4 + 2 \times 5$ 22 iii) $3 \times (4 + 2) \times 5$ 90
iv) $3 \times (4 + 2) + 5$ 23 v) $3 \times 4 \times 2 + 5$ 29 vi) $3 + 4 + 2 \times 5$ 17
b) All the expressions in part a have the same numbers and the same operations. Why are the answers different?
The indicated operations are in different positions in the expressions. So, different pairs of numbers are multiplied and added each time.

366 UNIT 10: Patterning and Algebra

Order of Operations

Remind students of the work they did in grade 6 using the order of operations. Write the acronym B(E)DMAS on the board. (The E may be omitted until students learn the order of operations including exponents.) Tell students they can use this acronym to help them remember the order of operations. B represents brackets, D represents division, M represents multiplication, A represents addition, and S represents subtraction. Encourage students to write a 5-word sentence, where each word begins with one of the letters b, d, m, a, and s, in that order; for example, *Betty doing math at school*. Ensure students understand that multiplication and division are done in the order in which they appear. The same applies for addition and subtraction.

Common Misconceptions

➤ Students perform the operations in left-to-right order.

How to Help: Remind students that brackets are done first, then exponents, then multiplication and division, and then addition and subtraction.

➤ Students always perform addition before subtraction.

How to Help: Remind students that these operations should be performed in the order in which they appear. Use the example $10 - 2 + 5$. When the addition and subtraction are performed in the order in which they appear, the result is 13. When addition is performed before subtraction, the result is 3, which is incorrect. Ensure students understand that multiplication and division must also be performed in the order in which they appear.

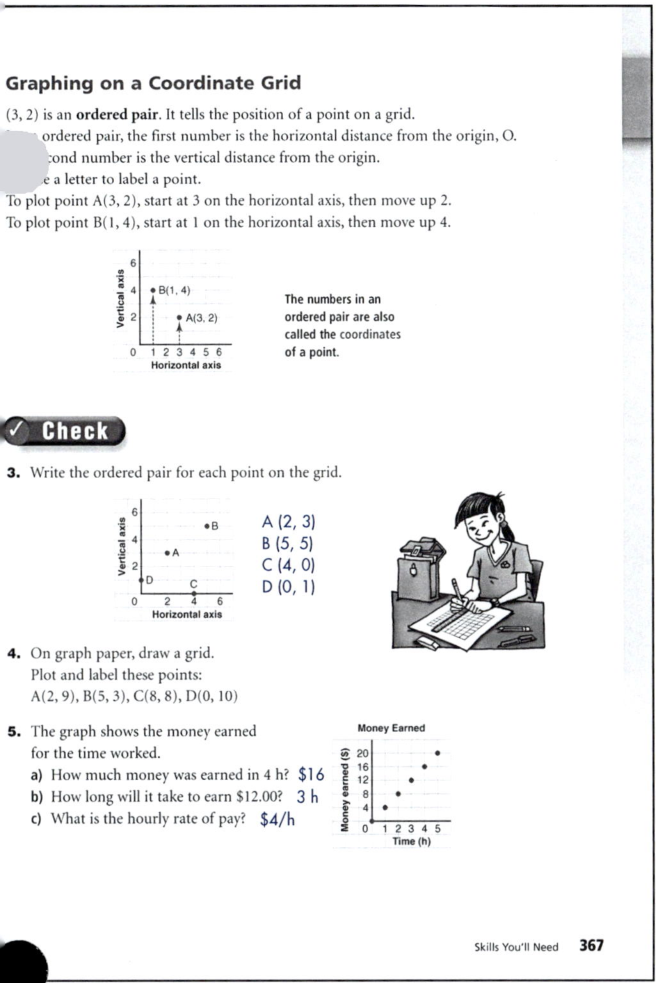

Graphing on a Coordinate Grid

(3, 2) is an **ordered pair**. It tells the position of a point on a grid.
… ordered pair, the first number is the horizontal distance from the origin, O.
…cond number is the vertical distance from the origin.
…e a letter to label a point.
To plot point A(3, 2), start at 3 on the horizontal axis, then move up 2.
To plot point B(1, 4), start at 1 on the horizontal axis, then move up 4.

The numbers in an ordered pair are also called the coordinates of a point.

✓ **Check**

3. Write the ordered pair for each point on the grid.

A (2, 3)
B (5, 5)
C (4, 0)
D (0, 1)

4. On graph paper, draw a grid.
Plot and label these points:
A(2, 9), B(5, 3), C(8, 8), D(0, 10)

5. The graph shows the money earned for the time worked.
a) How much money was earned in 4 h? $16
b) How long will it take to earn $12.00? 3 h
c) What is the hourly rate of pay? $4/h

Skills You'll Need 367

Alternative Example 2

On graph paper, draw a grid. Plot and label each set of points. Join the points in order. Which letter do you see?

a) A(3, 1), B(1, 1), C(1, 3), D(1, 5)
b) E(2, 2), F(2, 6), G(4, 4), H(6, 6), J(6, 2)

Solution

a) I see the letter L.

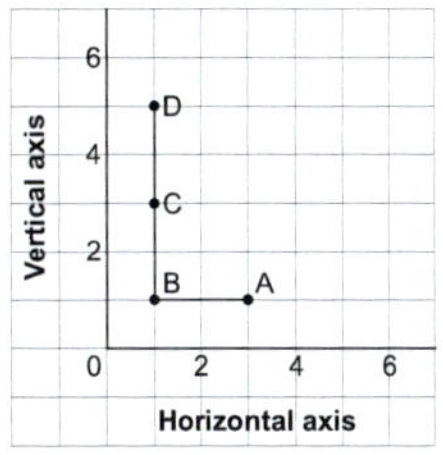

b) I see the letter M.

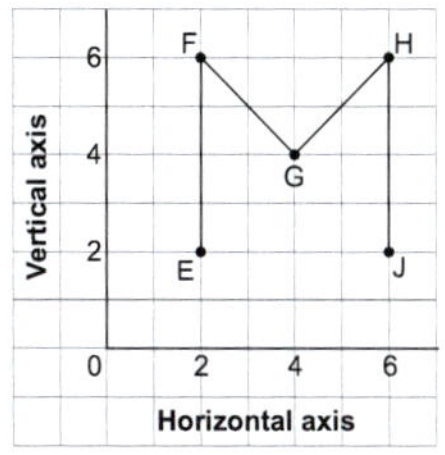

Sample Answers

4.

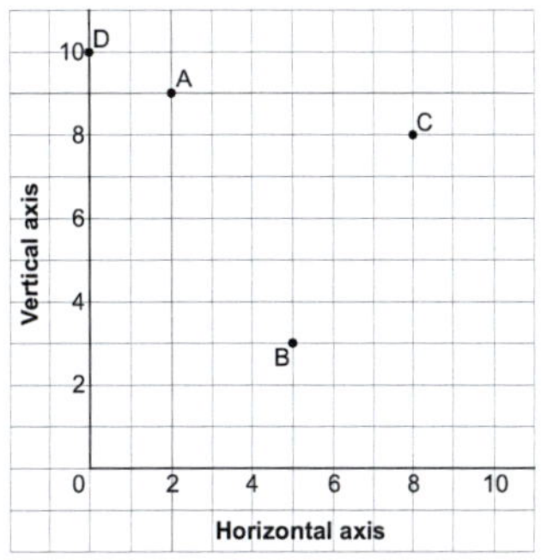

Graphing on a Coordinate Grid

Remind students of the work they did in grade 6, plotting points on a grid. On a coordinate grid, any point can be described by an ordered pair. In grades 6 and 7, the only points considered are these where grid lines intersect, and the numbers in an ordered pair are whole numbers. A line graph can be drawn by plotting ordered pairs to represent two related pieces of data, such as time and temperature, or time and height. On a line graph, individual ordered pairs are not usually labelled. Use a 1-cm grid transparency on the overhead projector. Have volunteers plot ordered pairs named by other volunteers.

Common Misconceptions

➤ Students think, for example, that (4, 1) and (1, 4) represent the same point.

How to Help: Model how to plot these points on a grid. To plot the point (4, 1), start at 4 on the horizontal axis, then move up 1. To plot the point (1, 4), start at 1 on the horizontal axis, then move up 4. The two ordered pairs represent different points.

➤ Students have difficulty plotting an ordered pair with 0 as one of its coordinates.

How to Help: If one coordinate in an ordered pair is 0, then the point lies on an axis. Have students think of the 0 as zero movement. When the first coordinate is 0, do not move horizontally. When the second coordinate is 0, do not move vertically.

Number Patterns

SECTION ORGANIZER (80–100 min)

Curriculum Focus: Extend patterns and use them to make predictions. (7m70, 7m71, 7m72, 7m75)

Student Materials
- counters
- Pattern Blocks (PM 25)
- square dot paper (PM 22)

Optional
- 0.5-cm grid paper (PM 14)
- geoboards
- geobands
- Step-by-Step 1 (Master 10.9)
- Extra Practice 1 (Master 10.17)

Assessment: Master 10.2 Ongoing Observations: Patterning and Algebra

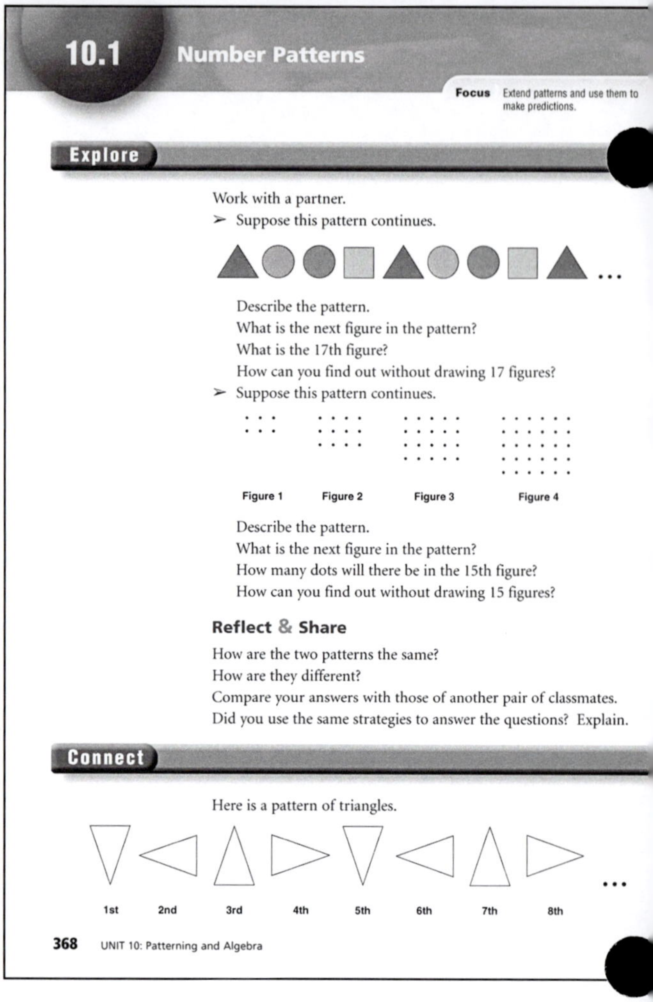
10.1 Number Patterns

Focus Extend patterns and use them to make predictions.

Explore

Work with a partner.

➢ Suppose this pattern continues.

Describe the pattern.
What is the next figure in the pattern?
What is the 17th figure?
How can you find out without drawing 17 figures?

➢ Suppose this pattern continues.

Figure 1 Figure 2 Figure 3 Figure 4

Describe the pattern.
What is the next figure in the pattern?
How many dots will there be in the 15th figure?
How can you find out without drawing 15 figures?

Reflect & Share

How are the two patterns the same?
How are they different?
Compare your answers with those of another pair of classmates.
Did you use the same strategies to answer the questions? Explain.

Connect

Here is a pattern of triangles.

1st 2nd 3rd 4th 5th 6th 7th 8th

368 UNIT 10: Patterning and Algebra

Key Math Learning

A pattern can be extended. It can also be used to make predictions about terms when it is not practical to continue the pattern.

Mental Math

Students could round each decimal to the nearest whole number before multiplying. Answers may vary depending on how students estimate. If students use a calculator to check, their answers will be different from these stated.

Math Note

For your information, if the only way to find the 100th term in a pattern is to find all of the previous 99 terms, then the pattern has a *recursive relationship.* If a rule exists that relates the number of objects in a frame to the frame number, then the pattern has a *functional relationship.* If this is the case, the 100th term can be found without finding the previous 99 terms. Students do not need to know these terms.

BEFORE Get Started

Remind students of the different patterns they saw in earlier grades. Write the pattern: star, moon, sun, star, moon, sun, . . . on the board.

Ask questions, such as:

- What type of pattern is this?
  (*A repeating pattern*) How do you know?
  (*It has a core that repeats.*)
- What is the core?
  (*Star, moon, sun*)

Draw the pattern ❤ ❤❤❤ ❤❤❤❤❤ on the board. Ask:

- What type of pattern is this?
  (*A growing pattern*) How do you know?
  (*Each frame has 2 more hearts than the frame before.*)
- How many hearts will be in the next frame?
  (7) How do you know?
  (*I add 2 hearts to Frame 3; 5 + 2 = 7.*)

Present *Explore.* Have square dot paper, counters, Pattern Blocks, and other plastic figures available for students who want them.

DURING Explore

Ongoing Assessment: Observe and Listen

As students work, ask questions, such as:

- Which type of pattern is the first pattern?
  (*A repeating pattern*) How do you know?
  (*It has a core that repeats.*)
- What is the core?
  (*Red triangle, green circle, blue circle, yellow square*)

The pattern is made up of different positions of an isosceles triangle.
To get the next term each time, rotate the triangle a $\frac{1}{4}$ turn clockwise about its centre.
The core of the pattern is 4 triangles.
The 5th term is the same as the 1st term.
The 6th term is the same as the 2nd term, and so on.
To find any term in the pattern, we find which of the first 4 terms it matches.
Think of multiples of 4: 4, 8, 12, 16, 20, 24, 28, …
All the 4th, 8th, 12th, 16th, 20th, 24th, 28th, … terms have the triangle pointing to the right.

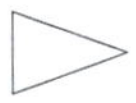

To find the 99th term, we find the closest multiple of 4.
100 is a multiple of 4, so the 100th term is the same as the 4th term.
The 99th term will be the same as the 3rd term:

The 99th term is the triangle pointing up.

We can use the same ideas to make predictions with number patterns.

Example

Each pattern continues.
i) Describe each pattern.
ii) Write the next 3 terms.
iii) Find the 50th term.

a) 4, 7, 10, 13, … b) 1, 4, 9, 16, …

Solution

a) 4, 7, 10, 13, …
i) The pattern begins with 4.
To get the next term, add 3 each time.
ii) The next 3 terms are: $13 + 3 = 16$
$16 + 3 = 19$
$19 + 3 = 22$
The next 3 terms are 16, 19, 22.

10.1 Number Patterns 369

REACHING ALL LEARNERS

Alternative Explore

Materials: Pattern Blocks (PM 25), isometric dot paper (PM 23), square dot paper (PM 22)
Have students use Pattern Blocks to create a repeating pattern. Students record and describe the pattern, then find the next figure and the 20th figure. Students explain how they can find the 20th figure without extending the pattern to find all terms up to the 20th term.
Have students use square dot paper to create a growing pattern. Students describe the pattern, then find the next figure and the 20th figure. Students explain how they can find the 20th figure without extending the pattern to find all terms up to the 20th term.

Early Finishers

Have students complete question 1 of the Extra Practice on page 447 of the Student Book.

Common Misconceptions

➤ Students have difficulty relating the term number to the term.
How to Help: Suggest students try to write an expression for each term number using the same pattern; for example, $1 + 2$, $2 + 2$, $3 + 2$, $4 + 2$; or 1^2, 2^2, 3^2, 4^2; or 1×3, 2×3, 3×3, 4×3. Ensure students understand that this may take a lot of searching at first but students should not get discouraged.

- What will the next figure be?
(*A green circle*)
- Which figures in the given pattern are triangles?
(*Figures 1, 5, and 9*)
- How can you find out what the 17th figure will be?
(*Each of the figure numbers for the triangles is one more than a multiple of 4. Since 17 is 1 more than 16, and 16 is a multiple of 4, then the 17th figure is a red triangle.*)
- Which type of pattern is the second pattern?
(*A growing pattern*) How do you know?
(*The number of dots added increases in a predictable way each time.*)
- What is the pattern rule for the number of dots?
(*Start at 6. Add 6. Increase the number added by 2 each time.*)
- What is the shape of each figure?
(*A rectangle*)
- What will the next figure look like?
(*It will have 42 dots arranged in 6 rows and 7 columns; 30 + 12 = 42.*)
- How many dots will be in the 15th figure?
(272) How do you know?
(*I continued the number pattern to the 15th term.*)

AFTER Connect

Invite students to share their descriptions, answers, and strategies. Ask:

- How are the patterns the same?
(*Both of them are geometric patterns and each changes in a predictable way.*)
- How are they different?
(*The first pattern is a repeating pattern with two attributes changing: colour and shape. The second pattern is a growing pattern. The number of dots increases in a predictable way each time but the shape remains rectangular.*)

Sample Answers

1. a) This is a repeating pattern with core: triangle, square, pentagon.

b)

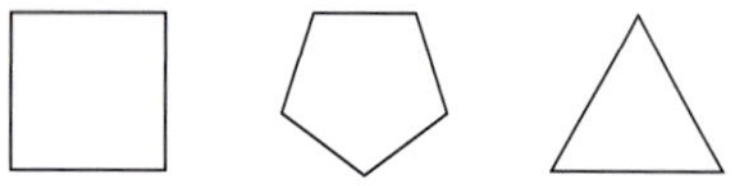

c)

29th figure 49th figure

2. a) The pattern is: Start with 3 counters in the shape of an "L." Add 1 counter to each arm each time.

b)

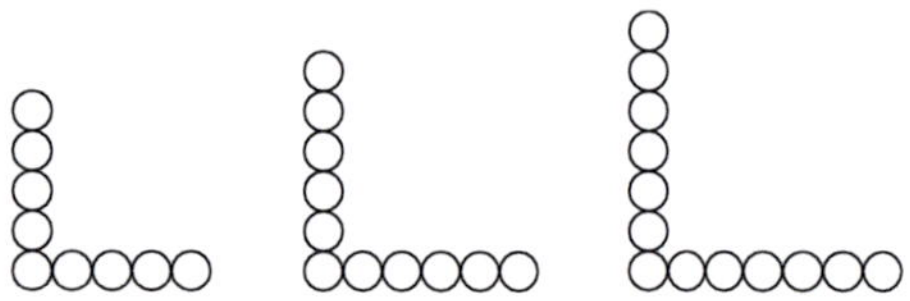

c) The 18th term has 19 counters in each arm.
The 38th term has 39 counters in each arm.

iii) Since the terms increase by 3 each time, compare the pattern with multiples of 3.
Pattern: 4, 7, 10, 13, 16, 19, 22, ...
Multiples of 3: 3, 6, 9, 12, 15, 18, 21, ...
Each term in the pattern is 1 more than a multiple of 3.
So, the terms in the pattern are multiples of 3, plus 1.
The 1st term: $1 \times 3 + 1 = 4$
The 2nd term: $2 \times 3 + 1 = 7$
The 3rd term: $3 \times 3 + 1 = 10$
The 4th term: $4 \times 3 + 1 = 13$, and so on
. .
. .
. .
The 50th term: $50 \times 3 + 1 = 151$
The 50th term is 151.

b) 1, 4, 9, 16, ...
i) The pattern begins with 1.
To get the 2nd term, add 3.
To get the 3rd term, add 5.
To get the 4th term, add 7.
To get each successive term, increase the number you add by 2 each time.
ii) The next 3 terms are: $16 + 9 = 25$
$25 + 11 = 36$
$36 + 13 = 49$
The next 3 terms are 25, 36, 49.

Recall that a perfect square is the product of a number and itself.

iii) To use the same method to get the 50th term, we would need to know the 49th term and what to add.
So, we look at the pattern a different way.
The pattern is: 1, 4, 9, 16, 25, 36, 49, ...
These are the perfect squares: $1^2, 2^2, 3^2, 4^2, 5^2, 6^2, 7^2, \ldots$
So, the 50th term is: $50^2 = 2500$
The 50th term is 2500.

370 UNIT 10: Patterning and Algebra

Assignment Guidelines

If your students do not have time to complete all the *Practice* questions on pages 371 and 372, these questions provide minimum curriculum coverage: 1, 3, 6, 7, 8, *Reflect*
To assess the 4 Achievement Chart categories listed in the curriculum document, have students complete these *Practice* questions: Understanding Concepts: 3; Application: 8; Problem Solving: 9; Communication: *Reflect*

For the second pattern, ensure students understand how to determine the number of dots in the 15th figure, using a rule that involves the position of the figure, rather than finding all preceding terms first.

There are 6 dots in Figure 1.
The dots are arranged in 2 rows of 3.
The rectangle is 2 by 3.
There are 12 dots in Figure 2.
The dots are arranged in 3 rows of 4.
The rectangle is 3 by 4.
There are 20 dots in Figure 3.
The dots are arranged in 4 rows of 5.
The rectangle is 4 by 5.
There are 30 dots in Figure 4.
The dots are arranged in 5 rows of 6.
The rectangle is 5 by 6.

Record the pattern in a table.

Figure	Number of Rows	Number of Columns	Number of Dots
1	2	3	6
2	3	4	12
3	4	5	20
4	5	6	30

There is a relationship between the number of rows and columns and the total number of dots. The product of the number of rows and the number of columns is the total number of dots; for example, in Figure 1,
$2 \times 3 = 6$, which is the number of dots.
To find the number of rows, I add 1 to the figure number.
To find the number of columns, I add 2 to the figure number.
We can use these patterns to predict how many dots will be in the 15th figure.

Practice

1. This pattern continues.

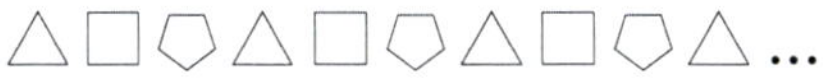

a) Describe the pattern.
b) Sketch the next 3 terms.
c) Sketch the 29th term and the 49th term.

2. This pattern continues.

a) Describe the pattern.
b) Sketch the next 3 terms.
c) Describe the 18th term and the 38th term.
Sketch them if you can.

3. For each pattern:
i) Describe the pattern.
ii) Write the next 3 terms.
iii) Find the 40th term. Explain how you found it.
a) 6, 9, 12, 15, … 18, 21, 24 b) 6, 10, 14, 18, … 22, 26, 30 c) 6, 11, 16, 21, … 26, 31, 36

4. There is a pattern in the patterns in question 3.
Write the first 5 terms of the next pattern. Justify your answer.
6, 12, 18, 24, 30

5. For each pattern:
i) Describe the pattern.
ii) Write the next 3 terms.
iii) Find the 20th term. a) $2^{20} = 1\ 048\ 576$; b) $2^{19} \times 3 = 1\ 572\ 864$
a) 2, 4, 8, 16, … 32, 64, 128 b) 3, 6, 12, 24, … 48, 96, 192

6. Look at the patterns below.
How are they the same? How are they different?
i) Write the next 3 terms for each pattern.
ii) Write the 20th term in each pattern.
a) 2, 5, 10, 17, 26, … 37, 50, 65 b) 0, 3, 8, 15, 24, … 35, 48, 63
a) $20^2 + 1 = 401$; b) $20^2 - 1 = 399$

10.1 Number Patterns **371**

3. a) i) Start at 6. Add 3 each time.
iii) The terms in the pattern are multiples of 3, starting with the second multiple.
So, the 40th term is the 41st multiple of 3, which is $41 \times 3 = 123$.
b) i) Start at 6. Add 4 each time.
iii) The terms in the pattern are 2 more than multiples of 4.
So, the 40th term is 2 more than the 40th multiple of 4; that is, $40 \times 4 + 2 = 162$.
c) i) Start at 6. Add 5 each time.
iii) The terms in the pattern are 1 more than multiples of 5.
So, the 40th term is 1 more than the 40th multiple of 5; that is $40 \times 5 + 1 = 201$.

4. The first term is always 6. In part a, 3 was added each time. In part b, 4 was added each time. In part c, 5 was added each time. So, the next pattern is: Start at 6. Add 6 each time.

5. a) i) Start at 2. Multiply by 2 each time.
Each term is a power of 2.
b) i) Start at 3. Multiply by 2 each time.

6. The starting number for each pattern is different but, in both cases, the rule is: Add 3. Increase the number added by 2 each time.

7. a) Each term is a rectangle. The number of rows starts at 1 and increases by 2 each time. The number of columns starts at 3 and increases by 2 each time. The pattern for the number of squares is: Start at 3. Add 12. Increase the number added by 8 each time.
b) Students' pictures should show these rectangles:
11 by 9, 13 by 11, and 15 by 13.

There will be 15 + 1, or 16 rows and 15 + 2, or 17 columns; $16 \times 17 = 272$.
The 15th figure will have 272 dots.

Once students have created a table, they have two representations of a pattern: a drawing or model of the pattern, and the number patterns in the table. Some students will find it easier to see a pattern in a table, while others will prefer to work with the physical model.

Review *Connect*. The first pattern is similar to the first pattern in *Explore*. The *Example* illustrates how to determine the terms in patterns without listing all preceding terms.

Practice

Have Pattern Blocks available for question 1. Have counters available for question 2. Have 0.5-cm grid paper available for questions 7 and 9. Have geoboards and geobands available for question 9.

Assessment Focus: Question 8

Students could create simple repeating patterns, such as 12, 32, 12, 32, . . ., or simple growing patterns such as 12, 22, 32, . . . Encourage students to look for more complex patterns by exploring squares and common factors. Students may also create shrinking patterns. Ensure students understand that 12 does not have to be the first term of the pattern.

Students who need extra support to complete Assessment Focus questions may benefit from the Step-by-Step masters (Masters 10.9–10.14).

c) The 17th term is a 33 by 35 rectangle.
The 37th term is a 73 by 75 rectangle.

8. 32, 28, 24, 20, 16, 12, . . .
The pattern is: Start at 32. Subtract 4 each time.
The next 4 terms are 8, 4, 0, −4.
2, 7, 12, 17, 22, 27, 32, . . .
The pattern is: Start at 2. Add 5 each time.
The next 4 terms are 37, 42, 47, and 52.
The terms are 3 less than multiples of 5.

9. a) The number of squares in each figure starts at 5 and increases by 3 each time.
c) The perimeter of the 4th figure is: (4 + 1) × 6 = 30 and the perimeter of the 5th figure is: (5 + 1) × 6 = 36.
d) The perimeter of the 10th figure is: (10 + 1) × 6 = 66.
e) The 11th figure has 11 × 3 + 2 = 35 squares.
f) The number of squares in a figure is 2 more than 3 times the figure number. If there are 27 squares, then 3 times the figure number must be 25. Since 25 is not divisible by 3, I cannot make a figure using exactly 27 small squares.

10. 10, 11, 13, 16, 20, 25, . . . Start at 10. Add 1. Increase the number added by 1 each time.
16, 17, 20, 25, 32, . . . Start at 16. Add 1. Increase the number added by 2 each time.

REFLECT: To identify a number pattern, I look to see if each new term can be obtained by adding on to the previous term; for example, in the pattern 6, 9, 12, 15, . . . each term is the previous term, plus 3. I also look to see if each term is related to the term number; for example, in the pattern 6, 11, 16, 21, . . . each term is obtained by multiplying the term number by 5, then adding 1.

Mental Math

Estimate each product.
Order the products from least to greatest.

1 • 24.8 × 3.2 75
4 • 35.23 × 2.89 105
3 • 13.21 × 5.78 78
2 • 5.5 × 15.5 90

What strategies did you use?

7. This pattern continues.

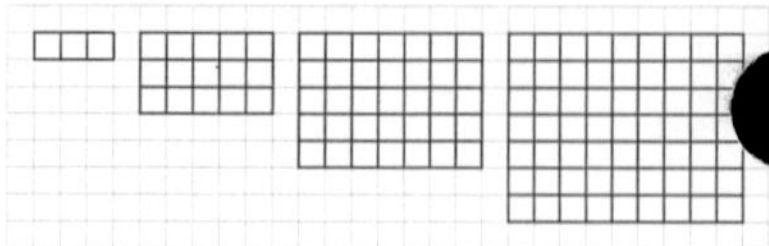

a) Describe the pattern.
b) Sketch the next 3 terms.
c) Describe the 17th term and the 37th term.
Sketch them if you can.

8. Assessment Focus Create two different number patterns.
Each pattern must contain the numbers 12 and 32.
Describe each pattern in words.
Write the next 4 terms in each pattern.

Take It Further

9. a) Describe this pattern. The pattern continues.
b) How many squares would be in the 10th figure? 32 squar
c) What are the perimeters of the 4th figure and 5th figure? 30 36
d) What is the perimeter of the 10th figure? 66
e) How many squares are there in the figure with perimeter 72?
f) Could you make one of the figures using exactly 27 small squares? Explain. No

Use a geoboard and geoband if they help.

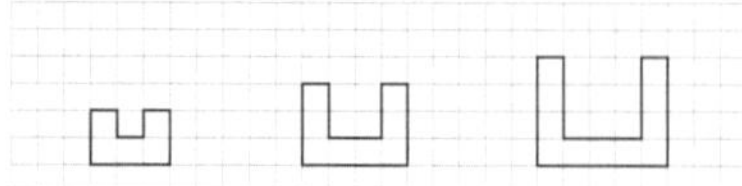

10. Create two different number patterns that contain the numbers 16, 20, and 25. Write the first 5 terms in each pattern.

Reflect

Describe how you identify a number pattern.
Use two different examples from this lesson.

372 UNIT 10: Patterning and Algebra

ASSESSMENT FOR LEARNING

What to Look For	What to Do
Understanding concepts ✔ Students understand that geometric patterns can be represented with numbers. ***Applying procedures*** ✔ Students can use a pattern to make predictions about later terms in the pattern. ***Communicating*** ✔ Students can describe a pattern using mathematical terminology.	***Extra Support:*** Students who have difficulty identifying a pattern rule in a geometric pattern may benefit from modelling the pattern with manipulatives. Students can use Step-by-Step 1 (Master 10.9) to complete question 8. ***Extra Practice:*** Have students use a table to represent the patterns in *Practice* questions 2 and 7, then use the table to find the 15th terms. Students can complete Extra Practice 1 (Master 10.17). ***Extension:*** Have students create a growing pattern on 0.5-cm grid paper. Students record and describe the pattern in as many ways as they can, then predict the number of squares in the 20th figure. Students trade patterns with a classmate and check each other's work.

Recording and Reporting
Master 10.2 Ongoing Observations: Patterning and Algebra

10.2 Graphing Patterns

Focus Use a table and a graph to describe a pattern.

Explore

Work with a partner.
You will need grid paper.
One CD costs $10.
➢ Copy and complete this table.
Find the cost for up to 10 CDs.
➢ Graph the data in the table.

Number of CDs	Cost ($)
0	0
2	20
4	40
6	60
8	80
10	100

Reflect & Share

Describe the patterns in the table.
How are these patterns shown in the graph?

Connect

We can use a table and a graph to illustrate number patterns.
Recall this pattern from *Section 10.1, Example, page 369.*

Term 1: 4
Term 2: 7
Term 3: 10
Term 4: 13
Term 5: 16
Term 6: 19
We write these terms in a table.

Term Number	Term Value
1	4
2	7
3	10
4	13
5	16
6	19

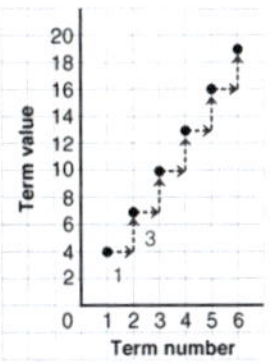

We plot these data on a graph.
The *Term number* is plotted on the horizontal axis.
The *Term value* is plotted on the vertical axis.

The graph is a set of points that lie on a straight line.
To get from one point to the next, move 1 unit right and 3 units up.
Moving 1 unit right is the same as adding 1 in the first column to get the next term number.
Moving 3 units up is the same as adding 3 in the second column to get the next term value.

10.2 Graphing Patterns 373

Graphing Patterns

SECTION ORGANIZER — 80–100 min

Curriculum Focus: Use a table and a graph to describe a pattern. (7m70, 7m71, 7m72, 7m75)

Student Materials
- rulers
- 0.5-cm grid paper (PM 14)
- calculators

Optional
- Step-by-Step 2 (Master 10.10)
- Extra Practice 2 (Master 10.18)

Vocabulary: term number, term value

Assessment: Master 10.2 Ongoing Observations: Patterning and Algebra

Key Math Learning

A table and a graph can be used to illustrate number patterns and to make predictions about the patterns.

Calculator Skills

Students could divide 24.5 by 0.25 to get 98. Students then find 2 numbers that multiply to 98. If students use whole numbers, they could find 1 and 98, 2 and 49, and 7 and 14. If students do not restrict themselves to whole numbers, there are many more possibilities, including 24.5 and 4, and 19.6 and 5.

Math Note

The data in this lesson are discrete data; that is, the data are the counting numbers: 0, 1, 2, 3, 4, 5, 6, . . . There are no values between these counting numbers; that is, there are no decimal or fractional values. So, it makes no sense to join the points when graphing discrete data.

BEFORE — Get Started

Review how to complete a table. Draw a table on the board as shown.

Number of Items	Cost ($)
1	
2	
3	
4	
5	

Ask a volunteer to tell the cost of an item she has recently bought.

Ask:
- What would 2 of these items cost? 3 items? 4 items? 5 items?

Show students how to record the results in the table. Remind students that we can use a table, as well as a graph, to illustrate a number pattern.

Present *Explore.* Distribute 0.5-cm grid paper.

DURING — Explore

Ongoing Assessment: Observe and Listen

As students work, ask questions, such as:

- How did you find the cost of 2 CDs?
(I multiplied $10 by 2 to get $20.)
- What label did you put on the horizontal axis of your graph? *(Number of CDs)*
On the vertical axis? *(Cost, in dollars)*
- How did you graph the data?
(I plotted a point on the grid for each pair of entries in the table. The first number is the distance along

REACHING ALL LEARNERS

Alternative Explore

Materials: 0.5-cm grid paper (PM 14), rulers
One T-shirt costs $14. Have students make a table for the costs of 1, 2, 3, 4, 5, and 6 T-shirts, then graph the data in the table. Students describe the patterns in the table and tell how these patterns are shown in the graph.

Early Finishers

Have students make a graph for each Input/Output table in *Practice* questions 1, 2, and 5.

Common Misconceptions

➤ Students think that the first number in an ordered pair indicates the vertical distance moved on a grid.

How to Help: Remind students that, in an ordered pair, the first number is the horizontal distance and the second number is the vertical distance. Since *horizontal* comes before *vertical* alphabetically, we always move the first number, the horizontal distance, first.

We can use a table related to an Input/Output machine to make a pattern.

Example 1

a) Complete the table for this pattern:
Multiply each number by 2, then add 3.
b) Graph the pattern.
Explain how the graph shows the pattern.

Input	O
1	
2	
3	
4	
5	

Solution

Input	Output
1	5
2	7
3	9
4	11
5	13

a) Multiply each Input number by 2, then add 3.
$1 \times 2 + 3 = 5$
$2 \times 2 + 3 = 7$
$3 \times 2 + 3 = 9$
$4 \times 2 + 3 = 11$
$5 \times 2 + 3 = 13$

b) The points lie on a straight line.
To get from one point to the next, move 1 unit right and 2 units up.
Moving 1 unit right is the same as adding 1 to an Input number to get the next Input number.
Moving 2 units up is the same as adding 2 to an Output number to get the next Output number.

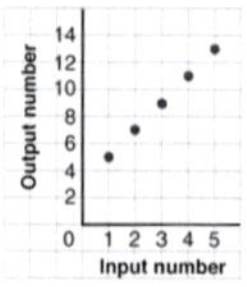

Example 2

a) Describe the patterns in this table.
b) Use the patterns to extend the table 3 more rows.
c) Graph the table in part b. Explain how the graph shows the patterns.

Input	Output
1	10
2	9
3	8
4	7
5	6

374 UNIT 10: Patterning and Algebra

Sample Answers

3. b) The numbers in the Input column start at 2 and increase by 2 each time. The numbers in the Output column start at 3 and increase by 4 each time.
Each Output number is 1 less than twice the Input number.

c) I added 2 to the Input number each time.
I added 4 to the Output number each time.

the horizontal axis and the second number is the distance along the vertical axis.)

- What scale did you use on the horizontal axis? (*I let 1 square represent 2 CDs.*)
On the vertical axis? (*I let 1 square represent $20.*)

AFTER Connect

Invite volunteers to share their patterns, graphs, and tables.
What you might see:

Number of CDs	Cost ($)
0	0
2	20
4	40
6	60
8	80
10	100

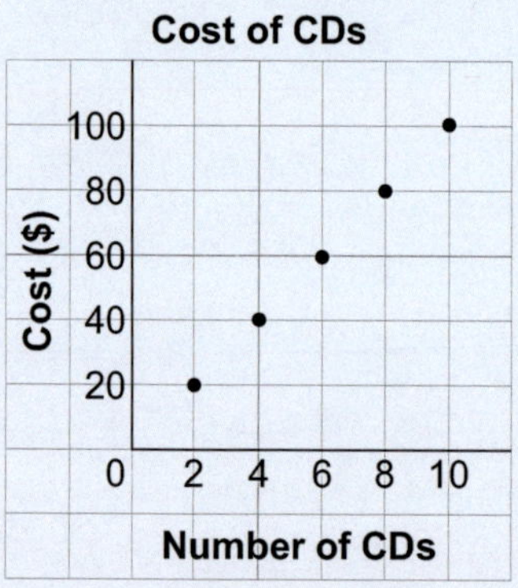

Ask questions, such as:

- What patterns do you see in the table? (*The number of CDs starts at 0 and increases by 2 each time. The cost of the CDs starts at 0 and increases by $20 each time. The cost of the CDs is the product of the number of CDs and $10.*)
- How would you describe your graph? (*It is a set of points that lie on a straight line.*)
- How do you get from one point to the next point on the graph? (*I move 1 square right and 1 square up.*)

Solution

a) The numbers in the Input column start at 1 and increase by 1 each time.
The numbers in the Output column start at 10 and decrease by 1 each time.
The sum of matching Input and Output numbers is 11.

b) The next 3 Input numbers are 6, 7, 8.
The next 3 Output numbers are 5, 4, 3.

Input	Output
1	10
2	9
3	8
4	7
5	6
6	5
7	4
8	3

c) The graph is a set of points that lie on a straight line.

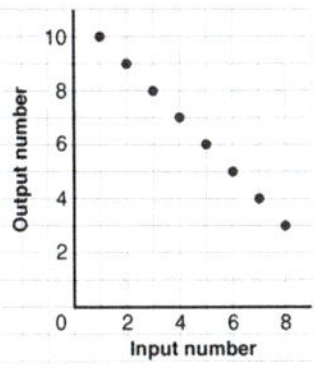

The line goes down to the right.
As the Input numbers increase from 1 to 8, the Output numbers decrease from 10 to 3.

Practice

1. Copy and complete this table for each pattern.
   a) Multiply each Input number by 3.
   b) Add 2 to each Input number.
   c) Multiply each Input number by 3, then add 2.
   d) Add 2 to each Input number, then multiply by 3.

Input	Output a	b	c	d
1	3	3	5	9
2	6	4	8	12
3	9	5	11	15
4	12	6	14	18
5	15	7	17	21

2. Copy and complete this table for each pattern.
   a) Divide each Input number by 10.
   b) Subtract 3 from each Input number.
   c) Divide each Input number by 10, then subtract 3.

Input	Output a	b	c
100	10	97	7
80	8	77	5
60	6	57	3
40	4	37	1
20	2	17	−1

10.2 Graphing Patterns 375

4. b)

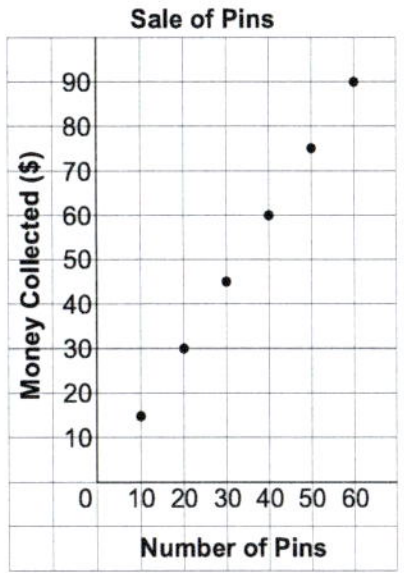

6. a) Number of students: 5, 10, 15, 20, 25, 30
Number of sandwiches: 13, 23, 33, 43, 53, 63

b) Number of students: 5, 10, 15, 20, 25, 30
Number of drinks: 10, 15, 20, 25, 30, 35

c)

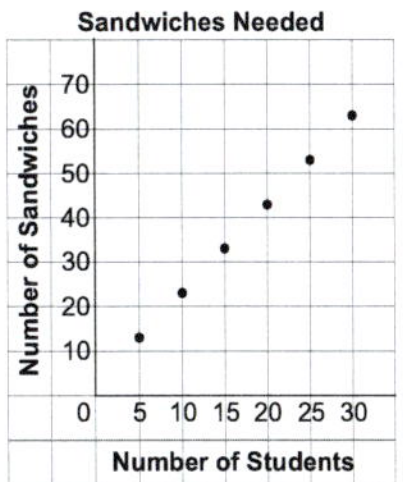

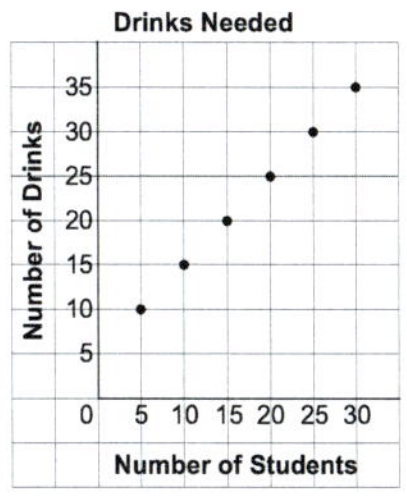

For the number of sandwiches, to get from one point to the next on the graph, I move 5 students right and 10 sandwiches up. This is the same as adding 5 to the number of students and 10 to the number of sandwiches in the table. For the number of drinks, to get from one point to the next on the graph, I move 5 students right and 5 drinks up. This is the same as adding 5 to the number of students and 5 to the number of drinks in the table.

How can you describe this movement using the scales on the axes?
(I move 2 CDs right and $20 up.)

- How could you use the graph to find the cost of 12 CDs?
  (I could extend the graph by moving 2 CDs right and $20 up from the last plotted point; 12 CDs cost $120.)

Survey the class to find how many students joined the points with a straight line. Make students understand that it does not make sense to join the points because, for example, there is no such thing as $1\frac{1}{2}$ or $2\frac{3}{4}$ CDs. Ensure students understand that they should not join the points for any graph they draw in this section.

Remind students that they now have 4 ways to represent a pattern: by drawing or making a model, by using a pattern rule, by making a table, and by drawing a graph.

Have students sit in pairs as you review the explanation in *Connect*. One student's book can be open at page 369, for easy reference. Review the examples in *Connect*. Ask questions, such as:

- Look at *Example 1*. How can we use the graph to find the Output number when the Input number is 9?
  (I can redraw the graph on a larger grid, then use a ruler to extend the graph to 9 on the horizontal axis. From the graph, I draw a horizontal line to the vertical axis. The line meets the axis at 21. When the Input number is 9, the Output number is 21.)
- How can we use the pattern to find the Output number when the Input number is 9?
  (Multiply the Input number by 2, then add 3: $9 \times 2 + 3 = 21$. The Output number is 21.)
- How can we find the Output number when the Input number is 0?
  (We can extend the graph backward. We move 1 unit left and 2 units down from the point (1, 5). We end up at the point (0, 3). So, the Output number is 3 when the Input number is 0.)

7. a)

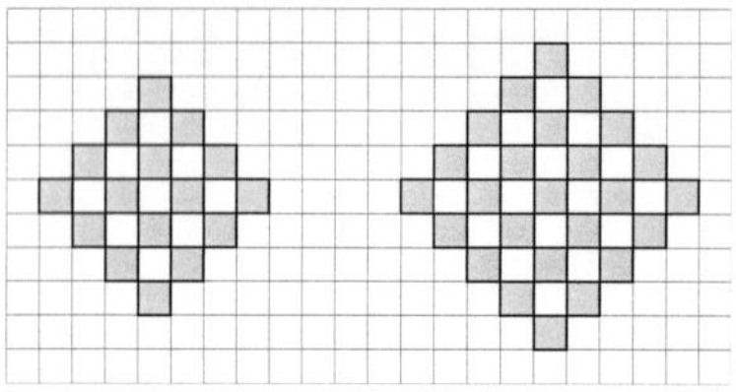

b)

Figure Number	Number of Blue Squares
1	1
2	4
3	9
4	16
5	25

c)

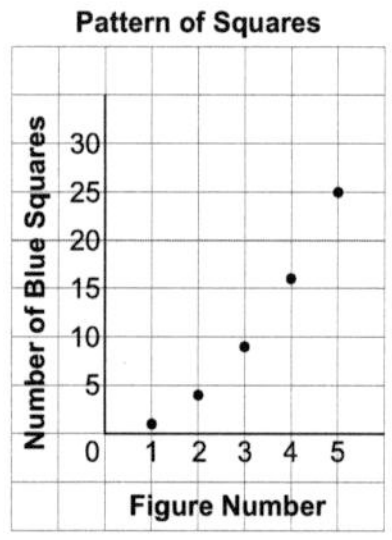

d) The points do not lie on a straight line.

e) If I use the table, the number of blue squares is equal to the square of the figure number: $9^2 = 81$. The 9th figure will have 81 blue squares. I cannot use the graph because it is not a straight line.

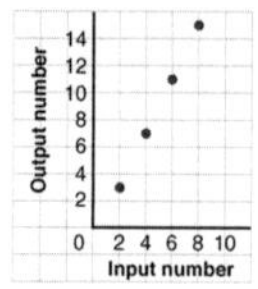

3. a), c)

Input	Output
2	3
4	7
6	11
8	15
10	19
12	23
14	27

5. iii) a) b) c)

Input	Output		
12	16	36	26
14	18	42	30
16	20	48	34

3. Look at this graph.
a) Make an Input/Output table for the graph.
b) What patterns do you see in the table?
c) Extend the table 3 more rows. Explain how you did this.

4. The students at a school sell pins at a school fair to raise money for charity.
The students charge $1.50 per pin.
a) Copy and complete this table.
b) Graph the data in the table in part a.
c) Suppose you know how many pins were sold.
How can you find how much money was collected:
i) by using the table? ii) by using the graph?

Number of Pins	Money Collecte
10	$15
20	$30
30	$45
40	$60
50	$75
60	$90

5. For each table:
i) Describe the pattern in the Output column.
ii) How can you find an Output number when you know an Input number?
iii) Write the next 3 rows in each table.

a)

Input	Output
2	6
4	8
6	10
8	12
10	14

b)

Input	Output
2	6
4	12
6	18
8	24
10	30

c)

Input	Output
2	6
4	10
6	14
8	18
10	22

6. Assessment Focus Mr. Francis is planning a school picnic.
a) Mr. Francis estimates he needs 2 sandwiches for each student, plus 3 extras. Make a table for the number of sandwiches needed for 5, 10, 15, 20, 25, 30 students.
b) Mr. Francis estimates he needs 1 drink for each student, plus 5 extras. Make a table for the number of drinks needed for up to 30 students.
c) Draw graphs for the tables in parts a and b.
Explain how each graph shows the patterns in the tables.

376 UNIT 10: Patterning and Algebra

Have students look at the graph in *Example 2*. Ask:

- How far can we extend the graph?
(*We can extend the graph until the line intersects the horizontal axis. This happens when the Input number is 11.*)
- Does anyone disagree with this answer? Explain.
(*Yes. The line does not have to stop at the horizontal axis. We learned about negative numbers in Unit 9. If we were graphing the daily temperatures in Ontario during the month of January, we would probably have to graph temperatures below zero, or negative temperatures. So, we could extend this line below the horizontal axis. We would then have negative Output numbers.*)

Practice

Have 0.5-cm grid paper available for questions 4, 6, 7, and *Reflect*. Encourage students to use a ruler to make their tables and to extend their graphs. Teachers should be aware that the Input/Output table in *Practice* question 2c has a negative number in the Output column. Challenge early finishers to graph this pattern.

Assessment Focus: Question 6

Ensure students understand that there should be 3 extra sandwiches and 5 extra drinks for any number of students. Students should make 2 tables and draw 2 graphs, then relate the patterns in each table to the corresponding graph.

Take It Further

7. a) Copy this pattern on grid paper.
Extend the pattern to show the next 2 figures.

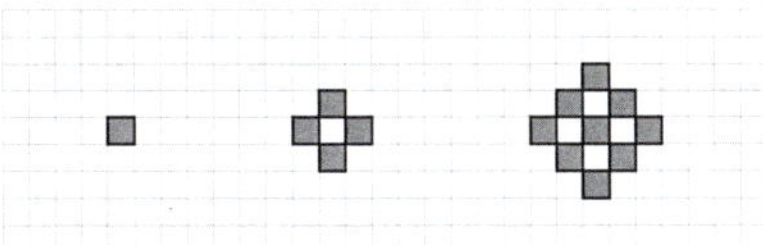

b) Copy and complete this table for the first 5 figures.

Figure Number	Number of Blue Squares
1	1
2	4
3	9
4	16
5	25

c) Draw a graph to show the data in the table.

d) How is this graph different from other graphs you have drawn?

e) How could you use the graph or the table to find the number of blue squares in the 9th figure?

alculator Skills

hree numbers have product of 24.5.
ne number is 0.25.
Vhat might the other wo numbers be?

example, 1 and 98, nd 49, 7 and 14

Reflect

Explain how a pattern in words can be represented by a table and a graph.
Use an example in your explanation.

Math Link

History
The word "algebra" comes from the Arabic world "al-jabr." This word appeared in the title of one of the earliest algebra texts, written around the year 825 by al-Khwarizmi. He lived in what is now Uzbekistan.

REFLECT: A pattern in words can be represented in an Input/Output table. The Input numbers are the term numbers. The Output numbers are the term values. Each pair of entries in the table can be plotted as a point on a grid. As an example, the pattern is: Multiply each term by 3, then subtract 2.
The Input/Output table is:

Input	Output
1	1
2	4
3	7
4	10
5	13

The graph that represents this pattern is:

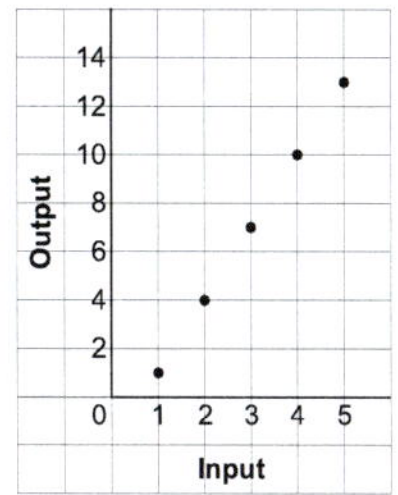

Assignment Guidelines

If your students do not have time to complete all the *Practice* questions on pages 375, 376, and 377, these questions provide minimum curriculum coverage: 1, 2, 3, 4, 6, *Reflect*
To assess the 4 Achievement Chart categories listed in the curriculum document, have students complete these *Practice* questions:
Understanding Concepts: 1
Communication: 3
Application: 4
Problem Solving: 7

ASSESSMENT FOR LEARNING

What to Look For	What to Do
Applying procedures ✔ Students can make a table and draw a graph to represent a number pattern. ✔ Students can use a table or a graph to make predictions about patterns. ***Communicating*** ✔ Students can explain how a pattern in words can be represented by a table and a graph. ***Problem solving*** ✔ Students can solve patterning problems and explain their solutions.	***Extra Support:*** Students who have difficulty seeing a pattern on a graph may benefit from drawing a vertical and a horizontal line segment from each point on the graph to the next, then labelling each line segment with the corresponding distances. Students can use Step-by-Step 2 (Master 10.10) to complete question 6. ***Extra Practice:*** Students choose a pattern rule for an Input/Output machine. Students complete a table for the Input numbers 1 to 6, then graph the data and explain how the graph shows the pattern. Students can complete Extra Practice 2 (Master 10.18). ***Extension:*** Have students make an Input/Output table, then erase the numbers from the Input column. Students trade tables with a partner, then complete each other's table.

Recording and Reporting
Master 10.2 Ongoing Observations: Patterning and Algebra

Variables in Expressions

SECTION ORGANIZER (80–100 min)

Curriculum Focus: Use a variable to represent a set of numbers. (7m73, 7m77)

Student Materials

Optional

- Step-by-Step 3 (Master 10.11)
- Extra Practice 3 (Master 10.19)

Vocabulary: variable, algebraic expression

Assessment: Master 10.2 Ongoing Observations: Patterning and Algebra

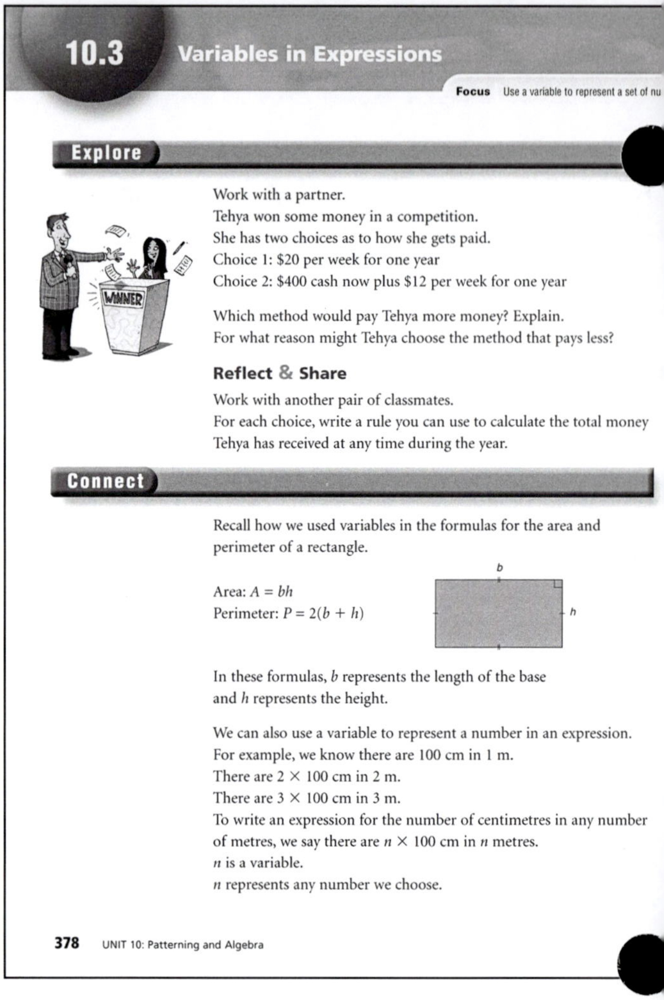

10.3 Variables in Expressions

Focus Use a variable to represent a set of nu

Explore

Work with a partner.
Tehya won some money in a competition.
She has two choices as to how she gets paid.
Choice 1: $20 per week for one year
Choice 2: $400 cash now plus $12 per week for one year

Which method would pay Tehya more money? Explain.
For what reason might Tehya choose the method that pays less?

Reflect & Share

Work with another pair of classmates.
For each choice, write a rule you can use to calculate the total money Tehya has received at any time during the year.

Connect

Recall how we used variables in the formulas for the area and perimeter of a rectangle.

Area: $A = bh$
Perimeter: $P = 2(b + h)$

In these formulas, *b* represents the length of the base and *h* represents the height.

We can also use a variable to represent a number in an expression.
For example, we know there are 100 cm in 1 m.
There are 2 × 100 cm in 2 m.
There are 3 × 100 cm in 3 m.
To write an expression for the number of centimetres in any number of metres, we say there are $n \times 100$ cm in *n* metres.
n is a variable.
n represents any number we choose.

378 UNIT 10: Patterning and Algebra

Key Math Learnings

1. An algebraic expression is a mathematical expression that contains a variable.
2. A variable in an algebraic expression represents a set of numbers.
3. Variables are written in italics so they are not confused with units of measurement.

BEFORE — Get Started

Talk to students about allowances they get. Ask questions, such as:

- Suppose you get $5 a week. About how much would you get in a year? (*$5 × 50 = $250*)
- Suppose you are offered $100 now, plus $1 a week for the rest of the year. Which would you prefer and why? (*$100 now, so I can buy the DVD I want without having to save up for it.*)
- Which choice gives you more money in one year? (*The first choice*) How do you know? (*The first choice gives me about $250; the second choice gives me about $150.*)

Present *Explore.* Tell students they will use the same kind of logical thinking to investigate the choices in *Explore.*

DURING — Explore

Ongoing Assessment: Observe and Listen

As students work, ask questions, such as:

- If Tehya chooses Choice 1, how much money will she be paid? (*$1040*) How do you know? (*There are 52 weeks in a year; 52 × $20 = $1040.*)
- If Tehya chooses Choice 2, how much money will she get paid? (*$1024*) How do you know? (*There are 52 weeks in a year; 52 × $12 = $624, and $624 + $400 = $1024.*)
- Which method would pay Tehya more money? Explain. (*Choice 1; $1040 is greater than $1024.*)
- Why might Tehya choose the method that pays less? (*She might be short of money and have an immediate use for $400. She only loses $16 by taking $400 cash now.*)

We can choose any letter as a variable.
The letters n and x are frequently used.
The expression $n \times 100$ is written $100n$.
$100n$ is an **algebraic expression**.

les are written in italics so they are not confused with units of measurement.

Here are some other algebraic expressions, and their meanings.
In each case, n represents the number.

- Three more than a number: $3 + n$ or $n + 3$
- Seven times a number: $7n$
- 8 less than a number: $n - 8$
- Twenty divided by a number: $\frac{20}{n}$

Example 1

A car travels at an average speed of 50 km/h.
How far will the car travel in: a) 3 h? b) t hours?

Solution

$t \times 50$ is equal to $50 \times t$, which is written $50t$.

In 1 h, the car travels 50 km.
a) In 3 h, the car travels: 3×50 km = 150 km
b) In t hours, the car travels: $t \times 50$ km = $50t$ kilometres

Example 2

Write an algebraic expression for each statement.
a) the amount of money earned at \$5/h
b) the perimeter of a square
c) eight more than three times a number
d) double a number and subtract 5

Solution

We often choose a letter to remind us what the variable represents.
t for time
s for side length
n for number

For each statement, choose a variable to represent the number.
a) Let t hours represent the time worked.
Then, the amount earned is $5 \times t$, or $5t$ dollars.
b) Let s centimetres represent the side length of the square.
Then, the perimeter in centimetres is $4 \times s$, or $4s$ centimetres.
c) Let n represent the number.
Three times the number: $3n$
Then add 8: $3n + 8$
d) Let x represent the number.
Double the number means 2 times the number: $2x$
Then subtract 5: $2x - 5$

10.3 Variables in Expressions 379

REACHING ALL LEARNERS

Early Finishers

Have students write algebraic expressions, then trade with a partner and write each of their partner's expressions in words.

Common Misconceptions

➤ Students think that the expressions $4x + 2$ and $4b + 2$ are different.

How to Help: Remind students that a variable is a symbol that represents any one of a set of numbers. Students may use different variables in expressions that represent the same statement, but the choice of variable does not affect the expression.

➤ Students ignore the order of operations when writing an algebraic expression.

How to Help: Remind students of the order of operations. Write the following example on the board: Subtract 2 from a number, then multiply by 3. Students may erroneously write the expression: $n - 2 \times 3$. Since the multiplication must be performed first, the expression $n - 6$ results. This is the same as subtracting 6 from a number. To ensure that 2 is subtracted from the number first, brackets must be used: $(n - 2) \times 3$, or $(n - 2)3$, or $3(n - 2)$.

ESL Strategies

Have students make index cards with different kinds of statements and their related expressions. For example, students could write: "Five times a number: $5n$," "A number increased by five: $n + 5$." Students can refer to these cards as they work through the *Practice* questions.

AFTER Connect

Have students share their rules with the class.

Ask:

- Use Choice 1. How can you calculate the money Tehya has received after 6 weeks?
(Multiply 6 by \$20 to get \$120.)
After 25 weeks?
(Multiply 25 by \$20 to get \$500.)
- What rule can you write to calculate the money received at any time during the year for Choice 1?
(Multiply the number of weeks by \$20.)
- Did anyone write this rule differently?
(Yes, I let w represent the number of weeks. My rule is \$20 $\times$ w.)
- Use Choice 2. How can you calculate the money Tehya has received after 6 weeks?
(Multiply 6 by \$12, then add \$400 to get \$472.)
After 25 weeks?
(Multiply 25 by \$12, then add \$400 to get \$700.)
- What rule can you write to calculate the money received at any time during the year for Choice 2?
(Multiply the number of weeks by \$12, then add \$400.)
- Did anyone write this rule differently?
(Yes, I let n represent the number of weeks. My rule is: \$12 $\times$ n + \$400.)

Review *Connect*. Some students may have difficulty with the concept that $50 \times t$ can be written as $50t$. When multiplying two numbers, such as 15×3, students have always included the multiplication sign. If they were to omit the multiplication sign, they would get 153, and $15 \times 3 \neq 153$. It may take students a while to become comfortable with the idea of omitting the multiplication sign when working with variables, but stress that it is omitted to avoid possible confusion by having a variable and a symbol adjacent to each other; for example, $3 \times x$.

Sample Answers

5. a) Eight more than a number
   b) A number multiplied by six
   c) A number divided by five
   d) A number decreased by eleven
   e) A number subtracted from twenty-seven
   f) A number squared
7. a) i) Subtract three from forty, then multiply by a number.
   ii) Subtract three times a number from forty.
   b) The expressions use the same numbers, the same operations, and the same variable, but different terms are multiplied and subtracted.
8. b) All expressions involve a number and 3. The order in which the variable and 3 appear varies, and the operation is either addition or subtraction.
9. a) Multiply a number by six, then add five.
   b) Subtract three from a number, then divide by four.
   c) Divide a number by four, then add twelve.
   d) Subtract three from a number, then multiply by three.
   e) Subtract a number divided by five from thirty-two.
   f) Divide a number by five, then subtract thirty-two.
10. b) Thirty-six minus a number: $9 \times 4 - n$
    A number plus thirty-six: $n + 9 \times 4$

REFLECT: In an algebraic expression, the variable represents any number. For example, we can write an expression for the cost of different numbers of movie tickets. Suppose one ticket is \$8. We can use the variable n to represent the number of tickets. The expression for the cost is \$8n. We can use the expression to find the cost of any number of tickets. It is easier to write \$8n, rather than listing all possible prices, such as \$8, \$16, \$24, \$32, \$40, and so on.

Practice

If you use x as a variable, write it so it is not confused with a multiplication sign, ×.

Remember that the fraction bar indicates division.

1. Write an algebraic expression for each statement.
   a) six more than a number $n + 6$
   b) a number multiplied by eight $8n$
   c) a number decreased by six $n - 6$
   d) a number divided by four $\frac{n}{4}$
2. A person earns \$4/h baby-sitting. Find the money earned for each time.
   a) 5 h \$20 b) 8 h \$32 c) t hours \$4t
3. Find the area of a rectangle for each length and width.
   a) length: 8 cm; width: 6 cm $A = 48$ cm²
   b) length: 10 cm; width: 5 cm $A = 50$ cm²
   c) length: l centimetres; width: w centimetres $A = lw$ square centimet
4. A person walks at an average speed of 5 km/h. Find the distance walked in each time.
   a) 2 h 10 km b) 5 h 25 km c) t hours $5t$ kilometres
5. Write each algebraic expression in words. Use the words "a number" in place of the variable.
   a) $n + 8$ b) $6a$ c) $\frac{p}{5}$
   d) $k - 11$ e) $27 - n$ f) x^2
6. Write an algebraic expression for each statement.
   a) Double a number and add three. $2n + 3$
   b) Subtract five from a number, then multiply by two. $(n - 5) \times 2$
   c) Subtract one-half of a number from 17. $17 - \frac{n}{2}$
   d) Divide a number by seven, then add six. $\frac{n}{7} + 6$
   e) A number is subtracted from twenty-eight. $28 - n$
   f) Twenty-eight is subtracted from a number. $n - 28$
7. a) Write each expression in words.
   i) $(40 - 3)r$ ii) $40 - 3r$
   b) How are the expressions and statements in part a similar? Different?

380 UNIT 10: Patterning and Algebra

Remind students that they have seen variables before. They have seen variables in formulas for area, perimeter, volume, and surface area.

Practice

Have index cards available for question 10, for students who want to make their own set of cards.

Assessment Focus: Question 10

Remind students to be aware of the order of operations. Some students may want to make their own set of cards. This may make it easier for students to see more expressions and will ensure they use a card only once in each expression. For part a) i), students may interpret this two ways: nine times a number, then subtract 4 ($9n - 4$), or nine times 4 less than a number ($9(n - 4)$). Either way is acceptable. We have given answers for the first interpretation. For part a) iv), students need to understand that finding one-quarter of a number is the same as dividing the number by 4.

Number Strategies

egular price of a running shoes is . What is the sale price in each case?

- 50% off $37.50
- 25% off $56.24
- 30% off $52.49
- 70% off $22.50

8. a) Write an algebraic expression for each statement.
   i) three more than a number $n + 3$
   ii) a number added to three $3 + n$
   iii) three less than a number $n - 3$
   iv) a number subtracted from three $3 - n$

b) How are the expressions in part a alike? How are they different? Explain.

9. Write each expression in words.

a) $6h + 5$ b) $\frac{(n-3)}{4}$ c) $\frac{t}{4} + 12$
d) $3(x - 3)$ e) $32 - \frac{w}{5}$ f) $\frac{w}{5} - 32$

10. Assessment Focus

a) Use the cards below to make an algebraic expression for each statement. Write the expression.

9	4	+	−	×	÷	n

   i) nine times a number subtract 4 $9n - 4$
   ii) the sum of four times a number and nine $4n + 9$
   iii) a number plus five $n + 9 - 4$
   iv) nine more than one-quarter of a number $\frac{n}{4} + 9$

b) Create two more expressions using the cards. Write each expression in words.
Show your work.

11. A pizza with cheese and tomato toppings costs $8.00.
There is a cost of $1 for each extra topping.
Write an algebraic expression for the cost of a pizza with e extra toppings.
$8.00 + $1e

Reflect

Why do we write algebraic expressions? How are they useful?

10.3 Variables in Expressions 381

Number Strategies

Students may use the fact that 25% off means you pay 75% of the original price, 30% off means you pay 70% of the original price, and 70% off means you pay 30% of the original price, then find the corresponding percent of $74.99. Other students may find the discount, then subtract from the original price. Remind students that since we are working with money, the answers have 2 decimal places.

Assignment Guidelines

If your students do not have time to complete all the *Practice* questions on pages 380 and 381, these questions provide minimum curriculum coverage: 1, 2, 5, 6, 7, 10, *Reflect*
To assess the 4 Achievement Chart categories listed in the curriculum document, have students complete these *Practice* questions:
Understanding Concepts: 1
Application: 4
Communication: 7
Problem Solving: 10

ASSESSMENT FOR LEARNING

What to Look For

Understanding concepts

✔ Students understand that an algebraic expression is a mathematical expression that contains a variable.
✔ Students understand that a variable can be used to represent a set of numbers.

Applying procedures

✔ Students can write an algebraic expression for a mathematical statement.
✔ Students can write an algebraic expression in words.

What to Do

Extra Support: Students who have difficulty writing an algebraic expression for a statement may benefit from additional practice with simpler expressions, such as two times a number, a number plus 1, and a number minus 1.
Students can use Step-by-Step 3 (Master 10.11) to complete question 10.

Extra Practice: Have students write as many different algebraic expressions as they can using 3, 7, +, −, ×, ÷, and *t*. Students write each expression in words.
Students can complete Extra Practice 3 (Master 10.19).

Extension: The Grade 7 students are buying T-shirts for gym class. T-shirts with logos on the front cost $15. T-shirts with logos on the front and back cost $20. Write an expression to represent the total cost of all T-shirts purchased. (*Answer: $15f + $20g*).

Recording and Reporting

Master 10.2 Ongoing Observations: Patterning and Algebra

MID-UNIT REVIEW

SECTION ORGANIZER

Student Materials
- calculators
- rulers
- 0.5-cm grid paper (PM 14)

Assessment:
Masters 10.1 Unit Rubric: Patterning and Algebra, 10.4 Unit Summary: Patterning and Algebra

Mid-Unit Review

LESSON

10.1 **1.** For each pattern:
i) Describe the pattern.
ii) Write the next 3 terms.
iii) Find the 10th term.
a) 5, 8, 11, 14, … 17, 20, 23
b) 14, 25, 36, 47, … 58, 69, 80
c) 1, 8, 27, 64, … 125, 216, 343
d) 1, 3, 7, 15, 31, … 63, 127, 255

2. a) Describe this pattern.

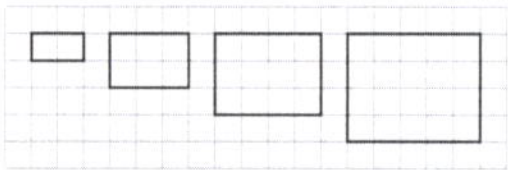

The pattern continues.
b) Write the dimensions of the next 2 rectangles. 5 by 6, 6 by 7
c) Write the areas of the first 5 rectangles. 2, 6, 12, 20, 30 square units
d) What are the dimensions and area of the 19th rectangle? 19 by 20 $A = 380$ square units
e) Which rectangle has area 110 square units? The 10th rectangle

10.2 **3.** a) Complete the table in the next column for this pattern: Multiply each term by 4, then subtract 1.
b) Graph the pattern. Explain how the graph shows the pattern.

Input	Output
1	3
2	7
3	11
4	15
5	19
6	23

4. a) Describe the pattern in the Output column.
b) How can you find an output number when you know an input number?
c) Write the next 3 rows in the table.
d) Graph the table. Explain how the graph shows the pattern.

Input	Output
1	8
2	11
3	14
4	17
5	20
6	23

10.3 **5.** Write an algebraic expression for each statement.
a) eleven more than a number n -
b) four less than a number $n - 4$
c) a number divided by three $\frac{n}{3}$
d) a number multiplied by nine 9
e) the sum of five times a number, and 2 $5n + 2$
f) seventeen more than two times a number $2n + 17$

6. Write each expression in words. Use the words "a number" in place of each variable.
a) $n + 3$ b) $21 - h$ c) $9n$ d) $\frac{a}{4}$

382 UNIT 10: Patterning and Algebra

Sample Solutions

1. a) i) Start at 5. Add 3 each time.
iii) The 10th term is: $10 \times 3 + 2 = 32$
b) i) Start at 14. Add 11 each time.
iii) The 10th term is: $10 \times 11 + 3 = 113$
c) i) Start at 1. Cube it. Increase the number cubed by 1 each time.
iii) The 10th term is: $10^3 = 1000$
d) i) Start at 1. Multiply by 2, then add 1 each time.
iii) The 10th term is: $2^{10} - 1 = 1023$
2. a) All the figures are rectangles. Each rectangle has length and width 1 unit greater than the preceding rectangle.
d) The dimensions of the 1st rectangle are: 1 by 2
The dimensions of the 2nd rectangle are: 2 by 3
So, the dimensions of the 19th rectangle are: 19 by 20
The area of the 19th rectangle is 19 units × 20 units = 380 square units.

(*Solutions continue below.*)

(*Sample Solutions, continued*)
e) We need to find factors of 110 that are 2 consecutive numbers: 1, 110; 2, 55; 5, 22; 10, 11.
The 10th rectangle has dimensions 10 by 11.
So, the area of the 10th rectangle is 10 units × 11 units = 110 square units.

3. b)

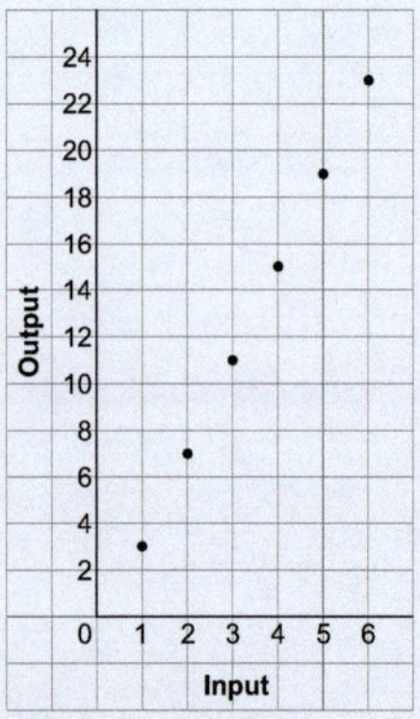

To get from one point to the next, I move 1 unit right and 4 units up. Moving 1 unit right is the same as adding 1 in the first column to get the next Input number. Moving 4 units up is the same as adding 4 in the second column to get the next Output number.

4. a) The Output numbers start at 8 and increase by 3 each time.
b) Recognize that each Output number is 5 more than a multiple of 3. Multiply the Input number by 3, then add 5.
c) Input: 7, 8, 9; Output: 26, 29, 32
d)

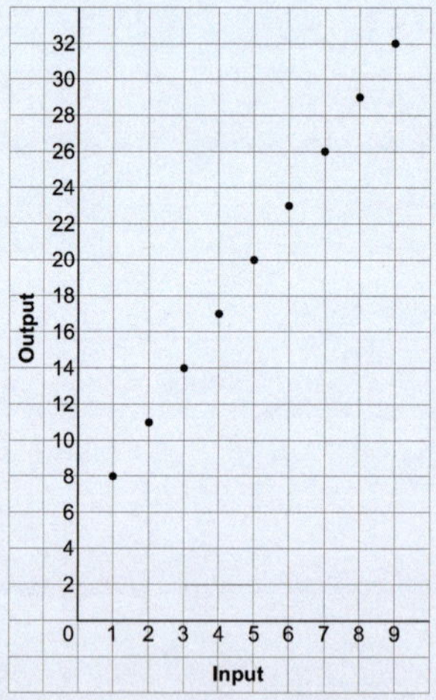

To get from one point to the next, I move 1 unit right and 3 units up. Moving 1 unit right is the same as adding 1 to an Input number to get the next Input number. Moving 3 units up is the same as adding 3 to an Output number to get the next Output number.

6. a) Three more than a number
b) A number subtracted from twenty-one
c) A number multiplied by nine
d) A number divided by four

10.4 Evaluating Algebraic Expressions

Focus Substitute a number for a variable in an algebraic expression.

Explore

Work with a partner.
Ms. Prasad plans to hold a party for a group of her friends.
The cost of renting a room is $25.
The cost of food is $3 per person.
Which algebraic expression gives the total cost, in dollars, of the party for n people?

$3 + 25n$ $\quad$ $28n$ $\quad$ $28 + n$ $\quad$ $25 + 3n$

Check your answer by finding the cost for 10 people.

Reflect & Share

Compare your answer with that of another pair of classmates.
How did you decide which expression was correct?
How does the expression change in each of the following cases?

- The cost of food doubles.
- The rent of the room doubles.

Connect

When we replace a variable with a number, we substitute a number for the variable.

When we replace a variable with a number in an algebraic expression, we **evaluate** the expression. That is, we find the value of the expression for a particular value of the variable.

Recall the work you did in *Unit 6 Measuring Perimeter and Area*. You substituted numbers for variables in the formulas for area and perimeter.
We use the same method to evaluate algebraic expressions.

Example

Write each algebraic expression in words.
Then evaluate for the value of the variable given.

a) $5k + 2$ for $k = 3$ $\quad$ b) $\frac{(x-3)}{5}$ for $x = 13$

10.4 Evaluating Algebraic Expressions 383

SECTION 10.4

Evaluating Algebraic Expressions

SECTION ORGANIZER 80–100 min

Curriculum Focus: Substitute a number for a variable in an algebraic expression. (7m73, 7m76, 7m77)

Student Materials

Optional

- Step-by-Step 4 (Master 10.12)
- Extra Practice 4 (Master 10.20)

Vocabulary: evaluate, substitute

Assessment: Master 10.2 Ongoing Observations: Patterning and Algebra

Key Math Learnings

1. To evaluate an algebraic expression, replace a variable with a number, then simplify.
2. Substitute consecutive numbers in an algebraic expression to get a pattern.

BEFORE Get Started

Remind students of the algebraic expression they wrote in Section 10.3 for the cost of a pizza with e extra toppings: $8.00 + 1.00e$.

Ask:

- What does the $8.00 represent? (*The cost of a pizza with no extra toppings*)
- What does the $1.00 represent? (*The cost of each extra topping*)
- What does the variable e represent? (*The number of extra toppings*)
- How much would a pizza with 3 extra toppings cost? (*$11*) How do you know? (*I replaced e with 3 in the expression $8.00 + $1.00e: $8.00 + $1.00 × 3 = $8.00 + $3.00 = $11.00.*)

Present *Explore*.

DURING Explore

Ongoing Assessment: Observe and Listen

As students work, ask questions, such as:

- How much does it cost to rent the room for 5 people? (*$25*) For 10 people? (*$25*) For 100 people? (*$25*) Explain. (*The cost of the room is not dependent on the number of people.*)
- What is the cost of food for 5 people? (*$15*) How do you know? (*The cost of food is $3 per person; 5 × $3 = $15.*)
- What is the cost of food for 10 people? (*$30*) For 100 people? (*$300*)
- What is the total cost of the party for 5 people? (*$25 + $15 = $40*) For 10 people? (*$25 + $30 = $55*)
- What is the cost of food for n people? (*$3n*)
- What is the total cost for n people? (*$25 + $3n*)

REACHING ALL LEARNERS

Early Finishers

Have students evaluate each expression in Section 10.3, *Practice* questions 5 and 9, by substituting 5 for the variable.

Common Misconceptions

➤ Students do not use the order of operations to evaluate an expression.

How to Help: Show students that if they do not use the order of operations, they may get a different answer. For example, evaluate the expression $3 + 4k$ for $k = 2$.
Use the order of operations.
Replace k with 2.

$3 + 4k = 3 + 4 \times 2$ Multiply first.
$= 3 + 8$ Add.
$= 11$

Now, do not use the order of operations.

$3 + 4k = 3 + 4 \times 2$
$= 7 \times 2$
$= 14$

Students see that the answer is different if the order of operations is not followed.

Mental Math

Some students may need to use a number line or a pattern to help them add the integers. Other students may be able to write the sums directly.

Solution

a) $5k + 2$ means 5 times a number, then add 2.
Replace k with 3 in the expression $5k + 2$.
Use the order of operations.

5*k* means $5 \times k$.

$5k + 2 = 5 \times 3 + 2$ Multiply first.
$= 15 + 2$ Add.
$= 17$

b) $\frac{(x-3)}{5}$ means subtract 3 from a number, then divide by 5.
Replace x with 13.

$\frac{(x-3)}{5} = \frac{(13-3)}{5}$ Do the operation in brackets first.
$= \frac{10}{5}$ Divide.
$= 2$

Recall that a variable is a symbol that can represent a set of numbers.
If we substitute consecutive numbers in an algebraic expression, we get a pattern.
Use the algebraic expression $3n + 2$.
Substitute $n = 1, 2, 3, 4$, and 5.

When $n = 1$, $3n + 2 = 3(1) + 2$
$= 3 + 2$
$= 5$

When $n = 2$, $3n + 2 = 3(2) + 2$
$= 6 + 2$
$= 8$

When $n = 3$, $3n + 2 = 3(3) + 2$
$= 9 + 2$
$= 11$

When $n = 4$, $3n + 2 = 3(4) + 2$
$= 12 + 2$
$= 14$

When $n = 5$, $3n + 2 = 3(5) + 2$
$= 15 + 2$
$= 17$

Use the values of n as the Input.
Use the values of $3n + 2$ as the Output.
Then, write the patterns in a table.
To get each Output number, multiply the Input number by 3, then add 2.

Input n	Output $3n + 2$
1	5
2	8
3	11
4	14
5	17

- Which algebraic expression gives the total cost, in dollars, of the party for n people? *($25 + 3n$)*
- How did you check your answer? *(I replaced n in the expression with 10. The total cost, in dollars, for 10 people is $25 + 3 \times 10 = 55$. This answer is the same as the answer I got when I didn't use the algebraic expression.)*

AFTER Connect

Have volunteers share their answers with the class.

Ask:

- How does the expression change if the cost of food doubles? *(If the cost of food doubles, the cost of food will be \$3 × 2 = \$6 per person. The algebraic expression becomes \$25 + \$6n.)*
- What is the cost of the party for 10 people now? *(\$25 + \$6 × 10 = \$85)*
- How does the expression change if the rent of the room doubles? *(If the rent of the room doubles, the cost of renting a room will be \$25 × 2 = \$50. The algebraic expression becomes \$50 + \$3n.)*
- What is the cost of the party for 10 people now? *(\$50 + \$3 × 10 = \$80)*
- How does the expression change if both the rent of the room and the cost of the food doubles? *(The expression becomes \$50 + \$6n.)*
- What is the cost of the party for 10 people now? *(\$50 + \$6 × 10 = \$110)*

Work through the examples in *Connect*. Ensure students understand that the order of operations must be followed when they evaluate an algebraic expression.

Show students how they can use an algebraic expression to make a pattern.
Use the algebraic expression from *Explore:* $25 + 3n$
Substitute $n = 5, 10, 15, 20$, and 25.
When $n = 5$, $25 + 3n = 25 + 3(5) = 40$
When $n = 10$, $25 + 3n = 25 + 3(10) = 55$

Practice

1. Evaluate each expression by replacing x with 4.
   a) $x + 5$ 9 b) $3x$ 12 c) $2x - 1$ 7
   d) $\frac{x}{2}$ 2 e) $3x + 1$ 13 f) $20 - 2x$ 12

2. Evaluate each expression by replacing z with 7.
   a) $z + 12$ 19 b) $10 - z$ 3 c) $\frac{(z+5)}{2}$ 6
   d) $3(z - 1)$ 18 e) $35 - 2z$ 21 f) $3 + \frac{z}{7}$ 4

...ental Math

Find each sum.
- $(-2) + (+10) = +8$
- $(-6) + (-9) = -15$
- $(+8) + (-7) = +1$
- $(+11) + (+7) = +18$

3. Write each algebraic expression in words. Then, evaluate the expression for $n = 3$.
   a) $n - 1$ 2 b) $5n + 2$ 17 c) $\frac{n}{3} + 5$ 6
   d) $n + 1$ 4 e) $2(n + 9)$ 24 f) $\frac{(n+7)}{2}$ 5

4. Copy and complete each table. Explain how to get an Output number when you know the Input number.

a)

Input x	Output $2x$
1	2
2	4
3	6
4	8
5	10

b)

Input m	Output $10 - m$
1	9
2	8
3	7
4	6
5	5

c)

Input p	Output $3p + 4$
1	7
2	10
3	13
4	16
5	19

5. Jason works at a local fish and chips restaurant. He earns \$7/h during the week, and \$9/h on the weekend.
   a) Jason works 8 h during the week and 12 h on the weekend. Write an expression for his earnings. $8 \times \$7 + 12 \times \$9$
   b) Jason works x hours during the week, and 5 h on the weekend. Write an algebraic expression for his earnings. $\$7x + 5 \times \$9$
   c) Jason needs \$115 to buy sports equipment. He worked 5 h on the weekend. How many hours does Jason need to work during the week to have the money he needs? 10 h

Sample Answers

3. a) One less than a number
   b) Five times a number, then add two.
   c) Divide a number by three, then add five.
   d) One more than a number
   e) Add nine to a number, then multiply by two.
   f) Add seven to a number, then divide by two.
4. a) Multiply the Input number by 2.
   b) Subtract the Input number from 10.
   c) Multiply the Input number by 3, then add 4.
5. c) Jason needs to work 10 h to have the money he needs.
6. a) If 5 people go, the trip will cost $\$20 + (5 \times \$9) = \$65$.
   If 10 people go, the trip will cost $\$20 + (10 \times \$9) = \$110$.
   b) $\$20 + \$9p$
   c) If the cost of food doubles, the cost of food will be $\$9 \times 2 = \$18$ per person. $\$20 + \$18p$
   d) If the cost of the cabin doubles, the cost of renting a cabin will be $\$20 \times 2 = \$40$. $\$40 + \$9p$
   e) I can write an expression for each different scenario, then evaluate each expression for different numbers of people by substituting a number for the variable p. The variable p is used because "p" is the first letter of "people."
7. a) Think: What do I multiply by 5 to get 30?; $n = 6$; $5 \times 6 = 30$
   b) Think: What do I take 1 away from to get 11? *Answer: 12;* then, what do I multiply 3 by to get 12?; $n = 4$; $3 \times 4 - 1 = 11$
   c) Think: What do I add to 7 to get 15? *Answer: 8;* then, what do I multiply 4 by to get 8? $n = 2$; $4 \times 2 + 7 = 15$

When $n = 15$, $25 + 3n = 25 + 3(15) = 70$
When $n = 20$, $25 + 3n = 25 + 3(20) = 85$
When $n = 25$, $25 + 3n = 25 + 3(25) = 100$

Use the values of n as the Input.
Use the values of $25 + 3n$ as the Output.

Input n	Output $25 + 3n$ (\$)
5	40
10	55
15	70
20	85
25	100

The Input numbers start at 5 and increase by 5 each time.
The Output numbers start at 40 and increase by 15 each time.
To get each Output number, multiply the Input number by 3, then add 25.

Students could graph the table. Students could use the table, the expression, or the graph to evaluate the expression for different values of n.

Practice

Encourage students to show their work when evaluating an expression. For question 7, students could set up an Input/Output table for each part. Students could start with Input numbers 1, 2, 3, and 4, then use any patterns they see to extend the table if necessary.

Assessment Focus: Question 6

Students realize that the cost of renting the cabin does not depend on the number of people and that the cost of food does depend on the number of people who go on the trip. Students understand that the variable, p, is associated with the cost of the food. Students can use their results from *part a* to check the expression they write in *part b*.

d) Think: What do I take 4 away from to get 11? *Answer: 15;* then, what do I multiply 5 by to get 15? $n = 3$; $5 \times 3 - 4 = 11$

e) Think: What do I add to 4 to get 40? *Answer: 36;* then, what do I multiply 6 by to get 36? $n = 6$; $4 + 6 \times 6 = 40$

f) Think: What do I add to 1 to get 5? *Answer: 4;* then, what do I divide by 8 to get 4? $n = 32$; $\frac{32}{8} + 1 = 4 + 1 = 5$

9. There are many different ways to do this. In each case, p is 1 more than 3 times q.

REFLECT: It is important to use the order of operations when evaluating an algebraic expression to ensure that the correct answer is obtained. For example, if I use the order of operations to evaluate the expression $3 + 2 \times n$ for $n = 4$, I get $3 + 2 \times 4 = 3 + 8 = 11$. If I do not use the order of operations, I get $3 + 2 \times 4 = 5 \times 4 = 20$. We need to use the order of operations so all of us get the same answer.

Assignment Guidelines

If your students do not have time to complete all the *Practice* questions on pages 385 and 386, these questions provide minimum curriculum coverage: 1, 3, 5, 6, 7, *Reflect*

To assess the 4 Achievement Chart categories listed in the curriculum document, have students complete these *Practice* questions: Understanding Concepts: 3; Application: 5; Problem Solving: 7; Communication: *Reflect*

6. **Assessment Focus** Kouroche is organising an overnight camping trip. The cost of renting a cabin is \$20. The cost of food is \$9 per person.
   a) How much will the trip cost if 5 people go? 10 people go?
   b) Write an algebraic expression for the cost of the trip if p people go. \$20 + \$9p
   c) Suppose the cost of food doubles. Write an expression for the total cost of the trip for p people.
   d) Suppose the cost of the cabin doubles. Write an expression for the total cost of the trip for p people.
   e) Explain why using the variable p is helpful.

7. A value of n is substituted in each expression to get the number in the box. Find each value of n.

a) $5n$	30	$n = 6$	b) $3n - 1$	11	$n = 4$
c) $4n + 7$	15	$n = 2$	d) $5n - 4$	11	$n = 3$
e) $4 + 6n$	40	$n = 6$	f) $\frac{n}{8} + 1$	5	$n = 32$

Take It Further

8. Each table shows patterns. Write an algebraic expression to describe how each Output relates to the Input.

a)

Input x	Output $3x$
1	3
2	6
3	9
4	12

b)

Input x	Output $3x - 2$
1	1
2	4
3	7
4	10

c)

Input x	Output $x - 3$
5	2
10	7
15	12
20	17

9. Find a value for p and a value for q so that $p - 3q$ has a value of 1. How many different ways can you do this? Explain.
   For example, $q = 1$ and $p = 4$; $q = 2$ and $p = 7$; $q = 3$ and $p =$

Reflect

Explain why it is important to use the order of operations when evaluating an algebraic expression. Use an example to explain.

386 UNIT 10: Patterning and Algebra

ASSESSMENT FOR LEARNING

What to Look For

Understanding concepts

✔ Students understand that to evaluate an algebraic expression, they replace a variable with a number, and simplify.

Applying procedures

✔ Students can evaluate an algebraic expression.

✔ Students can write an algebraic expression to represent a situation.

Communicating

✔ Students can explain why it is important to use the order of operations when evaluating an algebraic expression.

What to Do

Extra Support: Students who have difficulty using the order of operations when evaluating an expression may benefit from putting brackets around the operation that should be completed first. For example, to evaluate $5n - 4$ for $n = 2$, students rewrite $5 \times 2 - 4$ as $(5 \times 2) - 4$.
Students can use Step-by-Step 4 (Master 10.12) to complete question 6.

Extra Practice: Students can play the Additional Activity *Substitution Toss* (Masters 10.5a, 10.5b).
Students can complete Extra Practice 4 (Master 10.20).

Extension: Students write an algebraic expression, then use the expression to make an Input/Output table. Students trade expressions and Input numbers with a classmate, then complete each other's table.

Recording and Reporting
Master 10.2 Ongoing Observations: Patterning and Algebra

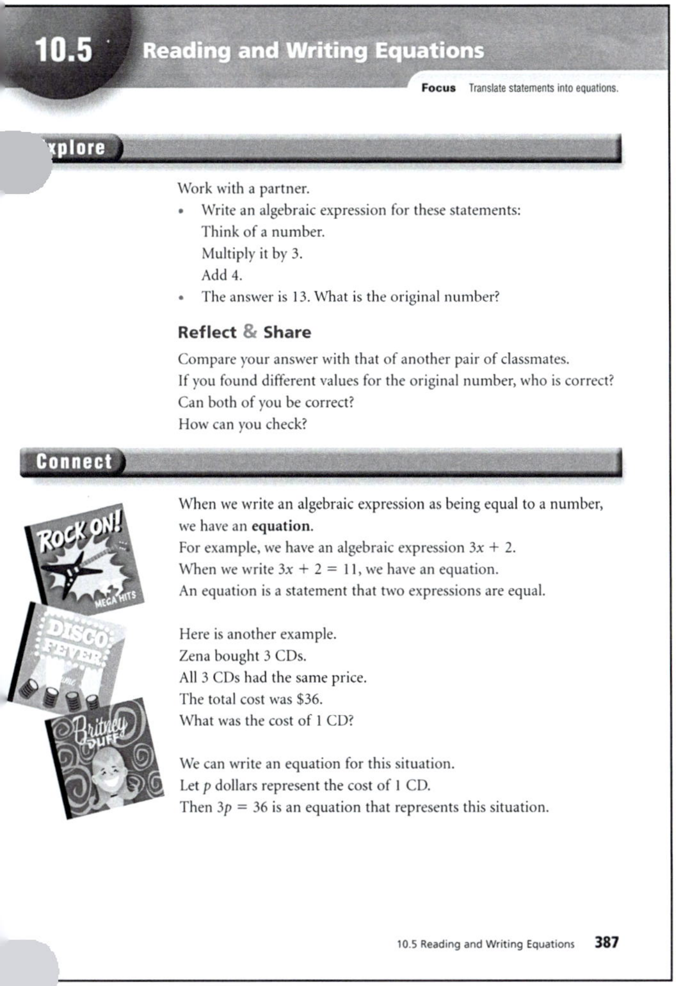

10.5 Reading and Writing Equations

Focus Translate statements into equations.

xplore

Work with a partner.
- Write an algebraic expression for these statements:
  Think of a number.
  Multiply it by 3.
  Add 4.
- The answer is 13. What is the original number?

Reflect & Share

Compare your answer with that of another pair of classmates.
If you found different values for the original number, who is correct?
Can both of you be correct?
How can you check?

Connect

When we write an algebraic expression as being equal to a number, we have an **equation**.
For example, we have an algebraic expression $3x + 2$.
When we write $3x + 2 = 11$, we have an equation.
An equation is a statement that two expressions are equal.

Here is another example.
Zena bought 3 CDs.
All 3 CDs had the same price.
The total cost was $36.
What was the cost of 1 CD?

We can write an equation for this situation.
Let p dollars represent the cost of 1 CD.
Then $3p = 36$ is an equation that represents this situation.

10.5 Reading and Writing Equations 387

Reading and Writing Equations

SECTION ORGANIZER (80–100 min)

Curriculum Focus: Translate statements into equations. (7m77)
Student Materials
Optional
- Step-by-Step 5 (Master 10.13)
- Extra Practice 5 (Master 10.21)

Vocabulary: equation
Assessment: Master 10.2 Ongoing Observations: Patterning and Algebra

Key Math Learnings

1. An equation is a statement that two numbers or expressions are equal.
2. A variable in an equation represents one number. To solve the equation means to find this number.

Sample Answers

2. a) Twelve more than a number is 19.
   b) Three times a number is 18.
   c) A number subtracted from twelve is 5.
   d) A number divided by two is 6.
4. a) Seven subtracted from five times a number is 37.
   b) The sum of one-third of a number and four is 9.
   c) Two times a number subtracted from seventeen is 3.

BEFORE Get Started

Review algebraic expressions. Ask:
- What algebraic expression can you write for the statement "nine less than a number?" ($n - 9$)
- What is the meaning of the expression $6n + 2$? (*Multiply a number by six, then add two.*)
- How can you evaluate the expression $5n + 3$ for $n = 4$? (*I replace n with 4:* $5 \times 4 + 3 = 23$.)

Present *Explore.*

DURING Explore

Ongoing Assessment: Observe and Listen

Ask questions, such as:
- Which variable did you use for the number? (*I used n, the first letter of "number."*)
- What expression did you write to represent "Multiply it by 3?" ($3n$)
- What expression did you write to represent "Multiply it by 3. Add 4?" ($3n + 4$)
- How did you use the answer to find the original number? (*I wrote the expression as being equal to the answer:* $3n + 4 = 13$. *I know that* $9 + 4 = 13$. *So, 3 times which number is 9? I know that* $3 \times 3 = 9$; *so* $n = 3$. *The original number is 3.*)

AFTER Connect

Invite students to share their answers with the class.

Ask:
- How did you check your answer? (*I worked through the written statements with my number. My result is 13, so my answer is correct.*)

REACHING ALL LEARNERS

Alternative Example

Write an algebraic expression for these statements:
Think of a number.
Add 7.
Divide it by 4.
The answer is 3. What is the original number?
(*Answer*: 5)

Early Finishers

Have students write 5 equations in words on index cards. Students then write the corresponding algebraic equations on index cards. Students shuffle the cards, then trade cards with a partner. Students match each algebraic equation with the correct word equation.

Common Misconceptions

➤ Students do not know when to write an equation and when to write an expression.

How to Help: Students learn in English that a sentence has a verb, and a phrase does not. Relate this to math: A sentence that contains the verb "is" or "equals" may be written as an equation. A phrase that has no verb may be written as an algebraic expression.

ESL Strategies

Suggest students refer to the index cards they made in Section 10.3 that show different kinds of statements and their related expressions. These may be helpful as students write equations.

Example 1

Mark thinks of a number.
He multiplies the number by 2, then adds 15.
The answer is 35. Write an equation for the problem.

Solution

Let n represent the number Mark thinks of.
Multiply the number by 2: $2n$
Then add 15: $2n + 15$
The equation is: $2n + 15 = 35$

Example 2

Write an equation for each sentence.
a) Three more than a number is 15.
b) Five less than a number is 7.
c) A number subtracted from 5 is 1.
d) A number divided by 3 is 10.

Solution

a) Three more than a number is 15.
Let x represent the number.
Three more than x: $x + 3$
The equation is: $x + 3 = 15$

b) Five less than a number is 7.
Let x represent the number.
Five less than x: $x - 5$
The equation is: $x - 5 = 7$

c) A number subtracted from 5 is 1.
Let x represent the number.
x subtracted from 5: $5 - x$
The equation is: $5 - x = 1$

d) A number divided by 3 is 10.
Let x represent the number.
x divided by 3: $\frac{x}{3}$
The equation is: $\frac{x}{3} = 10$

Ensure students understand that the variable in an algebraic expression can represent any number. But, as soon as we equate the expression to a given number, that is, we write an equation, the variable has only one value. So, in *Reflect & Share*, only one value for the original number is possible.

Ask students to suggest an alternative way to solve this problem. They may suggest working backward and using the inverse operations:
Begin with 13. Subtract 4 to get 9.
Divide by 3 to get 3.
The original number is 3.

Review the explanation and *Examples* in *Connect*. Point out to students how we explain what a variable represents before we use it in an equation, and how this is an important part of writing an equation.

Practice

Assessment Focus: Question 7

Remind students to begin each answer with a statement that tells what the variable represents. If students have difficulty with the wording of any sentence, suggest they rewrite the sentence in their own words. For *part c*, students should recall the formula for the perimeter of a rectangle. Some students may erroneously write $15 + w = 38$, forgetting the definition of perimeter.

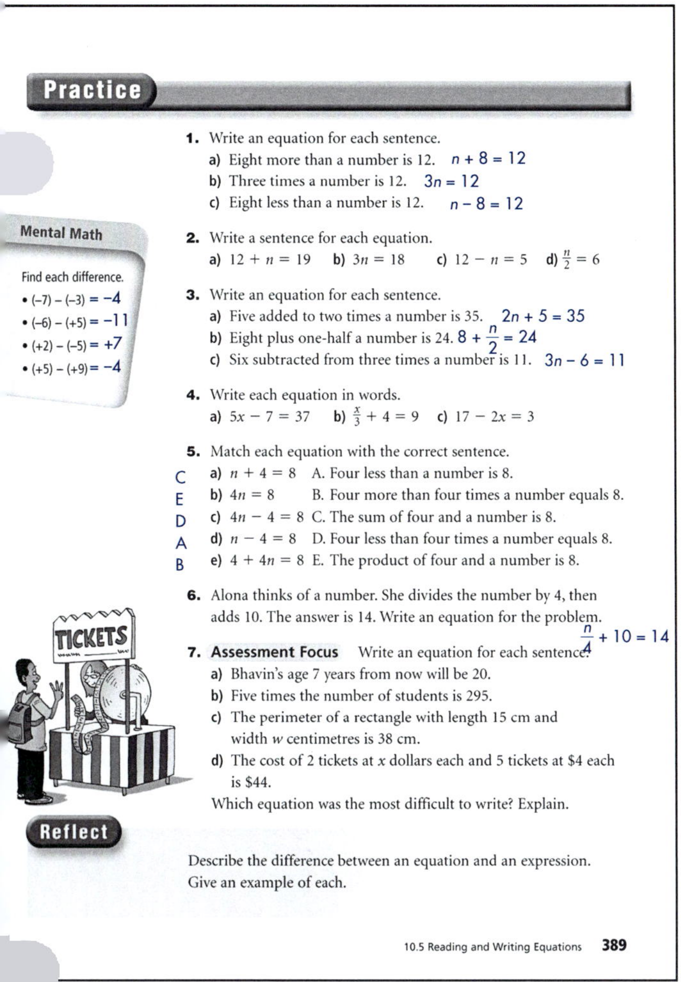

Practice

1. Write an equation for each sentence.
   a) Eight more than a number is 12. $n + 8 = 12$
   b) Three times a number is 12. $3n = 12$
   c) Eight less than a number is 12. $n - 8 = 12$

2. Write a sentence for each equation.
   a) $12 + n = 19$ b) $3n = 18$ c) $12 - n = 5$ d) $\frac{n}{2} = 6$

3. Write an equation for each sentence.
   a) Five added to two times a number is 35. $2n + 5 = 35$
   b) Eight plus one-half a number is 24. $8 + \frac{n}{2} = 24$
   c) Six subtracted from three times a number is 11. $3n - 6 = 11$

4. Write each equation in words.
   a) $5x - 7 = 37$ b) $\frac{x}{3} + 4 = 9$ c) $17 - 2x = 3$

5. Match each equation with the correct sentence.
   C a) $n + 4 = 8$ A. Four less than a number is 8.
   E b) $4n = 8$ B. Four more than four times a number equals 8.
   D c) $4n - 4 = 8$ C. The sum of four and a number is 8.
   A d) $n - 4 = 8$ D. Four less than four times a number equals 8.
   B e) $4 + 4n = 8$ E. The product of four and a number is 8.

6. Alona thinks of a number. She divides the number by 4, then adds 10. The answer is 14. Write an equation for the problem. $\frac{n}{4} + 10 = 14$

7. **Assessment Focus** Write an equation for each sentence.
   a) Bhavin's age 7 years from now will be 20.
   b) Five times the number of students is 295.
   c) The perimeter of a rectangle with length 15 cm and width w centimetres is 38 cm.
   d) The cost of 2 tickets at x dollars each and 5 tickets at $4 each is $44.
   Which equation was the most difficult to write? Explain.

Mental Math

Find each difference.
- $(-7) - (-3) = -4$
- $(-6) - (+5) = -11$
- $(+2) - (-5) = +7$
- $(+5) - (+9) = -4$

Reflect

Describe the difference between an equation and an expression. Give an example of each.

10.5 Reading and Writing Equations 389

7. a) Let n represent Bhavin's age in years now. $n + 7 = 20$
   b) Let n represent the number of students. $5n = 295$
   c) The perimeter of a rectangle is: $P = 2l + 2w$
   $2(15) + 2w = 38$; or $30 + 2w = 38$
   d) $\$2x + 5(\$4) = \$44$; or $\$2x + \$20 = \$44$
   Equation c was the most difficult to write because I had to remember the formula for the perimeter of a rectangle before I could write the equation.

REFLECT: An algebraic expression is a mathematical expression that contains a variable; for example, $4b + 6$. The variable represents any number. An equation is a statement that two expressions are true; for example, $4b + 6 = 18$ is an equation. The variable represents one number. An equation always has an equal sign. An expression does not have an equal sign.

Assignment Guidelines

If your students do not have time to complete all the *Practice* questions on page 389, these questions provide minimum curriculum coverage: 1, 3, 4, 6, 7, *Reflect*

To assess the 4 Achievement Chart categories listed in the curriculum document, have students complete these *Practice* questions: Understanding Concepts: 3; Application: 6; Problem Solving: 7; Communication: *Reflect*

Mental Math

Some students may need to use a number line, colour tiles, or related addition equations to subtract the integers.

ASSESSMENT FOR LEARNING

What to Look For	What to Do
Understanding concepts ✔ Students understand that an equation is a statement that two expressions are equal. ✔ Students understand that an equation is made when we equate an algebraic expression to a number. ***Applying procedures*** ✔ Students can write an equation for a mathematical sentence, and a sentence for an equation. ***Communicating*** ✔ Students can describe the difference between an equation and an expression.	***Extra Support:*** Students who have difficulty writing an equation may benefit from breaking the sentence into two parts: the algebraic expression and the number that it equals. Students write the expression first, then use an equal sign to relate it to the number. Students can use Step-by-Step 5 (Master 10.13) to complete question 7. ***Extra Practice:*** Students can play the Additional Activity *Algebra Concentration* (Master 10.6). Students can complete Extra Practice 5 (Master 10.21). ***Extension:*** Have students find as many different ways as they can to express the number 8; for example, 4 + 4 or 9 – 1. Students use their results to rewrite the equation $2x = 8$ in as many different ways as they can.

Recording and Reporting

Master 10.2 Ongoing Observations: Patterning and Algebra

Solving Equations

SECTION ORGANIZER

80–100 min

Curriculum Focus: Solve equations by inspection and by systematic trial. (7m77, 7m78, 7m79, 7m80)
Student Materials
Optional
- Step-by-Step 6 (Master 10.14)
- Extra Practice 6 (Master 10.22)

Vocabulary: solve an equation
Assessment: Master 10.2 Ongoing Observations: Patterning and Algebra

Key Math Learnings

1. To solve an equation means to find the value of the variable that makes the equation true.
2. An equation can be solved by systematic trial or by inspection.

10.6 Solving Equations

Focus Solve equations by inspection and by systematic trial.

Explore

Work with a partner.
On the way home from school, 3 students get off the bus at the first stop. Seven get off at the next stop. Five get off at the next stop. Ten get off at the next stop. There are now 2 students left on the bus. How many students were on the bus when it left the school? 27
How many different ways can you solve the problem?

Reflect & Share

Discuss your strategies for finding the answer with another pair of classmates.
Did you use an equation? Did you use reasoning?
Did you draw a picture? Explain.

Connect

Recall the equation about the cost of 1 CD, from *Section 10.5 Reading and Writing Equations*, page 387.
The equation is $3p = 36$, where p is the cost of 1 CD.
When we use the equation to find the value of p, we **solve the equation.**

Here are 2 ways to solve this equation.

Method 1: By Systematic Trial
$3p = 36$
We choose a value for p and substitute.
When $p = 10$, $3p = 30$
30 is too small, so choose a greater value of p.

When $p = 20$, $3p = 60$
60 is too large, so choose a lesser value of p.

When $p = 15$, $3p = 45$
45 is too large, so choose a lesser value of p.

390 UNIT 10: Patterning and Algebra

BEFORE Get Started

Show students how they use mathematical thinking to solve simple word problems.

Ask:
- I ate 3 soda crackers with my soup at lunch. I have one left. How many soda crackers did I have to start with? (*4*) How do you know? (*3 + 1 = 4*)
- There were 25 copies of the daily newspaper in the paper box. There are 5 papers left. How many papers have been sold? (*20*) How do you know? (*25 – 5 = 20*)

Present *Explore.*

DURING Explore

Ongoing Assessment: Observe and Listen

Ask questions, such as:

- Which strategy did you use to solve the problem? (*I worked backward.*) Explain. (*There are 2 students on the bus. Before the last stop, there were 10 + 2, or 12 students on the bus. Before the third stop, there were 12 + 5, or 17 students on the bus. Before the second stop, there were 17 + 7, or 24 students on the bus. Before the first stop, there were 24 + 3, or 27 students on the bus.*)
- Did anyone use a different strategy? (*I added the number of students who got off the bus: 3 + 7 + 5 + 10 = 25. There are 2 students still on the bus. So, when the bus left the school, there were 25 + 2, or 27 students on the bus.*)

When $p = 12$, $3p = 36$
This is correct.
The cost of 1 CD is $12.

Method 2: By Inspection
$3p = 36$
We find a number which, when multiplied by 3, has product 36.
We know that $3 \times 12 = 36$; so, $p = 12$.
The cost of 1 CD is $12.

We say that the value $p = 12$ makes the equation $3p = 36$ true.
A value $p = 10$ would not make the equation true because 3×10 does not equal 36.
The value $p = 12$ is the only solution to the equation.
That is, there is only one value of p that makes the equation true.

Example 1

Solve by inspection.
a) $x + 7 = 10$
b) $\frac{24}{n} = 6$
c) $40 - y = 30$
d) $9z + 2 = 38$

Solution

a) $x + 7 = 10$
Which number added to 7 gives 10?
We know that $3 + 7 = 10$; so, $x = 3$.

b) $\frac{24}{n} = 6$
This means $24 \div n = 6$.
Which number divided into 24 gives 6?
We know that $24 \div 4 = 6$; so, $n = 4$.

c) $40 - y = 30$
Which number subtracted from 40 gives 30?
We know that $40 - 10 = 30$; so, $y = 10$.

d) $9z + 2 = 38$
9 times which number, plus 2, gives 38?
We know $36 + 2 = 38$
So, 9 times which number is 36?
We know that $9 \times 4 = 36$; so, $z = 4$.

10.6 Solving Equations 391

REACHING ALL LEARNERS

Alternative Example

The class planted a tomato plant in the spring. As the tomatoes ripened, different students picked the tomatoes. On Day 1, four tomatoes were picked. On Day 2, six tomatoes were picked. On Day 3, three tomatoes were picked. On Day 4, two tomatoes were picked. On Day 5, three tomatoes were picked. There are 3 unripe tomatoes left on the plant. How many tomatoes did the plant produce? How many different ways can you solve the problem?

Early Finishers

Have students solve the equations in Section 10.5, *Practice* questions 2, 4, 6, and 7.

Common Misconceptions

➤ Students write an incorrect solution to an equation.

How to Help: Model how to substitute to check the solution to an equation. For example, use the equation $2c + 1 = 9$ and the solution $c = 4$. Remind students that the value of c must make the equation true.
Find the value of the expression on the left side of the equal sign: Replace c with 4.
$2 \times 4 + 1 = 9$
Now look at the number on the right side of the equation: 9
Since the numbers are equal, the solution is correct. If the two numbers were not equal, the solution would be incorrect and students should try to solve the equation again.

- Did anyone use a different strategy? (*I used guess and check. I assumed there were 30 students on the bus. I subtracted the students as they got off at each stop. I had 5 students left on the bus. This is 3 students too many. So, I reduced the number of students I started with by 3: 30 – 3 = 27.*)
- Did anyone use a different strategy? (*I drew a picture. I drew 2 circles. I labelled the circles, "On the bus," and "Off the bus." I drew stick people in the circle labelled "Off the bus" to represent the students who left the bus. There were 25 stick people in the circle. I drew 2 stick people in the circle labelled "On the bus." I added to find the total number of students: 25 + 2 = 27.*)

AFTER — Connect

Invite students to share their strategies with the class.

Ask questions, such as:

- Did anyone use an equation? Explain. (*Yes. I let n represent the number of students on the bus when the bus left the school. So,* $n - 3 - 7 - 5 - 10 = 2$, *or* $n - 25 = 2$.)
- How can you write this equation in words? (*Twenty-five less than a number is two.*)
- How can you use the equation to solve the problem? (*I know that* $27 - 25 = 2$; *so,* $n = 27$.)

Tell students that they are familiar with many equations already; for example:

$3 + 4 = 7$
$5 \times 5 = 25$
$28 \div 7 = 4$
$21 - 11 = 10$

Sample Answers

6. a) The perimeter of a square = 4 × side length.
   Let s represent the side length, in centimetres.
   The perimeter is 156 cm; so, $156 = 4s$.
   b) I know that $4 \times 39 = 156$; so, $s = 39$.
   The side length of the square is 39 cm.
7. a) The perimeter of a regular hexagon = 6 × side length.
   Let P represent the perimeter, in centimetres.
   The side length is 9 cm; so, $P = 6 \times 9$.
   b) $P = 54$; so, the perimeter of the regular hexagon is 54 cm.
8. a) The perimeter of a regular octagon is 64 cm. Write an equation you can solve to find the side length of the octagon.
   b) The perimeter of a regular octagon = 8 × side length.
   Let s represent the side length, in centimetres.
   The perimeter is 64 cm; so, $8s = 64$.
   c) I know that $8 \times 8 = 64$; so, $s = 8$.
   The side length of the octagon is 8 cm.
9. a) Let c represent the number of friends who shared the comic books.
   Before sharing with his friends, Eli had 130 – 10 comic books.
   Then, each friend was given $\frac{(130 - 10)}{c}$ comic books.
   I know each friend was given 24 comic books.
   So, the equation is: $\frac{(130 - 10)}{c} = 24$.
   b) $130 - 10 = 120$. I know that $120 \div 5 = 24$; so, $c = 5$.
   Five friends were given comic books.

Example 2

Solve by systematic trial.

a) $2a - 28 = 136$

b) $\frac{y}{4} = 220$

Solution

a) $2a - 28 = 136$

When the numbers are large, use a calculator.

Try $a = 50$; then, $2 \times 50 - 28 = 72$

72 is too small, so choose a greater value of a.

Try $a = 100$; then, $2 \times 100 - 28 = 172$

172 is too big, so choose a lesser value of a.

Try $a = 75$; then, $2 \times 75 - 28 = 122$

122 is too small, so choose a greater value of a.

Try $a = 80$; then, $2 \times 80 - 28 = 132$

132 is too small, but it is close to the value we want.

Try $a = 82$; then, $2 \times 82 - 28 = 136$

This is correct.

$a = 82$ is the solution.

b) $\frac{y}{4} = 220$

Use a calculator. We know the number is much greater than 220, because the number is divided by 4 to get 220.

Try $y = 1000$; then, $\frac{1000}{4} = 250$ This is too big.

Try $y = 900$; then, $\frac{900}{4} = 225$ This is closer, but still too big.

Try $y = 850$; then, $\frac{850}{4} = 212.5$ This is too small.

Try $y = 880$; then, $\frac{880}{4} = 220$ This is correct.

$y = 880$ is the solution.

We can write, then solve, an equation to solve a problem.

Example 3

Kiera shared 420 hockey cards equally among her friends.
Each friend had 105 cards.

a) Write an equation that describes this situation.

b) Solve the equation to find how many friends shared the cards.

392 UNIT 10: Patterning and Algebra

Show students that we can replace one of the numbers in an equation with a variable to make an equation like the ones in this section; for example,

$3 + v = 7$

$5 \times a = 25$

$t \div 7 = 4$

$z - 11 = 10$

This illustrates how to use basic facts to solve an equation; for example, to solve $3 + v = 7$, students use the fact that $3 + 4 = 7$, to find $v = 4$.

Review the explanation in *Connect* that illustrates solving by systematic trial and by inspection.

In *Example 1*, ensure students understand that $x + 7 = 10$ and $10 = x + 7$ are the same equation, just as $3 + 4 = 7$ and $7 = 4 + 3$ are the same. Point out that it does not matter which side of the equal sign has the algebraic expression and which side has the number.

In *Example 1*, after students have seen the solution to $\frac{24}{n} = 6$, have students use what they know to solve the equation $\frac{24}{x} = 4$. Students should see that they use the fact $6 \times 4 = 24$ to solve both equations, and that in this equation, $x = 6$.

Ask:

- Which other pairs of equations of this form can you write?
  ($\frac{35}{n} = 5$, $\frac{35}{x} = 7$; $\frac{56}{n} = 8$, $\frac{56}{x} = 7$)
- Would you use systematic trial or inspection to solve these equations? Why?
  (I would use inspection because I can use the basic facts 5 × 7 = 35, and 7 × 8 = 56.)

In *Example 2*, systematic trial is used to solve the equation $2a - 28 = 136$. Ask:

- Why was inspection not used?
  (Because we do not know a basic fact for 136 and because the numbers are large.)

Solution

a) Let h represent the number of friends who shared the cards.
Then, each friend had $\frac{420}{h}$ cards.
Also, each friend had 105 cards.
So, the equation is: $\frac{420}{h} = 105$

b) Solve $\frac{420}{h} = 105$ by inspection.
Think: $420 \div h = 105$
Which number divides into 420 to give the quotient 105?
We know $400 \div 4 = 100$; so, try $h = 4$.
$420 \div 4 = 105$
So, the solution is $h = 4$.
Four friends shared the cards.

Practice

1. Solve each equation.
   a) $x + 3 = 12$ $x = 9$ b) $y + 9 = 9$ $y = 0$
   c) $10 + 2z = 20$ $z = 5$ d) $17 + 3c = 26$ $c = 3$
2. Solve each equation.
   a) $x - 4 = 3$ $x = 7$ b) $10 - n = 10$ $n = 0$
   c) $2z - 7 = 1$ $z = 4$ d) $13 - 4k = 5$ $k = 2$

3. Shenker has 45 CDs.
   He gives 10 CDs to his brother.
   a) Write an equation you can solve to find how many CDs Shenker has left. $45 - 10 = n$
   b) Solve the equation. $n = 35$
4. Solve by inspection.
   a) $x + 4 = 15$ $x = 11$ b) $2k - 13 = 3$ $k = 8$
   c) $3y = 24$ $y = 8$ d) $\frac{z}{9} = 2$ $z = 18$
5. Solve by systematic trial.
   a) $n + 5 = 33$ $n = 28$ b) $8z = 88$ $z = 11$
   c) $43 - 3y = 16$ $y = 9$ d) $\frac{x}{7} = 4$ $x = 28$

10. a) I know $3 \times 9 = 27$; so, $n = 9$.
    b) I know $24 + 3 = 27$ and $2 \times 12 = 24$; so, $n = 12$.
    c) I know $30 - 3 = 27$ and $2 \times 15 = 30$; so, $n = 15$.
    d) I know $81 \div 3 = 27$; so, $n = 81$.
    e) I know $24 + 3 = 27$ and $48 \div 2 = 24$; so, $n = 48$.
    f) I know that $54 \div 2 = 27$ and $3 \times 18 = 54$; so, $n = 18$.
11. a) Jason bought two slices of pizza and was given a $1 discount. He paid $5 in total. How much was each slice of pizza? (*Answer:* $x = 3$)
    b) The perimeter of a square is 24 cm. What is the side length of the square? (*Answer:* $y = 6$)
    c) The students in the school are divided into 38 groups. Each group has 57 students. How many students are in the school? (*Answer:* $z = 2166$)
    d) Jasmine had 5 hockey cards. She buys 5 packages of hockey cards. She now has 30 hockey cards. How many cards were in each package? (*Answer:* $x = 5$)
    e) There are 25 students in the class. The teacher divides the students into groups to play a game. There are 5 students in each group. How many groups are there? (*Answer:* $y = 5$)
    f) The aces are removed from a deck of 52 playing cards. The remaining cards are dealt equally among 4 players. How many cards does each player get? (*Answer:* $x = 12$)
    Equation c was the most difficult to solve because I didn't know number facts for 38×57. I had to use a calculator.

REFLECT: Knowing my number facts helps me find a solution to an equation quickly. For example, to solve the equation $4s = 36$, I recall that $4 \times 9 = 36$. I am able to see immediately that $s = 9$. I can save a lot of time if I know my number facts.

- Could you solve the equation $\frac{y}{4} = 220$ by inspection? Explain.
  (*Yes. This equation means that a number divided by 4 is 220. I can find this number by multiplying 4 by 220. Since the numbers are large, I use a calculator to find y = 880.*)

Some students find problems, such as the one in *Example 3*, difficult. After you have worked through the solution, have volunteers write similar problems in preparation for *Practice* question 8.

Ask:

- What problem did you write? (*Jenny shared 280 baseball cards equally among her brothers. Each of her brothers had 70 cards. How many brothers does Jenny have? Answer: 4*)

Practice

Encourage students to check their solutions to ensure they are correct.

Assessment Focus: Question 11

Students will demonstrate the depth of their understanding of equations by the problems they write. Encourage students to relate the equations to real-life situations rather than to direct translations; for example, discourage students from writing, "Four times a number is 24. Which number am I?" Students solve the equations, then relate the solutions to their problems.

Mental Math

Students could round each whole number to the nearest whole number that has the corresponding denominator as a factor. For $\frac{1}{4}$ of 22, students could find $\frac{1}{4} \times 20 = 5$; for $\frac{2}{5}$ of 36, students could find $\frac{2}{5} \times 35 = 14$; for $\frac{2}{3}$ of 91, students could find $\frac{2}{3} \times 90 = 60$; and for $\frac{3}{8}$ of 79, students could find $\frac{3}{8} \times 80 = 30$.

Assignment Guidelines

If your students do not have time to complete all the *Practice* questions on pages 393 and 394, these questions provide minimum curriculum coverage: 1, 4, 5, 6, 9, 11, *Reflect*
To assess the 4 Achievement Chart categories listed in the curriculum document, have students complete these *Practice* questions:
Understanding Concepts: 4
Application: 6
Problem Solving: 9
Communication: *Reflect*

Mental Math

Estimate.
- $\frac{1}{4}$ of 22 About 5
- $\frac{2}{5}$ of 36 About 14
- $\frac{2}{3}$ of 91 About 60
- $\frac{3}{8}$ of 79 About 30

6. The perimeter of a square is 156 cm.
a) Write an equation you can solve to find the side length of the square. $156 = 4s$
b) Solve the equation. $s = 39$

7. The side length of a regular hexagon is 9 cm.
a) Write an equation you can solve to find the perimeter of the hexagon. $P = 6 \times 9$
b) Solve the equation. $P = 54$

8. Use questions 6 and 7 as a guide.
a) Write your own problem about side length and perimeter of a figure.
b) Write an equation you can use to solve the problem.
c) Solve the equation.

9. Eli has 130 comic books.
He gives 10 to his sister, then shares the rest equally among his friends.
Each friend has 24 comic books.
a) Write an equation you can solve to find how many friends were given comics. $\frac{(130-10)}{c} = 24$
b) Solve the equation. $c = 5$

10. Find the value of n that makes each equation true.
a) $3n = 27$ $n = 9$
b) $2n + 3 = 27$ $n = 12$
c) $2n - 3 = 27$ $n = 15$
d) $\frac{n}{3} = 27$ $n = 81$
e) $\frac{n}{2} + 3 = 27$ $n = 48$
f) $\frac{3n}{2} = 27$ $n = 18$

11. **Assessment Focus** Write a problem that can be described by each equation. Solve each equation.
Which equation was the most difficult to solve? Explain.
a) $2x - 1 = 5$ $x = 3$
b) $4y = 24$ $y = 6$
c) $\frac{z}{38} = 57$ $z = 2166$
d) $5x + 5 = 30$ $x = 5$
e) $\frac{25}{y} = 5$ $y = 5$
f) $52 - 4 = 4x$ $x = 17$

Reflect

How does knowing your number facts help you solve an equation by inspection? Give examples in your explanation.

394 UNIT 10: Patterning and Algebra

ASSESSMENT FOR LEARNING

What to Look For	What to Do
Understanding concepts ✔ Students understand that an equation has only one solution and that solution makes the equation true. ***Applying procedures*** ✔ Students can solve an equation by systematic trial or by inspection. ***Problem solving*** ✔ Students can write, then solve, an equation to solve a problem. ***Communicating*** ✔ Students can explain the steps they used to solve an equation.	***Extra Support:*** Students having difficulty solving an equation by inspection should review the basic addition, subtraction, multiplication, and division facts. Students may benefit from using addition and multiplication charts. Students can use Step-by-Step 6 (Master 10.14) to complete question 11. ***Extra Practice:*** Students can play the Additional Activity *Algebra Game* (Masters 10.7a, 10.7b). Students can complete Extra Practice 6 (Master 10.22). ***Extension:*** Students can complete the Additional Activity *Algebra Word Search* (Master 10.8).

Recording and Reporting
Master 10.2 Ongoing Observations: Patterning and Algebra

Clothes Buyer

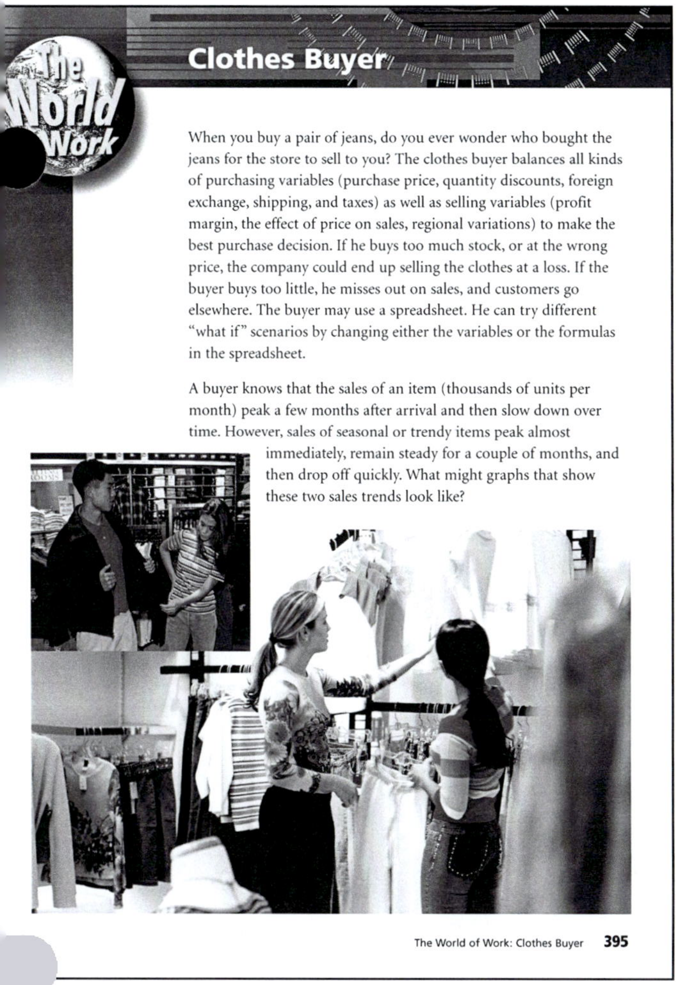

Clothes Buyer

When you buy a pair of jeans, do you ever wonder who bought the jeans for the store to sell to you? The clothes buyer balances all kinds of purchasing variables (purchase price, quantity discounts, foreign exchange, shipping, and taxes) as well as selling variables (profit margin, the effect of price on sales, regional variations) to make the best purchase decision. If he buys too much stock, or at the wrong price, the company could end up selling the clothes at a loss. If the buyer buys too little, he misses out on sales, and customers go elsewhere. The buyer may use a spreadsheet. He can try different "what if" scenarios by changing either the variables or the formulas in the spreadsheet.

A buyer knows that the sales of an item (thousands of units per month) peak a few months after arrival and then slow down over time. However, sales of seasonal or trendy items peak almost immediately, remain steady for a couple of months, and then drop off quickly. What might graphs that show these two sales trends look like?

The World of Work: Clothes Buyer 395

Sample Solution

Here is a sample of the graphs that show the two different sales trends.

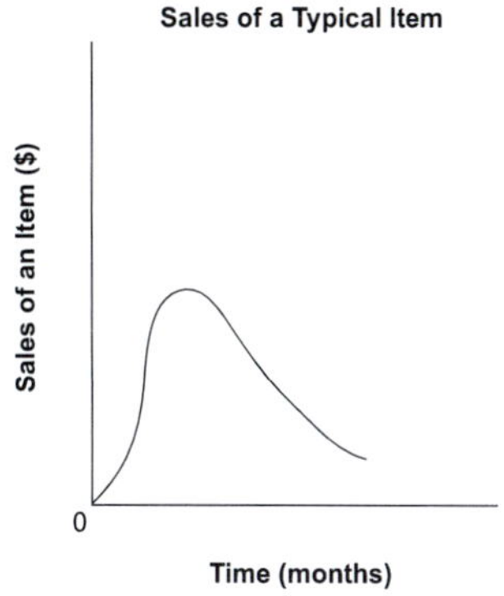

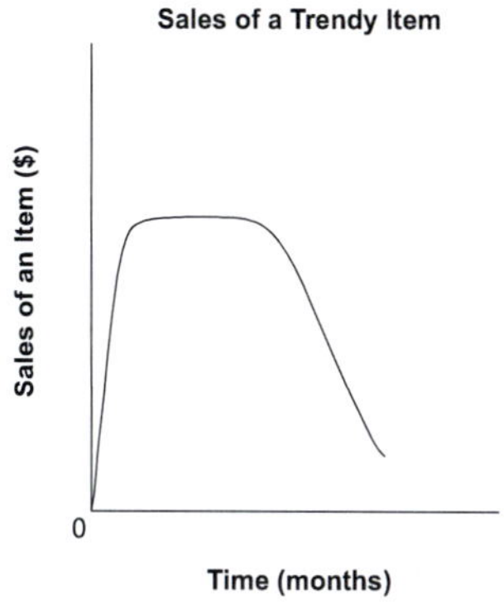

Here are some other careers that involve the use of variables and equations.

Applied Mathematician: An applied mathematician uses equations and variables to solve problems related to economic, social, scientific, and business situations. For example, an applied mathematician could study the cost-effectiveness of an alternative manufacturing process, the aerodynamic qualities of experimental cars and planes, or the behaviour of financial markets.

Clinical Laboratory Technologist: A clinical laboratory technologist examines and analyses body fluids, cells, and tissues, and performs tests to help detect, diagnose, and treat disease. A technologist uses equations to analyse the results of these tests, then relays her findings to a physician.

Choosing a Strategy

SECTION ORGANIZER

Student Materials
- calculators
- red and blue tiles (optional)
- 0.5-cm grid paper (PM 14) (optional)

Vocabulary: solve an equation
Assessment: Master 10.2 Ongoing Observations: Patterning and Algebra

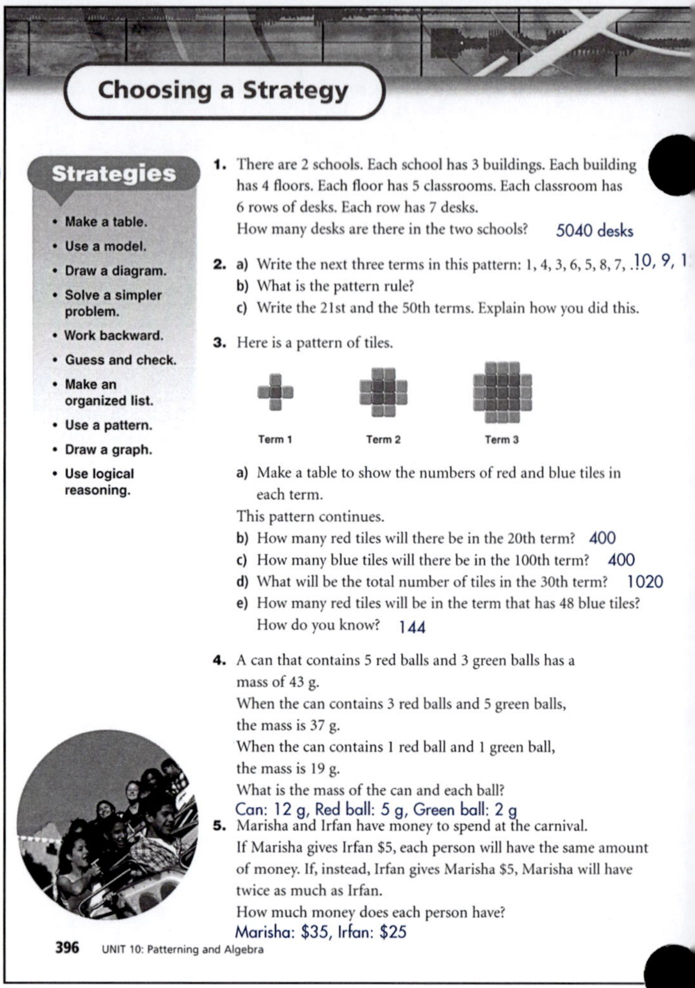

Choosing a Strategy

Strategies
- Make a table.
- Use a model.
- Draw a diagram.
- Solve a simpler problem.
- Work backward.
- Guess and check.
- Make an organized list.
- Use a pattern.
- Draw a graph.
- Use logical reasoning.

1. There are 2 schools. Each school has 3 buildings. Each building has 4 floors. Each floor has 5 classrooms. Each classroom has 6 rows of desks. Each row has 7 desks.
How many desks are there in the two schools? 5040 desks

2. a) Write the next three terms in this pattern: 1, 4, 3, 6, 5, 8, 7, . . . 10, 9, 1
b) What is the pattern rule?
c) Write the 21st and the 50th terms. Explain how you did this.

3. Here is a pattern of tiles.

Term 1 Term 2 Term 3

a) Make a table to show the numbers of red and blue tiles in each term.
This pattern continues.
b) How many red tiles will there be in the 20th term? 400
c) How many blue tiles will there be in the 100th term? 400
d) What will be the total number of tiles in the 30th term? 1020
e) How many red tiles will be in the term that has 48 blue tiles? How do you know? 144

4. A can that contains 5 red balls and 3 green balls has a mass of 43 g.
When the can contains 3 red balls and 5 green balls, the mass is 37 g.
When the can contains 1 red ball and 1 green ball, the mass is 19 g.
What is the mass of the can and each ball?
Can: 12 g, Red ball: 5 g, Green ball: 2 g

5. Marisha and Irfan have money to spend at the carnival.
If Marisha gives Irfan $5, each person will have the same amount of money. If, instead, Irfan gives Marisha $5, Marisha will have twice as much as Irfan.
How much money does each person have?
Marisha: $35, Irfan: $25

396 UNIT 10: Patterning and Algebra

Sample Solutions

2. b) Start at 1. Add 3 to get the next term. Subtract 1 to get the next term. Continue to add and subtract in this way.
c) Each odd-numbered term is equal to the term number. Each even-numbered term is equal to the term number, plus 2.
Since 21 is an odd number, the 21st term is 21.
Since 50 is an even number, the 50th term is $50 + 2 = 52$.

3. a)

Term Number	Number of Red Tiles	Number of Blue Tiles
1	1	4
2	4	8
3	9	12

b) The number of red tiles in each term is the square of the term number.
So, the number of red tiles in the 20th term is:
$20^2 = 400$
c) The number of blue tiles in each term is the term number multiplied by 4.
So, the number of blue tiles in the 100th term is:
$100 \times 4 = 400$
d) The total number of tiles in the 30th term is:
30^2 red tiles + 30×4 blue tiles $= 900 + 120 = 1020$
e) The number of blue tiles = the term number $\times$ 4
If there are 48 blue tiles, 48 = the term number $\times$ 4.
$4 \times 12 = 48$, so the term number is 12.
The number of red tiles in term 12 is: $12^2 = 144$.

4. Can + 5 red + 3 green = 43
Can + 3 red + 5 green = 37
Can + 1 red + 1 green = 19
We know the masses of the can, 1 red ball, and 1 green ball are 19.
So, if we subtract 19 from 43, we have taken away the masses of the can, 1 red ball, and 1 green ball from the masses of the can, 5 red balls, and 3 green balls.
So, we are left with 4 red + 2 green = $43 - 19 = 24$.
Similarly, if we subtract 19 from 37, we have taken away the masses of the can, 1 red ball, and 1 green ball from the masses of the can, 3 red balls, and 5 green balls.
So, we are left with 2 red + 4 green = $37 - 19 = 18$.
Use guess and check: If a red ball has a mass of 5 g, 4×5 + 2 green = 24; so, 20 + 2 green = 24. I know $20 + 4 = 24$, so the 2 green balls have a mass of 4 g.
The mass of each green ball, in grams, is: $4 \div 2 = 2$.

Reading and Writing in Math

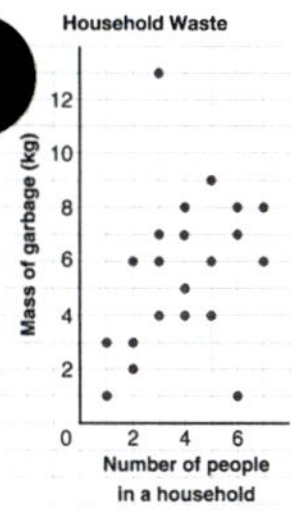

6. The graph shows the garbage put out by 21 households in one week.
   a) How does the mass of garbage relate to the number of people in the household?
   b) Give three possible reasons why one household has 13 kg of garbage.
   c) Give three possible reasons why one household has 1 kg of garbage.
7. For a school trip, the charge for using the school bus is $50. The cost of food is $10 per student.
   a) Copy and complete this table for up to 10 students.

Number of students	1	2	3	4	5
Total cost of trip ($)	60	70	80	90	100

   $110, $120, $130, $140, $150
   b) What is the total cost for each number of students?
   i) 12 $170 ii) 15 $200 iii) 20 $250
   c) Each person pays a fair share. What is the cost per person when each number of students goes on the trip?
   i) 5 $20 ii) 10 $15 iii) 15 About $13.33

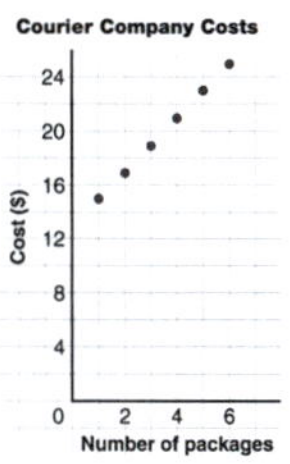

8. The graph shows the price charged by a local courier company to collect and deliver packages.
   a) What is the cost to have 6 packages collected and delivered? $25
   b) Extend the pattern in the graph. What is the cost to have 8 packages collected and delivered? $29
   c) Why does it cost $15 to collect and deliver one package, but only $17 to collect and deliver 2 packages?
9. I am a 3-digit number.
   My hundreds digit is the square of my ones digit.
   My tens digit is the product of my hundreds digit and my ones digit.
   a) What number, or numbers, could I be? 111 or 482
   b) What do you notice about your answer(s)?
   The digits in each number are either all odd or all even.

Reading and Writing in Math: Choosing a Strategy 397

Question Number	Possible Strategy
1	Work backward; draw a diagram
2	Use a pattern; use logical reasoning
3	Make a table; use a pattern
4	Use logical reasoning; guess and check
5	Guess and check; use logical reasoning
6	Use logical reasoning
7	Use a pattern; draw a diagram
8	Use a pattern; use logical reasoning
9	Use logical reasoning; guess and check

I use these results to check if 2 red + 4 green have a mass of 18 g:
$2 \times 5 + 4 \times 2 = 10 + 8 = 18$
Since the mass is 18 g, the mass of each ball is correct.
So, since Can + 1 red + 1 green = 19 g, the mass of the can, in grams, is: $19 - 5 - 2 = 12$.

5. Use guess and check.
Try: Marisha has $30 and Irfan has $20.
If Marisha gives Irfan $5, Marisha will have $30 – $5 = $25 and Irfan will have $20 + $5 = $25.
Both people have the same amount of money.
If Irfan gives Marisha $5, Irfan has $20 – $5 = $15, and Marisha has $30 + $5 = $35. $35 is more than twice as much as $15.
Try: Marisha has $35 and Irfan has $25.
If Marisha gives Irfan $5, Marisha will have $35 – $5 = $30 and Irfan will have $25 + $5 = $30.
Both people have the same amount of money.
If Irfan gives Marisha $5, Irfan has $25 – $5 = $20, and Marisha has $35 + $5 = $40.
$40 is twice as much as $20.
So, Marisha has $35 and Irfan has $25.

6. a) The mass of garbage generally increases as the number of people in the household increases.
   b) Three possible reasons are: the people don't recycle; they had a spring clean up; or they put a heavy item out for garbage.
   c) Three possible reasons are; they were away for a few days; they recycle and use a composter, or there is only 1 person in the household.

8. c) Extend the graph backward. It costs $13 to deliver 0 parcels; that is, the cost that does not depend on the number of parcels is $13. Then, each parcel costs an extra $2.

SECTION ORGANIZER

Student Materials
- calculators
- 0.5-cm grid paper (PM 14)

Assessment:
Masters 10.1 Unit Rubric: Patterning and Algebra, 10.4 Unit Summary: Patterning and Algebra

Unit Review

Review any lesson with etext online tutorial

What Do I Need to Know?

✓ A variable is a letter or symbol that represents a number, or a set of numbers.
A variable can be used to write an expression:
"3 more than a number" is $3 + n$.
A variable can be used to write an equation:
"4 more than a number equals 11" is $4 + n = 11$.

✓ We can solve equations by:
- inspection
- systematic trial

What Should I Be Able to Do?

For extra practice, go to page 447.

LESSON

10.1 **1.** For each pattern:
i) Describe the pattern.
ii) Write the next 3 terms.
iii) Find the 20th term.
Explain how you did this.
a) 5, 12, 19, 26, .. 33, 40, 47
b) 3, 9, 27, 81, … 243, 729, 2187
c) 96, 93, 90, 87, … 84, 81, 78
d) 10, 21, 32, 43, … 54, 65, 76
e) 9, 13, 17, 21, 25, 29, 33

2. Your favourite aunt gives you 1¢ on April 1, 2¢ on April 2, 4¢ on April 3. She continues doubling the daily amount until April 12.
a) How much will you get on April 12? 2048¢ or \$20.48
b) What is the total amount you will receive? 4095¢ or \$40.95

3. a) Describe this pattern: 2, 5, 11, 23, 47, … a) Start at 2. Multiply by 2, then add 1 each time.
b) Write the next 3 terms. b) 95, 191, 383
c) Write a similar pattern. Use a different start number.

4. This pattern continues.

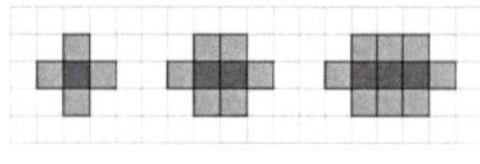

a) Describe the pattern.
b) Sketch the next 3 figures.
c) Describe the 12th figure and the 22nd figure. Sketch them if you can.

398 UNIT 10: Patterning and Algebra

Sample Solutions

1. a) i) The terms are multiples of 7, minus 2.
iii) The 1st term is: $1 \times 7 - 2 = 5$
The 2nd term is: $2 \times 7 - 2 = 12$
The 3rd term is: $3 \times 7 - 2 = 19$
So, the 20th term is: $20 \times 7 - 2 = 138$

b) i) The terms are powers of 3.
iii) The 1st term is: $3^1 = 3$
The 2nd term is: $3^2 = 9$
The 3rd term is: $3^3 = 27$
So, the 20th term is: $3^{20} = 3\ 486\ 784\ 401$

c) i) The terms are decreasing multiples of 3, beginning with 96.
iii) The 1st term is: $32 \times 3 = 96$
The 2nd term is: $31 \times 3 = 93$
The 3rd term is: $30 \times 3 = 90$
To find each term, subtract the term number from 33, then multiply by 3.
So, the 20th term is: $(33 - 20) \times 3 = 13 \times 3 = 39$

d) i) The terms are 1 less than multiples of 11.
iii) The 1st term is: $1 \times 11 - 1 = 10$
The 2nd term is: $2 \times 11 - 1 = 21$
The 3rd term is: $3 \times 11 - 1 = 32$
So, the 20th term is: $20 \times 11 - 1 = 219$

e) i) The terms are 1 more than multiples of 4, beginning with the 2nd multiple.
iii) The 1st term is: $2 \times 4 + 1 = 9$
The 2nd term is: $3 \times 4 + 1 = 13$
The 3rd term is: $4 \times 4 + 1 = 17$
To find each term, add 1 to the term number, multiply by 4, then add 1.
So, the 20th term is: $21 \times 4 + 1 = 85$

2. The pattern, in cents, is: 1, 2, 4, 8, 16, 32, 64, 128, 256, 512, 1024, 2048

3. c) For example: 3, 7, 15, 31, . . .

4. a) The number of purple squares starts at 1 and increases by 1 each time. The number of green squares starts at 4 and increases by 2 each time. Each time, the green squares are added above and below the additional purple square.

b)

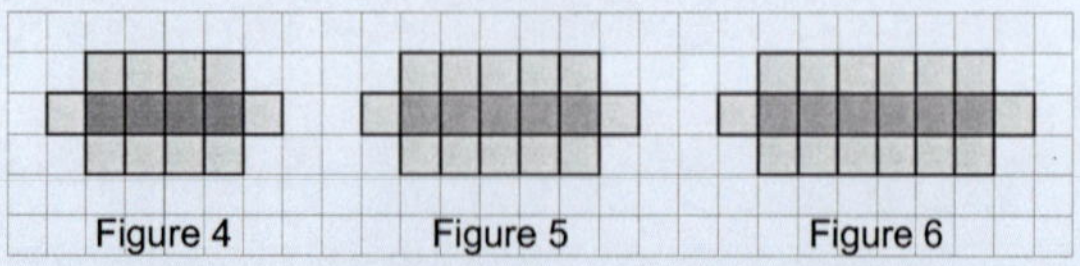

c) The number of purple squares = figure number
The number of green squares = figure number × 2 + 2
So, Figure 12 has 12 purple squares and 12 × 2 + 2, or 26 green squares.

LESSON

10.2

5. Copy and complete this table for each pattern.

Input	Output
4	
6	
8	
10	
12	

a) Add 3 to each Input number. Output numbers: 7, 9, 11, 13, 15

b) Multiply each Input number by 2. Output numbers: 8, 12, 16, 20, 24

c) Subtract 3 from each Input number. Output numbers: 1, 3, 5, 7, 9

d) Divide each Input number by 2. Output numbers: 2, 3, 4, 5, 6

e) Divide each Input number by 2, then add 3. Output numbers: 5, 6, 7, 8, 9

f) Multiply each Input number by 2, then subtract 3. Output numbers: 5, 9, 13, 17, 21

6. Look at this graph.

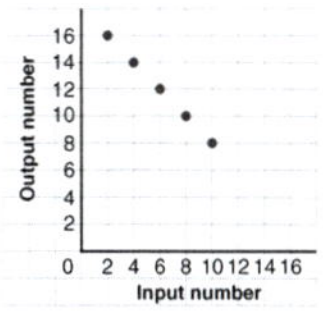

a) Make an Input/Output table for the graph.

b) What patterns do you see in the table?

c) Extend the table 3 more rows. Explain how you did this.

d) What happens if you try to extend the table further?

7. a) Describe the patterns in this table.

b) Use the patterns to extend the table 3 more rows.

Input	Output
5	1
15	3
25	5
35	7
45	9
55	11

10.3 **8.** Write an algebraic expression for each statement.

a) twenty more than a number $n + 20$

b) one less than a number $n - 1$

c) a number increased by ten $n + 10$

d) a number multiplied by thirteen $13n$

9. Write each algebraic expression in words.

a) $n + 4$ **b)** $25 - h$

c) $\frac{a}{5}$ **d)** $5 - 2n$

10.4 **10.** Evaluate each expression for $x = 3$.

a) $x + 8$ 11 **b)** $9x$ 27

c) $2x - 1$ 5 **d)** $\frac{x}{2}$ $\frac{3}{2}$

e) $10x + 4$ 34 **f)** $9 - 3x$ 0

11. A value of n is substituted in each expression to get the number in the box. Find each value of n.

a) $5n$ 40 $n = 8$

b) $6n - 1$ 11 $n = 2$

c) $2n + 8$ 16 $n = 4$

d) $3n - 4$ 14 $n = 6$

Unit Review **399**

YOUR NOTES

Figure 22 has 22 purple squares and $22 \times 2 + 2$, or 46 green squares.

6. a), c)

Input	Output
2	16
4	14
6	12
8	10
10	8
12	6
14	4
16	2

b) The Input numbers: Start at 2. Add 2 each time. The Output numbers: Start at 16. Subtract 2 each time. The sum of an Input number and an Output number is 18.

d) The Output numbers become negative numbers.

7. a) The Input numbers start at 5 and increase by 10 each time. The Output numbers start at 1 and increase by 2 each time. The Output number equals the Input number divided by 5.

b) The Input numbers are: 65, 75, 85; the Output numbers are: 13, 15, 17

9. a) A number increased by four

b) A number subtracted from twenty-five

c) A number divided by five

d) Two times a number subtracted from five

13. a) The sum of three and a number is 17.

b) The product of three and a number is 24.

c) A number divided by four is 5.

d) Four less than three times a number is 20.

e) The sum of four times a number and seven is 35.

14. a) Five students got on the school bus at the last stop. There are now twenty-one students on the bus. How many students were on the bus before the last stop?

b) I bought five packages of hockey cards. I gave two cards to a friend. I now have 28 cards. How many cards were in each package?

16. a) There are twenty-three classrooms in the school. Two of the classrooms are portables. How many classrooms are in the main building?

b) A number subtracted from four is twelve. What is the number?

c) The class is divided into five groups. There are thirty-five students in the class. How many students are in each group?

d) The students were divided into five teams. There were nine students on each team. How many students were there altogether?

LESSON

12. One pair of running shoes costs $70.
   a) What is the cost of 3 pairs? 7 pairs? $210, $490
   b) What is the cost of r pairs of running shoes? $70r$
   c) Write an algebraic expression for the number of pairs of shoes you could buy for d dollars. $\frac{d}{70}$

10.5 13. Write each equation in words.
   a) $x + 3 = 17$
   b) $3y = 24$
   c) $\frac{x}{4} = 5$
   d) $3y - 4 = 20$
   e) $7 + 4x = 35$

14. Write a problem that can be represented by each equation.
   a) $x + 5 = 21$
   b) $5n - 2 = 28$

15. Write an equation for each sentence.
   a) Six times the number of people in the room is 258. $6n = 258$
   b) The area of a rectangle with length 6 cm and width w centimetres is 36 cm². $6w = 36$
   c) One-half of a number is 6. $\frac{n}{2} = 6$

16. Write a problem that can be represented by each equation.
   a) $x + 2 = 23$
   b) $4 - x = 12$
   c) $5x = 35$
   d) $\frac{x}{9} = 5$

17. Write an equation to find the length of one side of an equilateral triangle with perimeter 24 cm. $3s = 24$

10.6 18. Solve each equation.
   a) $12 = 3n$ $n = 4$
   b) $21 - n = 18$ $n = 3$
   c) $\frac{27}{n} = 9$ $n = 3$
   d) $\frac{n}{9} = 27$ $n = 243$
   e) $n - 21 = 30$ $n = 51$
   f) $3n + 2 = 11$ $n = 3$

19. Solve each equation.
   a) $17 - 3n = 2$ $n = 5$
   b) $17 + 3n = 47$ $n = 10$
   c) $3n - 17 = 4$ $n = 7$
   d) $\frac{n}{17} = 25$ $n = 425$

20. At Queen Mary School, 98 students walk to school. There are 250 students in the school.
   a) Write an equation you can solve to find how many students do not walk to school. $250 - 98 =$
   b) Solve the equation. $n = 152$

21. At Sir Robert Borden School, twice as many students take the bus as walk to school. Seventy-four students walk to school.
   a) Write an equation you can solve to find how many students take the bus. $2 \times 74 =$
   b) Solve the equation. $n = 148$

400 UNIT 10: Patterning and Algebra

Correlation of Extra Practice questions on page 447:

Section	Questions
10.1	1
10.2	2
10.3	3, 4
10.4	5
10.5	6, 7, 8
10.6	9, 10

ASSESSMENT FOR LEARNING

What to Look For

Understanding of concepts

✔ **Question 8:** Student understands that an algebraic expression is a mathematical expression that contains a variable.

✔ **Questions 15 and 17:** Student understands that an equation is a statement that two expressions are equal.

Application of mathematical procedures

✔ **Question 1, 2, 3, and 4:** Student can identify and extend a pattern, then use the pattern to make predictions.

✔ **Question 6:** Student can make an Input/Output table to represent a graph.

✔ **Questions 8 and 12:** Student can write an algebraic expression.

✔ **Questions 18 and 19:** Student can solve an equation by systematic trial or by inspection.

Communicating

✔ **Question 1:** Student can explain how a specific term of a pattern was found.

Problem solving

✔ **Questions 20 and 21:** Student can write, then solve, an equation to solve a problem.

Recording and Reporting

Master 10.1 Unit Rubric: Patterning and Algebra
Master 10.4 Unit Summary: Patterning and Algebra

Practice Test

Input	Output
1	2
2	7
3	12
4	17
5	22

1. a) Copy and complete the table for this pattern:
Multiply each number by 5, then subtract 3.
b) Graph the pattern.
Explain how the graph shows the pattern.
c) Extend the table 3 more rows.
Plot the point for each row on the graph.
d) How can you find the Output number when the Input number is 47?
e) How can you find the Input number when the Output number is 47?
f) Can the Input number be 100? Explain. Yes
g) Can the Output number be 100? Explain. No

2. Angelina wins money in a competition.
She is given the choice as to how she is paid.
Choice 1: Get \$1 the 1st day, \$2 the 2nd day, \$4 the 3rd day, \$8 the 4th day, and so on.
This pattern continues for 3 weeks.
Choice 2: Get \$1 000 000 today.
a) With which method of payment will Angelina get more money? Choice 1
b) How did you use patterns to solve this problem?
c) After how many days will the money Angelina gets from Choice 1 be approximately \$1 000 000? After 20 days

3. Here are 5 algebraic expressions: $2 + 3n$, $2n + 3$, $3n - 2$, $\frac{2n}{2}$, $\frac{3n}{2}$
Are there any values of n that will produce the same number when substituted in two or more of the expressions? Yes
Investigate to find out. Show your work.

4. Solve each equation by systematic trial or by inspection.
a) $3x + 90 = 147$ $x = 19$ b) $\frac{84}{h} = 12$ $h = 7$
c) $\frac{26}{y} + 3 = 16$ $y = 2$ d) $147 - 3x = 90$ $x = 19$
Explain your choice of method in each case. Show your work.

Practice Test 401

SECTION ORGANIZER

Student Materials
- 0.5-cm grid paper (PM 14)
- calculators

Assessment:
Masters 10.1 Unit Rubric: Patterning and Algebra, 10.4 Unit Summary: Patterning and Algebra

To assess the 4 Achievement Chart categories listed in the curriculum document, use these test questions:
Understanding Concepts: 1
Application: 2
Problem Solving: 3
Communication: 4

Sample Solutions

1. b)

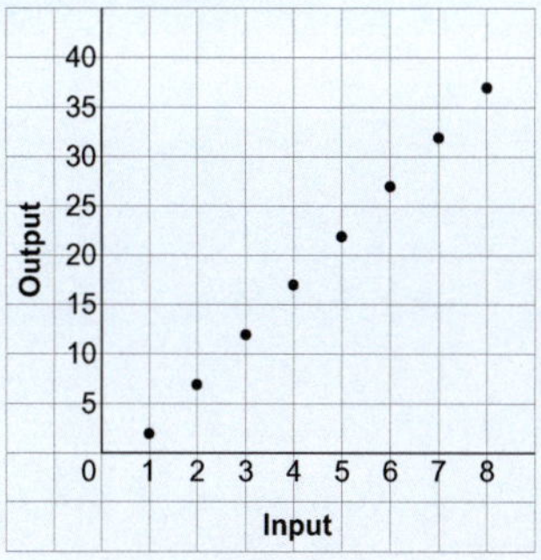

To get from one point to the next, I move 1 unit right and 5 units up. Moving 1 unit right is the same as adding 1 in the first column to get the next Input number. Moving 5 units up is the same as adding 5 in the second column to get the next Output number.

c)

Input	Output
6	27
7	32
8	37

d) The Output number = Input number × 5 − 3;
so, when the Input number is 47, the Output number is 47 × 5 − 3 = 232.

e) Let n represent the Input number. $47 = 5n - 3$;
I know 50 − 3 = 47, and 5 × 10 = 50;
so, the Input number is 10.

f) The Input number increases by 1 each time;
so, 100 can be an Input number.

g) All the Output numbers end in either 2 or 7;
so, 100 cannot be an Output number.

2. b) I started with Choice 1. I found how much money Angelina gets on the 21st day. The pattern for each term is: raise 2 to the power of the term number minus 1. To find term 21, I found 2^{20} = 1 048 576. Since this term alone is greater than \$1 000 000, Choice 1 pays more money.

3. Yes. For example, when $n = 1$, $2 + 3n = 2 + 3 \times 1 = 5$, and $2n + 3 = 2 \times 1 + 3 = 5$.
When $n = 5$, $2n + 3 = 2 \times 5 + 3 = 13$, and $3n - 2 = 3 \times 5 - 2 = 13$
When $n = 1$, $3n - 2 = 3 \times 1 - 2 = 1$,
and $\frac{2n}{2} = \frac{2 \times 1}{2} = 1$

4. a) I chose systematic trial because the numbers are large.
Try $x = 15$; then $3 \times 15 + 90 = 45 + 90 = 135$
135 is too small, so choose a greater value for x.
Try $x = 20$; then $3 \times 20 + 90 = 60 + 90 = 150$
150 is too big, so choose a lesser value for x.
Try $x = 19$; then $3 \times 19 + 90 = 57 + 90 = 147$
This is correct.
$x = 19$ is the solution.

Fund Raising

SECTION ORGANIZER 40–50 min

Student Grouping: Individual
Student Materials
- calculators
- 0.5-cm grid paper (PM 14)
- rulers

Assessment:
Masters 10.3 Performance Assessment Rubric: Fund Raising, 10.4 Unit Summary: Patterning and Algebra

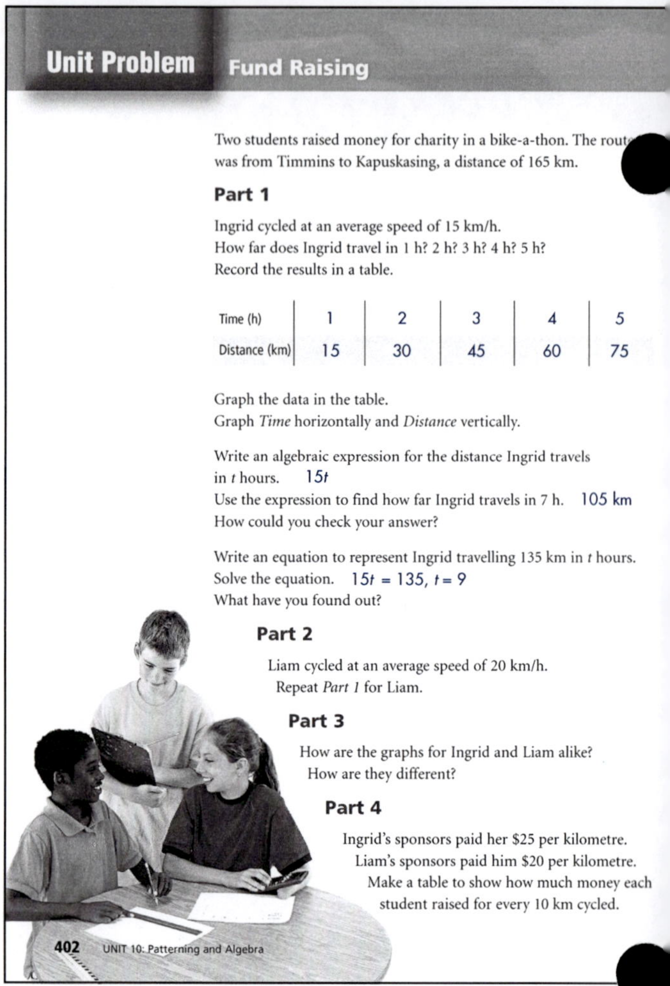

Sample Solution

Part 1:

Time (h)	1	2	3	4	5
Distance (km)	15	30	45	60	75

How Far Ingrid Travels

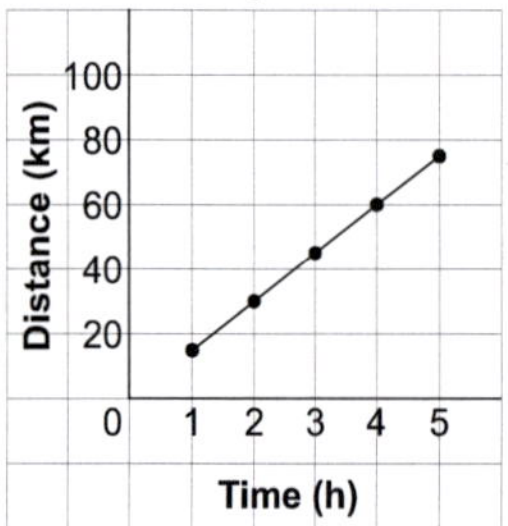

Distance Ingrid travels: $15t$
Distance Ingrid travels in 7 h:
$15 \times 7 = 105$
Ingrid travels 105 km in 7 h.
I could check my answer by extending the table or by extending the graph.
$15t = 135$
To solve this equation, I know $15 \times 9 = 135$; so, Ingrid travels 135 km in 9 h.

Have students turn to pages 364 and 365 of the Student Book.

Review *What You'll Learn,* and discuss the meanings of the Key Words. Tell students they will use the skills and concepts they learned in this unit to complete the *Unit Problem.*

Present the *Unit Problem.* Invite volunteers to read the introduction and instructions for the problem aloud. Ensure students understand what they are expected to do.

Have one student read the *Check List* aloud. Remind students that they should use the *Check List* to assess their work before handing it in. You may also wish to provide students with copies of Master 10.3 Performance Assessment Rubric: Fund Raising so they will know how their work will be assessed.

Tell students that they should check their equations by substituting values they know, then comparing the solutions they get with values in their completed tables. Ensure students give each graph a title.

Encourage students to use the same scale on both graphs so they can compare the graphs easily. If students use different scales, the steepness of the two graphs may look the same.

REFLECT ON THE UNIT: Number patterns are related to algebra because when we substitute consecutive numbers in an algebraic expression, we get a number pattern. For example, if we substitute the Input numbers $n = 1, 2, 3, 4,$ and 5 into the expression $2n + 1$, we get the Output numbers 3, 5, 7, 9, and 11. The Output numbers follow the pattern: Start at 3. Add 2 each time.
We have an equation when we write an algebraic expression as being equal to a number. So, an equation is a statement that two expressions are equal. For example, $3n - 2$ is an algebraic expression, while $3n - 2 = 10$ is an equation. A variable in an equation has only one value.

Distance (km)	Money Raised by Ingrid ($)	Money Raised by Liam ($)
10		
20		
30		

How much money did Ingrid raise if she cycled *d* kilometres? $25*d*

How much money did Liam raise if he cycled *d* kilometres? $20*d*

Liam and Ingrid raised equal amounts of money.
How far might each person have cycled? Explain.

Check List

Your work should show:

✓ all tables and graphs, clearly labelled

✓ the equations you wrote and how you solved them

✓ how you know your answers are correct

✓ explanations of what you found out

Reflect on the Unit

How are number patterns related to algebra?
How are algebraic expressions related to equations?
Give examples in your explanation.

Part 2:

Time (h)	1	2	3	4	5
Distance (km)	20	40	60	80	100

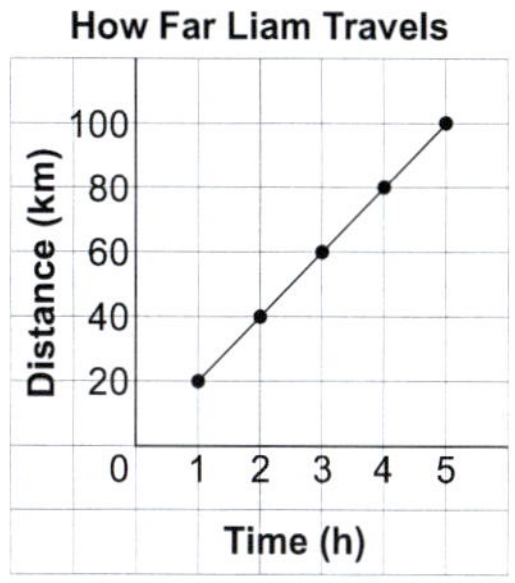

Distance Liam travels: $20t$
Distance Liam travels in 7 h:
$20 \times 7 = 140$
Liam travels 140 km in 7 h.
I could check my answer by extending the table or by extending the graph.
$20t = 135$; $t = 6.75$;
so, Liam travels 135 km in 6.75 h.

Part 3: Both graphs are straight lines that go up to the right. Liam's graph is steeper than Ingrid's graph.

Part 4:

Distance (km)	Money Raised by Ingrid ($)	Money Raised by Liam ($)
1	25	20
10	250	200
20	500	400
30	750	600
40	1000	800
50	1250	1000
60	1500	1200

Ingrid raises: $25*d*   Liam raises: $20*d*

For example, looking at the table above, if Ingrid cycled 40 km and Liam cycled 50 km, both would raise $1000.

ASSESSMENT FOR LEARNING

What to Look For

Understanding concepts

✔ Students use patterning and algebra to explain answers, compare results, and justify methods and solutions.

Applying procedures

✔ Students identify and extend number patterns, represent a pattern as a graph, write and evaluate algebraic expressions, and write and solve simple equations.

Problem solving

✔ Students can choose appropriate patterning strategies to create and solve problems.

What to Do

Extra Support: Make the problem accessible.
Some students may have difficulty understanding the terms "horizontally" and "vertically." Remind students that the horizon is the line where the earth and sky meet, and the line runs from right to left, or vice versa.

Some students may not know whether to join the points on each graph. Ensure students understand that the data are continuous and show progressions from one hour to the next, so the points can be joined. The points on the graph between those plotted from data in the table do have meanings.

Recording and Reporting

Master 10.3 Performance Assessment Rubric: Fund Raising
Master 10.4 Unit Summary: Patterning and Algebra

Evaluating Student Learning: Preparing to Report: Unit 10 Patterning and Algebra

This unit provides an opportunity to report on the **Patterning and Algebra** strand.
Master 10.4: Unit Summary: Patterning and Algebra provides a comprehensive format for recording and summarizing evidence collected.

Here is an example of a completed summary chart for this Unit:

Strand: *Patterning and Algebra*	**Problem Solving**	**Understanding of Concepts**	**Application of mathematical procedures**	**Communication**	***Overall***
Ongoing Observations	3	4	4	4	4
Work samples or portfolios; conferences	4	3	3	4	3/4
Unit Review	4	4	4	4	4
Practice Test	3	3	3	3	3
Unit Problem Fund Raising	3	4	3	4	3/4
Achievement Level for reporting					3/4

Recording	**How to Report**
Ongoing Observations	Use *Master 10.2 Ongoing Observations: Patterning and Algebra* to determine the most consistent level achieved in each category. Enter it in the chart. Choose to summarize by achievement category, or simply to enter an overall level. Observations from late in the unit should be most heavily weighted.
Portfolios or collections of work samples; conferences, or interviews	Use *Master 10.1 Unit Rubric: Patterning and Algebra* to guide evaluation of collections of work and information gathered in conferences. Teachers may choose to focus particular attention on the Assessment Focus questions. Work from late in the unit should be most heavily weighted.
Unit Review	*Master 10.1 Unit Rubric: Patterning and Algebra* may be helpful in determining levels of achievement. #1, 3, 8, 15, 17, 18, and 19 provide evidence of Understanding of concepts; #2, 4, 6, 8, and 12 provide evidence of Application of mathematical procedures; #16 and 17 provide evidence of Problem solving; #1 provides evidence of Communication.
Practice Test	*Master 10.1 Unit Rubric: Patterning and Algebra* may be helpful in determining levels of achievement. #1 provides evidence of Understanding of concepts; #2 provides evidence of Application of mathematical procedures; #3 provides evidence of Problem solving; #4 provides evidence of Communication.
Unit Problem	Use *Master 10.3 Performance Assessment Rubric: Fund Raising*. The *Unit Problem* offers a snapshot of students' achievement. In particular, it shows their ability to synthesize and apply what they have learned.
Student Self-Assessment	Note students' perceptions of their own progress. This may take the form of an oral or written comment, or a self-rating.
Comments	Analyse the pattern of achievement to identify strengths and needs. In some cases, specific actions may need to be planned to support the learner.

Learning Skills	**Ongoing Records**
PM 4: Learning Skills Check List Use to record and report throughout a reporting period, rather than for each unit and/or strand.	*PM 10: Summary Class Records: Strands* *PM 11: Summary Class Records: Achievement Categories* *PM 12: Summary Record: Individual* Use to record and report evaluations of student achievement over several clusters, a reporting period, or a school year. These can also be used in place of the Unit Summary.

Name ____________________ Date ______________

Master 10.1

Unit Rubric: Patterning and Algebra

	Level 1	Level 2	Level 3	Level 4
Problem solving • chooses and carries out a range of patterning strategies (tables, graphs, equations) to create and solve problems	with assistance, chooses and carries out a limited range of appropriate patterning strategies to solve problems, rarely resulting in an accurate solution	with limited assistance, chooses and carries out appropriate patterning strategies to solve problems that frequently result in an accurate solution	chooses and carries out appropriate patterning strategies to solve problems that usually result in an accurate solution	chooses and carries out appropriate patterning strategies; may offer an innovative approach; results in an accurate solution
Understanding of concepts • shows understanding by demonstrating and explaining: – patterns in a variety of sequences – the use of patterns to make predictions – variables – algebraic expressions – simple algebraic equations	shows little understanding; may be unable to demonstrate or explain: – patterns in a variety of sequences – using patterns to make predictions – variables – algebraic expressions – simple algebraic equations	shows some understanding; partially able to demonstrate or explain: – patterns in a variety of sequences – using patterns to make predictions – variables – algebraic expressions – simple algebraic equations	shows understanding; able to clearly and appropriately demonstrate or explain: – patterns in a variety of sequences – using patterns to make predictions – variables – algebraic expressions – simple algebraic equations	shows thorough understanding; able to accurately and effectively demonstrate, and explain: – patterns in a variety of sequences – using patterns to make predictions – variables – algebraic expressions – simple algebraic equations
Application of mathematical procedures • accurately: – identifies and extends number patterns (including completing a table) – represents patterns as graphs – reads and writes algebraic expressions – evaluates simple algebraic expressions – reads and writes simple equations – solves simple algebraic equations	limited accuracy; major errors or omissions in: – identifying and extending number patterns – representing patterns as graphs – reading and writing algebraic expressions – evaluating algebraic expressions – reading and writing simple equations – solving simple algebraic equations	somewhat accurate; several minor errors or omissions in: – identifying and extending number patterns – representing patterns as graphs – reading and writing algebraic expressions – evaluating algebraic expressions – reading and writing simple equations – solving simple algebraic equations	generally accurate; few minor errors or omissions in: – identifying and extending number patterns – representing patterns as graphs – reading and writing algebraic expressions – evaluating algebraic expressions – reading and writing simple equations – solving simple algebraic equations	accurate and precise; no errors in: – identifying and extending number patterns – representing patterns as graphs – reading and writing algebraic expressions – evaluating algebraic expressions – reading and writing simple equations – solving simple algebraic equations
Communication • explains reasoning and procedures clearly using appropriate terminology	unable to explain reasoning and procedures clearly	explains reasoning and procedures with some clarity	explains reasoning and procedures clearly and precisely	explains reasoning and procedures clearly, precisely, and confidently
• presents work clearly, including appropriate symbols	presents work with little clarity	presents work with some clarity	presents work clearly	presents work clearly and precisely

Name ____________________ Date ________________

Master 10.2

Ongoing Observations: Patterning and Algebra

The behaviours described under each heading are examples; they are not intended to be an exhaustive list of all that might be observed. More detailed descriptions are provided in each lesson under *Assessment for Learning.*

STUDENT ACHIEVEMENT: Patterning and Algebra				
Student	**Problem solving**	**Understanding of concepts**	**Application of mathematical procedures**	**Communication**
	▪ Chooses and carries out appropriate patterning strategies to solve problems; usually results in an accurate solution	▪ Demonstrates and explains: – patterns and patterning strategies – variables, expressions, and equations	▪ Identifies, extends, and graphs patterns ▪ Evaluates simple expressions ▪ Solves simple equations	▪ Explains reasoning clearly using appropriate terms (for example, variable, expression, equation) ▪ Presents work clearly

Level 1 – very limited; Level 2 – somewhat or limited; Level 3 – satisfactory; Level 4 – thorough

Name ____________________ Date ______________

Master 10.3

Performance Assessment Rubric: Fund Raising

	Level 1	Level 2	Level 3	Level 4
Problem solving • chooses appropriate patterning strategies (for example, tables, graphs, estimating, equations) to solve and create problems	uses few simple patterning strategies to solve and create problems; limited success	uses some appropriate patterning strategies to solve and create problems; some success	uses appropriate patterning strategies to solve and create problems; successful	uses innovative and appropriate patterning strategies to solve and create problems; successful and effective
Understanding of concepts • shows understanding by using concepts of patterning and algebra in explaining answers, comparing results, and justifying methods and solutions	shows very limited understanding by giving few appropriate explanations and using few required concepts in explanations and justifications	shows limited understanding by giving appropriate but incomplete explanations and justifications that use some required concepts	shows understanding by giving appropriate explanations and justifications that use required concepts	shows thorough understanding by giving appropriate and complete explanations and justifications that use all required concepts
Application of mathematical procedures • accurately: – identifies and extends number patterns (including completing a table) – represents a pattern as a graph – writes and evaluates algebraic expressions – writes and solves simple equations	limited accuracy; major errors or omissions in: – identifying and extending patterns – representing a pattern as a graph – writing and evaluating algebraic expressions – writing and solving simple equations	somewhat accurate; several minor errors or omissions in: – identifying and extending patterns – representing a pattern as a graph – writing and evaluating algebraic expressions – writing and solving simple equations	generally accurate; few minor errors or omissions in: – identifying and extending patterns – representing a pattern as a graph – writing and evaluating algebraic expressions – writing and solving simple equations	accurate and precise; no errors in: – identifying and extending patterns – representing a pattern as a graph – writing and evaluating algebraic expressions – writing and solving simple equations
Communication • explains reasoning clearly, using appropriate mathematical terminology	explains reasoning unclearly and imprecisely, using few mathematical terms	explains reasoning with some clarity, using some appropriate mathematical terms	explains reasoning clearly and precisely, using appropriate mathematical terms	explains reasoning clearly, precisely, and confidently, using a range of appropriate mathematical terminology
• presents work, including diagrams, clearly	presents work with little clarity	presents work with some clarity	presents work clearly	presents work clearly and precisely

Name ____________________ Date ______________

Master 10.4

Unit Summary: Patterning and Algebra

Review assessment records to determine the most consistent achievement levels for the assessments conducted. Some cells may be blank. *Overall* achievement levels may be recorded in each row, rather than identifying levels for each achievement category.

	Most Consistent Level of Achievement*				
Strand: *Patterning and Algebra*	**Problem solving**	**Understanding of concepts**	**Application of mathematical procedures**	**Communication**	***Overall***
Ongoing Observations					
Work samples or portfolios; conferences					
Unit Review					
Practice Test					
Unit Problem: Fund Raising					
Achievement Level for reporting					

* Use Ontario Achievement Levels 1, 2, 3, 4.

Self-Assessment:

Comments: (Strengths; Needs, Next Steps)

Name ____________________ Date ______________

Master 10.5a

Additional Activity 1: Substitution Toss

Play with a partner.

You will need *Substitution Expressions*, scissors, and 2 number cubes labelled 1 to 6.

How to Play:

1. Cut out the expressions to make cards.
Shuffle the cards.
Place them face down in a pile.

2. Player A draws a card from the pile, then places it face up on the table.
Player B rolls the number cubes.
The sum of the numbers rolled is the number to substitute for x.

3. Player A evaluates the expression by replacing this number for x.
Player B checks the answer.

4. If Player A is correct, he keeps the card.
If Player A is incorrect, the card is returned to the bottom of the pile.

5. Players switch roles.
Play continues until all expressions have been correctly evaluated.
The player with more cards wins.

Take It Further: Players say the algebraic expression in words before evaluating it.

Name ____________________ Date ________________

Master 10.5b

Substitution Expressions

Cut out these expressions for use with the Additional Activity *Substitution Toss*.

$5x$	$3 + 7x$	$10x - 6$
x^3	$0x$	$2x + 1$
$4x$	$15 - x$	$4(x + 1)$
$2x - 5$	x^2	$13 - 2x$
$2x + 9$	$\frac{4x}{2}$	$20 - 3x$
$\frac{10x}{2}$	$3x + 4$	$32 - 4x$
$3(x + 5)$	$\frac{24}{x}$	$3(x - 2)$
$4 + x \times 2$	$x + 3 \times 2$	$2x + 3 \times 5$
$2(x + 2 \times 4)$	$3x - 1 + 3$	$\frac{(3 + x)}{2}$
$12 - x + 2$	$x^2 + 2$	$36 - x \times 2$

Name ____________________ Date ______________

Master 10.6

Additional Activity 2: Algebra Concentration

Play with a partner.

You will need a pair of scissors.

How to Play:

1. Cut out the cards below.
   Lay them out face down on the table.
2. Player A turns over a card.
   If the card contains a word, she tries to find the matching description.
   If the card contains a description, she tries to find the matching word.
   Player A turns over a second card.
3. If Player A finds a matching pair, she keeps the cards.
   If the two cards do not match, both cards are turned over.
4. Player B takes a turn.
   Play continues until all matches have been made.
   The player with the greater number of cards wins.

Take It Further: Students make cards for other words and their descriptions, then add the cards to the game. Students play the game again.

A letter representing a quantity that can vary	The result when two or more numbers are multiplied	Substitute	Equation
Ordered pair	Variable	To replace a variable with a letter	A statement that two expressions are equal
It tells the position of a point on a grid.	Quotient	Product	Difference
The result of a division question	Algebraic expression	A mathematical expression containing a variable	The answer to a subtraction question

Name ____________________ Date ______________

Master 10.7a

Additional Activity 3: Algebra Game

Play with a partner.

You will need an *Algebra Game Board* and tiles.

1. Cover all the questions with tiles or counters.

2. Player A chooses a category and a point value.
The question is uncovered and Player A answers the question.

3. If Player A is correct, he scores the points.
If Player A is incorrect, Player B can answer the question.
If Player B is correct, she scores the points.

4. Player B takes a turn.
Play continues until all questions have been revealed.

5. The player with the greater number of points wins.

Take It Further: Players create their own Algebra Game Boards, then exchange boards with another pair of students.

Name ____________________ Date ______________

Master 10.7b

Algebra Game Board

	100	200	300
Write the expression.	12 times a number	A number subtracted from 19	One-fifth of a number
Use order of operations to find the answer.	$16 \div 8 \times 2$	$440 \div (2 + 18)$	$3 \times 5 - 8 \div 4$
Write the equation.	Three more than a number is 8.	The product of 2 and a number is 24.	Six more than three times a number is 21.
Solve the equation.	$2x + 5 = 13$	$\frac{x}{3} + 2 \times 3 = 9$	$25 - 3x = 7$
Evaluate the expression.	$7x$ when $x = 3$	$63 - 5x$ when $x = 7$	$3 + \frac{x}{2}$ when $x = 18$

Name ____________________ Date ________________

Master 10.8

Additional Activity 4: Algebra Word Search

Work on your own.

Find the words listed below in the grid.
The words may appear horizontally, vertically, or diagonally.
They may be read forward or backward. Circle the words as you find them.

EQUATION	ALGEBRA	COORDINATE
PATTERN	GRAPH	GRID
VARIABLE	PRODUCT	EXPRESSION
INPUT		

E	X	P	R	E	S	S	I	O	N
T	T	O	P	O	L	A	N	H	V
C	B	A	A	S	M	L	E	P	A
U	G	S	N	G	P	G	T	A	R
D	R	T	P	I	V	E	G	R	I
O	I	U	V	E	D	B	Y	G	A
R	D	P	Q	Z	L	R	S	B	B
P	O	N	Y	S	M	A	O	T	L
N	O	I	T	A	U	Q	E	O	E
I	P	A	T	T	E	R	N	C	C

Take It Further: Write a meaning for each word you find.

Name ____________________ Date ______________

Master 10.9

Step-by-Step 1

Section 10.1, Question 8

Step 1 Which ones digit is in both 12 and 32? ______

Which number between 12 and 32 has this ones digit? ______

Which number before 12 has this ones digit? _______

Which number after 12 has this ones digit? _______

Step 2 List the numbers in *Step 1* from least to greatest:

____, ____, ____, ____, ____, …

Describe the pattern in words. ____

____

Write the next 4 terms of the pattern. ____, ____, ____, ____

Step 3 List the factors of 12: __________________________

List the factors of 32: __________________________

List the common factors: _____________

Choose a common factor. Start at 12. Count on by this factor to 32.

____

Describe the pattern in words. ____

____

Write the next 4 terms of the pattern. ____, ____, ____, ____

Name ____________________ Date ______________

Master 10.10 **Step-by-Step 2**

Section 10.2, Question 6

Step 1 Mr. Francis needs 2 sandwiches for each student, plus 3 extra sandwiches.
Complete the table for the number of sandwiches.

Number of Students	Number of Sandwiches
5	
10	
15	
20	
25	
30	

Step 2 Use 0.5-cm grid paper. Label the horizontal axis "Number of Students."
Choose a scale for the horizontal axis:
1 square represents __________.
Write the scale along the horizontal axis.

Step 3 Label the vertical axis "Number of Sandwiches."
Choose a scale for the vertical axis: 1 square represents __________.
Start at 0 and write the scale along the vertical axis.
Plot the data on the grid. Give the graph a title.
How does the graph show the patterns in the table?

____

____

Step 4 Mr. Francis needs 1 drink for each student, plus 5 extra drinks.
Complete the table for the number of drinks.

Number of Students	Number of Drinks
5	
10	
15	
20	
25	
30	

Step 5 Use 0.5-cm grid paper. Label the horizontal axis "Number of Students."
Choose a scale for the horizontal axis:
1 square represents __________.
Write the scale along the horizontal axis.

Step 6 Label the vertical axis "Number of Drinks."
Choose a scale for the vertical axis: 1 square represents __________.
Start at 0 and write the scale along the vertical axis.
Plot the ordered pairs on the grid. Give the graph a title.
How does the graph show the patterns in the table?

____

____

Name ____________________ Date ______________

Master 10.11 **Step-by-Step 3**

Section 10.3, Question 10

9	4	+	–	×	÷	*n*

Use the cards above.

Step 1 Which card represents any number? ____________________

Write an expression for 9 times a number. ____________________

Subtract 4 from the expression. ____________________

Step 2 Write an expression for 4 times a number. ____________________

The word "sum" means add. Add 9 to the expression. ____________________

Step 3 Use the cards to make 5. Try subtraction: ____ – ____ = 5

Write an expression for a number plus 5. ____________________

Step 4 Write an expression for $\frac{1}{4}$ of a number. Remember that finding $\frac{1}{4}$ is the same as dividing by 4. The words "more than" mean add.

Add 9 to the expression. ____________________

Step 5 Use the cards to create a different expression: ____________________

Write the expression in words. ____________________

Step 6 Use the cards to create another expression: ____________________

Write the expression in words. ____________________

Name ____________________ Date ________________

Master 10.12

Step-by-Step 4

Section 10.4, Question 6

Step 1 The cost of food is \$9 per person.

Multiply to find the cost of food for 5 people: ___ × \$9 = ________

The cost of renting a cabin is \$20.

Add the cost of the cabin and the cost of food to find the cost of the trip for 5 people:

______ + ______ = ______

Step 2 Multiply to find the cost of food for 10 people: ___ × \$9 = ________

Add the cost of the cabin and the cost of food to find the cost of the trip for 10 people:

______ + ______ = ______

Step 3 Multiply to find the cost of food for *p* people: ___ × \$9 = ________

Write an algebraic expression for the cost of the food and cabin for *p* people. ______________________________________

Step 4 The cost of food doubles. Multiply the cost of food per person by 2 to get the new cost:

______ × 2 = \$______

Write an algebraic expression for the cost of the food and cabin for *p* people. _______________

Step 5 The cost of the cabin doubles. Multiply the cost of the cabin by 2 to get the new cost:

______ × 2 = \$______

Write an algebraic expression for the cost of the food and cabin for *p* people. _______________

Step 6 Explain why using the variable *p* is helpful.

____

____

Name ____________________ Date ______________

Master 10.13 Step-by-Step 5

Section 10.5, Question 7

Step 1 Bhavin's age 7 years from now will be 20.

Let ___ represent Bhavin's age now.

Add 7 to his age: __________

The equation is: ______________________

Step 2 Five times the number of students is 295.

Let ___ represent the number of students.

Multiply the number of students by 5: ______________________

The equation is: ______________________

Step 3 The perimeter of a rectangle with length 15 cm and width *w* centimetres is 38 cm.

An expression to find the perimeter of a rectangle is:

$2 \times \text{length} + 2 \times \text{width}$.

Multiply the length by 2: __________

Multiply the width by 2: __________

The equation is: _____________________________

Step 4 The cost of 2 tickets at *x* dollars each and 5 tickets at $4 each is $44.

Find the cost of 2 tickets at *x* dollars each: ______________________

Add the cost of 5 tickets at $4 each: ______________________

The equation is: ______________________

Step 5 Which equation was the most difficult to write? Explain.

____

____

Name ____________________ Date ________________

Master 10.14

Step-by-Step 6

Section 10.6, Question 11

Step 1 Write a problem that can be described by the equation $2x - 1 = 5$.

____

We know: A number – 1 = 5. The number is ___.

Two times which number is 6? ______

So, $x =$ ___

Step 2 Write a problem that can be described by the equation $4y = 24$.

____

We know $4 \times$ a number = 24. The number is ___.

So, $y =$ ___

Step 3 Write a problem that can be described by the equation $\frac{z}{38} = 57$.

____

Use a calculator: $38 \times 57 =$ ___; so, ___ $\div 38 = 57$.

So, $z =$ ___

Step 4 Write a problem that can be described by the equation $5x + 5 = 30$.

____

We know: A number + 5 = 30. The number is ___.

Five times which number is 25? ______

So, $x =$ ___

Step 5 Write a problem that can be described by the equation $\frac{25}{y} = 5$.

____

We know $25 \div$ a number = 5. The number is ___.

So, $y =$ ___

Step 6 Write a problem that can be described by the equation $52 - 4 = 4x$.

____

We know: 52 – 4 = a number. The number is ___.

Four times which number is 48? _____

So, $x =$ ___

Step 7 Which equation was the most difficult to solve? Explain.

____

Name ____________________ Date ________________

Master 10.15a Unit Test: Unit 10 Patterning and Algebra

1. For each pattern:

i) Describe the pattern.

ii) Write the next 3 terms.

iii) Find the 16th term.

a) 2, 6, 10, 14, …

b) 1, 2, 4, 8, 16, …

2. a) Look at the pattern in question 1a. Is 108 a term in the pattern? How do you know?

b) Look at the pattern in question 1b. Is 256 a term in the pattern? How do you know?

3. Complete the table for each pattern.

a) Multiply each Input number by 6, then add 2.

Input	Output
3	
4	
5	
6	
7	

b) Add 8 to each Input number, then multiply by 3.

Input	Output
5	
6	
7	
8	
9	

4. a) Look at the completed table in question 3a. Could 96 be an Output number? Explain.

b) Look at the completed table in question 3b. Could 111 be an Output number? Explain.

Name ____________________ Date ________________

Master 10.15b **Unit Test continued**

5. Write an algebraic expression for each statement.

a) Eight more than three times a number

b) Twenty divided by a number

c) Subtract one-half of a number from 10.

d) Double a number and subtract nine.

6. Write each expression in words.

a) $3c + 5$

b) $4(x - 2)$

7. Evaluate each expression by replacing w with 4.

a) $2w + 10$

b) $\frac{w + 4}{2}$

c) $\frac{w}{2} + 9$

8. Write an equation for each sentence, then solve the equation.

a) Three more than a number is 15.

b) Six subtracted from three times a number is 12.

9. Adrian cuts the neighbours' lawns for $8.50/h.

a) Copy and complete the chart that shows the money he earns.

Time (h)	1	2	3	4	5
Money Earned ($)					

b) Graph the data in the table.

Unit Test continued

c) Use the variable t to write an algebraic expression that describes the amount of money Adrian earns.

d) How much does Adrian earn in 3.5 h? How did you get the answer?

10. Susan is looking after the neighbours' cat while they are on vacation.
She is given a choice as to how she is paid.
Choice 1: Get 10¢ the 1st day, 20¢ the 2nd day, 40¢ the 3rd day, 80¢ the 4th day, and so on.
Choice 2: Get $75.00 today.
The neighbours are away for 10 days.
With which method of payment will Susan get more money? Explain.

11. a) Evaluate the expression $2(3p + 4)$ for $p = 2$.

b) Explain why it is important to use the order of operations when evaluating an algebraic expression.

Name ____________________ Date ______________

Master 10.16 **Sample Answers**

Unit Test – Master 10.15

1. a) i) Start at 2. Add 4 each time.
ii) 18, 22, 26
iii) Another way to look at the pattern is to say that each term is 2 less than 4 times the term number. So, the 16th term is $4 \times 16 - 2 = 62$

b) i) Start at 1. Multiply by 2 each time.
ii) 32, 64, 128
iii) Another way to look at this pattern is to say that, after the first term, each term is 2 raised to a number that is 1 less than the term number. So, the 16th term is $2^{15} = 32\,768$

2. a) Since each term is 2 less than 4 times the term number, each term is 2 less than a multiple of 4. Since 108 *is* a multiple of 4, it cannot be a term in this pattern.
b) Each term is a power of 2. Since $256 = 2^8$, and 2^8 *is* a power of 2, then 256 is the 9th term in the pattern.

3. a)

Input	Output
3	20
4	26
5	32
6	38
7	44

b)

Input	Output
5	39
6	42
7	45
8	48
9	51

4. a) In exercise 3a, each Output number is 2 more than a multiple of 6. 96 *is* a multiple of 6, so 96 cannot be an Output number.
b) In exercise 3b, each Output number is a multiple of 3. Since 111 *is* a multiple of 3, 111 can be an Output number.

5. a) $3n + 8$ **b)** $\frac{20}{n}$
c) $10 - \frac{n}{2}$ **d)** $2n - 9$

6. a) Three times a number increased by five
b) Two less then a number, multiplied by four

7. a) 18 **b)** 4 **c)** 11

8. a) $n + 3 = 15, n = 12$
b) $3n - 6 = 12, n = 6$

9. a)

Time (h)	1	2	3	4	5
Money Earned ($)	8.50	17.00	25.50	34.00	42.50

b) **Money Earned by Cutting Grass**

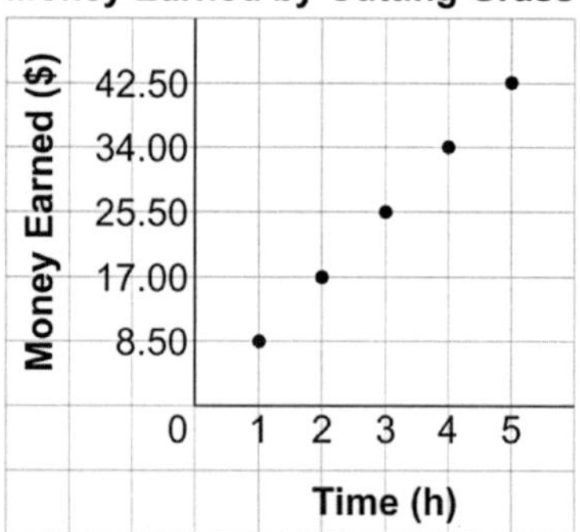

c) 8.50t$
d) In the algebraic expression, substitute $t = 3.5$. Then $8.50t$ becomes $8.50 \times 3.5 = 29.75$. Adrian earns $29.75 in 3.5 h.

10. Choice 1: Choice 1 pays $102.30 after 10 days. Choice 2 only pays $75.

11. a) 20
b) If the order of operations is not followed, the answer will be different; for example, $2 \times 3 \times 2 + 4 = 16$

Extra Practice Masters 10.17–10.23

Go to the CD-ROM to access editable versions of these Extra Practice Masters.

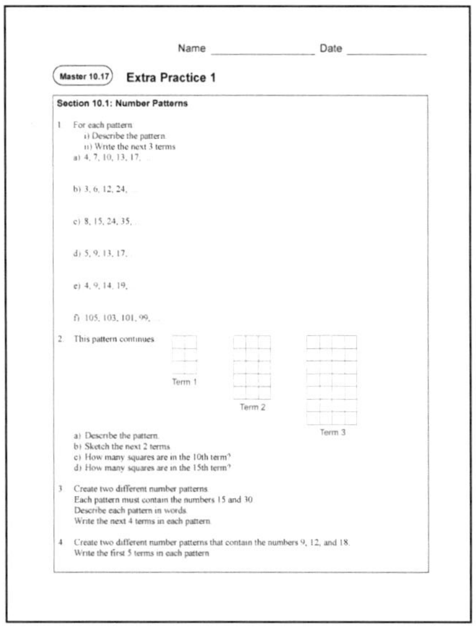

Name ________ Date ________

Master 10.17 Extra Practice 1

Section 10.1: Number Patterns

1. For each pattern:
i) Describe the pattern.
ii) Write the next 3 terms.
a) 4, 7, 10, 13, 17, ...
b) 3, 6, 12, 24, ...
c) 8, 15, 24, 35, ...
d) 5, 9, 13, 17, ...
e) 4, 9, 14, 19, ...
f) 105, 103, 101, 99, ...

2. This pattern continues.
Term 1 Term 2 Term 3
a) Describe the pattern.
b) Sketch the next 2 terms.
c) How many squares are in the 10th term?
d) How many squares are in the 15th term?

3. Create two different number patterns.
Each pattern must contain the numbers 15 and 30.
Describe each pattern in words.
Write the next 4 terms in each pattern.

4. Create two different number patterns that contain the numbers 9, 12, and 18.
Write the first 5 terms in each pattern.

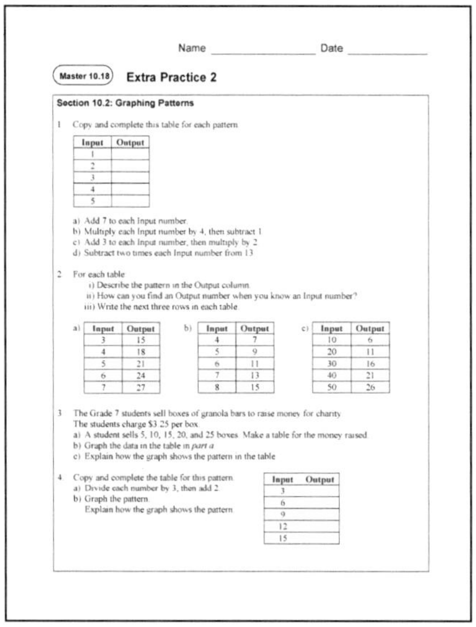

Name ________ Date ________

Master 10.18 Extra Practice 2

Section 10.2: Graphing Patterns

1. Copy and complete this table for each pattern.

Input	Output
1	
2	
3	
4	
5	

a) Add 7 to each Input number.
b) Multiply each Input number by 4, then subtract 1.
c) Add 3 to each Input number, then multiply by 2.
d) Subtract two times each Input number from 13.

2. For each table:
i) Describe the pattern in the Output column.
ii) How can you find an Output number when you know an Input number?
iii) Write the next three rows in each table.

a)

Input	Output
3	15
4	18
5	21
6	24
7	27

b)

Input	Output
4	7
5	9
6	11
7	13
8	15

c)

Input	Output
10	6
20	11
30	16
40	21
50	26

3. The Grade 7 students sell boxes of granola bars to raise money for charity.
The students charge $3.25 per box.
a) A student sells 5, 10, 15, 20, and 25 boxes. Make a table for the money raised.
b) Graph the data in the table in *part a*.
c) Explain how the graph shows the pattern in the table.

4. Copy and complete the table for this pattern.
a) Divide each number by 3, then add 2.
b) Graph the pattern.
Explain how the graph shows the pattern.

Input	Output
3	
6	
9	
12	
15	

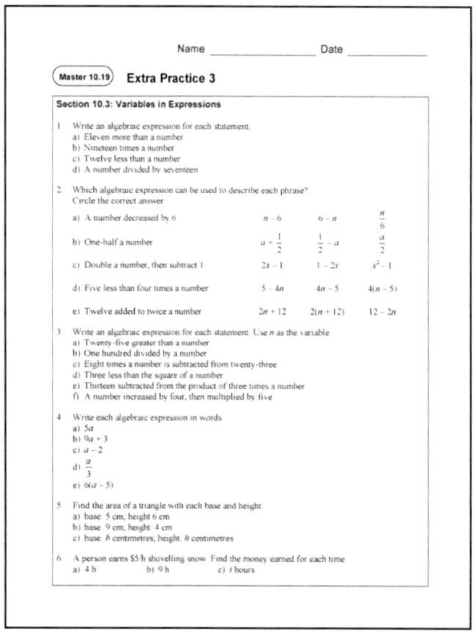

Name ________ Date ________

Master 10.19 Extra Practice 3

Section 10.3: Variables in Expressions

1. Write an algebraic expression for each statement.
a) Eleven more than a number
b) Nineteen times a number
c) Twelve less than a number
d) A number divided by seventeen

2. Which algebraic expression can be used to describe each phrase?
Circle the correct answer.

a) A number decreased by 6	$n-6$	$6-n$	$\frac{n}{6}$
b) One-half a number	$a+\frac{1}{2}$	$\frac{1}{2}-a$	$\frac{a}{2}$
c) Double a number, then subtract 1	$2x-1$	$1-2x$	x^2-1
d) Five less than four times a number	$5-4n$	$4n-5$	$4(n-5)$
e) Twelve added to twice a number	$2n+12$	$2(n+12)$	$12-2n$

3. Write an algebraic expression for each statement. Use *n* as the variable.
a) Twenty-five greater than a number
b) One hundred divided by a number
c) Eight times a number is subtracted from twenty-three
d) Three less than the square of a number
e) Thirteen subtracted from the product of three times a number
f) A number increased by four, then multiplied by five

4. Write each algebraic expression in words.
a) $5a$
b) $9a+3$
c) $a-2$
d) $\frac{a}{3}$
e) $6(a-5)$

5. Find the area of a triangle with each base and height.
a) base: 5 cm; height 6 cm
b) base: 9 cm; height: 4 cm
c) base: *b* centimetres; height: *h* centimetres

6. A person earns $5/h shovelling snow. Find the money earned for each time.
a) 4 h b) 9 h c) *t* hours

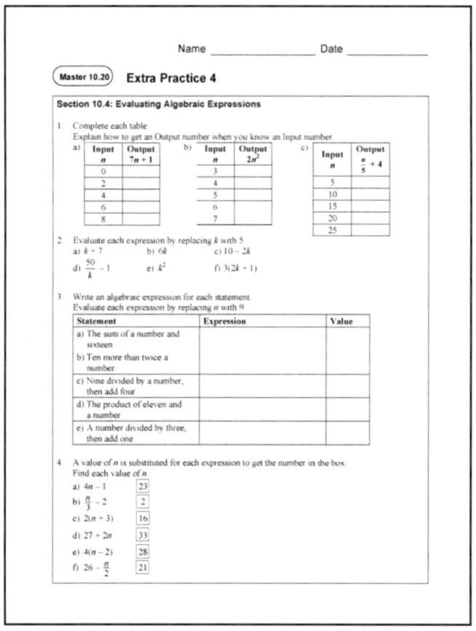

Name ________ Date ________

Master 10.20 Extra Practice 4

Section 10.4: Evaluating Algebraic Expressions

1. Complete each table.
Explain how to get an Output number when you know an Input number.

a)

Input n	Output $7n+1$
0	
2	
4	
6	
8	

b)

Input n	Output $2n^2$
3	
4	
5	
6	
7	

c)

Input n	Output $\frac{n}{5}+4$
5	
10	
15	
20	
25	

2. Evaluate each expression by replacing *k* with 5.
a) $k+7$ b) $6k$ c) $10-2k$
d) $\frac{50}{k}-1$ e) k^2 f) $3(2k+1)$

3. Write an algebraic expression for each statement.
Evaluate each expression by replacing *n* with 9.

Statement	Expression	Value
a) The sum of a number and sixteen		
b) Ten more than twice a number		
c) Nine divided by a number, then add four		
d) The product of eleven and a number		
e) A number divided by three, then add one		

4. A value of *n* is substituted for each expression to get the number in the box.
Find each value of *n*.
a) $4n-1$ 23
b) $\frac{n}{3}-2$ 2
c) $2(n+3)$ 16
d) $27+2n$ 33
e) $4(n-2)$ 28
f) $26-\frac{n}{2}$ 21

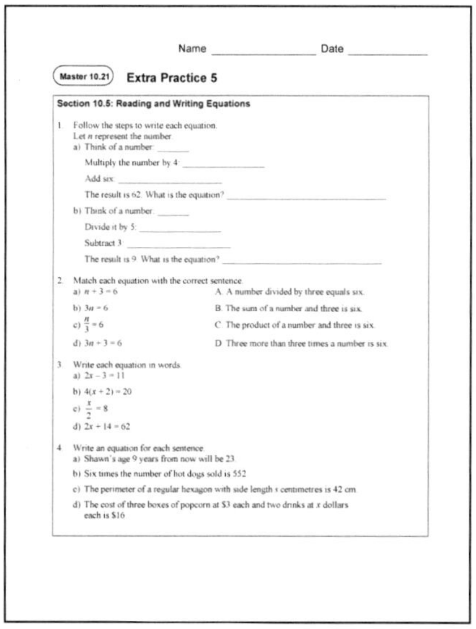

Name ________ Date ________

Master 10.21 Extra Practice 5

Section 10.5: Reading and Writing Equations

1. Follow the steps to write each equation.
Let *n* represent the number.
a) Think of a number: ______
Multiply the number by 4: ______
Add six: ______
The result is 62. What is the equation? ______
b) Think of a number: ______
Divide it by 5: ______
Subtract 3: ______
The result is 9. What is the equation? ______

2. Match each equation with the correct sentence.
a) $n+3=6$ — A. A number divided by three equals six.
b) $3n=6$ — B. The sum of a number and three is six.
c) $\frac{n}{3}=6$ — C. The product of a number and three is six.
d) $3n+3=6$ — D. Three more than three times a number is six.

3. Write each equation in words.
a) $2x-3=11$
b) $4(x+2)=20$
c) $\frac{x}{2}=8$
d) $2x+14=62$

4. Write an equation for each sentence.
a) Shawn's age 9 years from now will be 23.
b) Six times the number of hot dogs sold is 552.
c) The perimeter of a regular hexagon with side length *s* centimetres is 42 cm.
d) The cost of three boxes of popcorn at $3 each and two drinks at *x* dollars each is $16.

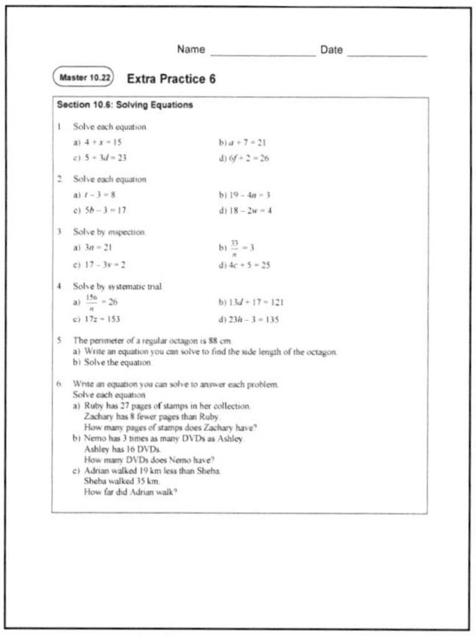

Name ________ Date ________

Master 10.22 Extra Practice 6

Section 10.6: Solving Equations

1. Solve each equation.
a) $4+x=15$ b) $a+7=21$
c) $5+3d=23$ d) $6f+2=26$

2. Solve each equation.
a) $t-3=8$ b) $19-4n=3$
c) $5b-3=17$ d) $18-2w=4$

3. Solve by inspection.
a) $3n=21$ b) $\frac{33}{n}=3$
c) $17-3x=2$ d) $4c+5=25$

4. Solve by systematic trial.
a) $\frac{156}{n}=26$ b) $13d+17=121$
c) $17z=153$ d) $23h-3=135$

5. The perimeter of a regular octagon is 88 cm.
a) Write an equation you can solve to find the side length of the octagon.
b) Solve the equation.

6. Write an equation you can solve to answer each problem.
Solve each equation.
a) Ruby has 27 pages of stamps in her collection.
Zachary has 8 fewer pages than Ruby.
How many pages of stamps does Zachary have?
b) Nemo has 3 times as many DVDs as Ashley.
Ashley has 16 DVDs.
How many DVDs does Nemo have?
c) Adrian walked 19 km less than Sheba.
Sheba walked 35 km.
How far did Adrian walk?

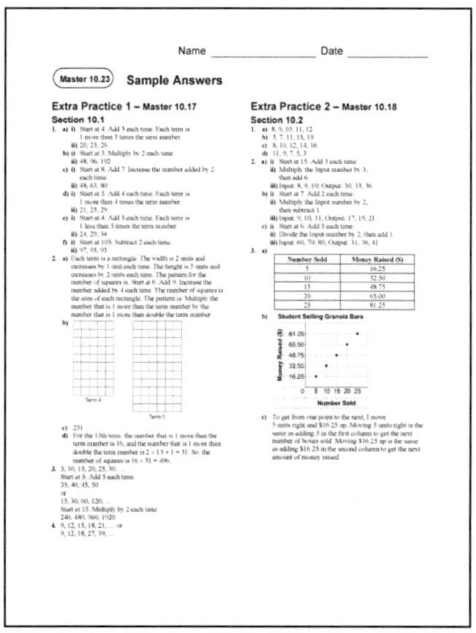

Name ________ Date ________

Master 10.23 Sample Answers

Extra Practice 1 – Master 10.17

Section 10.1

Extra Practice 2 – Master 10.18

Section 10.2

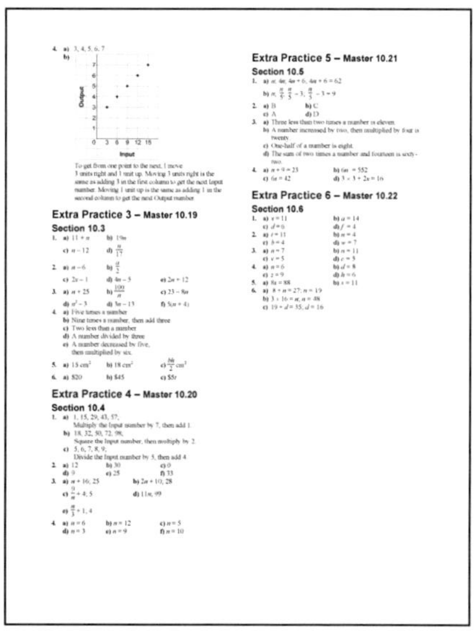

Extra Practice 5 – Master 10.21

Section 10.5

Extra Practice 6 – Master 10.22

Section 10.6

Extra Practice 3 – Master 10.19

Section 10.3

Extra Practice 4 – Master 10.20

Section 10.4

Addison Wesley

Mathematics Makes Sense

Program Authors

Jason Johnston
Bryn Keyes
Mary Doucette
Antonietta Lenjosek
Steve Thomas
Margaret Sinclair
Trevor Brown
Cathy Heideman
Don Jones
Michael Davis
Jennifer Paziuk
Ken Harper
Sharon Jeroski
Ray Appel
Laura Weatherhead
Betty Milne
Jim Mennie
Lynn Strangway

Printed and bound in Canada

10 17

PEARSON
Education Canada

ADDISON WESLEY

Ontario

Math Makes Sense 7

Ontario

Teacher Guide

Unit 11: Probability

PEARSON
Addison Wesley

UNIT 11

Probability

". . .probability is more than spinning spinners and flipping coins. It helps us answer questions about our world in terms of chances of future events occurring or not."

John A. Van de Walle

FOCUS STRAND
Data Management and Probability

SUPPORTING STRAND
Number Sense and Numeration

TIPS
Adolescent students learn mathematics best in environments that allow for physical activity and social interaction. Effective use of manipulatives helps students move from concrete and visual representations to more abstract and cognitive levels.

Mathematics Background

What Are the Big Ideas?

- The likelihood of an event can be described using terms, such as impossible, less likely, equally likely, more likely, or certain, or by assigning a number between 0 (impossible) and 1 (certain).
- A tree diagram can be used to investigate theoretical probability.
- The more times an experiment is conducted, the closer the experimental probability is to the theoretical probability.

How Will the Concepts Develop?

Students conduct probability experiments, draw tree diagrams to list all possible outcomes, and determine experimental probabilities. They review that experimental probability is the number of times an outcome occurs divided by the total number of times the experiment is conducted.

Students investigate theoretical probability by analysing the possible outcomes. They learn that for equally likely outcomes, the probability of any outcome is the number of favourable outcomes divided by the number of possible outcomes.

Students understand that probability can be expressed as a fraction, a decimal, or a percent. Students learn that the probability of an outcome that is certain is 1, and the probability of an impossible outcome is 0.

Why Are These Concepts Important?

We read about probability everywhere: the probability of living to a certain age, the probability that it will rain tomorrow, the probability of a certain team winning the championship, and the probability of contracting a certain disease. Students need a solid foundation in probability to make sense of this information.

A strong conceptual understanding of probability will prepare students for problems they will encounter in later grades.

Curriculum Overview

Overall Expectations
- Use and apply a knowledge of probability. (7m88)

Specific Expectations
- Develop intuitive concepts of probability and understand how probability can relate to sports and games of chance. (7m106)
- List the possible outcomes of simple experiments by using tree diagrams, modelling, and lists. (7m107)
- Identify the favourable outcomes among the total number of possible outcomes and state the associated probability. (7m108)
- Apply a knowledge of probability in sports and games of chance. (7m109)

Launch

Section 11.1: Listing Outcomes

Section 11.2: Experimental Probability

Mid-Unit Review

Section 11.3: Theoretical Probability

Section 11.4: Applications of Probability

Unit Review
Practice Test

Unit Problem
Games of Chance

Curriculum across the Grades

Grade 6	Grade 7	Grade 8
Students connect the possible events and the probability of a particular event. They examine experimental probability results in the light of theoretical results. Students use tree diagrams to record the results of systematic counting. They show an understanding of probability in making relevant decisions.	Students develop intuitive concepts of probability and understand how probability can relate to sports and games of chance. They list the possible outcomes of simple experiments by using tree diagrams, modelling, and lists. Students identify the favourable outcomes among the total number of possible outcomes and state the associated probability.	Students use probability to describe everyday events, and identify 0 to 1 as a range from "never happens" to "always happens" when investigating probability. They list the possible outcomes of simple experiments by using tree diagrams, modelling, and lists. Students identify the favourable outcomes among the total number of possible outcomes and state the associated probability. They use definitions of probability to calculate complex probabilities from tree diagrams and lists. Students compare predicted and experimental results. They apply a knowledge of probability in sports and games, weather predictions, and political polling.

Additional Activities

The Conversion Game

For Extra Practice (Appropriate for use after Skills You'll Need)

Materials: *The Conversion Game* (Master 11.5), a deck of cards with face cards removed (Ace = 1), a calculator

Playing this game reinforces the skills of converting fractions and decimals to percents.

The work students do: Students play in groups of 2, 3, or 4. Students take turns to draw 2 cards from the deck, then use the numbers to make a proper fraction. The student converts the fraction to a decimal and a percent. Each student records these numbers in a table. After each student has had 10 turns, students find the sums of their decimals. The student with the greatest sum wins.

Take It Further: Students add 5 to each number drawn before making a fraction.

Kinesthetic/Social/Logical
Group Activity

Spinner Construction

For Extra Practice (Appropriate for use after Section 11.4)

Materials: *Spinner Construction* (Master 11.6a), *Spinners* (Master 11.6b), 2 number cubes labelled 1 to 6, protractors, pencil crayons

Playing this game reinforces the skill of using probability to construct spinners.

The work students do: Students play with a partner. Students construct spinners as instructed by their partners; for example, "Construct a spinner so that the chance of the pointer landing on red is $\frac{1}{5}$." The student who accurately constructs the greater number of spinners in 6 turns wins.

Take It Further: Players use percents in their instructions instead of fractions. For example, "Construct a spinner so that the chance of the pointer landing on red is 80%."

Visual/Social/Kinesthetic
Partner Activity

Planning for Unit 11

Planning for Instruction

Suggested Unit time: About 2 weeks

Section	Time	Materials	Program Support
Launch, page 2	15–20 min		
Skills You'll Need, page 4	15–20 min	calculators	
11.1: Listing Outcomes, page 5 Investigate outcomes of experiments.	80–100 min	number cubes labelled 1 to 6 spinners with 4 equal sectors coloured pencils rulers open paper clip as a pointer (optional)	Master 11.6b: Spinners Master 11.7: Step-by-Step 1 Master 11.13: Extra Practice 1
11.2: Experimental Probability, page 9 Determine probability from experiments.	80–100 min	coins paper cups paper bags calculators counters (red and yellow) octahedra 3-column charts (optional)	PM 18: 3-Column Chart Master 11.8: Step-by-Step 2 Master 11.14: Extra Practice 2
Mid-Unit Review, page 13		cubes of 2 different colours rulers calculators	
11.3: Theoretical Probability, page 14 Explore and apply theoretical probability.	80–100 min	linking cubes paper bags spinners coloured pencils 4-column charts (optional)	PM 19: 4-Column Chart Master 11.6b: Spinners Master 11.9: Step-by-Step 3 Master 11.15: Extra Practice 3
11.4: Applications of Probability, page 18 Solve probability problems.	80–100 min	blank cards (4 per pair of students) paper bags calculators	Master 11.10: Step-by-Step 4 Master 11.16: Extra Practice 4
Reading and Writing in Math: Choosing a Strategy, page 22		square dot paper red octahedra labelled from 1 to 8 white number cubes labelled from 1 to 6 calculators play money (optional)	PM 22: Square Dot Paper
Game: Empty the Rectangles, page 24		number cubes labelled 1 to 6 counters	
Unit Review, page 25		calculators	Extra Practice: Student Book page 448
Practice Test, page 27		calculators	
Unit Problem: Games of Chance, page 28	40–50 min	spinners paper clips as pointers coloured pencils or crayons number cubes regular polyhedra with numbered faces coins	Master 11.6b: Spinners

etext online tutorial

This web-based tutorial uses voice, animation, and an optional quiz to present each core lesson, so that students can review content with a new approach.

Planning for Assessment

Purpose	Tools and Process	Recording and Reporting
Diagnostic	*Unit Launch* Question; conference; scaffold problems throughout the unit	PM 8: Conference Prompts
Formative	*Explore* – Ongoing Assessment: Observe and Listen	Master 11.2 Ongoing Observations: Probability PM 1: Inquiry Process Check List PM 6: Observation Record 1 PM 7: Observation Record 2 PM 8: Conference Prompts PM 2: Self-Assessment PM 3: Self-Assessment: Problem Solving PM 9: Work Sample Records
Summative	Unit Review *Unit Problem* – Performance Assessment Unit Test Review assessment records; add unit results to ongoing records	Master 11.1 Unit Rubric: Probability Master 11.3 Performance Assessment Rubric: Games of Chance Master 11.4 Unit Summary: Probability PM 10: Summary Class Records: Strands PM 11: Summary Class Records: Achievement Categories PM 12: Summary Record: Individual
Learning Skills/ Mathematical Disposition	Observe and record throughout unit	PM 4: Learning Skills Check List PM 5: Mathematical Dispositions and Learning Skills

Program Masters (PM) are in the *Grade 7 Planning and Program Masters* module.
Extra Practice Masters are on the CD-ROM and are printed in reduced format on page 49 of this module.

SECTION ORGANIZER

15–20 min

Curriculum Focus: Activate prior learning about probability.
Vocabulary: probability

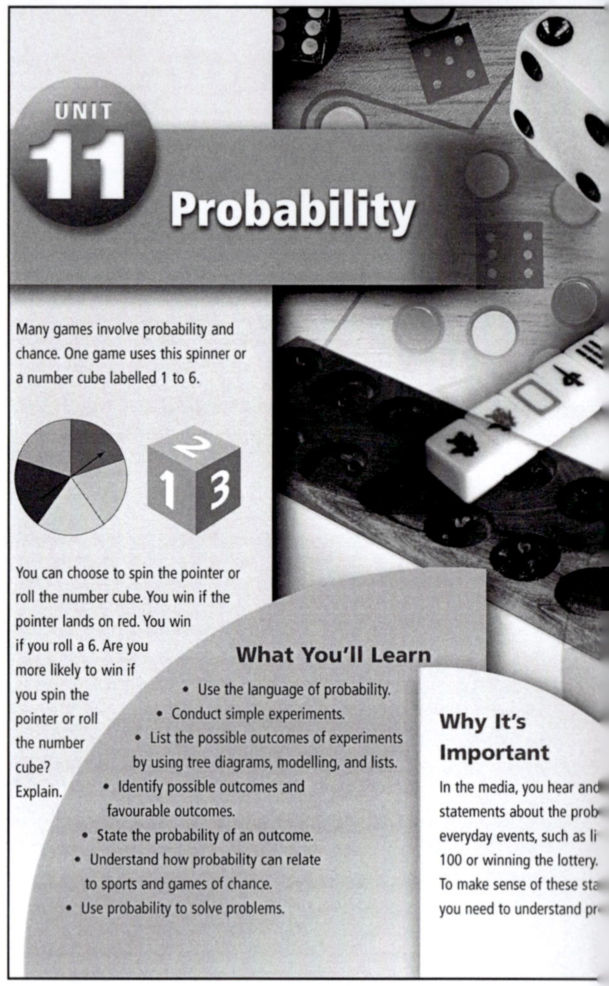

UNIT 11

Probability

Many games involve probability and chance. One game uses this spinner or a number cube labelled 1 to 6.

You can choose to spin the pointer or roll the number cube. You win if the pointer lands on red. You win if you roll a 6. Are you more likely to win if you spin the pointer or roll the number cube? Explain.

What You'll Learn

- Use the language of probability.
- Conduct simple experiments.
- List the possible outcomes of experiments by using tree diagrams, modelling, and lists.
- Identify possible outcomes and favourable outcomes.
- State the probability of an outcome.
- Understand how probability can relate to sports and games of chance.
- Use probability to solve problems.

Why It's Important

In the media, you hear and statements about the prob everyday events, such as li 100 or winning the lottery. To make sense of these sta you need to understand pr

ASSUMED PRIOR KNOWLEDGE

- ☑ Students can relate the possible outcomes to the probability of a particular outcome.
- ☑ Students can use fractions to describe probability.
- ☑ Students can use appropriate language to describe probabilities.

ACTIVATE PRIOR LEARNING

Have students look at the pictures on pages 404 and 405 of the Student Book. Have students identify some games that involve probability and chance (*backgammon, Monopoly, dominoes, Twister*). Invite students to look at the picture of the spinner and the number cube on page 404. Ask questions, such as:

- Which colours can the pointer land on? (*Red, blue, black, yellow, and green*)
- Are these outcomes equally probable? Explain. (*Yes, because the sectors are congruent.*)
- What is the probability that the spinner will land on red? (*The probability is 1 out of 5, or $\frac{1}{5}$.*)
- How many possible outcomes are there if you roll the number cube? (*There are 6 possible outcomes: 1, 2, 3, 4, 5, 6.*)
- Are these outcomes equally probable? Explain. (*Yes, because each number appears on the cube once.*)
- What is the probability that you will roll a 6? (*The probability is 1 out of 6, or $\frac{1}{6}$.*)
- Are you more likely to win if you spin the pointer or roll the number cube? Explain. (*I am more likely to win if I spin the pointer because $\frac{1}{5} > \frac{1}{6}$.*)

Tell students that, in this unit, they will investigate probability. They will conduct simple experiments, list possible outcomes of experiments, identify favourable outcomes, state the probability of an outcome, learn how probability relates to sports and games of chance, and use probability to solve problems. At the end of the unit, students will use their understanding of probability to investigate a spinner game, and to design their own games of chance.

Key Words

- probability
- outcome
- tree diagram
- relative frequency
- experimental probability
- theoretical probability

FROM THE LIBRARY

Graphing, Statistics, and Probability: Grades 6–8+: Inventive Exercises to Sharpen Skills and Raise Achievement (Basic, Not Boring 6 to 8) by Imogene Forte and Marjorie Frank. Incentive Publications, 2000
ISBN: 0865034467
The exercises in this book are based on a sports theme, allowing students to develop probability skills while entering a world of fun and exciting activities.

Fractions, Ratio, Probability, and Standard Measurement: Reproducible Skill Builders and Higher Order Thinking Activities Based on NCTM Standards by Brenda Opie, Douglas McAvinn, and Lory Jackson. Incentive Publications, 1995
ISBN: 0865303029
This book is designed to improve concept understanding and skills mastery. With meaningful practice materials, students connect classroom learning to real-life situations. Students should find the activities stimulating and fun.

REACHING ALL LEARNERS

e-tools Some students may benefit from using the virtual manipulatives on the e-Tools CD-ROM.
The e-Tool appropriate for this unit is *Probability*.

DIAGNOSTIC ASSESSMENT

What to Look For	What to Do
✔ Students can relate the possible outcomes to the probability of a particular outcome.	***Extra Support:*** Students who have difficulty relating the possible outcomes to the probability of a particular outcome may benefit from working with simple problems; for example, students could look at a number cube labelled 1, 2, 2, 3, 3, 3, . . ., list the possible outcomes, then find the probability of each outcome. *Work on this skill during Sections 11.1 and 11.2.*
✔ Students can use fractions to describe probability.	Students who have difficulty using fractions to describe probability should write the fraction: $\text{Probability} = \frac{\text{number of favourable outcomes}}{\text{total number of outcomes}}$, and keep this fraction where it is easily available for reference. *Work on this skill throughout the unit.*
✔ Students can use appropriate language to describe probabilities.	Students who cannot use appropriate language to describe probabilities may benefit from writing a sentence that uses each term (such as likely, unlikely, equally probable, more probable, certain, and impossible) in a context they understand. *Work on this skill during Section 11.2.*

SECTION ORGANIZER

15-20 min

Skills in Review
- Converting fractions and decimals to percents

Student Materials
- calculators

Vocabulary: percent, equivalent fraction

Alternative Example 1

Express each fraction as a decimal, then as a percent.

a) $\frac{17}{25}$ b) $\frac{4}{5}$ c) $\frac{27}{40}$ d) $\frac{123}{150}$

Solution

a) $\frac{17}{25} = \frac{68}{100}$ (multiply the numerator and the denominator by 4)
$= 0.68$, or 68%

b) $\frac{4}{5} = \frac{80}{100}$ (multiply the numerator and the denominator by 20)
$= 0.80$, or 80%

c) $\frac{27}{40} = 27 \div 40$
$= 0.675$
$= 67.5\%$

d) $\frac{123}{150} = 123 \div 150$
$= 0.82$
$= 82\%$

UNIT 11

Skills You'll Need

Converting Fractions and Decimals to Percents

Percent (%) means "per hundred" or out of one hundred.

Example

Express each fraction as a decimal, then as a percent.

a) $\frac{9}{50}$ b) $\frac{1}{4}$ c) $\frac{5}{8}$ d) $\frac{7}{16}$

Solution

To convert a fraction to a decimal, try to write an equivalent fraction with denominator 100.

a) $\frac{9}{50} = \frac{18}{100}$ (× 2, × 2) b) $\frac{1}{4} = \frac{25}{100}$ (× 25, × 25)

$\frac{18}{100} = 0.18$, or 18% $\frac{25}{100} = 0.25$, or 25%

When you cannot write an equivalent fraction, use a calculator to divide.

c) $\frac{5}{8} = 5 \div 8$
$= 0.625$
$= 62.5\%$

d) $\frac{7}{16} = 7 \div 16$
$= 0.4375$
$= 43.75\%$

✓ Check

1. Express each decimal as a percent.
   a) 0.1 10% b) 0.01 1% c) 0.24 24% d) 0.05

2. Express each fraction as a decimal, then as a percent.
   a) $\frac{7}{10}$ 0.7, 70% b) $\frac{3}{5}$ 0.6, 60% c) $\frac{9}{25}$ 0.36, 36% d) $\frac{3}{4}$ 0.7

3. Express each fraction as a decimal, then as a percent.
   a) $\frac{7}{40}$ 0.175, 17.5% b) $\frac{3}{8}$ 0.375, 37.5% c) $\frac{13}{16}$ 0.8125, 81.25% d) $\frac{51}{200}$ C

406 UNIT 11: Probability

Converting Fractions and Decimals to Percents

Have volunteers list the factors of 100 on the board (1, 2, 4, 5, 10, 20, 25, 50, 100). Have students use each factor (except for 1 and 100) as a denominator and any number as the numerator, to write a proper fraction; for example, $\frac{1}{2}, \frac{3}{4}, \frac{2}{5}, \frac{9}{10}, \frac{17}{20}, \frac{13}{25}, \frac{33}{50}$. Have students write an equivalent fraction with denominator 100 for each fraction. Ask:

- What did you multiply each fraction by? Explain. (*I multiplied both numerator and denominator by 50, 25, 20, 10, 5, 4, and 2 to get the denominator 100.*)

Since each fraction now has denominator 100, the decimal and percent can be read from the numerator; for example, $\frac{17}{20} = \frac{85}{100} = 0.85$, or 85%.

Ensure students understand that they use division to convert a fraction that does not have a denominator that is a factor of 100. Point out that some decimals terminate, or stop, after 2, 3, or 4 decimal places. Other decimals repeat. If this happens, ensure students understand they should round each decimal to 3 or 4 decimal places.

Students can play the Additional Activity *The Conversion Game* (Master 11.5).

Common Misconceptions

➤Students divide the denominator by the numerator.

How to Help: Model how to write a division statement as a fraction. Tell students that we replace the division sign with the fraction line. For example, write $4 \div 7$ on the board. Write 4 as the numerator, then the fraction line, then 7 as the denominator: $\frac{4}{7}$. Students can use this model to work backward from a fraction to get a division statement.

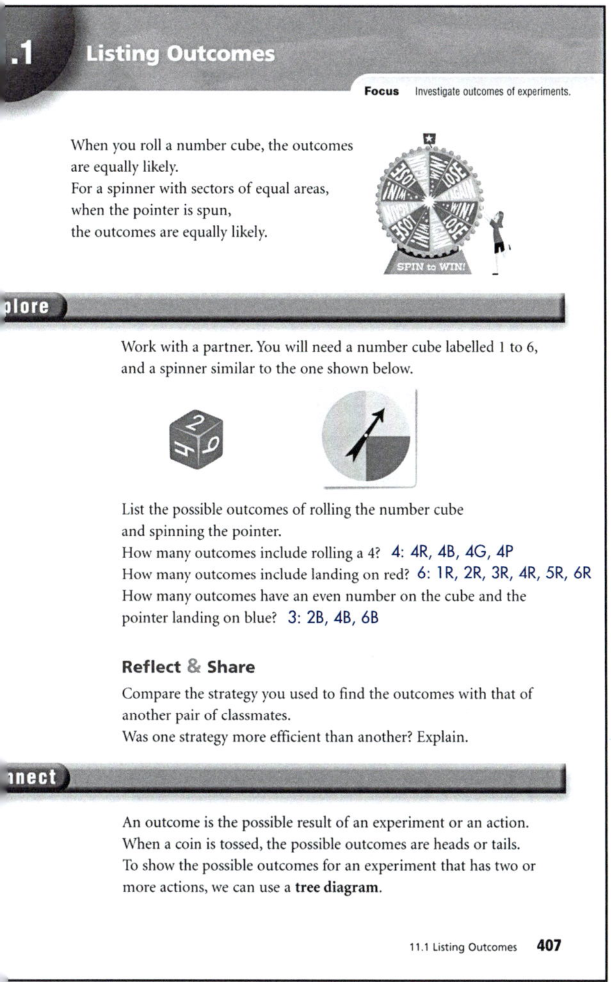

.1 Listing Outcomes

Focus Investigate outcomes of experiments.

When you roll a number cube, the outcomes are equally likely.
For a spinner with sectors of equal areas, when the pointer is spun, the outcomes are equally likely.

plore

Work with a partner. You will need a number cube labelled 1 to 6, and a spinner similar to the one shown below.

List the possible outcomes of rolling the number cube and spinning the pointer.
How many outcomes include rolling a 4? 4: 4R, 4B, 4G, 4P
How many outcomes include landing on red? 6: 1R, 2R, 3R, 4R, 5R, 6R
How many outcomes have an even number on the cube and the pointer landing on blue? 3: 2B, 4B, 6B

Reflect & Share

Compare the strategy you used to find the outcomes with that of another pair of classmates.
Was one strategy more efficient than another? Explain.

nnect

An outcome is the possible result of an experiment or an action.
When a coin is tossed, the possible outcomes are heads or tails.
To show the possible outcomes for an experiment that has two or more actions, we can use a **tree diagram**.

11.1 Listing Outcomes 407

Listing Outcomes

SECTION ORGANIZER (80–100 min)

Curriculum Focus: Investigate outcomes of experiments. (7m107)

Student Materials
- number cubes labelled 1 to 6
- spinners with 4 equal sectors (Master 11.6b)
- coloured pencils
- rulers

Optional
- open paper clip as a pointer
- Step-by-Step 1 (Master 11.7)
- Extra Practice 1 (Master 11.13)

Vocabulary: outcome, tree diagram
Assessment: Master 11.2 Ongoing Observations: Probability

Key Math Learnings

1. An outcome is the possible result of an experiment or an action.
2. A tree diagram can be used to show the possible outcomes for an experiment that has two or more actions.

BEFORE Get Started

Show students a number cube, labelled from 1 to 6. Ask:

- What are the possible outcomes of rolling the number cube? (*1, 2, 3, 4, 5, 6*)
- What are the possible outcomes for a spinner with 5 congruent sectors, coloured red, blue, yellow, green, and orange? (*Red, blue, yellow, green, orange*)
- Why do we say that these outcomes are equally likely? (*For the number cube, each number appears only once on the cube, so the likelihood of rolling each number is the same. For the spinner, each sector is the same size, so the likelihood of the spinner landing on each colour is the same.*)
- When would the outcomes not be equally likely? (*If one number on the number cube appeared more than once, it would have a greater likelihood of being rolled. If one colour on the spinner had a larger sector, or appeared more than once, that colour would have a greater likelihood of being spun.*)

Present *Explore*. Distribute a number cube and a spinner to pairs of students. If commercial spinners are not available, have students make the spinner by using the spinner divided into quarters on *Spinners* (Master 11.6b) by colouring the sectors red, blue, green, and pink.

Ensure students understand that they are to find the outcomes of the two combined actions and not the two separate actions. Encourage students to experiment with the number cube and spinner, if necessary, when determining the possible outcomes.

REACHING ALL LEARNERS

Early Finishers

Have students extend *Explore*. List the possible outcomes when 2 number cubes are rolled. (*Answer: there are 36 possible outcomes.*) List the possible outcomes when the spinner is spun twice. (*Answer: there are 16 possible outcomes.*) What do you notice about the number of total outcomes in each experiment? (*Answer: The total number of possible outcomes is the square of the total number of possible outcomes when the action is performed once.*)

Common Misconceptions

➤ Students have difficulty drawing a tree diagram and mix up the possible outcomes.

How to Help: Have students write down the number of possible actions in the experiment. This is the number of columns in the tree diagram. Students list the possible outcomes of the first action in column 1, leaving appropriate spacing between them. Students list the possible outcomes of the second action in column 2, beside each of the first outcomes, forming branches. Students continue this method for each additional action.

ESL Strategies

Students for whom English is a second language may benefit from using number cubes, coins, spinners, and pictures related to some of the exercises. For example, for question 4, pictures of eggs, fruit, toast, pancakes, cereal, milk, and juice will help them understand the vocabulary, and they can use the pictures to form possible combinations.

When 2 coins are tossed, the outcomes for each coin are heads (H) or tails (T).
List the outcomes of the first coin toss.
For each outcome, list the outcomes of the second coin toss.
Then list the outcomes for the coins tossed together.

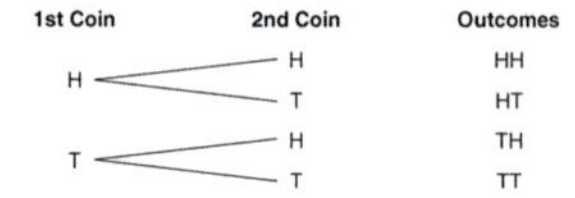

There are 4 possible outcomes: HH, HT, TH, TT

Example

Farah tosses a coin and spins the pointer on this spinner.

a) Draw a tree diagram to show the possible outcomes.
b) List all the possible outcomes.
c) How many outcomes include the pointer landing on pink?
d) How many outcomes include tails?

Solution

a) The sectors on the spinner have equal areas, so the outcomes are equally likely. The possible outcomes for the spinner are: pink (P), yellow (Y), or blue (B). For each colour, the possible outcomes for tossing the coin are: heads (H) or tails (T)

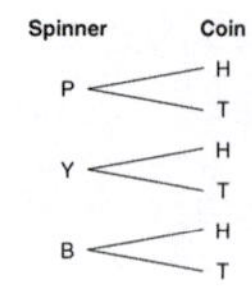

b) The outcomes are: pink/heads, pink/tails, yellow/heads, yellow/tails, blue/heads, blue/tails
c) There are two outcomes with the colour pink: pink/heads, pink/tails
d) There are three outcomes with tails: pink/tails, yellow/tails, blue/tails

408 UNIT 11: Probability

DURING Explore

Ongoing Assessment: Observe and Listen

As students work, ask questions, such as:

- What are the possible outcomes of spinning the pointer on the spinner? (*Red, blue, green, pink*)
- What are the possible outcomes of rolling the number cube and spinning the pointer? (*1R, 1B, 1G, 1P, 2R, 2B, 2G, 2P, 3R, 3B, 3G, 3P, 4R, 4B, 4G, 4P, 5R, 5B, 5G, 5P, 6R, 6B, 6G, 6P*)
- How many outcomes include rolling a 4? (*4: 4R, 4B, 4G, 4P*)
- How many outcomes include landing on red? (*6: 1R, 2R, 3R, 4R, 5R, 6R*)
- How many outcomes have an even number on the cube and the pointer landing on blue? (*3: 2B, 4B, 6B*)

AFTER Connect

Invite students to share their strategies. Students could post their findings on chart paper. Have two students explain how they displayed their outcomes and why they chose that particular method. Discuss as a class if any one particular method of displaying the outcomes is more suitable.

Ask:

- How many actions does this experiment have? (*2*)

Suggest an organized way of listing the outcomes. (*For each of the numbers 1, 2, 3, 4, 5, 6, there are 4 colours: red, blue, green, pink. Write each colour with the number 1, then with the number 2, and so on. There are 24 possible outcomes.*)

What you might see:

1 red	2 red	3 red
1 blue	2 blue	3 blue

ctice

1. List the possible outcomes in each case.
   a) spinning the pointer Red, green, yellow
   b) rolling a number cube labelled 1 to 6 1, 2, 3, 4, 5, 6

2. List the possible outcomes in each case.
   a) the colour of a traffic light when you reach it Red, yellow, green
   b) the gender of a baby who is born Boy, girl
   c) the points scored in a hockey game 0, 1, 2
   d) the suit of a card pulled from a deck of playing cards Diamonds, hearts, clubs, spades
3. The Scenic Railroad sells tickets for trips on Saturdays and Sundays. All-day and half-day trips are available. There are adult, child, and senior fares. Draw a tree diagram to show the possible ticket types.
4. Use a tree diagram to show the possible combinations for breakfast. You must choose one of each:
   - eggs or fruit
   - toast, pancakes, or cereal
   - milk or juice
5. Jim has to choose an outfit. His choices of pants are black, grey, or navy. His sweater choices are red, beige, white, or yellow.
   a) Draw a tree diagram to display all the possible outfits.
   b) How many outfits have either black pants or a white sweater? 6
   c) How many outfits do not have black pants or do not have a white sweater? 6
   d) How many outfits have a black sweater? 0
6. A deli offers 2 soups, 4 salads, 5 sandwiches, and 3 beverages. How many choices are there for a customer who wants each of the following meals?
   a) a salad and a beverage 12
   b) soup, a sandwich, and a beverage 30
   c) soup, a salad, and a beverage 24
   d) a sandwich or salad, and a soup 18

lath

+5) = +2
−5) = +8
−5) = −2
+5) = −2

11.1 Listing Outcomes 409

Mental Math

Students may use a number line, a pattern, coloured tiles, or related equations. Stronger math students may be able to write the sums and the difference directly.

Assignment Guidelines

If your students do not have time to complete all the *Practice* questions on pages 409 and 410, these questions provide minimum curriculum coverage: 2, 3, 6, 7, *Reflect*
To assess the 4 Achievement Chart categories listed in the curriculum document, have students complete these *Practice* questions:

Understanding Concepts: 3	Application: 6
Problem Solving: 7	Communication: *Reflect*

Sample Answers

3. There is insufficient room to show a tree diagram. Here is a description of it.
   1st column: Day – Saturday, Sunday
   2nd column: adjacent to each day in the first column: Trip – Half day, All day
   3rd column: adjacent to each trip in the second column: Fare – Adult, child, senior
4. Here is a description of a tree diagram.
   1st column: 1st Choice – Eggs, Fruit
   2nd column: adjacent to each 1st choice in the first column: 2nd Choice – Toast, Pancakes, Cereal
   3rd column: adjacent to each 2nd choice in the second column: 3rd Choice – Milk, Juice

1 green	2 green	3 green
1 pink	2 pink	3 pink
4 red	5 red	6 red
4 blue	5 blue	6 blue
4 green	5 green	6 green
4 pink	5 pink	6 pink

An alternative method is to write each number once, then list the outcomes of the spinner for each number. Students then draw a line or branch from each number to each of the 4 colours to form a **tree diagram.**

Review *Connect.* Point out that another column is added to the tree diagram to list all the possible outcomes.

Practice

Some students may use multiplication to determine the number of choices in *Practice* question 6. Other students may draw diagrams.

Some of the tree diagrams will be long because of the number of possible outcomes for each choice.

Assessment Focus: Question 7

Some students may benefit from using two number cubes as they complete the chart. Students use the completed chart to answer the other parts of the question. Ensure students understand that the order of the cubes matters; for example, cube one showing 2 and cube two showing 4 is different from cube one showing 4 and cube two showing 2.

Students who need extra support to complete Assessment Focus questions may benefit from the Step-by-Step masters (Masters 11.7–11.10).

5. a) Here is a description of a tree diagram.
   1st column: Pants – Black, Grey, Navy
   2nd column: adjacent to each entry in the first column: Sweater – Red, Beige, White, Yellow

7. b) 11 different outcomes: 2, 3, 4, 5, 6, 7, 8, 9, 10, 11, 12
   c) 5 ways: 5 + 1 = 6; 4 + 2 = 6; 3 + 3 = 6; 2 + 4 = 6; 1 + 5 = 6
   d) 4 ways: 6 + 3 = 9; 5 + 4 = 9; 4 + 5 = 9; 3 + 6 = 9
   e) 2 ways: 1 + 1 = 2; 6 + 6 = 12
   f) Seven is the sum that appears most often.
   g) Here is a description of a tree diagram.
   1st column: 1st cube 1, 2, 3, 4, 5, 6
   2nd column: adjacent to each number in the first column are 1, 2, 3, 4, 5, 6
   3rd column: a list of the outcomes – 1, 1; 1, 2; 1, 3; 1, 4; 1, 5; 1, 6; 2, 1; 2, 2; 2, 3; 2, 4; 2, 5; 2, 6; 3, 1; 3, 2; 3, 3; 3, 4; 3, 5; 3, 6; 4, 1; 4, 2; 4, 3; 4, 4; 4, 5; 4, 6; 5, 1; 5, 2; 5, 3; 5, 4; 5, 5; 5, 6; 6, 1; 6, 2; 6, 3; 6, 4; 6, 5; 6, 6
   The table is easier to read, and the tree diagram does not show the sums.

REFLECT: A tree diagram is helpful to list the outcomes of an experiment with more than one action. It is a visual and organized method of listing all possible first actions followed by all possible second actions. All possible combinations of actions can be read from the tree diagram.

7. Assessment Focus
a) Copy and complete this table.
Show the sums when two number cubes are rolled.

When one cube shows 1 and the other cube shows 4, then the sum is 5.

Sum of Numbers on Two Cubes					
Number on Cube	1	2	3	4	5
1	2	3	4	5	6
2	3	4	5	6	7
3	4	5	6	7	8
4	5	6	7	8	9
5	6	7	8	9	10
6	7	8	9	10	11

b) How many different outcomes are there for the sum of the numbers on the cubes? 11
c) In how many ways can the sum be 6? 5 ways
d) In how many ways can the sum be 9? 4 ways
e) In how many ways can the sum be 2 or 12? 2 ways
f) Why do you think 7 is a lucky number? Seven is the
g) Draw a tree diagram to show these results.
Why do you think a table was used instead of a tree diagram?
Show your work.

Take It Further

8. A lock combination comprises the four digits from 1 to 4 in any order.
How many possible combinations are there in each case?
a) The digits cannot repeat within the code. 24
b) The digits can repeat within the code. 256

Reflect

Explain why a tree diagram is helpful to list the outcomes of an experiment.

410 UNIT 11: Probability

ASSESSMENT FOR LEARNING

What to Look For

Understanding concepts
✔ Students understand that an outcome is the possible result of an experiment or an action.

Applying procedures
✔ Students can draw a tree diagram to show all possible outcomes for an experiment that has two or more actions.

Communicating
✔ Students can explain why a tree diagram is helpful to list the outcomes of an experiment.

What to Do

Extra Support: Students who have difficulty drawing a tree diagram to show possible outcomes may benefit from making a table first.
Students can add additional columns as necessary, then draw lines between adjacent columns to make a tree diagram.
Students can use Step-by-Step 1 (Master 11.7) to complete question 7.

Spinner	Coin
Red	H
	T
Blue	H
	T
Green	H
	T

Extra Practice: Have students use a tree diagram to show the possible combinations for lunch, using different choices for: type of sandwich, type of juice, and type of fruit.
Students can complete Extra Practice 1 (Master 11.13).

Recording and Reporting
Master 11.2 Ongoing Observations: Probability

1.2 Experimental Probability

Focus Determine probability from experiments.

plore

Work with a partner.
You will need a coin.
When you toss a coin, which outcome do you think is more likely?
Do you think the outcomes are equally likely? Explain.

Outcome	Tally	Frequency
Heads		
Tails		

➢ Toss the coin 50 times.
How many times do you think you will get heads?
Record the results in a table.

➢ Write the number of heads as a fraction of the total number of tosses.
Write the number of tails as a fraction of the total number of tosses.
Add the fractions. What do you notice?

Reflect & Share

How do the results compare with your prediction?
Combine your results with those of another pair of classmates.
This is same as tossing the coin 100 times.
Write the new fractions for 100 tosses.
Add the fractions. What do you notice?

nnect

The **relative frequency** is the number of times an outcome occurs divided by the total number of times the experiment is conducted.

$$\text{Relative frequency} = \frac{\text{Number of times an outcome occurs}}{\text{Number of times experiment is conducted}}$$

The relative frequency may be written as a fraction, a decimal, or a percent. Relative frequency is also called **experimental probability**.

11.2 Experimental Probability **411**

Experimental Probability

SECTION ORGANIZER (80–100 min)

Curriculum Focus: Determine probability from experiments. (7m106, 7m107, 7m109)

Student Materials
- coins
- paper cups
- paper bags
- calculators
- counters (red and yellow)
- octahedra

Optional
- 3-column charts (PM 18)
- Step-by-Step 2 (Master 11.8)
- Extra Practice 2 (Master 11.14)

Vocabulary: relative frequency, experimental probability

Assessment: Master 11.2 Ongoing Observations: Probability

Key Math Learnings

1. The relative frequency is the number of times an outcome occurs divided by the total number of times the experiment is conducted. Relative frequency may be written as a fraction, a decimal, or a percent.

2. Relative frequency is also called experimental probability.

3. The sum of the relative frequencies for an experiment is 1.

BEFORE Get Started

Prompt a short class discussion about the value of conducting an experiment.

Ask questions, such as:

- Why is an experiment conducted? (*An experiment is conducted to test a hypothesis and to collect information.*)
- What kind of experiment could we perform to find how often a coin lands heads or tails when tossed? (*We could toss a coin 10, 20, or 30 times, and record how often the coin lands heads or tails.*)

Present *Explore.* Distribute coins and copies of a 3-column chart (PM 18) to pairs of students. One student should toss the coin and the other student should record the results. Remind students that when writing a fraction, the numerator represents either the number of heads or the number of tails, and the denominator represents the total number of tosses.

DURING Explore

Ongoing Assessment: Observe and Listen

As students work, ask questions, such as:

- When you toss a coin, do you think the outcomes are equally likely? Explain. (*Yes. The coin lands heads or tails, and each outcome appears once on the coin.*)
- How many times do you think you will get heads if you toss the coin 50 times? (*Since each outcome is equally likely, heads should appear about one-half of the time. So, heads should appear about 25 times.*)
- How many times did you get heads? (*28*) What fraction did you write? ($\frac{28}{50}$)
- How many times did you get tails? (*22*) What fraction did you write? ($\frac{22}{50}$)

REACHING ALL LEARNERS

Alternative Explore

Work with a partner. You will need a spinner with 3 congruent sectors: red, yellow, green, and an open paper clip as a pointer. When you spin the pointer, which outcome do you think is most likely? Do you think the outcomes are equally likely? Explain.
Spin the pointer 50 times. How many times do you think the pointer will land on red?
Record the results in a table.
Write the number of spins for each colour as a fraction of the total number of spins.
Add the fractions. What do you notice?

Early Finishers

Ask: Suppose you roll a number cube 50 times. How many times do you think you will roll a 6?
Have students roll a number cube 50 times.
Record the results in a table.
Write the number of 6s rolled as a fraction of the total number of rolls. Do this for each number rolled. Add the fractions. What do you notice?

Common Misconceptions

➤ Students think that after 50 tosses of a coin, there should be exactly 25 heads and 25 tails.

How to Help: Remind students that even though the outcomes are equally likely, this is an experiment and there may not be equal numbers of heads and tails. The greater the number of tosses, the closer the relative frequencies will be to $\frac{1}{2}$, or 0.5.

When a thumbtack is dropped, it can land with its point up or on its side.
Here are the results of 100 drops:

Outcome	Frequ
Point up	4
On its side	5

Relative frequency of Point up $= \frac{\text{Number of times Point up}}{\text{Total number of drops}}$

$= \frac{46}{100}$, or 0.46

Relative frequency of On its side $= \frac{\text{Number of times On its side}}{\text{Total number of drops}}$

$= \frac{54}{100}$, or 0.54

Outcome	Frequency	Relative Frequency
Point up	46	0.46
On its side	54	0.54

The sum of the relative frequencies fo experiment is 1.
That is, $\frac{46}{100} + \frac{54}{100} = 0.46 + 0.54$
$= 1$

Example

The number of times a player goes up to bat is referred to as the player's "at bats."
This table shows the number of at bats and hits for some of the greatest players in the Baseball Hall of Fame.

In baseball, a "batting average" is a relative frequency.

a) Calculate the batting average for each player.
b) Order the players from greatest to least batting average.

Players in Base Hall of Fame	
Player	**At Bats**
Aaron	12 364
Cobb	11 429
Gehrig	8 001
Jackson	9 864
Mantle	8 102
Mays	10 881

Solution

a) To calculate each player's batting average, divide the number of hits by the number of at bats.
Round each batting average to 3 decimal places.

Use a calculator to write each fraction as a decimal.

Aaron $= \frac{3771}{12\,364} \doteq 0.305$ Cobb $= \frac{4191}{11\,429} \doteq 0.367$

Gehrig $= \frac{2721}{8001} \doteq 0.340$ Jackson $= \frac{2584}{9864} \doteq 0.262$

Mantle $= \frac{2415}{8102} \doteq 0.298$ Mays $= \frac{3283}{10\,881} \doteq 0.302$

412 UNIT 11: Probability

AFTER Connect

Ask questions, such as:

- How do the results compare with your predictions?
(*Our results were close to what we predicted.*)
- When you combined your results with another pair of classmates, how many times did you get heads? (*48*) Tails? (*52*)
- What fraction did you write to represent heads? ($\frac{52}{100}$) Tails? ($\frac{48}{100}$)
- What do you notice about the sum of the new fractions? (*The sum is 1.*)

Ensure students understand that the results they have obtained are experimental because they are based on an experiment rather than a theoretical analysis of the coin.

Introduce the terms **relative frequency** and **experimental probability**. Use the explanation and *Example* in *Connect* as further illustrations of this concept.

Practice

Question 4 requires a paper cup. Question 5 requires 3 red counters, 3 yellow counters, and a paper bag. Question 7 requires 2 regular octahedra, labelled 1 to 8. Students may use the octahedra they made in Unit 3, if they are still on hand. Students label the faces of each octahedron from 1 to 8.

Assessment Focus: Question 7

Students could make a table to record the results of their experiment. Some students may record all possible sums in the "Outcomes" column, while other students may record only 2 possible outcomes: "Sum of 7" and "Not a sum of 7." A level 4 response could include a chart that shows the theoretical probabilities, and the fact that the probability for a sum of 7 is $\frac{6}{64} \doteq 0.094$. "The greater the number of experiments, the closer the experimental probability comes to the calculated probability."

b) The batting averages, from greatest to least, are:
0.367, 0.340, 0.305, 0.302, 0.298, 0.262
The players, from greatest to least batting average, are:
Cobb, Gehrig, Aaron, Mays, Mantle, and Jackson

actice

	At Bats	Hits
si	58	26
	41	20
	54	23
	36	11
	49	18
	42	15
	46	22
s	45	17

1. This table shows data for a baseball team.
Find the batting average of each player.
Round each answer to 3 decimal places.

2. Write each relative frequency as a decimal to 3 decimal places.
   a) A telemarketer made 200 phone calls and 35 new customers signed up. What is the relative frequency of getting a customer? Not getting a customer? $\frac{35}{200}$, or 0.175; $\frac{165}{200}$, or 0.825
   b) A quality controller tested 175 light bulbs and found 5 defective. What is the relative frequency of finding a defective bulb? Finding a good bulb? $\frac{5}{175}$, or 0.029; $\frac{170}{175}$, or 0.971

3. A paper cup is tossed.
The cup lands with the top up 27 times, the top down 32 times, and on its side 41 times.
   a) What are the possible outcomes of tossing a paper cup? Top up, top down, on its side
   b) Are the outcomes equally likely? Explain. No
   c) State the relative frequency of each outcome.
   Top up: $\frac{27}{100}$, Top down: $\frac{32}{100}$, On its side: $\frac{41}{100}$

4. a) Conduct the paper cup experiment in question 3.
   Decide how to hold the cup to drop it.
   Repeat the experiment until you have 100 results.
   b) Compare your results with those from question 3.
   Are the numbers different? Explain.

5. Use 3 red counters and 3 yellow counters.
You may place some or all of the counters in a bag.
You then pick a counter without looking.
How many different ways can you place the counters in the bag so you are more likely to pick a red counter than a yellow counter? Explain.

here are 6 ways: red; 2 red; 1 red; red and 1 yellow; red and 2 yellow; red and 1 yellow.

Sample Answers

1. Batting Averages: Yang Hsi: 0.448, Aki: 0.488, David: 0.426, Yuk Yee: 0.306, Eli: 0.367, Aponi: 0.357, Leah: 0.478, Devadas: 0.378
3. b) No. There is a greater likelihood that the cup will land on its side because when it initially lands on its top or base, it frequently falls sideways before it comes to rest.
4. a) Results will vary.
   b) The numbers are different because I performed an experiment and experiments do not usually give the same results.
5. As long as there are more red counters than yellow counters in the bag, the likelihood of picking a red counter is greater.
6. a), b) Answers will vary.
   c) The sum of the relative frequencies is 1. This makes sense because each denominator is 31 (the total number of "experiments;" that is, the total number of students who wrote their birthdays in the table), the sum of the numerators is also 31 (the total number of possible outcomes); and $\frac{31}{31} = 1$.
7. a) I rolled the two octahedra 10 times.

Outcome	Frequency	Relative Frequency
Sum of 7	1	$\frac{1}{10} = 0.1$
Not Sum of 7	9	$\frac{9}{10} = 0.9$

(Answers continue below.)

(Sample Answers, continued)

I rolled the two octahedra 50 times.

Outcome	Frequency	Relative Frequency
Sum of 7	5	$\frac{5}{50} = 0.1$
Not Sum of 7	45	$\frac{45}{50} = 0.9$

I rolled the two octahedra 100 times.

Outcome	Frequency	Relative Frequency
Sum of 7	9	$\frac{9}{100} = 0.09$
Not Sum of 7	91	$\frac{91}{100} = 0.91$

b) I noticed that each time, the relative frequencies were approximately the same. The relative frequency does not seem to be affected much by the number of times I do the experiment.

REFLECT: If a coin is tossed 50 times and it lands heads 27 times, then the relative frequency is $\frac{27}{50}$, or 0.54. If I conduct the experiment again, this time tossing the coin 60 times, I can predict that heads will land about $60 \times 0.54 \doteq 32$ times.

Number Strategies

For 10% of $325.00, students could move the decimal point 1 place to the left to get $32.50. For 15% of $114.00, students could find 10% of $114.00, or $11.40, then divide $11.40 by 2 to find 5%; $5.70. Students then add to find 15%: $11.40 + $5.70 = $17.10. For 20% of $99.99, students could round $99.99 to $100.00, then divided by 5 to get $20.00. For 25% of $500.00, students could divide $500.00 by 4 to get $125.00.

Assignment Guidelines

If your students do not have time to complete all the *Practice* questions on pages 413 and 414, these questions provide minimum curriculum coverage: 2, 3, 6, 7, *Reflect*
To assess the 4 Achievement Chart categories listed in the curriculum document, have students complete these *Practice* questions:
Understanding Concepts: 2
Application: 6
Problem Solving: 7
Communication: *Reflect*

6. Copy and continue the table to show all months of the yea
Have each student write her or his month of birth on the
Find the number of students who were born in each mont

a) Complete the table.

Month	Tally	Frequency	Relative Frequency
January			
February			
March			

b) What is the relative frequency for birthdays in the same month as yours?

c) Find the sum of the relative frequencies. Explain why this sum makes sense.

Number Strategies

Find each percent.
- 10% of $325.00 $32.50
- 15% of $114.00 $17.10
- 20% of $99.99 $20.00
- 25% of $500.00 $125.00

7. Assessment Focus A regular octahedron has faces lab
1 to 8. Two of these octahedra are rolled.
The numbers on the faces the octahedra land on are adde
Work with a partner. Use the regular octahedra you made
Unit 3. Label the faces of each octahedron from 1 to 8.

Conduct an experiment to find the relative frequency of g
sum of 7 when two regular octahedra are rolled.

a) Report your results.

b) How are the results affected if you conduct the experir
10 times? 50 times? 100 times? Explain.

Reflect

Suppose you know the relative frequency of one outcome of an experiment.
How can you use that to predict the likelihood of that outcor
occurring if you conduct the experiment again?
Use an example to explain.

414 UNIT 11: Probability

ASSESSMENT FOR LEARNING

What to Look For

Understanding concepts
- ✔ Students understand how to find relative frequency.
- ✔ Students understand that the sum of the relative frequencies for an experiment is 1.

Applying procedures
- ✔ Students can conduct experiments and determine the relative frequency of outcomes.

Communicating
- ✔ Students can explain the relationship between relative frequency and experimental probability.

What to Do

Extra Support: Students who have difficulty finding relative frequency may benefit from first writing the fraction in words; for example, $\frac{\text{Number of heads}}{\text{Number of tosses}} = \frac{28}{50}$.
Students can use Step-by-Step 2 (Master 11.8) to complete question 7.

Extra Practice: Have students repeat the paper cup experiment in question 4, compare the results with their initial experiment, and explain any differences.
Students can complete Extra Practice 2 (Master 11.14).

Extension: Have students design an experiment of their choice and determine the relative frequency of the outcomes of the experiment.

Recording and Reporting
Master 11.2 Ongoing Observations: Probability

Mid-Unit Review

LESSON

11.1 **1.** Jenna plays a video game on her computer. Each time she plays, she can choose an easy, intermediate, or challenging level of difficulty. She can also choose 1 or 2 players. Use a tree diagram to show the possible game choices.

2. Use a tree diagram to show the possible lunch choices.

LUNCH SPECIAL
1 side dish • 1 main dish • 1 drink

SIDE DISH	MAIN DISH	DRINK
Egg roll	Sweet and sour chicken	Low-fat milk
Soup	Chop suey	Juice
Fried rice	Broccoli beef	Pop

11.2 **3.** Write each relative frequency as a decimal.

a) An air traffic controller's records show 512 planes landed one day. Seventeen planes were 727s. What is the relative frequency of a 727 landing? About 0.033

b) A cashier served 58 customers in one shift. Thirty-two customers paid cash. What is the relative frequency of a customer paying cash? About 0.552

c) Qam spun a pointer on a spinner 95 times. The pointer landed on purple 63 times. What is the relative frequency of landing on purple? About 0.663

4. You will need 4 cubes: 2 of one colour, 2 of another colour; and a bag. Place the cubes in the bag. Pick 2 cubes without looking. Design and conduct an experiment to find the relative frequency of choosing 2 matching cubes.

5. A number cube is labelled 1 to 6.

a) What are the possible outcomes when this cube is rolled? 1, 2, 3, 4, 5, 6

b) Are these outcomes equally likely? Explain.

c) Design and conduct an experiment to find the relative frequency of each outcome.

d) Do the results confirm your prediction in part b? Explain.

e) How does your answer to part d depend on the number of times you roll the number cube? Explain.

6. There are 3 blue counters and 3 green counters in a bag. You may add to the bag or remove from the bag, as listed below. You put:

a) 1 red counter in the bag

b) 1 more green counter in the bag

c) 2 blue counters in the bag

You then pick a counter without looking. Which of the actions above would make it more likely that you would pick a green counter? Explain. Action b

Mid-Unit Review 415

SECTION ORGANIZER

Student Materials

- cubes of 2 different colours
- rulers
- calculators

Assessment: Masters 11.1 Unit Rubric: Probability, 11.4 Unit Summary: Probability

Sample Solutions

1. Level — Number of Players — Outcomes

2.

Level	Number of Players	Outcomes
Easy	1	Easy, 1
	2	Easy, 2
Intermediate	1	Intermediate, 1
	2	Intermediate, 2
Challenging	1	Challenging, 1
	2	Challenging, 2

There is insufficient room to show a tree diagram.
Here is a description of it.
1st column: Side Dish – Egg Roll, Soup, Fried Rice
2nd column: adjacent to each side dish in the first column: Main Dish – Chicken, Chop Suey, Broccoli Beef
3rd column: adjacent to each main dish in the second column: Drink – Milk, Juice, Pop
For a list of outcomes, see the answers on page 489 of the Student Book or the CD-ROM.

3. a) $\frac{17}{512} \doteq 0.033$ **b)** $\frac{32}{58} \doteq 0.552$ **c)** $\frac{63}{95} \doteq 0.663$

(Solutions continue below.)

(Sample Solutions, continued)

4. Experiment: Place 2 green and 2 red number cubes in a bag. Pick two cubes without looking. Record the colour of each cube. Repeat this experiment 50 times. What is the relative frequency of picking 2 cubes with matching colours? For example,

$$\text{Relative frequency} = \frac{\text{Number of times matching cubes occurred}}{\text{Number of times experiment was conducted}}$$

$= \frac{19}{50}$

$= 0.38$

5. b) Yes. Each number appears only once on the cube. The probability of each outcome is $\frac{1}{6}$.

c) Roll the number cube. Record the number rolled. Repeat this experiment until you have 60 results. What is the relative frequency of rolling each number? For example,

Outcome	Frequency	Relative Frequency
1	12	0.200
2	9	0.150
3	8	0.133
4	11	0.183
5	9	0.150
6	11	0.183

d) Yes, although no relative frequency was $\frac{10}{60}$, or $\frac{1}{6}$, the relative frequencies are close to $\frac{1}{6}$, or about $0.1\dot{6}7$.

e) The more times the number cube is rolled, the closer the results are likely to be to the calculated probabilities.

6. Action b: If I put 1 more green counter in the bag, the probability of picking a green counter increases from $\frac{3}{6}$ to $\frac{4}{7}$.

a) One more red counter in the bag decreases the likelihood of picking a green counter. The probability decreases from $\frac{3}{6}$ to $\frac{3}{7}$.

c) Two more blue counters in the bag decreases the likelihood of picking a green counter. The probability decreases from $\frac{3}{6}$ to $\frac{3}{8}$.

SECTION 11.3

Theoretical Probability

SECTION ORGANIZER 80–100 min

Curriculum Focus: Explore and apply theoretical probability. (7m106, 7m108, 7m109)

Student Materials
- linking cubes
- paper bags
- spinners (Master 11.6b)
- coloured pencils

Optional
- 4-column charts (PM 19) (optional)
- Step-by-Step 3 (Master 11.9)
- Extra Practice 3 (Master 11.15)

Vocabulary: theoretical probability

Assessment: Master 11.2 Ongoing Observations: Probability

Key Math Learnings

1. When the outcomes of an experiment are equally likely, the probability of any outcome is the ratio of the number of favourable outcomes to the number of possible outcomes. This is called the theoretical probability.
2. The theoretical probability is found by analysing the possible outcomes.
3. The more times an experiment is conducted, the closer the experimental probability is to the theoretical probability.

11.3 Theoretical Probability

Focus Explore and apply theore

Explore

Work in a group.
A carnival game has a bucket of different-coloured balls.
Each player is asked to predict the colour of the ball he or she will select.
The player then selects a ball, without looking.
If the guess is correct, the player wins a prize.
After each draw, the ball is returned to the bucket.

Use linking cubes.
Put 4 red, 3 blue, 2 yellow, and 1 green cube in a bag.
Suppose you take 1 cube without looking.
Predict the probability that you will pick each colour.
Play the game 50 times.
What is the experimental probability for picking each colour?
How does each predicted probability compare with the experimental probability?

Reflect & Share

Combine your results with those of another group of students
How does each experimental probability compare with the predicted probability now?

Connect

Recall that when the outcomes of an experiment are equally li the probability of any outcome is:

$$\text{Probability} = \frac{\text{Number of favourable outcomes}}{\text{Number of possible outcomes}}$$

This is called the **theoretical probability**, but we usually say "probability."
You find the probability by analysing the possible outcomes ra than by experimenting.

416 UNIT 11: Probability

BEFORE Get Started

Prompt a short discussion about carnivals or fairs. Encourage students to name different games they might find at a carnival or fair.

Put several handfuls of different-coloured counters in a large plastic container. Ask a volunteer to predict the colour of counter he or she will pick. Have the student pick a counter, without looking. Was her or his prediction correct? Return the counter to the container. Repeat this procedure with other students.

Present *Explore*. Distribute linking cubes and paper bags to groups of students. Have students record their predictions before beginning the game. Encourage students to record their results in a table, such as:

Colour	Tally	Frequency	Relative Frequency

DURING Explore

Ongoing Assessment: Observe and Listen

As students work, ask questions, such as:

- What probability did you predict for each colour? (*Red:* $\frac{4}{10}$ *= 0.4; blue:* $\frac{3}{10}$ *= 0.3; yellow:* $\frac{2}{10}$ *= 0.2; and green:* $\frac{1}{10}$ *= 0.1*)
- Which colour did you pick the greatest number of times? (*Red*) The least number of times? (*Green*)
- How did you find the experimental probability for red? (*I divided the number of times red was picked by 50, the number of times the game was played:* $\frac{22}{50}$ *= 0.44*)

you pick an
without
g, the object is
at random.

Twenty counters were put in a bag:
7 green, 6 black, 5 orange, and 2 purple
You take one counter from the bag without looking.
There are 4 outcomes: green, black, orange, and purple
Suppose the favourable outcome is black.
Then, the probability of picking a black counter is: $\frac{6}{20} = 0.3$

Suppose the favourable outcome is green.
Then, the probability of picking a green counter is: $\frac{7}{20} = 0.35$

Note that the outcomes are not equally likely.

We can predict the possible number of times an outcome will occur by multiplying the probability by the number of repetitions.
Suppose we pick a counter at random 54 times.
Then, the predicted number of times a black counter is picked is:
$54 \times 0.3 = 16.2$
We would expect to pick a black counter about 16 times.
However, we may never pick a black counter, or we might always pick a black counter.

xample

Suppose you roll a number cube 100 times. Predict how many times:
a) a 1 will show **b)** a 5 will show
c) a 1 or a 5 will show **d)** a 1 or a 5 will not show
How are the answers to parts c and d related?

olution

When a number cube is rolled, there are six possible outcomes.
The outcomes are equally likely.

a) The probability of rolling a 1 is $\frac{1}{6}$.
So, the predicted number of times a 1 will show in 100 rolls is:
$\frac{1}{6} \times 100 = \frac{100}{6} \doteq 17$

b) The probability of rolling a 5 is also $\frac{1}{6}$.
So, the predicted number of times a 5 will show is also about 17.

11.3 Theoretical Probability **417**

REACHING ALL LEARNERS

Alternative Explore

Work with a partner. Remove 4 spades, 3 hearts, 2 clubs, and 1 diamond from a deck of cards. Shuffle the cards you removed, then spread them out face down on the desk. Suppose you select 1 card without looking. Predict the probability that you will pick each suit.
Play the game 50 times. What is the experimental probability for picking each suit?
How does each predicted probability compare with the experimental probability?

Early Finishers

Have students repeat the steps in *Explore* but this time use 5 red, 4 blue, 3 yellow, and 2 green cubes.
Determine the experimental probability for picking each colour when the game is played 50 times, 80 times, and 100 times.
How does each predicted probability and experimental probability compare the more times the game is repeated?

Common Misconceptions

➤ Students think that the theoretical probability is equal to the experimental probability.

How to Help: Remind students that experimental probability depends on the outcome of an experiment. The outcome may be different every time the experiment is conducted. The theoretical probability is calculated from the numbers of possible outcomes and is constant.

- What experimental probabilities did you find for the other colours? (*Blue: $\frac{14}{50}$ = 0.28; yellow: $\frac{9}{50}$ = 0.18; green: $\frac{5}{50}$ = 0.1*)
- What do you notice about the sum of the experimental probabilities? (*The sum is 1.*)
- How does each predicted probability compare with the experimental probability? (*The values are quite close.*)

AFTER Connect

Have students share their results with the class.

What you might see:

Colour	Tally	Frequency	Relative Frequency
Red	卌 卌 卌 卌 //	22	0.44
Blue	卌 卌 ////	14	0.28
Yellow	卌 ////	9	0.18
Green	卌	5	0.1

Possible combined results:

Colour	Tally	Frequency	Relative Frequency
Red	卌 卌 卌 卌 卌 卌 卌 卌 /	41	0.41
Blue	卌 卌 卌 卌 卌 ////	29	0.29
Yellow	卌 卌 卌 ////	19	0.19
Green	卌 卌 /	11	0.11

Ask:

- How do the experimental probabilities compare with the predicted probabilities after you combined results with another group of students? (*The experimental probabilities are closer to the predicted probabilities.*) Explain. (*Combining the results is the same as playing the game a greater number of times, 50 × 2 = 100.*)
- How can we use the probability of picking a green cube to predict how many times a green cube will be picked in 80 games? (*We can multiply the probability of picking green by the number of times the game is played: 0.1 × 80 = 8.*)

Number Strategies

Students could use equivalent fractions that have the same denominators, fraction strips, or number lines to add or subtract.

Sample Answers

3. a) False. It is not likely that you will get 10 heads, but it could happen in an experiment.
   b) False. The theoretical probability is 0.5, but the experimental probability could be different.
   c) True. For many tosses, the experimental probability is close to the theoretical probability.
4. a) True. The 3 sectors are congruent. The 3 outcomes are equally likely: $100 \div 3 \doteq 33$.
   b) False. In an experiment, equally likely outcomes may occur a different number of times.
   c) False. The pointer *may* land on *Lose* exactly 33 times but it may never land on *Lose*.
6. a) I found a common denominator of 12, then used the common denominator to write equivalent fractions.
   $\frac{1}{4} = \frac{3}{12}; \frac{1}{2} = \frac{6}{12}; \frac{1}{6} = \frac{2}{12}; \frac{1}{12}$
   I used the spinner that was divided into 12 congruent sectors. I looked at the numerators of the equivalent fractions, then coloured 3 sectors red, 6 sectors yellow, 2 sectors blue, and 1 sector green.

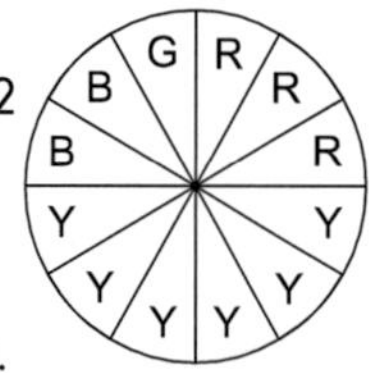

   b) To find how many times the pointer may land on each colour in 200 trials, I multiplied each probability by 200:
   Red: $\frac{1}{4} \times 200 = 50$ Yellow: $\frac{1}{2} \times 200 = 100$
   Blue: $\frac{1}{6} \times 200 \doteq 33$ Green: $\frac{1}{12} \times 200 \doteq 17$

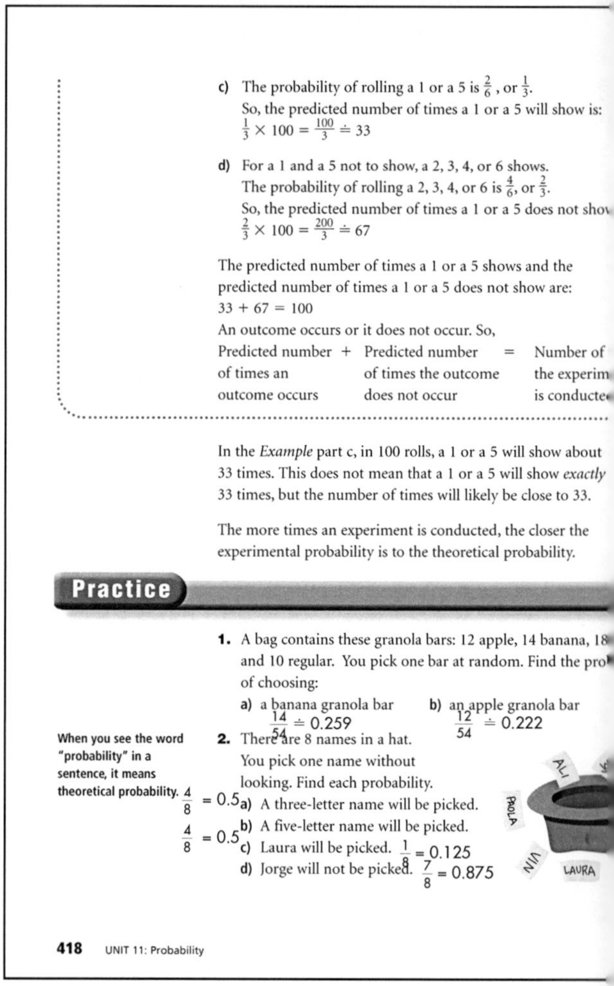
c) The probability of rolling a 1 or a 5 is $\frac{2}{6}$, or $\frac{1}{3}$.
So, the predicted number of times a 1 or a 5 will show is:
$\frac{1}{3} \times 100 = \frac{100}{3} \doteq 33$

d) For a 1 and a 5 not to show, a 2, 3, 4, or 6 shows.
The probability of rolling a 2, 3, 4, or 6 is $\frac{4}{6}$, or $\frac{2}{3}$.
So, the predicted number of times a 1 or a 5 does not show
$\frac{2}{3} \times 100 = \frac{200}{3} \doteq 67$

The predicted number of times a 1 or a 5 shows and the predicted number of times a 1 or a 5 does not show are:
$33 + 67 = 100$
An outcome occurs or it does not occur. So,
Predicted number of times an outcome occurs + Predicted number of times the outcome does not occur = Number of the experim is conducte

In the *Example* part c, in 100 rolls, a 1 or a 5 will show about 33 times. This does not mean that a 1 or a 5 will show *exactly* 33 times, but the number of times will likely be close to 33.

The more times an experiment is conducted, the closer the experimental probability is to the theoretical probability.

Practice

1. A bag contains these granola bars: 12 apple, 14 banana, 18 and 10 regular. You pick one bar at random. Find the pro of choosing:
   a) a banana granola bar $\frac{14}{54} \doteq 0.259$
   b) an apple granola bar $\frac{12}{54} \doteq 0.222$

When you see the word "probability" in a sentence, it means theoretical probability.

2. There are 8 names in a hat. You pick one name without looking. Find each probability.
   a) A three-letter name will be picked. $\frac{4}{8} = 0.5$
   b) A five-letter name will be picked. $\frac{4}{8} = 0.5$
   c) Laura will be picked. $\frac{1}{8} = 0.125$
   d) Jorge will not be picked. $\frac{7}{8} = 0.875$

418 UNIT 11: Probability

- Does this mean that in 80 games, 8 green cubes will be picked? Explain. (*No; we would expect to pick a green cube about 8 times, but we might pick 15 green cubes or no green cubes. In an experiment, no outcome is certain.*)
- Why do we say that a cube should be picked without looking? (*So that the probability of picking a cube is not influenced by outside factors*)

Introduce the term **theoretical probability.** Use the explanation and *Example* in *Connect* as further illustrations of this concept.

Practice

Question 6 requires students to construct a spinner. Students can use a blank spinner from *Spinners* (Master 11.6b), a protractor, and pencil crayons; or students can choose a spinner that has already been divided into the necessary number of equal sectors, and colour as required.

Assessment Focus: Question 6

Students have to recognize that the probabilities dictate how many of each sector should be each colour. Most students will use 12 sectors; some students may use 24 or 36. Students may alternate colours or draw the spinner with sectors the same colour together. For part c, different answers are possible. The yellow sector is smaller; it may affect only one other colour or all other colours. For example, the probability of landing on red may change to $\frac{1}{2}$, then the probabilities of landing on blue and green remain the same.

3. Is each statement true or false? Explain.
   a) If you toss a coin 10 times, you will never get 10 heads. False
   b) If you toss a coin 10 times, you will always get exactly 5 heads. False
   c) If you toss a coin many times, the number of heads should be approximately $\frac{1}{2}$ the number of tosses. True

4. The pointer on this spinner is spun 100 times.
   Is each statement true or false? Justify your answer.
   a) The pointer will land on *Win* about 33 times. True
   b) The pointer will land on *Win*, *Lose*, and *Tie* an equal number of times. False
   c) The pointer will land on *Lose* exactly 33 times. False

5. Two hundred fifty tickets for a draw were sold.
   The first ticket drawn wins the prize.
   a) Joe purchased 1 ticket. What is the probability Joe will win? $\frac{1}{250} = 0.004$
   b) Maria purchased 10 tickets.
   What is the probability Maria will win? $\frac{10}{250} = 0.04$
   c) Ivan purchased 25 tickets.
   What is the probability Ivan will *not* win? $\frac{250 - 25}{250} = \frac{225}{250} = 0.9$

6. **Assessment Focus**
   a) Construct a spinner with red, yellow, blue, and green sectors, so the following probabilities are true.
      - The probability of landing on red is $\frac{1}{4}$.
      - The probability of landing on yellow is $\frac{1}{2}$.
      - The probability of landing on blue is $\frac{1}{6}$.
      - The probability of landing on green is $\frac{1}{12}$.

   Explain how you drew your spinner.
   b) In 200 trials, about how many times would the pointer land on each colour?
   c) Suppose the spinner had been constructed so the probability of landing on yellow was $\frac{1}{4}$.
   What effect would this have on the probability of landing on each other colour? Explain.

Reflect

How are theoretical probability and experimental probability similar? Different?
Use an example to explain.

11.3 Theoretical Probability 419

c) If the probability of landing on yellow was $\frac{1}{4}$, the probability of landing on at least one other colour would increase because the sum of the probabilities is always 1.

REFLECT: Theoretical probability and experimental probability are similar in that both of them predict the likelihood of an outcome. Experimental probability is based on results from experiments. The outcomes do not have to be equally likely. Theoretical probability (or probability) is based on analysing possible outcomes that are equally likely without experimenting. The theoretical probability and experimental probabilities may not be equal. The more an experiment is performed, the closer the experimental probability is to the theoretical probability. For example, if a coin is tossed 50 times and lands heads 19 times, the experimental probability of landing heads is $\frac{19}{50}$. The theoretical probability of landing heads in 50 tosses is 0.5, or $\frac{25}{50}$ because landing heads and landing tails are equally likely.

Assignment Guidelines

If your students do not have time to complete all the *Practice* questions on pages 418 and 419, these questions provide minimum curriculum coverage: 2, 3, 5, 6, *Reflect*
To assess the 4 Achievement Chart categories listed in the curriculum document, have students complete these *Practice* questions:
Understanding Concepts: 2
Application: 5
Problem Solving: 6
Communication: *Reflect*

ASSESSMENT FOR LEARNING

What to Look For	What to Do
Understanding concepts ✔ Students understand that theoretical probability is found by analysing the possible outcomes. ✔ Students understand that the more times an experiment is conducted, the closer the experimental probability is to the theoretical probability. ***Applying procedures*** ✔ Students can solve problems involving theoretical probability. ***Communicating*** ✔ Students can explain the difference between theoretical and experimental probability.	***Extra Support:*** Students who are having difficulty determining theoretical probability may benefit from making a list of all possible outcomes first. Have students count the number of possible outcomes, then write this number in the denominator. Students make a list of the favourable outcomes. Students count the number of favourable outcomes and write this number in the numerator. Students can use Step-by-Step 3 (Master 11.9) to complete question 6. ***Extra Practice:*** Have students write problems similar to *Practice* question 1, then solve their problems. Students can complete Extra Practice 3 (Master 10.15). ***Extension:*** Have students determine the probability of rolling an even number and obtaining a tail when a number cube labelled 1 to 6 is rolled and a coin is tossed.

Recording and Reporting
Master 11.2 Ongoing Observations: Probability

Applications of Probability

SECTION ORGANIZER — 80–100 min

Curriculum Focus: Solve probability problems. (7m106, 7m107, 7m108, 7m109)

Student Materials
- blank cards (4 per pair of students)
- paper bags
- calculators

Optional
- Step-by-Step 4 (Master 11.10)
- Extra Practice 4 (Master 11.16)

Vocabulary: chance, certain, impossible

Assessment: Master 11.2 Ongoing Observations: Probability

11.4 Applications of Probability

Focus Solve probability problems

Explore

Work with a partner.
You will play the *Sum and Product* game.
You will need 4 blank cards and a bag.
Write the numbers from 1 to 4 on the cards.
Place the cards in the bag.
Each person picks a card.
Both of you find the sum and the product of the two numbers
One of you is Player A, the other is Player B.
If the sum is less than or equal to the product, Player A gets a
If the sum is greater than the product, Player B gets a point.

- ➢ Who is likely to win? Explain your reasoning.
- ➢ Play the game several times; you choose how many times. Who won?
- ➢ How does your prediction of the winner compare with your result?

Reflect & Share

Compare your results with those of another pair of classmates
Work together to come up with an explanation of who is mor
to win.

Connect

- ➢ Probability can be expressed as a fraction, a decimal, or a
When probability is expressed as a percent, we use the wo
"chance."
For example, the weather forecast is a 40% chance of rain
This means that the probability of rain is: $\frac{40}{100} = 0.4$
- ➢ When an outcome is certain, the probability of it occurrir
For example, when we toss a coin, the probability of it lan
heads or tails is 1.
When an outcome is impossible, the probability of it occu
0. For example, when we roll a number cube labelled 1 to
probability of a 7 showing is 0.

420 UNIT 11: Probability

Key Math Learnings

1. When probability is expressed as a percent, the word "chance" is used.
2. The probability of an impossible outcome is 0. The probability of an outcome that is certain is 1.

BEFORE — Get Started

Review the meaning of: sum, product, less than or equal to, and greater than.

Ask questions, such as:

- When you find a sum, which operation is involved? (*Addition*)
- What is the sum of 15 and 10? (*25*)
- When you find a product, which operation is involved? (*Multiplication*)
- What is the product of 15 and 10? (*150*)
- Which of the numbers 7, 12, 5, 2, and 4 are less than or equal to 5? (*5, 2, 4*)
- Which of the numbers 3, 8, 10, 4, and 7 are greater than 7? (*8, 10*)

Present *Explore*. Distribute blank cards and paper bags to pairs of students.

DURING — Explore

Ongoing Assessment: Observe and Listen

As students work, ask questions, such as:

- Who do you think is likely to win? Explain. (*Player A because multiplication often results in a greater answer; for example, 10 + 2 = 12 and 10 × 2 = 20.*)
- Who won most of your games? (*Player A won 6 games and Player B won 5 games.*)
- Is this what you predicted? (*No, I thought Player A would win by a much greater amount.*)
- What results did other pairs of classmates get? (*In most pairs, Player A won about the same number of times as Player B.*)

xample

Flick This is an Ultimate Frisbee team.
The team plays 3 games against 3 other teams.
All 4 teams have equal chances of winning.

a) What is the chance that Flick This will win all three of its games?
b) What is the chance that Flick This will win exactly one game?
c) What is the chance that Flick This will win at least two games?

olution

For any game, the possible outcomes are win (W) or lose (L). These outcomes are equally likely. Draw a tree diagram to list the possible results of 3 games for Flick This.

1st Game	2nd Game	3rd Game	Outcomes
W	W	W	WWW
		L	WWL
	L	W	WLW
		L	WLL
L	W	W	LWW
		L	LWL
	L	W	LLW
		L	LLL

There are 8 possible outcomes.

a) There is 1 outcome in which Flick This wins all three games: WWW
So, the probability of 3 wins is: $\frac{1}{8} = 0.125$
So, the chance of winning 3 games is 12.5%.

e word "exactly" is uded because inning one game" ght be interpreted winning one or re games.

b) There are 3 outcomes in which Flick This wins exactly one game: WLL, LWL, LLW
So, the probability of winning exactly 1 game is: $\frac{3}{8} = 0.375$
So, the chance of winning exactly 1 game is 37.5%.

c) There are 4 outcomes in which Flick This wins at least two games: WWW, WWL, WLW, LWW
So, the probability of winning at least 2 games is: $\frac{4}{8} = \frac{1}{2} = 0.5$
So, the chance of winning at least 2 games is 50%.

REACHING ALL LEARNERS

Alternative Explore

Work with a partner. You will play the *Product Game*.
You will need two number cubes, labelled 1 to 6.
Each person rolls one number cube. Both of you find the product of the two numbers. One of you is Player A, the other is Player B. If the product is less than or equal to 10, player A gets a point. If the product is greater than 10, Player B gets a point. Who is likely to win? Explain your reasoning.
Play the game several times; you choose how many times. Who won? How does your prediction of the winner compare with your result?
(*There are 19 outcomes in favour of Player A. There are 17 outcomes in favour of Player B. Player A is more likely to win.*)

Early Finishers

Have students repeat the steps of *Explore*, this time adding a fifth card, the number 5, to the bag. Compare the results to the results of four cards. How are they similar or different?

Common Misconceptions

➤ Students assume that the sum of two numbers will usually be less than their product.

How to Help: Have students make addition tables and multiplication tables for different sets of 4 numbers. When the numbers do not include 1, the product is always greater than or equal to the sum. Two numbers that include 1 have a sum greater than the product.

AFTER Connect

Have volunteers share their results with the class.

Ask:

- How can you use probability to decide who is most likely to win? (*I can draw a tree diagram to list all possible combinations of numbers, then find the sum and product of the numbers in each pair. I then find whether the sum or product is greater.*)

What you might see:

Card 1	Card 2	Outcome	Sum	Product
1	2	1, 2	3	2
	3	1, 3	4	3
	4	1, 4	5	4
2	1	2, 1	3	2
	3	2, 3	5	6
	4	2, 4	6	8
3	1	3, 1	4	3
	2	3, 2	5	6
	4	3, 4	7	12
4	1	4, 1	5	4
	2	4, 2	6	8
	3	4, 3	7	12

- What other ways could you find the probability of each outcome? (*I made a multiplication table for 1 to 4, and an addition table for 1 to 4, then compared corresponding terms in the two tables.*)
- How many pairs of cards have a sum less than or equal to the product? (*6: 2 and 3, 2 and 4, 3 and 2, 3 and 4, 4 and 2, 4 and 3*)
- How many pairs of cards have a sum greater than the product? (*6: 1 and 2, 1 and 3, 1 and 4, 2 and 1, 3 and 1, 4 and 1*)
- Who is more likely to win? (*Since both outcomes occur 6 times, each of Player A and Player B is likely to win 50%, or $\frac{1}{2}$ of the time.*)

Work through the example in *Connect*. Have volunteers list examples of probability that they have read or heard about in the media. (*For example, the chance of winning the lottery, the chance of the Blue Jays winning the World Series, the chance of living to 100*)

Sample Answers

1. d) The answers are the same. If all the winners are female, none of the winners can be male.
3. b) The words "at least" mean that both 2 tails, and 3 tails are included. If the words were left out, the phrase may be interpreted as exactly 2 tails. The chance would then be 37.5% instead of 50%.
   c) The word "exactly" means there can be no more than 2 heads; that is, the outcome 3 heads is not included. If this word was left out, the phrase may be interpreted as including 3 heads. The chance would then increase to 50% from 37.5%.
4. The game with the least chance of winning often has the greatest prize because people are least likely to win. The carnival owners can afford to be generous with the prize because it will rarely be given away.
6. **Sandwich** **Vegetable** **Dessert**

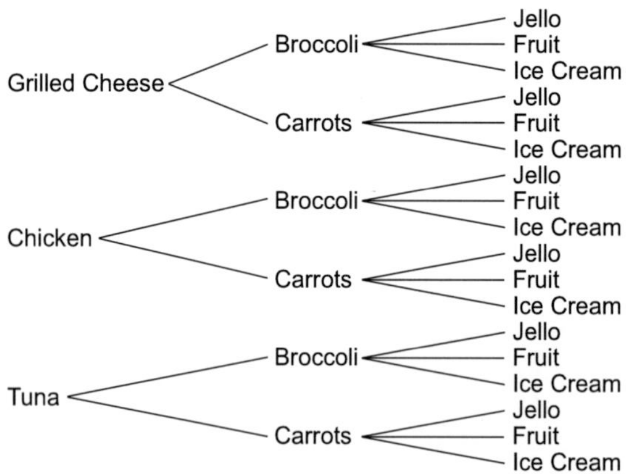

(Answers continue below right.)

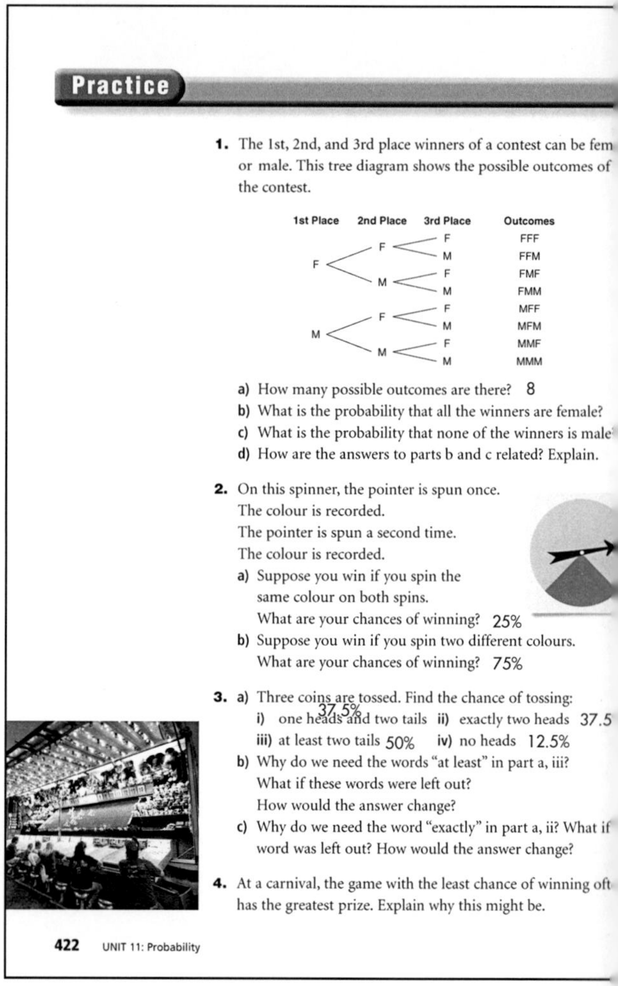
Practice

1. The 1st, 2nd, and 3rd place winners of a contest can be fem or male. This tree diagram shows the possible outcomes of the contest.

1st Place	2nd Place	3rd Place	Outcomes
F	F	F	FFF
		M	FFM
	M	F	FMF
		M	FMM
M	F	F	MFF
		M	MFM
	M	F	MMF
		M	MMM

a) How many possible outcomes are there? 8
b) What is the probability that all the winners are female?
c) What is the probability that none of the winners is male
d) How are the answers to parts b and c related? Explain.

2. On this spinner, the pointer is spun once. The colour is recorded. The pointer is spun a second time. The colour is recorded.
a) Suppose you win if you spin the same colour on both spins. What are your chances of winning? 25%
b) Suppose you win if you spin two different colours. What are your chances of winning? 75%

3. a) Three coins are tossed. Find the chance of tossing:
i) one heads and two tails 37.5% ii) exactly two heads 37.5
iii) at least two tails 50% iv) no heads 12.5%
b) Why do we need the words "at least" in part a, iii? What if these words were left out? How would the answer change?
c) Why do we need the word "exactly" in part a, ii? What if word was left out? How would the answer change?

4. At a carnival, the game with the least chance of winning oft has the greatest prize. Explain why this might be.

422 UNIT 11: Probability

Practice

Encourage students to draw a tree diagram for questions 3, 5, 6, and 7.

Assessment Focus: Question 6

Students may draw a tree diagram to show all sandwich/vegetable combinations. Students find that the outcomes are equally likely. Students add a third column to the tree diagram to show all sandwich/vegetable/dessert combinations. Students find that the outcomes are equally likely, but since there are many more outcomes, the probabilities of possible combinations decrease.

(Sample Answers, continued)

a) There are 6 possible combinations of sandwich and vegetable. Each combination occurs once. So, the probability of each combination is $\frac{1}{6}$.
b) There are 18 possible combinations of sandwich, vegetable, and dessert. Each combination occurs once. So, the probability of each combination is $\frac{1}{18}$. The probabilities of possible combinations decrease when dessert is added.

7. There are 12 outcomes for spinning the pointer on each spinner once: Pink-pink, pink-purple, pink-yellow, yellow-pink, yellow-purple, yellow-yellow, purple-pink, purple-purple, purple-yellow, pink-pink, pink-purple, pink-yellow. The probability of getting pink and yellow is: $\frac{3}{12}$, or a 25% chance.
There are 16 outcomes for spinning the pointer on Spinner A twice: Pink-pink, pink-yellow, pink-purple, pink-pink, yellow-pink, yellow-yellow, yellow-purple, yellow-pink, purple-pink, purple-yellow, purple-purple, purple-pink, pink-pink, pink-yellow, pink-purple, pink-pink. The probability of getting pink and yellow is: $\frac{4}{16}$, or a 25% chance.

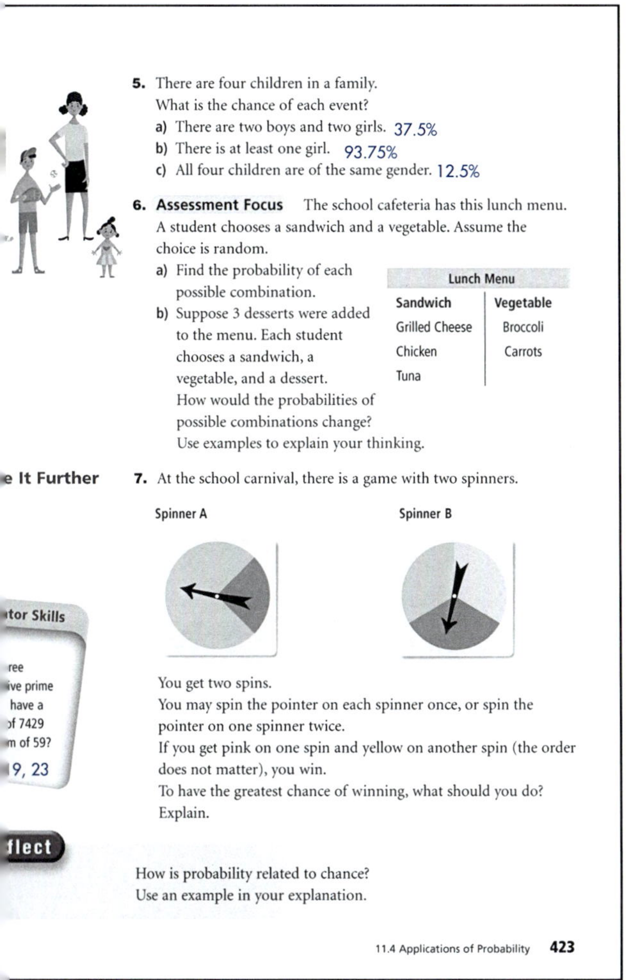

5. There are four children in a family.
What is the chance of each event?
a) There are two boys and two girls. 37.5%
b) There is at least one girl. 93.75%
c) All four children are of the same gender. 12.5%

6. **Assessment Focus** The school cafeteria has this lunch menu.
A student chooses a sandwich and a vegetable. Assume the choice is random.
a) Find the probability of each possible combination.
b) Suppose 3 desserts were added to the menu. Each student chooses a sandwich, a vegetable, and a dessert.
How would the probabilities of possible combinations change?
Use examples to explain your thinking.

Lunch Menu

Sandwich	Vegetable
Grilled Cheese	Broccoli
Chicken	Carrots
Tuna	

e It Further

7. At the school carnival, there is a game with two spinners.

Spinner A

Spinner B

You get two spins.
You may spin the pointer on each spinner once, or spin the pointer on one spinner twice.
If you get pink on one spin and yellow on another spin (the order does not matter), you win.
To have the greatest chance of winning, what should you do?
Explain.

tor Skills

ree
ive prime
have a
of 7429
m of 59?
9, 23

flect

How is probability related to chance?
Use an example in your explanation.

11.4 Applications of Probability 423

There are 9 outcomes for spinning the pointer on Spinner B twice: Pink-pink, pink-purple, pink-yellow, purple-pink, purple-purple, purple-yellow, yellow-pink, yellow-purple, yellow-yellow. The probability of getting pink and yellow is: $\frac{2}{9}$, or about a 22% chance.
The greatest chance of winning is either to spin each pointer once or to spin the pointer on Spinner A twice. The least chance of winning is to spin the pointer on Spinner B twice.

REFLECT: The word "chance" is used when probability is expressed as a percent. For example, the probability of tossing a coin and getting heads is $\frac{1}{2}$, or 0.5.
To get a percent: $0.5 = \frac{50}{100} = 50\%$
The chance of getting heads when tossing a coin is 50%.

Calculator Skills

Students should recall that a prime number is a whole number with exactly 2 factors, itself and 1. Students could list consecutive prime numbers less than 30: 2, 3, 5, 7, 11, 13, 17, 19, 23, 29. Students then add 3 consecutive numbers until they get a sum of 59, and a product of 7429.

Assignment Guidelines

If your students do not have time to complete all the *Practice* questions on pages 422 and 423, these questions provide minimum curriculum coverage: 1, 2, 5, 6, *Reflect*
To assess the 4 Achievement Chart categories, have students complete these *Practice* questions:

Understanding Concepts: 1	Problem Solving: 2
Application: 5	Communication: *Reflect*

ASSESSMENT FOR LEARNING

What to Look For	What to Do
Understanding concepts ✔ Students understand that the probability of a certain event is 1, and the probability of an impossible event is 0. ***Applying procedures*** ✔ Students can use tree diagrams to solve problems involving chance. ***Communicating*** ✔ Students can explain how probability is related to chance.	***Extra Support:*** Have students identify situations that are certain, and situations that are impossible. Students can use Step-by-Step 4 (Master 11.10) to complete question 6. ***Extra Practice:*** Students can play the Additional Activity *Spinner Construction* (Masters 11.6a and 11.6b). Students can complete Extra Practice 4 (Master 11.16). ***Extension:*** Students write a question related to chance and solve it. Students write their questions on the board for others to solve.

Recording and Reporting
Master 11.2 Ongoing Observations: Probability

Choosing a Strategy

SECTION ORGANIZER

Student Materials
- calculators
- play money (optional)
- square dot paper (PM 22)
- octahedron labelled +1 to +8
- number cube labelled +1 to +6

Assessment: Master 11.2 Ongoing Observations: Probability

Choosing a Strategy

Strategies
- Make a table.
- Use a model.
- Draw a diagram.
- Solve a simpler problem.
- Work backward.
- Guess and check.
- Make an organized list.
- Use a pattern.
- Draw a graph.
- Use logical reasoning.

1. For her birthday, Janine was given a row of 25 pennies. Her father replaced every second coin with a nickel. Her mother replaced every third coin with a dime. Her brother replaced every fourth coin with a quarter. Her uncle replaced every fifth coin with a loonie. How much did Janine get on her birthday? $6.97
2. Arif has a part-time job. He was offered $96 per week or $4.50/h. Which is the better deal? Explain.
3. a) The perimeter of a rectangle is 36 cm. What is the maximum possible area of the rectangle? 81 cm²
   b) The sum of the length, width, and height of a rectangular prism is 18 cm. What is the maximum possible volume of the prism? 216 cm³
4. What fraction of this figure is shaded?

$\frac{1}{64}$

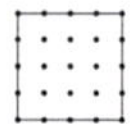

5. Divide the square at the left into four congruent figures. Record each way you find on dot paper. Find at least ten different ways to do this.
6. Running shoes cost $79.99. They are on sale for 20% off. The sales tax of 15% has to be added. Which would you choose? Explain. a and b are the same; the final price is $73.59
   a) Take the 20% off the price, then add the 15% sales tax.
   b) Add the 15% sales tax, then take off the 20%.
7. The Magic Money Box doubles any amount of money placed in it, then adds $1 to it. Yesterday I placed a sum of money in the box and got a new amount. Today I put the new amount in the box and got $75 out. How much did I put in the box yesterday? $18

424 UNIT 11: Probability

Sample Solutions

1. Draw a diagram. Follow the instructions in the book.

P P P P P P P P P P P P P P P P P P P P P P P P P
P N P N P N P N P N P N P N P N P N P N P N P N P
P N D N P D P N D N P D P N D N P D P N D N P D P
P N D Q P D P Q D N P Q P N D Q P D P Q D N P Q P
P N D Q L D P Q D L P Q P N L Q P D P L D N P Q L

Count the numbers of coins and their values.
7 pennies, 3 nickels, 5 dimes, 5 quarters, 5 loonies
Total value is $0.07 + $0.15 + $0.50 + $1.25 + $5.00 = $6.97

2. Divide $96.00 by $4.50 to find how many hours Arif would have to work to earn about the same money both ways.
$96.00 ÷ $4.50 = 21.3
If Arif works more than 21 h, then he should opt for $4.50/h because 22 × $4.50 = $99.
If Arif works 21 h or less, he should opt for $96 per week, because 21 × $4.50 = $94.50.

3. a) The perimeter is 36 cm, so the length + width = 18 cm. Make a table to show each possible value of length and width. Use lengths and widths in whole numbers of centimetres. Find the area for each length and width.

Length (cm)	Width (cm)	Area (cm²)
17	1	17
16	2	32
15	3	45
14	4	56
13	5	65
12	6	72
11	7	77
10	8	80
9	9	81

The greatest possible area is 81 cm², when the rectangle is a square with side length 9 cm.

b) I know that the greatest volume is when the rectangular prism is closest to a cube. So, I chose values of length, width, and height that were closest. I found three numbers whose sum is 18.

Length (cm)	Width (cm)	Height (cm)	Volume (cm³)
6	6	6	216
7	5	6	210
8	4	6	192
8	5	6	200

I checked measurements that were close to a cube to make sure the cube had the greatest volume. The maximum possible volume is 216 cm³.

Reading and Writing in Math

8. Play this game with a partner.
Each of you needs an octahedron and a cube like these:
The faces of a red octahedron are labelled from +1 to +8.
The faces of a white cube are labelled from +1 to +6.
Take turns to roll the two solids.
Subtract the red number from the white number.
The person with the lesser number scores a point.
The first person to reach 20 points is the winner.

9. On your first birthday, you have 1 candle on your cake.
On your second birthday, you have 2 candles on your cake, and so on, every year.
How many candles will be needed to celebrate your first 16 birthdays? 136

10. A radio station plays an average of 16 songs every hour.
One-half the songs are pop, one-quarter are jazz, one-eighth are country, and the rest are classical.
One show is 3 h long. The songs are played at random.
a) How many classical songs would be played? 6
b) What is the probability that the first song played is jazz? 0.25

11. An octahedron has eight faces labelled 1 to 8.
A cube has six faces labelled 1 to 6.

a) Both solids are rolled. What is the probability that the sum of the numbers is 8? 0.125
b) Both solids are rolled. What is the probability that the sum of the numbers is a prime number? about 0.396

Question Number	Possible Strategy
1	Use a model; draw a diagram
2	Use logical reasoning
3	Make a table; use a pattern
4	Use logical reasoning
5	Guess and check
6	Use logical reasoning
7	Work backward
9	Solve a simpler problem; use a pattern
10	Use logical reasoning; draw a diagram
11	Use logical reasoning

5.

9. I wrote the sum of all the candles on two lines:

1	+ 2	+ 3	+ 4	+ 5	+ 6	+ 7	+ 8
+ 16	+ 15	+ 14	+ 13	+ 12	+ 11	+ 10	+ 9
17	17	17	17	17	17	17	17

There are 8 pairs of numbers. The sum of the numbers in each pair is 17.
So, the total number of candles is $8 \times 17 = 136$.

10. a) 6 songs in 1 h
One-half of 16 = 8 — So, 8 pop songs
One-quarter of 16 = 4 — So, 4 jazz songs
One-eighth of 16 = 2 — So, 2 country songs
Total songs above: 8 + 4 + 2 = 14
The number of classical songs played in 1 h is 16 − 14 = 2
So, in 3 h, 6 classical songs will be played.

b) Since one-quarter of the songs are jazz, and assuming the songs are chosen at random, the probability that the first song played is jazz is $\frac{1}{4}$, or 0.25.

Empty the Rectangles

SECTION ORGANIZER

Student Materials

- 2 number cubes labelled 1 to 6
- counters (6 per students)

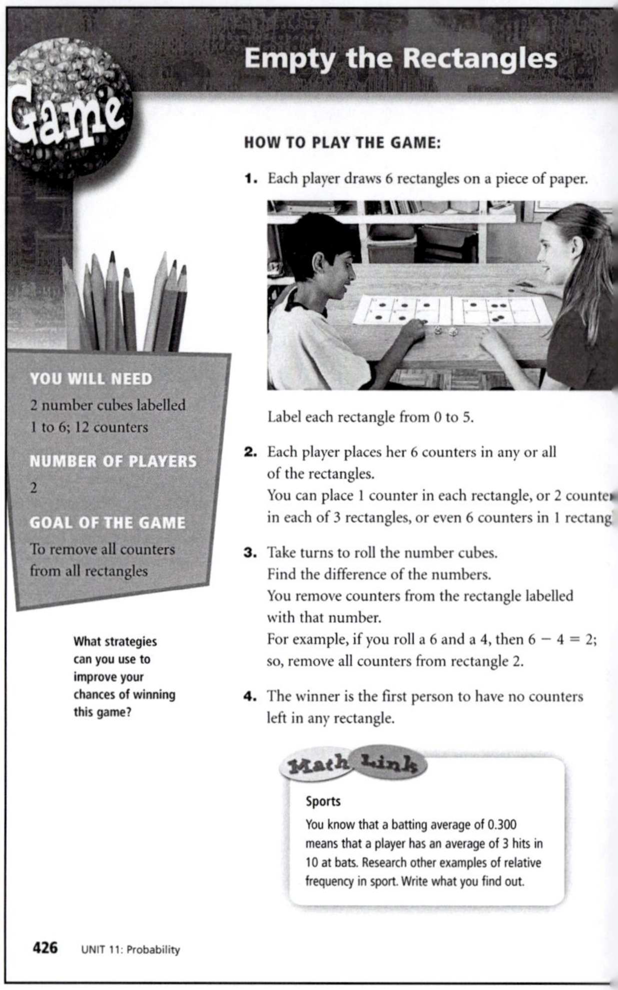

Empty the Rectangles

HOW TO PLAY THE GAME:

1. Each player draws 6 rectangles on a piece of paper.

Label each rectangle from 0 to 5.

2. Each player places her 6 counters in any or all of the rectangles.
You can place 1 counter in each rectangle, or 2 counters in each of 3 rectangles, or even 6 counters in 1 rectangle.
3. Take turns to roll the number cubes.
Find the difference of the numbers.
You remove counters from the rectangle labelled with that number.
For example, if you roll a 6 and a 4, then 6 − 4 = 2; so, remove all counters from rectangle 2.
4. The winner is the first person to have no counters left in any rectangle.

YOU WILL NEED
2 number cubes labelled 1 to 6; 12 counters

NUMBER OF PLAYERS
2

GOAL OF THE GAME
To remove all counters from all rectangles

What strategies can you use to improve your chances of winning this game?

Math Link

Sports
You know that a batting average of 0.300 means that a player has an average of 3 hits in 10 at bats. Research other examples of relative frequency in sport. Write what you find out.

426 UNIT 11: Probability

Take It Further

Suppose you created a similar game using the sum of the number cubes. How many rectangles would you draw? Which numbers would you use to label the rectangles? Which rectangle would have the greatest chance of emptying first? The least chance of emptying first?

Invite a volunteer to read the game rules. Ensure students understand the rules.

Sample Solution

The number cubes are labelled 1 to 6.
This chart shows the differences of all possible combinations of numbers rolled.
The difference 0 occurs 6 times, the difference 1 occurs 10 times; the difference 2 occurs 8 times; the difference 3 occurs 6 times; the difference 4 occurs 4 times, and the difference 5 occurs 2 times.

Difference	1	2	3	4	5	6
1	0	1	2	3	4	5
2	1	0	1	2	3	4
3	2	1	0	1	2	3
4	3	2	1	0	1	2
5	4	3	2	1	0	1
6	5	4	3	2	1	0

The probability of getting a difference of:

- 0 is $\frac{6}{36} \doteq 0.167$, or about a 17% chance
- 1 is $\frac{10}{36} \doteq 0.278$, or about a 28% chance
- 2 is $\frac{8}{36} \doteq 0.222$, or about a 22% chance
- 3 is $\frac{6}{36} \doteq 0.167$, or about a 17% chance
- 4 is $\frac{4}{36} \doteq 0.111$, or about an 11% chance
- 5 is $\frac{2}{36} \doteq 0.056$, or about a 6% chance

Getting a difference of 1 has the greatest probability or chance. Therefore, all the counters should be placed in rectangle 1 to have the greatest chance of winning the game.

Unit Review

Review any lesson with etext online tutorial

What Do I Need to Know?

✓ Relative frequency = $\frac{\text{Number of times an outcome occurs}}{\text{Number of times experiment is conducted}}$

✓ Theoretical probability = $\frac{\text{Number of favourable outcomes}}{\text{Number of possible outcomes}}$

What Should I Be Able to Do?

For extra practice, go to page 448.

LESSON

11.1 **1.** a) Use a tree diagram to show the possible combinations for a breakfast. You can choose:
- a banana, an orange, or an apple
- carrots, celery, or cucumber, and
- yogurt or cheese

b) How many outcomes have a banana and cheese? 3

c) How many outcomes have an orange, celery, or a yogurt? 14

d) How many outcomes do not have an apple? 12

2. Four coins are tossed.

a) List all the possible outcomes.

b) How many outcomes have exactly 1 head? 4

c) How many outcomes have exactly 2 tails? 6

d) How many outcomes have at least 3 tails? 5

11.2 **3.** A biologist tested a new vaccine. She found that in 500 trials, the test was successful 450 times.

a) What is the relative frequency that the vaccine is successful? $\frac{450}{500}$, or 0.9

b) Suppose the vaccine is used on 15 000 people. How many successes can be expected? 13 500

4. The owner of a shop recorded customer sales for one week.

Gender	Purchase	No Purchase	Total
Male	125	65	190
Female	154	46	200

Determine the relative frequency of each outcome.

a) A customer is male.

b) A customer is female.

c) A customer makes a purchase.

d) A male does not make a purchase.

e) A female makes a purchase.

Unit Review **427**

SECTION ORGANIZER

Student Materials
- calculators

Assessment: Masters 11.1 Unit Rubric: Probability, 11.4 Unit Summary: Probability

Sample Solutions

1. a)

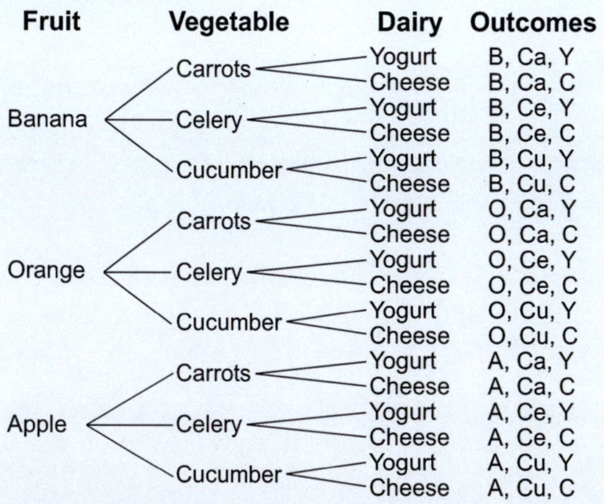

2. a) HHHH, HHHT, HHTH, HHTT, HTHH, HTHT, HTTH, HTTT, THHH, THHT, THTH, THTT, TTHH, TTHT, TTTH, TTTT

3. b) $0.9 \times 15\,000 = 13\,500$

4. a) $\frac{190}{390}$, or about 0.487 **b)** $\frac{200}{390}$, or about 0.513

c) $\frac{125 + 154}{390} = \frac{279}{390}$, or about 0.715 **d)** $\frac{65}{190}$, or about 0.342

e) $\frac{154}{200}$, or 0.77

5. a) False. It may show tails 100 times in an experiment, but it is unlikely.

b) True. In 100 tosses it is more likely to show some tails and some heads.

c) False. The theoretical probability is 0.5, but the experimental probability could be different.

d) True. The theoretical probability is $\frac{1}{2}$. For many tosses, the experimental probability is usually close to the theoretical probability.

6. a) The sectors are congruent and each money amount appears once.

7. a) 10 numbers are odd.

b) 5 numbers are multiples of 4: 4, 8, 12, 16, 20

c) 16 numbers are not perfect squares: 2, 3, 5, 6, 7, 8, 10, 11, 12, 13, 14, 15, 17, 18, 19, 20

d) 8 numbers are prime numbers: 2, 3, 5, 7, 11, 13, 17, 19

8. a) $\frac{1}{15} \times 99 \doteq 7$

b) $\frac{5}{15} \times 99 \doteq 33$

c) $\frac{9}{15} \times 99 \doteq 59$

d) $\frac{7}{15} \times 99 \doteq 46$

9. a) Possible outcomes are: HH, HT, TH, TT
   i) $\frac{1}{4}$, or 25% ii) 0%
   b) Possible outcomes are: HHH, HHT, HTH, HTT, THH, THT, TTH, TTT
   i) $\frac{3}{8}$, or 37.5% ii) $\frac{7}{8}$, or 87.5%

10. Possible outcomes are: RR, RY, RG, YR, YY, YG, GR, GY, GG
The chance of two consecutive colours being the same is: $\frac{3}{9}$, or about 33%

Correlation of Extra Practice questions on page 448:

Section	Questions
11.1	1
11.2	2
11.3	3
11.4	4, 5

LESSON

5. Is each statement true or false? Explain.
   a) When a coin is tossed 100 times, it will never show tails 100 times.
   b) When a coin is tossed 100 times, it is unlikely to show heads 100 times.
   c) When a coin is tossed 100 times, it will show tails exactly 50 times.
   d) The more often a coin is tossed, the more likely that $\frac{1}{2}$ the results will be tails.

11.3 6. In a game show, each contestant spins the wheel once to win the money shown.

   a) Are the probabilities of winning the amounts equally likely? Explain. Yes
   b) What is the probability of winning $100? $\frac{1}{10}$, or 0.1
   c) What is the probability of winning less than $50? $\frac{4}{10}$, or 0.4
   d) What is the probability of winning from $30 to $70? $\frac{5}{10}$, or 0.5

7. Twenty cards are numbered from 1 to 20. The cards are shuffled. A card is drawn. Find the probability that the card has:
   a) an odd number $\frac{10}{20}$, or 0.5
   b) a multiple of 4 $\frac{5}{20}$, or 0.25
   c) a number that is not a perfect square $\frac{16}{20}$, or 0.8
   d) a prime number $\frac{8}{20}$, or 0.40

11.4 8. Each of the numbers 1 to 15 is written on a separate card. The cards are shuffled and placed in a pile face down. A card is picked from the pile. Its number is recorded. The card is returned to the pile. In 99 trials, about how many times would you expect each outcome?
   a) a 6 about 7 times
   b) a multiple of 3 about 33 times
   c) a number less than 10 about 59 t
   d) an even number about 46 times

9. What is the chance of each outcome?
   a) tossing 2 coins and getting:
      i) 2 heads
      ii) 1 tail and 2 heads
   b) tossing 3 coins and getting:
      i) 1 head and 2 tails
      ii) at least 1 tail

10. An electronic game has three coloured sectors. A colour lights up at random, followed by a colour lighting up at random again. What is the chance the two consecutive colours are the same?

UNIT 11: Probability

ASSESSMENT FOR LEARNING

What to Look For

Understanding of concepts

✔ **Question 1:** Student understands that an outcome is the possible result of an experiment or an action.
✔ **Question 4:** Student understands how to find relative frequency.

Application of mathematical procedures

✔ **Question 1:** Student can draw a tree diagram to show all possible outcomes.
✔ **Question 7:** Student can find theoretical probability by analysing the possible outcomes.

Communicating

✔ **Question 5:** Student can explain the differences between relative frequency and theoretical probability.

Problem solving

✔ **Questions 8, 9, and 10:** Student can solve problems involving theoretical probability.

Recording and Reporting

Master 11.1 Unit Rubric: Probability
Master 11.4 Unit Summary: Probability

Practice Test

1. A theatre shows movies on Saturday and Sunday.
There are matinee and evening shows.
There are adult, child, and senior rates.
Draw a tree diagram to show the possible ticket types.

2. A number cube is labelled 1 to 6.
The cube is rolled 60 times.
Predict how many times each outcome will occur.
Explain each answer.
   a) 1 is rolled. 10
   b) An even number is rolled. 30
   c) A number greater than 3 is rolled. 30
   d) 9 is rolled. 0

3. a) In Sarah's first 30 times at bat, she had 9 hits.
What is Sarah's batting average? $\frac{9}{30} = 0.300$
   b) In Sarah's next game, she had 3 hits in 4 times at bat.
What is Sarah's new batting average? $\frac{12}{34} \doteq 0.353$
   c) How many hits would you expect Sarah to have in 90 times at bat? Explain your reasoning.

4. A number cube is labelled 1 to 6.
Suppose you roll a number cube twice.
Is it more likely you will get a 3 then a 5, or a 3 then a 3?
Explain your reasoning.

5. In the game "rock, paper, scissors," 2 players make hand signs.
Players can make a hand sign for rock, paper, or scissors.
On the count of 3, players show their hand signs.
Suppose the players choose their signs at random.
In 75 games, how many times would you expect to see both players showing rock?
About 8 times

Practice Test 429

SECTION ORGANIZER

Student Materials
- calculators

Assessment: Masters 11.1 Unit Rubric: Probability, 11.4 Unit Summary: Probability

Assignment Guidelines

To assess the 4 Achievement Chart categories listed in the curriculum document, use these test questions:
Understanding Concepts: 1
Application: 3
Communication: 4
Problem Solving: 5

Sample Solutions

1.

Day	Time	Rate	Ticket Types
Saturday	Matinee	Adult	Sa, M, A
		Child	Sa, M, C
		Senior	Sa, M, S
	Evening	Adult	Sa, E, A
		Child	Sa, E, C
		Senior	Sa, E, S
Sunday	Matinee	Adult	Su, M, A
		Child	Su, M, C
		Senior	Su, M, S
	Evening	Adult	Su, E, A
		Child	Su, E, C
		Senior	Su, E, S

2. a) The probability of rolling 1 is $\frac{1}{6}$. Multiply the probability by the number of repetitions, 60.
   b) There are 3 even numbers: 2, 4, 6. The probability of rolling an even number is $\frac{3}{6}$, or 0.5. Multiply the probability by the number of repetitions, 60.
   c) There are 3 numbers greater than 3: 4, 5, 6. The probability of rolling a number greater than 3 is $\frac{3}{6}$, or 0.5. Multiply the probability by the number of repetitions, 60.
   d) 0; 9 is not a number on the cube. The probability of an impossible outcome is 0.

3. c) I multiplied her most recent batting average by 90 to find the number of hits:
$\frac{12}{34} \times 90 \doteq 32$

4. There are 36 possible outcomes when you roll a number cube twice. Each outcome occurs once; so, the probability of each outcome is $\frac{1}{36}$, or about 0.028. To get a 3 then
a 5, or a 3 then a 3 are equally likely.

5. The possible outcomes are: RR, RP, RS, PR, PP, PS, SR, SP, SS
The probability of both players showing rock is $\frac{1}{9}$, or about 0.111. So, in 75 games, I would expect to see both players showing rock about 8 times:
$75 \times \frac{1}{9} \doteq 8.333$.

Games of Chance

SECTION ORGANIZER (40–50 min)

Student Grouping: 2
Student Materials
- spinners (Master 11.6b)
- paperclips as pointers
- coloured pencils or crayons
- number cubes
- regular polyhedra with numbered faces
- coins

Assessment: Masters 11.3 Performance Assessment Rubric: Games of Chance, 11.4 Unit Summary: Probability

Teaching notes for Cross Strand Investigation *A Population Simulation* are in the *Additional Assessment Support* module.

REFLECT ON THE UNIT: I use probability when I hear the weather forecast. If it says there is a 90% chance it will rain, I take an umbrella. If it says there is a 10% chance it will rain, I do not take an umbrella. My older sister does not buy lottery tickets because she has only a 1 in a 14 million chance of winning the jackpot.

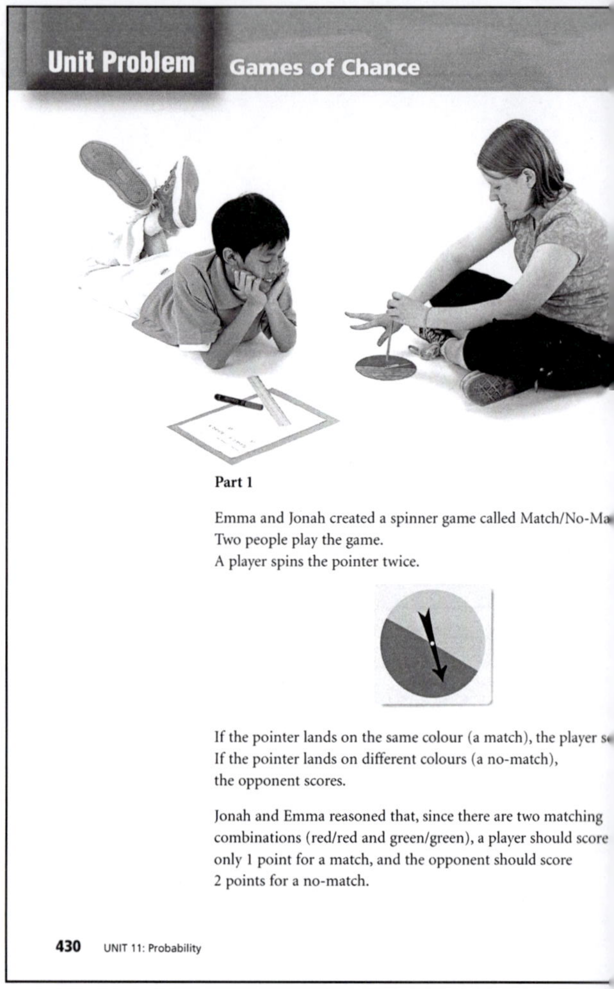
Unit Problem Games of Chance

Part 1

Emma and Jonah created a spinner game called Match/No-Ma
Two people play the game.
A player spins the pointer twice.

If the pointer lands on the same colour (a match), the player s
If the pointer lands on different colours (a no-match),
the opponent scores.

Jonah and Emma reasoned that, since there are two matching combinations (red/red and green/green), a player should score only 1 point for a match, and the opponent should score 2 points for a no-match.

430 UNIT 11: Probability

Have students turn to pages 404 and 405 of the Student Book.

Review *What You'll Learn,* and discuss the meanings of the Key Words. Tell students they will use the skills and concepts they learned in this unit to complete the *Unit Problem.*

Present the *Unit Problem.* Invite volunteers to read the introduction and instructions for the problem aloud. Ensure students understand what they are expected to do.

Have one student read the *Check List* aloud. Remind students that they should use the *Check List* to assess their work before handing it in. You may also wish to provide students with copies of Master 11.3 Performance Assessment Rubric: Games of Chance so they will know how their work will be assessed.

Sample Solution

Part 1

We played the Match/No-Match game 50 times. I scored a point when the pointer landed twice on the same colour. My partner scored a point when the pointer landed on different colours. Here are the results:

	Tally	Frequency
Me (Match)	卌 卌 卌 卌 |||	23
My Partner (No-match)	卌 卌 卌 卌 卌 ||	27

The relative frequency of a match is $\frac{23}{50} = 0.46$.
The relative frequency of a no-match is $\frac{27}{50} = 0.54$.
The possible outcomes of two spins are shown in this tree diagram. The outcomes are equally likely.

First Spin	Second Spin	Outcomes
red	red	rr
	green	rg
green	red	gr
	green	gg

There are two outcomes for a match: rr, gg
There are two outcomes for a no-match: rg, gr
So, the theoretical probability for a match is $\frac{2}{4} = \frac{1}{2}$, or 0.5.
And, the theoretical probability for a no-match is $\frac{2}{4} = \frac{1}{2}$, or 0.5.

Play the Match/No-Match game. Take at least 50 turns each.

Use the results to find the relative frequency of a match and of a no-match.

List the possible outcomes of a turn (two spins).
Find the theoretical probability of a match and a no-match.

Do you think the players have equal chances of winning? Explain.

Part 2

Design a game using spinners, number cubes, coins, or any other materials.
The game should use two different items.

Play the game.

Do the players have equal chances of winning? Explain.
Calculate some probabilities related to your game.
Show your work.

eck List

ır work
ɔuld show:

- calculations of quency or ɔbability, in detail
- grams, tables, or s to show possible comes and results ɜach game
- explanation of yers' chances of nning each game
- rect use of the guage of ɔbability

ɜflect on the Unit

Give at least two examples of how you use probability in everyday life.

Since these probabilities are equal, the players have equal chances of winning.

Part 2

We designed a game with a regular octahedron labelled 1, 1, 2, 2, 3, 3, 4, 4 and a regular tetrahedron labelled 1 to 4. It is a game for two players.

Octa Tetra Roll

Here is how to play.
Players take turns to roll the polyhedra.
We multiplied and added the numbers on the faces the polyhedra land on. If the sum is 5 or greater, Player A gets a point. If the product is 6 or less, Player B gets a point.
The winner is the first person to get 20 points.

Player A and Player B have equal chances of winning. There are 32 sums and 32 products. There are 20 ways to get a sum of 5 or more: 1 + 4, 1 + 4, 2 + 3, 2 + 3, 2 + 4, 2 + 4, 3 + 2, 3 + 2, 3 + 3, 3 + 3, 3 + 4, 3 + 4, 4 + 1, 4 + 1, 4 + 2, 4 + 2, 4 + 3, 4 + 3, 4 + 4, 4 + 4
There are 20 ways to get a product of 6 or less: 1 × 1, 1 × 1, 1 × 2, 1 × 2, 1 × 3, 1 × 3, 1 × 4, 1 × 4, 2 × 1, 2 × 1, 2 × 2, 2 × 2, 2 × 3, 2 × 3, 3 × 1, 3 × 1, 3 × 2, 3 × 2, 4 × 1, 4 × 1
The probability that Player A gets a point is $\frac{20}{32} = 0.625$.
The probability that Player B gets a point is $\frac{20}{32} = 0.625$.

ASSESSMENT FOR LEARNING

What to Look For	What to Do
Understanding concepts ✔ Students understand how to calculate relative frequency and theoretical probability. ***Applying procedures*** ✔ Students apply their knowledge of probability to decide whether the Match/No-Match Game is fair. ***Problem solving*** ✔ Students design a game of chance and use probability to decide who is likely to win. ***Communicating*** ✔ Students can describe their game and how they know whether outcomes are equally likely.	***Extra Support:*** Make the problem accessible. *Part 1* Have students record the result of each turn in a frequency table, then draw a tree diagram to determine the theoretical probability. *Part 2* Encourage students to use ideas from the unit to create a game. Have them use tree diagrams or charts to help determine probabilities.

Recording and Reporting
Master 11.3 Performance Assessment Rubric: Games of Chance
Master 11.4 Unit Summary: Probability

Cumulative Review

SECTION ORGANIZER

Student Materials

- 1-cm grid paper (PM 20)
- fraction strips (Master 4.22)
- number lines (Master 4.24)
- 0.5-cm grid paper (PM 14)
- coloured tiles
- 3 colours of counters, or 3 coins

Assessment: PM 9 Work Sample Record

Units 1–11 Cumulative Review

UNIT

1 **1.** Write the first 5 multiples of each number.
a) 6 — 6, 12, 18, 24, 30
b) 9 — 9, 18, 27, 36, 45
c) 12 — 12, 24, 36, 48, 60

2. Write all the factors of each number.
a) 36 — 1, 2, 3, 4, 6, 9, 12, 18, 36
b) 57 — 1, 3, 19, 57
c) 75 — 1, 3, 5, 15, 25, 75

2 **3.** There are two patchwork quilts.
In quilt A, the ratio of red squares to green squares is 5:7.
In quilt B, the ratio of red squares to green squares is 4:5.
The quilts are the same size.
Which quilt has more red squares? Quilt B
Use grid paper to show your answer.

3 **4.** a) Write the formula for the surface area of a cube, with edge length *c* units. $SA = 6c^2$
b) Write the formula for the surface area of a rectangular prism with dimensions *l* units by *w* units by *h* units. $SA = 2lw + 2lh + 2wh$
c) How can you get the formula for the surface area of a cube from the formula for the surface area of a rectangular prism? Use pictures in your explanation.

4 **5.** Add or subtract.
a) $2\frac{3}{4} - 1\frac{1}{3}$ $1\frac{5}{12}$
b) $3\frac{1}{3} + 2\frac{3}{5}$ $5\frac{14}{15}$
c) $3\frac{4}{5} - 2\frac{1}{10}$ $1\frac{7}{10}$
d) $\frac{3}{10} + 1\frac{1}{2}$ $1\frac{4}{5}$
e) $\frac{3}{8} + \frac{7}{4} + \frac{7}{2}$ $\frac{45}{8}$, or $5\frac{5}{8}$
f) $\frac{9}{10} + \frac{1}{2} + \frac{6}{5}$ $\frac{26}{10}$, or $2\frac{3}{5}$

6. Divide. Round the quotient nearest tenth where necessa
a) 7.22 ÷ 1.9 3.8
b) 7.22 ÷ 2.1 3.4
c) 8.97 ÷ 2.3 3.9
d) 8.98 ÷ 2.4 3.7

5 **7.** a) The people who run the survey students about th favourite foods.
How might the survey re affect the menu?
b) A local hair salon collect on the number of clients who would like hair appointments on Sunda How might these data affect the days the salon

8. Annette's practice times for downhill ski run, in second 122, 137, 118, 119, 124, 118
a) Find the mean time.
b) Find the median time.
c) Find the mode time.
d) Which measure of centr tendency best represents times? Explain. 120s o
e) What is the range? 19
f) What time must Annette her next run so the med 120 s? Explain.
g) What time must Annette her next run so the mea Is this possible? Explain.

434 Units 1–11

Students can use this review to evaluate their progress in the mathematical content of Units 1 through 11.

Remind students that the unit containing the content required to answer each question is listed in red beside or above the question.

Encourage students to refer to the *Connect* sections of the relevant units.

Encourage students to draw on each other's skills as they work through the review.

Students who have identified areas in which they are strong may wish to act as volunteer tutors for students who require assistance.

Sample Solutions

3. Find an equivalent ratio for each ratio.
Add the terms in each ratio. Keep adding until the sums are equal for quilt A and quilt B.

Quilt A		Quilt B	
Ratio	Sum of terms	Ratio	Sum of terms
5:7	12	4:5	9
10:14	24	8:10	18
15:21	36	12:15	27
20:28	48	16:20	36

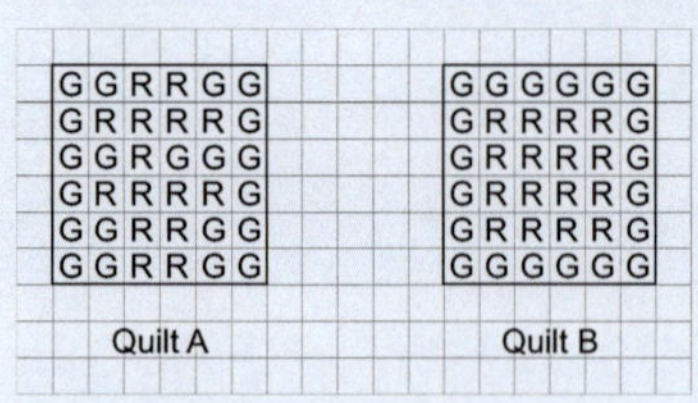

Each quilt has 36 squares
Quilt A has 15 red squares and 21 green squares.
Quilt B has 16 red squares and 20 green squares.
So, quilt B has more red squares.
Diagrams will vary.

What does this table show?

Toronto Blue Jays' Average Game Attendance	
Year	Average Attendance
1991	47 966
1992	49 402
1993	49 732
1994	50 098
1995	39 257
1996	31 600
1997	31 967
1998	30 300
1999	26 710
2000	21 058
2001	23 690
2002	20 209
2003	22 215

Do you think the average is the mean, the median, or the mode? Explain your choice.
Draw a line graph to display these data.
What trends does the graph show?
Find out what happened to change the trend.
Draw a graph to display the data each way.
i) The marketing department wants attendance to look as great as possible.
ii) The shareholders want to show that the attendance is too low.
f) Explain how each graph in part e shows what was intended.

6 **10.** Find the area of each figure.

a)

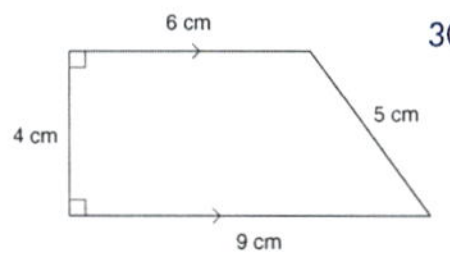

30 cm²

b)

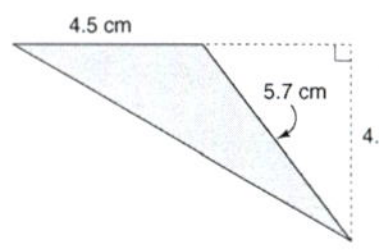

10.125 cm²

c)

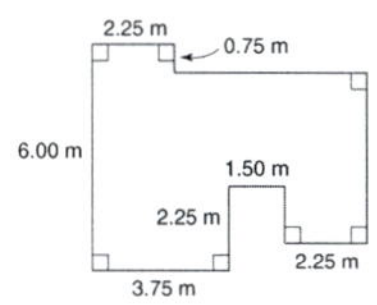

36 m²

d)

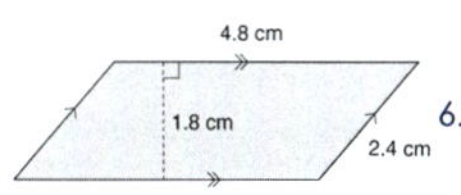

6.64 cm²

(Sample Solutions, continued)

4. c) For a cube: $SA = 6c^2$

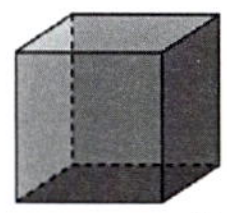

For a rectangular prism: $SA = 2lh + 2lw + 2hw$

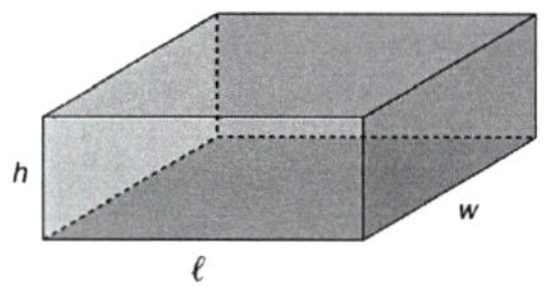

The edge lengths of a cube are equal.
So, each of l, h, and w is equal to c.
Substitute for c in the formula for surface area.
$SA = 2cc + 2cc + 2cc$
cc means $c \times c$, which we can write as c^2.
$SA = 2c^2 + 2c^2 + 2c^2$
$2c^2$ represents the area of 2 faces. There are three $2c^2$, which represent the area of 6 faces.
So, $SA = 6c^2$

(Solutions continue below.)

(Sample Solutions, continued)

5. Use equivalent fractions.

a) $2\frac{3}{4} - 1\frac{1}{3}$

Subtract the whole numbers: $2 - 1 = 1$

Subtract the fractions: $\frac{3}{4} - \frac{1}{3}$

The lowest common denominator is 12.

$\frac{3}{4} = \frac{9}{12}$ and $\frac{1}{3} = \frac{4}{12}$

$\frac{3}{4} - \frac{1}{3} = \frac{9}{12} - \frac{4}{12} = \frac{5}{12}$

So, $2\frac{3}{4} - 1\frac{1}{3} = 1\frac{5}{12}$

b) $3\frac{1}{3} + 2\frac{3}{5}$

Add the whole numbers: $3 + 2 = 5$

Add the fractions: $\frac{1}{3} + \frac{3}{5}$

The lowest common denominator is 15.

$\frac{1}{3} = \frac{5}{15}$ and $\frac{3}{5} = \frac{9}{15}$

$\frac{1}{3} + \frac{3}{5} = \frac{5}{15} + \frac{9}{15} = \frac{14}{15}$

So, $3\frac{1}{3} + 2\frac{3}{5} = 5\frac{14}{15}$

e) $\frac{3}{8} + \frac{7}{4} + \frac{7}{2}$

The lowest common denominator is 8.

$\frac{7}{4} = \frac{14}{8}$ and $\frac{7}{2} = \frac{28}{8}$

$\frac{3}{8} + \frac{7}{4} + \frac{7}{2} = \frac{3}{8} + \frac{14}{8} + \frac{28}{8} = \frac{45}{8} = 5\frac{5}{8}$

9. c)

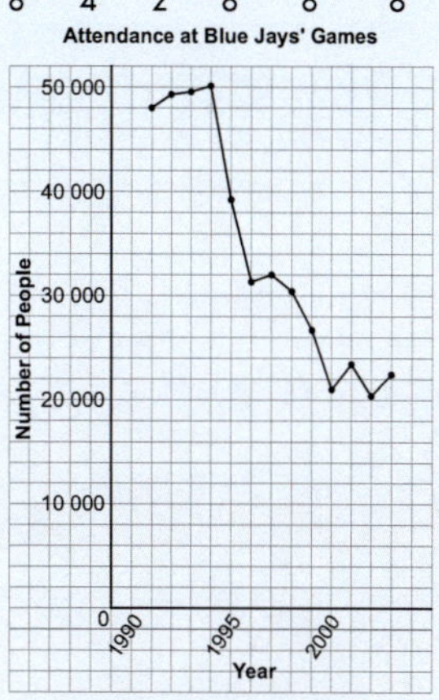

e) i)

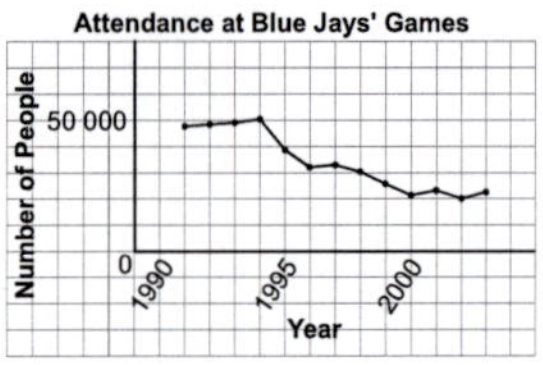

ii)

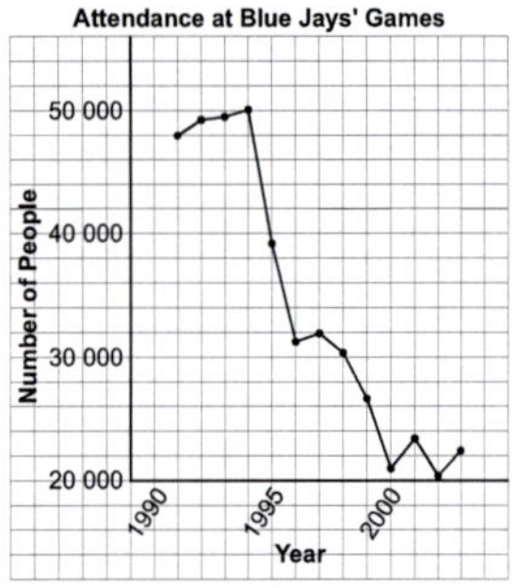

10. a) Divide the trapezoid into a rectangle and triangle.
The area of the rectangle is $6\text{ cm} \times 4\text{ cm} = 24\text{ cm}^2$.
The area of the triangle is $\frac{3\text{ cm} \times 4\text{ cm}}{2} = 6\text{ cm}^2$. So, the area of the trapezoid is $24\text{ cm}^2 + 6\text{ cm}^2 = 30\text{ cm}^2$.

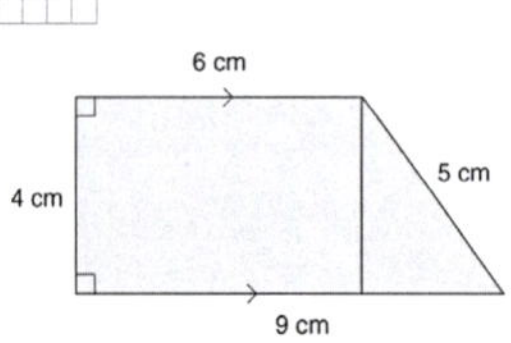

b) Both the base and height of the triangle are 4.5 cm.
So, the area of the triangle is $\frac{4.5\text{ cm} \times 4.5\text{ cm}}{2} = 10.125\text{ cm}^2$

c) Divide the figure into 4 rectangles.
The area of rectangle A is
$2.25\text{ m} \times 0.75\text{ m} = 1.6875\text{ m}^2$
The area of rectangle B is

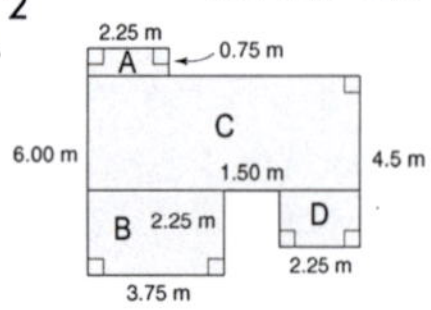

(Solutions continued below.)

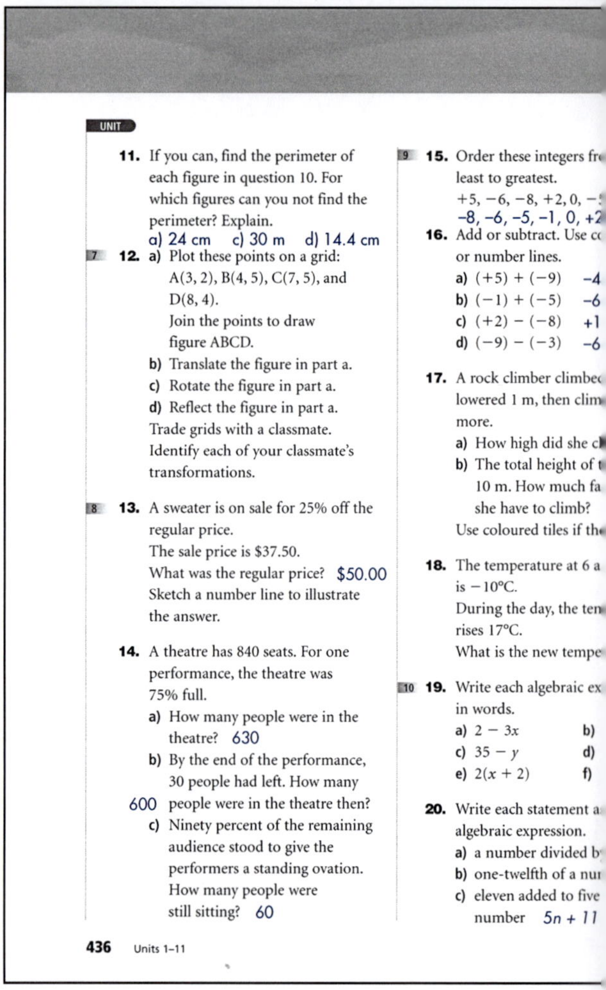

UNIT

11. If you can, find the perimeter of each figure in question 10. For which figures can you not find the perimeter? Explain.
a) 24 cm c) 30 m d) 14.4 cm

7 **12. a)** Plot these points on a grid:
A(3, 2), B(4, 5), C(7, 5), and D(8, 4).
Join the points to draw figure ABCD.
b) Translate the figure in part a.
c) Rotate the figure in part a.
d) Reflect the figure in part a.
Trade grids with a classmate.
Identify each of your classmate's transformations.

8 **13.** A sweater is on sale for 25% off the regular price.
The sale price is \$37.50.
What was the regular price? \$50.00
Sketch a number line to illustrate the answer.

14. A theatre has 840 seats. For one performance, the theatre was 75% full.
a) How many people were in the theatre? 630
b) By the end of the performance, 30 people had left. How many people were in the theatre then? 600
c) Ninety percent of the remaining audience stood to give the performers a standing ovation. How many people were still sitting? 60

9 **15.** Order these integers fr
least to greatest.
+5, −6, −8, +2, 0, −
−8, −6, −5, −1, 0, +2

16. Add or subtract. Use co
or number lines.
a) (+5) + (−9) −4
b) (−1) + (−5) −6
c) (+2) − (−8) +1
d) (−9) − (−3) −6

17. A rock climber climbe
lowered 1 m, then clim
more.
a) How high did she c
b) The total height of t
10 m. How much fa
she have to climb?
Use coloured tiles if th

18. The temperature at 6 a
is −10°C.
During the day, the ten
rises 17°C.
What is the new tempe

10 **19.** Write each algebraic ex
in words.
a) 2 − 3x **b)**
c) 35 − y **d)**
e) 2(x + 2) **f)**

20. Write each statement a
algebraic expression.
a) a number divided b
b) one-twelfth of a nu
c) eleven added to five
number 5n + 11

436 Units 1–11

(Sample Solutions, continued)
$2.25\text{ m} \times 3.75\text{ m} = 8.4375\text{ m}^2$
The length of rectangle C is
$3.75\text{ m} + 1.50\text{ m} + 2.25\text{ m} = 7.5\text{ m}$
The width of rectangle C is
$6.00\text{ m} - 0.75\text{ m} - 2.25\text{ m} = 3.0\text{ m}$
So, the area of rectangle C is $7.5\text{ m} \times 3.0\text{ m} = 22.5\text{ m}^2$
The length of rectangle D is 2.25 m.
The width of rectangle D is 4.5 m − width of rectangle C, or $4.5\text{ m} - 3.0\text{ m} = 1.5\text{ m}$.
So, the area of rectangle D is $2.25\text{ m} \times 1.5\text{ m} = 3.375\text{ m}^2$.
The area of the figure is the sum of the areas of the 4 rectangles:
$1.6875\text{ m}^2 + 8.4375\text{ m}^2 + 22.5\text{ m}^2 + 3.375\text{ m}^2 = 36\text{ m}^2$

12. Diagrams may vary.
a) The translation is 6 units right and 6 units up.
b) The rotation is $\frac{1}{2}$ turn about B(4, 5).
c) The reflection is in a horizontal line through 7 on the vertical axis.

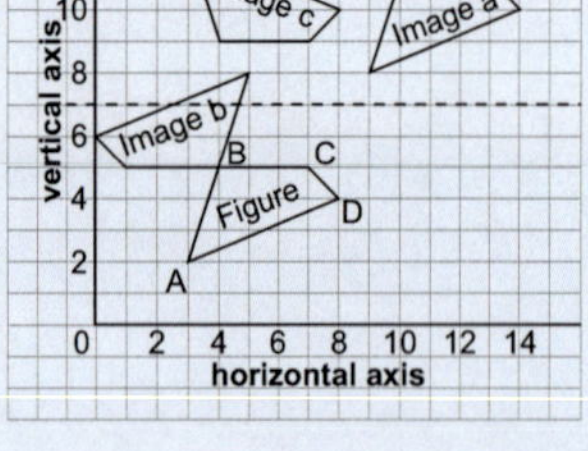

13. The sale price is \$37.50.
This is 100% − 25% = 75% of the regular price.
So, 1% of the regular price is $\$\frac{37.50}{75} = \$0.50$
The regular price is 100%: $100 \times \$0.50 = \$50.00$

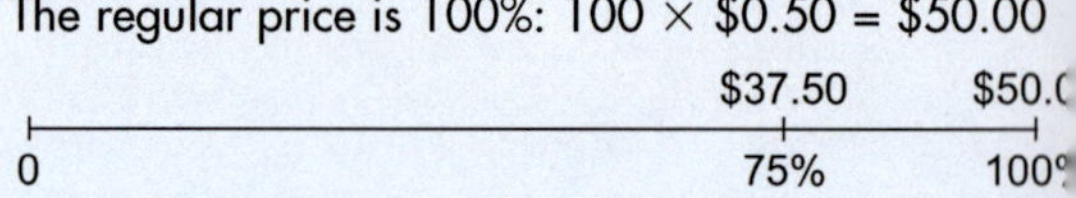

14. a) 75% of 840 = $0.75 \times 840 = 630$
630 people were in the theatre.
b) At the end of the performance, there were 630 −
or 600 people.
c) 90% of the people stood.
So, 10% were seated.
10% of 600 = $0.10 \times 600 = 60$
60 people were sitting.

21. a)

Number of Cars	Money Collected (\$)
5	30
10	60
15	90
20	120
25	150
30	180

21. Students are fund raising by washing cars.
The students charge $6.00 per car.

a) Copy and complete this table.

Numbers of Cars	Money Collected ($)
5	
10	
15	
20	
25	
30	

b) Graph the data in the table in part a.

c) What patterns do you see in the table? How could you extend each pattern?

d) Suppose you know how many cars were washed. How can you find how much money was collected in each case?
i) by using the table
ii) by using the graph

e) Suppose 27 cars were washed. How much money was collected? $162
How many different ways can you find the answer? Explain.

22. Solve each equation.

a) $2x + 3 = 15$ $x = 6$

b) $\frac{x}{3} = 15$ $x = 45$

c) $\frac{15}{x} = 3$ $x = 5$

d) $2x - 3 = 15$ $x = 9$

23. Evan had $852.00.
He shared the money equally with his brother and sister.

a) Write an equation you can solve to find out how much money each person got. $3p = 852.00$

b) Solve the equation. $p = \$284.00$

11 **24.** a) What are the possible outcomes when 3 coins are tossed?
HHH, HHT, HTH, HTT, THH, THT, TTH, TTT

b) What is the probability of each outcome?

c) Design and conduct an experiment to find the relative frequency of each outcome.

d) Write each relative frequency as a decimal.

e) How do the probabilities and relative frequencies compare? Is this what you expect? Explain.

25. Each letter of the word PROBABILITY is written on a card. The cards are placed in a box. Suppose you pick a card, at random, record the letter, then replace the card.
In 55 trials, about how many times would you expect each outcome?

a) a P 5 b) a B 10 c) a vowel 20 d) an X 0

26. Anca rolls two number cubes labelled 3 to 8. She adds the numbers that show on the cubes.
List the possible outcomes.
Use a tree diagram if it helps.
6, 7, 8, 9, 10, 11, 12, 13, 14, 15, 16

Cumulative Review 437

b) 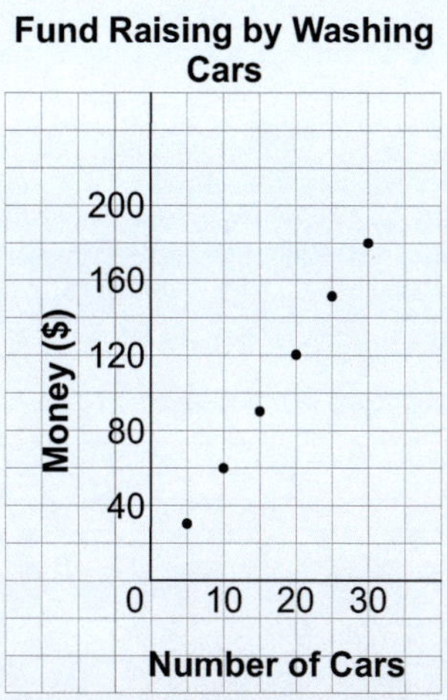

c) In the first column, the number of cars starts at 5 and increases by 5 each time. To extend the pattern, add 5 to the last term.
In the second column, the money collected starts at $30 and increases by $30 each time. To extend the pattern, add $30 to the last term.

d) i) I can only use the table to find the money collected for multiples of 5 cars. When I know the number of cars, I can read the money from the same row in the next column.

ii) I could draw the graph so 1 square represents 2 cars. I could draw a broken line through the points on the graph. Then, to find the cost of any number of cars, I draw a vertical line from that number on the horizontal axis to the broken line, then draw a horizontal line. This line meets the vertical axis at a point that represents the money collected.

e) For 27 cars washed, I find the money collected these ways:

- Multiply: $6 × 27 = $162
- Use a table, but the table would need multiples of 3 cars in the first column.
- Use the graph, as described in part d) ii).
  Draw a vertical line from 27 on the horizontal axis to meet the broken line drawn through the points. Draw a horizontal line through the point where the vertical line meets the broken line. The money collected is represented by the point where the horizontal line meets the vertical axis.

Evaluating Student Learning: Preparing to Report: Unit 11 Probability

This unit provides an opportunity to report on the **Data Management and Probability** strand. *Master 11.4 Unit Summary: Probability* provides a comprehensive format for recording and summarizing evidence collected.

Here is an example of a completed summary chart for this Unit:

Strand: *Data Management and Probability*	**Problem solving**	**Understanding of concepts**	**Application of mathematical procedures**	**Communication**	***Overall***
Ongoing Observations	2	3	2	3	2/3
Work samples or portfolios; conferences	2	3	3	3	3
Unit Review	3	3	3	3	3
Practice Test	2	3	2	3	2/3
Unit Problem Games of Chance	3	3	2	3	3
Achievement Level for reporting					3

Recording	**How to Report**
Ongoing Observations	Use *Master 11.2 Ongoing Observations: Probability* to determine the most consistent level achieved in each category. Enter it in the chart. Choose to summarize by achievement category, or to enter an overall level. Observations from late in the unit should be most heavily weighted.
Portfolios or collections of work samples; conferences, or interviews	Use *Master 11.1 Unit Rubric: Probability* to guide evaluation of collections of work and information gathered in conferences. Teachers may choose to focus particular attention on the *Assessment Focus* questions. Work from late in the unit should be most heavily weighted.
Unit Review	*Master 11.1 Unit Rubric: Probability* may be helpful in determining levels of achievement. #1 provides evidence of Understanding of concepts; # 2, 3, and 4 provide evidence of Application of mathematical procedures; all provide evidence of Communication.
Practice Test	*Master 11.1 Unit Rubric: Probability* may be helpful in determining levels of achievement. #1 provides evidence of Understanding of concepts; #3 provides evidence of Application of mathematical procedures; #5 provides evidence of Problem solving; #4 provides evidence of Communication.
Unit Problem	Use *Master 11.3 Performance Assessment Rubric: Games of Chance.* The *Unit Problem* offers a snapshot of students' achievement. In particular, it shows their ability to synthesize and apply what they have learned.
Student Self-Assessment	Note students' perceptions of their own progress. This may take the form of an oral or written comment, or a self-rating.
Comments	Analyse the pattern of achievement to identify strengths and needs. Specific actions may be planned to support the learner.

Learning Skills	**Ongoing Records**
PM 4: Learning Skills Check List Use to record and report throughout a reporting period, rather than for each unit and/or strand.	*PM 10: Summary Class Records: Strands* *PM 11: Summary Class Records: Achievement Categories* *PM 12: Summary Record: Individual* Use to record and report evaluations of student achievement over several clusters, a reporting period, or a school year. These can also be used in place of the Unit Summary.

Name ______________ Date ______________

Master 11.1

Unit Rubric: Probability

	Level 1	Level 2	Level 3	Level 4
Problem solving • uses a range of strategies (for example, tables, tree diagrams, logical reasoning) to design simple experiments and solve problems involving probability	with assistance, chooses and carries out a limited range of appropriate strategies to design simple experiments and solve problems involving probability	with limited assistance, chooses and carries out appropriate strategies to design simple experiments and solve problems that involve probability	chooses and carries out appropriate strategies to design simple experiments and solve problems that involve probability	chooses and carries out appropriate strategies to design simple experiments and solve problems that involve probability; strategies may be innovative
Understanding of concepts • shows understanding by using concepts of probability to explain: – how probability relates to sports and games of chance – the probability of a favourable outcome among possible outcomes (for example, getting heads in a fair coin toss)	shows little understanding; may be unable to explain: – how probability relates to sports and games of chance – the probability of a favourable outcome among possible outcomes	shows some understanding; partially able to explain: – how probability relates to sports and games of chance – the probability of a favourable outcome among possible outcomes	shows understanding; able to clearly and appropriately explain: – how probability relates to sports and games of chance – the probability of a favourable outcome among possible outcomes	shows thorough understanding; able to accurately and effectively explain: – how probability relates to sports and games of chance – the probability of a favourable outcome among possible outcomes
Application of mathematical procedures • accurately: – lists possible outcomes of simple experiments – identifies possible outcomes and favourable outcomes – states the probability of an outcome	limited accuracy; major errors or omissions in: – listing possible outcomes of simple experiments – identifying possible outcomes and favourable outcomes – stating the probability of an outcome	somewhat accurate; several minor errors or omissions in: – listing possible outcomes of simple experiments – identifying possible outcomes and favourable outcomes – stating the probability of an outcome	generally accurate; few minor errors or omissions in: – listing possible outcomes of simple experiments – identifying possible outcomes and favourable outcomes – stating the probability of an outcome	accurate and precise; no errors in: – listing possible outcomes of simple experiments – identifying possible outcomes and favourable outcomes – stating the probability of an outcome
Communication • explains concepts, reasoning, and procedures clearly, using appropriate mathematical language (for example, probability, relative frequency, chance)	unable to explain reasoning and procedures clearly	partially explains reasoning and procedures	explains reasoning and procedures clearly	explains reasoning and procedures clearly, precisely, and confidently
• presents work clearly including labels and symbols	presents work with little clarity	presents work with some clarity	presents work clearly	presents work clearly and precisely

Name ____________________ Date ______________

Master 11.2

Ongoing Observations: Probability

The behaviours described under each heading are examples; they are not intended to be an exhaustive list of all that might be observed. More detailed descriptions are provided in each lesson under *Assessment for Learning.*

STUDENT ACHIEVEMENT: Probability				
Student	**Problem solving** ▪ Uses a range of strategies to design simple experiments and solve problems involving probability	**Understanding of concepts** ▪ Explains how probability relates to sports and games of chance ▪ Explains the probability of a favourable outcome	**Application of mathematical procedures** ▪ Lists possible outcomes and favourable outcomes ▪ States the probability of an outcome	**Communication** ▪ Explains concepts, reasoning, and procedures clearly ▪ Presents work clearly, including labels and symbols

Level 1 – very limited; Level 2 – somewhat or limited; Level 3 – satisfactory; Level 4 – thorough

Name ____________________ Date ______________

Master 11.3

Performance Assessment Rubric: Games of Chance

	Level 1	Level 2	Level 3	Level 4
Problem solving • Uses a range of strategies (for example, tables, tree diagrams, logical reasoning) to: – determine whether players have equal chances of winning – design a game and determine the probabilities of winning	uses few simple strategies, with limited success, to: – solve the problem posed in Part 1 – design a game and determine the probabilities of winning	uses some appropriate strategies, with partial success, to: – solve the problem posed in Part 1 – design a game and determine the probabilities of winning	uses appropriate strategies to successfully: – solve the problem posed in Part 1 – design a game and determine the probabilities of winning	uses innovative and appropriate strategies to successfully and effectively: – solve the problem posed in Part 1 – design a game and determine the probabilities of winning
Understanding of concepts • shows understanding of how probability relates to games of chance by using relevant concepts in explanations of whether players in each game have equal chances of winning	shows very limited understanding; may be unable to give appropriate explanations, using concepts of probability	shows limited understanding by giving some appropriate but incomplete explanations, using some concepts of probability	shows understanding by giving appropriate explanations, using required concepts of probability	shows thorough understanding by giving appropriate and complete explanations, using all relevant concepts of probability
Application of mathematical procedures • Records results of games accurately • Determines relative frequencies of results • Lists possible outcomes • Calculates theoretical probabilities	limited accuracy; major errors or omissions in: – recording results of the games – determining relative frequencies of results – listing possible outcomes – calculating theoretical probabilities	somewhat accurate; several minor errors or omissions in: – recording results of the games – determining relative frequencies of results – listing possible outcomes – calculating theoretical probabilities	generally accurate; few minor errors or omissions in: – recording results of the games – determining relative frequencies of results – listing possible outcomes – calculating theoretical probabilities	accurate and precise; no errors in: – recording results of the games – determining relative frequencies of results – listing possible outcomes – calculating theoretical probabilities
Communication • explains reasoning clearly using appropriate mathematical terminology (for example, outcome, relative frequency, theoretical probability, experimental probability)	explains reasoning unclearly and imprecisely, using few mathematical terms	explains reasoning with some clarity, using some appropriate mathematical terms	explains reasoning clearly and precisely, using appropriate mathematical terms	explains reasoning clearly, precisely, and confidently, using a range of appropriate mathematical terminology
• presents work clearly, including tables and lists	presents work with little clarity	presents work with some clarity	presents work clearly	presents work clearly and precisely

Name ____________________ Date ______________

Master 11.4

Unit Summary: Probability

Review assessment records to determine the most consistent achievement levels for the assessments conducted. Some cells may be blank. *Overall* achievement levels may be recorded in each row, rather than identifying levels for each achievement category.

	Most Consistent Level of Achievement*				
Strand: *Data Management and Probability*	**Problem solving**	**Understanding of concepts**	**Application of mathematical procedures**	**Communication**	***Overall***
Ongoing Observations					
Work samples or portfolios; conferences					
Unit Review					
Practice Test					
Unit Problem Games of Chance					
Achievement Level for reporting					

*Use Ontario Achievement Levels 1, 2, 3, 4.

Self-Assessment:

Comments: (Strengths, Needs, Next Steps)

Name ____________________ Date ______________

Master 11.5

Additional Activity 1: The Conversation Game

Play in groups of 2, 3, or 4.

You will need a deck of cards with the face cards removed, and a calculator.

How to Play:

1. Decide who will go first.
Player A draws 2 cards from the deck.
Use the numbers drawn to make a proper fraction. An ace counts as 1.
For example, if the numbers are 4 and 7, the fraction is $\frac{4}{7}$.

2. Player A converts her fraction to a decimal and to a percent.
She records these numbers in this table.

Turn	Fraction	Decimal	Percent
1			
2			
3			
4			
5			
6			
7			
8			
9			
10			

3. Players check each other's answers.
Each time, the cards are returned to the bottom of the deck.

4. Players take turns until each player has had 10 turns.
Players find the sums of their decimals.
The player with the greatest sum wins.

Take It Further:
Players add 5 to each number drawn before making a proper fraction.

Name ____________________ Date ______________

Master 11.6a

Additional Activity 2: Spinner Construction

Play with a partner.

You will need *Spinners*, two number cubes labelled 1 to 6, protractors, and pencil crayons.

How to Play:

1. Players take turns to roll two number cubes.
When the sum of the numbers is even, Player A instructs Player B to make a spinner.
When the sum of the numbers is odd, Player B instructs Player A to make a spinner.

Students use the numbers rolled to make proper fractions, then use these fractions in their instructions. The wording of the instructions to make the spinner should be: "Construct a spinner so that the chance of the pointer landing on (*choose one of: red, blue, green, yellow*) is (*the fraction made with the numbers rolled*)."

For example, "Construct a spinner so the probability of the pointer landing on yellow is $\frac{1}{5}$."

2. If a player makes the spinner correctly, he gets 1 point.
If a player does not know how to make the spinner, or the spinner is wrong, the other player makes the spinner.
If the other player is correct, she gets 1 point.

3. The player who has more points after 12 spinners have been constructed wins.

Take It Further:
Players use percents in their instructions instead of fractions. The wording of the instructions to make the spinner should be: "Construct a spinner so that the chance of the pointer landing on (*choose one of: red, blue, green, yellow*) is (*choose a percent that is a multiple of 10, but not greater than 100%*)."
For example, "Construct a spinner so that the chance of the pointer landing on red is 80%."

Name ____________________ Date ______________

Master 11.6b

Spinners

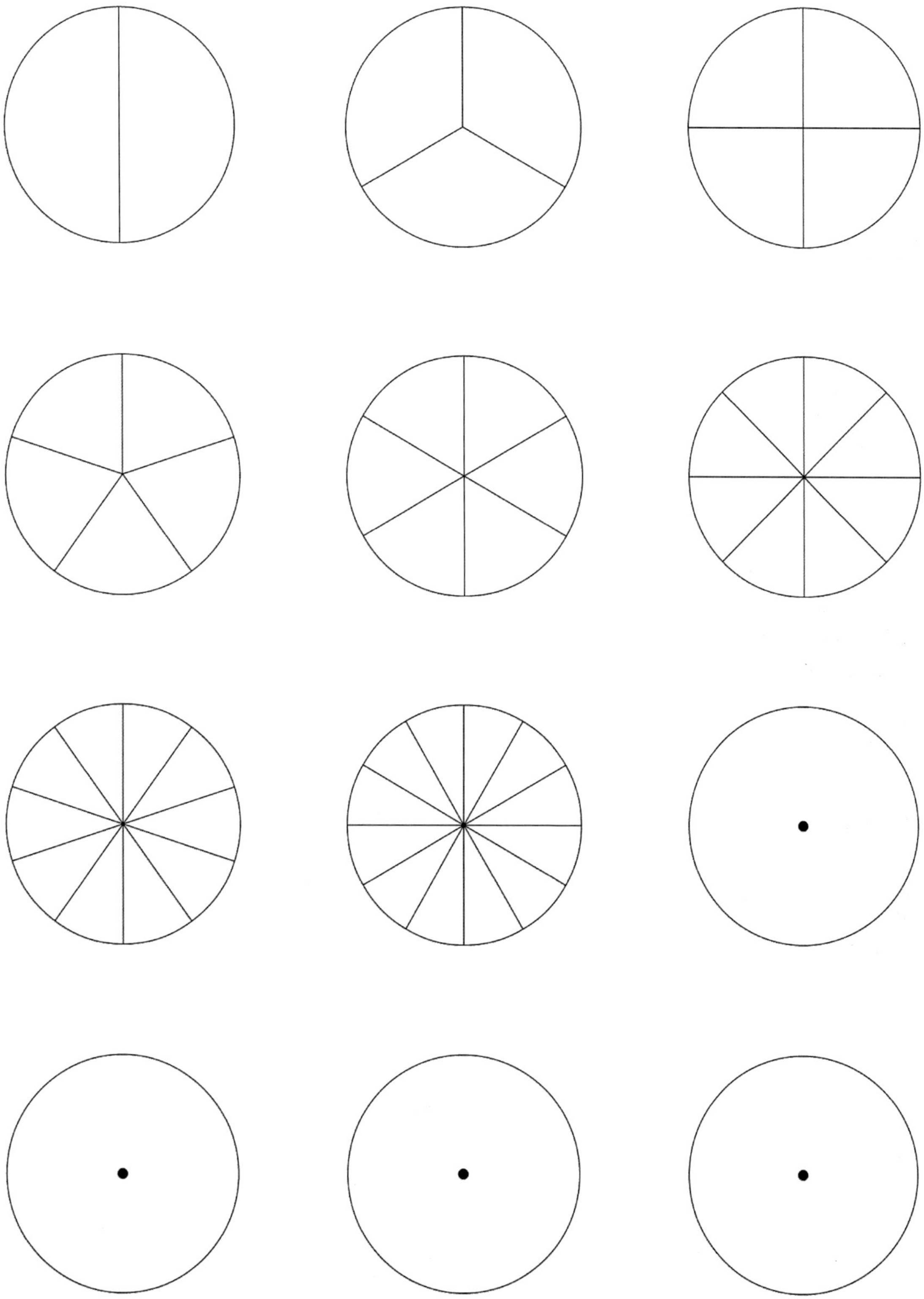

Name ____________________ Date ______________

Master 11.7

Step-by-Step 1

Section 11.1, Question 7

Step 1 Complete this table. Add each number in the 1st column to each number in the 1st row.

Sum of Numbers on Two Cubes						
Number on Cube	**1**	**2**	**3**	**4**	**5**	**6**
1	2	3	4			
2						
3						
4						
5						
6						

Step 2 List the different sums from the completed table.

_____, _____, _____, _____, _____, _____, _____, _____, _____, _____, _____

How many different outcomes are there for the sum of the numbers on the cubes? ______

Step 3 Count the number of 6s in the table that are sums.
In how many ways can the sum be 6? _____

Step 4 Count the number of 9s in the table.
In how many ways can the sum be 9? _____

Step 5 Count the number of 2s and 12s that are sums.
In how many ways can the sum be 2 or 12? _____

Step 6 Count the number of 7s in the table.
In how many ways can the sum be 7? _____
Are there other sums that appear more often than 7? ____
Why do you think 7 is a lucky number? ________________________
____

Step 7 Use the back of this paper. Draw a tree diagram to show these results.
List the outcomes for the first cube.
For each outcome, list the outcomes of the second cube.
Then list the sum of the two cubes in each pair.
Label the 1st column "Number on First Cube."
Label the 2nd column "Number on Second Cube."
Label the 3rd column "Sum of Cubes."
Is it easy to see how many times each sum occurs from the tree diagram?
____
Explain. ____
Why do you think a table was used instead of a tree diagram? ______
____

Name ____________________ Date _______________

Master 11.8

Step-by-Step 2

Section 11.2, Question 7

Step 1 Use this table to record the results of your experiment.

Outcome	Tally	Frequency	Relative Frequency
Sum of 7			
Not Sum of 7			

Step 2 Label the faces of each of the two regular octahedra from 1 to 8.
Roll the octahedra. Which number is on each face? ____ ____
What is their sum? _______

Step 3 If the sum is 7, put a tally mark beside "Sum of 7" in the Tally column.
If the sum is not 7, put a tally mark beside "Not Sum of 7" in the Tally column.

Step 4 Conduct the experiment 10 times.
What is the frequency of getting a sum of 7? ________
What is the relative frequency of getting a sum of 7? _______

Step 5 Conduct the experiment 50 times.
What is the frequency of getting a sum of 7? __________
What is the relative frequency of getting a sum of 7? _______

Step 6 Conduct the experiment 100 times.
What is the frequency of getting a sum of 7? ________
What is the relative frequency of getting a sum of 7? _______

Step 7 How are the results affected as you increase the number of times the experiment is conducted?

____

____

____

____

Name ____________________ Date ______________

Master 11.9

Step-by-Step 3

Section 11.3, Question 6

Step 1 Find a common denominator for the fractions $\frac{1}{4}$, $\frac{1}{2}$, $\frac{1}{6}$, and $\frac{1}{12}$. ______

To find each sector angle, divide 360° by the common denominator:
Use a protractor. Divide the spinner into congruent sectors with this angle.
How many congruent sectors are there? ______

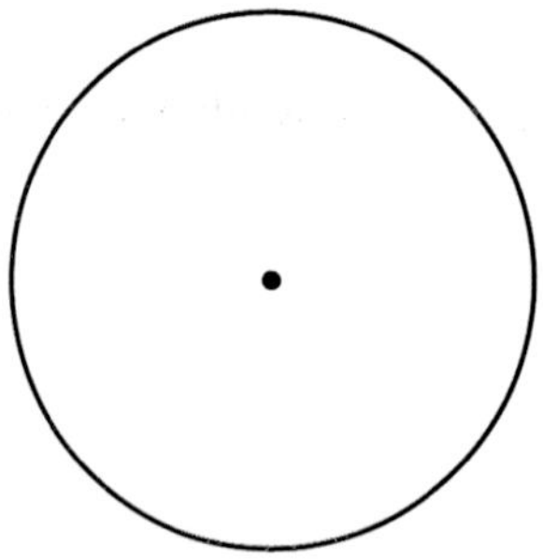

Step 2 Use the common denominator from *Step 1*. Write an equivalent fraction for each fraction.

Red: $\frac{1}{4}$ = Yellow: $\frac{1}{2}$ = Blue: $\frac{1}{6}$ = Green: $\frac{1}{12}$ =

Step 3 Use the numerator of each equivalent fraction in *Step 2*.
How many sectors should there be of each colour?
There should be ____ red sectors, ____ yellow sectors, ____ blue sectors, and _____ green sectors.
Colour the spinner.

Step 4 Multiply to find how many times the pointer may land on each colour in 200 trials.

Red: $\frac{1}{4} \times 200 =$ ______ Yellow: $\frac{1}{2} \times 200 =$ ______

Blue: $\frac{1}{6} \times 200 \doteq$ ______ Green: $\frac{1}{12} \times 200 \doteq$ ______

Step 5 The probability of landing on yellow was $\frac{1}{2}$; now it is $\frac{1}{4}$.
How has the probability changed? ____________________________
What effect would this have on the probability of landing on each other colour? Explain.

____

____

____

Name ____________________ Date ______________

Master 11.10

Step-by-Step 4

Section 11.4, Question 6

Look at the table on page 423 of your book.

Step 1 Use the back of this paper.
Draw a tree diagram. List the possible choices of sandwiches.
For each sandwich choice, list the possible vegetable choices.

Step 2 List the possible combinations of sandwich and vegetable.

Step 3 How many combinations are possible? __________
Does any combination occur more than once? _____
What is the probability of each combination? _____________

Step 4 List 3 possible lunch desserts: ____________________________________
Extend your tree diagram. For each vegetable choice, list the possible dessert choices.

Step 5 List the possible combinations of sandwich, vegetable, and dessert.

What is the probability of each combination? _____________

How do the probabilities of possible combinations change when dessert is added to the choice?

____

____

Name ______________________ Date ______________________

Master 11.11a

Unit Test: Unit 11 Probability

1. A jar is filled with 48 yellow jelly beans, 43 red jelly beans, 52 orange jelly beans, and 57 green jelly beans. One jelly bean is picked at random.

   a) What are the possible outcomes?

   b) What is the probability of picking each colour of jelly bean?

2. A regular tetrahedron is labelled 1 to 4. A number cube is labelled 1 to 6.
   The tetrahedron and cube are rolled.

   a) Record the numbers on the faces that do not show.
   Are you more likely to get the answer 8 if you add these numbers or multiply them?
   Explain your answer.

   ____

   ____

   ____

   b) Make up your own problem about the tetrahedron and cube. Solve the problem.
   Show your work.

Unit Test continued

3. Each of two spinners has congruent sectors. Spinner A has 4 sectors coloured red, green, yellow, and black. Spinner B has 3 sectors coloured red, green, and purple.

a) The pointer on each spinner is spun. Use a tree diagram to list the possible outcomes.

b) What is the probability that the colours are different? Explain.

c) What is the probability that only one colour is red? Explain.

d) What is the probability that no colour is red? Explain.

e) What is the probability that no colour is orange? Explain.

4. a) In her 85 times at bat, Jillian got 55 hits. What is her batting average?

b) A home cleaning service solicits new business by telephone. On one day, 500 telephone calls were made. They produced 111 new customers.
What is the relative frequency of getting a customer over the phone? Explain.

c) A quality controller at a battery manufacturing company tested 360 batteries from the production line. She found that 19 were defective.
A box contains 5000 batteries.
How many might you expect *not* to be defective?
Show two different ways to solve this problem.

Master 11.12 Sample Answers

Unit Test – Master 11.11

1. a) Yellow, red, orange, green

b) The total number of jelly beans is 200:
$48 + 43 + 52 + 57 = 200$.
The probability of picking a:

- yellow jelly bean is $\frac{48}{200} = \frac{6}{25}$ or 0.24
- red jelly bean is $\frac{43}{200}$ or about 0.22
- orange jelly bean is $\frac{52}{200} = \frac{13}{50}$ or 0.26
- green jelly bean is $\frac{57}{200}$ or 0.28

2. a) Students can draw addition and multiplication tables.
There are 2 ways to get 8 if you multiply:
2×4 and 4×2.
There are 3 ways to get 8 if you add: $6 + 2$, $5 + 3$, $4 + 4$.
So, you are more likely to get 8 if you add the numbers that show.

b) **Sample problem:** You can divide the number on the cube by the number on the tetrahedron, or you can subtract the number on the tetrahedron from the number on the cube. With which operation are you more likely to get the answer 2?
Solution: There are 3 ways to get the answer 2 if you divide: $2 \div 1$, $4 \div 2$, $6 \div 3$.
There are 4 ways to get the answer 2 if you subtract: $3 - 1$, $4 - 2$, $5 - 3$, $6 - 4$. So, you are more likely to get 2 if you subtract.

3. a)

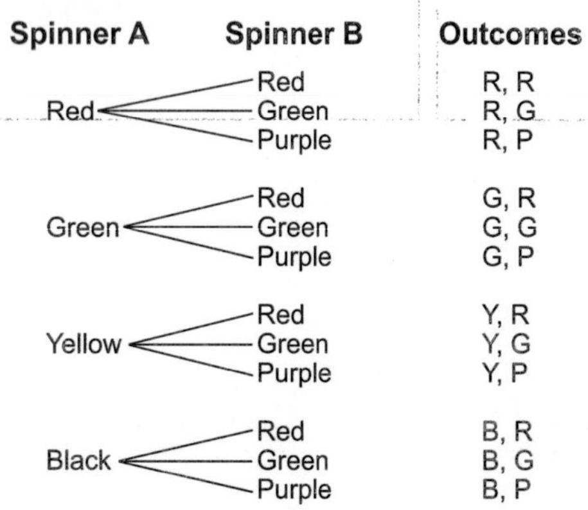

b) $\frac{10}{12} = \frac{5}{6}$; 10 out of 12 outcomes have 2 different colours.

c) $\frac{5}{12}$; 5 out of 12 outcomes have only 1 red sector.

d) $\frac{6}{12} = \frac{1}{2}$; 6 out of 12 outcomes have no red sectors.

e) 1; there are no orange sectors, so all outcomes never have orange.

4. a) $\frac{55}{85} \doteq 0.647$, or approximately 65%

b) $\frac{111}{500} \doteq 0.222$, or approximately 22%

c) *Solution Method 1:* 19 are defective, so $360 - 19 = 341$ are not defective. So, the probability of not being defective is $\frac{341}{360} \doteq 0.947$.
Multiply the probability by the number of batteries. $\frac{341}{360} \times 5000 \doteq 4736$
So, approximately 4736 batteries should not be defective.
Solution Method 2: The probability of being defective is $\frac{19}{360} \doteq 0.053$.
Find out how many batteries will be defective. Multiply the probability of being defective by 5000.
$\frac{19}{360} \times 5000 \doteq 263.9$ or approximately 264 batteries will be defective. The number of non-defective batteries will be $5000 - 264 = 4736$.
So, approximately 4736 batteries should not be defective.

Extra Practice Masters 11.13–11.17

Go to the CD-ROM to access editable versions of these Extra Practice Masters.

Name ________________ Date ____________

Master 11.13 **Extra Practice 1**

Section 11.1: Listing Outcomes

1. List the possible outcomes in each case.
   a) spinning the pointer

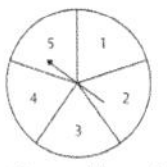

   b) picking a card from a pile of 11 cards, each of which has one of the letters of the word MATHEMATICS written on it
2. A dairy bottles 4 kinds of milk: regular, 2%, skim, and chocolate. There are 3 different sizes available: 2 L, 1 L, and 500 mL. Draw a tree diagram to show the possible milk types and sizes.
3. Stacy wears a uniform to school. Her choices of skirts are blue or beige. She can wear a white blouse, a blue turtleneck, or a beige sports shirt. She can wear knee socks or leotards.
   a) Draw a tree diagram to display all the possible outfits.
   b) How many outfits have either a blue skirt or a blue turtleneck?
   c) How many outfits do not have leotards?
   d) How many outfits have a beige skirt and a white blouse?
4. An entertainment park offers 5 rollercoaster rides, 3 water rides, 4 magical rides, 3 musical shows, and 2 Imax movies. How many choices are there for a customer who wants to purchase the following ticket combinations?
   a) a roller coaster ride, a water ride, a magical ride, and an Imax movie
   b) a water ride, a magical ride, a musical show, and an Imax movie
   c) a roller coaster ride, a water ride, and a musical show
   d) a ride and a musical show or a movie

Name ________________ Date ____________

Master 11.14 **Extra Practice 2**

Section 11.2: Experimental Probability

1. This table shows data for the New York Yankees Major League Baseball team on June 15, 2004. Find the batting average of each player. Round each answer to 3 decimal places.

Name	At Bats	Hits
A. Rodriguez	236	72
G. Sheffield	226	68
M. Cairo	87	26
K. Lofton	73	21
H. Matsui	223	64
J. Posada	169	46
R. Sierra	131	35
B. Williams	210	54
J. Giambi	152	38
D. Jeter	247	61
B. Crosby	25	6
T. Clark	100	22
E. Wilson	134	28
J. Flaherty	50	9
T. Lee	19	2
H. Bush	7	0

2. Use 4 white marbles and 4 blue marbles. You may place some or all of the marbles in a bag. You then pick a marble without looking.
   a) How many different ways can you place the marbles in the bag so you are more likely to pick a blue marble? Explain.
   b) How many different ways can you place the marbles in the bag so that picking either a blue marble or a white marble is equally likely?
3. Write each relative frequency as a decimal rounded to 3 decimal places.
   a) A quality controller tested 350 CDs and found 12 defective. What is the relative frequency of finding a defective CD? Finding a good CD?
   b) From a shuffled deck of cards, a card was withdrawn, at random, its colour was recorded, then it was returned to the deck. In 85 trials, there were 47 black cards. What was the relative frequency of drawing a red card?
4. You will need a deck of cards. A deck of cards (with the jokers removed) is shuffled and one card is drawn.
   a) What are the possible outcomes for the suit of the card?
   b) Do you think the outcomes in part a are equally likely? Explain.
   c) Pick a card from the deck and record its suit in a table. Return the card to the deck. Repeat this 50 times. Record the outcomes in the table.
   d) Calculate the relative frequency of each outcome in the table.
   e) Do the results confirm your prediction in part b? Explain.

Name ________________ Date ____________

Master 11.15 **Extra Practice 3**

Section 11.3: Theoretical Probability

1. A pencil case contains 7 blue pens, 9 red pens, 6 pencils, 7 red coloured pencils, and 8 green coloured pencils.
   You pick one item at random. Find the probability of choosing:
   a) a red pen
   b) a coloured pencil
   c) a pencil
   d) a pen
2. A number cube is labelled 1 to 6. Is each statement true or false? Explain.
   a) If you roll the number cube 18 times, you will never get 18 ones.
   b) If you roll the number cube 18 times, you will always get exactly 3 fours.
   c) If you roll the number cube 18 times, you may get a two approximately 3 times.
   d) If you roll the number cube many times, each number 1, 2, 3, 4, 5, 6 may occur approximately $\frac{1}{6}$ of the number of rolls.
3. There are these markers in a box: 3 purple, 5 black, 8 pink, and 4 red.
   You pick one marker without looking.
   Find each probability.
   a) A black marker will be picked.
   b) A purple or red marker will be picked.
   c) A pink marker will not be picked.
4. One hundred twenty first-prize tickets were sold. Eighty-five second-prize tickets were sold. Seventy third-prize tickets were sold.
   a) Kendall purchased 8 first-prize tickets.
      What is the probability that Kendall will win the first prize?
   b) Laura purchased 9 second-prize tickets.
      What is the probability that Laura will win the first prize? The second prize?
   c) Anthony purchased 25 third-prize tickets.
      What is the probability that Anthony will not win the third prize?

Name ________________ Date ____________

Master 11.16 **Extra Practice 4**

Section 11.4: Applications of Probability

1. A coin is tossed and the pointer on the following spinner is spun.

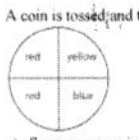

   a) Suppose you win if the coin lands heads and you spin red.
      What are your chances of winning?
   b) Suppose you win if you spin red.
      What are your chances of winning?
2. A coin is tossed three times. Find the chances of tossing:
   a) two heads and one tail
   b) three heads
   c) at least one tail
3. Two number cubes are rolled. Each cube is labelled 1 to 6.
   Determine the probability of each event.
   a) A 3 and a 4 are rolled.
   b) A sum of seven is rolled.
   c) Two even numbers are rolled.
   d) An even and an odd number are rolled.
   e) A double is rolled.
   f) A double is not rolled.
4. A pointer on this spinner is spun and a 2-coloured counter is tossed.
   The counter is red and blue.

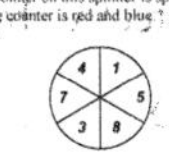

   What is the chance of each event? Give the answer to the nearest percent.
   a) Spinning 4 and tossing red
   b) Spinning an odd number and tossing blue
   c) Not spinning 5
   d) Not tossing blue

Name ________________ Date ____________

Master 11.17 **Sample Answers**

Extra Practice 1 – Master 11.13
Section 11.1

1. a) 1, 2, 3, 4, 5
   b) M, A, T, H, E, M, A, T, I, C, S
2.

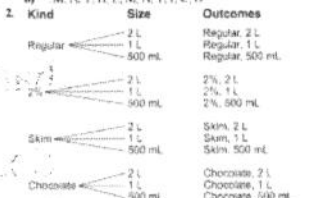

3. a)

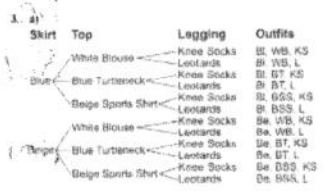

   b) 6 (the outfits that have both a blue skirt and a blue turtleneck were not counted)
   c) 6
   d) 2
4. a) 120
   b) 72
   c) 45
   d) 60

Extra Practice 2 – Master 11.14
Section 11.2

1.

Name	Batting Average
A. Rodriguez	0.305
G. Sheffield	0.301
M. Cairo	0.299
K. Lofton	0.288
H. Matsui	0.287
J. Posada	0.272
R. Sierra	0.267
B. Williams	0.257
J. Giambi	0.250
D. Jeter	0.247
B. Crosby	0.240
T. Clark	0.220
E. Wilson	0.209
J. Flaherty	0.180
T. Lee	0.105
H. Bush	0.000

2. a) 10 ways. You are more likely to pick a blue marble whenever there are more blue marbles than white marbles in the bag. This can happen if the following combinations of marbles are in the bag:
   i) 1 blue ii) 2 blue iii) 3 blue iv) 4 blue
   v) 2 blue, 1 white vi) 3 blue, 2 white
   vii) 3 blue, 1 white viii) 4 blue, 3 white
   ix) 4 blue, 2 white x) 4 blue, 1 white
   b) 4 ways. For the outcomes of picking either blue or white to be equal, there must be the same number of each colour in the bag. This can happen if the following combinations of marbles are in the bag:
   i) 1 white, 1 blue
   ii) 2 white, 2 blue
   iii) 3 white, 3 blue
   iv) 4 white, 4 blue
3. a) $\frac{12}{350} = 0.034$, $\frac{338}{350} = 0.966$
   b) $\frac{38}{85} = 0.447$
4. a) Heart, spade, club, diamond
   b) Yes, the outcomes are equally likely, because there are 13 cards of each suit (the same number of cards for each suit).

c), d) Answers will vary.

Outcomes	Tally	Frequency	Relative Frequency
Spade	卌 卌 |||	13	$\frac{13}{50} = 0.260$
Diamond	卌 卌 |	11	$\frac{11}{50} = 0.220$
Heart	卌 卌 ||||	14	$\frac{14}{50} = 0.280$
Club	卌 卌 ||	12	$\frac{12}{50} = 0.240$

e) Answers will vary depending on the original prediction and the results in the table.

Extra Practice 3 – Master 11.15
Section 11.3

1. a) $\frac{9}{37} = 0.243$ b) $\frac{15}{37} = 0.405$ c) $\frac{6}{37} = 0.162$
   d) $\frac{16}{37} = 0.432$
2. a) False. In an experiment, it is possible to get 18 ones. This could happen but it is unlikely.
   b) False. You are not guaranteed exactly 3 fours. It could be more or less.
   c) True. In 18 rolls, it is possible to roll a two 3 times.
   d) True. There are 6 numbers, and the probability of rolling each number is $\frac{1}{6}$.
3. a) $\frac{5}{20} = 0.250$ b) $\frac{3+4}{20} = \frac{7}{20} = 0.350$
   c) $\frac{20-8}{20} = \frac{12}{20} = 0.600$
4. a) $\frac{8}{120} = 0.067$ b) 0, $\frac{9}{85} = 0.106$
   c) $\frac{70-25}{70} = \frac{45}{70} = 0.643$

Extra Practice 4 – Master 11.16
Section 11.4

1. a) $\frac{1}{4} = 0.250$, or 25%
   b) $\frac{1}{2} = 0.5$, or 50%
2. a) $\frac{3}{8} = 0.375$, or 37.5%
   b) $\frac{1}{8} = 0.125$, or 12.5%
   c) $\frac{7}{8} = 0.875$, or 87.5%
3. a) $\frac{2}{36} = 0.056$ b) $\frac{6}{36} = 0.167$ c) $\frac{9}{36} = 0.250$
   d) $\frac{18}{36} = 0.5$ e) $\frac{6}{36} = 0.167$ f) $\frac{30}{36} = 0.833$
4. a) $\frac{1}{12} = 0.083$, or about 8%
   b) $\frac{4}{12} = 0.333$, or about 33%
   c) $\frac{10}{12} = 0.833$, or about 83%
   d) $\frac{6}{12} = 0.5$, or 50%

Addison Wesley
Mathematics
Makes Sense

Program Authors

Jason Johnston
Bryn Keyes
Mary Doucette
Antonietta Lenjosek
Steve Thomas
Margaret Sinclair
Trevor Brown
Cathy Heideman
Don Jones
Michael Davis
Jennifer Paziuk
Ken Harper
Sharon Jeroski
Ray Appel
Laura Weatherhead
Betty Milne
Jim Mennie
Lynn Strangway

Printed and bound in Canada

10 17

PEARSON
Education Canada